BIOLOGICAL SCIENCE

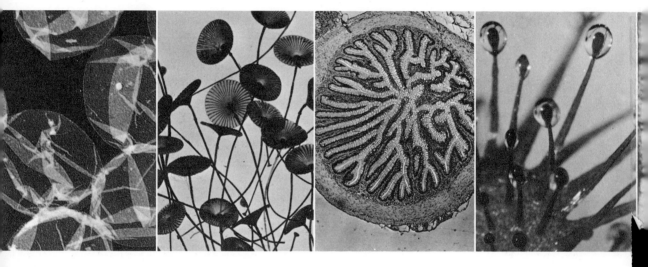

BIOLOGICAL SCIENCE

WILLIAM T. KEETON
CORNELL UNIVERSITY

Illustrated by Paula DiSanto Bensadoun

NEW YORK W · W · NORTON & COMPANY · INC ·

Photographic credits. *Title page:* J. F. Hoffman (1); General
Biological Supply House, Inc., Chicago (2, 5); Warren Andrew
(3); Thomas Eisner (4). *Part I:* K. R. Porter. *Part II:* David
Pramer; J. Arthur Herrick; W. C. Dilger. *Part III:* General Bio-
logical Supply House. *Part IV:* Elmer S. Phillips. *Part V:*
General Biological Supply House; Verne N. Rockcastle; New York
Zoological Society.

CONTENTS

PART II   THE BIOLOGY OF ORGANISMS

PART III   THE PERPETUATION OF LIFE

PART IV
THE BIOLOGY OF POPULATIONS AND COMMUNITIES

PART V   THE ORIGIN AND DIVERSITY OF LIFE

PREFACE

BIOLOGICAL SCIENCE CAN AND SHOULD BE one of the most stimulating subjects a college student encounters. Nothing else, after all, has such immediate personal relevance as the phenomenon of life; and biological science, as the study of life, sheds light on what every individual experiences in himself and observes around him. Given the inherent excitement of the subject, there is no excuse for an introductory biology course to be dull. If large numbers of students in the past found biology a disappointing subject, one seemingly beset with long lists of names and cut-and-dried "facts" to memorize, then the blame must rest with those of us who were their teachers rather than with the students themselves.

Fortunately, the last decade has witnessed a nationwide effort to reorganize and redesign our approach to the teaching of elementary biology. The results of the Biological Sciences Curriculum Study and other projects to improve high school science courses are being increasingly felt by the colleges. Each year the entering students are better prepared than the ones the year before. This, together with the recent rapid pace of biological discovery, has led to an extraordinary growth of interest on the part of students. Many intend to enter some branch of biological science as their life's work; many others, who intend to pursue a career in some other field, nevertheless rightly see that in our day no liberal education is complete if it has not included biological science.

A textbook for today's better-prepared students must do justice to the newer areas of biological science without neglecting the older areas that provide the foundation upon which the new rests. Attempting an accurate and honest picture of the current state of our knowledge (and ignorance) in each of the major areas, without prejudice to any one of them, I have given extensive treatment to such topics as cellular ultrastructure, the mechanism of photosynthesis, molecular genetics, and developmental biology, but not at the expense of "whole organism" and population biology.

This book does not follow the once-traditional phylum-by-phylum organization; nor does it put plant and animal biology in separate sections, as is commonly done. Instead, it discusses the basic problems faced by all forms of life, whether plant, animal, or microbe (I have tried hard to avoid slighting the plants, a tendency to which integrated texts are prone), and compares, in the light of modern evolutionary theory, the various alternative "solutions" to these problems seen in a variety of organisms. In this way, students are constantly reminded of the unity in diversity that characterizes life.

There is much disagreement among teachers about the sequence in which the various topics in an introductory biological science course should be taught. The disagreement is a legitimate one, since a good case can be made for each of several sequences. The plain fact is that each topic can best be understood if all the other topics have preceded it. This being impossible, every teacher must choose the sequence that best suits his conceptual approach to the subject. Thus, although strong arguments can be given for placing the discussions of cell division, genetics, and development with the other cellular topics at the beginning of the sequence, I have deferred them until later (Part III) for two reasons: First, I feel that study of genetics benefits more from prior knowledge of anatomical and physiological characteristics than study of anatomy and physiology benefit from prior knowledge of genetics. Second, since evolutionary theory rests upon genetics, there is considerable advantage in having the chapters on these two subjects close together. Those who find these justifications unconvincing can easily move Part III forward and follow the sequence I, III, II, IV, V. The treatment is flexible enough so that diverse sequences of chapters can be followed.

It is a particularly difficult decision whether to cover the major groups of organisms near the beginning of a textbook, so that students will be familiar with them when they are mentioned in other chapters, or whether to leave them until the end of the course, when students may approach their examination with more insight. I have followed the latter alternative here (although the major groups are briefly introduced in Chapter 3) for the sake of a more meaningful discussion of evolutionary patterns in the plant and animal kingdoms.

This book goes deeper into many topics than has been customary in the past in introductory biology courses. Whenever possible, it includes discussions of important experiments and investigations, even though this takes much more space than a simple recitation of "facts"; the investment will be justified if the student gets a feel for the way new information is obtained.

It is my conviction that it is useless merely to mention a topic for the sake of "completeness" of coverage, that if it is mentioned at all it should be given sufficient depth of treatment to make it meaningful. My experience in teaching the introductory biology course at Cornell (one taken by both science majors and students of the humanities) has shown me that it is often more difficult for a student to understand an oversimplified "elementary" presentation than one that is rigorous enough to engender some insight into the relevance of the material. For example, it was a frustration to me for several years that too many of my students seemed to find genetics a hurdle they could not master. I finally tried extending my treatment of the subject considerably beyond that given in most elementary biology textbooks; the result was that most of the students who would formerly never have grasped the essentials of genetics now did so, and some of them even became especially enthusiastic about that part of the course.

Given the rate at which our knowledge is advancing, no biological science textbook can be fully up to date at the time a student reads it. It is important that the student understand this as one aspect of the dynamic, searching, inquiring nature of science. Hence I have not hesitated to warn repeatedly that more research is needed before some of the ideas discussed can be reliably evaluated, and I have added footnotes to draw attention to the fact that while the book was in press doubt was cast on some of the theories to which it gives major emphasis (e.g. the unit membrane theory). Often evidence is cited both for and against two or three opposing hypotheses, and it is made clear that a final decision is not yet possible. This approach, which encourages the student to evaluate the evidence for himself, can bring it home to him that much remains to be done and that the effort will be exciting.

Because no one book can give adequate coverage to all the diverse aspects of biological science, students should be encouraged to consult other sources. Lists of authoritative references and of readings accessible to the beginner will be found at the end of each chapter; guides to identification are listed at the end of Chapters 21 and 22. Many of the suggested readings are articles from *Scientific American;* the majority of these are available as numbered separates (called offprints).

A good index can be an important learning aid. Proceeding on what I believe to be the sound assumption that too many entries are better than too few, Ann M. Kingsbury has prepared an index through which the student can readily locate any topic, term, or proper name mentioned in the text.

In order to avoid encouraging students to memorize isolated and often sterile definitions, I have not included a glossary. Definitions of terms in context can be found through italicized page references in the index.

Many people read parts of this book in manuscript and offered valuable advice and criticism. I wish to acknowledge especially the aid of the following of my colleagues at Cornell University: David W. Bierhorst, A. W. Blackler, W. C. Dilger, Richard D. O'Brien, Richard B. Root, and H. T. Stinson. The criticisms of Peter H. Klopfer of Duke University and Lester Ingle of the University of Illinois were also most helpful.

My thanks are due to the many individuals, museums, and business firms that lent me photographs and permitted me to publish them; their names are given in the pertinent legends. I am particularly indebted to four of my colleagues who spent long hours preparing special photographs: Thomas Eisner, Herbert Israel, Edgar M. Raffensperger, and Verne N. Rockcastle.

It is a special pleasure to acknowledge the imaginative and tireless help of my illustrator, Paula DiSanto Bensadoun. Her drawings add immeasurably to the value of the book.

My thanks also to Ruth Thalheimer and Hugh O'Neill of W. W. Norton, who were responsible for the copy editing and the design.

Finally, I wish to express my gratitude to my wife for her endless patience and interest during the years of writing when I must have been a constant trial to my family.

Ithaca, New York
October, 1966

W.T.K.

BIOLOGICAL SCIENCE

CHAPTER

1

INTRODUCTION

THE SUBJECT OF THIS BOOK IS BIOLOGICAL science—the study of life. But what is life? We all have some intuitive idea. After all, we have life, and many of the things with which we come in contact every day have life. But when asked to say explicitly what life is, few of us can give a satisfying answer. One dictionary defines "life" as "the condition which distinguishes animals and plants from inorganic objects and dead organisms." This same dictionary defines "dead" as "deprived of life." In other words, life is what animals and plants have when they are not dead, and dead is what those same organisms are when they lack life. Clearly, such circular definitions get us nowhere. Here is a word for something at the very center of our concern, and yet we are at a loss to offer a meaningful definition of it.

In lieu of a definition, many biology books give a list of attributes that, taken together, are said to characterize life. The list usually includes metabolism, reproduction, growth, responsiveness, and movement. And there can be no doubt that investigation of these attributes does help us toward an understanding of what life is. But merely setting down one-paragraph descriptions of each of these properties and attempting to explain how they distinguish life seems a singularly inadequate way to describe something so rich and varied, so marvelous in its complexity, so constantly changing. This entire book is about life; yet when you have finished it, you still won't be able to define life convincingly or describe it satisfactorily, although you will, we hope, have a deeper appreciation and understanding of what it means to be alive.

BIOLOGY AS A SCIENCE

We have said that we are here concerned with biological science, with the science of life. Perhaps it will be well to pause a moment and consider what a science is. We live in a science-conscious age. Radio and television advertise every product as the latest result of "scientific" research. Commercials are full of "scientists" in starched white lab coats. The news media deal every day with the latest developments in space science or medical science or agricultural science. The President and Congress have scientific advisers, and millions of dollars are spent every year by both the national and the state governments on scientific research and development. Yet, surprisingly, most people have no real understanding of what science is. They view it as something akin to magic or as a cold and relentless mathematical game. They often believe—though less now than in the past—that this game is played exclusively by strange men so narrow and specialized that they have only the most simple-minded notions about anything falling outside their specialty.

The advent of space vehicles and moon probes changed the public image of at least some scientists. But the new conception of glamorous adventurers is as erroneous as the older one. Most scientists are just people who have a deep curiosity about the world in which they live. They want to know more about the earth and stars, rocks and rivers, atoms and molecules, plants and animals. For many scientists, the need to know is sufficient motivation in itself. For others, the possibility that what they discover may benefit mankind is additional motivation. But whatever the incentive, they are usually neither naïve recluses nor glamorous adventurers. And they are not some strange breed of modern magician waving a wand called "scientific method."

The Scientific Method

So much has been said about the powers of the scientific method that many seem to think it involves some formula too complicated for ordinary people to understand. It doesn't. It is used to some extent by almost everyone every day. Its power in the hands of a good scientist stems from the rigor of its application. Let us briefly examine the elements of this method.

Science is concerned with the material universe. It seeks to discover facts about that universe and to fit those facts into conceptual schemes, called theories or laws, that will give them order and meaning. Science must therefore begin with observations of objects or events in the physical universe. The objects or events may occur naturally, or they may be the products of planned experiments, but the important point is that they must be observed, either directly or indirectly. Science cannot deal with anything that cannot be observed. A frequent criticism leveled at scientists is that they will accept as valid evidence only what they can perceive with their senses, that they ignore other ways of knowing. This charge is often made with the implication that scientists should be ashamed of their reliance on observation. But scientists are not ashamed. Science rests upon the conviction (justified by its pragmatic success) that all events of the universe can be described by physical theories and laws, and that we get the data with which to formulate those theories and laws through our senses. (Notice that we said physical theories and laws *describe* events; they are summary statements of how things are and predictions of how they probably will be, not of how they should be. They are *a posteriori* laws, not *a priori* laws.) Scientists readily acknowledge the imperfection of sensory perception. They themselves have studied sensory perception and have found it disconcertingly variable and unreliable. Furthermore, they know that there is always an unavoidable interaction between the observer and the phenomenon observed. As George Gamow has said, "There is no such thing as a physical phenomenon *per se*—the observer and his instruments become an integral part of the phenomenon under investigation." But to recognize the imperfection of sensory perception is not to admit that we may get information by other means (except, of course, by genetic transmission, which is also a physical process). That is not a possibility open to us as scientists.

Once a scientist has made careful observations, he must do something with his data. It is not enough simply to amass data; the data must be fitted into some sort of generalization. The observation that a particular fly has three pairs of legs is interesting, but it will remain an essentially useless isolated fact until it is incorporated into a generalization such as, "All flies have three pairs of legs," or the even broader generalization, "All insects have three pairs of legs." The step from isolated observations to generalizations can be made with confidence only if enough observations have been made to give a firm basis for generalization and only if the individual observations have been reliably made.

Having reasoned inductively from the specific to the general (i.e. from specific observations to a general statement), the good scientist must next reverse his field and reason deductively, from the general to the specific. Suppose, for example, he has observed thirty kinds of flies, ten kinds of beetles, four kinds of wasps, and six kinds of grasshoppers and

has found that all have three pairs of legs. And suppose he has arrived at the following generalization from these observations: "All insects have three pairs of legs." He may now reason deductively that if all insects have three pairs of legs, and if cockroaches, crickets, moths, and bees are insects, then they must have three pairs of legs. In other words, he uses his generalization to formulate a hypothesis about things that he has not yet observed. Then he proceeds to test his hypothesis, in this case by examining as many kinds of cockroaches, crickets, moths, and bees as he can to check if they really do have three pairs of legs. When he finds that all these insects do indeed have three pairs of legs and that his hypothesis was therefore a good one, he feels more confidence in his generalization. But he doesn't stop there; he makes new hypotheses designed to test his generalization still further. Perhaps he will predict that since immature flies and moths are insects they too must have three pairs of legs. But observation shows him that many grubs (immature flies) and caterpillars (immature moths) have no legs at all. His generalization must therefore take the more restricted form: "All adult insects have three pairs of legs."

Let us summarize the steps followed up to this point by our hypothetical scientist. He began, as all good scientists must begin, with observations. He used these observations to formulate a generalization, which he then tested by basing simple predictions on it and seeing if the predictions were accurate. When he found a discrepancy between his generalization and observable fact, he changed his generalization. Any good scientist must be ready to alter or even abandon his most cherished generalizations when new facts contradict them. He must always remember that his generalizations, his theories, even his physical laws, are dependent upon observable facts and not vice versa.

Our discussion here has been limited to a case involving very simple data and a very elementary generalization, but the same considerations would apply to data obtained by the most elaborate experiment and to the most sophisticated and complex generalization based on those data. And it would apply also to higher levels of generalization, such as purported explanations for biological events. At this higher level of generalization the steps one must follow may be less clear. For example, hypotheses may not flow so obviously from previous generalizations; they may often depend more on educated guesses or hunches than on simple deduction. But in the final analysis the basic rules are the same. The hypothesis must be testable, or it is of no value, and as testing proceeds the hypothesis must be altered when necessary to conform with the evidence. The scientist's query must always be: "What is the evidence?"

Perhaps the scientific attitude to evidence can be made clearer by outlining how a critical scientist would evaluate a controversial new paper in his field, a paper reporting a discovery that calls into question certain long-held and widely accepted ideas. Now, we must admit that scientists, being human, have a strong attachment to the conceptual schemes they have erected, and that the history of science abounds with examples of lack of objectivity on the part of a scientific community psychologically unprepared for radically different new ideas. But we are here assuming an "ideal" scientist, a "perfect" blend of hard, rigorous skepticism and objective open-mindedness. Such a scientist would at first disregard the claims and interpretations of the author of the paper and carefully examine the data presented and the methods whereby those data were obtained. Having provisionally satisfied himself that the data justify proceeding further, he would evaluate the author's interpretation of them. Do the data support the author's claims? What are the alternative interpretations, and on what basis did the author reject them? If he failed to consider some possible alternatives, do these fit the data better or worse than the

one he adopted? If several interpretations fit the data equally well, which is the simplest, and what sort of additional data might facilitate a choice among them? Finally, if the scientist thinks the author's basic interpretation of the data is a reasonable one, he can examine the more elaborate conceptual scheme the author has built upon this base and analyze it for logical consistency in the arguments used. Suppose the paper successfully withstands all critical scrutiny. That, of course, is only the beginning. Attempts must now be made to duplicate the author's research procedures to see if similar results can be obtained by other people. And new procedures must be devised to test the new idea. Eventually, if all the evidence continues to support the new idea, it may become generally accepted as probably true and be dignified by being called a ***theory***.[1] But the testing never completely stops. No theory in science is ever absolutely and finally proved. Einstein's theory that nothing in the universe can attain a speed greater than the speed of light was proposed more than fifty years ago, and it is now fundamental to much of modern physics; yet new tests of it are still being devised. If someone were to demonstrate conditions under which the theory does not hold, he would doubtless win a Nobel Prize, as Tsung-Dao Lee and Chen Ning Yang did in 1957 for showing that one of the basic conservation laws, the Law of Conservation of Parity, fails in certain inherently slow decay processes of fundamental particles.

By now you are probably tired of following

---

[1] Notice that scientists do not use the word "theory" the way the general public does. To many people, a theory is a highly tentative statement, a poor makeshift for fact. But when scientists dignify a statement by calling it a theory, they imply that it has a very high degree of probability and that they have great confidence in it. A theory is a hypothesis that has been repeatedly and extensively tested and always found to be true. It is supported by the facts and helps order and explain those facts. Many scientific theories, such as the cell theory and the theory of evolution, are so well supported by all known facts that they themselves are "facts" in the nonscientific usage of that term.

this elementary exposition of the scientific method. After all, every high school student today is familiar with all that we have said, and none of it is unique to science. True. But nowhere is the method applied with such good results as in science, for nowhere is it consistently applied with such rigor. That rigor of application implies the fulfillment of at least three requirements. First, hypotheses must be testable by observation of the physical universe. Hypotheses that are not testable are inadmissible in science, but they are frequently proposed in other contexts and often form the basis for elaborate conceptual schemes. Second, all generalizations and hypotheses must actually be tested. Yet in areas other than science, when testable generalizations and hypotheses appear self-evident, they are often accepted as true without testing. Third, generalizations and hypotheses that are found upon testing to be contradicted by the evidence must be modified or abandoned. In many contexts, however, resistance to changing them may be such that the evidence is dismissed as irrelevant. A telling comparison between scientific method used correctly and the same procedures used less rigorously was made by T. H. Huxley in the following statement: "Science is, I believe, nothing but trained and organized common sense, differing from the latter only as a veteran may differ from a raw recruit; and its methods differ from those of common sense only so far as the guardsman's cut and thrust differ from the manner in which a savage wields his club."

Limitations of the Scientific Method. Science's insistence on testability imposes limitations on what it can do. For example, the hypothesis that there is a God working through the natural laws of the universe is not testable and hence cannot be evaluated by science. Science cannot say that there is such a God, nor can it say that there is not. This does not mean that science cannot legitimately say something about certain attributes ascribed to God. Throughout history men have made statements about the physical universe in the name of their gods, and have insisted that denial of their statements is a denial of their gods. If this is so, then science may well have to deny those gods. Any part of the physical universe can be studied by science, and he who makes the existence of his God stand or fall on some supposed fact about the universe risks having science destroy his God.

Science cannot make value judgments; it cannot say that a painting or a sunset is beautiful. And science cannot make moral judgments; it cannot say that war is immoral. Science can, however, analyze elements in a painting that are regarded as contributing to its beauty, and it can analyze the biological and cultural implications of war. It can, in short, try to predict what people will consider beautiful or moral, and it can provide people with information that they can use in making value or moral judgments. But the act of making the judgment itself is not science.

THE RISE OF MODERN BIOLOGICAL SCIENCE

The scientific approach discussed above is of relatively recent origin. It may seem obvious to you that the way to learn about nature is to look at nature, to seek evidence by observation, but for many centuries such an approach was not in the least obvious. True, major scientific discoveries were made in several of the ancient civilizations, especially those of Greece, Egypt, and Babylonia, but this early scientific activity was limited to a tiny handful of the populace, and it began a steady decline more than a century before the birth of Christ. Between about 200 and 1200 A.D., there were almost no important scientific advances, and much of what the ancients had known was forgotten. During this period, most people placed greater reliance on religious dogma and superstition and on the writings of a few venerated ancient scholars than on observation of the universe itself. They often preferred haggling over the exact meaning of a sentence from one of Aristotle's books on plants or animals to studying the plants or animals themselves to see if Aristotle was right. Indeed, the possibility that Aristotle might sometimes have erred seems to have been quite beyond their grasp. They seldom questioned the theology of the times, and since they made no real distinction between science and theology, they didn't question the science either.

Then came a time of intellectual reawakening in Europe. Two very influential theologians and philosophers, Albertus Magnus (1193–1280) and Thomas Aquinas (1225–1274), both of whom taught at the University of Paris, accepted the idea of a distinction between natural truth and revealed truth. This rationalistic approach, separating large segments of human knowledge and speculation from theology, prepared the way for a relatively independent development of science. At about the same time, Roger Bacon (ca. 1210–1293) of Oxford University was calling for an end to unthinking acceptance of traditionally authoritative writings such as Aristotle's: "Cease to be ruled by dogmas and authorities; look at the world!" Three centuries later, Francis Bacon (1561–1626) vigorously championed the experimental approach to knowledge, urging men to trust no statements without verification, to test all things with the utmost rigor.

The New Era in the Physical Sciences. The intellectual climate was changing; it was no longer beneath the dignity of an educated man to look at the material objects of nature. Thus Nicolaus Copernicus (1473–1543), a Polish astronomer, analyzed the movements of the heavenly bodies and announced that the earth moves around the sun rather than the sun around the earth. Now, the intellectual climate may have been changing and becoming more friendly to science, but it had not yet changed enough to be ready for such a

proposition as this. After all, if the earth moved around the sun, then the earth was not the center of the universe and man, therefore, did not stand at the center of all creation. This was too much! When the great Galileo Galilei (1564–1642) embraced Copernicus' theory, he was forced to recant publicly under threat of excommunication. H. G. Wells[2] describes this early clash between science and dogma:

the church . . . decided that to believe that the earth was smaller and inferior to the sun made man and Christianity of no account . . . so Galileo, under threats of dire punishment, when he was an old man of sixty-nine, was made to recant this view and put the earth back in its place as the immovable centre of the universe. He knelt before ten cardinals in scarlet, an assembly august enough to overawe truth itself, while he amended the creation he had disarranged. The story has it that as he arose from his knees, after repeating his recantation, he muttered, "Eppur si Muove"— "it moves nevertheless."

Galileo may have publicly recanted, but the ideas of Copernicus, Galileo, and the other great scientists that followed them could not be suppressed. It wasn't long before educated men became convinced that the physical universe could indeed be understood in terms of orderly relationships, of universal laws, that physical events have impersonal causes which men can hope to understand, that capricious whims of gods and magicians and evil spirits need no longer be invoked to explain a physical event. No other name stands out so prominently during this period as that of Isaac Newton (1642–1727), who was born in the year of Galileo's death. His discovery of the Law of Gravitation and his explanation in 1685 of the movements of the planets caused a revolution in human thought and carried physical science into a new era. In a very real

[2] In *The Outline of History* (3rd ed.; Macmillan, 1922), pp. 732–733.

sense, the work of Newton marks the birth of modern physics.

The science of the new era was largely restricted to physics, astronomy, and chemistry, i.e. to the physical sciences. If men were now ready to give up their place at the center of the universe and admit that the earth circles the sun, they were nevertheless not yet ready to admit that they themselves and other living creatures could be understood in terms of impersonal forces. Life seemed too full of purpose, of design, to be studied in the same way chemicals and moving particles are studied. And besides, if Copernicus was a threat to human dignity and pride, how much greater a threat would be an explanation of life processes in mechanistic terms! It was not until 1859, nearly two hundred years after Newton, that biological science experienced its own revolution and entered its modern era.

The New Era in the Biological Sciences. The year 1859 is taken as the beginning of the modern era of biology because it was in that year that Charles Darwin (1809–1882), the great British naturalist, published *The Origin of Species,* in which he proposed his theory of evolution by natural selection.[3] We do not wish to imply that no important biological work was done before the time of Darwin—that would be nonsense. Andreas Versalius (1514–1564) described in greater detail than anyone had ever done before the anatomy of the hu-

man body; Ulisse Aldrovandi (1522–1605) published three large books on birds and a monumental treatise on insects; William Harvey (1578–1657) discovered the circulation of the blood; Marcello Malpighi (1628–1694) extended Harvey's work and also made major contributions to the understanding of embryological development; Robert Hooke (1635–1703) first detected the presence of cells in biological material; Antoni van Leeuwenhoek (1632–1723) studied and described many microscopic organisms; John Ray (1627–1705) made major contributions to knowledge of plants and correctly explained fossils as remains of organisms that lived in past ages; and Carolus Linnaeus (1707–1778) founded the modern system of classification of living organisms. But important as the work of these men was, it did not spark the sort of explosive growth of biological science that Newton's work stimulated in the physical sciences. However, an explosion is precisely what Darwin's book did cause. Men had long since reconciled themselves to living on a small planet far from the center of the universe, but they were not prepared to accept the ultimate indignity, that they had descended from some lowly form of life in the distant past and shared common ancestors with monkeys and apes and even worms. Again, the old cry of heresy was raised. Again, some men felt that the very basis of all they held dear had been challenged, that if Darwin's views should prevail their religion would be destroyed. The outcry was loud and anguished and has not fully subsided yet, although most major Western religions and denominations now accept the theory of evolution and no longer consider it a threat to their existence.

Copernicus' theory was not generally accepted until long after his death, as we have seen. But delayed recognition was not to be the fate of Darwin's theory. And despite violent denunciations from some quarters, Darwin never had to recant as Galileo had been obliged to do. The times were ripe for Darwin. A major

---

[3] Actually, the theory was first announced in a short paper read before the Linnaean Society of London in 1858. A paper by Alfred Russel Wallace (1823–1913) containing essentially the same conclusions was also presented on this occasion. Darwin had conceived the theory first and had labored many years to prepare a massive tome that would provide convincing proof. For this reason and because what he published the following year was far more complete than anything Wallace ever published on the theory of evolution, the theory is usually attributed to him. It is, however, a good indication that the times were ripe for such a theory that two men should advance it independently at almost the same time. In fact, earlier in the nineteenth century several other workers had published comments that foreshadowed the ideas of Darwin and Wallace.

part of the scientific community welcomed and promptly championed his views. In fact, he himself seldom debated the merits of his theory in public. He didn't need to. Some of his greatest contemporaries eagerly acted as his defenders. His spark had ignited an excitement in the scientific community that was not to be extinguished. Biology was never again to be the same. Almost immediately, interest in biological research began to grow rapidly. Whether to prove or disprove Darwin, men began to investigate the phenomena they had so long considered beyond the scope of science. The dynamic growth of biological research, begun more than a century ago, has never slackened; in fact, the rate of growth is greater now than ever before. And to this day, the theory of evolution by natural selection remains one of the most important unifying principles in all biology. We shall have cause to refer to it in every chapter of this book.

DARWIN'S THEORY

The theory of evolution, as modified in the years since Darwin, will be treated at some length in a chapter in the second half of this book. But since we shall have to refer to this all-important unifying principle of biology in interpreting much of the material covered in earlier chapters, let us pause here and briefly examine the central concepts of Darwin's theory.

The theory consists of two major parts: the concept of evolutionary change and the concept of natural selection. First, Darwin rejected the notion that living creatures are the immutable products of a sudden creation, that they exist now in precisely the form in which they have always existed. He insisted, instead, that change is the rule, that the organisms living today have descended by gradual changes from ancient ancestors quite unlike themselves. Second, Darwin said that it is *natural selection* that determines the course of the change, that

natural selection is the guiding factor. He showed that this guiding factor can be understood in completely mechanistic terms, that no conscious purpose or design need be invoked. Let us examine the two parts of Darwin's theory separately.

The Concept of Evolutionary Change

To people living in the mid-twentieth century, the idea that lineages of organisms change with time seems far from revolutionary. We are used to change. We see change on every hand. We should probably be surprised to find anything that remained the same for any very long period of time. But in Darwin's day things moved more slowly. The idea of a world in constant flux had only few adherents. The vast majority accepted without question the notion that the universe was created a few thousand years before the birth of Christ, and that all the species of plants and animals were put on the earth at that time and had perpetuated themselves without change ever since. What sorts of evidence could Darwin bring forward to combat this static view?

First, he could point to the fossils. During the latter part of the eighteenth and the first half of the nineteenth century, geologists had unearthed many fossils and had realized that most of them were species no longer living on the earth and that few living species were represented in the fossil record. In other words, forms of life different from those known today inhabited the earth in past ages. This is a point now familiar to grade-school children, who are aware that dinosaurs once roamed the earth in vast numbers, but that one seldom sees a dinosaur nowadays. They can go to museums and see dioramas of ancient seas filled with strange fish and shelled creatures unlike anything living today, or they can see reconstructions of weird coal-age forests with plants that became extinct millions of years ago. They study about the early cavemen, who, though clearly human, were also clearly different in many ways from modern men. To us the existence of fossils seems convincing evidence that the history of life on earth has been marked by change. But when it was first suggested that the extinct creatures whose remains are preserved in the rocks as fossils represented the ancestors from which the organisms living today are descended, it was urged instead that these extinct species indicated the occurrence of catastrophic extinctions at various times in the history of the earth, followed by new episodes of divine creation. According to this hypothesis, each species would have remained unchanged from the time of its creation until the time of its extinction; there would have been no evolution.

Soon, however, the fossil record itself made this hypothesis untenable. As more and more fossils were discovered and studied, it became evident that gradual shifts in characters could be traced through time. If an investigator studied the fossils in one rock layer and then studied the fossils in a slightly more recent layer, he would often find that those in the more recent layer were very similar to the older ones but showed slight differences. If he then studied a third layer slightly more recent than the second, he would again find that slight changes in the characters of the fossil species could be detected. In this way, by studying a series of successive rock layers, he could reconstruct the sequence of changes through which a given lineage had passed. He could even predict what the fossils in some intermediate layer not yet studied would be like and then test his hypothesis by locating and studying such a layer. The notion of catastrophic extinctions and repeated creations hardly seemed adequate to explain such fossil sequences. It was far more likely that the changes seen in the fossils were the result of accumulation of many small alterations as the generations passed.

Second, Darwin could point to resemblances between living species. If one looks at the forelimbs of a variety of different mammals, for example, one will find essentially the same bones arranged in the same order; the basic bone structure of a man's arm, a dog's front leg, or a seal's flipper is the same. The same bones are even present in a bird's wing. True, the size and shape of the individual bones vary from species to species, and some bones may be missing entirely in one or another species, but the basic construction is unmistakably the same. To Darwin, the resemblance suggested that all these species had descended from a common ancestor from whom each had inherited, with distinctive modifications, its forelimb. The fact that some species possess in reduced and nonfunctional form structures that in other species have important functions further convinced Darwin of the validity of his theory. Why would the Creator have given pigs, which walk on only two toes per foot, two other toes that dangle uselessly well above the ground? Why would he have given human embryos gill pouches and well-developed tails only to make them disappear again before the time of birth? It seemed much simpler to assume that such structures were inherited vestiges of structures that functioned in ancestral forms and that still function in other species descended from the same ancestor.

Third, and particularly convincing, Darwin could point to changes produced in domesticated plants and animals. How could anyone doubt that great changes can occur in organisms with time when he has before him the historical evidence of the changes in domesticated forms? Where were French poodles and Mexican Chihuahuas two thousand years ago? Where were Guernsey cattle and Leghorn chickens? Where were the modern strains of tomatoes and corn and roses? None of them existed. Their ancestors existed, but those ancestors bore little resemblance to poodles or Chihuahuas or Guernseys or Leghorns or garden tomatoes, corn, and roses. Obviously, radical changes have occurred in a few thousand, or even a few hundred, years. The ancestors of the poodles and Chihuahuas were wolves. The ancestors of modern corn were small wild plants with ears less than an inch long. Let anyone who would still insist that species cannot change explain these facts.

The Concept of Natural Selection

It was easy for Darwin to see that evolutionary change had occurred. But it took him many years to figure out what caused the changes. His first clue came from the breeding of domesticated plants and animals. When pigeon breeders, for example, are developing a new strain, they exploit the variation always seen among individuals by selecting the ones best endowed with the characteristics they want to propagate and using them as the parents for the next generation. The same procedure is followed in each successive generation; those individuals that most nearly approximate the desired type are selected as breeders, and individuals that deviate markedly from the desired type are eliminated. After many generations of such selection, the pigeons will be very different from the ones with which the breeders began (Fig. 1.1). Essentially the same procedure is used in developing a new breed of dog or horse or wheat or chrysanthemum. Since individual variation occurs in all populations of wild organisms, just as it does in populations of domesticated ones, Darwin reasoned that evolutionary change in these populations must be caused by some sort of natural selection for individuals with certain characteristics and elimination of individuals with other characteristics. But what sort of selective force might be at work in nature? The answer eluded Darwin for several years.

Then in 1838 he happened to read a book entitled *An Essay on the Principle of Population,* written by Thomas R. Malthus (1766–1834) in 1798. This book suggested to him how he could account for the selection he felt sure must be operating in nature. Consider for a moment a population of gray squirrels. If this population is to be perpetuated at a stable level, each pair of squirrels must leave enough offspring to replace itself—two, if we assume that all the offspring survive to reproduce. If the average number of progeny per pair were more than two, then the population density would rise; if the average number were less than two, then the population density would fall. Now, even a casual study of actual populations will reveal that the average number of offspring per pair is always more than two, usually far more. A single female frog may lay many thousands of eggs each year; a single pair of robins usually has two clutches per year of four to five eggs each; and a pair of gray squirrels usually has two litters per year containing two to four young each. A single oak tree may produce millions of seeds during its lifetime. Very large reproductive potentials are, in short, the rule in all types of organisms. Yet natural populations usually remain relatively stable over long stretches of time; they may fluctuate noticeably, but they never even approach the level that would be expected if all their progeny survived to reproduce. It is obvious, therefore, that a very high percentage of the young of any species fail to survive and reproduce.

Once Darwin recognized that in nature the majority of the offspring of any species die before they reproduce, he had the clue he needed to explain natural selection. If survival of the young organisms were totally random, if each individual in a large population had exactly the same chance of surviving and reproducing as every other individual, then there would probably be no significant evolutionary change in the population. But survival and reproduction are never totally random. Some individuals are born with such gross defects that they stand almost no chance of surviving to reproduce. And even among individuals not so severely afflicted, differences in the ability to escape predators or obtain nutrients or withstand the rigors of the climate or find a mate,

Fig. 1.1. Breeds of Pigeons. (A) The wild rock pigeon of Europe is thought to be the ancestor of the domesticated breeds shown here. (B) Fantail. (C) Frillback. (D) Satinette oriental frill. (E) English pouter. (F) Pomeranian pouter. (G) Carrier. [Based on photographs in W. W. Levi, *The Pigeon,* Levi Publishing Co., 1957.]

etc. ensure that survival will not be totally random. The individuals with characteristics that weaken their capacity to escape predators or obtain nutrients or withstand the rigors of the climate, etc. will have a poorer chance of surviving and reproducing than individuals with characteristics enhancing these capacities. In each generation, therefore, a slightly higher percentage of the well-adapted individuals will leave progeny. If the characteristics are inherited, those favorable to survival will slowly become more common as the generations pass and those unfavorable to it will become less common. Given enough time, these slow shifts can produce major evolutionary changes.

Now let us compare the propagation of favorable characteristics in nature, as outlined above, with their propagation in domesticated organisms. In each case, far more offspring are born than will survive and reproduce. In other words, in each case there is selection, by which we mean differential reproduction. In the breeding of domesticated plants and animals, the selection (differential reproduction) results from the deliberate choice of the breeder. In nature the selection (differential reproduction) results simply from the fact that individuals with different inherited characteristics have unequal chances of surviving and reproducing. Both sorts of selection, artificial and natural, cause some inherited characteristics to become more prominent in the population and others to become less so as the generations pass. Notice that individuals, once born, are not changed by selection. An individual cannot evolve. The change is in the makeup of the population.

One difference between evolutionary change in nature and the change produced by breeders

should be noted. That is the rate of the change. Breeders can practice very rigorous selection, eliminating all undesirable individuals at every generation and allowing only a few of the most desirable to reproduce. They can thus produce very rapid change, as we all know. Natural selection is usually much less rigorous. Some poorly adapted individuals manage to survive and reproduce, and some well-adapted individuals are eliminated. Hence evolutionary change is usually rather slow; major changes may take many thousands or even millions of years. Fortunately for Darwin and his theory, the geologists of his day, particularly Charles Lyell (1797–1875), one of the greatest geologists of all time and a close friend of his, had provided evidence that the earth could not possibly have been created in 4004 B.C. as many churchmen insisted, but that it must be very much older. Without the geologists' gift of immense spans of time, Darwin's theory of natural selection could not adequately have explained evolutionary change.

In summary, we see that Darwin's explanation of evolutionary change in terms of natural selection depends upon five basic assumptions: (1) Many more individuals are born in each generation than will survive and reproduce. (2) There is variation among individuals; they are not identical in all their characteristics. (3) Individuals with certain characteristics have a better chance of surviving and reproducing than individuals with other characteristics. (4) At least some of the characteristics resulting in differential reproduction are heritable. (5) Enormous spans of time are available for slow, gradual change. All the known evidence supports the validity of these five assumptions.

PART I

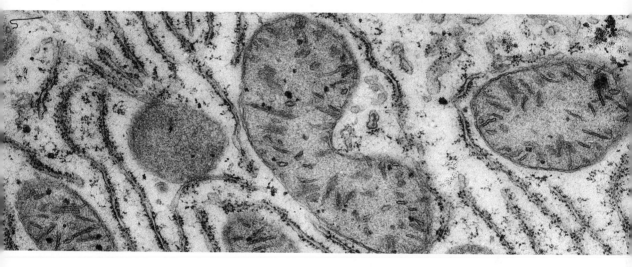

THE CHEMICAL
AND CELLULAR BASIS OF LIFE

CHAPTER

2

SOME SIMPLE CHEMISTRY

ONE OF THE MOST COMMON COMPLAINTS OF students in introductory biology courses is that they are expected to learn too much chemistry. They protest that they are in the course because they want to learn biology, not chemistry. It seems only fair, therefore, to pause a moment and consider their objections before plunging determinedly into a chapter devoted almost exclusively to chemistry.

Admittedly, some aspects of biology can be understood reasonably well without reference to chemistry or physics. Someone with an exclusively descriptive approach to living things and little or no concern with underlying mechanisms might conceivably avoid knowledge of the physical sciences and yet make meaningful contributions to biological knowledge. It is certainly true that not many years ago much of the fundamental biological research was done without reference to the physical sciences, and many unanswered questions and undiscovered facts could still be studied in this manner. But it is also true that in recent years biologists have gained a new appreciation and awareness of the contributions chemistry and physics can make to biology. More and more, living organisms are being viewed as integral parts of the physical universe, to which the fundamental physical laws have as important an application as to atoms and molecules, rocks and minerals, planets and stars. It is becoming increasingly plain that a person without background in the physical sciences is severely limited in his choice of biological pursuits. Even if he chooses an area of biology in which work can be done without this background, his outlook is likely to be so narrow and restricted that he will never achieve the insight and productivity his abilities might otherwise gain him.

If other sciences are important to biology today, they will unquestionably be of greater importance still a decade from now. Chemistry and physics are becoming ever more closely intertwined with biology, and the person who would understand the biology of the future must swallow any hesitancy he may feel and plunge into the study of the physical sciences determined not only to familiarize himself with the facts of those sciences but also to learn to think in their terms. The day of the neat compartmentalization of the sciences is past, and it will never return.

For those of you who plan to go on to more advanced work in the biological sciences, these arguments may seem convincing. But some of you are taking biology now only because you want to know something about the subject as part of your liberal education (or because the course is required and you couldn't get out of it), and you may object that for your purposes a simplified version of biology, omitting all chemistry, would be sufficient. Such an objection misses the basic point of taking an introductory science course. One of the fundamental purposes of such a course is to give you insight into what the science is today, what questions it asks, how it attempts to answer them, and what its probable future lines of development will be. If all chemistry were omitted from this book, you would get an untrue picture of modern biology, for biology without the physical sciences is not the biology of today or of tomorrow. You would hardly wish to get so superficial a view of the facts and methods of biology that it has no relevance to the present or to the future.

THE ELEMENTS

The matter of the universe is composed of a limited number of basic substances called elements. Elements are substances that cannot be decomposed into simpler substances by chemical reactions. There are 92 naturally occurring elements; additional synthetic, or man-made, elements have been manufactured in the laboratory in recent years, raising the current total for both natural and artificial elements to 103. (Quite likely, more artificial elements will have been made by the time you read this book. Here is but one example of why it is so difficult to write a truly up-to-date book on science: Advances are being made so rapidly that statements are often outdated before the ink is dry.)

Each element is designated by a chemical symbol of either one or two letters that stands for its English or Latin name. Thus H is the symbol for hydrogen, O for oxygen, C for carbon, Cl for chlorine, Mg for magnesium, K for potassium (the Latin name is *kalium*), Na for sodium (the Latin name is *natrium*), etc.

Matter is not continuous; i.e. it cannot be subdivided without limit. It is, instead, discontinuous, and progressive subdivision leads ultimately to units indivisible by ordinary chemical means. These units are called *atoms.* The atoms of a particular element are alike in many essential characteristics and differ in many measurable ways from the atoms of other elements. A single atom is customarily represented by the chemical symbol of the element concerned; e.g. N stands for a single atom of nitrogen.

Elements Important in Biology

Not all 92 naturally occurring elements are of particular importance in living organisms. Some of the important ones are shown in Table 2.1. Of these, six play such a salient role in the phenomenon of life that they should be given special mention. They are hydrogen, carbon, oxygen, nitrogen, phosphorus, and sulfur. They occur in all living creatures and are indispensable to life as we know it on this planet. We shall have countless occasions to refer to them during the course of our examination of life processes.

TABLE 2.1

Elements Important in Living Material

Element	Symbol	Atomic number	Approximate percentage of earth's crust	Approximate percentage of human body
Hydrogen	H	1	0.1	9.5
Boron	B	5	Trace	Trace
Carbon	C	6	0.03	18.5
Nitrogen	N	7	Trace	3.3
Oxygen	O	8	46.6	65.0
Fluorine	F	9	0.03	Trace
Sodium	Na	11	2.9	0.2
Magnesium	Mg	12	2.1	0.1
Phosphorus	P	15	0.1	1.0
Sulfur	S	16	0.05	0.3
Chlorine	Cl	17	0.05	0.2
Potassium	K	19	2.6	0.4
Calcium	Ca	20	3.6	1.5
Manganese	Mn	25	0.1	Trace
Iron	Fe	26	5.0	Trace
Cobalt	Co	27	Trace	Trace
Copper	Cu	29	0.01	Trace
Zinc	Zn	30	Trace	Trace
Selenium	Se	34	Trace	Trace
Molybdenum	Mo	42	Trace	Trace
Iodine	I	53	Trace	Trace

You should not get the impression that these six are the only elements essential for life, however. Others such as calcium, sodium, potassium, magnesium, and iron are of great importance in most organisms. Still others, commonly called trace elements, are present in minute amounts in many cells and, despite the extremely small quantities in which they occur, may be indispensable for the maintenance of life. Table 2.1 gives a rough idea of the relative quantities of the various elements in the human body.

Atomic Structure

Atoms are basic units of matter. Even so, it is possible to study the composition of the atoms themselves. Anyone living today in the so-called atomic age is well aware that atoms are composed of still smaller particles, and that if appropriate methods are used these particles can be separated from each other. Atoms, then, are complex entities, and if we are to understand their chemical behavior we must consider their detailed structure.

The Atomic Nucleus. In 1911 the great physicist Lord Rutherford performed a critical series of experiments which demonstrated that the earlier conception of the atom as an essentially homogeneous sphere of positive electricity with negative particles embedded in it was no longer tenable. He suggested instead that the positive charge and almost all of the mass of an atom are concentrated in its center, or *nucleus.* An atomic nucleus is still postulated today. Scientists now think that the nucleus contains two primary particles, *protons* and *neutrons.* Each proton carries an electronic charge of +1. The neutrons, as their name implies, have no charge. Protons and neutrons have roughly the same mass, which is close to one (see Table 2.2).[1]

---

[1] Mass is measured in atomic mass units. They are relative units based on the arbitrary assignment of 16 atomic mass units as the atomic weight of oxygen.

TABLE 2.2

Fundamental Particles

Particle	Mass (atomic mass units)	Charge (electronic charge units)
Electron	0.00055	−1
Proton	1.00732	+1
Neutron	1.00866	0

The number of protons in the nucleus is unique for each element. This number, called the *atomic number,* is usually symbolized by the letter Z and is sometimes written as a subscript immediately before the chemical symbol. Thus $_1H$ indicates that the Z number of hydrogen is one; i.e. its nucleus contains only one proton. Similarly, $_8O$ indicates that oxygen nuclei contain eight protons. Often it is desirable to indicate the total number of protons and neutrons in a nucleus; this number is called the *mass number,* because it approximates the total mass of the nucleus. The mass number is commonly written as a superscript immediately following the chemical symbol. For example, most atoms of oxygen contain eight protons and eight neutrons; the mass number is therefore 16, and the nucleus can be symbolized as O^{16} or, if we wish to show both Z number and mass number, as $_8O^{16}$.

We have indicated that the number of protons (Z) is the same for all atoms of the same element. But the number of neutrons is not always the same, and neither, consequently, is the mass number. For example, most oxygen atoms, as we have said, contain eight protons and eight neutrons and have a mass number of 16; some, however, contain nine neutrons and thus have a mass number of 17 (symbolized as O^{17}), and still others have ten neutrons and a mass number of 18 (symbolized as O^{18}). Atoms of the same element that differ in mass, because they contain different numbers of neutrons, are called *isotopes.* Thus O^{16}, O^{17}, and O^{18} are three isotopes of oxygen.[2] Some elements have as many as 20 isotopes; others have as few as two. Modern nuclear reactors have made it possible to create many new artificial isotopes that do not occur in nature. Apparently the number of neutrons in the nucleus does not affect the chemical properties of an atom, for all isotopes of the same element have essentially the same chemical characteristics.

The number of neutrons does, however, affect the physical properties of a nucleus. Some isotopes are unstable and tend to break down to more stable forms, emitting high-energy radiation in the process. This radiation from the so-called radioactive isotopes is increasingly important in the modern world. Later in this book we shall discuss some of the profound effects high-energy radiation can have upon living material. We shall also refer to some of the ways scientists can use radioactive isotopes as research tools.

The Electrons. The portion of the atom outside the nucleus contains only negatively charged particles, the electrons. Electrons have very little mass (see Table 2.2). As a result, almost the total mass of the atom is contributed by the protons and neutrons in the nucleus, even though the extranuclear region constitutes most of the volume of the atom. Each electron carries a charge of -1; i.e. its charge is exactly opposite that of a proton.

In a normal neutral atom, the number of electrons orbiting around the nucleus is exactly the same as the number of protons in the nucleus of that atom. The positive charges of the protons and the negative charges of the electrons cancel each other, making the total atom neutral. Consequently, in a neutral atom, the Z number represents both the number of

protons inside the nucleus and the number of electrons outside the nucleus. If, then, we see the symbol $_{17}Cl^{35}$, we can tell that a neutral atom of this isotope of chlorine has 17 protons, 18 neutrons, and 17 electrons (Fig. 2.1). Similarly, the symbol $_{19}K^{39}$ means that this isotope of potassium contains 19 protons, 20 neutrons, and 19 electrons.

If we arrange the elements in sequence according to their Z numbers, beginning with hydrogen, which has the number one, and proceeding to uranium, the last of the natural

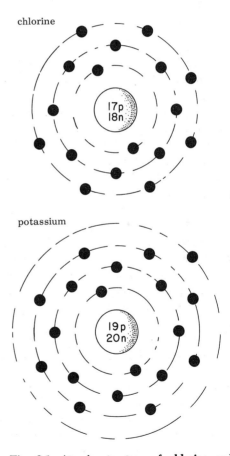

Fig. 2.1. **Atomic structure of chlorine and potassium.** Chlorine has 17 protons and 18 neutrons in its nucleus, and 17 electrons (dark balls) distributed in three orbitals outside the nucleus. Potassium has 19 protons and 20 neutrons in its nucleus and 19 electrons in four orbitals.

2 Three other isotopes of oxygen are known: O^{14}, O^{15}, and O^{19}.

elements, which has the number 92, we are struck by an interesting fact. The various chemical properties of the elements recur at regular intervals in the list. For example, fluorine, number 9, is more like chlorine, number 17, bromine, number 35, and iodine, number 53, than it is like oxygen, number 8, or neon, number 10, the two elements immediately adjacent to it in the list. This tendency for chemical properties to recur periodically throughout the sequence of elements is called the Periodic Law, and is particularly identified with the important work of Dmitri Mendeleev in Russia about 1870.

The explanation for this periodicity must be that it is the electrons of an atom that determine its chemical properties. Electrons are not simply distributed at random around the nucleus but, instead, move very rapidly around the nucleus at statistically predictable distances from it. Since electrons moving at different distances from the nucleus possess different amounts of energy (the greater the distance, the greater the energy), we can say that the different distances represent different energy levels. Apparently, then, not all conceivable energy levels are possible for electrons; electrons can orbit at certain energy levels only. The various possible energy levels, in effect, form a series of concentric shells around the nucleus. There is a maximum number of electrons that each of these shells can contain at any one time. The maximum population for the first energy level is 2, for the second 8, for the third 18, for the fourth 32, etc.

The chemical properties of elements are largely determined by the number of electrons in their outermost shell. If that shell is full, as in helium ($Z = 2$) or neon ($Z = 10$), the element is inert; i.e. it tends not to react chemically with other atoms (Fig. 2.2).[3] If the outermost shell has one electron less than the

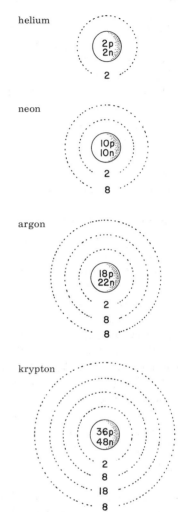

Fig. 2.2. Atomic structure of the inert gases. Each of these elements has a complete outer shell (two electrons for helium and eight electrons for each of the other three) and hence is chemically less active than most other elements (though not totally inactive, as was once thought).

full complement, the element has certain characteristic chemical properties; if it lacks two electrons the element has somewhat different properties; if it lacks seven electrons it has very different properties. Although the most stable configuration for an atom is that in which all its electron shells are complete, it turns out that the third and all later shells

[3] Recently it has been demonstrated that under appropriate conditions even the so-called inert gases can react chemically with some other elements.

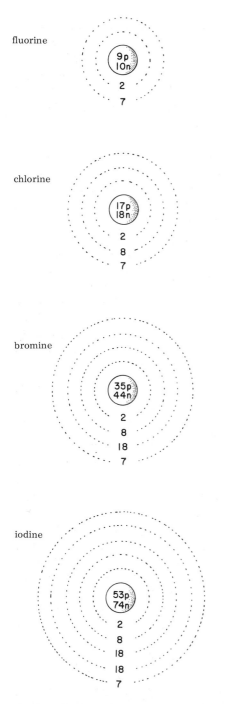

fluorine

chlorine

bromine

iodine

Fig. 2.3 Atomic structure of the halogens. These four elements have similar chemical properties because each has seven electrons in its outermost shell.

behave in many ways as though they were complete when they contain only eight electrons, even though they can hold more than eight.[4] For example, argon $(Z = 18)$ and krypton $(Z = 36)$ are inert gases because they have eight electrons in their outermost energy levels (Fig. 2.2). For our purposes, then, we can consider the first shell complete when it holds two electrons and every other shell complete when it holds eight electrons.

The periodicity of chemical properties in the table of elements now becomes understandable. We said earlier that fluorine is chemically similar to chlorine, bromine, and iodine even though these elements are not close to each other in the list of elements. The critical characteristic shared by these four elements is that each has seven electrons in its outer shell (Fig. 2.3). Oxygen (Fig. 2.4), the element immediately preceding fluorine, has six electrons in its outer shell and hence is chemically rather different from fluorine, despite its proximity in the list. Neon, the element just after fluorine, has a full eight electrons in its outer shell and therefore lacks the reactivity of fluorine.

Since it is the outermost shell of electrons alone that determines most of the chemical properties of an atom, we commonly disregard

[4] The reasons for this are not fully clear.

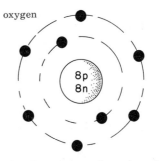

oxygen

Fig. 2.4. Atomic structure of oxygen. There are six electrons in the outer shell; hence oxygen needs two more electrons for a complete shell of eight electrons.

the inner shells. A convenient way to represent the electronic configuration of the outer shell is to symbolize each electron by a dot placed near the chemical symbol for the element under consideration. Thus fluorine and chlorine, which, as we have said, have seven electrons in their outer energy level, would have the electronic symbols

$$: \overset{\cdot\cdot}{\underset{\cdot\cdot}{F}} \cdot \qquad : \overset{\cdot\cdot}{\underset{\cdot\cdot}{Cl}} \cdot$$

Similarly, hydrogen with one electron in its shell, carbon with four in its outer shell, nitrogen with five, and oxygen with six would be shown as follows:

$$H \cdot \qquad \cdot \overset{\cdot}{\underset{\cdot}{C}} \cdot \qquad \cdot \overset{\cdot\cdot}{\underset{\cdot}{N}} \cdot \qquad : \overset{\cdot\cdot}{\underset{\cdot}{O}} \cdot$$

It should be emphasized that the placement of the dots has no significance and in no way indicates the actual positions of the electrons concerned.

CHEMICAL BONDS

The atoms of most elements possess the property of binding to other atoms to form new and more complex aggregates. When two or more atoms are bound together in this fashion, the attraction that holds them together is called a chemical bond. Each bond represents a certain amount of potential chemical energy. The atoms of a particular element characteristically can form only a certain precise and limited number of such bonds; atoms of some other element may be capable of forming a different but equally precise and limited number of bonds. Our previous examination of the nature of atoms should now help us understand how atoms bond together and why each element has its own characteristic bonding capacity.

Ionic Bonds

We have said that atoms are in a particularly stable configuration when their outer electron shell is complete, i.e., in most cases, when it contains eight electrons. There is consequently a general tendency for atoms to form complete outer shells by reacting with other atoms. These reactions are the stuff of chemistry, and it is clear that the tendency of atoms to gain complete outer shells forms the basis upon which all chemistry is built.

Consider, for example, an atom of sodium ($Z = 11$). This atom has two electrons in its first shell, eight in its second shell, and only one in its third shell. One way sodium might gain a complete outer shell would be to acquire seven more electrons from some other atom or atoms. But the sodium would then have an enormous excess of negative charge, and, since like charges repel each other, the electrons would tend to push each other away from the sodium. In point of fact, sodium cannot obtain a full outer shell by appropriating seven additional electrons. An alternative way, and the way actually followed in nature, is for the sodium atom to give up the lone electron in its third shell to some electron acceptor, leaving the complete second shell as the new outer shell (Fig. 2.5).

Next, consider an atom of chlorine ($Z = 17$). This atom has two electrons in its first shell, eight in its second shell, and seven in its third shell. In other words, its outer shell is almost complete, lacking only a single electron. It cannot lose the seven electrons in its outer shell for reasons similar to those preventing sodium from gaining seven electrons; the electrons are too strongly attracted to the protons of the chlorine nucleus for seven to be removed, an operation that would leave an excess charge of $+7$ in the atom. It is by gaining an extra electron from some electron donor that chlorine can acquire a complete outer shell.

If a strong electron donor like sodium (i.e. an atom with a strong tendency to get rid of an electron) and a strong electron acceptor like chlorine (i.e. an atom with a strong tendency to acquire an extra electron) come into

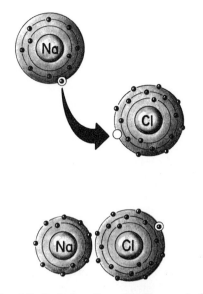

Fig. 2.5. Ionic bonding of sodium and chlorine. Sodium has only one electron in its outer shell, while chlorine has seven. Sodium acts as an electron donor, giving up the lone electron in its outer shell, whereupon the complete second shell functions as its new outer shell. Chlorine acts as an electron acceptor, picking up an additional electron to complete its outer shell. But after sodium has donated an electron to chlorine (top), the sodium, left with one more proton than it has electrons, has a positive charge. Conversely, the chlorine, with one more electron than it has protons, has a negative charge. The two charged atoms, called ions, are attracted to each other by their unlike charges (bottom). The result is sodium chloride (NaCl).

contact, an electron may be completely transferred from the donor to the acceptor. The result, in the present example, is a sodium atom with one less electron than normal and a chlorine atom with one more electron than normal. Once it has lost an electron, the sodium is left with one more proton than it has electrons, and it therefore has a net charge of $+1$. Similarly, the chlorine atom that gained an electron has one more electron than it has protons and has a net charge of -1. Such charged atoms or aggregates of atoms are called *ions,* and are symbolized by the appropriate chemical symbol followed by a superscript indi-

cating the charge. Sodium and chlorine ions are written as Na^+ and Cl^-.

A sodium ion with its positive charge and a chlorine ion with its negative charge tend to attract each other, since opposite charges attract. Consequently the two ions are held together by an electrical attraction and form the compound we know as table salt, or sodium chloride, NaCl. Such a bond, involving the complete transference of an electron from one atom to another and the binding together of the two ions thus formed, is termed an *ionic bond.*

Ionic bonding may involve the transfer of more than one electron, as in calcium chloride, another common salt. Calcium $(Z = 20)$ has two electrons in its outermost shell, and it loses both to form the calcium ion Ca^{++} (Fig. 2.6).

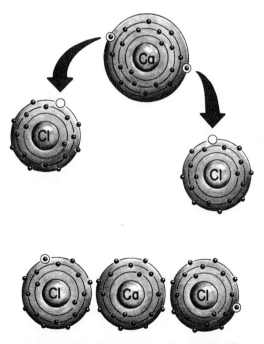

Fig. 2.6. Ionic bonding of calcium and chlorine. Calcium has two electrons in its outer shell. It donates one to each of two chlorine atoms, and the two negatively charged chlorine ions thus formed are attracted to the positively charged calcium ion (Ca^{++}) to form calcium chloride $(CaCl_2)$.

Chlorine, however, need gain only one electron to complete an octet in its outer shell, as we have already seen. As a result, it takes two chlorine atoms to act as acceptors for the two electrons from a single calcium atom, and the calcium chloride formed involves the bonding together of a total of three ions, symbolized as $CaCl_2$, where the subscript 2 indicates that there are two chlorine atoms for each calcium atom in this compound. We can say, then, that calcium has a bonding capacity, or valence, of $+2$, while sodium has a valence of $+1$ and chlorine a valence of -1.

Ionic bonds are formed primarily in reactions between atoms or aggregates of atoms that must lose only a few electrons to gain a complete outer shell and atoms that must gain only a few electrons. In other words, ionic bonds occur between strong electron donors (which are configurations with only a few electrons in their outer energy level) and strong electron acceptors (which are configurations with nearly eight electrons in their outer energy level). Ionic bonding is not common between configurations that have intermediate numbers of electrons in the outer shells, or between units both of which are strong electron donors or electron acceptors.

In many instances *ionization* (i.e. the transfer of one or more electrons from one atom to another to form ions) occurs without true molecular formation. A molecule is generally defined as an electrically neutral aggregate of atoms bonded together strongly enough to be regarded as a single entity. Substances like sodium chloride (NaCl) or calcium chloride ($CaCl_2$), in which the bonds are almost exclusively ionic, have a pronounced tendency to dissociate into separate ions when in solution. When they are dissociated or ionized in this manner, they do not exist as molecules. In solution, NaCl forms two separate entities, a Na^+ ion and a Cl^- ion (Fig. 2.7). Similarly, $CaCl_2$ in solution forms three separate entities, a Ca^{++} ion and two Cl^- ions. Even in the

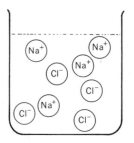

Fig. 2.7. Ionization of sodium chloride. When in solution, the NaCl dissociates into separate Na^+ and Cl^- ions.

solid state, ionic compounds often do not form discrete molecules in the usual sense. In solid sodium chloride, many sodium and chlorine atoms are bound together into a large crystal; there are no separate molecules composed of one sodium atom bonded to one chlorine atom, as the molecular symbol NaCl might seem to indicate. In a sense, the entire crystal is a single molecule, although in practice the term "molecule" is not used in such cases.

Substances wholly or partly ionized in water play many important roles in the functioning of biological systems. Therefore we should briefly mention some of the properties of such ionized materials. A first and obvious fact is that ions, being charged particles, behave differently from neutral atoms or molecules in living systems. In a later chapter, we shall refer, for instance, to the effects of charge upon the movements of materials through the membranes of living cells. Another characteristic of some importance is the fact that solutions containing dissociated ions can conduct electric currents. Because ionic compounds produce conducting solutions, they are called electrolytes. Other types of compounds that do not dissociate into ions in water and therefore do not produce conducting solutions are called non-electrolytes.

Two classes of ionic compounds are of such immense importance that they deserve special mention. These are the *acids* and the *bases.*

There are a number of different definitions of acids and bases, but for our purposes an acid can be defined simply as a substance that increases the concentration of hydrogen ions (H^+) in water, a base as a substance that increases the concentration of hydroxyl ions (OH^-) in water. The degree of acidity or basicity (usually called alkalinity) of a solution is usually measured in terms of a scale known as the *pH scale.* A solution is neutral, neither acidic nor basic (i.e. it contains equal concentrations of H^+ ions and OH^- ions), if its pH is exactly 7. Substances with a pH of less than 7 are acidic (i.e. contain a higher concentration of H^+ ions than of OH^- ions); the lower the pH, the more acidic the substance. Conversely, substances with a pH higher than 7 are basic (i.e. contain a higher concentration of OH^- ions than of H^+ ions); the higher the pH, the more basic the substance.

Covalent Bonds

Ionic bonds, as we have just seen, involve complete transfer of electrons from one atom to another. But in many, indeed most, cases bonding occurs without complete transfer, by a sharing of electrons between the atoms involved. Bonds of this sort, based on shared electrons, are called *covalent bonds.*

Consider the first element, hydrogen ($Z = 1$). An atom of hydrogen has only one orbital electron. A complete first shell would contain two electrons. If the hydrogen gained an electron, it would have a full shell, but there would be twice as much negative charge as positive charge in the atom (one proton and two electrons). Hydrogen does not, in fact, ionize in this manner. It tends to do the reverse; it loses its single electron, forming H^+ ions, which are simply isolated protons since the hydrogen nucleus contains no neutrons. But suppose there is no strong electron acceptor available and the hydrogen cannot ionize. One possible

reaction is for two atoms of hydrogen to bond with each other to form what we call molecular hydrogen, H_2

$$H \cdot + H \cdot \rightarrow H : H$$

In this molecule, each atom shares its electron with the other atom, so that each hydrogen has, in a sense, two electrons in its shell (Fig. 2.8). Clearly, when two atoms of the same element bond together, as in this case, the likelihood is, not that one will have more attraction for the two electrons than the other, but that these will be shared equally by the two atoms. In other words, there is no more probability that the negative charges will be nearer one atom than that they will be nearer the other atom. Such a bond is said to be a *nonpolar* covalent bond.

Suppose now that, instead of being bonded to each other, two hydrogen atoms are covalently bonded to an oxygen atom, forming water, H_2O

$$H \cdot + H \cdot + : \overset{\cdot \cdot}{\underset{\cdot}{O}} \cdot \rightarrow H : \overset{\cdot \cdot}{\underset{\cdot \cdot}{O}} : H$$

Oxygen ($Z = 8$) has only six electrons in its outer shell and needs two more. By sharing electrons with two hydrogen atoms, the oxygen atom can obtain a full outer octet, while at the same time each hydrogen obtains a complete first shell of two electrons. A covalent bond between a hydrogen atom and an oxygen atom is somewhat different from one between two hydrogen atoms or between two oxygen atoms, however. No two elements have exactly the

Fig. 2.8. Covalent bonding of two hydrogen atoms. The electrons are shared, so that, in a sense, each atom has two electrons in its shell.

same affinity for electrons. Consequently, when a covalent bond forms between two different elements, the shared electrons tend to be pulled closer to one element than to the other. Such a bond is called a *polar* covalent bond; i.e. the charge is distributed asymmetrically within the bond. In water, the electrons are closer to the oxygen than to the hydrogen.

Once we realize that many covalent bonds are polar, and that there are all degrees of polarity, from bonds where the electrons are much closer to one atom than to the other to bonds where they are only slightly closer to one than to the other, we begin to see that there is actually no sharp distinction between ionic bonds and covalent bonds. Ionic bonds are simply one extreme, where the electrons are pulled completely from one atom to the other, and nonpolar covalent bonds are the other extreme, where the electrons are pulled exactly equally by two atoms. Polar covalent bonds represent the middle ground between these two extremes; the electrons are pulled closer to one atom than to the other, but not all the way. Further, electrons do not remain in one position, but are constantly moving. Consequently, a bond may exhibit resonance; i.e. it may be essentially ionic one instant and covalent the next instant. Thus even a compound that is primarily covalent may be very slightly ionized.

An understanding of the phenomenon of polarity helps us understand many of the properties of various molecules in living systems. Whole molecules can be polar as a result of the polarity of bonds within the molecules. If we return to the example of water, we can see (Fig. 2.9) that even though the two hydrogen-oxygen bonds are polar, it would be possible to arrange the atoms in the molecule in such a way that the charge would be distributed symmetrically within the molecule as a whole and the water molecule itself would be nonpolar. But this is apparently not the actual arrangement; the three atoms, instead of being in a straight line, which would be a nonpolar

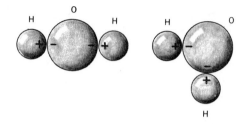

Fig. 2.9. Molecular structure of water. Two hydrogen atoms are bonded covalently to one oxygen atom, but the shared electrons are pulled closer to the oxygen than to the hydrogen. The bonds are thus polar, with the oxygen side more negative. If the three atoms were arranged linearly, as at left, the charge distribution within the whole molecule would be symmetrical and the molecule would be nonpolar. But in reality the atoms are arranged as shown at right; so the charge distribution is asymmetrical and the molecule is polar.

arrangement, probably form a bent chain or V-shaped structure, with the oxygen forming the apex of the V and the two hydrogen atoms forming the ends of the arms. We have already said that the electrons are closer to the oxygen than to the hydrogen; it follows that there is a concentration of negative charge near the oxygen end of the molecule and a concentration of positive charge near the hydrogen end. Therefore the water molecule is polar.

In our discussion of covalent bonds so far, we have mentioned only the sharing of one electron pair between two atoms, i.e. the formation of a single bond. Sometimes two atoms share two or three electron pairs and form double or triple bonds. When two atoms of oxygen bond together, they form a double bond (remember that an oxygen atom needs two electrons to complete its outer shell), and when two atoms of nitrogen $(Z = 7)$ bond together, they form a triple bond because each nitrogen atom needs three additional electrons to fill its outer shell:

$$: \overset{..}{O} : : \overset{..}{O} : \qquad : N : : : N :$$

We have so far been diagraming covalent bonds by a pair of dots representing a pair of electrons. Often, however, each pair of shared electrons, which constitute a covalent bond, is simply indicated by a line between the two atoms, and the other electrons in the outer shells are ignored. Shown in this manner, H_2, H_2O, O_2, and N_2, the molecules we have discussed, appear as follows:

$$H—H \quad H—O—H \quad O=O \quad N≡N$$

You will note that, for convenience, the water molecule is shown as if the atoms were in a straight line, even though we know that they are not. If we wished to be fully accurate, we would also indicate that O_2 molecules do not always contain double bonds; often each oxygen atom in the molecule has an unpaired electron, through which the molecule acquires special magnetic properties, but such considerations go beyond the scope of our treatment here.

We have seen that hydrogen atoms tend to form only one bond, oxygen two bonds, and nitrogen three bonds. In other words, hydrogen has a covalent bonding capacity, or valence, of one; oxygen a valence of two; and nitrogen usually a valence of three. Notice that for covalent bonding we do not put a plus or minus in front of the valence, as we do for ionic bonding. The reason, of course, is that electrons are not completely captured or lost, but are simply shared.

Hydrogen Bonds

One other type of bond, which is extremely important in biological systems, should be mentioned here. This is the so-called *hydrogen bond* or hydrogen bridge. It forms only between a few small very electronegative atoms like oxygen, fluorine, and nitrogen. It is a low-energy bond in which a hydrogen atom is apparently bonded simultaneously to two other atoms; i.e. the hydrogen atom is shared between two other atoms and forms a bridge between them. For example, water molecules are commonly bonded together by hydrogen bonds between the oxygen atoms of the water;

the result is a kind of giant molecule or super-molecule (Fig. 2.10). Similarly, hydrogen bonds often serve to bind water molecules loosely to the molecules of many other compounds. We shall refer to hydrogen bonds again when we discuss such critically important substances as proteins and nucleic acids.

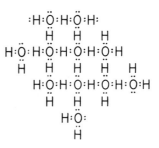

Fig. 2.10. **Hydrogen bonding between water molecules.** The hydrogen atoms tend to be shared between two oxygen atoms, so that it is difficult to say where one H_2O molecule ends and another begins.

SOME IMPORTANT INORGANIC MOLECULES

Chemists have traditionally referred to complex molecules containing the element carbon as *organic* compounds. All other compounds are called inorganic compounds. The designation "inorganic" should not mislead you into assuming that these compounds play no role in the lives of living organisms, however. On the contrary, many inorganic substances are basic to the chemistry of life and will often have to be considered in our examination of the phenomenon of life. We cannot mention all such critical inorganic molecules at this point, but a few must be examined now if we are to have any hope of understanding the more complex organic compounds to which we will soon turn our attention.

Water

We have already said that a molecule of water is composed of two atoms of hydrogen bonded to one atom of oxygen and is therefore symbolized as H_2O. We have also indicated that the bonds between the hydrogen and oxygen are primarily polar covalent (although there is always a small degree of ionization—roughly one molecule out of 554 million is ionized), that the water molecule itself is polar, and that in the liquid and solid states many water molecules are bound together by hydrogen bonds. What more can we say about water here?

Living things are composed largely of water; roughly 80 to 90 percent of living material is water. Not only is water the major internal component, but it is also one of the principal external environmental factors affecting organisms. The chemistry of life, and indeed much of the chemistry of the earth, is water chemistry (i.e. the chemical reactions take place within a water medium). One of the main reasons is that water is among the best solvents known; more different substances will dissolve in water, and in greater quantity, than in almost any other liquid. It is even sometimes called the "universal solvent"—a rather misleading phrase, as there are actually many materials, such as oxygen, gasoline, and oils, for which water is a poor solvent. Nonetheless, its excellent properties as a solvent in general and its tendency to produce ionization of substances in solution certainly play important roles in facilitating chemical reactions. But this ubiquitous substance does more than simply facilitate reactions; it is itself often a reactant or a product of chemical reactions. Water is the principal source of the hydrogen and one of the principal sources of the oxygen that becomes incorporated into the many organic compounds in the bodies of living things.

Aside from its essential chemical roles, water also plays many important physical roles in the world of living things. It is a medium of transport for substances within the bodies of plants and animals. It is almost certainly the medium within which life arose, and vast numbers of organisms still live all or part of their lives in it. The great amount of heat necessary to increase the temperature of water or to change liquid water to water vapor and, conversely, the great amount of heat liberated into the environment when liquid water changes to ice all play crucial roles in stabilizing temperatures on the earth; since the quantity of water on the earth's surface is enormous, it follows that the warming or cooling of this water is necessary if any major widespread temperature changes are to occur. Water is not limited to maintaining a high degree of constancy of temperature, however; it also plays an immensely important role in determining the absolute temperature value. The water vapor in the atmosphere exerts what has been called a "greenhouse effect"; i.e. the vapor absorbs much of the sunlight striking it and also much of the radiation re-emitted by the earth. The absorbed radiation warms the atmosphere, which, in turn, warms the earth's surface below it.

One other curious property of water may be mentioned. Unlike most other substances, when it is frozen it is less dense than when it is a few degrees above the freezing point; it has its greatest density at 4°C. Consequently, ice floats and water at 4°C sinks. This means that bodies of water usually freeze from the top down instead of from the bottom up. Organisms living near the bottom of ponds and lakes are thus protected.

Carbon Dioxide

Carbon $(Z = 6)$ has only four electrons in its outer electron shell and, as a result, has a covalent bonding capacity of four. Carbon dioxide (CO_2) is the compound formed when two atoms of oxygen bond to one atom of carbon. Though this substance contains carbon, it is often thought of as inorganic, because it is simpler than most other organic compounds.

Only a very small fraction of the atmosphere, roughly 0.03 percent, is CO_2; yet atmospheric carbon dioxide is the principal inorganic source of carbon, and carbon is the principal structural element of living matter. Before CO_2 can take part in chemical reactions, it must usually first dissolve in water, which it does very readily, and then react with the water to form carbonic acid, H_2CO_3

$$CO_2 + H_2O \rightarrow H_2CO_3$$

This reaction involves so little energy change that it is easily reversible, and CO_2 can readily be released from water solution when conditions are appropriate:

$$H_2CO_3 \rightarrow CO_2 + H_2O$$

Carbon dioxide and water are the raw materials from which green plants manufacture many complex organic compounds essential to life, as we shall see in detail in a later chapter. And when these complex compounds have run their course in the life system, they are broken down again to carbon dioxide and water, and the carbon dioxide is eventually released into the atmosphere. The simple compound carbon dioxide, then, is the beginning and the end of the immensely complex carbon cycle in nature.

Oxygen

Molecular oxygen (O_2) constitutes approximately 20 percent of the atmosphere. It is a necessary material for maintenance of life in most organisms, although a few can live without it. It can be utilized directly, without change, by both plants and animals. Although oxygen is not very soluble in water, as we have already mentioned, enough dissolves to supply the needs of aquatic organisms, provided that the water is not too hot and that its surface is exposed to the air or that green plants are growing in it and constantly release O_2 into it by the process of photosynthesis, a process we shall examine in detail in a later chapter.

Although most organisms require O_2, most

of the oxygen incorporated into the structures of living things comes, not from O_2, but from H_2O. The principal functions of O_2 in the life system are seen to be—once the intricacies of its reactions are stripped away—essentially janitorial; it combines with waste hydrogen and carbon to form water and carbon dioxide, two waste substances of which organisms can easily rid themselves.

SOME SIMPLE ORGANIC CHEMISTRY

Organic compounds are based on the element carbon ($Z = 6$), which has a covalent bonding capacity of four. This element is present in an enormous number of known chemical compounds; of all the elements, only hydrogen has more known compounds. Although carbon can and does bond to a variety of different elements, it is most commonly bonded to hydrogen, oxygen, nitrogen, or more carbon.

Of central importance in organic chemistry are the compounds containing carbon and hydrogen; the number of different compounds of this kind, called hydrocarbons, is immense. A basic reason for the great variety of hydrocarbons is the readiness with which carbon-to-carbon bonds can form, producing chains of varying lengths and shapes (Fig. 2.11). These chains may be simple, as in methane, ethane, butane, decane, and other still longer substances; or they may be branched, as in isobutane and isopentane; or they may form circles of varying numbers of carbons, as in cyclopropane and cyclohexane. Obviously, the more atoms there are in a molecule, the more different arrangements of those atoms are possible, giving compounds of the same atomic content and molecular formula but differing structures and hence differing properties (Fig. 2.12). Such compounds are called *isomers* (do not confuse these with isotopes, which are very different things). Very large organic molecules may have hundreds of different isomers.

Hydrocarbon chains may be

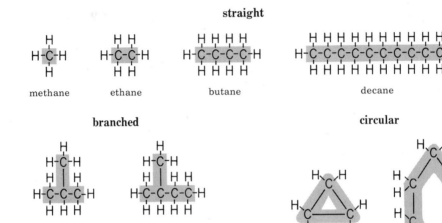

straight

methane   ethane   butane   decane

branched   **circular**

isobutane   isopentane

cyclopropane

cyclohexane

Carbon-to-carbon bonds may be

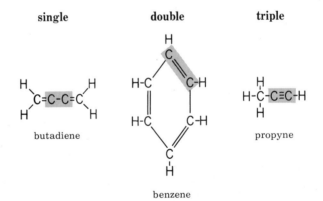

single   **double**   **triple**

butadiene   propyne

benzene

Fig. 2.11. Examples of hydrocarbons. Hydrocarbon chains may be straight, branched, or circular (top). Carbon-to-carbon bonds may be single, double, or triple (bottom).

Another factor adding variety to hydrocarbon compounds is the capacity of adjacent carbon atoms to form single, double, or triple bonds, as in butadiene, benzene, and propyne (Fig. 2.11). And, of course, substitution of other elements or groups of elements for hydrogen atoms makes possible an almost infinite number of derivative hydrocarbons. The total number of hydrocarbons and derivatives has been estimated at more than half a million, and this may be a conservative estimate.

Obviously, we cannot even attempt in these few pages to cover the enormous field of organic chemistry, but as the word "organic" suggests, organisms are composed of organic substances, and we cannot understand many of the most important attributes of life unless we are familiar with a few simple facts of

ISOMERIC HEXOSES

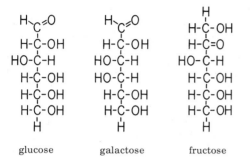

glucose   galactose   fructose

Fig. 2.12. Three isomeric hexoses. Each of these six-carbon sugars has the same molecular formula, $C_6H_{12}O_6$; hence each is an isomer of the others. Fructose, which is a ketone sugar (one with the double-bonded oxygen attached to an internal carbon), is a structural isomer of the other two. Glucose and galactose, which are both aldehyde sugars (with the double-bonded oxygen attached to a terminal carbon), are optical isomers of each other.

organic chemistry. We shall mention only four major classes of organic compounds: carbohydrates, lipids, proteins, and nucleic acids.

Carbohydrates

Carbohydrates are compounds that contain only carbon, hydrogen, and oxygen. Characteristically, the hydrogen and oxygen are present in the same proportions as in water; i.e. there are two hydrogen atoms and one oxygen atom for each carbon atom. Consequently the grouping CH_2O, diagrammed as

H—C—OH

recurs frequently in carbohydrate molecules.

Some carbohydrates, like starch and cellulose, are very large and complex molecules. Fortunately for our grasp of them, however, they, like most very large organic molecules, are composed of many simpler "building-block" compounds bonded together. Almost an infinity of various complex substances can thus be synthesized from only a few, relatively simple constituent molecules. If we understand the constituent or building-block compounds, then we shall be able to understand much about the more complex substances.

Simple Sugars. The basic carbohydrate molecules are simple sugars, or monosaccharides. All sugars, when in straight-chain form, contain a C=O group (Fig. 2.12); if the double-bonded O is attached to the terminal C of a chain, the combination is called an aldehyde group, while if it is attached to a nonterminal C, the combination is called a ketone group. The carbon chain that forms the backbone of the sugar can be of different lengths. Some sugars contain as few as three carbons (trioses); others contain five carbons (pentoses), six carbons (hexoses), or more. Though both trioses and pentoses play important biological roles and will be mentioned in later chapters, it is the hexoses, six-carbon sugars, that are the most important as building-block compounds for more complex carbohydrates.

There are many six-carbon sugars, of which glucose and fructose (Fig. 2.12) are two of the most important. Since these two sugars contain the same number of carbon atoms, and since the proportions of oxygen and hydrogen atoms are constant in carbohydrates, it follows that glucose and fructose (and other six-carbon sugars) are isomers of each other; i.e. they have the same molecular formula, $C_6H_{12}O_6$.

In addition to this kind of structural isomerism, which is readily understandable, there is another more subtle kind, called stereoisomerism. In a given pair of stereoisomers, identical groups are attached to the carbon atoms, but the spatial arrangements of the attached groups are different. The two middle compounds shown in Fig. 2.13 are geometric stereoisomers; if all the carbon-to-carbon bonds in these two molecules were single bonds, the two would in fact be the same compound, because free rotation is possible around a single bond, though not around a double bond. The optical stereoisomers shown at the bottom of

STRUCTURAL ISOMERS

ethyl alcohol　　　　dimethyl ether

GEOMETRIC ISOMERS

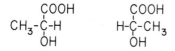

maleic acid　　　　fumaric acid

OPTICAL ISOMERS

l-lactic acid　　　　d-lactic acid

Fig. 2.13. Three types of isomerism. The two structural isomers differ in the basic grouping of their constituent atoms, one being an alcohol (characterized by an OH group) and the other an ether (characterized by an oxygen bonded between two carbons). The two geometric isomers are fixed in different spatial arrangements by their inability to rotate around the double bond between the middle two carbons. The two optical isomers are mirror images of each other; as shown in Fig. 2.14, the two asymmetrical molecules cannot be superimposed.

Fig. 2.13 are harder to understand at first than geometric stereoisomers. You must keep in mind that molecules are not flat, even though we often draw them that way for convenience. In all likelihood, the carbon valences are arranged around the carbon like the apexes of a tetrahedron, and if the groups attached to each of the four valences are different, there will be some alternative arrangements of these

groups that will not be superimposable (Fig. 2.14). If you compare the two sugars glucose and galactose, shown in Fig. 2.12, you will see that they, too, are optical isomers of each other; the position of one OH group is different. Isomers of this sort tend to rotate the plane of polarized light when such light is passed through a solution of the compound. If an optically active isomer rotates the plane of polarized light to the right, it is called a *d* isomer (for *dextro*, from the Latin for right), and if it rotates the plane of the light to the left, it is called an *l* isomer (for *levo*, from the Latin for left).[5] The *d* and *l* isomers of a com-

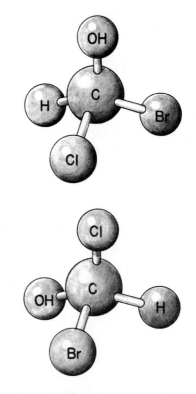

Fig. 2.14. Models of two optical isomers. No matter which way you turned these models, you could not superimpose them so as to make all like atoms face each other.

[5] Actually, the *d* and *l* designations were first used with reference to the direction of rotation of polarized light, but they later came by convention to be applied to two classes of compounds differentiated by the arrangement of the groups attached to the asymmetric

pound may appear very similar, but their biological properties are usually completely different. For reasons not clear to us, almost all naturally occurring sugars are of the *dextro* type.

We have said that glucose is one of the most important simple sugars; in fact, it is *the* most important. Let us look at it in more detail. You will see from Figure 2.12 that glucose is an aldehyde sugar; i.e. its double-bonded oxygen is attached to a terminal carbon. But now we must admit to you that glucose does not always exist as a straight-chain aldehyde compound; indeed, this is probably its least common form. Sometimes it exists in ring form —most often, probably, with the ring composed of five carbons and one oxygen (Fig. 2.15). Glucose is said to resonate between these forms; i.e. its internal configuration is constantly in a state of flux, and no single structural formula can fully depict it.

Glucose plays a unique role in the chemistry of life. It is in a very real sense the crossroads of the chemical pathways in the bodies of plants and animals. Other six-carbon *monosaccharides* (simple sugars) like fructose and galactose are constantly being converted into glucose or synthesized from glucose. The

more complex carbohydrates such as disaccharides and polysaccharides are composed of monosaccharides bonded together in sequence. And even such classes of compounds as fats and proteins can be converted into simple sugars in the living body.

Disaccharides. Disaccharides, or double sugars, are compound sugars composed of two simple sugars bonded together through a reaction that involves the removal of a molecule of water. This kind of reaction is called a condensation reaction or a dehydration reaction.

Let us first examine the double sugar maltose, or malt sugar. This compound is synthesized by a condensation reaction between two molecules of glucose, described by the following equation:

$$2C_6H_{12}O_6 \rightarrow C_{12}H_{22}O_{11} + H_2O$$

This equation tells us very little, however. Any simple six-carbon sugar has the formula $C_6H_{12}O_6$, and any double sugar synthesized from such building blocks will have the formula $C_{12}H_{22}O_{11}$. Consequently the above equation can describe many different reactions involving a variety of reactants and products. If we wish to see specifically what is involved in the condensation synthesis of maltose, we must look at a diagram that indicates the structures of the molecules (Fig. 2.16). Then we see that the hydrogen atom from a hydroxyl group (OH) of one molecule of glucose combines with a complete hydroxyl group from the other molecule of glucose to form water.[6] The oxygen valence vacated by removal of hydrogen and the carbon valence vacated by removal of OH are filled by the bonding together of the oxygen of one glucose molecule with the carbon of the other glucose molecule. As a result, the two glucose units are connected

FORMS OF GLUCOSE

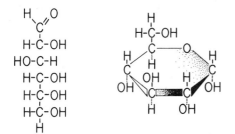

Fig. 2.15. Two forms of glucose. Glucose may exist in the straight-chain aldehyde form shown at left or as a ring structure, as shown at right. The ring structure is more common.

carbon atom farthest from the double-bonded oxygen. Thus fructose is a *d* sugar, but rotates light to the left and is described by *d* (−); glucose rotates light to the right and is described by *d* (+).

[6] It must be pointed out that this is not exactly the way sugars are combined in the bodies of living organisms. Phosphate groups are first attached to the sugars, and it is this group that is removed in the condensation reaction, but the end result is just what it would be if water had been directly removed.

SYNTHESIS OF A DOUBLE SUGAR

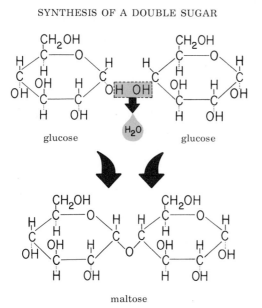

Fig. 2.16. Synthesis of a double sugar. Removal of a molecule of water between the two molecules of glucose results in formation of a bond between the two. The double sugar produced is maltose.

by way of an oxygen atom shared between them. The product is the double sugar maltose. *Sucrose,* our common table sugar, is also a disaccharide. It differs from maltose in that it is synthesized by a condensation between a molecule of glucose and a molecule of fructose.

Lactose, or milk sugar, is a double sugar composed of glucose and galactose.

Having seen how double sugars are synthesized, we should also consider the reverse, the breaking of the disaccharide into its constituent simple sugars. This reaction involves addition of a water molecule, and is called *hydrolysis:*

$$C_{12}H_{22}O_{11} + H_2O \rightarrow 2C_6H_{12}O_6$$

We will focus particular attention on hydrolysis reactions when we discuss digestion in a later chapter.

We are now in a position to define a simple sugar, or monosaccharide, more precisely than we have so far done. Unlike compound sugars, a monosaccharide is a sugar that cannot be hydrolyzed into smaller carbon-containing substances.

Polysaccharides. The prefix *poly* means many, and polysaccharides are complex carbohydrates composed of many simple-sugar building blocks bonded together in long chains (Fig. 2.17). They are synthesized by exactly the same kind of condensation reactions as the disaccharides. And like the disaccharides, they can be broken down to their constituent sugars by hydrolysis.

A number of complex polysaccharides are of great importance in biology. *Starches,* for example, are principal storage products of plants;

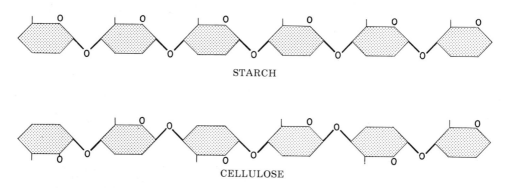

Fig. 2.17. Two polysaccharides. Small segments of molecules of starch and cellulose are shown. Each of these polymers consists of a very large number of glucose units bonded together, but the units are arranged differently in the two.

they are composed of many glucose units bonded together. There are many slightly different types of starch, varying in the number of constituent sugar molecules, the degree of branching, etc. *Glycogen* is a principal storage product in animals and is sometimes called "animal starch"; its molecules are more branched than those of starch. *Cellulose* is a highly insoluble polysaccharide occurring widely in plants, where it is a major supporting material; the bonds between its sugars are somewhat different from those of starch and glycogen, and seem to be more resistant to hydrolysis.

Reactions like those that form polysaccharides, i.e. reactions in which small molecules bond together to form long chains, are called polymerization reactions. The products formed are called *polymers.* From our examination of polysaccharides, it is plain that if polymerization between molecules A, B, C, D, etc. is to occur, one end of molecule A must be capable of interacting with the other end of molecule B so as to split out some small group such as water, and each molecule must contain two functional groups so that after the first two combine, the free ends can continue to react and extend the polymer. Polymers of several types play many critical roles in biology, as we shall see.

Lipids

Lipids constitute a second major group of important biological compounds. Like carbohydrates, they are composed principally of carbon, hydrogen, and oxygen; but unlike carbohydrates, they may sometimes also contain other elements, particularly phosphorus and nitrogen. They differ from carbohydrates in containing a much smaller proportion of oxygen. They are insoluble in water.

Fats.   Among the best-known lipids are the fats. Each molecule of fat is composed of two different types of building-block compounds, an alcohol called *glycerol* (also sometimes called glycerin) and *fatty acids.* Glycerol has a backbone of three carbon atoms; attached to each carbon is a hydroxyl (OH) group (Fig. 2.18). (It is the presence of an OH group attached to a carbon atom that characterizes a compound as an alcohol; hence the hydroxyl group is sometimes termed the alcoholic functional group.)

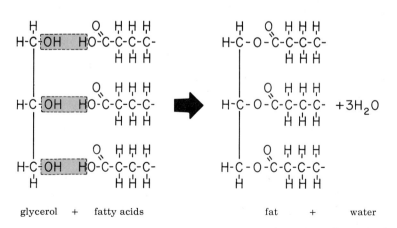

glycerol   +   fatty acids   fat   +   water

Fig. 2.18. Synthesis of a fat. Removal of three molecules of water results in the bonding of three molecules of fatty acid to a single molecule of glycerol. The carbon chains of the fatty acids are longer than shown here.

Fatty acids, like all organic acids, contain a COOH group (called a carboxyl group):

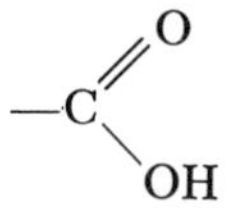

$$-C\begin{smallmatrix} \nearrow O \\ \searrow OH \end{smallmatrix}$$

(Notice that when both a double-bonded oxygen and an OH group are attached to the same carbon atom, the OH does not make the compound an alcohol; in this case the entire COOH unit acts as a single functional group, making the compound an acid.) There are many different fatty acids, varying in carbon-chain length, in the number of carbon-to-carbon bonds that are single or double, etc. Most of the fatty acids that enter into the formation of edible fats have relatively long carbon backbones, usually from 4 to 24 carbons, or more; three of the most common, for example, are stearic (18 carbons), palmitic (16 carbons), and oleic (18 carbons). For reasons that are not fully clear, the fatty acids in edible fats and oils contain an even number of carbon atoms.

Organic acids and alcohols have a tendency to combine through a condensation reaction. Since glycerol has three alcoholic groups, it can combine in this fashion with three molecules of fatty acid (Fig. 2.18); the result is a fat. In summary, then, a fat is composed of one molecule of glycerol and three molecules of fatty acid. Various fats differ in the specific fatty acids, or types of fatty acids, of which they are composed. Take saturated and unsaturated fats. (You have doubtless read in newspapers and magazines of the controversy in medical and nutritional circles concerning the relative effects of these upon our health.) Saturated fats are simply those whose fatty acids have the maximum possible number of hydrogen atoms attached to each carbon and which therefore do not contain any carbon-to-carbon double bonds (Fig. 2.19). Conversely, the fatty acids in unsaturated fats (or perhaps we should say oils, since they are usually liquid at

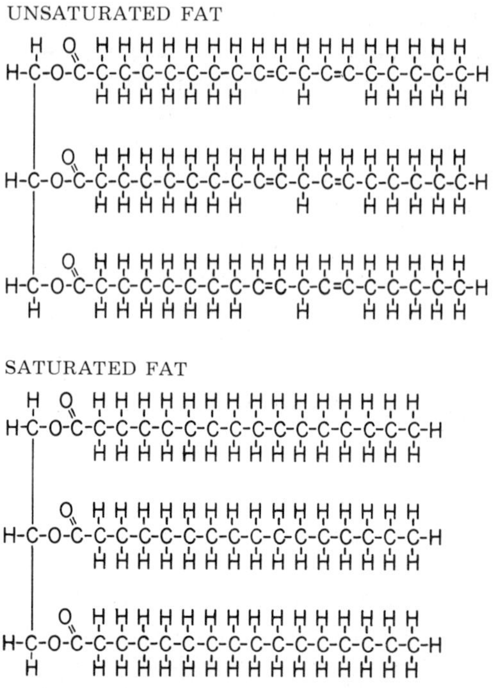

UNSATURATED FAT

SATURATED FAT

Fig. 2.19. Comparison of unsaturated and saturated fats. The fatty acids of an unsaturated fat contain less than the maximal amount of hydrogen.

room temperature) contain at least one carbon-to-carbon double bond; i.e. they are not completely saturated with hydrogen.

Since fats are synthesized by condensation reactions (removal of water), they, like complex carbohydrates, can be broken down to their building-block compounds by hydrolysis, as happens in digestion.

Other Lipids. Various other important lipids (fatlike substances) include waxes (in which the alcohol is larger than glycerol) and *phospholipids* (which are composed of glycerol, fatty acids, phosphoric acid, and a nitrogenous compound) (Fig. 2.20). Phospholipids are important components of many cellular membranes.

Another group of compounds, the **steroids,** are commonly classified as lipids because their solubility characteristics are similar to those of

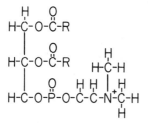

Fig. 2.20. A phospholipid. One of the fatty acids has been replaced by a group containing phosphorus and nitrogen. Because the group is charged, this portion of the molecule is water-soluble. (R stands for the long hydrocarbon chains of the fatty acids.)

fats, oils, waxes, and phospholipids; all are insoluble in water but soluble in ether. As you can see from Fig. 2.21, the structure of steroids is very different from the structures of the other lipids we have discussed. They are not based upon a bonding together of fatty acids and an alcohol. Instead, steroids are complex molecules composed of four interlocking rings of carbon atoms with various side groups attached to them. Steroids are very important biologically; some of the vitamins and hormones are steroids, and steroids are frequently important structural elements in living cells, particularly in cellular membranes.

Proteins

Proteins are far more complex than either carbohydrates or lipids. It is only in recent

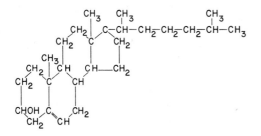

Fig. 2.21. A steroid. All steroids have the same basic unit of four interlocking rings. They differ in the side groups attached to those rings. This particular steroid is cholesterol.

years, in fact, that the structure of any protein has become known, and the number whose structure is known is still very small. One of the most active fields of research in biochemistry today is the study of protein structure. In spite of this, we can understand some basic facts about proteins, even in such an elementary book as this, because proteins, like carbohydrates and lipids, are composed of relatively few simple building-block compounds.

The Structure of Proteins. All proteins contain four essential elements: carbon, hydrogen, oxygen, and nitrogen. These four elements are bonded together to form compounds called *amino acids.* Being organic acids, these compounds contain the COOH group. In addition, they each have an amino group, NH_2. Theoretically, the amino group could be attached to any carbon atom in the molecule, but for reasons unknown to us the NH_2 group and the COOH group are both attached to the same carbon atom in all amino acids found in proteins:

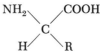

Such amino acids are known as α-amino acids. The various α-amino acids differ in their side chains, shown as R in the structural formula given above. R may be very simple, as in glycine, where it is only a hydrogen atom, or it may be very complex, as in tryptophane, where it includes two ring structures. Twenty-odd different amino acids, all of the *l* type, are commonly found in proteins; the structural formulas of some of them are shown in Fig. 2.22. We don't show you the structures of these compounds because we expect you to memorize them or even to learn their names (the majority of professional biologists don't remember all of them). We simply feel that you will have a better understanding of biology if you have at least seen them once and have

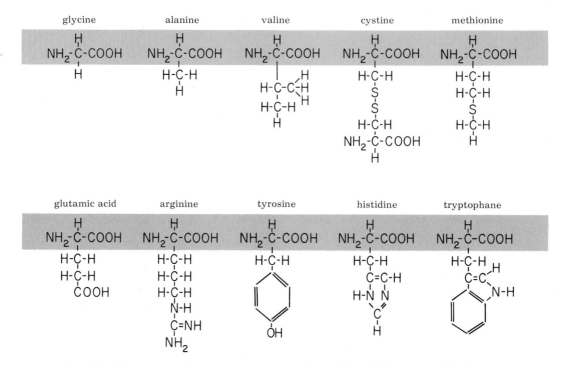

Fig. 2.22. The structure of some representative amino acids. All the amino acids that enter into the formation of protein have the same NH₂–CH–COOH unit at one end (shaded). They differ in their subsidiary groups (usually denoted as R). Glycine is the simplest, R being a single hydrogen atom. Some amino acids have straight-chain R groups and others have rings. Notice particularly cystine, a symmetrical molecule in which the two identical ends are held together by a disulfide linkage.

formed an impression of the types of structures involved.

Proteins are long and complex polymers of the twenty-odd amino acids. The amino acid building blocks bond together by condensation reactions between the COOH groups and the NH₂ groups (Fig. 2.23). Such bonds are called *peptide bonds,* and the chains they produce are called *polypeptide chains.* The number of amino acids in a single protein molecule may vary from about 50 to 50,000 or more. Since proteins may differ in the total number of amino acid units they contain, in the relative quantities of the different amino acids, and in the specific sequence in which the amino acids are bonded, enormous variation is obviously possible. The number of different proteins is almost endless, and we begin to understand

how it can be that every species and, in many cases, every individual organism has one or more proteins peculiar to it.

But protein molecules are even more complex than our discussion so far would indicate. We have mentioned amino acid content (number, type, and sequence), the so-called primary structure of the molecule. Now we must also mention the spatial arrangements of the polypeptide chains in which the amino acids are combined. Let us begin by examining the structure of one of the more unusual of the amino acids, cystine, shown in Fig. 2.22. Notice that this curious molecule is a sort of double molecule, a molecular twin as it were. At each end is a carbon to which are attached a carboxyl (COOH) group and an amino (NH₂) group. The two ends of the molecule are joined to-

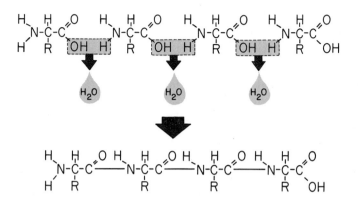

Fig. 2.23. Synthesis of a polypeptide chain. Condensation reactions between the –COOH and –NH₂ groups of adjacent amino acids result in peptide bonds between the acids.

gether by two atoms of sulfur, forming what is called a disulfide bond (–S–S–). Each half of a cystine molecule can, as a result of its structure, enter into reactions as though it were an independent amino acid. If one half of a cystine molecule were to enter into the formation of one polypeptide chain and the other half were to enter into the formation of a different polypeptide chain, the two polypeptide chains would be linked together by the disulfide bond in the cystine molecule and would constitute a single protein (Fig. 2.25). In a similar manner, one half of a cystine molecule might be incorporated into a polypeptide chain at one point and the other half incorporated into the same chain at a different point, causing the single polypeptide chain to fold back on itself (Fig. 2.26). Disulfide bonds, then, play a very important role in linking together the constituent polypeptide chains of complex proteins and in determining the folding pattern of proteins.

Proteins are not laid out simply as two-dimensional chains of amino acids, as our discussion so far might seem to imply. Instead, they are coiled and folded into very complex spatial patterns. Linus Pauling and Robert B. Corey of the California Institute of Technology postulated in 1951 that a basic configuration of polypeptide chains is the so-called α-helix (it may help you visualize this configuration if you think of the chain as wound around a

regular cylinder). Later research has tended to confirm this model. The helix is apparently maintained primarily by hydrogen bonds between adjacent oxygen and nitrogen atoms, although some other factors, like weak attractions between negatively charged portions of one amino acid and positively charged portions of another amino acid, are also involved.

Proteins can be roughly classified into two groups on the basis of the extent of their coiling and folding. Those arranged as long linear molecules are called fibrous proteins. They are relatively insoluble in water, salt solutions, and other aqueous media. Important structural elements of the body, they include collagen (the principal fibrous protein of skin, tendons, ligaments, cartilage, bone, the cornea of the eye, etc.), myosin (one of the chief proteins in muscle), keratin (the major protein in hair), and fibrin (a protein important in blood clotting). Proteins more highly coiled, and folded into a nearly spherical configuration, are termed globular proteins. They are soluble in aqueous media such as salt solutions, acids, bases, or aqueous alcohols. Most enzymes, proteinaceous hormones, and blood proteins are globular.

When normal (or "native," as they are called) proteins are exposed to excessive heat, radiation, electricity, excessive acidity, various chemical reagents, etc., their structure may become disorganized. One type of disorganization is called denaturation; apparently the hydrogen bonds are ruptured, causing the normally regular and rigid arrangement to unfold into a more diffuse formation (Fig. 2.24). Denaturation is partly or wholly reversible in some cases. Sometimes the process of breakdown and disorganization of the protein goes so far that there is loss of solubility. The protein is then said to be coagulated; coagulation cannot be reversed. Denatured or coagulated proteins ordinarily lose their normal properties and activity—a clear indication that the three-dimensional architecture is an essential aspect of protein structure; ultimately, any attempt to explain the biological properties of proteins must take this fact into account.

Determining the Structure. When we began this discussion of proteins, we said it is only recently that the structure of any protein has been discovered and that as yet we know the structure of only a very few. If, indeed, by "knowing the structure" we mean knowing all its aspects fully, including all details of the three-dimensional architecture, then at the time of this writing we could not say that we know the structure of any protein, although for a few like myoglobin we are nearing the goal. Since proteins are basic to both the structure and function of living material, it seems worthwhile at this point to examine briefly how we have learned what we do know about protein structure.

Figures 2.25 and 2.26 show the amino acid sequence of two proteins, insulin, a hormone produced by the pancreas, and ribonuclease, an important enzyme. Insulin was the first protein for which a structural formula could be written. Frederick Sanger and his colleagues at Cambridge University in England spent about ten years in exhaustive work before they could feel confident in 1954 that they finally knew the full sequence of amino acids in insulin, and they still did not know the three-dimensional arrangement. Nonetheless, Sanger's work constituted a milestone in the history of biochemical knowledge, and he was awarded

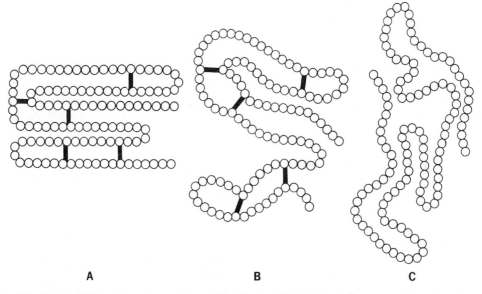

A   B   C

Fig. 2.24. Denaturation of a protein. First the weak attractions between adjacent parts of the folded molecule are destroyed, and then the disulfide linkages are ruptured. The three-dimensional configuration of the molecule is completely changed.

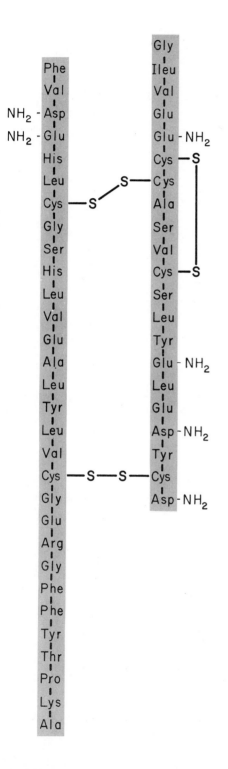

a Nobel Prize in 1958 for his great achievement.

Insulin was well suited to be the object of pioneering work on protein structure; it can be rather easily obtained in pure form, and it is one of the smallest proteins known (but note that even this "small" protein contains a total of 777 atoms). Sanger's method of determining the sequence of amino acids in insulin involved breaking the molecules into fragments and then trying to determine how the pieces fitted together. If a protein is heated in an acid solution for about 24 hours, all its peptide bonds are hydrolyzed; i.e. a water molecule is added at the site of each peptide bond, thereby breaking the bond and uncoupling the amino acids. The results can then be analyzed, and it can be determined which amino acids are present and in what amounts.

One of the best techniques for analyzing the amino acids is chromatography, a process that utilizes the different affinities of the unknown substances for two other materials. The analysis may be carried out as follows: A glass column is packed with some highly adsorbent material (an adsorbent is a substance to the surface of which the molecules of a gas, dissolved substance, or liquid tend to adhere). The adsorbent in question may be calcium carbonate, activated charcoal, various clays, silica gel, cellulose, starch, or fuller's earth. A solution of the test material is poured into the top of the column and allowed to filter through the adsorbent. The various substances in the test mixture tend to be adsorbed at different points in the column, and their rates of travel

Fig. 2.25. The structure of beef insulin. The molecule consists of two polypeptide chains joined by two disulfide linkages. There is also one disulfide linkage within the shorter chain. The amino acids are abbreviated as follows: Ala, alanine; Arg, arginine; Asp, aspartic acid; Asp-NH₂, asparagine; Cys, cystine; Glu, glutamic acid; Glu-NH₂, glutamine; Gly, glycine; His, histidine; Ileu, isoleucine; Leu, leucine; Lys, lysine; Met, methionine; Phe, phenylalanine; Pro, proline; Ser, serine; Thr, threonine; Tyr, tyrosine; Val, valine.

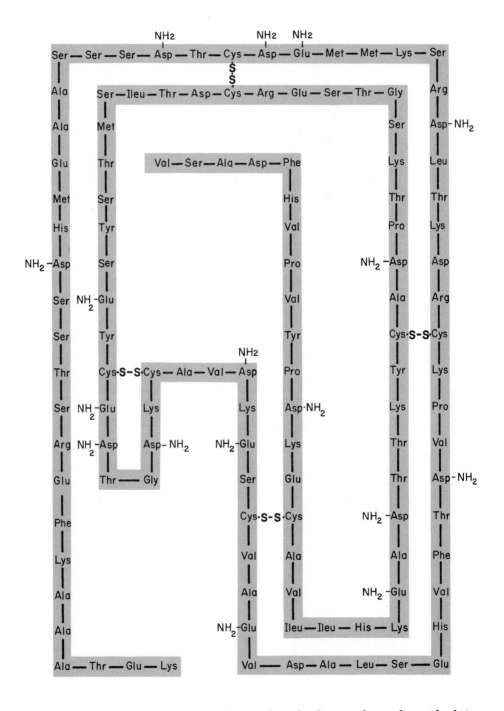

Fig. 2.26. The structure of beef ribonuclease.   The molecule is one long polypeptide chain with four disulfide cross linkages. For abbreviations, see Fig. 2.25.

are dependent upon their relative affinity for the solvent and for the adsorbent. Those substances which have a very pronounced tendency to adhere to the adsorbent will move slowly and will consequently be left behind in the upper part of the column. Other substances which have a greater affinity for the solvent will move more rapidly and will be left in a lower part of the column. Once the substances are separated in this fashion, the adsorbent column can be removed from its container and cut into pieces, and the contents of the pieces can be analyzed. Or more solvent can be poured into the top of the column to make the separated substances move slowly down the column until they come out at the lower end; since the different substances will emerge from the bottom at different times, they can be collected in different containers. Often a special reagent that reacts with amino acids to produce a blue color is then added to each glass container, and the results are analyzed by a photometer attached to a recorder. The photometer determines the intensity of blue color, which is proportional to the amount of amino acid, and the recorder graphs the results. The researcher thus obtains a graph showing the amount of amino acid that came out of the tube during each of a series of precise time intervals. Ordinarily there will be a peak on the graph indicating the emergence of each different amino acid. The researcher can identify each peak by comparing his experimental ones with those obtained by running known amino acids through a similar column with a similar solvent. In summary, the position of the peaks tells which amino acids were present in the original test material, and the height of the peaks tells the quantities.

There are many other ways chromatography can be performed. Some are technically complex and others are relatively simple. For example, in paper chromatography the test solution is simply placed at one corner of a piece of filter paper and allowed to migrate in a solvent along the paper. The relative affinities

of the different substances for the paper and for the solvent will determine what points on the paper these substances will reach at the end of a specified time interval. But all chromatographic techniques are limited in the types of information they can provide. The most Sanger could learn from these procedures was which amino acids insulin contained and in what amounts. To learn the amino acid sequence, he had to use other approaches.

By less drastic treatment of insulin with hydrolyzing agents, he could preserve some of the peptide bonds and thus obtain many protein fragments consisting of two, three, four, five, or more amino acids. He analyzed these fragments for their amino acid content, utilizing particularly a technique that enabled him to determine which amino acid was on the end having the free amino group. After analyzing vast numbers of such pieces, he attempted to fit them together in proper sequence, by identifying fragments with regions of apparent overlap. For example, he found the following two fragments that seemed to have overlapping sequences at their ends:

Leu–Val–Cy–Gly–Glu–Arg–Gly–Phe–Phe
            Gly–Phe–Phe–Tyr–Thr–Pro–Lys

He reasonably concluded that one part of the insulin molecule contained the sequence

Leu–Val–Cy–Gly–Glu–Arg–Gly–Phe–Phe–Tyr–Thr–Pro–Lys

He then hunted for other fragments that overlapped this sequence, so that he could extend it. After long and laborious investigations of this sort, he finally determined the entire amino acid sequence. But he still wasn't through. He knew that insulin contained two separate polypeptide chains (Fig. 2.25), but he didn't know the location of the disulfide bonds that linked them.

As we have already seen, disulfide bonds result from the incorporation of the two ends of a cystine molecule in two different places in a protein molecule; in insulin, the two ends are in different polypeptide chains. Sanger knew that there were three cystine units in insulin, and he therefore expected to find three disulfide bonds. The question was, "Where?" First he and his co-workers tried for a partial breakdown of the insulin molecule to obtain fragments containing cystine with the disulfide linkages still intact. The results were thoroughly confusing. There seemed to be no significant pattern for the distribution of the disulfide bonds. Every conceivable combination seemed to be present. Sanger soon found the explanation, however: During each hydrolysis, the disulfide bonds opened and a variety of rearrangements occurred. He eventually discovered ways to avoid this problem and finally located the disulfide linkages.

Since Sanger's monumental discovery of the structural formula of insulin, after more than a century of effort by scientists to learn the composition and structure of proteins, several other proteins have been similarly elucidated. One of these is ribonuclease, shown in Fig. 2.26. The more recent work has been aided, as you would expect, by many technological advances. Of particular importance has been the development of a method for splitting off amino acids one at a time from the end of the polypeptide chains.

The Three-Dimensional Configuration. Our knowledge of the three-dimensional structure of proteins has also moved forward. The use of X rays as analytical tools has been fundamental to this work. Proteins can be crystallized, an indication that all the molecules have the same detailed shape and that they are arranged in a regular three-dimensional array. It has been known for years that if X rays are sent through a crystal while it is being turned in various directions, the X rays do not travel in a straight line, but are scattered by the electrons of the atoms in the crystal. If these scattered X rays fall on a photographic plate, they produce a characteristic pattern; the pattern is determined by the angle at which the

X rays strike the planes of the crystal. A crystal can be rotated in a carefully planned way in an X-ray camera so that its sets of planes come into correct reflecting position one after another. The successive patterns thus produced make their imprint on photographic plates. Since crystals of different substances have different atomic and electron arrangements, they produce different X-ray patterns when studied in this manner. The patterns indicate, in a very complex way, the structure of the crystal.

This X-ray technique of crystal analysis has been applied to myoglobin, a protein similar to but smaller than hemoglobin, the red pigment in blood. John C. Kendrew and his associates at Cambridge University recorded thousands of reflections of X rays through myoglobin crystals at various angles and fed them into a computor for analysis. They then took the computor results and attempted to use them as a guide in constructing a three-dimensional model of myoglobin. This extremely tedious process has yielded the best picture we have to date of the three-dimensional structure of a protein (Fig. 2.27). Similar studies of hemoglobin are being performed by other workers.

The diagram of myoglobin shows that this protein contains a group different from the characteristic polypeptide chains, a so-called heme group, which is a flat grouping of atoms with an iron atom at its center. Hemoglobin contains four such heme groups. A nonproteinaceous grouping of this kind, known as a *prosthetic group,* is attached to many proteins and is usually essential to their characteristic chemical reactivity. For example, the heme group in myoglobin and hemoglobin is necessary to the interactions of those substances with oxygen.

Nucleic Acids

Nucleic acids, a fourth major class of biological compounds, are long polymers that play a fundamental role in the transmission of heredi-

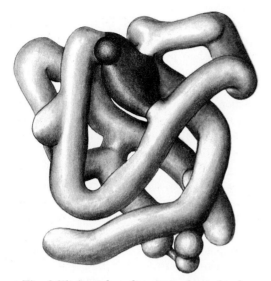

Fig. 2.27. Spatial configuration of a molecule of myoglobin. The molecule consists of a single complexly folded polypeptide chain of 151 amino acid units, with a nonproteinaceous prosthetic group attached to it. At the center of the prosthetic group, called heme, is an atom of iron, shown here as a large black ball. [Modified from J. C. Kendrew, *Science*, vol. 139, 1963.]

tary traits, in the control of the functioning of living cells, and in the synthesis of proteins. We shall study them in detail in a later chapter and so shall not examine them here.

CHEMICAL REACTIONS

In this chapter we have mentioned several chemical reactions that take place within the organism: condensation reactions between simple sugars to form polysaccharides, and hydrolysis of polysaccharides back to simple sugars; condensation reactions of fatty acids and glycerol to form fats, and the reverse hydrolysis; condensation of amino acids to form polypeptide chains and proteins, and the reverse hydrolysis. When we first discussed these reactions, we said nothing about the conditions under which they will take place. It is now time to examine those conditions briefly.

General Conditions for Chemical Reactions

Instead of talking at this point about condensation reactions or hydrolysis reactions or any other specific type of reaction, let us consider some hypothetical generalized reactions. Suppose, for example, that two substances, A and B, can react with each other to form two new substances, C and D:

$$A + B \rightarrow C + D$$

What factors determine the rate at which such a reaction occurs? First we must recognize that if A and B are to react with each other, their molecules must come into contact. It follows that anything that increases the probability of contact increases the rate of reaction. One obvious way to increase the probability of molecular contact is to increase the concentration of the reactants; the more molecules per unit volume, the more will bump into each other by chance per unit time. Raising the pressure on the reactant solutions has essentially the same effect; the molecules are pushed closer together and consequently come into contact more often. This concept of the importance of concentration in determining reaction rates is the basis of the Law of Mass Action, which simply states that, all other conditions being equal, the rate of reaction is proportional to the concentrations of the reactants.

Increasing the concentration of reactants is not the only way to speed up a reaction. Heating the reactants is another way. Heat is a form of energy. We shall discuss the concept of energy and energy transformations at some length in a later chapter; all we need to say at this point is that energy is the capacity to do work and that all forms of energy involve motion of some sort. For heat, the motion is that of the atoms and molecules of which the substance in question is composed. At all temperatures above the theoretical absolute zero ($-273°C$), all particles possess motion, ordinarily a vibratory randomly directed type of motion. This motion increases as the temperature increases. Clearly, the more of this sort of random heat motion (or thermal agitation, as it is often called) the molecules of the reactants possess, the greater will be the chance that they will bump into each other. Thus, applying heat to the reactants will increase the rate of the reaction. Application of heat is a standard and frequently used technique of chemists in their laboratories.

In our discussion so far, we have not mentioned the energy changes that take place in reactions. All substances contain free energy. Conversion of one substance into another, or of two substances into new ones, ordinarily involves changes in energy content. In some reactions, the products contain less energy than the reactants, the extra energy being released by the reaction:

$$A + B \rightarrow C + D + energy$$

Such reactions are said to be *exergonic,* and the energy released is called reaction energy. In other reactions, the products contain more energy than the reactants; an external source of energy is necessary if these reactions, called *endergonic* reactions, are to take place:

$$W + X + energy \rightarrow Y + Z$$

It should be clear that just increasing the concentrations of the reactant substances in an endergonic reaction is not sufficient effectively to increase the rate of the reaction; the energy supply must also be increased. In living things, it is very common for exergonic and endergonic reactions to be coupled, the energy released by the one being used to drive the other.

Let us now suppose that the reaction of A with B to form C and D has been going on for some time and that high concentrations of the products, C and D, are accumulating, while the concentrations of A and B are dwindling. This means that the probability of collisions between C and D is increasing, while that for A and B is decreasing. When the molecular

concentrations of C and D become greater than those of A and B, there may actually be more collisions per unit time between product molecules than between reactant molecules. What happens then? Does the direction of the reaction become reversed? The answer is perhaps. In principle, chemical reactions are reversible. It is possible, therefore, that as the concentrations of the products (C and D) start rising, these will begin to react to form A and B. At first, however, there will be very little C and D and much A and B. According to the Law of Mass Action, then, we would expect the forward reaction (written with an arrow pointing toward the right) to proceed at a much higher rate than the back reaction (written with an arrow pointing toward the left). We can symbolize the relative rates by the lengths of the arrows in our equations:

$$A + B \xrightleftharpoons{\quad\longrightarrow\quad} C + D$$

Later, however, when the concentrations of the substances on the two sides of the equation are approximately equal, the Law of Mass Action would lead us to expect the forward and back reactions to proceed at the same rate:

$$A + B \rightleftharpoons C + D$$

When such a point is reached, how can the concentrations of C and D increase further? Isn't the system now in equilibrium? If there were no energy considerations involved, the answer would be yes. If the energy content of C and D were exactly equal to that of A and B, equilibrium would be reached when the concentrations of C and D were equal to the concentrations of A and B. But suppose the reaction is slightly exergonic—in other words, that the forward reaction releases a small amount of reaction energy. Under these conditions, the equilibrium point is pushed to the right; the loss of energy means that the concentrations of C and D must be higher than the concentrations of A and B before the rate of the back reaction equals that of the forward reaction. If the reaction is highly exergonic, the equilibrium point is pushed so far to the right that, for all practical purposes, there will be no back reaction. If we consider energy one of the products of the reaction, such a result agrees with the Law of Mass Action; because one of the products (i.e. energy) is being lost, the concentration of products can never be sufficient to drive a back reaction. A similar effect occurs when one or more of the material products precipitates out of solution as a relatively insoluble solid or when a product escapes as a gas.

In summary, concentration, pressure, temperature, and free-energy changes all exert an influence on reactions. But these are not all the factors we should consider. Many exergonic reactions do not begin spontaneously even when the conditions of concentration, pressure, and temperature are adequate. They need, so to speak, a push to get them going. This push must come from some outside source and is called *activation energy.* For example, a sheet of paper can burn (i.e. combine with oxygen) easily once ignited, but that same paper may exist in direct contact with a plentiful oxygen supply for centuries without ever beginning to burn. Activation energy, usually in the form of extra heat from a match or some other hot object, must be applied to start the reaction of paper with oxygen. The magnitude of activation energy needed is different for each reaction and is not determined by the magnitude of the free-energy change of the reaction. It is a measure of the stability of the reactants under the given set of conditions.

Catalysis

In the laboratory, activation energy is generally provided by applying heat. But how can activation energy be supplied for reactions that take place within the bodies of living things? For example, how do hydrolysis reactions involving carbohydrates, fats, and proteins occur? We all know from everyday experience that the simple mixing of starch and water is not

followed by hydrolysis and the rapid production of sugar; similarly that the addition of water is not enough to hydrolyze fats and proteins. Hydrolysis reactions require activation energy of fairly high magnitude. Clearly, when such reactions occur in our bodies, the activation energy cannot be applied in the form of heat, or our bodies would be destroyed. The same is true for all other living things. Yet hundreds or thousands of reactions that in a test tube would require high activation energy take place every instant within an organism at relatively low temperatures. What is the answer?

The chemist knows that many reactions can be made to take place much more readily if a small quantity of *catalyst* is added to the mixture. For example, a simple mixture of hydrogen gas and oxygen gas shows no appreciable reaction. If, however, a small quantity of platinum is added, an explosive reaction takes place, and water is formed. At the end of the reaction, the platinum is still present, unchanged. This lack of alteration is a general property of catalysts; they are substances that speed up reactions but are unchanged themselves when the reactions are over (they may have been temporarily changed during the reactions). In the terms of our discussion, catalysts decrease the activation energy needed for reactions to take place. Just how they do this is not fully clear. Apparently, part of the answer is that they tend to adsorb molecules of the reactants to their surfaces, thereby increasing molecular contact or putting unusual strain on chemical bonds and facilitating the reactions. Note that catalysts simply speed up reactions that are possible to begin with; no catalyst can alter the direction of a reaction, its final equilibrium, or the reaction energy involved.

The principle of reduction of activation energy by catalysts is fundamental to life. Here is the explanation for the "cold" chemistry in living things. The vast majority of chemical reactions taking place within organisms are

catalyzed by special catalysts called **enzymes.**
All enzymes are proteins, usually globular proteins. Some fibrous proteins, like myosin in
muscle, also seem to act as enzymes, however;
and some scientists think that all proteins may
play some enzymatic role. At any rate, our
earlier discussion of the nature and structure
of proteins can now be considered a description of enzymes.

Current theory holds that the key to enzyme
function—as to the operation of simpler inorganic catalysts—is surface activity. Proteins,
as we have seen, are enormously complex molecules with intricate three-dimensional contours. This intricate surface geometry is distinctive for each different kind of protein. It
seems probable that an enzyme combines
briefly with reactants whose molecular surfaces
"fit" the enzyme surfaces (Fig. 2.28). In this
manner, two or more reactants may be brought

into close proximity, a state facilitating their
interaction; or, by being attached to an enzyme, a reactant molecule may be altered or
deformed in its configuration and thus become
more reactive.

We can now begin to understand some of
the distinctive properties of enzymes. Enzymes are inactivated at temperatures well
below that of boiling water (100°C). The explanation, in accordance with the theory of
surface activity of enzymes, is that the surface
is simply not the same at high temperatures
and reactivity is lost; we have already seen that
high temperatures break the hydrogen bonds
in protein molecules and disrupt their three-
dimensional shape. Similarly, we can understand the high sensitivity of enzymes to acidity
changes (some work best when the solution is
acid, others when the solution is basic, but very
few are active over a wide pH range); such

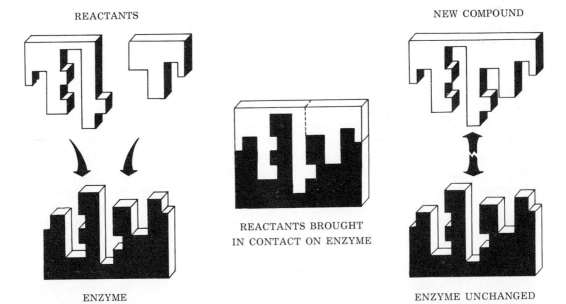

REACTANTS

NEW COMPOUND

REACTANTS BROUGHT
IN CONTACT ON ENZYME

ENZYME

ENZYME UNCHANGED

Fig. 2.28. Activity of enzymes. It is thought that enzymes have characteristic surface
configurations that "fit" their specific substrates. The enzyme probably combines briefly with
the reactant molecules in such a way as to bring them close together and facilitate their
interaction. When the reaction is complete and the enzyme-substrate complex dissociates,
the enzyme is left unchanged.

changes affect the three-dimensional configurations of proteins.

A characteristic of enzymes critical to the functioning of living systems is their specificity. Most enzymes are highly specific with regard to the reactants they affect (often called substrates in enzyme-catalyzed reactions) and with regard to the type of reactions they catalyze. Thus, for example, the enzymes that catalyze the hydrolysis of starch are different from those that catalyze the hydrolysis of glycogen, despite the fact that starch and glycogen are two very similar polysaccharides. Similarly, some protein-hydrolyzing enzymes are so specific that they will act only on peptide bonds involving the carboxyl groups of one or two particular amino acids and not on those involving any other amino acids; i.e. they will hydrolyze proteins at only a few specific points along the polypeptide chains. The specificity exhibited by enzymes confers upon living systems enormous potential for very precise control of chemical reactions; this precise control is a basic feature of life.

Most enzymes can, however, catalyze reactions in both the forward and back directions. It is not the enzyme that determines in which direction the reaction will proceed; it is the other factors we have discussed: concentration, pressure, temperature, and energy changes.

Enzyme specificity can be seen as a reflection of the distinctiveness of the proteins themselves. We have already seen that each different protein has a surface geometry that is uniquely its own. Since it can catalyze only those reactions that involve substrates capable of "fitting" its surfaces, its catalytic potential is severely limited and its specificity is the result.

Modern research on the structure of proteins has given impetus to the attempt to clarify one important aspect of the relation between the structure of proteins and their function as enzymes: the seeming presence of "active sites" on enzymes. Enzymes, as we have seen, are very large molecules; the substrates upon which they work are usually much smaller. It follows that only a small portion of the enzyme molecule can be in contact with the substrate when the two are joined in the enzyme-substrate complex. This small portion is the "active site." We don't mean to imply that the rest of the enzyme molecule is functionless; sometimes activity remains when a portion of the rest of the molecule is lost, but often it does not. It is one of the tasks of research to determine the nature of the active sites and the role played by the rest of the molecule in enzyme function.

One promising line of attack has involved the use of selective poisons. Many poisons exert their effect by inactivating critical enzymes. Since enzymes are not used up by the reactions they catalyze, only a small quantity of each enzyme is necessary to maintain a chemical system in functioning order; consequently a small amount of poison can inactivate all the enzyme. Some enzyme poisons apparently combine tightly with the enzymes, masking their active sites and making them unavailable for combinations with their substrates. Determining where on the enzyme molecule the inactivating poison attaches gives a clue to the location of the active site. For several proteins, this technique has made it possible to identify a sequence of three or four amino acids that is apparently at least a part of the active site. It is interesting that in some instances another amino acid, quite distant on the polypeptide chain from the others constituting the active site, also appears to be a part of the active site. Perhaps such an amino acid is brought into close spatial proximity with the others by the folding and coiling of the molecule; this would mean that denaturation would dismember the active site, rendering it inactive. It is possible that the large segments of the molecule that are not parts of the active site function in holding together the components of the active site and giving it the proper shape.

Some enzymes function only in conjunction with other substances called **coenzymes.** Coenzymes are sometimes simply metal ions; or they may be more complex organic compounds, but they are never proteins. They are not as specific with reference to substrate as enzymes. It seems probable that the enzyme and its co-enzyme combine to some extent during the course of a reaction, but the closeness of this combination may vary so much that in some cases it is largely a matter of definition whether a substance is to be considered a coenzyme or merely a relatively nonspecific accessory substance.

REFERENCES

FIESER, L. F., and M. FIESER, 1957. *Organic Chemistry*, 3rd ed. Heath, Boston.

———, 1961. *Advanced Organic Chemistry*. Reinhold, New York.

SIENKO, M. J., and R. A. PLANE, 1961. *Chemistry*, 2nd ed. McGraw-Hill, New York.

WATT, G. W., L. F. HATCH, and J. J. LAGOWSKI, 1964. *Chemistry*. Norton, New York.

WHITE, E. H., 1964. *Chemical Background for the Biological Sciences*. Prentice-Hall, Englewood Cliffs, N.J.

SUGGESTED READING

BAKER, J. J. W., and G. E. ALLEN, 1965. *Matter, Energy, and Life*. Addison-Wesley, Reading, Mass.

GRAY, G. W., 1951. "Electrophoresis," *Scientific American*, December. (Offprint 83.)

GREEN, D. E., 1960. "The Synthesis of Fat," *Scientific American*, February. (Offprint 67.)

KENDREW, J. C., 1961. "The Three-Dimensional Structure of a Protein Molecule," *Scientific American*, December. (Offprint 121.)

RAMSAY, J. A., 1965. *The Experimental Basis of Modern Biology*. Cambridge University Press, New York. (See esp. Chapter 3.)

ROBERTS, J. D., 1957. "Organic Chemical Reactions," *Scientific American*, November. (Offprint 85.)

STEIN, W. H., and S. MOORE, 1951. "Chromatography," *Scientific American*, March. (Offprint 81.)

———, 1961. "The Structure of Proteins," *Scientific American*, February. (Offprint 80.)

STERN, H., and D. L. NANNEY, 1965. *The Biology of Cells*. Wiley, New York. (See esp. Chapter 4.)

THOMPSON, E. O. P., 1955. "The Insulin Molecule," *Scientific American*, May. (Offprint 42.)

3

CELLS: UNITS OF STRUCTURE AND FUNCTION

W^E SAW IN THE LAST CHAPTER THAT OR- ganisms are composed of a great variety of chemicals, some simple and some complex. But these chemicals do not of themselves possess the properties we recognize as life; those properties are observable only in association with the organization superimposed on the chemicals in living systems. They are properties that do not necessarily follow from the properties of the molecules taken separately. Their existence suggests that the chemicals are not simply dispersed in a random fashion within an aqueous medium; and we shall see that they are, in fact, contained within discrete structural units. The fundamental organizational unit of life, to which we shall refer throughout this book, is the cell. It is the purpose of this chapter to examine the cell in some detail.

THE CELL THEORY

The discovery of cells, and of their structure, is inextricably bound up with the development of magnifying lenses, particularly the microscope. Some of the optical properties of curved surfaces were known as long ago as 300 B.C., but it was not until the seventeenth century that previous observations were brought to fruition in the development of the microscope. Antoni van Leeuwenhoek (1632–1723) and his contemporaries refined the production of lenses and made microscopes satisfactory for simple scientific observations. Thus in 1665 Robert Hooke (1635–1703) was able to present before the Royal Society of London the results of his investigations on the texture of cork. It is from this work of Hooke's that studies of cells must be dated. Let us pause a moment and examine Hooke's findings as presented in his own words in *Micrographia*.

I took a good clear piece of Cork, and with a Pen-knife sharpen'd as keen as Razor, I cut a piece of it off, and thereby left the surface of it exceeding smooth, then examining it very diligently with a Microscope, me thought I could perceive it to appear a little porous; but I could not so plainly distinguish them, as to be sure that they were pores, much less what Figure they were of: But judging from the lightness and yielding quality of the Cork, that certainly the texture could not be so curious, but that possibly, if I could use some further diligence, I might find it to be discernable with a Microscope, I with the same sharp Pen-knife, cut off from the former smooth surface an exceeding thin piece of it, and placing it on a black object Plate, because it was it self a white body, and casting the light on it with a deep plano-convex Glass, I could exceeding plainly perceive it to be all perforated and porous, much like a Honey-comb, but that the pores of it were not regular; yet it was not unlike a Honey-comb in these particulars.

First, in that it had a very little solid substance, in comparison of the empty cavity that was contain'd between, . . . for the Interstitia, or walls (as I may so call them) or partitions of these pores were neer as thin in proportion to their pores, as those thin films of Wax in a Honey-comb . . . are to theirs.

Next, in that these pores, or cells, were not very deep, but consisted of a great many little

Boxes, separated out of one continued long pore, by certain Diaphragms . . .

I no sooner discern'd these (which were indeed the first microscopical pores I ever saw, and perhaps, that were ever seen, for I had not met with any Writer or Person, that had made any mention of them before this) but me thought I had with the discovery of them, presently hinted to me the true and intelligible reason of all the Phaenomena of Cork; . . .

Despite Hooke's discovery, it was not until the early nineteenth century that intensive work on cells began in earnest. The first clear enunciation of one of the most important generalizations of modern biology, the so-called cell theory, is generally credited to two German investigators, the botanist Matthias Jakob Schleiden and the zoologist Theodor Schwann, who published their ideas in 1838 and 1839 respectively. The **cell theory** says that all living things are composed of cells. Actually, this concept had been stated in relatively clear form by a number of other workers in the earlier part of the nineteenth century; already in 1809 Lamarck had said, "no body can have life if its constituent parts are not cellular tissue or are not formed by cellular tissue." Schleiden and Schwann, then, were not the first to enunciate this principle, but they stated it with particular clarity, and it was their support of the idea that helped it gain general credence and come to be accepted by the majority of the biologists of their day.

A very important extension of the cell theory was contributed in 1858 by Rudolf Virchow of Germany. Virchow said that all living cells arise from pre-existing living cells, i.e. that there is no spontaneous creation of cells from nonliving matter—*omnis cellula e cellula*. Proof of Virchow's theory of **biogenesis** came only a few years later through the work of Louis Pasteur in France. Strange as it may seem to us, before the time of Virchow and Pasteur there was a widespread belief in the spontaneous creation of life, among scientists as well as nonscientists. Pasteur's now classic experiments finally settled the matter as far as most scientists were concerned. He placed various nutrient broths into long-necked flasks and then bent the necks of the flasks into curves (Fig. 3.1). Next he boiled the broths in the flasks to kill any microorganisms (germs) that might be in them. While the flasks were left standing, germ-laden dust particles in the air moving into the flasks were trapped in the films of moisture on the humid curves of the neck; the curved neck acted as a filter. Though the broths might be left standing in their "swan-neck" containers for months or even a year or more, no life appeared in them. Control broths boiled in flasks with straight necks did not remain free of microorganisms and were soon teeming with life. Similarly, if the swan-neck was broken off, the experimental broth rapidly developed colonies of molds and bacteria. Thus Pasteur showed that the source of the microorganisms that fermented or putrefied such substances as milk, wine, or sugar-beet juice was the air. The organisms did not arise spontaneously from the nutrient media.

The principle of biogenesis, life from life, has been somewhat modified in recent years, as we shall see in a later chapter. Current theory holds that spontaneous generation of life from nonliving matter does not occur under present conditions, but that it probably did occur under the conditions existing on the primitive earth when life first arose.

The two components of the cell theory—that all living things are composed of cells and that all cells arise from other cells—give us the basis for our first definition of living things: Living

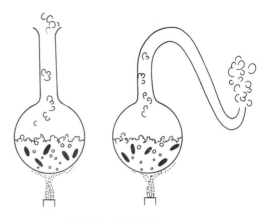

PROLONGED HEATING

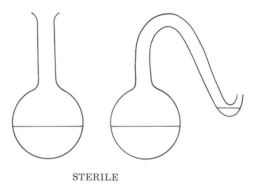

STERILE

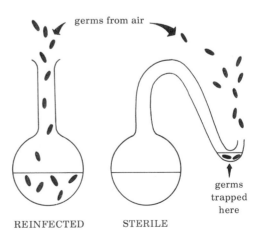

germs from air

REINFECTED STERILE

germs trapped here

Fig. 3.1. Pasteur's experiment. Nutrient broths were boiled to kill any organisms in them (top). The sterile broths were then allowed to sit in their open-mouthed containers for several weeks (middle). Germs (here shown vastly exaggerated in size) entered the straight-necked flask and contaminated the broth, but those entering the bent neck of the other flask were trapped in films of moisture in the curves of the neck and did not contaminate the broth (bottom).

things are chemical organizations composed of cells and capable of reproducing themselves. Notice we have said that this is our first definition of living things. It is a working definition that will allow us to proceed further, but it will not be the last definition we shall consider in this book. We shall see later that any attempt to draw a sharp line between the non-living and the living becomes essentially arbitrary. We shall see, for example, that it is often convenient to treat viruses as living things, even though they are not composed of cells in the usual sense.

CELL STRUCTURE

The years since Schleiden, Schwann, and Virchow laid the foundations of the cell theory have witnessed many major advances in our knowledge of cells. Most of the later work has been made possible by the development of better and more powerful microscopes. In the detailed analysis of subcellular structure, three attributes of microscopes are of particular importance: magnification, resolution, and contrast. Magnification is a means of increasing the apparent size of the object being viewed until it provides an adequate stimulus to our eyes. Resolution is the capacity to separate close objects from each other. Contrast is important in distinguishing one part of a cell from another.

Although ordinary light microscopes can be manufactured with very high magnification, their resolving power is somewhat limited. It is about 500 times better than that of the unaided human eye, but this is still not enough for viewing some of the smaller subcellular structures. Contrast is often obtained in microscopy by fixing and staining the material being studied. Different parts of the material often have different affinities for various dyes, and it is therefore possible to stain these parts different colors and make them stand out from each other.

The advent of the electron microscope (Fig. 3.2) in recent years has opened up whole new vistas in the study of cells. This microscope, as its name implies, uses a beam of electrons instead of light as its source of illumination. The electrons pass through the specimen and fall upon a photographic plate, where they produce an image of the specimen. Electron microscopes are capable of resolving objects about 10,000 times better than the unaided human eye. Many of the details of cellular structure discussed in this chapter would not be known but for the electron microscope.

Cell Size

Most cells are very small and can be distinguished only with a microscope. Some, how-

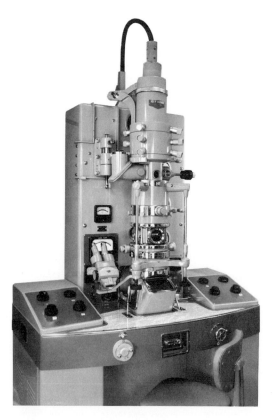

Fig. 3.2. Electron microscope. [Courtesy Perkin-Elmer Corp.]

ever, like the yolks of birds' eggs, are quite large. Others, like nerve cells, may be very small in some of their dimensions, but extremely long. A single human nerve cell may be as much as 3 or 4 feet long, and a nerve cell of an elephant could be even longer. To say that cells are generally small does not say much, however, because even among microscopic cells there is a wide range in size. The diameter of a human red blood cell is about 35 times greater than that of some very tiny microorganisms, while that of a human egg cell is about 14 times greater than that of a red blood cell; the diameter of an ostrich egg, in turn, is about 1,500 times greater than that of a human egg cell. Most cells, however, have a diameter of 0.5–40 microns. (A micron [μ] equals 0.001 millimeter [mm].)

It is not altogether clear why cell size has remained restricted throughout the course of evolution. One of several factors that have probably played a role is the ratio of surface area to volume, which has an important bearing on the functioning of cells. Cells obtain necessary materials such as oxygen and nutrients from the area surrounding them. These materials must enter across the surface of the cell, and waste products must leave by the same route. As cell size increases, the volume increases much more rapidly than the surface area (volume increases as the cube of the cell radius, surface area as the square of the cell radius). Thus increasing size entails the problem of adequate exchange surface for support of the greatly increased volume. Cells very active in carrying out chemical reactions tend to be smaller than cells with lower metabolic rates, for the problem of exchange of materials is much greater for them. This whole question of the ratio of surface area to volume is not limited to single cells; we shall encounter it again and again in reference to whole organisms.

Another factor limiting cell size is the ability of the cell's control center, the nucleus, to exert control over the rest of the cell. As a cell in-creases in size, more and more of its parts must be located far from the control center and proper interaction becomes progressively more difficult.

Colloids and Protoplasm

Before we examine the internal characteristics of cells, we must consider the physical nature of the cellular material. When substances are mixed, there are several possible distribution patterns they may assume. At one extreme, a *solution* may form. A solution is a homogeneous mixture of two or more components. These components may be gaseous, liquid, or solid. Whatever the state of the components, the sizes of the particles are always so small that the particles of the two substances cannot be distinguished in the mixture. Hence the term "homogeneous." Consider, for example, the solution of a solid in a liquid. If the solid is progressively subdivided, its particles are eventually broken down to individual atoms or molecules or very tiny clusters of these. At this point, a true solution is obtained. The two phases, solid and liquid, can no longer be distinguished. The solution is uniform throughout. The individual molecules cannot be detected even with the strongest microscope. No matter how long the solution is left standing, the dispersed particles do not settle out, nor can they be removed from the solution by filtration (Fig. 3.3).

True solutions represent one extreme, where the dissolved substance is divided into minute particles of atomic or molecular size. At the other extreme is a *suspension.* Here the dispersed substance consists of particles so large that it is only by constant agitation that they remain suspended within the liquid. A mixture of sand grains and water is an example. The sand can be kept dispersed in the water as long as the mixture is agitated. When agitation ceases, the sand grains soon settle to the bottom. A suspension, then, is a heterogeneous mixture. The two phases remain distinct.

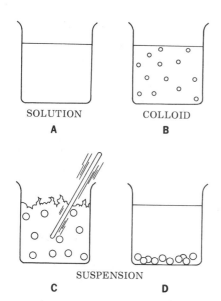

Fig. 3.3. Solutions, colloids, and suspensions. The tiny particles in a solution cannot be detected and they do not settle out (A). The large particles of a suspension remain distinct from the liquid and will settle out rapidly (D) unless agitated (C). The particles of a colloid are of intermediate size and do not settle out at an appreciable rate (B).

Between the extremes of a true solution and an obvious suspension are many possible gradations. The transition from homogeneity to heterogeneity is not an abrupt one. A substance may break down to particles that are so small they cannot be seen and do not form an obviously separate phase; yet these particles may still be too large to form a true solution. Often the substance has not broken down all the way to its constituent molecules; its particles remain molecular aggregates. Particles in this intermediate size range do not settle out at an appreciable rate. Such a system is called a *colloid.* Colloids may involve solids, liquids, or gases. Cigarette smoke is an example of a colloid of solid ash dispersed in air. Ordinary milk is an example of a colloid involving a liquid dispersed in another liquid, in this case fat globules dispersed through an aqueous solution. Colloids of this sort, involving dispersion of a

liquid in a liquid, are generally called emulsions.

Let us consider in more detail colloids in which a solid is dispersed in a liquid or a liquid in another liquid. The obvious initial question is: What prevents the small particles from settling to the bottom over a period of time? You will recall from the last chapter that the particles of all matter possess heat energy if the temperature is above absolute zero. This heat energy is manifest in the form of motion by atoms, molecules, and other small particles. If you watch dust particles in a drop of water through a microscope, you will notice the constant agitation of the particles, or if you watch the fat globules in a droplet of milk under a microscope, you will observe a similar sort of Brownian movement. The movement of these particles is not solely dependent on the heat energy of the particles you see. You must bear in mind that the molecules of water through which they are dispersed also possess heat energy and are moving, and that these water molecules are constantly bumping into one another and into the particles of dust or the globules of fat. Consequently the various types of particles are constantly jostling one another. The continual movement of the particles is one of the factors that interfere with the influence of gravity and maintain the particles of a colloid in suspension. The particles are so small that their own thermal agitation, along with the energy transmitted to them by the bombarding water molecules, is enough partly to counteract the pull of gravity.

Another important factor in maintaining the suspension of colloidal particles is their electric charge. In many cases, colloidal particles are surrounded by layers of electric charge. Since particles of the same material possess the same charge, they tend to repel one another. As they start to settle out, they come into closer contact with one another, their charges interact, and they are repelled.

Still another factor, one particularly important in colloids of living material, is called solvation. Solvation occurs when there is a mutual attraction between the dispersed phase and the aqueous continuous phase, or "dispersions medium" as it is often called. Particles of the dispersed phase tend to take up water, forming a halo of water around themselves. An emulsion of this sort is much more stable than one involving a hydrophobic (water-repelling) dispersed phase.

Colloidal particles (generally macromolecules) that have considerable affinity for their liquid dispersions medium exhibit a capacity for interconversion between *sol* and *gel* states. In the sol state, the colloidal particles are dispersed throughout the dispersions medium in random fashion. They constitute the dispersed phase, while the liquid in which they are dispersed is the continuous phase. In the sol state, the colloid is essentially fluid. In the gel state, the colloidal particles interact and form a more orderly three-dimensional spongy network extending throughout the dispersions medium, so that both phases, in effect, become continuous (Fig. 3.4). When in the gel state, the colloid forms a semisolid and shows mechanical properties such as viscosity, elasticity, and tensile strength. Changes between the sol and gel states are brought about by changes in such factors as temperature, concentration, pH, salt concentration, pressure, and agitation. Think, for example, of jello. At high temperatures, jello is a sol, a fluid; when the temperature is lowered, it is converted into a gel, a semisolid.

Some gels can easily be reconverted into sols; others cannot. Apparently, a critical factor is the orderliness of the arrangement of the dispersed particles while these are in the gel condition. If the particles form a rather random network, the gel is usually reconvertible into a sol. If, however, they become oriented in a very precise manner with reference to one another and take on a semicrystalline form, the gel is usually not reversible. The network of particles in the colloidal gel state is usually held together by weak covalent bonds, hydrogen bonds, and electrical attractions between

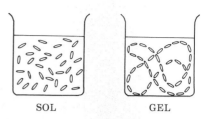

SOL   GEL

Fig. 3.4. Sol and gel states of a colloid. The particles in a sol are dispersed in a random and discontinuous fashion. The particles in a gel form a more orderly network.

molecules. The strength of these bonds also affects the stability of gels. Gels held together by fairly stable bonds are less easily reversible than those held by weaker bonds.

An understanding of the properties of colloidal systems is important in understanding the properties of living material. You will remember that protein molecules form the principal structural basis of living systems and that they are extremely large. In aqueous media, the individual protein molecules often separate to form a true solution, but being larger than the molecular aggregates of many other substances, they behave physically like colloidal particles. Protein solutions, then, have some of the properties of a true solution and some of the properties of a colloidal system; they have the greater reaction potential of a solution, but the sol-gel potential of a colloid.

Cells are generally said to be composed of *protoplasm,* or living substance. The word really isn't very specific, living material being composed of a wide variety of substances, intricately organized. Protoplasm may be regarded as both a complex solution and a heterogeneous colloid. The colloidal material is mostly protein molecules and fat globules. Various other materials such as inorganic salts, simple sugars, and amino acids are in solution. The sol-gel states to which protoplasm is subject because of its colloidal nature are a source of many of its unusual properties. Thus the different regions or structures revealed on close examination of cells are in part explained by

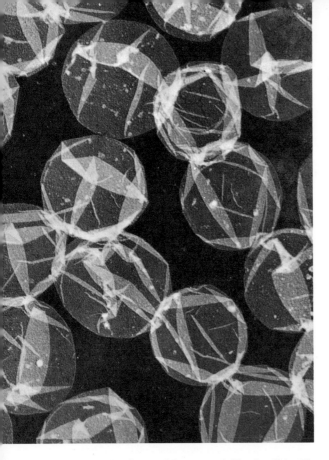

Fig. 3.5. Ghosts of human red blood cells. The whitish areas are places where the surface of the ghost is folded. The cells have been enlarged about 4,500 times. [Courtesy J. F. Hoffman, Yale University.]

the fact that given areas of the cell are in different sol or gel conditions. Through such organization, a system composed largely of water can maintain a high degree of structural integrity. Let us now examine the subcellular components, keeping in mind the properties of colloids.

The Cell Membrane

Structure of the Cell Membrane. For many years biologists have assumed that cells are bounded on their external surfaces by a *plasma membrane,* and they have explained many of the characteristics of cells in terms of properties they attribute to this membrane. Despite the widespread, almost routine, acceptance of its existence, it is only in the last few years that

any direct proof for it has been obtained. Most earlier ideas concerning the membrane were based on indirect reasoning from various characteristics of the cells themselves. The membrane was usually not visible even under the most powerful light microscopes; although something believed to be the membrane could be isolated from red blood cells, there was no conclusive proof that these red-cell "ghosts" (Fig. 3.5) were really cell membranes and not artifacts of the procedures used to obtain them.

It had been known for a long time that lipids and many substances soluble in lipids move with relative ease between the cell and the surrounding medium. From this fact it was deduced that the outer boundary of the cell, the cell membrane, must contain a layer of lipids, and that fat-soluble substances could move across the membrane by being dissolved in it. The lipid theory of the cell membrane was not sufficient to explain all the results of permeability studies, however. Because it was observed that many water-soluble substances also move quite freely between the inner portion of the cell and its external environment, the sieve theory was added to the lipid theory; this theory postulated pores or nonlipid patches in the cell membrane. But still another observation had to be accounted for. Many small water-soluble ions do not exhibit an equal facility for crossing the cell boundary; some move rather freely, others only very slightly. These different ions often possess different electric charges. It was therefore assumed that the cell membrane possesses charge and tends to attract some ions and repel others. The physical properties of the cell boundary, especially its wettability, made it necessary to hypothesize the presence of a layer of protein in the membrane.

These various ideas about the cell membrane —its lipid and protein layers and pores—all stemming primarily from permeability studies, were put together in 1940 by J. F. Danielli of King's College, London. He theorized that the membrane consisted of inner and outer layers of protein with two layers of lipid between them (Fig. 3.6), the whole membrane being about 80 angstroms thick (an angstrom is a hundred-millionth of a centimeter).

Despite the seemingly obvious need for a coating membrane to maintain the integrity of the cell, and despite all the indirect evidence concerning its structure gleaned from studies of permeability characteristics and red-cell "ghosts," some workers insisted that there was no compelling reason to believe that a cell membrane existed. They thought all the observations concerning the movement of materials could be explained by the formation of an interface between two liquid droplets of different substances. The question now seems to have been resolved, however, by recent electron-microscope studies of the outer boundaries of certain cells that envelop nerve cells and by X-ray diffraction studies. Electron micrographs made by J. David Robertson of the Harvard Medical School indicate that the cell mem-

Fig. 3.7. Electron micrograph showing cell membrane of human red blood cell. The cytoplasm of the cell is in the upper right half of the picture. The membrane consists of two dark lines (probably protein) separated by a lighter area, which is probably lipid. × 280,000. [Courtesy J. David Robertson, Harvard University.]

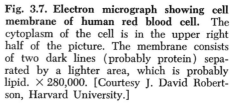

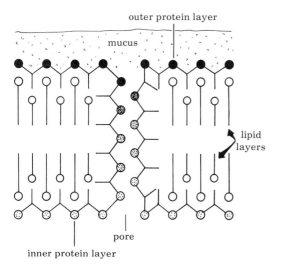

Fig. 3.6. Model of the cell membrane. Danielli suggested that there are two layers of lipids sandwiched between two layers of protein (as indicated here, the outer and inner protein layers are probably not identical). The molecules are oriented with their polar heads (circles) near the two surfaces and their nonpolar tails projecting at right angles from the surfaces. Tiny pores probably penetrate the membrane at some points. Many cells have a layer of mucoprotein on their outer surface.

brane is composed of two electron-dense layers separated by a somewhat wider lighter area (Fig. 3.7). His measurements of the total thickness of the membrane come to 75 angstroms, which is very close to the 80 angstroms hypothesized by Danielli in 1940. X-ray diffraction studies indicate that the molecules of the material in the lighter middle portion of the cell membrane are oriented parallel to the cell's radius. Again, this evidence supports Danielli's hypothesis of the arrangement of the lipid molecules (see Fig. 3.6). X-ray studies also seem to indicate that the outermost and innermost portions of the membrane are composed of molecules oriented perpendicular to the cell's radius—a confirmation of Danielli's idea of the arrangement of the proteins. Danielli's model of the cell membrane has been supported amazingly well by all later experimental approaches, and furnishes an excellent example of the value of model construction in science. Conceptual models often help us see more clearly both the current state of our knowledge and the problems yet to be tackled, and they often provide an impetus to further research.

Current information about the structure of the cell membrane is in full agreement with the known properties of lipids and proteins. The lipid portion of the membrane is probably composed primarily of phospholipids and/or steroids. Figure 2.20 on p. 37 shows that each phospholipid molecule is electrically charged at one end, and therefore polar; the charged or polar portion is attracted to water and is soluble, while the hydrocarbon chains of the fatty acids (shown simply as R groups in the figure) are nonpolar and hence insoluble in water. Similarly, the hydroxyl (OH) group of a steroid (Fig. 2.21, p. 37) is polar while the rest of the molecule is not. The differences between the polar and nonpolar ends tend to make these surface-active substances accumulate at interfaces, with the polar group attracted to the more aqueous medium and the nonpolar portion oriented at right angles away from the water. Thus it is not unexpected that lipid materials of this type constitute important components of membrane surfaces at points of junction between two media with different properties. When protein molecules are spread out on the surface of aqueous media, they too tend to form films with considerable regularity of structure similar to that shown in the membrane model; the main "backbone" portions of the protein molecules, with their partly ionized amino and carboxyl groups, tend to lie along the interface, while the R groups of the amino acids tend to be oriented at right angles to the interface. In the cell membrane, the charged portions of the lipids are probably loosely bound electrostatically to the charged groups of the proteins, forming lipoprotein complexes. We can see, then, that the plasma membrane is a very precisely arranged region of the protoplasm in the gel state—a state that is an outgrowth of the properties of the lipids

and proteins that are the two principal colloidal materials of protoplasm.

In this model of a membrane formed of regularly oriented layers of protein and lipid material, it seems also necessary to postulate a layer of carbohydrate-containing mucoprotein on the outer surface of the membrane of many cells (Fig. 3.6).

This lipoprotein sandwich, with lipids arranged between two layers of protein, has been termed by Robertson the *unit membrane.* Many other cellular membrane systems have been found to be based on this unit-membrane structure, as we shall see in later parts of this chapter and in other chapters to follow. The unit membrane is sometimes spoken of as a double membrane, but the whole unit really forms a single structurally and functionally integrated system.

This picture of the cell membrane should not, however, be accepted as the final version. Much remains to be learned. Continuing cooperation between electron microscopists and cell chemists promises to bring increasing knowledge of this critically important portion of the living cell.[1]

Function of the Cell Membrane. The cell membrane is not simply a passive envelope giving mechanical strength and shape and some protection to the cell, though these functions are important. It is an active component of the living cell, playing a complex and dynamic role in life processes. It regulates the traffic in materials between the precisely ordered interior of the cell and the essentially unfavorable and potentially disruptive outer environment. All substances moving between the cell's environment and the cellular interior

[1] In 1966, while this book was in press, serious doubt was cast on the general applicability of the concept of the unit membrane. It was pointed out in several papers that the concept of the unit membrane is based on myelin membranes, which may not be a valid model for other cellular membranes. There is increasing evidence that the arrangement of the proteins and lipids may vary considerably from one membrane to another. (See E. D. Korn, "Structure of Biological Membranes," *Science,* vol. 153, 1966, pp. 1491–1498.)

in either direction must pass through a membrane barrier.

Before attempting to examine in more detail the role of the membrane, we must discuss some of the factors affecting the movement of materials from one place to another in general. Several times already, we have mentioned the motion that characterizes small particles as a consequence of heat energy. This thermal agitation helped us explain, in part, the speeds of chemical reactions and the behavior of colloidal particles. It will also help us explain the topic now before us. Thermal agitation is a major factor in the tendency of particles to move from one place to another.

Let us consider a small rectangular box containing 20 marbles, all placed in a tight cluster near one end of the box (Fig. 3.8A). The marbles will remain close together at one end of the box as long as they are without motion. But suppose we now cause the marbles to move randomly. In a very short time, they will be distributed with relative uniformity throughout the box; the tight cluster at one end will have disappeared (Fig. 3.8B). Why? We said that the motion of the marbles was random; they were as likely to begin moving in one direction as in any other. But look at the marbles in Fig. 3.8A; among all the possible directions in which a given marble may move, there are more leading away from the center of the cluster than toward it. It is therefore more probable that random movement will result in disruption of the cluster than in its maintenance. Or, to word it another way, in the absence of any counteracting external influence, a dynamic system will tend to move toward the more probable disorganized state rather than toward the less probable organized state.

Besides the more numerous directions of movement away from the cluster than toward its center, there is another factor that plays an important role in the tendency of the marbles to scatter. Movement toward the cluster has a high probability of resulting in a collision of two or more marbles, with the effect of stop-

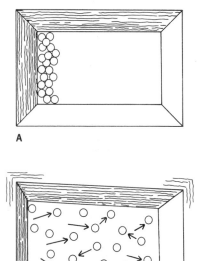

A

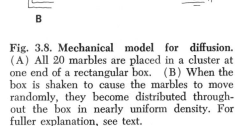

B

Fig. 3.8. **Mechanical model for diffusion.** (A) All 20 marbles are placed in a cluster at one end of a rectangular box. (B) When the box is shaken to cause the marbles to move randomly, they become distributed throughout the box in nearly uniform density. For fuller explanation, see text.

ping the forward motion of the colliding marbles and causing them to head off in other directions. Movement away from the cluster carries much less probability of collision; a marble has a good chance of continuing on an uninterrupted path to the outer portions of the box. On the average, then, more marbles move away from the center of concentration than toward it.

Notice that the above arguments are both statistical. It is possible that, as a result of random motion, 20 scattered marbles will all come to form a tight cluster at one end of the box. This result has a finite probability, but an extremely small one, so small that we generally feel justified in disregarding it. This kind of reasoning is typical of most scientific reasoning. Science cannot make absolute statements. Scientific facts and laws are statistical statements. They describe nature in terms of the probabilities of various events as the scientists see them.

We can now make a generalization based on our example of the marbles in the box and on others like it: *The net movement of the particles of a particular substance is from regions of greater concentration of that substance to regions of less concentration of that substance.* Note that we said the *net* movement. There will always be some individual particles moving, by chance, in the opposite direction, but when the movements of all the particles are considered jointly, the net movement is away from the centers of concentration. An obvious result is that the particles of a given substance tend to become distributed with relatively uniform density within any available space. When this uniform density is reached, the system is in equilibrium. The particles continue to move, but there is little net change in the system.

Movement of particles from one place to another in the manner we have been discussing is called **diffusion.** Diffusion is characteristic of the atoms and molecules of materials in all three principal states: gas, liquid, and solid. In all cases, the rate of diffusion increases as the temperature increases, since it is a consequence of heat motion. Diffusion is fastest by far in gases, where there is much space between the particles and consequently less chance of collision. If you open a bottle of oil of wintergreen at one end of a room, it won't be long before people at the other end of the room begin to smell it. Its movement is caused partly by air currents, but rapid diffusion is also a major factor. Diffusion in a liquid is much slower (Fig. 3.9). In the absence of convection currents, it takes a very long time, years in fact, for a substance to move in appreciable quantity only a few feet through water. Diffusion in solids is, of course, far slower still. There is very little space between the particles of a solid, and collisions occur almost before the particles get going. In all these instances, however, regardless of

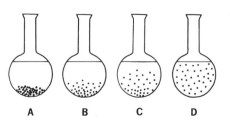

Fig. 3.9. Diffusion in a liquid. Particles are at the bottom of a flask of water in (A). The particles slowly diffuse away from the cluster until in (D) they are distributed with nearly uniform density through the water. If there are no convection currents, and all movement is by simple diffusion, it may take years to reach the condition shown in (D).

the rate of diffusion, the net effect is movement from the regions of higher concentration.

Now let us consider a somewhat more complicated situation, a chamber divided into two halves by a membrane partition. Let us assume, further, that particles of some substances can pass through the membrane while particles of other substances cannot. Such a membrane is said to be differentially permeable, or **semipermeable.** How will the semipermeable membrane affect the diffusion of materials between the two halves of the chamber? Suppose our chamber is a U tube like that shown in Fig. 3.10, divided in half by the semipermeable membrane. Suppose side A contains a solution of sugar in water and side B an equal quantity of pure water. If the membrane is permeable to water but not to sugar, water molecules will be able to pass in both directions, from A to B and from B to A. Since water is already present on both sides of the membrane, we might at first suppose that the net effect of the diffusion of water molecules across the membrane would be zero, but such a supposition would be wrong.

Consider the differences between the sugar solution and the pure water more carefully. Part of the space in the sugar solution is occupied by sugar molecules. Consequently there are more water molecules per unit volume in the pure water than in the sugar solution. This means that the probability is high that, per unit time, more water molecules will bump into the membrane on side B than on side A, simply because there are more water molecules near the membrane on side B than on side A. Furthermore, there will be some sugar molecules near the membrane on side A, and some of the water molecules moving toward the membrane in the sugar solution will strike these sugar molecules and be deflected before they hit the membrane. For these reasons, it is apparent that more water molecules will move across the membrane from side B to side A per unit time than in the opposite direction. You will note that this result is in full accord with our earlier generalization concerning diffusion; the net movement of the water molecules is from the region of their greater concentration (side B) to the region of their lesser concentration (side A). But this will mean that the volume of fluid will increase on side A and decrease on side B. How long can this process continue? Will an equilibrium point be reached?

Clearly, the concentration of water on the two sides of the membrane will never be equal, no matter how many water molecules move from B to A, because the fluid in A will remain a sugar solution, though an increasingly weak one, and the fluid in B will remain pure water if the membrane is completely impermeable to sugar molecules. We might therefore expect that the net movement of water from B to A would continue indefinitely. However, this is not in fact what happens. Under normal conditions, the fluid level in A will rise to a certain point and then cease to rise farther. Why? The column of fluid is, of course, being pulled downward by gravity, i.e. it has weight. As the column rises, therefore, it exerts increasing hydrostatic pressure upon the membrane at its base. Eventually the column of sugar solution becomes so high that the pressure it exerts against the membrane is great enough for water molecules to be forced across

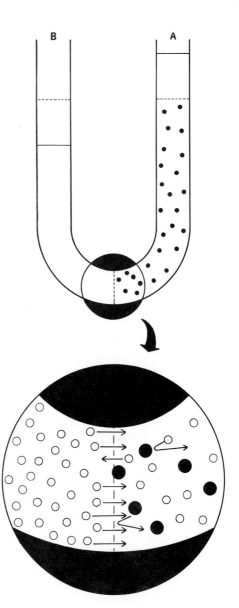

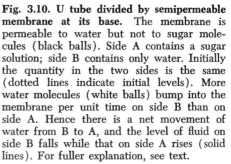

Fig. 3.10. U tube divided by semipermeable membrane at its base. The membrane is permeable to water but not to sugar molecules (black balls). Side A contains a sugar solution; side B contains only water. Initially the quantity in the two sides is the same (dotted lines indicate initial levels). More water molecules (white balls) bump into the membrane per unit time on side B than on side A. Hence there is a net movement of water from B to A, and the level of fluid on side B falls while that on side A rises (solid lines). For fuller explanation, see text.

the membrane from A to B as fast as they move into A from B. When this point is reached—when water is passing through the membrane in opposite directions at the same rate—the system is in equilibrium. Under given conditions of temperature and pressure, the equilibrium point is determined by the difference in particle concentration on the two sides of the membrane; the greater the difference, the higher the column will rise before equilibrium is reached. It is important to note that by concentration we here mean not concentration by weight, but rather molecular concentration, i.e. the number of particles per unit volume.

The diffusion of water through a semipermeable membrane is a special type of diffusion called *osmosis*.[2] Actually, osmosis is the diffusion of the principal solvent of a system, whether water or another substance, through a semipermeable membrane, but since the principal solvent in living systems is water, we shall always use the term "osmosis" with reference to water in this book. We can now also give a name to the hydrostatic pressure exerted by the column of sugar solution at equilibrium in our example; it is called *osmotic pressure*. Osmotic pressure is simply *the pressure that must be exerted on a solution or colloid to keep it in equilibrium with pure water when the two are separated by a semipermeable membrane*. Obviously, that pressure does not have to be exerted by a column of liquid; pressure upon the solution by any other means would also be effective.

It is customary to speak of any solution or colloidal system as having a characteristic potential osmotic pressure, the value of which is determined by the total number of dissolved or colloidal particles, regardless of what kind of particles they are. For example, when molecules of a substance ionize in water, it is not the number of original molecules that determines the osmotic activity of the solution, but the total number of dissociated ions, since each ion behaves as a separate and distinct particle. We can speak of the potential osmotic pressure of a solution even when the solution is not actually separated from pure water by a semipermeable membrane. What we mean, of course, is the pressure that would have to be put upon that solution to keep it from gaining water if it were separated from a supply of pure water by a semipermeable membrane. Clearly, then, *the osmotic pressure of a solution or colloid is a measure of the tendency of water to move by osmosis into it*. The more dissolved or colloidal particles there are in a solution, the more water will tend to move into it, and the higher the value of the solution's osmotic pressure will be.

You doubtless realize by now that we have discussed diffusion and osmosis and the role played by semipermeable membranes at such length because the cell membrane is semipermeable and the processes of diffusion and osmosis are fundamental to cell life. The membranes of different types of cells vary widely in their permeability characteristics. For example, the membrane of a human red blood cell is over 100 times more permeable to water than is the membrane of an amoeba, a single-celled organism. We can, however, make a few rough generalizations concerning the permeability of cell membranes: They are relatively permeable to water and to certain simple sugars, amino acids, and lipid-soluble substances; they are relatively impermeable to polysaccharides, proteins, and other very large molecules; their permeability to small inorganic ions differs greatly depending on the particular ion, but in general negatively charged ions can cross cellular membranes more rapidly than positively charged ions, though neither can do so as readily as uncharged particles.

---

[2] Recent evidence indicates that osmosis is more than simple diffusion of water through a semipermeable membrane. The movement of water in a membrane is far too rapid to be explained by the random molecular motions upon which diffusion depends. Apparently there is some sort of bulk flow in the membrane. However, both the direction of movement in osmosis and the equilibrium conditions can still be understood in terms of diffusion.

We have already seen how these permeability characteristics are related to our conceptions of the structure of the cell membrane, but let us here briefly review the implications of these characteristics for the structure of the membrane. From the preceding paragraph, it is evident that solubility in lipid, small molecular size, and lack of charge all facilitate penetration of the cell membrane. The first of these three characteristics is clearly related to the presence of lipid layers as major components of cell membranes; lipid-soluble substances probably move across the membrane by first dissolving in it. The second characteristic, small size, is one of the bases for the theory that there are small pores in the plasma membrane through which only very small particles can move (Fig. 3.6). That the electron microscope has so far failed to prove that such pores actually exist is disappointing but not unexpected, since the pores are thought to be very small. Their diameter is estimated at 5 to 10 angstroms, which is just at the lower limit of resolving power of the best electron microscopes now in existence, and they are probably far apart, comprising only one-thousandth or less of the total membrane area. Furthermore, the pores may not be stable; they may be constantly appearing and disappearing. It seems probable that they are important only in the passage of water molecules and a few very small negative ions. Most substances, even small ones like ions, must move through the membrane itself, and for this reason the membrane can exercise great selectivity as to what may cross it and what may not. The third characteristic, concerning charge, leads us to suppose that the membrane itself possesses charge, probably positive. This charge would hinder the movement of ions, particularly positive ions, which would be repelled (Fig. 3.11).

The above hypotheses, however, do not fully account for the high selectivity exhibited by cells toward different substances. It is probably necessary to hypothesize also that different areas of the membrane have different chemical specificities and have, as a result, slightly different permeability characteristics. We must stress, in addition, that our ideas concerning the cell membrane are still in flux and that some of the theories outlined here may have to be greatly modified in the future, or perhaps even abandoned.

So far, we have ignored any active role of the cell membrane and discussed the movement of substances through it as though all such movement were purely passive. And certainly some of the movement is passive, the result of concentration gradients between the cell contents and the external medium, or the result of electric-potential gradients between the inside and the outside of the cell, or the result (less often) of bulk flow through the pores. But this is far from the complete story. The membrane is a part of the living cell,

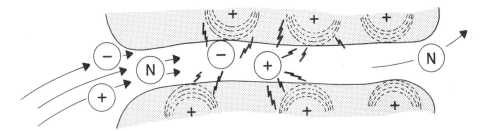

Fig. 3.11. Movement of particles through a pore in the cell membrane. The membrane is charged, probably positively. Hence positive ions are repelled by the surface of the membrane and negative ions are attracted, but the charge interferes with the movement of both types of ions. Neutral particles move through the pores most easily.

and as such it is an active, dynamic entity. Furthermore, the cell contents may also play a role in determining what shall enter freely and what shall not. We can, therefore, speak of *active transport,* movement of substances across cell membranes as a result of the doing of work by the cell. Doing work, of course, demands the expenditure of energy by the cell.

Often active transport involves moving into or out of the cells materials that passive diffusion would cause to move in the same direction, but not as rapidly. In other cases, it may involve moving substances against the concentration gradient. For example, many cells contain much less sodium than is found in the fluid surrounding them; i.e. there is a gradient between the low concentration of sodium inside the cells and the high concentration outside. Since the membrane is some-

what permeable to sodium, passive diffusion should result in movement of sodium into the cell until the concentrations on the two sides of the membrane become equal. Sodium does indeed diffuse into the cell, but as fast as it does so, the cell actively pumps it out again, against the concentration gradient. Conversely, many of these same cells actively transport potassium into the cell against a concentration gradient and thereby maintain a much higher concentration of potassium inside than outside.

The exact mechanism of active transport is not known. Most theories proposed to explain this phenomenon, which is so important to the maintenance of life, assume that some sort of carrier molecule is involved (Fig. 3.12). The carrier is presumed to react chemically with the molecule to be transported, forming a compound that is soluble in the lipid portion of

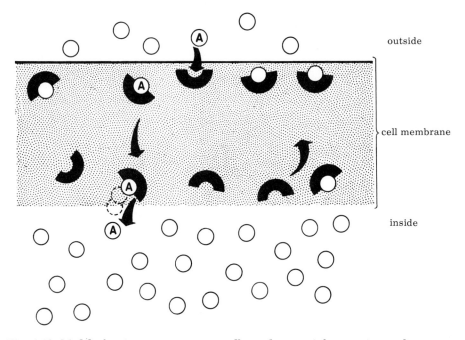

Fig. 3.12. Model of active transport across cell membrane. Substance A is in lower concentration outside the cell than inside; yet it continues to enter the cell. At the outer surface of the membrane, molecules of A combine with lipid-soluble carrier molecules (black arcs). The newly formed complex molecules diffuse across the membrane from the region of their higher concentration near the outer surface to the region of their lower concentration near the inner surface, where the A molecules are released into the interior of the cell. The free carrier molecules then diffuse back across the membrane to the outer surface. The chemical reactions involved require expenditure of energy.

the membrane. This compound then moves through the membrane along a concentration gradient to the other side, where it is broken apart by enzymes. The transported molecule is released, and the carrier diffuses back through the membrane, again along a concentration gradient, to pick up another load. Let us suppose, for example, that molecules of A are in lower concentration outside a cell than inside, but that A is being actively transported into the cell nonetheless. Suppose that the carrier molecule is X. Molecules of X near the outer surface of the membrane react with molecules of A to form XA. But if XA is constantly being synthesized at the outer edge of the membrane, it will be in higher concentration there than nearer the inner surface of the membrane. XA will therefore diffuse passively from the outer side of the membrane to the inner side. There an enzyme breaks XA apart, releasing A into the cell. But this means that X is being constantly resynthesized from XA near the inner suface of the membrane and is more concentrated there than nearer the outer surface. Therefore X will passively diffuse back across the membrane, where it is again available to pick up a molecule of A. This model of active transport, then, depends on passive diffusion of a compound molecule (XA) in a direction in which neither the transported molecule alone (A) nor the carrier molecule alone (X) would diffuse. The energy expenditure is in the chemical reactions involved, which make possible the pickup of molecule A by the carrier and its release from the membrane on the side where it is already in high concentration.

Carrier molecules may be involved in some passive transport as well. A molecule of sugar, for example, may be in higher concentration outside a liver cell than in it and hence tend to diffuse into the cell. But in order to cross the membrane, it may have to combine with a carrier and form a lipid-soluble compound. Since the movement is with the concentration gradient, however, no energy might be re-

quired; nonetheless, this sort of passive transport is certainly more complex than simple diffusion.

Another method by which the cell may play an active role in determining what substances will move into it, and in what quantities, depends more on the cellular contents than on the membrane. As a given substance passively diffuses into the cell, it may be bound to some other molecule and held in this compound form, thus preventing a buildup in concentration of the unbound substance and maintaining a concentration gradient that favors movement of more of the substance into the cell (Fig. 3.13). For example, substance B may be in higher concentration outside the cell than in it. It therefore tends to diffuse into the cell. Once inside, it is bound to a molecule of X to form XB. This means that the concentration of unbound B does not greatly increase inside the cell and B continues to diffuse rapidly into the cell.

Still another manner in which materials may enter cells involves the active engulfing of the material by the cell. When the material engulfed is in the form of large particles or chunks of matter, the process is called *phago-*

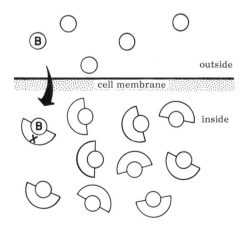

Fig. 3.13. Formation of a complex inside the cell. As fast as molecules of B enter the cell, they combine with molecules of X. Hence the concentration of free B inside the cell remains low and B continues to diffuse inward.

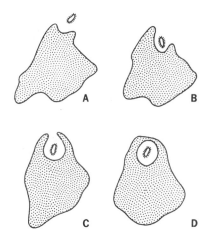

Fig. 3.14. Phagocytosis. Pseudopodia, arm-like processes of the cell, flow around the food particle until it has been entirely enclosed within a vacuole.

cytosis (Fig. 3.14). Usually portions of the cell flow around the prey, enclosing it within a chamber. The membrane of this chamber, or vesicle, then becomes detached from the membrane of the cell surface, and the vesicle migrates into the interior of the cell. When the engulfed material is liquid or consists of very small particles, the process is often called *pinocytosis* (Fig. 3.15). Pinocytosis is much like phagocytosis except that the material is not surrounded to the same extent by arms of the cell. Instead, the material apparently becomes adsorbed on the cell surface. Then the loaded membrane either flows inward into a deep narrow channel, at the end of which vesicles are formed, or the small vesicles are simply detached directly from the membrane of the cell surface.

When material is contained within vesicles formed through phagocytosis or pinocytosis, the material has not yet entered the cell in the fullest sense. It is still separated by a membrane from the cellular substance, and it must eventually cross that membrane (or the membrane must disintegrate) if it is to become incorporated into the cell. Usually the material is first acted upon by enzymes in the vesicles

and broken down to smaller, simpler substances that can move more easily across the vesicular membranes.

If we have given you the impression that the cell membrane can completely regulate the exchange of materials between the cell and the surrounding medium and always maintain optimum conditions within the cell, we must point out that such is not the case. Some poisons can apparently move freely across the cell membrane, much to the detriment of the cell. And some beneficial substances are lost to the cell because the membrane cannot prevent them

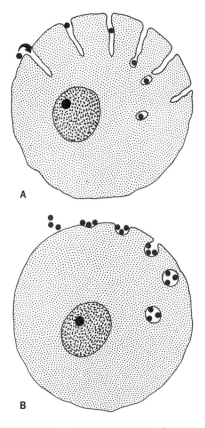

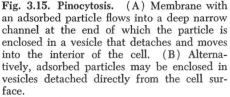

Fig. 3.15. Pinocytosis. (A) Membrane with an adsorbed particle flows into a deep narrow channel at the end of which the particle is enclosed in a vesicle that detaches and moves into the interior of the cell. (B) Alternatively, adsorbed particles may be enclosed in vesicles detached directly from the cell surface.

from diffusing out. Furthermore, the membrane's great permeability to water can sometimes result in harmful or even fatal effects upon the cell. When a cell is in a medium that is *hyperosmotic* relative to it (i.e. in a medium that has a higher concentration of osmotically active dissolved or colloidal particles and thus a higher osmotic pressure), the cell tends to lose water by osmosis to the medium (Fig. 3.16). As it loses water it shrinks, and if the process goes too far, the cell may die. Conversely, when a cell is in a medium *hypoosmotic* relative to it (i.e. in a medium that has a lower concentration of osmotically active particles and thus a lower osmotic pressure), the cell tends to gain water by osmosis from the medium. As it gains water it swells, and unless it has special mechanisms for expelling the excess water, or special structures that prevent excessive swelling (as in most plant cells), it may burst. A cell in an *isosmotic* medium (i.e. one that has the same concentration of osmotically active particles and thus the same osmotic pressure) neither loses nor gains appreciable quantities of water by osmosis.

Obviously, the osmotic relationship between the cell and the medium surrounding it is a critical factor in the life of the cell. Some cells are normally bathed by an isosmotic fluid and hence have no serious osmotic problems. Human red blood cells, to which we referred earlier, are an example; they are normally bathed by blood plasma, a fluid with which they are in relatively close osmotic balance. We can understand now why they are so permeable to water; in the absence of any significant selection for impermeable red blood cells, such cells have not evolved. Many of the simpler oceanic plants and animals also exemplify cells in an isosomotic medium; their cellular contents have an osmotic concentration closely approximating that of sea water. All protoplasm, however, has a higher osmotic concentration than fresh water. Fresh-water organisms thus live in a hypoosmotic medium

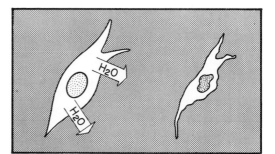

HYPEROSMOTIC MEDIUM

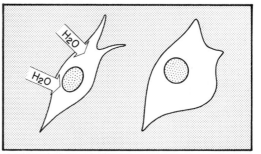

HYPOOSMOTIC MEDIUM

ISOSMOTIC MEDIUM

Fig. 3.16. Osmotic relationships of an animal cell. Cell in a hyperosmotic medium loses water (left) and shrivels (right). Cell in hypoosmotic medium gains water and swells. Cell in isosmotic medium has no net gain or loss of water.

and face the problem of a tendency to accumulate excessive water within their cells by osmosis. Their very existence has depended upon the evolution of ways of preventing their cells from becoming so turgid (i.e. so distended by their fluid contents) that they would burst. A variety of evolutionary solutions

Fig. 3.17. Electron micrographs of cell wall of the alga *Valonia ventricosa*, showing its development. (A) Very young primary wall. The cellulose fibrils are randomly arranged and form a loose network. × 10,500. (B–C) Later stages. Note increasing parallelism of fibrils. × 10,500. (D) Mature secondary wall. The cellulose fibrils lie parallel to each other in compact layers. Three layers, each oriented at 60 degrees to the one below it, can be seen here. × 14,800. [Courtesy F. C. Steward and K. Mühlethaler, *Ann. Botany* (*London*), vol. 17, 1953.]

to this problem will be examined in a later chapter. We can point out here, however, that amoebae, which we said earlier have membranes less permeable to water than those of human red blood cells, live in fresh water and hence have been exposed to selection pressures favoring evolution of such membranes.

Plant Cell Walls

One of the most striking differences between the cells of plants and those of animals is that the former possess a very conspicuous cell wall, while the latter do not. The cell wall is located outside the cell membrane. It is generally not considered part of the cellular protoplasm, although it is a product of the protoplasm.

The cell wall is composed primarily of the complex polysaccharide *cellulose* and other similar compounds. The cellulose is generally present in the form of long threadlike structures called fibrils. The spaces between the fibrils, though partly filled with other harder compounds like *pectin,* a complex polysaccharide, usually allow water, air, and dissolved materials to pass freely through the cell wall. The cell wall does not usually exert a discriminating effect as to which materials can enter the cell and which cannot. This function is reserved to the cell membrane located below the cell wall.

The first portion of the cell wall laid down by a young growing cell is the *primary wall.* The fibrils within the primary wall are arranged in a loose random network (Fig. 3.17A). Where the walls of two cells abut against each other, an intercellular layer known as the *middle lamella* is located between them. The middle lamella is common to both cells. Pectin, generally in the form of calcium pectate, is one of its primary constituents. It is this middle lamella between the primary walls of the two cells that binds the cells together. If the pectin of the middle lamella is dissolved away, the cells become less tightly bound to each other. This is what happens, for example, when fruits ripen. The calcium pectate of the middle lamella is partly converted into other more soluble forms, the cells become looser, and the fruit becomes softer. Many of the bacteria and fungi that produce soft rots of the tissues of higher plants do so by first dissolving the pectin, reducing the tissue to a soft pulp upon which they can feed.

Cells of the soft tissues of the plant have only primary walls and intercellular middle lamellae. The cells that eventually form the harder, more woody portions of the plant add additional layers to the cell wall, forming what is known as the *secondary wall.* Since this wall, like the primary wall, is deposited by the protoplasm of the cell, it is located internal to the earlier-formed primary wall, lying between it and the membrane (Fig. 3.18). The secondary wall is often much thicker than the primary wall and is composed of a succession of compact layers, or lamellae. The cellulose fibrils in these lamellae are not arranged in a loose network like those of the primary wall, but lie parallel to each other and are generally oriented at angles of about 60 degrees to the fibrils of the next lamella (Fig. 3.17D). This arrangement gives added strength to the cell wall. In addition to cellulose, secondary walls usually contain other harder materials such as *lignin,* which make them stiffer.

Deposition of the secondary wall usually begins when the cell is nearing the end of its growth. When deposition of the secondary wall has been completed, many cells die, leaving the hard tube formed by their cell walls to function in mechanical support and internal transport for the body of the plant.

The cellulose of the cell walls is commercially important as the main component of paper, cotton, flax, hemp, rayon, celluloid, and, obviously, wood itself. Lignin extracted from wood is sometimes used in the manufacture of synthetic rubber, adhesives, pigments, synthetic resins, and vanillin. It is also used in the food and drug industries.

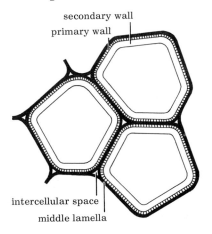

Fig. 3.18. Three adjacent plant cells, showing cell walls and middle lamella.

Cell walls generally do not form completely uninterrupted boundaries around the cells. There are often tiny holes in the walls through which delicate protoplasmic connections between adjacent cells may run. These connections are called *plasmodesmata* (see Fig. 3.24). In many cases, they are located in areas, called pits, where the cell wall is very thin (see Fig. 7.10, p. 230). Thus the protoplasm of an individual cell in a multicellular plant body is not isolated, but is in contact and communication with the protoplasm of other cells by way of the plasmodesmata. A large portion of the intercellular exchange of such materials as sugars and amino acids probably takes place through protoplasmic connections.

The presence of cell walls means that plant cells can withstand very dilute external media without bursting. In such media, they are of course in a condition of turgor (distention). Water tends to move by osmosis into the cell as a result of the high osmotic concentration of the protoplasm. The cell swells, building up *turgor pressure* against the cell walls. The walls, in turn, exert an equal opposing pressure against the swollen cell (from physics you may recall Newton's third law: To every action there is an equal and opposite reaction). The cell wall of a mature cell can usually be stretched only a minute amount. A point of equilibrium is eventually reached, therefore, when the resistance of the wall is so great that no further increase in the size of the cell is possible and, consequently, no more water can enter the cell. Hence, in their tendency to take in water, plants are not so fully dependent as are animal cells on the difference in osmotic concentration between the cellular material and the surrounding medium. Instead, their tendency to take in water, which we shall call *suction pressure,* S, is equal to the osmotic pressure, P, of the cellular contents, minus the wall pressure, W:

$$S = P - W$$

Plant cells, then, because of the wall pressure, can withstand much wider fluctuations in the osmotic makeup of the surrounding medium than can animal cells.

The Nucleus

Within the cells of most organisms (though not of bacteria and blue-green algae), the largest and one of the most conspicuous structural areas is the nucleus (Fig. 3.19), the control center of the cell. The nucleus plays the central role in cellular reproduction, the process whereby a single cell undergoes cell division and forms two new cells. It also plays a central role, in conjunction with the environment, in determining what sort of differentiation a cell will undergo and what form the cell will exhibit at maturity. And the nucleus directs the metabolic activities of the living cell. In short, it is from the nucleus that the "instructions" emanate that guide the life processes of the cell as long as it lives. Biologists attach so much importance to the nucleus that they even have a special name, *cytoplasm,* for all protoplasm other than the nucleus. We commonly think of the nucleus and the cytoplasm as the two major subdivisions of protoplasm.

Within the nucleus are several relatively distinct types of structures, notably the chromosomes and the nucleoli. These structures are embedded in a mass of relatvely amorphous, somewhat granular-appearing nucleoplasm. The entire nucleus is bounded by a nuclear membrane.

The *chromosomes* (Fig. 3.20) are elongate, threadlike bodies clearly visible only when the cell is undergoing division. They are composed of nucleic acid and protein bound together in a complex called nucleoprotein. The chromosomes bear, apparently in linear arrangement, the basic units of heredity, called *genes.* It is the genes that determine the characteristics of cells, as they are passed from generation to generation, and that act as the units of control in the day-to-day activities of living cells. They are the code units, if you will, whereby

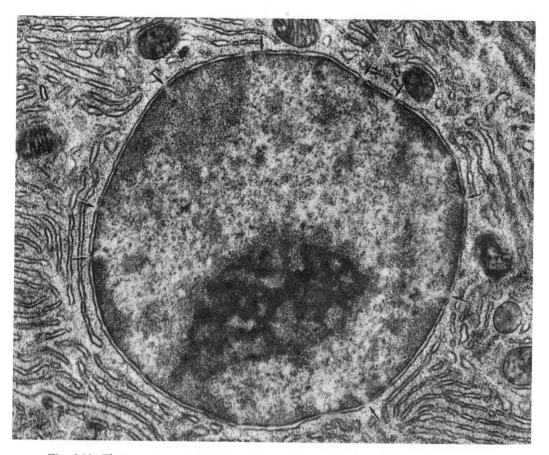

Fig. 3.19. Electron micrograph of the nucleus of a pancreatic cell. The dark area inside the nucleus is a nucleolus. Numerous "pores" (arrows) can be seen in the double nuclear membrane. × 16,000. [Courtesy D. W. Fawcett, *A Textbook of Histology*, Saunders, 1962.]

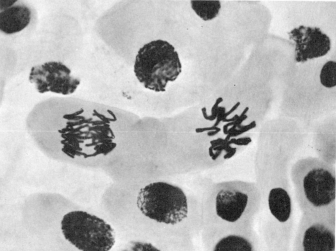

Fig. 3.20. Nuclei of dividing cells in root tip of onion, showing chromosomes. Separate chromosomes cannot be distinguished in the dark-stained nuclei of the nondividing cells at top and bottom of photograph. [Courtesy General Biological Supply House, Inc., Chicago.]

bits of information are passed from parent to offspring, and which determine the enzymes that so precisely regulate the myriad interdependent chemical reactions of life. Indeed, the genes are at the very focal point of life, and they and the chromosomes on which they lie are structures to which we must direct much attention in later chapters.

Nucleoli are dark-staining, generally oval bodies usually clearly visible within the nuclei of nondividing cells. There may be one or more nucleoli per nucleus, depending on the species of organism. Apparently nucleoli form in association with specific regions of specific chromosomes; however, the exact relationship between chromosomes and nucleoli is unclear. Nucleoli contain much protein and nucleic acid, as well as lesser quantities of other substances. Their chemical makeup probably varies considerably among different cell types and among cells of the same type in different metabolic states. Apparently the nucleoli are involved in the interactions between the nucleus and the cytoplasm.

The presence of a *nuclear membrane* surrounding the nucleus makes possible an environment within the nucleus different from that of the surrounding cytoplasm. Like the plasma membrane, the nuclear membrane probably has the unit-membrane structure (i.e. it is composed of two layers of lipid sandwiched between two layers of protein). Unlike the plasma membrane, the complete nuclear membrane actually involves two such unit membranes; i.e. it is double (Figs. 3.19 and 3.21). A distinct space is enclosed between the inner and outer membranes. Electron-microscope studies indicate that the double membrane is interrupted at intervals, leaving fairly large "pores" at points where the outer and inner membranes are continuous. It seems, however, that each such pore is filled by a formation called a "pore complex," and permeability experiments indicate that the pores do not make a sieve of the nuclear membrane. This membrane is, in fact, highly selective, and

some substances that can cross the cell membrane into the cytoplasm apparently cannot readily cross the nuclear membrane into the nucleus and are consequently restricted to the cytoplasm. For example, it has been found that when isotopically labeled albumin (i.e. albumin containing a radioactive isotope that acts as a label enabling us to locate it later) is injected into rats it enters certain cells of the liver, but microscopic studies of these cells have indicated that the labeled albumin is in the cytoplasm only. Such experiments with molecules much smaller than the so-called pores show clearly that simple unrestricted movement through them is definitely not possible.

The electron microscope has revealed another particularly interesting fact about the nuclear membrane. Apparently the outer portion of this double membrane is continuous at some points with an extensive cytoplasmic membrane system called the endoplasmic reticulum (Fig. 3.21). The significance of this connection for the functioning of the nucleus may be great. We turn next, therefore, to an examination of the intracellular membrane system.

The Endoplasmic Reticulum and Ribosomes

For many years, cell chemists have successfully used the technique of differential centrifugation to study the various fractions of cells. The first step is to grind up the tissue in a liquid medium of proper osmotic concentration to form a homogenate, which is then put in a centrifuge and spun. Initially it is spun at a relatively slow rate to separate out the larger, heavier parts of the homogenate, such as any remaining whole cells and the nuclei. When these fractions have been removed, the remaining material is again spun, this time at a higher speed, and cellular components of intermediate size, such as mitochondria, plas-

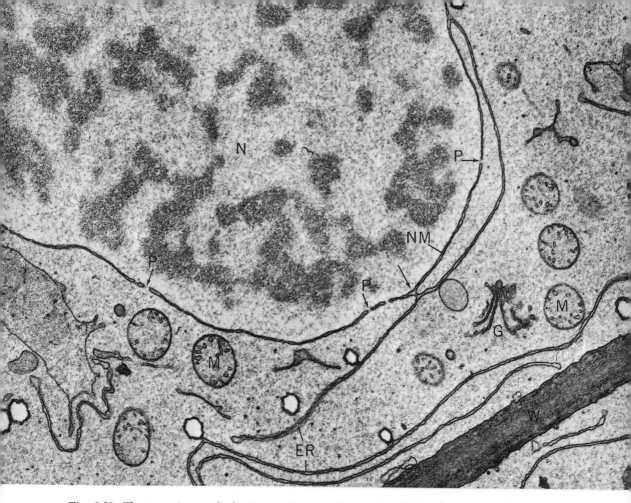

Fig. 3.21. Electron micrograph showing nuclear membrane of a cell from corn root. The nucleus is the large structure filling the upper left quarter of the picture. The unlabeled arrow indicates a point where the endoplasmic reticulum and the double nuclear membrane interconnect. ER, endoplasmic reticulum; G, Golgi apparatus; M, mitochondria; N, nucleus; NM, nuclear membrane; P, "pore" in nuclear membrane; W, cell wall. × 15,600. [Courtesy W. G. Whaley, H. H. Mollenhauer, and J. H. Leech, *Am. J. Botany,* vol. 47, 1960.]

tids, etc. (parts of the cell we shall discuss later), precipitate out and are removed. Thereupon the supernatant liquid can be spun at still higher speeds and smaller, lighter cellular fractions precipitated. By centrifuging the homogenate at increasing speeds in this manner, a series of fractions, segregated according to their particular size and density, can be obtained. These fractions can then be analyzed both morphologically and chemically to determine their characteristics and probable functions.

In 1938 Albert Claude of the Rockefeller Institute isolated by centrifugation at very high

speeds some essentially submicroscopic components of the cytoplasm, which were later termed microsomes (small bodies). This fraction made up as much as 15 to 20 percent of the total cell mass and could be isolated from almost any kind of cell, plant or animal. Chemical analysis showed that the microsomes had a very high nucleic acid content; in fact, they contained, almost all the cytoplasmic nucleic acid. They also contained a high percentage of the cytoplasmic phospholipids. Since, however, the microsomes were not visible under the light microscope, there was much argument as to whether they were

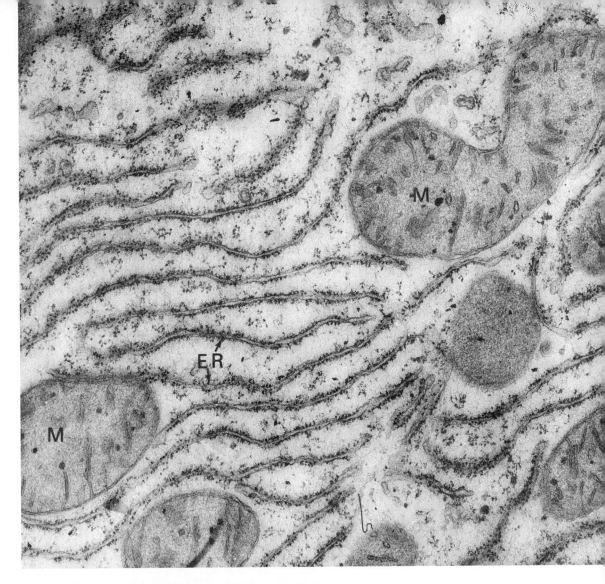

Fig. 3.22. Electron micrograph of rough endoplasmic reticulum of a rat liver cell. The dark particles studding the surface of the vesicles of the endoplasmic reticulum are ribosomes. Parts of several mitochondria can be seen. × 41,600. [Courtesy K. R. Porter, in *The Cell*, Academic Press, 1961.]

Fig. 3.23. Electron micrograph of smooth endoplasmic reticulum from interstitial cells of testis of an opossum. There are no ribosomes on the surfaces of the numerous vesicles. × 30,000. [Courtesy D. W. Fawcett, Harvard University.]

actually discrete portions of the living cells or simply artifacts produced by the breaking up and centrifugation of the cells.

Biologists long wondered if the cytoplasm had some sort of invisible structural organization, and faint traces of such a cytoplasmic "skeleton" were reported at various times. Finally, in 1945, Keith R. Porter of the Rockefeller Institute, using a phase microscope, which has much greater resolution than the usual light microscope, described a complex system of membranes forming a network in the cytoplasm. This system, called the *endoplasmic reticulum* by Porter, has since been extensively studied with the electron microscope. It has been shown to be present in all nucleated cells (though it is often not as well developed in Protozoa as in higher animals and plants).

Although the endoplasmic reticulum varies greatly in appearance in different cells—its components may look like long tubules or round or oblong vesicles—it always forms a system of membrane-enclosed spaces. In many cells, though not all, these spaces are interconnected, forming a true reticulum. Sometimes the membranes of the endoplasmic reticulum (ER) are lined on their outer surfaces by small particles called *ribosomes* (Fig. 3.22), in which case the ER is spoken of as "rough"; when no ribosomes line the membranes (Fig. 3.23), the ER is described as "smooth." Just as the ER may exist without associated ribosomes, ribosomes may occur independently of the ER.

It is now known that the microsomal fraction obtained by differential centrifugation is composed of ribosomes and fragments of the endoplasmic reticulum. It can be shown that ribosomes contain much nucleic acid; thus the high concentration of nucleic acid in the microsome is explained. Similarly, the phospholipids of the ER membranes account for the high concentrations of these materials in the microsome. Henceforth, we shall rarely use the term microsome, which simply designates a particular fraction produced by differential centrifugation, and shall refer, instead, to the endoplasmic reticulum or to ribosomes, more specific terms that designate actual subcellular structures.

There is now abundant evidence that ribosomes, which are present in almost all cells, are the sites of protein synthesis. For years it was noted that cells particularly active in protein synthesis contain large quantities of ribonucleic acid (RNA), and it was therefore supposed that this nucleic acid was in some way involved in the synthesis. When ribosomes were finally detected with the electron microscope and then studied chemically, it was found, as we have already said, that they contain almost all the cytoplasmic nucleic acid and some protein. It was also found that when radioactive amino acids are injected into cells active in protein synthesis, within 10 or 15 minutes a high percentage of the radioactivity is localized in the ribosomes. From such lines of evidence, the concept of protein synthesis on the ribosomes developed. There has been much exciting recent work supporting this idea, work so important to modern biology that we shall leave it for more extensive examination in a later chapter.

But what of the endoplasmic reticulum? What might the function of this ubiquitous membrane system be? Early in the electron-microscopic study of the ER, it was noticed that it almost always showed a close association with the nuclear membrane. Electron micrographs have repeatedly shown connections between the outer portion of the double nuclear membrane and adjacent elements of the ER (Fig. 3.21). Thus the spaces between the two components of the nuclear membrane are continuous with the membrane-enclosed spaces and channels of the ER. It seems, therefore, that the nuclear membrane is only a specialized part of the general cell-membrane system, a part of the endoplasmic reticulum.

One possible function of the ER is immediately apparent. Its channels could serve as

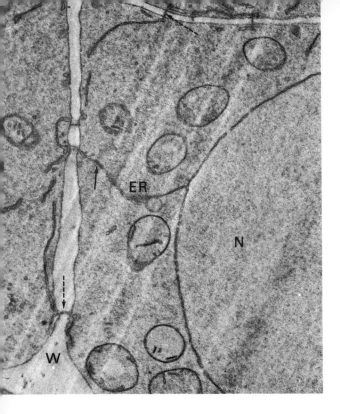

ER

N

W

Fig. 3.24. Electron micrograph of cell from corn root showing a canal of the endoplasmic reticulum (solid arrow) that may be continuous between the nuclear and the plasma membrane. In fact, this canal appears to run through the cell wall and join the ER of the adjacent cell. Two additional places where ER canals in the two cells seem to be continuous through plasmodesmata are indicated by dashed arrows. N, nucleus; ER, endoplasmic reticulum; W, wall. × 12,920. [Courtesy W. G. Whaley, H. H. Mollenhauer, and J. E. Kephart, *J. Biophys. Biochem. Cytol.*, vol. 5, 1959.]

routes for transport of materials between various regions of the cytoplasm or between the various parts of the cytoplasm and the nucleus, forming a communications network, as it were, between the nuclear control center and the rest of the cell. There is some evidence, in fact, that materials do move within the spaces of the ER. P. Siekevitz and G. E. Palade of the Rockefeller Institute have demonstrated that certain cells in the pancreas of guinea pigs synthesize large quantities of enzymes called zymogen. The zymogen, which is doubtless synthesized on the ribosomes, soon moves across the membranes and into the cavities of the ER. It then apparently moves within these cavities to other parts of the cell, particularly to the Golgi apparatus, an organelle of the cytoplasm to be discussed later.

But movement within the ER may not be limited to intracellular transport. There is evidence that in some cells (perhaps in all) the ER is continuous with the cell membrane, and that the channels of the ER open into the extracellular space. If this is so, and if the channels of the ER interconnect, as they ap-

parently do in at least some cases, what we have here is an open pathway extending from the exterior of the cell all the way to the spaces within the double nuclear membrane (Fig. 3.24). Products synthesized by the cell could then be moved within the ER to the cell surface and released—the process we call secretion—or materials from the environment could move into the channels of the ER and thence to the inner portions of the cytoplasm. Furthermore, environmental substances could move via the ER directly to the nucleus, without having to penetrate the enclosed portion of the cytoplasm, as was formerly thought necessary. In corroboration of this possibility, it has been shown that certain dyes stain elements in the nucleus of living cells without staining the cytoplasm, despite the fact that these same dyes can readily stain the cytoplasm of dead cells or of cells into which they have been injected; perhaps the explanation is that the cell membrane and ER membranes of the living cell are impermeable to the dyes while the nuclear membrane is permeable to them, and that the dyes move through the channels of the ER directly to the nuclear membrane. If the nucleus really has this sort of direct communication with the extracellular environment, all manner of environmental-nuclear interactions may occur, as yet hardly dreamed of. Obviously there are exciting possibilities for research here.

The apparent continuity of nuclear membrane, endoplasmic reticulum, and plasma membrane has led some biologists to hypothesize that the last two components evolved from the nuclear membrane (Fig. 3.25). However, the exact reverse is proposed by other biolo-

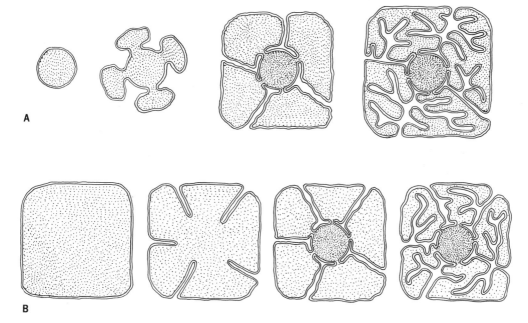

A

B

Fig. 3.25. Two theories of the evolution of cells of higher organisms. (A) begins with the nucleus. Parts of the nuclear membrane fold outward, and the vesicles they enclose become the cytoplasm; the outfolded areas of membrane become the endoplasmic reticulum and the plasma membrane. (B) begins with a cell that has no nucleus and no endoplasmic reticulum (essentially a bacterial cell). Parts of the plasma membrane fold inward and become the endoplasmic reticulum and nuclear membrane. Both theories consider the nuclear membrane, endoplasmic reticulum, and plasma membrane as segments of one continuous membrane system.

gists: that the nuclear membrane and the ER evolved from the plasma membrane. At the present stage of our knowledge, it is impossible to say which, if either, of these ideas is correct.

We have said that the endoplasmic reticulum may play an important role as a route of transport for numerous substances. But it would be surprising if its function were limited to that of a passageway. Remember that proteins may act both as structural elements in cells and as enzymes catalyzing chemical reactions. It would seem likely, therefore, that at least some of the many protein molecules of which the ER membranes are composed act as enzymes, and that the ER functions as a cytoplasmic framework providing manufacturing surfaces for the cell. In fact, by its complex folding it provides an enormous surface area. Evidence that the

ER functions as a manufacturing site comes from studies of the smooth ER found prominently in cells in which large quantities of lipids are synthesized. Apparently the enzymes involved in lipid synthesis are structural components of the ER membranes, for all efforts to separate them from the membranes have failed.

The Golgi Apparatus

In 1898 Camillo Golgi in Italy first described a new "reticular apparatus" in certain cells of the vertebrate brain. This "apparatus" was characterized by its reactions with certain chemicals (silver nitrate or osmium tetroxide), which became impregnated in it and made it visible under the light microscope. In the years that followed, similar cytoplasmic regions were found by numerous workers in a great variety of animal and plant cells. Although there was variation in their form and several different names were at first applied to them, all eventually came to be called Golgi apparatus (or Golgi bodies). A long controversy developed as to whether they represented actual structures of the living cell or were merely artifacts produced by the fixation process.

With the advent of the electron microscope and its extensive use on cells during the last twenty years, the controversy has at last been settled. It has been shown that subcellular elements identified as Golgi apparatus have a characteristic fine structure, regardless of the type of cell being studied. They consist of a system of membrane-delimited vesicles arranged approximately parallel to each other (Figs. 3.21 and 3.26). There is evidence that the smooth unit membranes of the Golgi apparatus are often continuous with the membranes of the endoplasmic reticulum and constitute, therefore, another portion of the complex cellular membrane system. They definitely are not artifacts.

The electron microscope may have settled the controversy as to the reality of the Golgi apparatus, but unfortunately the controversy concerning its function rages on. Many years ago, it was noticed that the Golgi apparatus was particularly prominent in cells thought to be involved in the secretion of various chemical products and that, as the level of secretory activity of these cells changed, corresponding changes occurred in the morphology of the Golgi apparatus. Consequently a widely held theory was developed that the Golgi apparatus played some part in the secretory process. In the discussion of the endoplasmic reticulum above, we mentioned that in certain cells of the pancreas of guinea pigs, zymogen, presumably synthesized on the ribosomes, apparently moves into the channels of the ER and through these to the Golgi apparatus. Here the zymogen seems to be stored until it is eventually released from the cell via channels of the ER. This evidence from electron microscopy seems to support the view that the Golgi apparatus is involved in secretion, but that its role is storage and perhaps modification (e.g. by removal of water or emulsification of lipids) of secretory products, not the actual synthesis of these products, as was once thought. Similar evidence for storage of a variety of substances, particularly lipids, in the Golgi apparatus has come from the work of many investigators, but in some of the cases studied the storage is of materials recently absorbed by the cell and not necessarily destined for secretory release. It seems possible, therefore, that the storage function of the Golgi apparatus is not limited to secretory products but may also involve materials being moved from one part of the cell to another or materials, such as enzymes, manufactured by the cell and held for its own use at a later time.

It must be emphasized that the function of

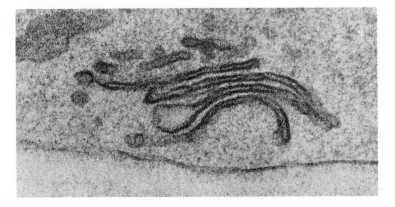

Fig. 3.26. Electron micrograph showing detail of Golgi apparatus. The apparatus is composed of vesicles, each bounded by a unit membrane. × 105,000. [Courtesy Herbert W. Israel, Cornell University.]

the Golgi apparatus is by no means clear yet; the storage function, if there is one, may be only a part of its role. The possibility still remains that some substances may be synthesized by this organelle. And recently another possible function, quite different from those so far discussed, has been proposed: that the Golgi apparatus may be the site of production of new membrane for the endoplasmic reticulum. Only much more research can answer the many remaining questions concerning this interesting, but perplexing, cellular component.

Mitochondria

During the latter part of the nineteenth century, a number of scientists carried out intensive investigations of those granules and formed inclusions of the cytoplasm that could be detected with the light microscopes of that time. Among these subcellular components were some small bodies of variable shape (granules, rods, filaments), but with numerous properties in common (particularly an affinity for certain stains), that seemed to be a constant feature of cytoplasm; they were found in almost all types of cells from most kinds of organisms (Figs. 3.21 and 3.22). These bodies were given the name mitochondria (the singular is mitochondrion, from the Greek for thread).

For years, speculation concerning the function of mitochondria ranged far and wide. Many extraordinarily elaborate theories were put forward. Finally, in 1934, a fraction containing the mitochondria was separated from the other cellular components by the process of differential centrifugation.[3] From this time forth, an enormous amount of research was done on the chemical properties of the mitochondrial fraction. It was found that these organelles are, in a sense, the "powerhouse"

of the cell. Many crucial chemical reactions take place within them, reactions that extract energy from foodstuffs and make it available to the cell for its innumerable energy-demanding activities. These chemical reactions are so important to life that we shall devote much time to their study in a later chapter.

Mitochondria are so small that the light microscope can reveal little about their morphology. But they are much larger than many other cytoplasmic bodies and can easily be studied in detail with the electron microscope. Consequently our knowledge of their structure has made notable progress during the last twenty years. Each mitochondrion is a double-walled vessel; the outer wall is a smooth membrane, and the inner wall is a membrane with many inwardly directed folds (Fig. 4.24, p. 145). These folds, called *cristae*, extend into a semifluid amorphous matrix. Small granules of uncertain function are sometimes embedded in the matrix.

It is clear that the mitochondrial membranes, which are composed of the alternating layers of protein and lipid characteristic of the other protoplasmic membranes already discussed, are semipermeable. Some substances apparently cannot pass from the cytoplasmic matrix into the mitochondria, while others can do so fairly easily. Furthermore, the permeability of the mitochondrial membranes changes in response to variation in the concentration of certain chemicals, particularly phosphate ions, in the surrounding cytoplasm. Because of the semipermeable nature of their membranes, mitochondria swell in hyposmotic media and shrink in hyperosmotic media. Such changes in volume, which presumably involve changes in the amount of stretching of the mitochondrial membranes, result in changes in the permeability of the membranes. Changes in permeability, with the resultant changes in what goes into or out of the mitochondria, would be expected to affect the rates at which chemical reactions take place within the mitochondria. Factors that alter the permeability may there-

[3] A mitochondrial fraction had already been prepared in the 1920's by Warburg, and some of its chemical properties had been determined; but, as has happened so often in the history of science, the importance of this work was not generally recognized, and it made little impression on other scientists.

fore be important in regulating the functions of the mitochondria.

Lysosomes

Lysosomes are very recently discovered organelles. They were first described in the 1950's by Christian de Duve of the Catholic University of Louvain in Belgium, and most of what we know about them today we owe to him and his co-workers. Lysosomes (Fig. 3.31) are membrane-enclosed bodies, slightly smaller than mitochondria (with which they were often confused in the past), that apparently function as storage vesicles for many powerful digestive enzymes. The lysosome membrane must be both impermeable to the outward movement of these enzymes and capable of resisting their digestive action. Thus packaged in the lysosomes, these important enzymes are prevented from digesting the material of the cell itself. If the lysosome membrane is ruptured, the enzymes are released into the surrounding cytoplasm and immediately begin to break down the cytoplasm.

It is now thought that the lysosomes act, in a sense, as the cell's "digestive system," enabling it to process some of the bulk materials taken in by phagocytosis or pinocytosis. They may also play a role in some developmental processes. We shall discuss their functions in more detail in later chapters.

Lysosomes were first discovered in rat liver cells. They have since been found in many kinds of animal cells, and may occur in all of them. They have also been found in some fungi, but it is not yet clear how widely they occur in other plant cells.

Plastids

Plastids are large cytoplasmic organelles found in plant cells but not in animal cells. They can easily be observed with an ordinary light microscope. There are two principal categories of plastids: *chromoplasts* (colored plastids)

and *leucoplasts* (white or colorless plastids).[4]

Chloroplasts, which are chromoplasts containing the green pigment *chlorophyll,* are extremely important to all life. In them energy from sunlight is trapped by chlorophyll and utilized in the manufacture of complex organic molecules (particularly sugar) from simple inorganic raw materials. Chloroplasts contain, in addition to chlorophyll, various yellow or orange pigments called *carotenoids.*

The electron microscope reveals that the typical chloroplast is bounded by a unit membrane and has a complex internal membranous organization (Fig. 3.27). The internal, rather homogeneous, proteinacious matrix is called the stroma. Numerous double-membrane lamellae are embedded in it. In most higher plants, these lamellae are differentiated into two varieties, separate lamellae running through the stroma and stacks of platelike lamellae forming regions known as **grana.** In some other plants, the brown algae for example, no grana occur; all the lamellae are stroma lamellae. The chlorophyll is located in the lamellae, apparently bound to the proteins and lipids of the membranes. The arragement of the protein, lipid, and pigment components of the lamellae is evidently a very precise one without which complete photosynthesis cannot take place. We shall consider this topic in more detail in a later chapter when we examine the photosynthetic process.

Chromoplasts lacking chlorophyll are usually yellow or orange (occasionally red) because of the carotenoids they contain. It is these kinds of chromoplasts that give the characteristic yellow or orange color to many flowers, ripe fruits, and autumn leaves. Some of these chromoplasts have never contained chlorophyll, while others are formed from chloroplasts whose chlorophyll has been lost. The latter are

[4] Some classifications of plastids recognize three principal categories: chloroplasts, chromoplasts, and leucoplasts. However, it seems more appropriate to consider chloroplasts, or green plastids, a subcategory of chromoplasts.

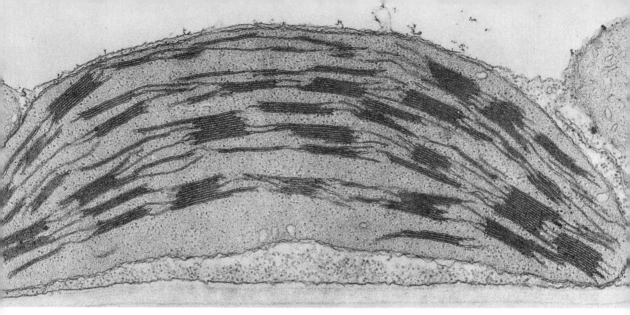

Fig. 3.27. Electron micrograph of chloroplast of tobacco. The stacks of disclike lamellae are the grana. The less tightly packed lamellae running between the grana are the stroma lamellae. × 35,000. [Courtesy Herbert W. Israel, Cornell University.]

particularly common in ripe fruits and autumn leaves, structures that were formerly green.

The colorless plastids, or leucoplasts, are primarily organelles in which materials such as starch, oils, and protein granules are stored. Plastids filled with starch (amyloplasts) are particularly common in storage roots and stems (e.g. carrots, potatoes) and in seeds, although they also occur in the cells of many other parts of the plant. The starch is deposited as a grain or group of grains in the plastid; no starch is found in other parts of the cell.

All types of plastids form from small colorless bodies called proplastids. Once formed, many kinds of plastids can be converted into other types under appropriate conditions. It can be demonstrated, for example, that synthesis of chlorophyll is dependent upon light and that under certain conditions leucoplasts exposed to light develop chlorophyll.

Vacuoles

Membrane-enclosed fluid-filled spaces called vacuoles are found in both animal and plant cells, though they have their greatest development in plant cells. There are various kinds of vacuoles with a corresponding variety of functions. In some Protozoa, specialized vacuoles, called contractile vacuoles, play an important role in expelling excess water and some wastes from the cell; we shall discuss them in greater detail in a later chapter. Many Protozoa also possess food vacuoles, chambers that contain food particles. Similar vacuoles, or vesicles, are formed by many kinds of cells when they take in material by phagocytosis or pinocytosis, processes discussed earlier in this chapter.

In most mature plant cells, a large vacuole occupies much of the volume of the cell. The immature cell usually contains many small vacuoles (Fig. 3.28). As the cell matures, the vacuoles take in more water and become larger, eventually fusing to form the very large definitive vacuole of the mature cell. This process pushes the cytoplasm to the periphery of the cell, where it forms a relatively thin layer.

The plant vacuole contains a liquid called cell sap—primarily water with a variety of substances dissolved in it or colloidally suspended in it. The cell sap is generally hyperosmotic relative to the external medium; consequently water tends to move into the cell by osmosis and the cell remains turgid. You will recall that the cell walls characteristic of plant cells prevent the cell from taking in so much water that it would be in danger of bursting.

Many substances of importance in the life of the plant cell are stored in the vacuoles. For example, high concentrations of soluble organic nitrogen compounds, including amino acids, are commonly found in the cell sap. Similarly, sugars, various organic acids, some proteins, and several pigments, particularly the *anthocyanin* pigments, are normal constituents of the cell sap. Apparently many substances are accumulated in the vacuoles and are selectively prevented from leaving by the vacuolar membrane (or tonoplast, as it is often called), which must have its own distinctive permeability characteristics and must be capable of actively regulating the direction of movement of substances across it. If living beet cells (whose red pigment is an anthocyanin in the cell sap) are placed in distilled water, the pigment does not diffuse out, even though it is in much higher concentration inside the vacuoles than outside. As soon as the beet cells die,

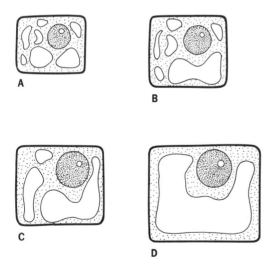

Fig. 3.28. Development of plant cell vacuole. The immature cell (A) has many small vacuoles. As the cell grows, these fuse to form the large vacuole occupying most of the space in the mature cell (D). The cytoplasm is pushed to the periphery of the cell.

their vacuolar membrane loses its selectivity and the anthocyanin diffuses out.

The anthocyanin pigments in the cell sap are responsible for many of the purples, blues, and dark reds commonly seen in flowers, fruits, and autumn leaves (we have already seen that the carotenoids in the plastids are responsible for orange, yellow, and sometimes light red in these same structures). The relative amounts of anthocyanins and carotenoids in autumn leaves differ for different species of plants and also differ under different conditions for the same species. A high accumulation of sugars, low temperatures, and adequate light favor anthocyanin formation.

Centrioles

Small dark bodies located just outside the nucleus of most animal cells in a region of specialized cytoplasm have been seen for many years and have been known to play a role in cell division. Recent electron-microscope studies of these bodies, called centrioles, have revealed that each is a cylindrical structure, and that two such centrioles normally lie close together, oriented at right angles to each other (Fig. 3.31). Centrioles do not occur in most higher-plant cells, although they are found in some algae and fungi and in a few reproductive cells of higher plants. We shall discuss both the structure and function of centrioles more fully when we describe the process of cell division in a later chapter.

Cilia and Flagella

Some cells of both plants and animals have one or more movable hairlike structures projecting from their free surfaces. If there are only a few of these appendages and they are relatively long in proportion to the size of the cell itself, they are called *flagella* (Fig. 8.7, p. 283). If there are many of them and they are short, they are called **cilia**. Actually the basic structure of flagella and cilia is the same,

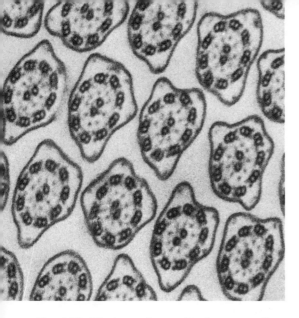

Fig. 3.29. Electron micrograph of cross sections of cilia. Note that each cilium has nine peripheral and two central fibrils. × 66,000. [Courtesy I. R. Gibbons, Harvard University.]

and the terms are often used interchangeably. Both usually function either in moving the cell or in moving liquids or small particles across the surface of the cell. They occur commonly on unicellular and small multicellular organisms and on the male reproductive cells of most animals and many plants, in both of which they may be the principal means of locomotion. They are also common on the cells lining many internal passageways and ducts in animals, where their beating aids in moving materials through the passageways.

Electron-microscopic studies of flagella and cilia during the last fifteen years have revealed a remarkable uniformity in their internal structure, regardless of the organism to which they belong, whether plant or animal, simple or complex. The slender cylindrical stalk consists of an extension of the cell membrane containing a cytoplasmic matrix, with eleven groups of fibrils embedded in the matrix. Invariably, nine of these groups of fibrils are arranged around the periphery of the cylinder and the other two are in the center (Fig. 3.29). At the base of the stalk, within the main portion of the cell, is a *basal body* (Fig. 3.31). The basal body is essential to the function of the cilium

or flagellum, and it is the part that gives rise to the stalk. Sometimes fibrous rootlets project from the basal body into the more internal cytoplasm of the cell.

"Typical" Cells

By now you realize that a living cell, small as it is, is far from simple. It is, in fact, an extraordinarily complex unit containing numerous components that are themselves relatively complex. The extent of this complexity has been fully appreciated for only a few years. The electron microscope and modern biochemical techniques have combined to change our whole picture of the cell. Not many years ago, biology books regularly included a diagram of a so-called typical cell that showed only five or six simple internal components, a diagram easily memorized by students (Fig. 3.30). No simple dia-

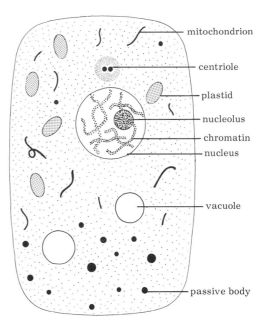

Fig. 3.30. Diagram of "typical" cell of about forty years ago. [Modified from E. B. Wilson, *The Cell in Development and Heredity*, Macmillan, 1925.]

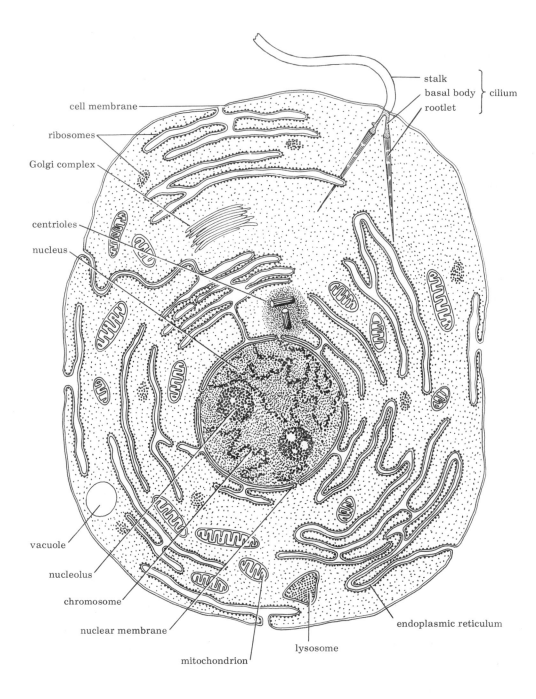

Fig. 3.31. Diagram of modern "typical" animal cell.

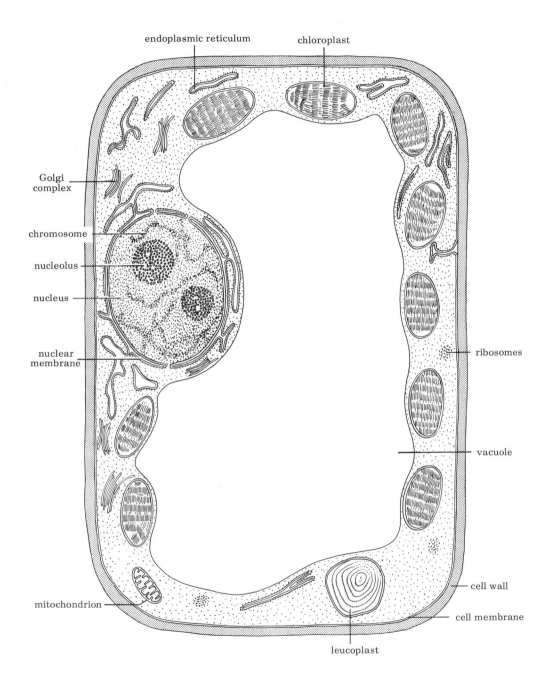

Fig. 3.32. Diagram of modern "typical" plant cell.

gram of this sort can be given today. In the first place, there is no such thing as a typical cell. Not only do plant and animal cells differ in many important ways, but the various cells of the body of any one plant or animal are often strikingly different from one another in shape, size, and function. This much, of course, has been known for a long time. But now that the number of known cellular components has grown so large and that their great variability has been demonstrated, it becomes even more obvious that no single diagram, or even series of diagrams, can really portray a "typical" cell. Nevertheless, in an effort to help you visualize the arrangement of the organelles discussed in the preceding pages, two such diagrams (Figs. 3.31 and 3.32) are given here. As you examine them, keep in mind that not all the components shown always occur together in any one real cell, and also that some of the arrangements shown (particularly those of the cyto-

plasmic membrane system) have not been verified conclusively.

Procaryotic Cells

You will have noticed that throughout the discussion of cellular components, we have had to caution you that the descriptions do not apply to bacteria or blue-green algae. The cells of these unicellular organisms differ in numerous basic ways from the cells of all other organisms. In recognition of their distinct characteristics, these cells are customarily termed *procaryotic cells*, while the cells of all other organisms, both plant and animal, are termed *eucaryotic cells*. The most striking difference between the two is that procaryotic cells lack the nuclear membrane characteristic of eucaryotic cells. For a long time it was thought that procaryotic cells have no nucleus at all, but in recent years it has been shown that they have

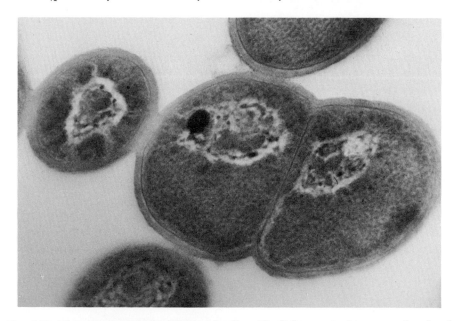

Fig. 3.33. Electron micrograph of bacterial cells. The light area in the center of each cell is the "nucleus," which lacks a membrane. The cell on the right has nearly finished dividing, but the new cell walls between the two daughter cells are not yet complete. Note that each daughter cell received "nuclear" material. × 37,000. [Courtesy G. B. Chapman, *J. Biophys. Biochem. Cytol.*, vol. 6, 1959.]

a nuclear region containing genetic material; however, this region is not enclosed by a membrane (Fig. 3.33). The genetic material is not organized into the type of chromosomes seen in eucaryotic cells, though it does apparently have an analogous structure. Some bacteria and all blue-green algae contain chlorophyll, which is associated with membranous vesicles, or lamellae; but the lamellae are not enclosed by membranes, and hence there are no distinct plastids. Procaryotic cells have no mitochondria, no endoplasmic reticulum, no Golgi apparatus, and no lysosomes. In short, they lack the internal membranous structures characteristic of eucaryotic cells. There is evidence, however, that the membrane that bounds the cell is folded inward at various points, and that this membrane carries out many of the enzymatic functions associated with the membranes of the mitochondria, endoplasmic reticulum, and other internal membranes of eucaryotic cells. Some bacteria have flagella, but these structures do not show the internal structure of nine peripheral fibrils and two central fibrils that is found universally in the flagella of other cells. Table 3.1 gives a summary of some of the most important differences between procaryotic and eucaryotic cells.

Knowledge of the correlation between function and internal structure in bacterial cells is still very rudimentary, and it is almost nonexistent for the blue-green algae. Much more research is needed on the functional morphology of procaryotic cells.

TABLE 3.1

A Comparison of Procaryotic and Eucaryotic Cells

Characteristic	Procaryotic cells	Eucaryotic cells
Nuclear membrane	Absent	Present
Chromosomes	Composed only of nucleic acid	Composed of nucleic acid and protein
Photosynthetic apparatus	May contain chlorophyll, but not in chloroplasts	Chlorophyll, when present, contained in chloroplasts
Mitochondria, Golgi apparatus, endoplasmic reticulum, etc.	Absent	Present
Flagella	Lack 9-2 fibrillar structure	Have 9-2 fibrillar structure
Cytoplasmic streaming or amoeboid movement	Does not occur	May occur
Cell wall	Contains amino sugars and muramic acid	When present, does not contain amino sugars or muramic acids

MULTICELLULAR ORGANIZATION

Some animals and some plants are unicellular (i.e. composed of a single cell), but most organisms are multicellular (i.e. composed of many cells). Ordinarily the bodies of multicellular organisms, particularly animals, are organized on the basis of tissues, organs, and systems. A *tissue* is composed of many cells, usually similar in both structure and function, that are bound together by intercellular material. An *organ,* in turn, is composed of various tissues (not necessarily similar) grouped together into a structural and functional unit. Similarly, a *system* is a group of interacting organs that "cooperate" as a functional complex in the life of the organism.

The following sections will introduce you briefly to some of the basic plant and animal tissues, organs, systems, and organisms. We shall refer to them repeatedly and examine them in more detail in later chapters.

PLANT TISSUES

Plant tissues have been classified in a variety of ways by different botanists. The system used here is not necessarily better than other possible systems; it is simply one of several acceptable ones. The lack of full agreement on any one classification springs from characteristics of the plant cells themselves. The different cell types intergrade, and a given cell may even change from one type to another during the course of its life. Consequently the tissues formed from such cells intergrade and may share structural and functional characteristics. Furthermore, plant tissues may contain cells of only one type, or they may be complex, containing a variety of cell types. In short, plant tissues cannot be fully characterized or distinguished on the basis of any single criterion

such as structure, function, location, or mode of origin.

We shall first divide all plant tissues into two major categories: *meristematic tissue* and *permanent tissue.* Meristematic tissues are composed of immature cells and are regions of active cell division; permanent tissues are composed of more mature, differentiated cells. This distinction is not an absolute one, however, for some permanent tissues may revert to meristematic activity under certain conditions.

We shall then divide the permanent tissues into three subcategories: surface tissues, fundamental tissues, and vascular tissues. Each of these, in turn, contains several different tissue types. The classification used here may be summarized as follows:

I. Meristematic tissue
II. Permanent tissue
    A. Surface tissue
        1. Epidermis
        2. Periderm
    B. Fundamental tissue
        1. Parenchyma
        2. Collenchyma
        3. Sclerenchyma
        4. Endodermis
    C. Vascular tissue
        1. Xylem
        2. Phloem

It is important to emphasize that this classification is based on the higher land plants, the vascular plants. It has little relevance for other plants, where multiple tissue types seldom occur.

Meristematic Tissue

Meristematic tissues are composed of embryonic, undifferentiated cells capable of cell division. Cell division occurs throughout the body of the very early embryo, but as the young plant develops, many regions of the body become specialized for other functions and cease playing a primary role in the production of new cells. Consequently cell division becomes restricted largely to certain undifferentiated tissues in localized regions; these tissues are the meristems.

It is difficult to make any general statement concerning the characteristics of meristematic cells, because they exhibit much variation. There is no such thing, in fact, as a "typical" meristematic cell. Nevertheless, we can say that these cells tend to be small, to have thin walls, to be rich in cytoplasm (i.e. to have only small vacuoles), and to lack intercellular spaces. New cells produced by a meristem are initially like those of the meristem itself, but, as they grow and mature, their characteristics slowly change and they become differentiated as components of other tissues.

There are regions of meristematic tissue at the growing tips of roots and stems. These apical meristems are responsible for increase in length of the plant body. In many plants, there are also meristematic areas toward the periphery of the roots and stems, and these lateral meristems are responsible for increase in girth.

Surface Tissue

As the term implies, surface tissues form the protective outer covering of the plant body. In young plants and herbaceous adult plants lacking active lateral meristems, the principal surface tissue of roots and stems is the *epidermis* (Fig. 3.34); epidermis is also the surface tissue of all leaves (Fig. 3.35). Often the epidermis is only one cell thick, though it may be thicker, as it is in some plants living in very dry habitats, where protection against water loss is critical. Most epidermal cells are relatively flat. They generally have a very large vacuole and only a thin layer of cytoplasm. Often their outer and radial walls are thicker than the inner wall. Epidermal cells on the aerial parts of the plant often secrete a waxy, water-resistant *cuticle* on their outer surface; this, combined with the thick outer wall, which is often impregnated with cutin, aids in protection against loss of water, mechanical injury, and invasion by parasitic fungi. What makes the barrier even more complete is that the irregularly shaped cells usually interlock tightly like pieces of a puzzle, leaving no intercellular space.

Epidermal tissues of the aerial parts sometimes give rise to unicellular or multicellular hairs, spines, or glands. Some epidermal cells, particularly of the leaves, are specialized as guard cells and regulate the size of small holes in the epidermis through which gases can move into or out of the leaf. Epidermal cells of the roots, which have no cuticle and function in water absorption, commonly bear long hairlike processes that greatly increase the total absorptive surface area.

As the stems and roots of plants with active lateral meristems increase in diameter, the epi-

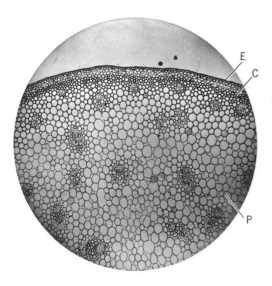

Fig. 3.34. Photograph of cross section of portion of lily stem. E, epidermis; C, collenchyma; P, parenchyma. [Courtesy General Biological Supply House, Inc., Chicago.]

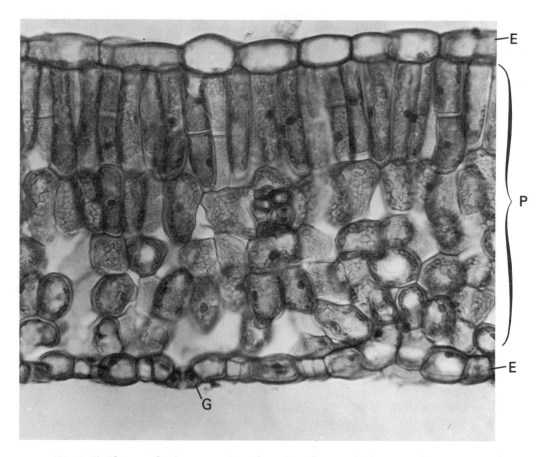

Fig. 3.35. Photograph of cross section of portion of privet leaf. E, epidermis; G, guard cell; P, parenchyma. Note the numerous chloroplasts in the parenchyma cells. × 540. [Courtesy Thomas Eisner, Cornell University.]

dermis is slowly replaced by another surface tissue, the *periderm* (Fig. 7.6, p. 226). This tissue constitutes the corky outer bark so characteristic of old trees. Functional cork cells are dead; it is their cell walls, waterproofed with suberin, that function as the protective outer covering of the plant.

Fundamental Tissue

Most of the fundamental tissues are simple tissues; i.e. each is composed of a single type of cell. Often these same types of cells also occur as components of the complex vascular tissues. The various fundamental tissues are not necessarily structurally similar, although they form from the same embryonic regions. They are often defined simply as those tissues that are neither surface tissues nor vascular tissues.

Parenchyma. Parenchyma tissue occurs in roots, stems, and leaves. The parenchyma cells of which this simple tissue is composed are relatively unspecialized vegetative cells, like those that make up almost the whole body of the lower plants. They have not lost the capacity for cell division, and in some circumstances they take on meristematic activity; they also sometimes undergo further specialization, forming other cell types. Parenchyma cells usually have thin primary walls and no secondary walls. They generally have a large vacuole surrounded by a peripheral layer of cytoplasm. The cells are ordinarily loosely packed;

consequently intercellular spaces are abundant in parenchyma tissue (Figs. 3.34 and 3.35). Most of the chloroplasts of leaves are in the cells of parenchyma tissue, and it is largely here that photosynthesis occurs. Parenchyma of stems and roots functions in storage of nutrients and water. When turgid, parenchyma is important in giving support and shape to the plant.

Collenchyma. Like parenchyma, collenchyma is a simple tissue whose cells remain alive during most of their functional existence. Though collenchyma cells are characteristically more elongate, they are structurally similar to parenchyma cells, except that their walls are irregularly thickened. The thickened areas are usually most prominent at the edges (the "corners" when viewed in cross section) (Fig. 3.36). Collenchyma functions as an important supporting tissue in young plants, in the stems of nonwoody older plants, and in leaves.

Sclerenchyma. Sclerenchyma is a type of simple fundamental tissue that, like collenchyma, functions in support. However, sclerenchyma cells are far more specialized than collenchyma cells; at functional maturity, most

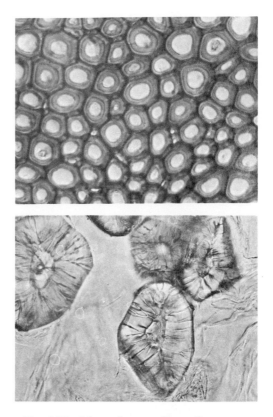

Fig. 3.37. Sclerenchyma. Top: Cross section of fibers from corn stem. Bottom: Stone cells of pear fruit. [Used by permission from J. D. Dodd, *Form and Function in Plants,* © 1962 by The Iowa State University Press.]

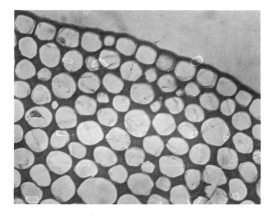

Fig. 3.36. Collenchyma cells from petiole of beet leaf. Notice the particularly thick walls at the corners of the cells. [Used by permission from J. D. Dodd, *Form and Function in Plants,* © 1962 by The Iowa State University Press.]

are dead, and their uniformly very thick, heavily lignified secondary walls give strength to the plant body. Often these walls are so thick that the lumen (internal space) of the cell has been nearly obliterated.

Sclerenchyma cells are customarily divided into two categories: *fibers* and *sclereids* (Fig. 3.37). Fibers are very elongate cells with tapered ends. They are tough and strong, but flexible; commercial flax and hemp are derived from strands of sclerenchyma fibers. Sclereids are of variable, often irregular, shape. The simpler, unbranched sclereids are frequently called stone cells; they are common in the shells of nuts and in the hard parts of seeds, and are scattered in the flesh of hard fruits (the gritty texture of pears is due to small clusters of stone cells; Fig. 3.37B).

Endodermis. Endodermis is a type of tissue difficult to place in any classification. It occurs as a layer surrounding the vascular-tissue core of roots and, less frequently, of stems (Fig. 5.4, p. 160). Endodermal cells are much like elongate parenchyma cells, except that a band of chemically distinctive thickening runs around the cell on its radial and end walls. This lignified and suberized ("waterproofed") band is called the *Casparian strip.* In older endodermal cells, the walls may become secondarily so thickened (sometimes almost obliterating the lumen) that the Casparian strip is obscured, but it can be detected with appropriate chemical tests. The cells of endodermal tissue occur in a single layer and are compactly arranged without intercellular spaces. Sometimes a few cells in this layer lack the thick walls of the other cells, though they do have Casparian strips; these thin-walled cells are called passage cells. The function of the endodermis is unclear; possible functions will be discussed in a later chapter.

Vascular Tissue

Vascular, or conductive, tissue is a distinctive feature of the higher plants that makes possible their extensive exploitation of the terrestrial environment. As the name implies, some of the cells of these tissues function as tubes or ducts within which water and numerous substances in solution move from one part of the plant body to another. There are two principal types of vascular tissue: xylem and phloem. Both of these are complex tissues; i.e. they consist of more than one kind of cell.

Xylem. Xylem is a vascular tissue that functions in the transport of water and dissolved substances upward in the plant body. It forms a continuous pathway running through the roots, the stem, and appendages of the stem such as leaves. It is a complex tissue, which in its most advanced form (i.e. in the form least like the ancestral one), in the flowering plants, commonly includes two types of cells unique to xylem—*tracheids* and *vessel elements*—and also numerous parenchyma and sclerenchyma cells (the latter may be represented in the xylem by both fibers and sclereids, but thick-walled fibers are by far the more prevalent). The parenchyma cells are the only living cells in mature functioning xylem, inasmuch as both the cytoplasm and the nucleus of tracheids, vessel elements, and sclerenchyma cells disintegrate at maturity, leaving the thick cell walls as the functional structures. In tracheids and vessels, the walls form passages or tubes within which vertical movement of materials can take place (Fig. 7.9, p. 230, and Fig. 7.11, p. 231).

Transport is not the only function of xylem. Another of its important functions is support, particularly of the aerial parts of the plant. The numerous fibers in the xylem function almost exclusively in this way, and the thick-walled tracheids are also important as supportive elements. One need only remember that the common name for xylem is "wood" to understand the enormous strength characteristic of this tissue.

Phloem. Like xylem, phloem is a vascular tissue; it is unlike xylem in that materials can move both up and down in it. Phloem functions particularly in the transport of organic materials such as carbohydrates and amino acids. For example, newly synthesized organic molecules are moved in the phloem from the leaves to the roots and stem for storage or to the growing points of the plant for immediate use. Like xylem, phloem is a complex tissue and contains both parenchyma cells and sclerenchyma cells in addition to the cells unique to it: *sieve cells* and *companion cells.* The sieve cells (Fig. 3.38) are the vertical transport units of phloem; at maturity, their nuclei disintegrate, but their cytoplasm remains. Com-

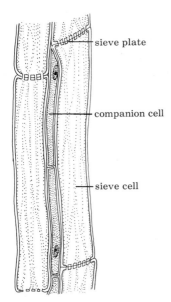

Fig. 3.38. **Longitudinal section of sieve cells and companion cells.**

panion cells, which retain both their nuclei and their cytoplasm at maturity, are closely associated with the sieve cells in the most advanced plants; their possible function will be discussed in a later chapter, where a more detailed treatment of both xylem and phloem will be given.

PLANT ORGANS

The body of the higher land plants is customarily divided into two major parts: the *root* and the *shoot* (Fig. 3.39). These two fundamental organ systems can be distinguished on the basis of numerous morphological characteristics, particularly the arrangement and mode of origin of the vascular tissue, differences in the way branch roots and branch stems are formed, and the presence of leaves on the shoot but not on the root. Yet note that many of the tissues are essentially continuous throughout the entire axis, both root and shoot. For example, the vascular tissue of root and shoot, despite a somewhat different

arrangement in each, forms an uninterrupted transport system.

The roots of a plant function particularly in procurement of inorganic nutrients such as minerals and water, in transport, in nutrient storage, and in anchoring the plant to the substrate. The shoot is somewhat more com-

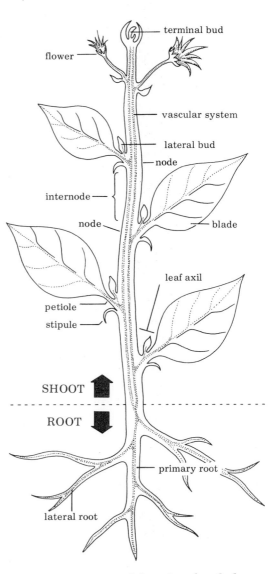

Fig. 3.39. **Diagram of flowering plant body.**

plex structurally. It consists of the stem and the appendages of the stem, particularly the foliage leaves and the reproductive organs. The stem, of course, functions in internal transport and in support, while the foliage leaves are organs in which the critical process of photosynthesis takes place.

You will notice that the number of distinct organs mentioned here—root, stem, foliage leaf, and reproductive organs—is much smaller than it would be for higher animals. In general, the plant body is simply not as clearly divided into readily distinguishable functional components, or organs, as the animal body. The parts of the plant grade more imperceptibly into each other and, in some ways, form a more continuous whole. Indeed, some botanists insist that there are only two organs, the root and the shoot. This seems to be an extreme position, however, because the foliage leaves and the reproductive structures, though derived from the stem and anatomically continuous with it, nevertheless constitute easily recognizable functional units composed of several types of tissues. Thus they fully meet our definition of the term "organ." The arrangement of the tissues within these organs will be covered in later chapters.

ANIMAL TISSUES

It is traditional to divide all animal tissues into four categories: epithelium, connective tissue, muscle, and nerve. Each of these, particularly the second, is a diverse assemblage containing numerous subtypes. It should be emphasized that the subtype classification is based primarily on the vertebrate animals, especially man, and that its application to other animals, particularly the lower invertebrates, is difficult and sometimes even meaningless.

The classification of animal tissues used here can be summarized as follows:

I. Epithelium
   A. Simple epithelium
      1. Squamous
      2. Cuboidal
      3. Columnar
   B. Stratified epithelium
      1. Stratified squamous
      2. Stratified cuboidal
      3. Stratified columnar

II. Connective tissue
   A. Vascular tissue
      1. Blood
      2. Lymph
   B. Connective tissue proper
      1. Loose connective tissue
      2. Dense connective tissue
   C. Cartilage
   D. Bone

III. Muscle
   A. Skeletal muscle
   B. Smooth muscle
   C. Cardiac muscle

IV. Nerve

Epithelium

Epithelial tissue forms the covering or lining of all free body surfaces, both external and internal. The outer portion of the skin, for example, is epithelium, as are the linings of the digestive tract, the lungs, the blood vessels, the varous ducts, the body cavity, etc. Epithelial cells are packed tightly together, with only a small amount of cementing material between them and almost no intercellular spaces. Consequently they provide a continuous protective barrier between the underlying cells and the external medium. Anything entering or leaving the body must cross at least one layer of epithelium, which means that the permeability characteristics of the cells of the various epithelia play an exceedingly important role in regulating the exchange of materials between different parts of the body and between the body and the external environment.

Since one surface of an epithelium is generally exposed to air or fluid and the opposite surface rests upon other cell layers, and since the epithelium plays a crucial part in the directional passage of materials, it is no surprise that epithelial cells are usually polarized; i.e. there are significant differences between their free ends and their attached ends. The free end is often highly specialized, commonly bearing cilia, hairs, or short fingerlike processes, or having deep depressions, or sometimes being covered with waxy or mucous secretions. Inside the cells, pigments and such organelles as mitochondria are often more abundant at one end than at the other (Fig. 3.40). Recent studies have shown that, as we might expect, the plasma membrane of an epithelial cell is not uniform in its permeability characteristics; the portion of the membrane on the outer surface of the cell, exposed to the extracellular environment, is quite different from the portions of the membrane adjacent to other epithelial cells. When a form of sodium fluorescent in ultraviolent light is injected into a single epithelial cell, it can be detected within a few minutes in neighboring cells, but it does not appear in the external medium. Apparently the sodium can move across the cell membranes at the junctions between epithelial cells, but cannot penetrate the cell membrane where it is in contact with the external medium. Clearly, then, the chemical and/or physical properties of the membrane are not the same at those two locations.

Although there is considerable variation in the shapes of epithelial cells, it is customary to group them into three categories: *squamous,* *cuboidal,* and *columnar.* Squamous cells are much broader than they are thick and have the appearance of thin flat plates (Fig. 3.41). Cuboidal cells are roughly as thick as they are wide and, as their name implies, have a rather square or cuboidal shape when viewed in a section perpendicular to the tissue surface; in surface view, however, they appear as polygons, often with six sides. Columnar cells are

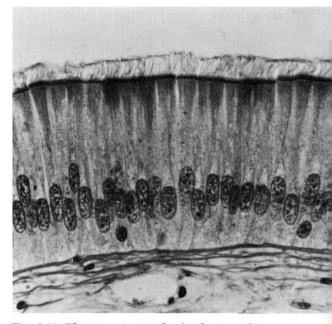

Fig. 3.40. Electron micrograph of columnar ciliated epithelium from digestive tract of a freshwater mussel. The dark basal bodies of the cilia and the long cones of fibrous rootlets are plainly visible. Mitochondria are prominent in the basal portion of the cells. Note the dark basement membrane upon which the epithelial cells rest. × 840. [Courtesy D. W. Fawcett, Harvard University.]

much thicker than they are wide and, in vertical section, appear as rectangles set on end.

Epithelial tissue may be only one cell thick, in which case it is called *simple epithelium,* or it may be two or more cells thick and is then known as *stratified epithelium.* There is, in addition, a third category, called *pseudostratified epithelium,* in which the tissue looks stratified but actually is not; whereas in true stratified epithelium only the cells in the lowest layer are in contact with the underlying membrane, in pseudostratified epithelium all the cells are in contact with it. The various types of epithelia are named on the basis of the cell type and the number of cell layers (it is the cells in the outermost layer of stratified epithelia that determine the name). Thus we can recognize simple squamous epithelium, simple cuboidal epithelium, simple columnar

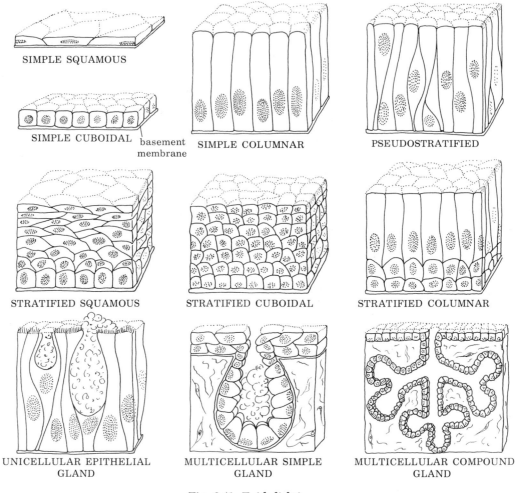

SIMPLE SQUAMOUS

SIMPLE CUBOIDAL   basement
                  membrane

SIMPLE COLUMNAR

PSEUDOSTRATIFIED

STRATIFIED SQUAMOUS

STRATIFIED CUBOIDAL

STRATIFIED COLUMNAR

UNICELLULAR EPITHELIAL
GLAND

MULTICELLULAR SIMPLE
GLAND

MULTICELLULAR COMPOUND
GLAND

Fig. 3.41. Epithelial tissues.

epithelium, stratified squamous epithelium (Fig. 3.42), stratified cuboidal epithelium, stratified columnar epithelium, etc. Epithelium, regardless of type, is usually separated from the underlying tissue by an extracellular fibrous *basement membrane* (Fig. 3.43).

Epithelial cells often become specialized as gland cells, secreting substances at the epithelial surface (Fig. 3.41). Sometimes a portion of the epithelial tissue becomes invaginated, and a multicellular gland is formed.

Connective Tissue

In connective tissue, the cells are always embedded in an extensive intercellular matrix. Much of the total volume of connective tissue is matrix, the cells themselves often being widely separated. The matrix may be liquid, semisolid, or solid. Connective tissue is often divided into four main types: (1) blood and lymph, (2) connective tissue proper, (3) cartilage, and (4) bone. The last three are sometimes collectively described as "supporting tissues."

Blood.   Blood and lymph are rather atypical connective tissues with liquid matrixes. They will be discussed in some detail in a later chapter.

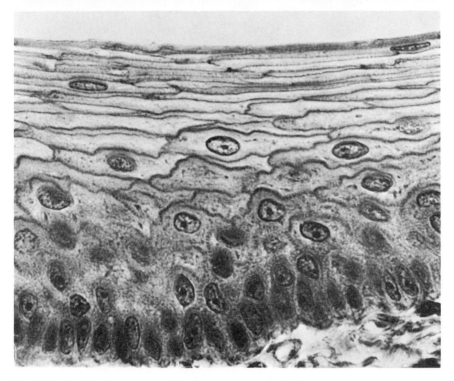

Fig. 3.42. Stratified squamous epithelium from a kitten. × 1,245. [Courtesy D. W. Fawcett, *A Textbook of Histology*, Saunders, 1962.]

Fig. 3.43. Electron micrograph of basement membrane of body-wall epidermis of a tadpole (*Rana catesbeiana*). The bases of the epidermal cells (top portion of micrograph) rest on a wide basement membrane, within which collagen fibers are arranged with unusual regularity—in a series of layers, with the fibers in each layer oriented at right angles to those in the adjacent layers. In the micrograph, the fibers in some layers are shown in cross section (dark round dots) and the fibers in the adjacent layers are shown in longitudinal section. It is not known how the orderly arrangement of fibers located outside living cells is established during development in larval amphibians. The fibers of most basement membranes, including those of adult amphibians, are much more randomly arranged. × 21,900. [Courtesy Miriam M. Salpeter, Cornell University.]

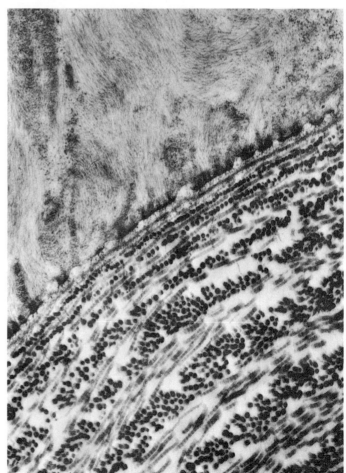

Connective Tissue Proper. Connective tissue proper is very variable, but its intercellular matrix always contains numerous fibers. These fibers are of three types. The first type, called *collagenous fibers* (or white fibers), is very common (Fig. 3.44). Each collagenous fiber is composed of numerous fine fibrils of collagen, a protein that constitutes a very high percentage of the total protein in the animal body. Such fibers are flexible but resist stretching and confer considerable strength on the tissues containing them. Fibers of the second type are called *elastic fibers* (or yellow fibers), and, as their name implies, can be easily stretched. When the stretching force ceases, the fibers return to their former length. Elastic fibers are often much thinner than collagenous fibers. They are composed of the protein elastin. Fibers of the third type are called *reticular fibers.* As the term "reticular" indicates, they branch and interlace to form complex networks. They are important at points where connective tissues and other tissues join. There are many of them, for example, in the basement membrane between epithelium and connective tissue.

Several kinds of cells are generally found in connective tissue proper. These include: (1) fibroblasts, which are believed to secrete the proteins from which the fibers form; (2) macrophages, irregularly shaped cells particularly common near blood vessels, which become very active when there is an inflammation and which can move by amoeboid motion and actively engulf particles such as dead red blood cells, bacteria, and other foreign material; (3) mast cells, which may produce a substance that tends to prevent blood clotting; (4) fat cells, which are cells highly specialized for fat storage (when these are very numerous in a region of connective tissue, the tissue is often called adipose tissue); and (5) various sorts of white blood cells, some of which can move fairly easily between the blood or lymph and the connective tissue proper—a clear demonstration of the close

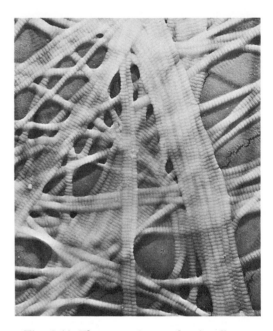

Fig. 3.44. Electron micrograph of collagen fibrils from human skin. × 12,300. [Courtesy Jerome Gross, Harvard University.]

interrelationship between these tissues. Both cells and fibers are embedded in a rather amorphous ground substance, which is a mixture of water, proteins, carbohydrates, and lipids. Associated with the ground substance is the *tissue fluid,* a liquid derived from the blood.

Connective tissue proper is customarily subdivided into two basic types—*loose connective tissue* and *dense connective tissue*—though there is no rigid separation between them, and intermediate types sometimes occur. Loose connective tissue is characterized by the loose, irregular arrangement of its fibers, the extensive amount of ground substance, and the presence of numerous cells of a variety of types (Fig. 3.45). It is very widely distributed in the animal body, no microscopic section of which is free of it. It has been said that if all other tissues were destroyed, the loose connective tissue alone would still show the exact contours of the body and the detailed shape of most internal organs. Much of the framework of the lymph glands, bone marrow, and liver is loose connective tissue; and loose connective tissue supports, surrounds, and connects the elements of all other tissues. For example, it binds muscle fibers together; attaches the skin to underlying tissues; forms the membranes that line the heart and abdominal cavities;

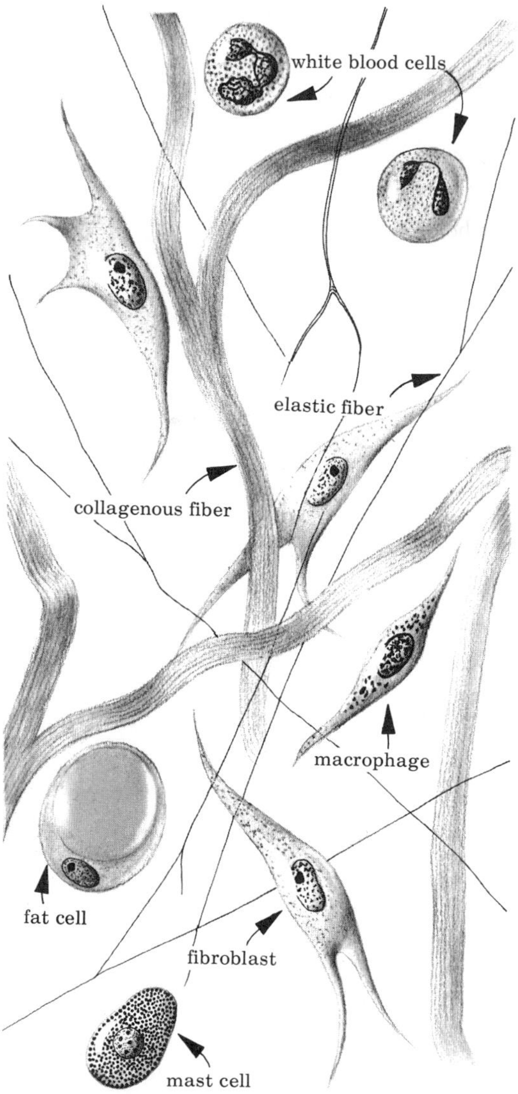

Fig. 3.45. Loose connective tissue. The several varieties of cells are embedded in an extensive extracellular matrix of fibers and ground substance.

forms the membranes, called mesenteries, that suspend the internal organs in their proper position and the membranes that bind together the parts of internal organs or that bind various organs together; functions as packing material in the spaces between organs; and forms a thin sheath around blood vessels, consequently penetrating with them into the interior of most organs. Because of its flexibility, loose connective tissue allows movement between the units it binds or connects.

But the functions of loose connective tissue are not limited to these mechanical ones. Since most substances exchanged between the blood and the cells of other tissues must pass through a layer of loose connective tissue, it is clear that this tissue plays an important role in the exchange process itself. And we have already mentioned the presence in connective tissue of cells that function in the destruction of noxious foreign substances by phagocytosis, an activity that often produces a local area of inflammation. It also seems probable that some of the cells of the connective tissue function in the production of antibodies, by means of which the body develops immunity to some diseases.

Dense connective tissue is characterized by the compact arrangement of its many fibers, the limited amount of ground substance, and the relatively small number of cells (Fig. 3.46A). The fibers may be irregularly arranged into an interlacing network, as in the dermis of the skin or the sheaths (periostea) of bone, or they may be arranged in a definite pattern, usually parallel bundles oriented to withstand tension from one direction, as in tendons connecting muscle to bone, or ligaments connecting bone to bone.

Cartilage. Cartilage (gristle) is a specialized form of dense fibrous connective tissue in which the intercellular matrix has a rubbery consistency (Fig. 3.46B). The relatively few cells are located in cavities in the matrix. Cartilage can support great weight; yet it is often flexible and somewhat elastic. It varies

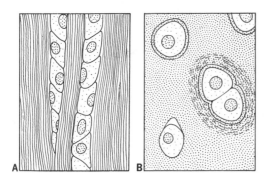

Fig. 3.46. Dense connective tissue and cartilage. (A) Rows of cells and collagenous fibers alternate in tendon. (B) The nearly spherical cells of cartilage are widely spaced in an extracellular matrix that looks almost homogeneous under an ordinary microscope. Actually, the matrix contains a dense network of thin fibrils.

in texture, color, and elasticity, and several different major types are recognized.

Cartilage is found in your body in such places as the nose and ears (where it forms pliable supports), the larynx and trachea (you can feel the rings of cartilage in the front of your throat), intervertebral discs, surfaces of skeletal joints, and ends of ribs. Most of the skeleton of the early vertebrate embryo is composed of cartilage; the developing bones follow this model and slowly replace it. Some vertebrate groups, the sharks for example, retain a cartilagenous skeleton even in the adult.

Bone. Bone has a hard, relatively rigid matrix. This matrix contains numerous collagenous fibers and a surprising amount of water, but it is impregnated with inorganic salts such as calcium carbonate and calcium phosphate (the calcium and phosphate probably associate to form a more complex inorganic compound in the bone). This inorganic material may constitute as much as 65 percent of the dry weight of an adult bone. The few bone cells are widely separated and are located in spaces in the matrix (Fig. 11.6, p. 436). We shall discuss the histology of bone in more detail in a later chapter.

Muscle

The cells of muscle have greater capacity for contraction than most other cells, although all protoplasm probably possesses this capacity to some extent. Muscles are responsible for most movement in higher animals. The individual muscle cells are usually elongate and are bound together into sheets or bundles by connective tissue. Three principal types of muscle tissue are recognized in vertebrates: skeletal or striated muscle, which is responsible for most voluntary movement; smooth muscle, which is involved in most involuntary movements of internal organs; and cardiac muscle, the tissue of which the heart is composed (Fig. 11.8, p. 438). This classification does not hold for many invertebrate animals, where one or more of these types may be missing entirely, and where the distribution of the types within the body is nearly always different from that outlined here for vertebrates.

Nerve

To some extent, all protoplasm possesses the property of irritability, the ability to respond to stimuli, but nerve tissue is highly specialized for such response. Nerve cells are easily stimulated and can transmit impulses very rapidly. Each cell is composed of a cell body, containing the nucleus, and one or more long thin extensions called fibers (Fig. 3.47). They are thus admirably suited to serve as conductors of messages over long distances. An individual nerve cell may be 3 or 4 feet long, or even longer; no other kinds of cells even approach such length. Many nerve fibers bound together by connective tissue constitute a nerve.

The functional combination of nerve and muscle tissue is fundamental to all multicellular animals except sponges. It is these tissues that confer upon animals their characteristic ability to move rapidly in response to stimuli.

ANIMAL ORGANS

The bodies of some of the simpler multicellular animals generally show few clearly distinct organs, but most larger, more advanced animals characteristically have numerous such organs, which, in turn, are organized into functional complexes called organ systems. Structural organization at the organ and organ-system levels is far more advanced in the higher animals than in the higher plants. This fundamental difference between these two great groups of organisms is doubtless correlated with the different modes of life that character-

ize them, particularly their different feeding methods and their different adaptations for a sedentary existence on the one hand (plants), and active locomotion on the other (animals).

Human skin has traditionally been used as an example of the complex integration of different types of cells and tissues to form an animal organ (Fig. 3.48). The illustration of skin, and the description of it in the caption, show that such an organ is far more complex than a first impression might indicate. For example, skin contains elements of all four primary animal tissue types: epithelium, connective tissue, muscle, and nerve. Portions of these tissues, in turn, are organized into relatively complex structures like glands, ducts, hairs, blood vessels, and sensory devices. All these structural elements are integrated to form the functional organ. In this case, the organ functions in many ways: as a protective covering for the body that resists penetration by many harmful substances and disease-producing organisms and that resists excessive water loss from the body; as an organ of excretion for several different waste materials; as an aid in regulating the temperature of the body; as an organ whose sensory nerve endings receive impulses from the outside environment; and as a depot in which reserve nutrients are stored.

The numerous organs, besides skin, that together constitute the body of a higher animal will be discussed in later chapters. For the moment, it is sufficient to indicate that these are commonly grouped into organ systems, of which the following will be of particular concern to us: (1) the digestive system, which functions in procuring and processing nutrients; (2) the respiratory system, which functions in the gas-exchange process whereby oxygen is taken into the body and waste carbon dioxide released; (3) the circulatory system, which is the internal transport system of animals; (4) the excretory system, which functions in the release of certain metabolic wastes from the body and also acts as a critically important

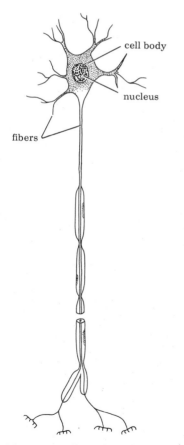

Fig. 3.47 Nerve cell. The shorter fibers (dendrites) carry impulses toward the cell body. The long fiber (axon) carries impulses away from the cell body.

regulator of the chemical makeup of the body fluids; (5) the endocrine system, whose glands and the hormones they produce play an important role in internal control; (6) the nervous system, a control system essential in coordinating the myriad functions of a complex multicellular animal; (7) the skeletal system, which provides support and determines shape in some animals; (8) the muscular system, of fundamental importance in the movement so typical of animals; and (9) the reproductive system, which functions in the production of new individuals, a capacity basic to life itself.

THE VARIETY OF ORGANISMS

In our discussion in later chapters of the many different problems faced by all living things and the numerous alternative solutions to them evolved in different kinds of organisms, we shall need to refer repeatedly to representative organisms drawn from a variety of plant and animal groups. Consequently a brief synopsis of a selected few such groups will be given here, so that you will be familiar with them when they are mentioned. A much more complete treatment of these and other groups will be given in another section of the book.

Bacteria

Bacteria do not fit well into either the plant kingdom or the animal kingdom, and it is meaningless to insist that they must belong to one or the other. Bacteria are very small single-celled procaryotic organisms. They are not usually green (though a few have a distinctive type of chlorophyll and carry out photosynthesis). They can be seen only under magnification. As we shall see, bacterial cells differ in many significant ways from the cells of most other organisms. Many bacteria are important as disease-producing agents. Others are important scavengers destroying the dead bodies of other organisms.

Fig. 3.48. Section of human skin. The outer portion of the skin, the epidermis, is composed of stratified squamous epithelial tissue. Its outermost layer (*stratum corneum*) consists of hardened dead cells that are constantly being sloughed off. Active cell division in the deeper layers of the epidermis produces new cells that are pushed outward and take the place of those that are lost. Beneath the epidermis is a layer, called the dermis, composed chiefly of connective tissue. Blood vessels penetrate into the dermis but not into the epidermis. Sweat glands are embedded in the deeper layers of the dermis, and their ducts push outward through both dermis and epidermis to open onto the surface of the skin through sweat pores. Both the glands and their ducts are derived from the epidermis; they form initially as invaginations of the epidermis that push downward into the connective tissue of the dermis. Hairs, and the inner layers of the hair follicles in which they are encased, are also derived from the epidermis and also develop as invaginations into the dermis. When fully developed, the bulbous base of the follicle and the hair root lie deep in the dermis; the shaft of the hair extends at a slant from the root to the surface of the skin and beyond.

A small muscle runs diagonally from the upper portion of the dermis to the hair follicle near its lower end; when this muscle contracts, it pulls the hair erect. One or more sebaceous (oil) glands empty into the hair follicle. Numerous nerves penetrate into the dermis, and a few even penetrate into the epidermis. Among them are nerves to the hair muscles, sweat glands, and blood vessels, and also nerves terminating in the sensory structures for touch, temperature, and pain.

Beneath the dermis, and not sharply delimited from it, is a subcutaneous layer, which is not considered a part of the skin itself. This is a layer of very loose connective tissue, usually with abundant fat cells. It is this layer that binds the skin to the body. The extent and form of its development determine the amount of possible skin movement.

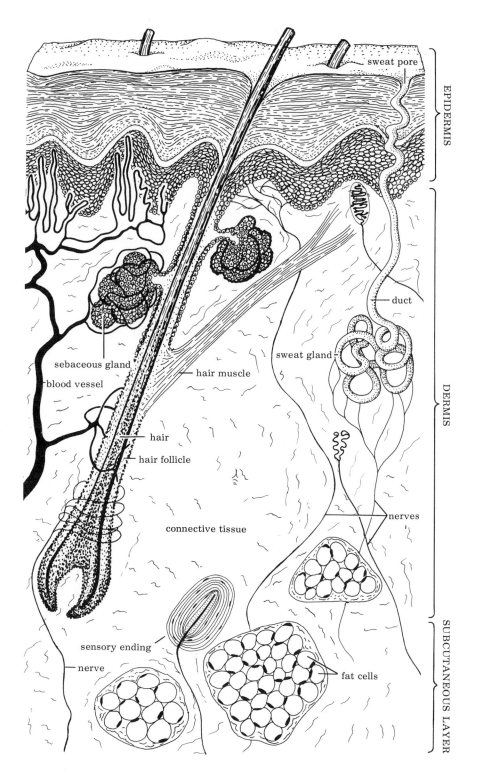

sweat pore

EPIDERMIS

sebaceous gland

blood vessel

hair muscle

sweat gland

duct

hair

hair follicle

connective tissue

nerves

DERMIS

sensory ending

nerve

fat cells

SUBCUTANEOUS LAYER

Plant Groups

Green Algae. Green algae are relatively simple plants that live only in the water or in very moist environments on land. Some are unicellular, others multicellular. In the latter case, most of the cells are similar to each other and are not highly specialized; consequently there are no separate layers or regions of different tissue types. The essentially parenchymatous cells form what might be considered a single continuous tissue, which is the plant body. These algae possess chlorophyll, as the name "green algae" implies. They are of special interest because it is believed that many (if not all) of the higher-plant groups evolved from ancestral flagellated green algae.

Brown Algae and Red Algae. Both the brown algae and the red algae are primarily marine and are commonly known as seaweeds. Their bodies are fairly complex and are always multicellular; some of them are very large. In most cases, there is relatively little differentiation into distinct tissue types. A few species of brown algae do show such differentiation and have evolved many other characteristics resembling those of the higher land-plant groups, but this evolution is generally considered to have been entirely independent and not an indication of close phylogenetic relationships. The common names of these two groups refer to the presence of brown and red pigments, which frequently mask the green chlorophylls that the plants also contain.

Fungi. Fungi are a group of relatively primitive plants whose members lack chlorophyll and are therefore unable to manufacture their own food. Like animals, they must obtain their complex high-energy nutrients in an already synthesized form. Some fungi are unicellular (e.g. yeast), but most are multicellular (e.g. bread mold, fruit molds, mushrooms, toadstools, bracket fungi). Like algae, their bodies show little differentiation into distinct tissue types.

Mosses. Mosses are green and photosynthetic. They live on land, but are not entirely free of dependence on the ancestral aquatic environment; thus they occur only in very moist habitats. Their restriction to such habitats is correlated with the fact that they have not evolved the highly specialized vascular tissues xylem and phloem, and hence lack an efficient internal transport system.

Vascular Plants. These plants, as their name implies, all possess vascular tissue and thus have an effective internal transport system. As a result, they are more independent of water in the surrounding environment than are the previously discussed plants, and they constitute the dominant plant group on land today. Of all members of the plant kingdom, this group shows the greatest internal specialization into tissues and organs, and it is to the higher members of the group, particularly the flowering plants, that our earlier description of plant tissue types and body form applies.

The vascular-plant group is usually subdivided into several sections, three of which are doubtless familiar to you; they are the ferns, the conifers and their allies (gymnosperms), and the flowering plants (angiosperms). Of these three groups, the ferns are the most primitive; they appeared on the ancient earth before the other two groups, dominated the land for a long time, but eventually gave way to the other groups and are now largely overshadowed by them.

The gymnosperms and flowering plants are known collectively as the *seed plants;* they are more highly specialized for a terrestrial existence than the ferns. Some commonly encountered gymnosperms are pine, cedar, spruce, fir, and hemlock; all of these bear cones and have needlelike leaves, though not all gymnosperms do.

The angiosperms, or flowering plants, are the most advanced of the three groups. The majority of the land plants familiar to you belong to this group, which includes plants of every shape and size from grasses to cactuses, and from tiny herbs and wild flowers to large oaks and maple trees. This huge and very diverse group is customarily further divided into two subgroups, the *dicots* and the *monocots*. The dicot subgroup includes such plants as beans, buttercups, privets, dandelions, oak trees, maple trees, roses, potatoes, and a great variety of others. The monocot subgroup includes the grasses and other grasslike plants such as corn, lilies, irises, and palm trees.

Animal Groups

Protozoa. The Protozoa are single-celled organisms, but in many cases the single cell is so highly specialized and complex that it resembles a multicellular organism. They are usually much larger than bacteria and are generally very mobile, swimming rapidly through the water in which they live or crawling along the bottom or on submerged objects. Some of them, like *Euglena* (Fig. 8.7, p. 283), possess long flagella and propel themselves by their whiplike motion. Others, like *Paramecium* (Fig. 5.15, p. 178), bear many cilia, which often function in both locomotion and feeding. Still others, like *Amoeba* (Fig. 22.3, p. 844), have neither flagella nor cilia, but move by a complex flowing of the cytoplasm as the cell, constantly changing shape, sends out extensions into which the rest of the cytoplasm then flows. We shall refer to representative Protozoa many times as we examine their fascinating evolutionary adaptations.

Coelenterates. The coelenterates constitute a large group of aquatic animals. Their saclike bodies are composed of two distinct tissue layers with a much less distinct third layer between them. They have a digestive cavity, but it has only one opening, which must serve as both mouth and anus. Tentacles are often present around the mouth and are used in capturing prey. The nerves and muscles of these simple animals are of an exceedingly primitive type, and no circulatory system is present. The body plan, or symmetry, is radial rather than bilateral, a reflection of the fact that many coelenterates are relatively sedentary during at least part of their life cycle. The group includes jellyfish, sea anemones, and corals. A fresh-water form to which we shall often refer as representative is the hydra (Fig. 5.17, p. 181).

Flatworms. The flatworms (Platyhelminthes) are more complex than the coelenterates in some ways, but they, too, have a digestive tract with only one opening. The body is composed of three primary tissue layers, and the symmetry is bilateral. Many flatworms, such as flukes and tapeworms, are parasites and show numerous interesting specializations for this mode of existence. Others, like planaria (Fig. 5.18, p. 182), a small animal to which we shall refer repeatedly, are free-living aquatic organisms.

Molluscs. The molluscs are fairly complex animals, most of which possess shells. Snails, clams, oysters, scallops, etc. belong to this group, as do octopuses and squids, which do not have obvious shells. These animals are particularly abundant in the oceans, as anyone who has collected their shells along the seashore will know. They are also common in fresh water. Some snails have evolved lungs and become fully terrestrial.

Annelids. The annelids are often called the segmented worms. As this term implies, the bodies of these highly evolved worms are divided into a series of units or segments, which are often clearly visible externally Though most of these animals are aquatic, some, like the earthworm, occur on land, though always in moist places. We shall generally take the earthworm as representative of this group; occasionally, however, we shall mention *Nereis,* a marine worm with large lobes growing from each side of the body segments (Fig. 6.9, p. 211).

Arthropods. The arthropods constitute an immense group of very advanced animals that includes more different species than all other animal groups combined. All arthropods have jointed legs and a hard outer skeleton. Spiders, scorpions, crabs, lobsters, crayfish, centipeds, millipeds, and insects all belong to this major group; of these, the insects are by far the largest subgroup and are among the most successful of all land animals, rivaled only by the mammals and man himself.

Echinoderms. All echinoderms are strictly marine; they have apparently never been able to invade either the fresh-water or the terres- trial habitats. Though their symmetry is radial, they are fairly advanced in many ways. The group included starfish, sand dollars, sea ur- chins, sea cucumbers, and a variety of other forms. Despite their unlikely appearance, the echinoderms are regarded by most biologists as the group of animals most closely related to the next group, the chordates, to which man himself belongs.

Chordates. This very important group in- cludes a major subgroup called the *vertebrates,* which comprises all those animals possessing an internal bony skeleton, particularly a back- bone. Fish, amphibians (e.g. frogs, salaman- ders), reptiles (e.g. snakes, lizards, turtles, alligators), birds, and mammals (including man) belong to this group. We shall pay particular attention to the chordates through- out this book.

REFERENCES

AREY, L. B., 1963. *Human Histology.* Saunders, Philadelphia.

BLOOM, W., and D. W. FAWCETT, 1962. *A Text- book of Histology,* 8th ed. Saunders, Philadel- phia.

BRACHET, J., and A. E. MIRSKY, ed., 1961. *The Cell,* vol. 2. Academic Press, New York.

BROWN, R., 1960. "The Plant Cell and Its Inclu- sions," in vol. 1A of *Plant Physiology,* ed. by F. C. Steward. Academic Press, New York.

CHRISTENSEN, H. N., 1962. *Biological Transport.* Benjamin, New York.

DE ROBERTIS, E. D. P., W. W. NOWINSKI, and F. A. SAEZ, 1965. *Cell Biology,* 4th ed. (titled *General Cytology* in older editions). Saunders, Philadelphia.

EAMES, A. J., and L. H. MACDANIELS, 1947. *An Introduction to Plant Anatomy.* McGraw-Hill, New York.

ESAU, K., 1965. *Plant Anatomy,* 2nd ed. Wiley, New York.

SUGGESTED READING

BRACHET, J., 1961. "The Living Cell," *Scientific American,* September. (Offprint 90.)

DE DUVE, C., 1963. "The Lysosome," *Scientific American,* May. (Offprint 156.)

DIPPELL, R. V., 1962. "Ultrastructure of Cells in Relation to Function," in *This Is Life,* ed. by

W. H. Johnson and W. C. Steere. Holt, Rine- hart & Winston, New York.

GREULACH, V. A., and J. E. ADAMS, 1962. *Plants: An Introduction to Modern Botany.* Wiley, New York. (See esp. Chapters 4–5.)

GROSS, J., 1961. "Collagen," *Scientific American,* May. (Offprint 88.)

HOKIN, L. E., and M. R. HOKIN, 1965. "The Chemistry of Cell Membranes," *Scientific American,* October. (Offprint 1022.)

HOLTER, H., 1961. "How Things Get into Cells," *Scientific American,* September. (Offprint 96.)

JENSEN, W. A., 1964. *The Plant Cell.* Wadsworth, Belmont, Calif.

LOEWY, A. G., and P. SIEKEVITZ, 1963. *Cell Structure and Function.* Holt, Rinehart & Winston, New York.

MONTAGNA, W., 1965. "The Skin," *Scientific American,* February. (Offprint 1003.)

PRESTON, R. D., 1957. "Cellulose," *Scientific American,* September.

RAMSAY, J. A., 1965. *The Experimental Basis of Modern Biology.* Cambridge University Press, New York. (See esp. Chapters 4–8.)

ROBERTSON, J. D., 1962. "The Membrane of the Living Cell," *Scientific American,* April. (Offprint 151.)

SATIR, P., 1961. "Cilia," *Scientific American,* February. (Offprint 79.)

SIEKEVITZ, P., 1957. "Powerhouse of the Cell," *Scientific American,* July. (Offprint 36.)

SOLOMON, A. K., 1960. "Pores in the Cell Membrane," *Scientific American,* December. (Offprint 76.)

STERN, H., and D. L. NANNEY, 1965. *The Biology of Cells.* Wiley, New York. (See esp. Chapters 1, 3.)

SWANSON, C. P., 1964. *The Cell,* 2nd ed. Prentice-Hall, Englewood Cliffs, N.J.

ZAMECNIK, P. C., 1958. "The Microsome," *Scientific American,* March. (Offprint 52.)

CHAPTER

4

ENERGY TRANSFORMATIONS

IT IS A BASIC PRINCIPLE OF PHYSICS THAT ALL systems have a natural tendency toward increasing disorder. The more orderly any arrangement of matter is, the less probable it is, and the less likely it is to be maintained if energy is not expended to counteract the tendency toward greater disorder. For example, the organization of wood, bricks, and other materials in the form of a house is one of an infinitely large number of possible arrangements of those materials, but it is so orderly an arrangement that it is extremely improbable that it would occur spontaneously. Similarly, if all the type used to print this page were dropped from a box onto the floor, one possible arrangement in which it could come to rest is the one you see before you, but this orderly arrangement of letters into words, sentences, and paragraphs is so very unlikely to occur by chance that you doubtless feel certain it could be achieved only if energy were expended by a typesetter. The living cell, whose complex structure we examined in the last chapter, is also an inherently unstable and improbable organization. Only by constant use of energy can it maintain itself and keep from falling into the more stable and more probable random and disorganized state. The acquisition of energy in usable form is thus a necessity for every living cell.

CHARACTERISTICS OF ENERGY

Energy is generally defined as the capacity to do work. Since it is a capacity, it need not at any given moment actively accomplish work. Instead of taking the form of active or kinetic energy, it can be stored as potential energy. But before work can actually be done, the energy must become kinetic, which is to say that there must be motion of some sort. Thus a car parked on a steep hill has potential energy by virtue of its position; when its brake is released, the car rolls down the hill, converting its potential energy into the kinetic energy of motion. Similarly, a lump of coal contains potential energy, which is released as kinetic energy when the coal burns.

Energy can occur in many different forms. Light is energy, and so is electricity; there is heat energy, mechanical energy, chemical energy, etc. All these involve motion, whether motion of photons, as in light, motion of electrons, as in electricity, or motion of atoms and molecules, as in heat. All forms of energy are interconvertible, at least partly. According to the *First Law of Thermodynamics* (also called the Law of Conservation of Energy), when energy is converted from one form into another no energy is either gained or destroyed (for this law to be strictly valid in all cases, matter must be considered a form of energy, but in biological systems interconversions between energy and matter can generally be disregarded).

Living cells draw primarily on chemical energy; they do work by utilizing the potential energy in chemical bonds. Every bond in every molecule represents an amount of chemical-bond energy equal to the amount of energy that was necessary to link the atoms together originally. Living cells, then, are transducers that turn other forms of energy into chemical-bond energy, or the reverse.

We have already seen that the molecules of many of the compounds of living cells are often highly complex and are composed of many thousands of atoms bonded together. Many of these bonds are relatively rich in chemical-bond energy. Hence a living organism is a veritable storehouse of potential chemical energy, which can be used, when necessary, to do work. But as this stored energy is converted into other forms, less and less remains in reserve. There must be a source of usable energy outside the organism, which can be utilized to replenish its supply of chemical-bond energy. For many organisms, that outside energy source is other organisms; i.e. one living thing obtains new supplies of energy-rich molecules by eating the bodies of other living things. Since according to the First Law of Thermodynamics all these energy conversions are accomplished without reduction of the total amount of energy, it might seem at first glance that the same energy could be passed continuously from organism to organism and that no source of energy outside the system composed of all living things would be required. A little further thought shows immediately that this is not true, since energy is constantly passed from organisms to nonliving matter, as when you throw a rock or move a pencil or when heat from your body warms the air; such energy is lost to the life system. Furthermore, the molecules of substances that leave the body retain some energy, and this energy, too, may be lost. But there is another basic reason why life on earth would run down if there were no nonliving source of energy to be tapped. The *Second Law of Thermodynamics* says that every energy transformation results in a reduction in the usable or free energy of the system; or, to put it another way, there is a steady increase in the amount of energy that cannot be used to do work, an increase in entropy as the physicists call it. Entropy is a measure of the unavailable or useless energy in a system; hence we may also think of it as a measure of the randomness of the system. Thus the Second Law is essentially a more formal statement of the idea, mentioned earlier, that there is a general tendency toward greater disorder.

PHOTOSYNTHESIS

As you doubtless know, the ultimate energy source for most living things is sunlight, and the organisms that transform the light energy into chemical-bond energy are primarily the green plants. The process by which this transformation is carried out is called photosynthesis. There is still much about the process that is not known, but the last few years have witnessed an enormous growth in our understanding of the chemical pathways involved. It is not our purpose here to discuss in detail all the chemistry of photosynthesis, or to mention all reactions and compounds now thought to be involved in it; but photosynthesis is so fundamental to life that we ought to grasp at least the broad outlines of the process and some of the principles of energy transformations in living systems exemplified by it.

Historical Development

As early as 1772, an English clergyman and chemist, Joseph Priestley (1733–1804), demonstrated that green plants affect air so as to reverse the effects of breathing (Fig. 4.1). In his words:

I flatter myself that I have accidentally hit upon a method of restoring air which has been injured by the burning of candles, and that I have discovered at least one of the restoratives which nature employs for this purpose. It is vegetation. In what manner this process in nature operates, to produce so remarkable an effect, I do not pretend to have discovered; but a number of facts declare in favour of this hypothesis. I shall introduce my account of them, by reciting some of the observations which I made on the growing of plants in confined air, which led to this discovery.

One might have imagined that, since common air is necessary to vegetable, as well as to animal life, both plants and animals had affected it in the same manner, and I own I had that expectation, when I first put a sprig of mint into a glass-jar, standing inverted in a vessel of water; but when it had continued growing there for some months, I found that the air would neither extinguish a candle, nor was it at all inconvenient to a mouse, which I put into it.

Finding that candles burn very well in air in which plants had grown a long time, and

Fig. 4.1. Priestley's experiment. A lone plant in a closed jar died and a lone mouse in another closed jar died, but when plant and mouse were together in the same jar, both lived.

having had some reason to think, that there was something attending vegetation, which restored air that had been injured by respiration, I thought it was possible that the same process might also restore the air that had been injured by the burning of candles.

Accordingly, on the 17th of August, 1771, I put a sprig of mint into a quantity of air, in which a wax candle had burned out, and found that, on the 27th of the same month, another candle burned perfectly well in it. This experiment I repeated, without the least variation in the event, not less than eight or ten times in the remainder of the summer. Several times I divided the quantity of air in which the candle had burned out, into two parts, and putting the plant into one of them, left the other in the same exposure, contained, also, in a glass vessel immersed in water, but without any plant; and never failed to find, that a candle would burn in the former, but not in the latter. I generally found that five or six days were sufficient to restore this air, when the plant was in its vigour; whereas I have kept this kind of air in glass vessels, immersed in water many months without being able to perceive that the least alteration had been made in it.

This restoration of air I found depended upon the vegetating state of the plant; for though I kept a great number of the fresh leaves of mint in a small quantity of air in which candles had burned out, and changed them frequently, for a long space of time, I could perceive no melioration in the state of the air.

This remarkable effect does not depend upon any thing peculiar to mint, which was the plant that I always made use of till July 1772; for on the 16th of that month, I found a quantity of this kind of air to be perfectly restored by sprigs of balm, which had grown in it from the 7th of the same month.

Priestley's important experiments were the first demonstration that plants produce oxygen, though he himself did not realize that this was what was happening. Not only did he not know about oxygen, but he also did not realize that light was essential for the process he ob-

served. Nonetheless, his findings stimulated interest in photosynthesis, as we now call it, and led to further work. Only seven years later, the Dutch physician Jan Ingen-Housz (1730–1799) demonstrated the necessity of sunlight for oxygen production (though he, like Priestley, knew nothing about oxygen at that time and explained his results in other terms), and he also showed that only the green parts of the plant could photosynthesize. He reported his results in a book with the highly explicit title, *Experiments upon Vegetables, Discovering Their Great Power of Purifying the Common Air in the Sun-Shine, and of Injuring It in the Shade and at Night.* In 1782 a Swiss pastor and part-time scientist, Jean Senebier (1742–1809), showed that the process was dependent upon a particular kind of gas, which he called "fixed air" (and we call carbon dioxide). Finally, in 1804, another Swiss worker, Nicolas Théodore de Saussure (1767–1845), found that water is necessary for the photosynthetic production of organic materials.

Thus, early in the nineteenth century, all the important materials of the photosynthetic process were at least vaguely known, and could be summarized by the following equation:

$$\text{carbon dioxide} + \text{water} \xrightarrow[\text{light}]{\text{green plants}}$$
$$\text{organic material} + \text{oxygen}$$

Later, scientists came to believe that light energy trapped by *chlorophyll* (the green pigment of plants) splits carbon dioxide, CO_2, and that the carbon is then combined with water, H_2O, to form the unit (CH_2O), which is essentially the grouping upon which carbohydrates are based (the parentheses indicate that this combination of atoms does not represent an actual molecule, but only a grouping within some larger compound; thus, it takes six of these groupings to make a simple six-carbon sugar, $C_6H_{12}O_6$). According to this view, the oxygen released by the plant during photosynthesis comes from CO_2. This idea received a severe blow about 1930, when C. B.

van Niel of Stanford University showed that some photosynthetic bacteria do not give off molecular oxygen. For example, some of these bacteria use hydrogen sulfide (H_2S) instead of water as a raw material for photosynthesis, and they give off sulfur instead of oxygen as a by-product. Now, H_2S and H_2O have obvious chemical similarities, and if the sulfur produced by the bacteria during photosynthesis comes from H_2S, it seemed reasonable to suppose that the oxygen produced by higher plants during photosynthesis might come from H_2O, not from CO_2. This was at last conclusively shown to be true by use of a heavy isotope of oxygen (O^{18} instead of the usual O^{16}). If photosynthesizing plants are given normal carbon dioxide plus water composed of heavy oxygen, the heavy isotope appears as molecular oxygen:

$$CO_2 + 2H_2O^{18} \rightarrow O_2^{18} + (CH_2O) + H_2O$$

If, however, normal water plus carbon dioxide prepared with heavy oxygen are given to the plant, some of the labeled oxygen goes into the carbohydrate produced and some of it appears in water, but none of it forms free oxygen:

$$CO_2^{18} + 2H_2O \rightarrow O_2 + (CH_2O^{18}) + H_2O^{18}$$

We can summarize these findings by writing a new equation for green-plant photosynthesis and indicating the fates of all the atoms involved by dotted lines:

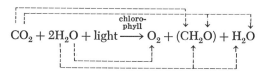

Or, if we prefer, we can write the same summary equation multiplied by 6, thereby indicating that glucose, a six-carbon simple sugar, is the end product:

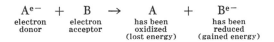

It may seem curious to write water on both sides of the equation, but it is necessary to do so because the water produced by the photosynthetic process is new water; it is not the same water as that used as a raw material.

The above equation is a convenient summary of photosynthetic carbohydrate synthesis, but it tells us nothing about how the synthesis is actually achieved. The process is certainly not one gross chemical reaction, as the summary equation might imply. It was recognized years ago that many reactions are involved and that some of these are "dark" reactions—ones that can take place with or without light. It is only in very recent years, however, that scientists have begun to learn the actual reactions of photosynthesis and that the role of light has been clarified.

The Chemical Nature of Photosynthesis

Carbon dioxide is an exceedingly energy-poor compound. Sugar is energy-rich. Photosynthesis, then, is a process that converts light energy into chemical-bond energy and stores it by synthesizing energy-rich sugar from energy-poor carbon dioxide. In chemical terms, the energy is stored by the reduction of carbon dioxide.

Before proceeding further, we should consider the term **reduction** and its converse **oxidation**. Basically, reduction means the addition of an electron (e^-), and oxidation means the removal of an electron. Since an electron added to one molecule must have been removed from some other molecule, it follows that whenever one substance is reduced another is oxidized.

A^{e-}	+	B	$\rightarrow$	A	+	B^{e-}
electron donor		electron acceptor		has been oxidized (lost energy)		has been reduced (gained energy)

Among the many ways a compound may be reduced, two of the most common involve removal of oxygen or addition of hydrogen; similarly, oxidation often involves addition of oxygen or removal of hydrogen:

$$A + BO \rightarrow AO + B$$

electron   electron   has been   has been
donor   acceptor   oxidized   reduced

or:

$$AH + B \rightarrow A + BH$$

electron   electron   has been   has been
donor   acceptor   oxidized   reduced

In biological systems, removal or addition of hydrogen constitutes the most frequent mechanism of oxidation-reduction reactions. In general, then, when we speak of reduction we shall mean addition of hydrogen, and when we speak of oxidation we shall mean removal of hydrogen. Reduction reactions store energy in the reduced compound, while oxidation reactions liberate energy.

It now becomes clear why the synthesis of sugar from carbon dioxide constitutes reduction of the carbon dioxide. Hydrogen obtained by splitting water molecules is added to the CO_2 to form compounds based on (CH_2O) units, and energy from light is stored in the process. Our attention must therefore be focused on two key points: the mechanism of trapping and handling energy and the mechanism of transferring hydrogen from water to carbon dioxide.

Light and Chlorophyll

Light waves constitute one small region of the spectrum of electromagnetic radiations (Fig. 4.2). Each radiation in this spectrum has a characteristic wavelength and energy content. These two characteristics are inversely related; i.e. the longer the wavelength, the smaller the energy content. Within the narrow band visible to man, the shortest light waves stimulate in us the sensation of violet and the longest stimulate the sensation of red. Radiations such as ultraviolet, X rays, and gamma rays, which are of shorter wavelength than violet, are invisible to us, as are infrared and radio-TV radiations, which are of longer wavelength than red.

With these facts in mind, let us examine again the statement that light energy is trapped by green plants and converted into chemical-bond energy. Does it imply that all light, regardless of wavelength, is equally effective? To answer this question, we must turn our attention to the all-important green pigment chlorophyll.

We have already mentioned that Ingen-Housz observed that only the green parts of a plant can photosynthesize. Years later, it was found that the green color is produced by a pigment called chlorophyll and that it is this

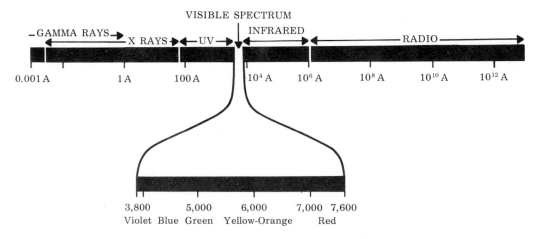

Fig. 4.2. Portion of the electromagnetic spectrum. Visible light constitutes only a very small portion of the total spectrum. Within the visible spectrum, light of different wavelengths stimulates in us different color sensations. Wavelengths are here given in angstroms.

chemical that is essential for photosynthesis. Actually there are several slightly different kinds of chlorophyll; the most widespread is chlorophyll *a*, and it will be to this compound that our discussion will primarily refer. Figure 4.3 shows the rather complex structure of a molecule of chlorophyll *a*.

Light falling on an object can pass through the object (be transmitted), be absorbed by it, or be reflected from it (Fig. 4.4). We can see transmitted or reflected light, but, obviously, we cannot see light that has been absorbed. Now, if chlorophyll is the material that traps the incident light, and if it appears green to our eyes, several facts should immediately be plain to us. First, chlorophyll cannot be absorbing much radiation of the wavelengths that stimulate in us the sensation of green, or we wouldn't see green color. Second, chlorophyll must be absorbing radiation of some wavelengths within the visible part of the spectrum, or the light transmitted or reflected to us would appear white (when all visible wavelengths are combined, they stimulate the

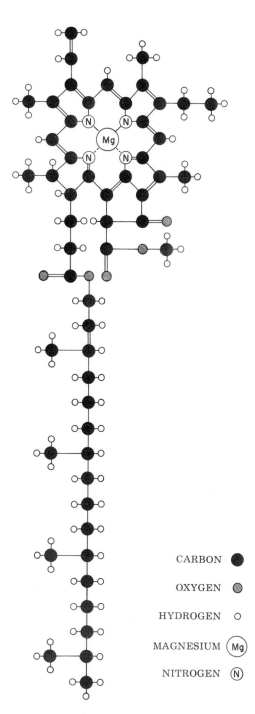

CARBON ●

OXYGEN ◉

HYDROGEN ○

MAGNESIUM (Mg)

NITROGEN (N)

Fig. 4.3. Molecular structure of chlorophyll *a*.

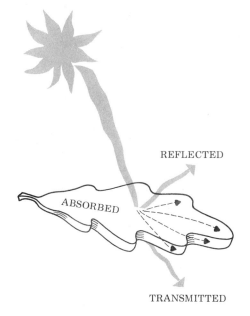

REFLECTED

ABSORBED

TRANSMITTED

Fig. 4.4. Light striking an object, such as a leaf, may be reflected, absorbed, or transmitted.

sensation of white). At this point we have already partly answered our question whether all light is equally effective for photosynthesis; we suspect that green light is not as effective as light of some other colors, since it is not absorbed as readily by chlorophyll. More precise information can be obtained if chlorophyll is extracted from the leaf and exposed to light of varying wavelengths to determine the amount of absorption at each wavelength. The absorption spectrum of chlorophyll *a* thus obtained (Fig. 4.5) shows that it is primarily light in the violet and red regions that is absorbed, while green, yellow, and orange light is absorbed only very slightly. It must be noted that the action spectrum of photosynthesis—a measure of the effectiveness of light of various wavelengths in driving photosynthesis (Fig. 4.6)—is somewhat different from the absorption spectrum of chlorophyll *a*, showing more activity in parts of the spectrum where the chlorophyll absorbs very little light. Apparently, other pigments, principally the yellow and orange carotenoids and other forms of chlorophyll, absorb light in these regions of the spectrum and then pass the energy to the chlo-

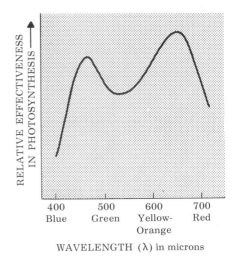

WAVELENGTH (λ) in microns

Fig. 4.6. Action spectrum of photosynthesis. Light of intermediate wavelengths is more effective in driving photosynthesis than would be predicted on the basis of the absorption spectrum of chlorophyll *a*. Apparently, other pigments absorb these intermediate wavelengths to some extent and pass the energy to chlorophyll *a* for photosynthesis. [Modified from A. W. Galston, *The Life of the Green Plant*, © 1964. By permission of Prentice-Hall, Inc., Englewood Cliffs, N.J.]

rophyll *a*. Accessory pigments like the carotenoids thus enable the plants to utilize light of more different wavelengths than could be trapped by chlorophyll *a* alone.

What happens when light of a proper wavelength strikes a chlorophyll molecule? We don't know exactly, but we can make some well-informed guesses. Light energy comes in discrete units or packets called photons. When a photon strikes a chlorophyll molecule and is absorbed, its energy is apparently transferred in some manner to an electron of the chlorophyll. This electron is raised from its normal stable energy level to a higher energy level (Fig. 4.7). This higher level is relatively unstable, and the "excited" electron will show a marked tendency to fall back to its normal level, giving up the absorbed energy. Isolated chlorophyll in a test tube promptly loses the energy it traps by re-emitting it as visible light; thus the chlorophyll alone is incapable of con-

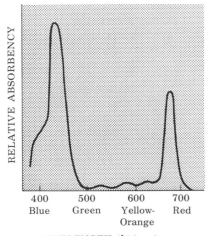

WAVELENGTH (λ) in microns

Fig. 4.5. Absorption spectrum of chlorophyll *a*. [Modified from A. W. Galston, *The Life of the Green Plant*, © 1964. By permission of Prentice-Hall, Inc., Englewood Cliffs, N.J.]

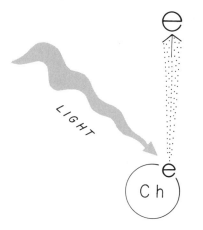

Fig. 4.7. Effect of light on chlorophyll. Light striking a chlorophyll molecule (Ch) causes an electron (e) of the chlorophyll to be raised to a higher energy level.

Cyclic Photophosphorylation

In the living photosynthesizing cell, the excited chlorophyll electron does not simply fall back to its normal lower energy level, losing its extra energy all at once. Instead, another molecule with a high affinity for electrons leads the high-energy electron away from the chlorophyll. One possible first electron-acceptor molecule passes the electron to another acceptor molecule, an iron-containing pigment called *cytochrome*, which in turn passes it to still another cytochrome acceptor molecule, and so forth (Fig. 4.8). After being passed from molecule to molecule in a chain of reactions, each catalyzed by an enzyme, the electron finally arrives back in the chlorophyll molecule whence it began. But when the electron leaves the chlorophyll it is energy-rich, and when it finally returns it is energy-poor. Obviously something happens to its extra energy while it is being passed along the circular chain of "electron carrier" molecules. What in fact happens is

verting light energy into chemical-bond energy. Once light energy has raised a chlorophyll electron to a high-energy state, other cellular components must come into play if the energy is to be captured and utilized.

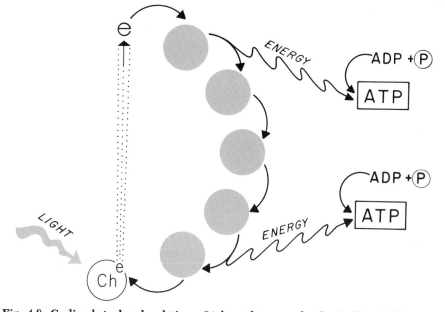

Fig. 4.8. Cyclic photophosphorylation. Light striking a molecule of chlorophyll causes an electron to be raised to a high energy level. The electron is picked up by an electron-acceptor molecule (dark circle), which passes it to a second acceptor molecule at a slightly lower energy level, which passes it to a third at a still lower energy level, etc. Some of the energy released as the electron is eased step by step down the energy gradient is used in the synthesis of ATP from ADP and inorganic phosphate.

that the electron is eased step by step down the energy gradient from the excited state to the normal state. As the electron is passed from carrier molecule to carrier molecule in the chain, it loses some energy. Thus, when the electron finally falls back into the chlorophyll, it has lost all its extra energy, but it has not lost it all at once, as would happen in the case of isolated chlorophyll in a test tube. Instead, the energy has been released in a series of small portions of manageable size.

Many everyday situations provide ready analogies to the step-by-step energy release by the excited chlorophyll electrons. Consider, for example, an automobile with its tank of gasoline. Locked in the chemical bonds of the gasoline is much energy. One way to release that energy would be to put a match to the entire supply. The energy would promptly be released, but it wouldn't do the automobile much good! A much more effective way to ensure that the released energy will be harnessed to propel the car is to burn the gasoline bit by bit. Or consider a waterfall where the water is not allowed to descend unobstructed, but is made to strike the paddles of a mill wheel, to which it imparts energy that can be used to do useful work. In each case—excited electron, gasoline, and waterfall—the total amount of energy released is unaffected by whether the change in energy levels is abrupt or gradual, but the results of the release are much affected.

The step-by-step reactions mentioned here provide an example of a general property of biological chemical systems. In living cells, almost all major chemical conversions are accomplished by a series of smaller conversions, each catalyzed by its own enzyme. Often some of the intermediate compounds formed are relatively unstable; i.e. they tend to break down very rapidly. They can be utilized in the chemistry of living cells because as soon as they are formed by one enzyme-catalyzed reaction they are acted upon by another enzyme and converted into a different compound before they

have time to break down in appreciable amounts.

We have implied that when the energy of the excited chlorophyll electron is released in a series of small bursts some of the energy can be harnessed to do useful work. How is this done? At several points along the carrier chain, part of the released free energy is captured and used in the synthesis of a compound named adenosine triphosphate, generally abbreviated to *ATP.* This compound, found in every living thing, is one of the most important substances of life. It plays the key role in biological energy transformations.

The ATP molecule (Fig. 4.9) is composed of a nitrogen-containing compound (adenosine) plus three phosphate[1] groups bonded in sequence:

$$\text{adenosine} - \textcircled{P} \sim \textcircled{P} \sim \textcircled{P}$$

It is to the bonds by which the second and third phosphate groups are attached that our attention must be directed if we are to understand the mechanism by which living cells handle energy. These bonds are not the usual kind of chemical bond; rather, they are energy-rich bonds (customarily represented in diagrams by the symbol $\sim$). If these bonds are broken, far more calories of energy are released than if the other bonds in the ATP molecule are broken. Actually, it is often only the terminal high-energy phosphate bond of ATP that is involved in energy conversions. The exergonic reaction by which this bond is broken and the terminal phosphate group removed leaves a compound called adenosine diphosphate or *ADP,* consisting of adenosine plus only two phosphate groups:

$$\text{ATP} \xrightarrow{\text{enzyme}} \text{ADP} + \textcircled{P} + \text{energy}$$

[1] The symbol $\textcircled{P}$ is customarily used to designate the entire phosphate group: $-\underset{\diagdown OH}{\overset{\diagup OH}{P}}\!\!=\!\!O$

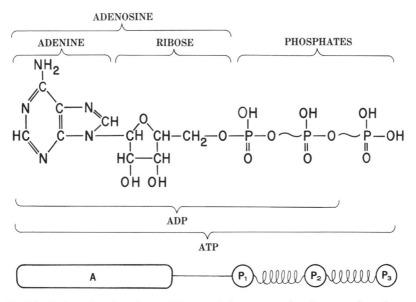

Fig. 4.9. The ATP molecule. As its full name, adenosine triphosphate, implies, this molecule is composed of an adenosine unit (a complex of adenine and ribose sugar) combined with three phosphate groups. The latter are arranged in sequence, with the last two attached by high-energy bonds (wavy lines). Mechanical analogue (bottom) shows low-energy bond as a string and the two high-energy bonds as extended springs.

New ATP can be synthesized from ADP and phosphate if adequate free energy is available to force a third phosphate group onto the ADP. Addition of phosphate is termed *phosphorylation:*

$$ADP + \textcircled{P} + energy \xrightarrow{\text{enzyme}} ATP$$

ATP is often called the universal energy currency of living things, and the designation is fully justified. It is energy stored in the energy-rich phosphate bonds that is used to do all manner of work: synthesis of more complex compounds, muscular contraction, nerve conduction, active transport across cell membranes, light production, etc. (Fig. 4.10). Whenever any organism is doing work of any kind, you can be certain that ATP is involved; the energy price of the work is paid in ATP's (i.e. the energy is obtained through the breaking down of ATP to ADP). It is as if in our country nickels were the only form of money and all bills had to be paid with them; an object worth 15 cents would be bought with three nickels, but what about an object worth 17 cents? Here a disadvantage of currency of only one denomination is apparent; there would be no choice but to pay four nickels for the 17-cent article. Similarly, a living cell doing one and a half ATP's worth of work must spend at least two molecules of ATP. But if the only monetary currency in our country were nickels, overpayment could be held to a minimum, because the nickel is a sufficiently small currency unit. Phosphate-bond energy is similarly suitable as energy currency; the unit is small enough to fill the energy requirements of the organism without releasing unnecessarily large amounts of energy in the process.

ATP molecules can be synthesized from ADP in a variety of ways in living organisms, as will be seen later in this chapter. But although neither synthesis of ATP nor step-by-step electron transport is unique to photosynthesis, the light-induced production of the high-energy electron that starts the process is.

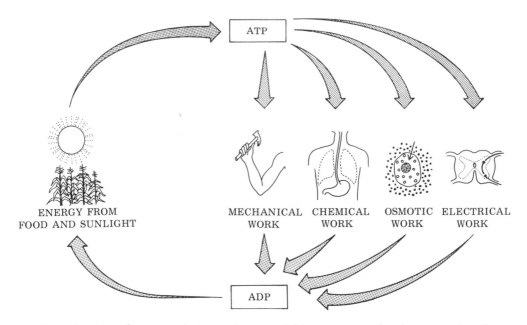

ENERGY FROM   MECHANICAL CHEMICAL   OSMOTIC   ELECTRICAL
FOOD AND SUNLIGHT   WORK   WORK   WORK   WORK

Fig. 4.10. ATP, the universal energy currency of life. ATP provides the energy for all
types of work performed by living organisms, whether plant or animal.

Any organism can manufacture energy currency by using up other energy-rich compounds, but only photosynthetic organisms
(and a few chemosynthetic bacteria) can
manufacture such currency from energy-poor
inorganic raw materials. In short, it is the
unique capacity of chlorophyll to absorb light
energy and act as a donor of high-energy electrons that is critical for photosynthesis.

In the photosynthetic phosphorylation process we have so far described, chlorophyll acts
both as electron donor and as the ultimate
electron acceptor, donating an excited electron
and eventually accepting the electron in a low-
energy state. Because the same electrons can
be carried round and round the system and no
outside source of electrons is involved, this
method of synthesizing ATP is called *cyclic
photophosphorylation.* The process was discovered in the mid-1950's by Daniel I. Arnon
and his co-workers at the University of California at Berkeley.

Noncyclic Photophosphorylation

It is possible that when the chlorophyll molecule first appeared in the evolution of life on
earth the sole energy-storing process driven by
light energy in the primitive organisms was
cyclic photophosphorylation. Under certain
conditions (as when CO_2 is not available), it
seems likely that modern green plants still
utilize light for this synthesis only. But most
present-day photosynthetic organisms usually
utilize light energy for another critical reaction
also. This reaction involves transfer of hydrogen from water to an intermediate compound,
which can then act as a hydrogen donor in the
reduction of carbon dioxide. Much remains to
be learned about this aspect of photosynthesis,
and there is much disagreement among authorities concerning the details of the process.
The overall scheme, however, has become
clearer in the past few years. The brief outline
given here is based largely on the model pro-

posed by Arnon, which may not be correct in all details.

This process, like that of cyclic photophosphorylation, already described, begins when photons of light strike molecules of chlorophyll and raise electrons to an excited state (Fig. 4.11). But here the first few electron-acceptor molecules that lead the excited electrons away from the chlorophyll are not the same as those involved in the previous process. According to Arnon, one of these acceptor molecules, probably the first, is an iron-containing compound called *ferredoxine,* which has a very high affinity for electrons. The ferredoxine passes the electrons to an extremely important compound called triphosphopyridine nucleotide, or **TPN** as it is usually abbreviated (it is also frequently called nicotinamide adenine dinucleotide phos-

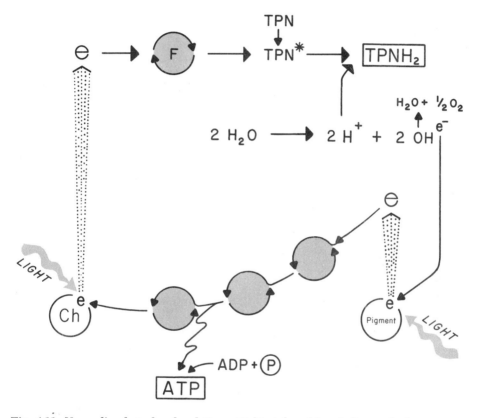

Fig. 4.11. Noncyclic photophosphorylation. Light strikes chlorophyll *a,* and electrons are raised to a high energy level (left). The electrons are picked up by ferredoxine (F), a very strong electron acceptor, and passed to TPN, which thus becomes activated (activation is symbolized by an asterisk). The activated TPN pulls hydrogen ions (H⁺) away from water and forms TPNH₂. A second light event raises electrons from a different pigment to a higher energy level (lower right). These electrons are passed along a series of acceptor compounds (dark circles) down an energy gradient until they reach chlorophyll *a,* where they replace the electrons lost from the chlorophyll as a result of the first light event; energy released from these electrons as they move down the energy gradient is used in synthesis of ATP from ADP and inorganic phosphate. Electrons to replace those lost from the second pigment come from the hydroxyl ions (OHᵉ⁻) from water. The (OH) radicals that remain combine to form new water and O₂ (four (OH) radicals are needed for one complete O₂ molecule to be formed). The two important products of noncyclic photophosphorylation, ATP and TPNH₂, make possible the synthesis of carbohydrate from CO₂.

phate and abbreviated NADP).[2] TPN, unlike the electron-acceptor molecules in cyclic photophosphorylation, does not promptly pass the electrons along to another acceptor molecule. Instead, the TPN retains the energized electrons, and the now energy-rich compound displays a great affinity for hydrogen ions (H^+). A small percentage of water is always in the ionized form and consists of hydrogen ions (H^+) and hydroxyl ions OH^-). The energized TPN apparently pulls two hydrogen ions away from water, forming reduced TPN, or $TPNH_2$. This utilization of light energy in the production of $TPNH_2$ by the splitting of water is crucial to photosynthesis by green plants, for $TPNH_2$ can act as a hydrogen donor in the reduction of carbon dioxide to carbohydrate. The electrons move from the chlorophyll to ferredoxine to $TPNH_2$ to carbohydrate (there may be other intermediate compounds involved).

If the excited electrons from chlorophyll are retained by TPN and eventually incorporated into carbohydrate, the chlorophyll molecules are left short of electrons. The electrons are replaced indirectly by some from hydroxyl ions (OH^-) derived from water. Thus water provides both the hydrogen for synthesis of $TPNH_2$ and new electrons for chlorophyll. Several cytochrome molecules (and other molecules, such as plastoquinone, that work in sequence with the cytochromes) act as electron carriers, passing the electrons step by step to chlorophyll. In this process, some free energy is released and is utilized in the synthesis of ATP from ADP and inorganic phosphate. (Several variants of this scheme suggest that ATP may also be synthesized at other points in the process; the experimental data are unfortu-

nately still insufficient to fix the sites of phosphorylation with certainty.)

It was thought at first that the electrons from the hydroxyl ions of water pass directly to a cytochrome chain and from this chain to the chlorophyll molecules with which the whole process began. There would thus be only one light-driven event—that which initially energized the chlorophyll electrons picked up by ferredoxin. There is strong evidence now, however, that two light-driven events are involved, the one we have already discussed and a second one more intimately related to the splitting of water. It is not yet clear precisely what pigment is involved in this second light event (though the substance will probably have been identified by the time you read this book). Some researchers think it is a form of chlorophyll *a* slightly different from that in-involved in the first light event (different forms of chlorophyll *a*, i.e. forms with maximal absorption at slightly different wavelengths, are known to exist); other workers think that the second pigment is chlorophyll *b* in land plants and green algae. Whatever the pigment is, the evidence that there are two light events in the process is compelling. Arnon suggests that light striking molecules of the second pigment energizes electrons that are then passed via the cytochrome chain to the chlorophyll *a* molecules involved in the first light event, and that this electron transport releases energy that can be utilized in ATP synthesis (Fig. 4.11). In other words, the electrons lost from the chlorophyll molecules involved in the first light event are replaced by electrons derived from molecules of the second pigment. The second pigment, in turn, receives electrons from hydroxyl ions as replacements for its lost electrons. The electrons involved in this second light event thus move from water to second pigment to cytochromes to first pigment (chlorophyll *a*). If we combine these steps with the electron movement associated with the first light event, as traced above, we obtain the following ab-

[2] Chemists now recognize NADP as the official designation, instead of TPN. Similarly, they recognize NAD (a compound to be discussed later) instead of DPN. Nonetheless, many of the leading research scientists working on photosynthesis continue to use TPN and DPN. The older names appear in almost all the references cited at the end of this chapter, and they are used in this book to avoid confusion.

breviated sequence showing the overall electron movement:

$$H_2O \rightarrow \text{pigment 2} \rightarrow \text{cytochromes} \rightarrow$$
$$\text{chlorophyll } a \rightarrow \text{ferredoxin} \rightarrow$$
$$TPNH_2 \rightarrow \text{carbohydrate}$$

We still have to account for the (OH) radicals left after the hydroxyl ions donate electrons to the pigment. These (OH) radicals, which are all that remains of the water, combine to form molecular oxygen (O_2) and new water, as shown in Fig. 4.11 (to yield a complete molecule of O_2, the equation for the splitting of water shown in the figure would have to be multiplied by 2).

Since electrons are not passed in a circular chain in this process, some leaving the system via $TPNH_2$ and others entering the system from water as replacements, this series of reactions is termed *noncyclic photophosphorylation.* The whole process results in formation of both ATP and $TPNH_2$ and in the release of molecular oxygen and new water as waste products. It can be summarized by the following equation:

$$2 \text{ ADP} + 2 \text{ ®} + 2 \text{ TPN} + 4H_2O + \text{light energy}$$
$$\rightarrow 2 \text{ ATP} + 2 \text{ TPNH}_2 + O_2 + 2H_2O$$

Whether the model proposed by Arnon is fully correct remains to be proved, but it serves to give you some notion of the processes involved in one aspect of photosynthesis and of current ideas about them.

Before leaving the topic of noncyclic photophosphorylation, we should point out that the details given above apply only to photosynthesis of green plants. As we have already indicated, some bacteria possess a form of chlorophyll and can utilize light energy in synthesis of ATP and $TPNH_2$, but they do not use water as the source of hydrogen ions and electrons. Some of these use hydrogen sulfide (H_2S), which is very much like water, and they give off sulfur instead of oxygen. Others use inorganic compounds that are not much like

water, but the basic processes involved remain essentially the same, although oxygen is not a by-product. Green plants themselves can be experimentally induced to use a source of electrons other than water. If oxidation of hydroxyl ions is blocked by chemical inhibitors, and then a strong electron donor is provided as a substitute, noncyclic photophosphorylation can continue without production of oxygen. In other words, green-plant photosynthesis has been experimentally converted into an essentially bacterial type of photosynthesis. Water is therefore only one of many possible electron sources for photosynthesis. It is not surprising, however, that the most successful photosynthetic organisms, the green plants, are those that evolved photosynthesis based on water, that ubiquitous solvent for and participant in the chemistry of life.

Carbohydrate Synthesis

Early in this chapter we said that in studying photosynthesis attention should be focused on two key points: the mechanism of trapping and handling energy and the mechanism of transferring hydrogen from water to carbon dioxide. Both of these key mechanisms have now been explained in terms of ATP and $TPNH_2$. What we must still do is indicate how these two energy-rich compounds make possible the synthesis of carbohydrates from carbon dioxide.

Actually we have already discussed the reactions that are unique to photosynthetic organisms and that are the heart of photosynthesis: the synthesis of ATP and $TPNH_2$ by means of light energy. The utilization of these two key compounds in the synthesis of carbohydrate can be carried out in the dark; the dark reactions of carbohydrate synthesis are fully separable from the light-driven synthesis of ATP and $TPNH_2$ upon which they depend. One way to separate the light and dark phases of photosynthesis experimentally in both time and space is to expose a suspension of chloroplasts to light under conditions of plentiful supply of ADP, inorganic phosphate, and TPN, but absence of carbon dioxide. Under such conditions, the chloroplasts will synthesize large quantities of ATP and $TPNH_2$. If the chloroplasts are then fractionated and the solid green portion in which photophosphorylation takes place is discarded, and if carbon dioxide is added to the remaining mixture in the dark, the carbon dioxide will be assimilated into carbohydrate at the expense of the earlier-synthesized ATP and $TPNH_2$. In other words, the production of ATP and $TPNH_2$, on the one hand, and the assimilation of carbon dioxide, on the other, may occur at different times, under different conditions, and even in different parts of the chloroplasts. It can be shown, furthermore, that almost any cell, whether it contains chlorophyll or not, and whether it is from a plant or an animal, can synthesize carbohydrate from carbon dioxide if it is furnished with the necessary ATP and $TPNH_2$, which function as free-energy donor and reducing agent respectively.

Now, carbohydrate contains much chemical-bond energy, while carbon dioxide contains very little. Hence we would predict from what we have already learned about the chemistry of living cells that the reduction of carbon dioxide to form glucose proceeds by many steps, each catalyzed by an enzyme. In effect, carbon dioxide is pushed up an energy gradient through a series of intermediate compounds, some of them unstable, until the stable carbohydrate end product is formed. An analogy would be a man moving a large and very heavy piece of furniture up a flight of stairs from the first floor of his home to the second floor. The man might be able to lift the article just high enough to get it up one step at a time, balancing it on each step just long enough to marshal his strength before the next heave. If the man let go (i.e. stopped applying energy) at any point between the stable level of the first floor and the stable but higher energy

level of the second floor, the furniture would come crashing to the bottom. The steps, then, make it possible to move the furniture up an energy gradient, but they themselves are unstable intermediate levels. In this case, the energy necessary to move the furniture through the series of unstable intermediate levels to the stable high energy level at the top is supplied by the man. In the case of synthesis of carbohydrate from carbon dioxide, the energy comes from light via ATP and $TPNH_2$ (Fig. 4.12).

If there are many sequential steps involved in the reduction of carbon dioxide to carbohydrate, and if many of the intermediate compounds occur also in other processes leading to different end products, you may well wonder how the exact sequence of steps could be discovered. The tool that made such discoveries possible was a radioactive isotope of carbon, designated C^{14}. This isotope was first found about 1940 by Samuel Ruben and Martin D. Kamen at the University of California at Berkeley. They immediately recognized its potential as a tool in research on photosynthesis, and showed that plants exposed to carbon dioxide containing the radioactive isotope ($C^{14}O_2$ instead of the normal $C^{12}O_2$) incorporated the isotope into a variety of compounds. Later, in 1946, Melvin Calvin and his associates at the University of California at Berkeley began an intensive long-term investigation of carbon dioxide fixation in photosynthesis, utilizing C^{14} as their principal tool. They exposed algal cells to light in an atmosphere of $C^{14}O_2$ for a few seconds and then killed the cells by immersing them in alcohol. The alcohol not only killed the cells but also inactivated the enzymes that catalyze the reactions of photosynthesis. With the enzymes inactivated, whatever amount of each intermediate compound existed in the cell at the moment of inactivation was, in effect, locked in. Calvin and his co-workers could then determine which of these locked-in intermediate compounds contained C^{14}. The length of time during which the algal cells were exposed to the $C^{14}O_2$ before being killed determined

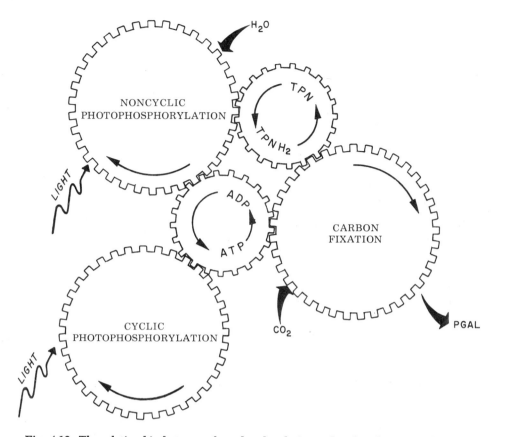

Fig. 4.12. The relationship between photophosphorylation and carbon fixation. The entire photosynthetic process can be visualized as a series of interlocking gears. Energy from light turns the two photophosphorylation gears. The turning of the cyclic-photophosphorylation gear causes the gear of ATP synthesis to turn, and the turning of the noncyclic-photophosphorylation gear causes both the ATP-synthesis and the TPNH$_2$-synthesis gears to turn. These two gears cause the carbon-fixation gear to turn, with resultant production of carbohydrate (PGAL) from CO$_2$.

the number of compounds in which C^{14} was detected; if the time was very short, the C^{14} would reach only the first few compounds in the photosynthetic sequence, while, if the time was longer, the isotope would have moved through more steps in the sequence and would appear in a great variety of compounds. After years of painstaking research, Calvin, who was awarded the Nobel Prize for his critically important work in 1961, worked out a sequence of reactions that we shall outline in very abbreviated form below.

It is not necessary here to discuss in detail the many reactions now believed to be involved in the reduction of carbon dioxide to glucose. Only the major steps will be mentioned briefly (Fig. 4.13). Under experimental conditions, the CO$_2$ first combines with a five-carbon compound called *ribulose.* The hypothetical six-carbon compound thus formed is promptly broken into two three-carbon molecules called phosphoglyceric acid, or PGA. Each of these three-carbon molecules of PGA is then phosphorylated by ATP. The new phosphorylated three-carbon compound thus produced is then reduced by the addition of

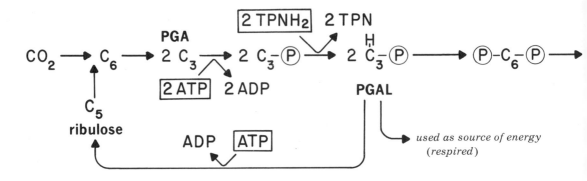

hydrogen from $TPNH_2$. The resulting energy-rich three-carbon compound is called phosphoglyceraldehyde, or *PGAL* for short. PGAL is a true sugar and is, in a sense, the stable end product of photosynthesis. Most of the molecules of PGAL are used in the formation of new ribulose (by a complicated series of reactions utilizing energy from ATP), with which more CO_2 can be processed. Some of the PGAL is used as a source of metabolic energy by the cell in which it is synthesized, and some is combined and rearranged in a series of steps to form the six-carbon sugar glucose, which is traditionally considered the end product of photosynthesis.

The glucose molecules, once synthesized, may be broken down to yield energy for the doing of work, or they may be used as raw material for synthesis of other classes of compounds such as fats, or they may be bonded together to form more complex carbohydrates such as sucrose or starch. The double sugar sucrose constitutes the form in which carbohydrate is most frequently transported in the vascular tissue of plants. Starch is the most common storage form of carbohydrate in higher plants. There are obvious advantages in storing carbohydrate as insoluble starch rather than soluble sugar. One of the most important is that starch, not being in solution, has much less osmotic activity than sugar, which is in solution. An excessive accumulation of sugar in cellular cytoplasm would raise the osmotic pressure of the cytoplasm to a very

high level and severely upset the osmotic balance between the cells and the surrounding fluid, with resulting excess uptake of water by the cells.

It is important to stress that the above-outlined sequence of reactions for carbon dioxide reduction to carbohydrate should not be accepted as definitive in all particulars (if, indeed, anything in science should ever be accepted as definitive). Changes in the scheme will almost certainly have to be made as more research results are obtained. Very likely, alternative pathways for the carbon will be found; it is rare indeed, as is becoming increasingly clear, that a particular end result can be accomplished through only one chemical pathway in a living system. Recent evidence already suggests that in living algal cells, as opposed to isolated enzyme systems, at least some of the carbon dioxide is directly reduced at the same time that it combines with the initial acceptor molecule (which may or may not always be ribulose, as postulated in Calvin's scheme), instead of forming PGA and then being reduced to PGAL several steps later, as shown in Fig. 4.13. In short, our discussion of the biochemical pathways by which photosynthesis is accomplished in the living cells of green plants should be regarded as no more than a model, a summary of the current state of our knowledge. Our account is probably accurate as to the general types of reactions involved in photosynthesis, but all details remain open to question.

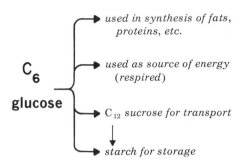

Fig. 4.13. Synthesis of carbohydrate. The CO_2 combines with ribulose, a five-carbon sugar, to form an unstable six-carbon compound, which promptly splits into two molecules of a three-carbon compound called PGA. The PGA is phosphorylated by ATP and then reduced (addition of hydrogen) by $TPNH_2$, to form PGAL, a three-carbon sugar. Much of the PGAL is used in synthesis of more ribulose by a complicated series of reactions (not shown separately here) driven by ATP. Some of the PGAL is respired. But some of the PGAL molecules are combined to form glucose, which can be used in a variety of ways by the organism.

The Leaf as an Organ of Photosynthesis

Photosynthesis is not restricted to the leaves; it occurs in all green parts of the plant. In most higher vascular plants, however, the leaves expose the greatest area of green tissue to the light and are therefore the principal organs of photosynthesis. As we briefly examine the structure of a representative leaf, always keep in mind the following question: What structural features of the leaf are of particular importance in making it an efficient organ for carrying on photosynthesis? Be sure you consider such requisites of the process as exposing large numbers of chloroplasts to sunlight and much moist cell-membrane surface to air, preventing excessive water loss, and moving the products of photosynthesis from their site of production to other parts of the plant.

Do not conclude, because our attention here will be focused on the leaves of the more advanced land plants, that only these are of importance as photosynthetic organisms. Indeed, it has been estimated that only about 10 percent of all photosynthesis is conducted by the land plants most familiar to us. The other 90 percent is carried out by algae, principally in the ocean. Many of these algae are microscopic, and all lack true leaves.

Figure 4.14 shows leaves of a variety of familiar land plants. Each dicot leaf typically consists of a stalk, or *petiole*, and a flattened *blade* (some leaves lack petioles, the blade

being sessile on the stem). In addition, some leaves bear small appendages, called stipules, at their bases. The blade is usually broad and thin and contains a complex system of veins. Because of the flatness of the blade, the leaf exposes to the light an area that is very large in relation to its volume.

If a transverse section of a leaf is examined microscopically (Fig. 4.15), the outer surfaces are seen to be formed by layers of epidermis, usually only one cell thick, but sometimes two, three, or more cells thick. A waxy layer, the *cuticle,* usually covers the outer surfaces of both the upper and lower epidermis; it is generally thicker on the former. The chief function of the epidermis is protection of the internal tissues of the leaf from excessive water loss, from invasion by fungi, and from mechanical injury. Most epidermal cells do not contain chloroplasts.

The entire region between the upper and lower epidermis contains parenchyma cells, which constitute the *mesophyll* portion of the leaf. The mesophyll is commonly divided into two fairly distinct parts: an upper *palisade* mesophyll consisting of cylindrical cells arranged vertically and a lower *spongy* mesophyll composed of irregularly shaped cells that are very loosely packed and have many intercellular spaces between them. These spaces are interconnected and communicate with the atmosphere outside the leaf by way of holes in the epidermis called *stomata.* The size of the stomatal openings is regulated by a pair

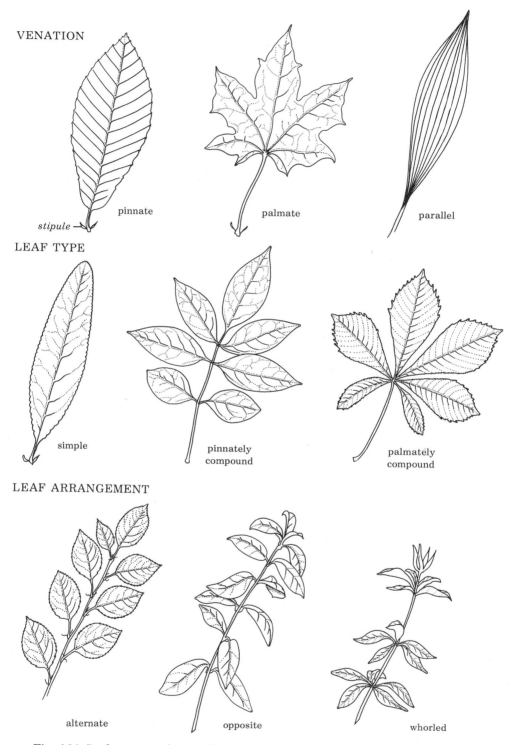

VENATION

pinnate palmate parallel

stipule

LEAF TYPE

simple pinnately compound palmately compound

LEAF ARRANGEMENT

alternate opposite whorled

Fig. 4.14. Leaf types. A leaf usually consists of a blade and a petiole, and sometimes stipules at the base of the petiole. Veins run from the petiole into the blade. The main veins may be parallel; or they may branch in succession off the midvein (pinnate venation); or they may branch together from the base of the blade (palmate venation). The blade may be simple, or it may be compound, i.e. divided into leaflets that may be pinnately or palmately arranged. The leaves may be attached to the stem in alternate, opposite, or whorled arrangements.

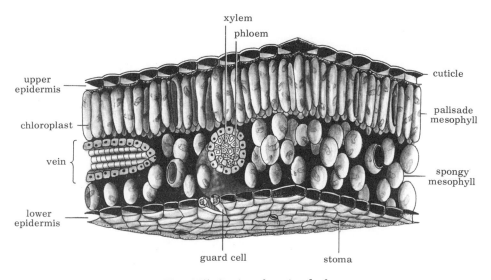

Fig. 4.15. Section of a privet leaf.

of modified epidermal cells called **guard cells.**

A rather conspicuous system of veins branches into the leaf blade from the petiole (Fig. 4.14). The veins form a structural framework for the blade and also act as transport pathways connecting the leaf with the transport system of the rest of the plant. Each vein contains cells of each of the two principal vascular tissues, xylem and phloem. In most cases, the veins branch profusely within the mesophyll tissues, with the result that no mesophyll cell is far removed from a veinlet.

The chloroplasts are located primarily in the cells of the mesophyll layers (Fig. 4.16). The chlorophyll is not simply distributed at random within the chloroplasts, but is arranged in a very precise and orderly fashion within lamellae. The lamellae, in turn, are embedded in a colorless protein matrix called the stroma (see the more complete description on p. 82 and in Fig. 3.27). In many parts of the chloroplasts of higher plants, numerous lamellae lie very close to each other, forming structures called grana, each of which has the appearance of a stack of coins (Fig. 4.17). Each lamella is basically a specialized unit membrane composed of a series of layers of protein, lipid, and

chlorophyll (Fig. 4.18). Although the general structure and appearance of the lamellar unit membranes are like those of the unit membranes of other parts of the cell, recent chemical analyses have indicated that most of the lipids, and probably the proteins, in the lamellae are of types found only there. Thus the chemical composition of the lamellar unit membranes mirrors the uniqueness of the photosynthetic function of these structures. The "light" reactions of photosynthesis (i.e. those of cyclic and noncyclic photophosphorylation) take place primarily in the lamellae, particularly those of the grana (except that ferredoxin is in the stroma, not the lamellae). The "dark" reactions of photosynthesis (i.e. those of carbon dioxide assimilation) take place in the more fluid stroma. As we have mentioned earlier, the stroma can continue to perform its carbon-assimilation function even after it has been physically separated from the lamellae by disruption of the chloroplasts; it is only necessary to ensure that the stroma has an adequate supply of CO_2, ATP, and $TPNH_2$.

There is considerable evidence that the individual molecules of chlorophyll in the lamellae do not function independently, but in-

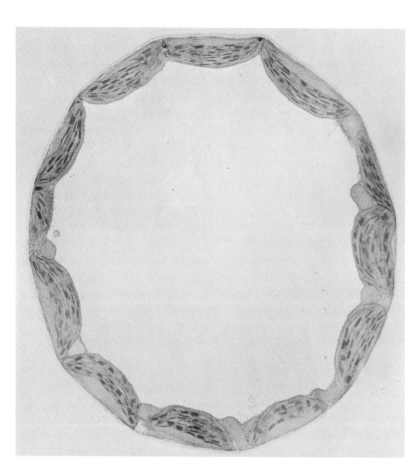

Fig. 4.16. Electron micrograph of cross section of a palisade cell from mesophyll of a tobacco leaf. The numerous chloroplasts almost completely fill the peripherally distributed cytoplasm. The large central area is the cell vacuole. ×5,360. [Courtesy Herbert W. Israel, Cornell University.]

Fig. 4.17. Electron micrograph of a granum from a chloroplast of tobacco. The lamellae in the granum are arranged like stacks of coins. Stroma lamellae run between the grana. The small dark spots in the stroma are ribosomes that were present inside the chloroplast. × 200,-000. [Courtesy Herbert W. Israel, Cornell University.]

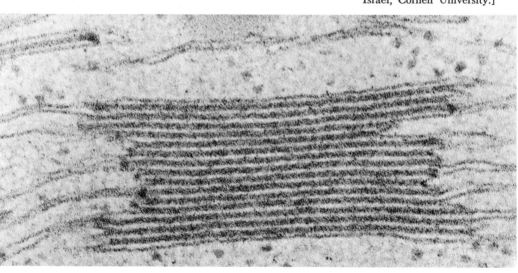

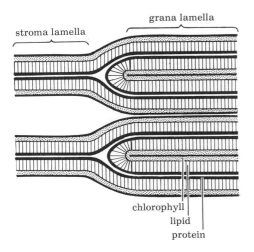

Fig. 4.18. Diagram of lamellar structure. Black layers, protein; stippled layers, chlorophyll; lined layers, lipid. [Modified from A. J. Hodge *et al.*, *J. Biophys. Biochem. Cytol.*, vol. 1, 1955.]

stead act in groups estimated to consist of as many as 200–400 or more chlorophyll molecules. Each such working group has been termed a photosynthetic unit; since light energy can presumably be passed from one pigment molecule to another within this unit, the chlorophyll molecule that actually loses its electron to ferredoxin may not be the one first activated by light. Recent electron-microscope studies of shadowed lamellae of chloroplasts have revealed that the inner surface of the lamellar membrane is not smooth, as was formerly thought, but instead shows a regular pattern of repeating structures with a granular, often spherical, appearance. These unit granular structures are called quantasomes, and many workers have speculated that they may be the structural expression of the functional photosynthetic units. Measurements of the quantasomes and studies of their chemical composition indicate that one quantasome may contain approximately 230 chlorophyll molecules, which puts the quantasome within the size range earlier estimated for the photosynthetic unit. It has not yet been demonstrated

conclusively, however, that the quantasome and the photosynthetic unit are the same thing, but if they should prove to be, it would be very satisfying to biologists, because the concept that structure and function are two sides of the same coin is both an intellectually appealing and an experimentally productive principle of biology.

Each chloroplast contains all the electron-carrier molecules and enzymes necessary for photosynthesis, and chloroplasts isolated from the rest of the cell can still carry out the complete photosynthetic process. Before 1954 it was thought that they could not, and even some recent textbooks maintain that complete photosynthesis, including carbohydrate production, cannot be expected to occur in experiments that do not involve whole living cells. This older idea dates particularly from work done in 1937 by R. Hill of Cambridge University, England, who removed chloroplasts from cells and then showed that they could perform only a part of photosynthesis; they could not assimilate carbon dioxide, but they could produce oxygen from water in the light if they were provided with a chemical that could act as a very strong electron acceptor. Hill's technique of providing illuminated isolated chloroplasts, or fragments of chloroplasts, with a strong electron acceptor (such as a ferric salt or a reducible organic dye) and then studying factors such as temperature, pH, etc. that influenced oxygen production from water by the chloroplasts became an important research approach. If we designate the artificially provided, nonphysiological electron acceptor as X, we can summarize the so-called Hill reaction by the following equation:

$$2\,X + 2H_2O + light \xrightarrow{\text{chloroplast}} 2\,H_2X + O_2$$

As long as X is continuously supplied (and other conditions are properly controlled), chloroplasts will produce oxygen from water in the light at nearly the same rate as a whole green cell.

How is it, in view of the evidence accumulated since 1954 that isolated chloroplasts can perform complete photosynthesis, that hundreds of research workers using variants of the Hill reaction over a period of about seventeen years remained convinced that isolated chloroplasts could not assimilate carbon dioxide? The answer apparently lies in the procedure used, and provides a good example of how minor, seemingly irrelevant details of technique may radically alter experimental results. The enzymes that fix carbon dioxide are very soluble, and they were simply lost from the chloroplasts in the process of separating the chloroplasts from the cells. If the chloroplasts are isolated by more careful procedures that leave the enzyme systems of the stroma intact, a single chloroplast can act as a complete photosynthetic factory. This was a very important discovery because it demonstrated clearly that any ATP used in carbon dioxide assimilation is synthesized in the chloroplasts themselves and not provided to the chloroplasts by the mitochondria, as was formerly thought. Recognition of this fact, in turn, led to the discovery of photophosphorylation and to our modern concept of the "light" reactions of photosynthesis.

CHEMOSYNTHESIS

Some bacteria are able to synthesize high-energy organic compounds from inorganic raw materials without utilizing light energy at all! Such bacteria oxidize inorganic compounds and trap the energy thus released. For example, one type of bacteria oxidizes ammonia (NH_4^+) as follows:

$$2NH_4^+ + 3O_2 \rightarrow$$
$$2NO_2^- + 2H_2O + 4H^+ + energy$$

Another bacterium oxidizes nitrite (NO_2^-) to nitrate (NO_3^-):

$$2NO_2^- + O_2 \rightarrow 2NO_3^- + energy$$

Still another oxidizes sulfur to sulfate:

$$2S + 3O_2 + 2H_2O \rightarrow 2SO_4^{--} + 4H^+ + energy$$

Many other examples of bacteria that oxidize various nitrogen and sulfur compounds, and even molecular hydrogen, could be cited. They share an ability to trap the small quantities of energy released by their oxidation of inorganic raw materials and to use this energy in synthesis of carbohydrate. Such organisms are called *chemosynthetic.* They are fascinating subjects for study, but their importance in the overall energy economy of nature is very small compared with that of the photosynthetic organisms. Some of the chemosynthetic bacteria that act on nitrogen compounds do, however, play an extremely important role in the movement of nitrogen within the life system, as we shall see in a later chapter.

CELLULAR RESPIRATION

Photosynthesis binds energy from solar radiation into complex organic compounds such as glucose and compounds synthesized from glucose. Before this potential energy can be utilized in the doing of work, either by the green plant itself or by some organism that has eaten the green plant, the large energy-rich molecules must be broken down chemically and the energy released. This oxidative breakdown is called *respiration;* it is a process that must occur in every living thing, and is thus a fundamental characteristic of life.

From what we have already learned in our examination of photosynthesis, we can anticipate some of the principles involved in respiration. We would expect that the breakdown does not occur as a single gross reaction, but rather as a series of smaller step-by-step reactions. We would expect that each of these reactions is catalyzed by an enzyme. And we would not be surprised to learn that the release of packets of free energy is coupled with phosphorylation reactions that synthesize ATP from ADP and inorganic phosphate.

The complete respiratory degradation of a compound such as glucose to carbon dioxide and water involves a very large number of reactions; it is not our purpose to discuss all of them here. Only the more important steps will be examined, although the others will be indicated in some of the diagrams simply to give you a clear impression of the complexity of this crucial metabolic process. The respiratory process will be discussed in two parts; the first series of reactions can take place whether or not oxygen is present, while the second series is dependent on oxygen.

Glycolysis and Fermentation

In our examination of cellular respiration, we shall concentrate first on the breakdown of carbohydrate—specifically, glucose. Glucose, as we have already seen, is a stable compound; i.e. it has little tendency to break down to simpler products. If the energy locked in its molecular configuration is to be released, it must first be made more reactive. Such a conversion requires energy expenditure by the organism. Earlier in this chapter, we mentioned the potential energy possessed by an automobile parked on a steep hill, and we saw that this potential energy could be transformed into the kinetic energy of motion if the brake were released. But the releasing of the brake requires an expenditure of energy by someone. Thus an initial energy investment precedes the major energy release that occurs when the car rolls down the hill. Such is also the case with the respiratory release of energy from glucose; a small amount of *activation energy* must be invested to initiate the process. Most exergonic chemical reactions in living things require activation energy, and the principle involved is an important one to understand.

We have already spoken of ATP as the universal "energy currency" of life, and it is therefore not unexpected that ATP should provide

the activation energy which initiates cellular respiration (Fig. 4.19). This initial reaction, like the succeeding ones, is facilitated by an enzyme, which reduces the amount of activation energy required. A molecule of ATP donates its terminal phosphate group to the glucose:

$$\underset{\text{glucose}}{C\text{–}C\text{–}C\text{–}C\text{–}C\text{–}C} + ATP \xrightarrow{\text{enzyme}}$$
$$C\text{–}C\text{–}C\text{–}C\text{–}C\text{–}C\text{–}\textcircled{P} + ADP$$

(The simplified equations given here show only the carbon skeleton, and you should bear in mind that oxygen and hydrogen are attached to the carbons; similarly, the symbol $\textcircled{P}$ is here used to represent an entire phosphate group.) When the phosphate group is transferred to glucose, some of the energy in the terminal phosphate bond of ATP is lost as heat; therefore the bond that attaches the phosphate group to the glucose is not energy-rich. After a reaction that converts the glucose-phosphate into a related six-carbon compound, another molecule of ATP donates its terminal phosphate group to the other end of the six-carbon chain, again with the loss of some energy as heat:

$$C\text{–}C\text{–}C\text{–}C\text{–}C\text{–}C\text{–}\textcircled{P} + ATP \xrightarrow{\text{enzyme}}$$
$$\textcircled{P}\text{–}C\text{–}C\text{–}C\text{–}C\text{–}C\text{–}C\text{–}\textcircled{P} + ADP$$

Next, the diphosphorylated six-carbon compound is split between the third and fourth carbons, forming two essentially similar three-carbon molecules:

$$\textcircled{P}\text{–}C\text{–}C\text{–}C\text{–}C\text{–}C\text{–}C\text{–}\textcircled{P} \xrightarrow{\text{enzyme}}$$
$$\textcircled{P}\text{–}C\text{–}C\text{–}C + C\text{–}C\text{–}C\text{–}\textcircled{P}$$

The three-carbon compound is one we have encountered before; it is PGAL, which you will recall as a major product of photosynthesis. The photosynthetic process involved synthesis of glucose from PGAL; so far, then, respiration has been the exact reverse of photosynthesis. And so far, instead of releasing energy from the carbohydrate and forming new ATP molecules, respiration has actually resulted in the loss of two molecules of ATP used as activation energy.

The next reaction is a rather complicated one. A molecule of inorganic phosphate is added to each of the two molecules of PGAL, and two atoms of hydrogen are removed from each molecule of PGAL. The hydrogen (a total of four atoms) is moved to acceptor molecules of diphosphopyridine nucleotide, commonly abbreviated **DPN** (also frequently called nicotinamide adenine dinucleotide and abbreviated NAD). (DPN, as its name indicates, is extremely similar to TPN, a hydrogen acceptor already encountered in photosynthesis.) The removal of the hydrogen from the PGAL (an oxidation reaction) has the effect of concentrating energy in the new phosphate bonds and converting them from energy-poor into energy-rich bonds. All of this can be summarized as follows:

$$2\ \textcircled{P}\text{--C--C--C} + 2\ \textcircled{P} + 2\ \text{DPN} \xrightarrow{\text{enzyme}}$$
$$2\ \textcircled{P}\text{--C--C--C}\sim\textcircled{P} + 2\ \text{DPNH}_2$$

Next, the two energy-rich phosphate groups are transferred to ADP, forming two ATP molecules:

$$2\ \textcircled{P}\text{--C--C--C}\sim\textcircled{P} + 2\ \text{ADP} \xrightarrow{\text{enzyme}}$$
$$2\ \textcircled{P}\text{--C--C--C} + 2\ \text{ATP}$$

Fig. 4.19. Glycolysis and fermentation. Activation energy for oxidation of glucose is supplied by two molecules of ATP. The resulting compound is then split into two molecules of PGAL. The PGAL is oxidized by removal of hydrogen, which is picked up by DPN to form two molecules of DPNH_2. A series of reactions then result in synthesis of four new molecules of ATP, for a net gain of two. The pyruvic acid produced by this anaerobic breakdown can be further oxidized if O_2 is present (by reactions not shown here). But in the absence of sufficient O_2, the pyruvic acid may accept hydrogen from DPNH_2 (reactions below dotted line) to form CO_2 and ethyl alcohol in most plants and many microorganisms or lactic acid in animals and some microorganisms. For fuller explanation, see text.

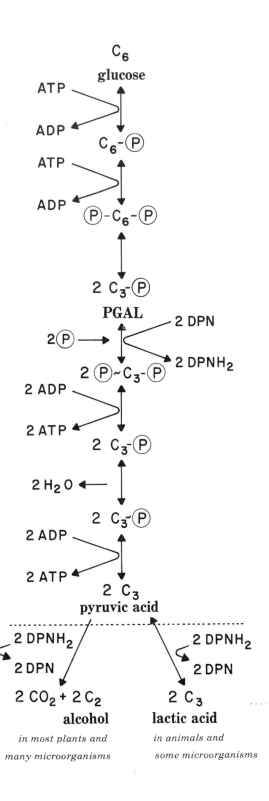

Then follow several reactions that result in concentrating energy in the remaining phosphate bonds, converting them into energy-rich bonds:

$$2 \; ⓟ\text{–C–C–C} \xrightarrow{\text{enzyme}} 2 \; ⓟ\sim\text{C–C–C} + 2H_2O$$

These energy-rich phosphate bonds are in turn transferred to ADP, forming two more ATP molecules:

$$2 \; ⓟ\sim\text{C–C–C} + 2 \text{ ADP} \xrightarrow{\text{enzyme}}$$
$$\underset{\text{pyruvic acid}}{2 \text{ C–C–C}} + 2 \text{ ATP}$$

The oxidation of carbohydrate to **pyruvic acid** by the pathway just described is called **glycolysis**.[3] This process can occur whether or not oxygen is present, because no molecular oxygen is used; it is frequently termed anaerobic respiration.[4] We can summarize the results of glycolysis as follows:

1. The breakdown of a molecule of glucose (a six-carbon compound) to two molecules of pyruvic acid (a three-carbon compound).
2. The use of two molecules of ATP as activation energy and the synthesis of four new molecules of ATP, for a *net* gain of two molecules of ATP.
3. The production of two molecules of DPNH$_2$.

---

[3] Some workers insist on restricting the term "glycolysis" to the anaerobic oxidation of glycogen to lactic acid. It is true, of course, that "glycolysis" is derived from "glycogen," but restriction of the term to the breakdown of only one carbohydrate by muscle tissue obscures the more general nature of the process. And to insist on lactic acid as the end product tends to confuse glycolysis with lactic acid fermentation, while also obscuring the more general nature of the pathway to pyruvic acid. Consequently we have followed the common practice of using the word "glycolysis" for this important chemical pathway, regardless of the carbohydrate with which it begins. We have taken glucose as the starting point for simplicity's sake, and because this compound is of more general occurrence than glycogen in both plants and animals.

[4] There is a recent tendency to restrict the term "respiration" to the aerobic components of the oxidative process. The older practice of referring to glycolysis as anaerobic respiration is followed in this book to emphasize that both the anaerobic and aerobic processes are components of the overall oxidation of food molecules.

If no oxygen is present, i.e. if the conditions are anaerobic, pyruvic acid formed by glycolysis will accept the hydrogen from DPNH$_2$, freeing the DPN for further use as a hydrogen acceptor and enabling glycolysis to continue. This addition of hydrogen to pyruvic acid results in the formation of **lactic acid** (a three-carbon compound) in animal cells and some unicellular organisms or in the formation of **ethyl alcohol** (a two-carbon compound) and carbon dioxide in plant cells and in many unicellular organisms:

$$\text{pyruvic acid} + \text{DPNH}_2 \xrightarrow{\text{enzyme}}$$
$$\text{lactic acid} + \text{DPN}$$

or

$$\text{pyruvic acid} + \text{DPNH}_2 \xrightarrow{\text{enzyme}}$$
$$\text{alcohol} + CO_2 + \text{DPN}$$

The process whereby the glycolytic pathway leads to production of alcohol or lactic acid from pyruvic acid is called **fermentation**.[5] We can thus speak of alcoholic fermentation or lactic acid fermentation, depending upon the end product formed by the process. (In a few organisms, fermentation forms products other than alcohol or lactic acid, but these are of less general importance and will not be discussed here.) Fermentation by yeast cells and other microorganisms is, of course, the basis for the extensive and economically vital fermentation industry.

---

[5] The term "fermentation" has been used in countless ways in the scientific literature. It is frequently restricted to the breakdown of glucose to alcohol, the breakdown of glucose to lactic acid being ignored. At other times, it is applied to the production of either alcohol or lactic acid by microorganisms, lactic acid production in animal cells being called glycolysis. Both of these uses lead to confusion between the terms "fermentation" and "glycolysis," and both tend to obscure the general occurrence of the same basic fermentation process in all living cells. Accordingly, "fermentation" is here applied to the process of production of alcohol or lactic acid, whether by plant, animal, or microorganism, and the glycolytic pathway is considered both as a preparatory reaction sequence leading to the Krebs citric acid cycle when sufficient oxygen is present and as the initial portion of fermentation in the absence of sufficient oxygen (a few microorganisms carry out fermentation in the presence of abundant oxygen).

The Cytochrome Carrier System

In our discussion of glycolysis and fermentation, we stressed the fact that in the absence of oxygen the hydrogen is unloaded from $DPNH_2$ by being passed to pyruvic acid, DPN being thus freed for further use in the respiration of more glucose molecules. Let us now find out what happens if oxygen is present, i.e. if the conditions are aerobic.

In this case, the $DPNH_2$ molecules are not forced to donate hydrogen to pyruvic acid. Instead, molecular oxygen can act as the ultimate hydrogen acceptor, and water is formed:

$$O_2 + 2\,DPNH_2 \rightarrow 2H_2O + 2\,DPN$$

The $DPNH_2$ does not, however, pass its hydrogen directly to the oxygen, as this summary equation might seem to indicate. Rather, the hydrogen is passed down a "respiratory chain" composed of a series of carrier compounds, most of which are cytochromes (Fig. 4.20). In this manner, the hydrogen is lowered step by step from its high energy level in $DPNH_2$ to a low energy level in H_2O. As the hydrogen is lowered down the energy gradient step by step through the cytochrome carrier system, energy is released, and this energy is used in the synthesis of ATP from ADP and inorganic phosphate. This process, often called *oxidative phosphorylation,* is very similar to the electron transport and ATP synthesis of photophosphorylation, which we have already discussed.

In both photo- and oxidative phosphorylation, some of the free energy released during the flow of electrons from a high-energy electron donor to an electron acceptor is used in ATP synthesis. A basic difference, however, between the two processes is that the overall effect of photophosphorylation is an increase in the amount of stored free energy within the organism, the additional energy input coming from light, while the overall effect of oxidative phosphorylation is a decrease in the amount of stored free energy within the organism because the process cannot be thermodynamically 100 percent efficient.

It can be shown that for every two hydrogens (actually electrons) moved through the respiratory carrier system from $DPNH_2$ to H_2O, three new ATP molecules are synthesized. Since two molecules of $DPNH_2$ were formed in the breakdown of glucose to pyruvic acid, it follows that six ATP molecules can be formed when the hydrogen of the two $DPNH_2$ molecules is moved to oxygen via the carrier system. Thus we see that in the absence of oxygen the respiration of a molecule of glucose to pyruvic acid yields a gain of only two ATP molecules, but that in the presence of oxygen the same breakdown yields a gain of eight ATP molecules (the two produced anaerobically plus the six formed by hydrogen transport).

Since under aerobic conditions the pyruvic acid does not have to act as a hydrogen ac-

Fig. 4.20. The cytochrome electron-transport system. Hydrogen removed from the substances being oxidized during cellular respiration is picked up by DPN, TPN, or other acceptor molecules and transported to the cytochrome system, where it is passed from one acceptor substance to the next, step by step down an energy gradient, until it is finally combined with O_2 to form water. Some of the energy released as the hydrogen electrons are lowered down the energy gradient is used in the synthesis of ATP from ADP and inorganic phosphate. During the complete oxidation of one molecule of glucose, a total of 24 hydrogens are transported through this system (4 from glycolysis, 4 from oxidation of pyruvic acid to acetyl-CoA, and 16 from the Krebs citric acid cycle). A total of three molecules of ATP are synthesized for every two hydrogens that enter the system via DPN or TPN. Since 20 of the 24 hydrogens enter in this manner, the result is a total of 30 ATP molecules ($20/2 \times 3$). Four of the 16 hydrogens from the Krebs cycle enter the system in a different manner and yield only two ATP's for every two hydrogens, for a total of four. Thus a grand total of 34 new ATP molecules are synthesized as a result of hydrogen transport during the complete oxidation of one molecule of glucose.

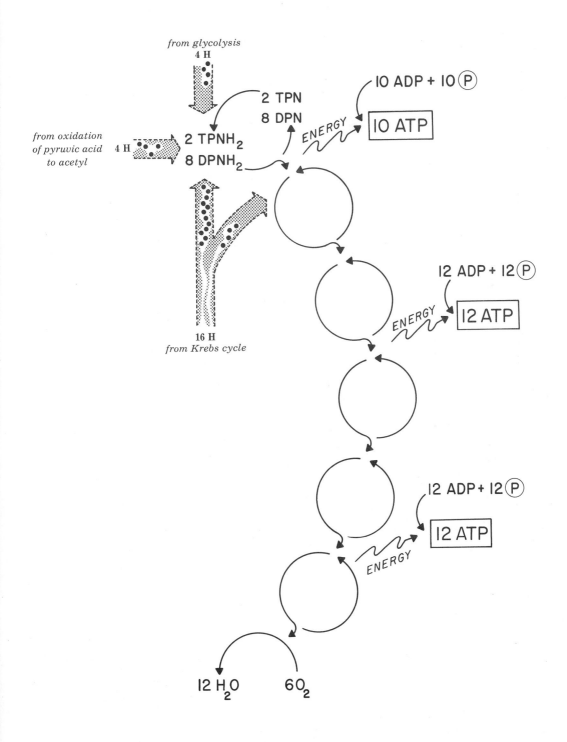

from glycolysis
4 H

2 TPN
8 DPN

10 ADP + 10 $\textcircled{P}$

*from oxidation
of pyruvic acid
to acetyl* **4 H**

2 TPNH$_2$
8 DPNH$_2$

ENERGY

10 ATP

16 H
from Krebs cycle

12 ADP + 12 $\textcircled{P}$

ENERGY

12 ATP

12 ADP + 12 $\textcircled{P}$

12 ATP

ENERGY

12 H$_2$O   6 O$_2$

ceptor and need not be converted into lactic acid or alcohol, it is free to be oxidized further. Similarly, if lactic acid has already been formed, it may be converted back into pyruvic acid, with the accompanying resynthesis of DPNH$_2$, when oxygen becomes available; the pyruvic acid thus formed may be used as raw material for resynthesis of carbohydrate, or it may be further oxidized aerobically. This further oxidation of pyruvic acid, described below, involves the removal of more hydrogen and the formation of many more molecules of DPNH$_2$. These DPNH$_2$ molecules, like those already discussed, pass their hydrogen to the cytochrome carrier system, with the result that more ATP molecules are synthesized by this system.

The Krebs Citric Acid Cycle

The aerobic oxidation of pyruvic acid begins with a complicated group of reactions that have the net effect of breaking down the three-carbon pyruvic acid to carbon dioxide and an activated form of the two-carbon compound acetic acid. We say the acetic acid is activated because it is not present as free acetic acid, but is bonded to a coenzyme called coenzyme A, or CoA for short; the complete compound is called *acetyl-CoA*. When a molecule of pyruvic acid is oxidized to acetyl-CoA and carbon dioxide, hydrogen is removed, and a molecule of DPNH$_2$ is formed. Since two molecules of

pyruvic acid were formed from each glucose molecule, two molecules of DPNH$_2$ are formed here. This complicated series of reactions can be summarized by the following equation:

$$2 \text{ pyruvic acid} + 2 \text{ CoA} + 2 \text{ DPN} \rightarrow$$
$$2 \text{ acetyl-CoA} + 2\text{CO}_2 + 2 \text{ DPNH}_2$$

The two DPNH$_2$ molecules then donate their hydrogen to the respiratory chain that we have called the cytochrome carrier system. As we have already seen, three molecules of ATP are formed for every two hydrogens carried down the system from DPNH$_2$; hence six more ATP molecules are synthesized at this point.

The acetyl-CoA is next fed into a complex circular series of reactions called the Krebs citric acid cycle (after the British scientist Sir Hans Krebs, who was awarded a Nobel Prize for his elucidation of this system). This cycle is shown in some detail in Fig. 4.21; its essential features are outlined in Fig. 4.22. Briefly, each of the two-carbon acetyl-CoA molecules formed from one molecule of glucose is combined with a four-carbon compound already present to form a new six-carbon compound called *citric acid.* Each of the citric acid molecules is then oxidized to a five-carbon compound and carbon dioxide. The five-carbon unit, in turn, is oxidized to a four-carbon compound and carbon dioxide. This four-carbon compound is then converted into the same four-carbon compound as the one to which acetyl-CoA was originally attached; it can now

Fig. 4.21. The Krebs citric acid cycle. The complete cycle is shown here simply to help you appreciate the complexity that characterizes many metabolic pathways; there is no point in your trying to learn all the reactions involved. The acetyl group (2 carbons) from acetyl-CoA is fed into the cycle by being combined with oxaloacetic acid (4 carbons) to form citric acid (6 carbons), as shown in the upper left of the figure. During the sequence of reactions in the cycle, two of the carbons are removed as CO$_2$ (between oxalosuccinic acid and α-ketoglutaric acid, and between α-ketoglutaric acid and succinyl-CoA), and a total of 8 hydrogens is removed (boxes). This hydrogen is picked up by DPN or some other acceptor molecule and fed into the cytochrome system. One molecule of ATP is synthesized at substrate level in the cycle (box). Finally, oxaloacetic acid is regenerated and can combine with a new acetyl group to start the cycle over again. The cycle is completed twice for each molecule of glucose oxidized. Black arrows indicate principal reactions, white arrows indicate water and cofactors fed into the cycle, and stippled arrows indicate substances removed during the cycle. The atoms removed at each step are shown in boldface in the structural formulas.

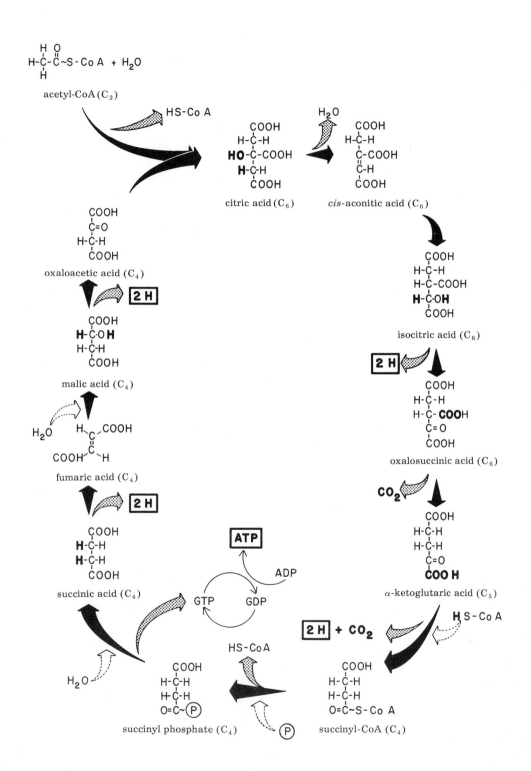

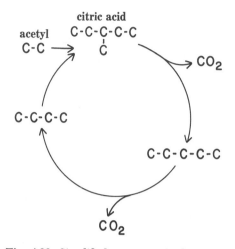

Fig. 4.22. Simplified version of the Krebs citric acid cycle. The two carbons of the acetyl group combine with a four-carbon compound to form citric acid, a six-carbon compound. Then one carbon is removed as CO_2, leaving a five-carbon compound. Then another carbon is removed as CO_2, leaving a four-carbon compound, which can combine with another acetyl group and start the cycle over again. Since one molecule of glucose gives rise to two acetyl units, two turns of the cycle occur for each molecule of glucose oxidized.

pick up more acetyl-CoA, forming new citric acid and beginning the cycle again.

The oxidative breakdown of each molecule of acetyl-CoA via the Krebs citric acid cycle involves the removal of much hydrogen and makes possible the synthesis of 12 molecules of ATP, or a total of 24 for the two acetyl-CoA molecules formed in the respiration of one glucose molecule. All but two of the 24 ATP molecules are produced by the cytochrome system, the hydrogen having been picked up by DPN (or the closely related TPN or other similar compounds) and then moved down the cytochrome system. The other two ATP molecules are synthesized within the Krebs cycle itself by a process called substrate-level phosphorylation.[6]

Summary of the ATP Yield of the Respiration of Glucose

We can summarize the yield of ATP molecules from the complete cellular respiration of one molecule of glucose to carbon dioxide and water as follows (Fig. 4.23):

1. A grand total of 38 ATP molecules are formed. This means that about 50–60 percent of the energy initially present in the glucose has been trapped; the rest has been lost as heat and entropy. An efficiency of 50–60 percent[7] is remarkably good for an energy-transforming system; most engines fall far below this mark.

2. Only two of the 38 ATP molecules are synthesized anaerobically; the other 36 are the product of aerobic respiration. We now see why oxygen is essential to the life of human beings and most other organisms. The importance of the anaerobic processes of glycolysis and fermentation should not be overlooked, however. Many microorganisms rely exclusively on fermentation for their energy. Our own tissues, particularly our muscles during violent activity, often need so much energy so fast that the oxygen supplied from breathing is insufficient. Under such circumstances, glycolysis provides the needed energy. Later, the oxygen debt is paid back by deep breathing or

---

[6] Substrate-level phosphorylation is the addition of inorganic phosphate to a substance being oxidized, followed by formation of an energy-rich phosphate bond in the oxidized product. The energy-rich phosphate group may then be transferred to ADP to form ATP.

[7] The efficiency figures given by different texts vary considerably, ranging from a low of 40 percent to a high of 70 percent. These discrepancies occur largely because of disagreement as to the exact energy content of ATP; what's more, there is no complete accord on the number of ATP molecules yielded by the complete respiration of one molecule of glucose, some workers claiming that this number is 40 rather than 38. The free-energy content of a gram molecule of glucose is about 686 kg.-calories. If we assume that the energy content of the terminal phosphate bonds of a gram molecule of ATP is 10 kg.-calories, and if 38 gram molecules of ATP are formed per gram molecule of glucose, then approximately 55.4 percent of the free energy initially present in the glucose has been trapped in the terminal high-energy phosphate bonds of the ATP. It is known that any overall efficiency value obtained represents a combination of two rather different efficiency values, that for glycolysis being considerably lower than the overall value and that for aerobic respiration being higher.

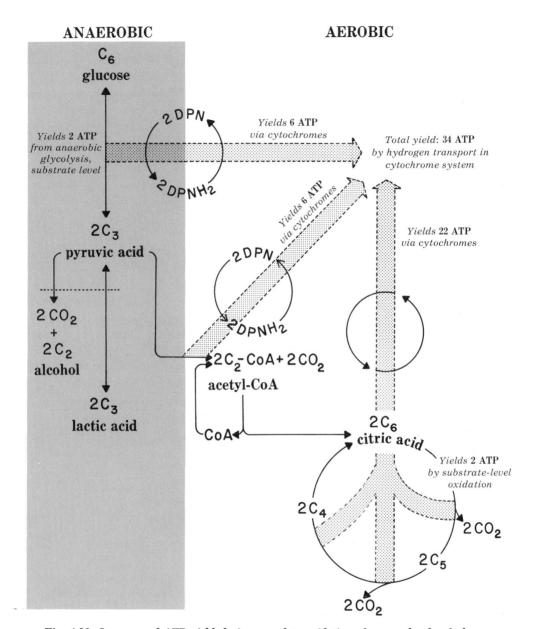

Fig. 4.23. Summary of ATP yield during complete oxidation of one molecule of glucose. If conditions are completely anaerobic, there is a net gain of only two ATP molecules, which are formed at substrate level. Under such conditions, the pyruvic acid must accept hydrogen from the $DPNH_2$ synthesized during glycolysis, and either alcoholic fermentation or lactic acid fermentation results. But if O_2 is present, the $DPNH_2$ may pass its hydrogen to the cytochrome system and ultimately to O_2 to form water. Thus the pyruvic acid may be further oxidized aerobically, yielding much more ATP. Of the grand total of 38 new ATP molecules formed by complete oxidation of glucose, 34 are formed via hydrogen-electron transport through the cytochrome system. The other four are formed at substrate level, two during the anaerobic reactions of glycolysis and two during the reactions of the Krebs citric acid cycle.

panting, and the lactic acid, which accumulated in the muscles as a result of glycolysis and fermentation, and which in excess contributes to muscle fatigue, is removed.

3. Of the 36 aerobically synthesized ATP molecules, 34 result from hydrogen transport via DPN (or similar electron acceptors) and the cytochrome system. It is thus evident that this system is of critical importance, and it is easy to understand why cyanide and certain other poisons that block the cytochrome system are so lethal.

Respiration of Fats and Proteins

Metabolism of fats begins with their hydrolysis to glycerol and fatty acids. The glycerol (a three-carbon compound) is then converted into PGAL and fed into the glycolytic pathway at the point where PGAL normally appears. The fatty acids are broken down into a number of two-carbon fragments, which are converted into acetyl-CoA and fed into the respiratory pathway at the appropriate point. Since fats are more completely reduced compounds than carbohydrates, their complete oxidation yields more energy per unit weight; one gram of fat yields slightly more than twice as much energy as one gram of carbohydrate.

The amino acids produced by hydrolysis of proteins are metabolized in a variety of ways. After the amino group is removed (deamination), some amino acids are converted into pyruvic acid, some into acetyl-CoA, and some into several different compounds of the citric acid cycle. Complete oxidation of a gram of protein yields roughly the same amount of energy as one gram of carbohydrate.

Since many of the respiratory reactions are reversible, such compounds as pyruvic acid, acetyl-CoA, and the compounds of the citric acid cycle, which are common to the metabolism of several different types of substances, not only play a crucial role in the oxidation of energy-rich compounds to carbon dioxide and

water, but they also function as important intermediates in interconversions between various types of compounds, serving as carbon skeletons from which a variety of substances can be synthesized.

Mitochondria

The precise and intricate nature of the reaction chains of cellular respiration would lead us to suspect that the enzymatic factors involved are not simply mixed randomly in the cellular cytoplasm. It is now clear that aerobic respiration is confined to the mitochondria—cellular structures already mentioned in the chapter on cells. The electron microscope, you will recall, shows that each mitochondrion has a wall composed of an outer and an inner membrane separated by a space filled with a watery fluid, and that the inner membrane has a series of folds, or cristae, which project into the lumen of the mitochondrion (Fig. 4.24). Recently, electron micrographs made at very high resolution by Humberto Fernández-Morán of the University of Chicago have revealed that the outside surface of the outer membrane and the inside surface of the inner membrane are covered with vast numbers of small particles. The particles on the inner membrane usually, but not always, consist of three parts: a spherical knoblike head, a cylindrical stalk, and a base piece to which the stalk attaches. The particles on the outer membrane are simpler and stalkless.

The evidence to date indicates that the particles are probably the physical units within which the various chemical functions of the mitochondria are performed. Apparently the oxidation reactions of the Krebs cycle occur in the particles on the outer membrane, while the reactions of the cytochrome electron-transfer system, which yield most of the ATP, occur in the particles on the inner membrane. DPN (and other electron acceptors similar to it) serves as the transport mechanism between the

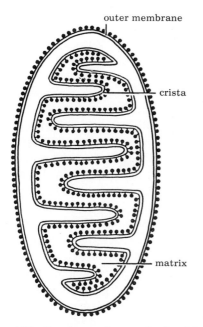

outer membrane

crista

matrix

Fig. 4.24. Structure of a mitochondrion. The outer surface of the outer membrane and the inner surface of the inner membrane are apparently covered with small particles that play an important role in oxidative metabolism.

BODY TEMPERATURE AND METABOLIC RATE

We have seen that cellular respiration is remarkably efficient at capturing the energy released by the oxidation of carbohydrates, fats, and proteins and converting it into the energy of the high-energy phosphate bonds of ATP. But efficient as it is, it nevertheless fails to capture between 40 and 60 percent of the released energy. A small amount of this energy is in the form of entropy and is useless, but most of the remainder is in the form of heat. The vast majority of animals and all plants promptly lose most of this heat energy to their environments; thus roughly half the energy from the food molecules such organisms oxidize is lost without appreciably benefiting them. Animals for which this is true are frequently said to be cold-blooded; a better term is *poikilothermic,* i.e. of variable temperature. Being determined by the environmental temperature, their body temperature is very nearly the same as that of the surrounding medium when they are at rest, particularly if the medium is water.

The metabolism[8] of an organism is very closely tied to temperature. Within the narrow range of temperatures to which the active organism is tolerant, the metabolic rate increases with increasing temperature and decreases with decreasing temperature in a very regular fashion. The relationship between metabolic rate and temperature is often expressed in terms of a value called the Q_{10}. This value is a measure of the rate increase for each 10°C rise in temperature. Thus if the rate doubles for each 10° rise in temperature, the Q_{10} is said to be 2; if the rate triples for each 10° rise, the Q_{10} is said to be 3; etc. Metabolic rates frequently have a Q_{10} of about 2. Let us sup-

two sets of particles, picking up the hydrogen (electrons) released by the reactions in the outer particles and ferrying it across the fluid-filled space between the two membranes to the inner particles.

The particles, like the other parts of the membrane, are composed of proteins and lipids (primarily phospholipids). It can be demonstrated that both of these materials are essential to the function of the inner particles. The proteins serve as components of the electron-transfer system itself, and are arranged in a very precise structural order. The lipids provide a medium essential for the transfer of electrons between component complexes. Both the proteins and the lipids are also, of course, essential structural elements of the particles, and serve as another example of the principle of the complementarity of structure and function.

[8] Metabolism means the chemical reactions of the body, both those, like respiration, that break down materials and those that build up complex molecules and structures.

pose that the metabolic rate of a given animal at 0°C is denoted by X. If the metabolic rate of this animal has a Q_{10} of 2, then at 10°C the rate will be denoted by 2X, at 20° it will be 4X, at 30° it will be 8X, and at 40° it will be 16X. Notice that the rate increases more and more rapidly as the temperature increases; when represented graphically, as in Fig. 4.25, this type of exponential increase produces a curve that becomes steeper and steeper as the temperature rises.

As would be expected, the activity of poikilothermic animals is radically affected by temperature changes in their environment. As the temperature rises (within narrow limits), they become more active; as the temperature falls, they become sluggish and lethargic. Such animals, then, are restricted as to the habitats they can effectively occupy, because they are at the mercy of the temperatures in those habitats.

A few animals, the mammals and birds, have evolved a mechanism that makes them much less dependent upon environmental tempera-

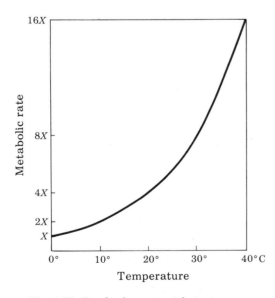

Fig. 4.25. Graph of exponential rise in metabolic rate with increasing temperature. The hypothetical organism has a Q_{10} of 2. See text for fuller explanation.

tures and frees them for successful exploitation of more varied habitats. Such animals are commonly called warm-blooded; biologists use the term *homeothermic* (or homoiothermic). These animals maintain a relatively constant body temperature, even when the environmental temperature fluctuates widely. The body temperature is quite high, usually higher than that of the environment, being between 36° and 39°C (96.8–102.2°F) for most mammals and between 40° and 43°C (104–109.4°F) for most birds. This means that the metabolic rate can be maintained at a uniformly high level and the animals can remain very active. Homeothermic animals, in short, put the heat lost during the exergonic reactions of their metabolism to work. They have evolved mechanisms, frequently involving insulation by fat, hair, feathers, etc., whereby heat loss to the environment is retarded, and the heat conserved makes possible a high rate for the very reactions that produce heat.

It is not surprising that homeothermic animals generally have body temperatures considerably higher than the average temperature of their environment. Not only does a high temperature produce a high metabolic rate and make possible a high activity level, as we have already seen, but also it is much easier to maintain a constant temperature higher than that of the surroundings than one lower than that of the surroundings. The animal can have very effective insulation, such as the thick fur of polar bears or the massive fat layers of seals and whales; it can shunt blood away from blood vessels near the body surface; and it can speed up heat production by such reactions as shivering, which is intensive muscle activity that rapidly uses up ATP energy and thus stimulates more cellular respiration and more heat production. In these ways, an arctic mammal like the Eskimo dog with a body temperature of 38.3°C may be comfortable at −30°C or less, a temperature over 60° below its body temperature. But no mammal or bird could live more than a very short time in an environment 60° hotter than its body temperature. In fact, few homeotherms can for long withstand environmental temperatures more than a few degrees above their body temperature. Their cooling mechanisms are simply not effective enough. Their metabolism, with its unavoidable heat production, is by its very nature a furnace, not a refrigeration unit; it can easily be speeded up to counteract environmental cold, but it cannot be made into a cooling device. The external heat will tend, in fact, to do just the reverse of what is needed: speed up the metabolic rate according to the relationship we have already discussed. The animal can, of course, avoid the heat to some extent by actively seeking out shady spots or retiring to cool burrows; it can shunt much blood into surface capillaries where heat loss is greatest; and it can utilize evaporative cooling such as sweating in man or panting in dogs or evaporation from licked parts in cats. But these methods are effective only in temperatures below, at, or just above body temperature; they cannot for long counteract very high temperatures. In short, the most effective thermal regulatory devices available to animals are based largely on heat production and conservation, not on heat loss and cooling. Homeothermy, then, involves mechanisms that can produce relative metabolic stability at a body temperature above that of the environment but not at one much below that of the environment.

We emphasized that homeothermic animals have evolved mechanisms enabling them to take systematic advantage of the heat energy unavoidably released during such chemical processes as cellular respiration. The implication that poikilothermic animals have not evolved such mechanisms needs qualification. Under certain conditions, many of these animals do, in fact, take advantage of metabolic heat energy. For example, on a cold day butterflies and moths frequently vibrate their wings for several minutes before launching into the air. The heat produced by cellular respiration in the vibrating muscles may increase the mus-

cle temperature by as much as 15°C in five or six minutes, the muscles thus getting into a condition where they can contract fast enough to produce normal flight. Obvious analogies are the warming-up of the engine of an automobile or an airplane and the warming-up exercises of athletes. Similarly, any rapidly moving poikilotherm produces metabolic heat faster than that heat can radiate away into the surrounding medium, and the animal's body temperature consequently rises well above that of the environment. Honeybees provide a particularly interesting example of thermal regulation by poikilotherms. When the temperature in their hive falls below a critical value, the bees become very active, releasing enough body heat to raise the hive temperature and maintain it at a level well above that of the outside environment. Conversely, when the hive temperature starts rising too high in summer, the bees create ventilating drafts with their wings.

In both homeothermic and poikilothermic animals and in plants, the normal metabolic rate is inversely related to body size; the smaller the organism, the higher the relative metabolic rate (Fig. 4.26). This is easily understood in the case of homeotherms, because the smaller the animal, the greater its surface-to-volume ratio and hence the greater its relative heat loss to the environment per unit time. If the small animal is to maintain its constant high body temperature despite the rapid heat loss across its body surface, it must oxidize food materials at a very fast rate. Because exesssively small size would necessitate more food intake, digestion, respiration, etc. per unit time than would be possible, there is a lower limit on the size of homeotherms. The smallest living mammals are shrews weighing only about 4 grams. They must eat nearly their own body weight of food every day, and can starve to death in a few hours if deprived of food.

It is more difficult to explain the inverse relationship between size and metabolic rate in poikilothermic animals and in plants. Since these organisms promptly lose their metabolic

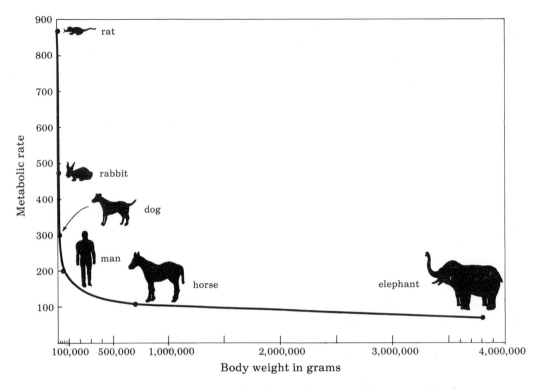

Fig. 4.26. Graph showing inverse relationship of relative metabolic rate and body size in mammals. Metabolic rate is given in cubic millimeters of oxygen per gram of body weight per hour.

heat to the environment and do not normally respond to heat loss by increased metabolism, the surface-to-volume ratio would not be expected to have much effect on metabolic rate; any effect it might have would be expected to be the reverse of that actually found, because larger size and smaller surface-to-volume ratio should retard heat loss slightly and the conserved heat should automatically speed up the metabolism. Why larger size actually slows down the metabolic rate has never been fully explained. One probable factor is that increasing size generally involves a disproportionate increase of such tissues as skeletal and other connective tissues in animals and of supportive fibers and mature xylem in plants; since these tissues are not particularly active metabolically, the average metabolic rate per unit weight for all tissues would fall as the proportion of these

less active tissues rises. This is seen in the course of the development of an embryo; the early embryo is composed almost exclusively of metabolically very active cells and has a high metabolic rate, while later embryos develop a higher proportion of the less active types of tissues and their metabolic rate falls.

The relationship between metabolic rate and body size in homeothermic animals has serious implications for small animals during the cold seasons of the year. Not only does the rate of heat loss rise at such times, but the food supply is generally low. Small mammals belonging to three groups—the insectivores, bats, and rodents—have evolved a mechanism that enables them partly to evade this problem. When winter comes, they **hibernate;** i.e. their body temperature falls far below its normal level, and their metabolism, heart rate, respiration, etc. are greatly depressed. The animal passes the winter in this dormant state, using up its energy reserves very slowly. Bats are of particular interest because they not only hibernate in winter in cold climates, but also go into a similar dormant state during the daylight hours every day, thus conserving the energy contained in the food they eat during the night. A very similar, but reversed, situation occurs in hummingbirds (which are very near the lower size limit for homeotherms); they are active during the day and become dormant, or "hibernate," during the night.

With a few exceptions, however, most birds do not hibernate during the winter; they either remain active, spending much of their time feeding, or they avoid the cold by migrating to a warmer region.

Large mammals like bears are good heat conservers and, as we have seen, have a relatively low metabolic rate. Consequently they do not hibernate during the winter. They become relatively inactive and spend much of their time sleeping, while using up their extensive fat reserves, but their body temperature decreases by only a few degrees and they are not truly dormant.

REFERENCES

BALDWIN, E., 1964. *Dynamic Aspects of Biochemistry*, 4th ed. Cambridge University Press, New York.

BLUM, H. F., 1962. *Time's Arrow and Evolution*, 2nd ed., rev. Harper Torchbooks, New York. (Paperback edition.)

CALVIN, M., and J. A. BASSHAM, 1962. *The Photosynthesis of Carbon Compounds*. Benjamin, New York.

CONN, E. E., and P. K. STUMPF, 1963. *Outlines of Biochemistry*. Wiley, New York.

DIXON, M., and E. C. WEBB, 1964. *Enzymes*, 2nd ed. Academic Press, New York.

FRUTON, J. S., and S. SIMMONDS, 1958. *General Biochemistry*, 2nd ed. Wiley, New York.

GAFFRON, H., 1960. "Energy Storage: Photosynthesis," in vol. 1B of *Plant Physiology*, ed. by F. C. Steward. Academic Press, New York.

GIBBS, M., and J. A. SCHIFF, 1960. "Chemosynthesis: The Energy Relations of Chemoautotrophic Organisms," in vol. 1B of *Plant Physiology*, ed. by F. C. Steward. Academic Press, New York.

LEHNINGER, A. L., 1964. *The Mitochondrion: Molecular Basis of Structure and Function*. Benjamin, New York.

WHITE, A., P. HANDLER, and E. L. SMITH, 1964. *Principles of Biochemistry*, 3rd ed. McGraw-Hill, New York.

SUGGESTED READING

ARNON, D. I., 1960. "The Role of Light in Photosynthesis," *Scientific American*, November. (Offprint 75.)

BASSHAM, J. A., 1962. "The Path of Carbon in Photosynthesis," *Scientific American*, June. (Offprint 122.)

DAWKINS, M. J. R., and D. HULL, 1965. "The Production of Heat by Fat," *Scientific American*, August. (Offprint 1018.)

GIESE, A. C., 1962. "Energy Release and Utilization," in *This Is Life*, ed. by W. H. Johnson and W. C. Steere. Holt, Rinehart & Winston, New York.

GREEN, D. E., 1964. "The Mitochondrion," *Scientific American*, January. (Offprint 175.)

LEHNINGER, A. L., 1961. "How Cells Transform Energy," *Scientific American*, September. (Offprint 91.)

LEHNINGER, A. L., 1965. *Bioenergetics*. Benjamin, New York.

McELROY, W. D., 1964. *Cell Physiology and Biochemistry*, 2nd ed. Prentice-Hall, Englewood Cliffs, N.J.

RABINOWITCH, E. I., 1948. "Photosynthesis," *Scientific American*, August. (Offprint 34.)

———, and GOVINDJEE, 1965. "The Role of Chlorophyll in Photosynthesis," *Scientific American*, July. (Offprint 1016.)

RAMSAY, J. A., 1965. *The Experimental Basis of Modern Biology*. Cambridge University Press, New York. (See esp. Chapters 9–20.)

SCHMIDT-NIELSEN, K., 1964. *Animal Physiology*, 2nd ed. Prentice-Hall, Englewood Cliffs, N.J. (See esp. Chapter 3.)

STERN, H., and D. L. NANNEY, 1965. *The Biology of Cells*. Wiley, New York, (See esp. Chapters 5–9.)

STUMPF, P. K., 1953. "ATP," *Scientific American*, April. (Offprint 41.)

PART II

THE BIOLOGY OF ORGANISMS

CHAPTER

5

NUTRIENT PROCUREMENT AND PROCESSING

OXIDATION OF HIGH-ENERGY ORGANIC COM- pounds—the process by which organisms obtain energy for carrying out life functions— and synthesis of new protoplasm entail procurement of two main categories of molecules from the environment: (1) already synthesized high-energy compounds, or else the raw materials from which they and new protoplasm can be synthesized; and (2) the oxygen used in the aerobic portion of cellular respiration. This chapter will deal with the procurement and processing of the first of these two categories, the nutrients.

Organisms can be divided into two classes on the basis of their methods of nutrition. Fully autotrophic ones can subsist in an exclusively inorganic environment because they can manufacture their own organic compounds from inorganic raw materials taken from the surrounding media. The molecules of these raw materials are small enough and soluble enough to pass through cell membranes. As a result, autotrophic organisms do not need to pretreat, or digest, their nutrients before taking them into their cells. As you would guess, most autotrophs are photosynthetic, although a few are chemosynthetic. The green plants are by far the most important of the earth's autotrophic organisms.

Heterotrophic organisms (most animals and all those plants, such as fungi, that lack chlorophyll) are incapable of manufacturing their own complex organic compounds from simple inorganic nutrients. Hence they must obtain prefabricated organic molecules from the environment. Many of the organic molecules found in nature are too large and not sufficiently soluble to be absorbed unaltered through cell membranes, and they must first be broken down into smaller, more soluble molecular units; i.e. they must be digested.

We can see, then, that autotrophic and heterotrophic organisms differ both in their nutrient requirements and in the problems associated with nutrient procurement. And we would expect that they have evolved radically different adaptations in response to the different selection pressures acting upon them. We shall therefore discuss these two great groups of organisms separately in this chapter, but shall indicate similarities between them where appropriate.

NUTRIENT REQUIREMENTS OF GREEN PLANTS

Raw Materials for Photosynthesis

The raw materials most obviously needed by higher photosynthetic organisms are of course carbon dioxide and water. These two compounds supply the carbon, oxygen, and hydrogen that are the predominant elements in organic molecules. Carbon dioxide, one of the constituent gases of our atmosphere, is obtained directly from the air by the leaves of terrestrial plants; submerged aquatic plants absorb the dissolved gas from the surrounding water. Terrestrial plants obtain the other raw material, water, from the substrate in which

they grow; most higher plants absorb water from the soil by roots.

If we recognize glucose as the central carbohydrate compound of protoplasm, and if we realize that a very high percentage of the total dry body weight of a large tree is carbohydrate and that much of the rest of it was synthesized from carbohydrate, we shall arrive at some interesting facts. The formula for glucose is $C_6H_{12}O_6$, which means, you will recall, that one molecule of glucose contains six atoms of carbon, twelve of hydrogen, and six of oxygen. The atomic weight of carbon is 12, that of hydrogen is 1, and that of oxygen is 16; consequently, the molecular weight of glucose is 180 (really 180.162 if isotopes are considered). Now, you will remember that all the carbon and oxygen incorporated into glucose by photosynthesis comes from carbon dioxide, which in turn comes from the air. But the combined weight of the six atoms of carbon and six atoms of oxygen in glucose is 168, which is about 93 percent of the total weight of glucose. This means that about 93 percent of the weight of a large, immensely heavy tree comes initially from the air. The hydrogen in glucose comes from water, and hydrogen constitutes roughly 7 percent of the weight of glucose; hence about 7 percent of the dry weight of the tree comes initially from water. Even with a modern knowledge of photosynthesis, it is hard to realize that most of the mass of a plant's body comes from air, not from the solid earth in which it grows.

As you would expect, this fact has not always been known. For many centuries, it was assumed that the structural material of the plant body comes from the soil. Then, about 1450, Cardinal Nicolai de Cusa (1401–1464) suggested that the weight gained by a growing plant comes from water, not earth. He was sure that if one were to put a carefully weighed quantity of earth in a pot, plant some seeds in it, wait until the seeds had germinated and the plants grown large and heavy, remove the plants, and again weigh the earth, very little loss of weight by the earth would be found. This, he thought, would prove that water had contributed the bulk of the weight of the plants. Curiously, there is no evidence that the Cardinal ever performed the experiment he had suggested. We must remember, however, that he lived in a day when the gathering of empirical data by experiments was not as commonplace a procedure as it is today.

The experiment suggested by Nicolai de Cusa was finally performed by Jean-Baptiste van Helmont (1577–1644), a Flemish physician; the results were published in 1648. Van Helmont describes his experiment as follows:

. . . I took an earthenware vessel, placed in it 200 lb. of soil dried in an oven, soaked this with rainwater, and planted in it a willow branch weighing 5 lb. At the end of five years, the tree grown from it weighed 169 lb. and about three ounces. Now, the earthenware vessel was always moistened (when necessary) only with rainwater or distilled water, and it was large enough and embedded in the ground, and, lest dust flying about be mixed with the soil, an iron plate coated with tin and pierced by many holes covered the rim of the vessel. I did not compute the weight of the fallen leaves of the four autumns. Finally, I dried the soil in the vessel again, and the same 200 pounds were found, minus about two ounces. Therefore 164 pounds of wood, bark, and root had arisen from water only.[1]

Though van Helmont clearly demonstrated that most of the material of a plant's body does not come from the soil, he was not prepared to consider the possibility that it might have come from so weightless a thing as air. Finally, in 1727, Stephen Hales (1677–1761), an Englishman, suggested that plants get at least part of their nourishment from the air, but it took many years for the extent of such nourishment to be fully realized. And only with the advent of isotopic tracer techniques in the mid-twentieth century could it be conclusively

[1] Translated from the original Latin.

demonstrated, as we saw in the last chapter, that CO_2 gas contributes the oxygen as well as the carbon for photosynthesis and that water contributes only hydrogen.

Mineral Nutrition

Clearly, carbon dioxide and water cannot be the only nutrient materials needed by a green plant. These two compounds provide only three elements: carbon, oxygen, and hydrogen; yet we know that some vital components of the plant contain other elements as well. Protein, for example, is an essential component of protoplasm, and the amino acids of which proteins are composed always contain nitrogen; several very important proteins also contain sulfur. ATP, the universal energy currency of life, contains phosphorus; phosphorus is also present in nucleic acids and many other critically important compounds. Chlorophyll, the essential mediator of photosynthesis, contains magnesium (see Fig. 4.3, p. 117). Where does the green plant obtain the nitrogen, sulfur, phosphorus, magnesium, and other elements it needs? Obviously not from carbon dioxide or water. Here, finally, we see the role of the soil itself as a source of plant nutrients. It is from the soil that the plant derives the minerals essential to its life. Perhaps those 2 ounces of weight lost from the soil in van Helmont's experiment were more important than he knew.

During the nineteenth century, there was much interest in Europe in determining the mineral needs of crop plants and in devising ways of supplementing the amounts of essential mineral elements in the soil. By 1900, seven of these were known: nitrogen, phosphorus, sulfur, potassium, calcium, magnesium, and iron. Three of them—nitrogen, phosphorus, and potassium—were stressed particularly, as they are to this day in the manufacture of fertilizer. Modern commercial fertilizers are often designated by their N-P-K percentages; e.g. the widely used garden fertilizer called 5-10-5 contains 5 percent nitrogen, 10 percent phosphoric acid, and 5 percent soluble potash by weight. These three are the elements most rapidly removed from the soil; consequently it is essential to replenish them if crops are to continue to flourish. Many modern fertilizers are also fortified by small amounts of some of the other essential minerals.

Much of the important research on the mineral requirements of plants was done by growing the plants in distilled water to which measured amounts of minerals were added. This water-culture technique allowed a degree of control and a precision of measurement unattainable with plants growing in soil. Nevertheless, it was not until 1911–1923, after more than fifty years of water-culture research, that it became apparent that other elements, in addition to the seven known, were essential to plants. These additional minerals are required in such small amounts that the traces present as contaminants in the water or salts used in the early experiments were sufficient to meet the needs of the plants. Only with very elaborate purification procedures could their presence be controlled and their effects determined. Such elements, essential in minute amounts but sometimes toxic in excess, are now called trace elements, or micronutrients.

The first trace elements added to the list of minerals essential to flowering plants were boron, manganese, copper, and zinc. More recently, it has been demonstrated that molybdenum is needed by some plants, and perhaps by all. And, still more recently, sodium and chlorine have been added to the list. It has been known for a long time that these two elements commonly occur in plant tissue, but their exclusion from culture media had not seemed to produce deleterious effects on the plants; the explanation is probably that such tiny amounts of sodium and chlorine as are essential to plant growth are extremely hard to eliminate from a water culture.

Table 5.1 lists all the essential nutrients known at the present time and gives some indication of the relative amounts needed and of

the known functions. Two other elements, vanadium and cobalt, are under investigation and may someday be added to the list. Silicon and aluminum, two of the commonest elements in the earth's crust, often occur in quantity in plants, but they seem to be dispensable; knowing, however, that the same thing was said of sodium and chlorine only a few years ago, and of other essential elements before that, we should keep our minds open and reserve judgment on these.

The functions listed in Table 5.1 make it clear why the trace elements are needed in such minute amounts. Most of them are components of enzymes or coenzymes. You will remember that enzymes can be used over and over and that a very small quantity of each is sufficient. Therefore only a small amount of mineral is required to synthesize the enzyme or coenzyme initially and to replenish the supply as the enzyme molecules are slowly broken down.

NUTRIENT PROCUREMENT BY GREEN PLANTS

We have seen that three classes of nutrients are needed by green plants: carbon dioxide, water, and minerals. Carbon dioxide is absorbed by the leaves (and occasionally by stems that are green and carry out photosynthesis). This gas, together with the other components of air, moves into the internal spaces of the leaf through openings in the epidermis called stomata. Inside the leaf, the air circulates throughout the numerous intercellular spaces (see Fig. 6.3, page 205); carbon dioxide dissolves in the film of water on the surfaces of the leaf cells and diffuses into the cells, where it is used as a raw material for photosynthesis. Details of leaf structure and adaptations for gas exchange, both photosynthetic and respiratory, will be discussed in more detail in the next chapter.

This chapter will be more concerned with

TABLE 5.1

Essential Minerals for Higher Plants

Element	Number of pounds (approx.) needed to grow 100 bushels of corn	Function
MACRONUTRIENTS		
Nitrogen (N)	160	Structural component of amino acids, nucleic acids, many hormones and coenzymes, etc.
Phosphorus (P)	40	Structural component of nucleic acids, phospholipids, ATP, coenzymes, etc.
Potassium (K)	125	Essential to a vast number of plant functions, but its exact role is not well understood
Sulfur (S)	75	Structural component of some amino acids, vitamins, enzymes, etc.
Magnesium (Mg)	50	Structural component of chlorophyll; cofactor for many enzymes involved in carbohydrate metabolism
Calcium (Ca)	50	Influences permeability of membranes; component of pectic salts in middle lamellae and perhaps necessary for wall formation; activator for several enzymes
Iron (Fe)	2	Structural component of iron-porphyrins (hemes), which are contained in cytochromes, peroxidases, catalases, and some other enzymes
MICRONUTRIENTS		
Manganese (Mn)	0.3	Cofactor of many enzymes involved in cellular respiration, photosynthesis, and nitrogen metabolism
Boron (B)	0.06	Function unknown; may play a role in translocation of sugar; perhaps necessary for utilization of calcium in wall formation
Chlorine (Cl)	0.06	Function unknown
Sodium (Na)	0.06	Function unknown
Zinc (Zn)	Trace	Necessary for synthesis of tryptophane (a precursor of auxin); component of the enzyme that catalyzes decomposition of carbonic acid to CO_2 and H_2O; may be a cofactor for some enzymes involved in oxidation of carbohydrates
Copper (Cu)	Trace	Structural component of many enzymes that catalyze oxidation reactions
Molybdenum (Mo)	Trace	Structural component of the enzyme that reduces nitrate to nitrite; essential for fixation of N_2 by nitrogen-fixing bacteria

the procurement of water and minerals. In the higher land plants, both of these enter the plant primarily through the roots. In such aquatic plants as the algae, minerals are absorbed from the surrounding water, in which they are in solution. These plants usually lack specialized procurement organs and absorb their nutrients through the general body surface. The structural organization of the algal body, when multicellular, is such that in general no cell is far from the surface or from intercellular spaces filled with fluid that is continuous with the external medium; hence there is a sufficient surface-to-volume ratio for absorption, and internal distribution of nutrients is adequate without a vascular system.

Roots as Organs of Procurement

Root Structure. The first root formed by the young seedling is called the *primary root.* Later, *secondary roots* branch from the primary root, and a root system is formed. If the branching results in a system of numerous slender roots, with no single root predominating, as in grass or clover, the plant is said to have a *fibrous root system* (Fig. 5.1A). If, however, the primary root remains dominant, with smaller secondary roots branching from it, the arrangement is called a *taproot system* (Fig. 5.1B). Dandelions, beets, and carrots, among others, are plants with taproots. As these examples suggest, taproots are frequently specialized as storage organs for the products of photosynthesis. Storage is a function of all roots, but particularly of taproots. Obviously, procurement of water and minerals and storage of high-energy organic compounds are not the only functions of roots; they also serve to anchor the plant to the substrate. Usually the substrate is soil, but climbing vines commonly have, in addition to their normal root system in the ground, short specialized roots branching from the stem, which fasten the plant to a vertical surface such as a tree

trunk or the side of a building. These aerial roots of vines are examples of *adventitious roots;* the term "adventitious" is applied to any root arising from a structure that is not a part

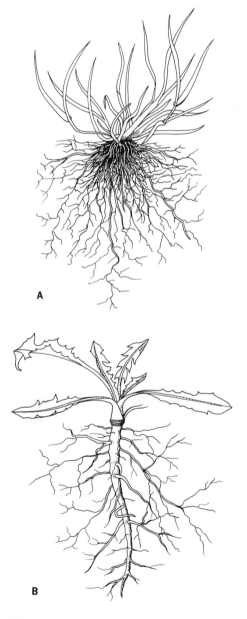

A

B

Fig. 5.1. Two types of root systems. (A) Fibrous root system of grass. (B) Taproot system of dandelion.

of the root system. The prop roots of corn are also adventitious roots; they arise from the lower portion of the stem (Fig. 5.2), penetrate the soil, and become important components of the root system.

The root system of a plant is normally very extensive, far more extensive than we ordinarily realize. When we pull up a plant, we seldom get anything even approaching the entire root system, since most of the smaller roots are so firmly embedded in the soil that they break off and are lost. The amplitude of the system is of course important both in anchoring the plant and in providing sufficient absorptive surface. When we discussed possible limitations on potential cell size in an earlier chapter, we mentioned the problem of the surface-to-volume ratio. We said then that as a cell or an organism gets bigger, its volume increases much faster than its surface area. A large multicellular organism thus faces a serious problem; it must have an absorptive surface extensive enough to enable it to obtain the nutrients it needs to support its large volume, particularly if most of the absorption is restricted to a limited region of the body, in this case the roots. As an adaptation solving this problem, many organisms have evolved absorptive surfaces that are extensively subdivided, so that the total absorptive area is very great, far greater than that of an undivided system of the same volume. The manifold branching of a typical root system is an example of this sort of adaptation. Approximately 14 million branch roots were found in the root system of a rye plant only 2 feet tall; their combined length was about 380 miles, and their total surface area exceeded 2,500 square feet, by contrast with a surface area for the shoots of only 51 square feet.

But calculations of surface area like that above, based simply on the number of branch roots and their length and diameter, fall far short of giving us a true picture of the total absorptive area. In the first place, there is relatively little absorption across the surfaces

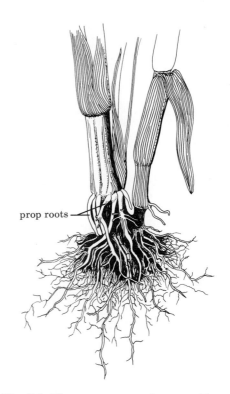

prop roots

Fig. 5.2. The prop roots of corn. These arise from a portion of the stem and are thus adventitious roots.

of the larger, older roots. Secondly, and much more important, an area just behind the growing tip of each rootlet usually bears a dense cluster of tiny hairlike extensions of the epidermal cells (Fig. 5.3). The zone of these *root hairs* on each rootlet may be only a fraction of an inch long (although in some species the zone may be several inches or even several feet long), but each such zone contains such vast numbers of root hairs that the total absorptive surface of the root is enormously increased. The rye plant cited above may have as many as 14 billion root hairs with a total surface of 4,300 square feet. This figure, combined with that already obtained for the main body of the rootlets, gives a total area of contact with the soil of approximately 6,800 square feet (slightly more than the floor area

Fig. 5.3. Root of radish seedling with many prominent root hairs. [Courtesy C. L. Wilson and W. E. Loomis, *Botany*, Holt, Rinehart & Winston, 1962.]

Fig. 5.4. Cross section of root of buttercup (*Ranunculus*). Bottom: Entire root. × 61. Top: Enlarged view of stele. × 262. (a) Epidermis; (b) cortex; (c) endodermis; (d) pericycle; (e) phloem; (f) xylem. The parenchyma cells of the cortex contain many dark-stained starch grains. The thinner-walled cells in the endodermal layer are passage cells; notice that they are mostly located opposite the ends of the xylem arms. [Top: Courtesy General Biological Supply House, Inc., Chicago. Bottom: Courtesy Thomas Eisner, Cornell University.]

of a square room with sides 80 feet long)—all for one small rye plant!

When viewed in cross section, a root of a young dicot plant can be seen to consist of a series of different tissue layers (Fig. 5.4). On its outer surface is a layer of *epidermis* one cell thick. Unlike the epidermis of the aerial parts of the plant, that of the root usually has no waxy cuticle on its surface; the explanation is obvious—the epidermis of a root functions in water absorption, while that of the aerial parts functions as a barrier against diffusion of water. We have already mentioned the small area just back of the growing tip of each rootlet where root hairs are produced. Each such root hair is an extension of a single epidermal cell (Fig. 5.5). The root hair is lined with a

thin layer of cytoplasm, but most of its volume is filled by a branch of the cell vacuole.

The next region beneath the epidermis is the *cortex*, a wide area composed primarily of parenchyma tissue, with numerous intercellular spaces. Sometimes the cortex also contains some sclerenchyma cells, commonly in the outer portion of the cortex adjacent to the epidermis. Large quantities of starch are often stored in the cells of the cortex. This tissue, so prominent and important in young roots, is frequently much reduced or even lost in older roots, where both cortex and epidermis may be replaced by a corky periderm.

Next interior to the cortex is the *endodermis*, a layer one cell thick (Fig. 5.4). You will recall that endodermal cells are characterized by

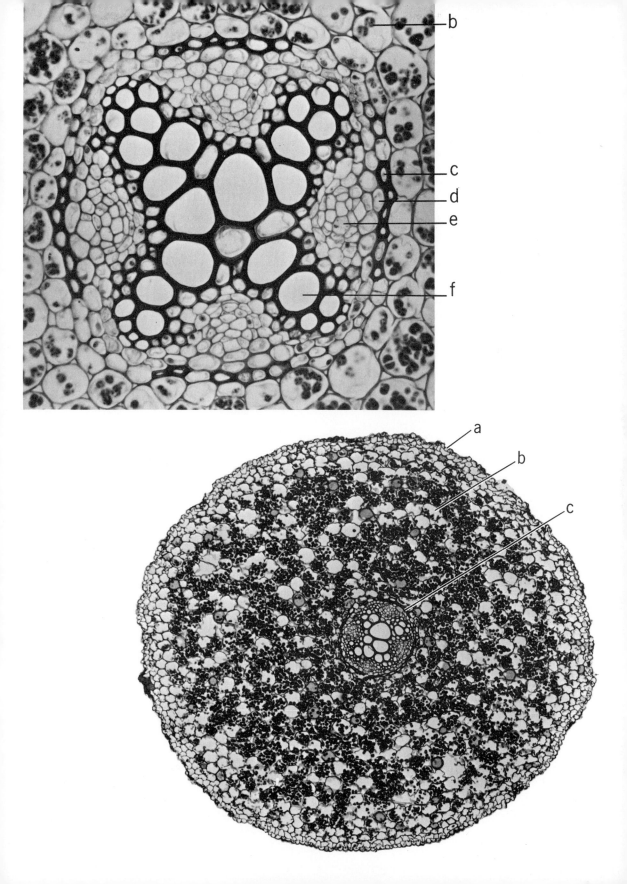

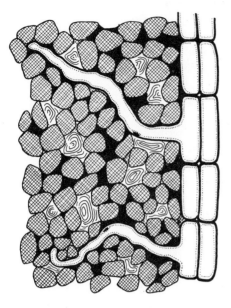

Fig. 5.5. Root hairs penetrating soil. Each root hair is an extension of a single epidermal cell.

a waterproof band, the **Casparian strip,** which runs through their radial (side) and end walls. The walls of mature endodermal cells are frequently very thick and lignified. A few endodermal cells, however, have relatively thin walls (though they still have Casparian strips); they are called **passage cells.** A well-differentiated endodermis is always present in roots, but occurs less regularly in stems. The endodermis forms the outer boundary of a central core of the root that contains the vascular cylinder; this core is called the **stele.** Just inside the endodermis is a layer, often only one cell thick, of thin-walled parenchymatous cells. The cells of this layer, called the **pericycle,** readily take on meristematic activity and may give rise to lateral roots (Fig. 5.6).

The central portion of the dicot stele, surrounded by endodermis and pericycle, is filled with the two vascular tissues, xylem and phloem. The thick-walled xylem cells frequently form a cross-shaped or star-shaped figure (Fig. 5.4). Bundles of phloem cells are located between the arms of the xylem. Consequently the phloem does not form a continuous cylinder like the epidermis, cortex, endodermis, and pericycle; instead, xylem and phloem alternate in this portion of the stele. Large roots of monocots commonly have a region of parenchyma tissue, called **pith,** located at the very center of the stele (Fig. 5.7); the xylem therefore does not form the star-shaped figure described as characteristic of dicots, but even in such roots the bundles of xylem and phloem alternate.

Absorption of Nutrients. When rain falls on the soil, some of the water fails to enter the soil and is lost as runoff to creeks and rivers. Of the water that does penetrate the soil, some percolates rapidly downward through the spaces around the soil particles and is soon beyond the reach of plants, and some is imbibed and held so strongly by colloidal soil particles, particularly those of clay, that it cannot be removed by roots and is thus unavailable to plants. But some of the water is held as a loose film around soil particles, and it is this so-called capillary water that is most important to plants. The roots, and particularly the root hairs, are in contact with the films of capillary water. Since the root epidermis lacks a cuticle, the water can easily move into the root.

Some of the water moves into epidermal cells by osmosis, and then moves from cell to cell across the cortex, either by osmosis or by diffusion along the plasmodesmata that interconnect the cytoplasm of the cells (Fig. 5.8). There is a fairly high concentration of dissolved substances such as sugar and other organic compounds in the epidermal cells, while the concentration of dissolved substances in the soil water is normally lower. The cell membranes are permeable to water, but not to the sugar or to the other organic compounds. What we have here, then, is a simple osmotic system; water is in higher concentration outside the cell than inside, and it therefore moves

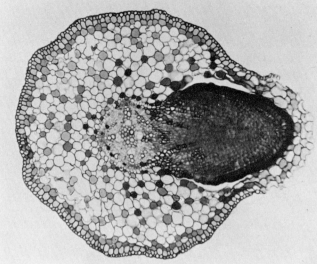

Fig. 5.6. Origin of lateral root from pericycle. As it develops, the young root pushes out through the cortex and epidermis and enters the soil. × 65. [Courtesy Thomas Eisner, Cornell University.]

Fig. 5.7. Cross section of a monocot root (*Smilax*). (a) Epidermis; (b) cortex; (c) endodermis with very thick walls; (d) pericycle, many cells thick; (e) phloem; (f) xylem; (g) pith. × 44. [Courtesy Thomas Eisner, Cornell University.]

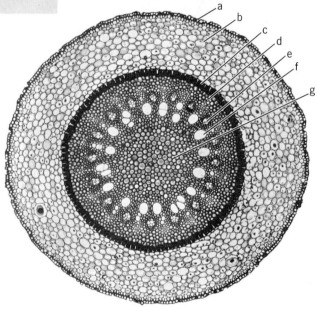

across the membrane into the cell, obeying the normal laws of diffusion. But once water has entered an epidermal cell, it dilutes the contents of that cell. This means that the total concentration of dissolved substances will now be lower in the epidermal cell than in the adjacent cell of the cortex, or, to word it another way, the osmotic pressure of the epidermal cell will now be lower than that of the cortex cell. Consequently water will tend to move from the epidermal cell to the adjacent cortex cell. But this, in turn, establishes another concentration gradient; water moving into the outermost cell of the cortex dilutes the contents of that cell and lowers its osmotic pressure to a point below that of the next cell of the cortex. As a result, water moves from the first cortex cell to the second cortex cell, following the concentration gradient. Again dilution of the recipient cell occurs, a new gradient is established, and water moves on to the next cell. In this way, water can move fairly easily from the capillary films of the soil across the epidermis and cortex to the stele. Once inside the xylem of the vascular cylinder, the water can rise to other parts of the plant body. Removal of water from the center of the root via the

xylem maintains the concentration gradient from the epidermis to the xylem and allows the process of water absorption to continue.

A word of caution is necessary here. The description of water absorption given in the above paragraph assumes passive diffusion along a simple concentration gradient, but there is a possibility, strongly supported by a few botanists, that at times roots may be capable of active, inwardly directed secretion of

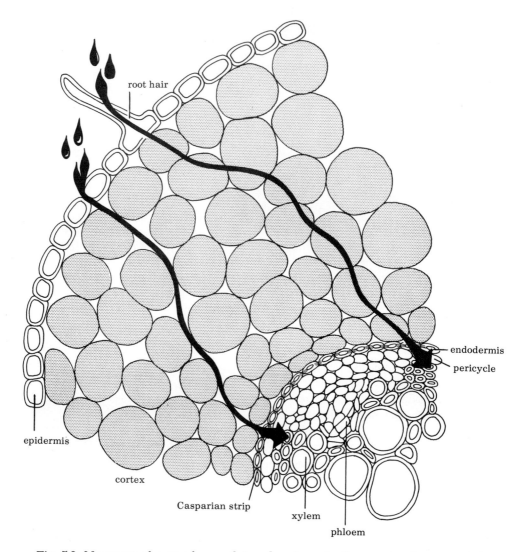

Fig. 5.8. Movement of water from soil to xylem in root. Some water (top arrow) is absorbed by the epidermal cells, particularly the root hairs, and moves from cell to cell, either by osmosis or by diffusion through plasmodesmata. Some water (lower arrow) flows along cell walls and does not cross membranes of living cells until it reaches the endodermis. The Casparian strip of the endodermal cells prevents flow of water along their radial and end walls; hence all water entering the stele must move through the living cells of the endodermis.

water. Such energy-consuming active transport would enable the plant to absorb water faster than would be possible by simple osmosis, especially when the concentration gradient between the soil and the root cells is not particularly favorable.

So far, we have discussed only one mode of absorption, that involving movement of water from the cytoplasm of one cell to the cytoplasm of the next cell, but there is another very important way that water can move across the epidermis and cortex of a root. The cellulose of plant cell walls has a strong tendency to imbibe water, and this water can flow along the cell walls from cell to cell. In this way, water may cross the epidermis and the entire cortex without ever actually penetrating a membrane or entering a cell (Fig. 5.8). But the water cannot flow across the endodermis in this manner, because the Casparian strips act as a barrier. Consequently all water entering the vascular cylinder must cross through the living cells of the endodermis. This gives the plant an opportunity for controlling the movement into the stele of substances dissolved in the water. A high percentage of the movement of water and dissolved substances across the endodermis takes place through the relatively thin-walled passage cells, which are located primarily opposite the ends of the xylem arms (Fig. 5.4). The alternation of xylem and phloem in the root can be viewed as an evolutionary adaptation that makes it unnecessary for incoming water and minerals to cross the phloem before entering the xylem.

The essential elements are usually absorbed in ionic form; e.g. nitrogen is absorbed as nitrate (NO_3^-) or ammonium (NH_4^+) ions; phosphorus as phosphate ions (PO_4^{---}); sulfur as sulfate ions (SO_4^{--}); and potassium, calcium, magnesium, and iron as their simple ions $(K^+, Ca^{++}, Mg^{++}, Fe^{++}$ or $Fe^{+++})$. These ions are in solution in the soil water, their concentration varying according to the fertility and the acidity of the soil and other factors. Often the minerals are not dissolved in quantity in the soil water, but are bound by ionic bonds to soil particles and are thus not available to plants. Agricultural soil management frequently involves changing the soil acidity to free more such bound minerals, so that they can be absorbed by roots. For example, the addition of lime to very acid soil may increase the availability of phosphorus, potassium, and molybdenum, but an excess of lime may decrease the available iron, copper, manganese, and zinc. Obviously, a carefully planned balance appropriate to the particular crop to be grown must be achieved for maximum yield.

Absorption of minerals by roots is essentially independent of the absorption of water. Furthermore, the absorption of each mineral is independent of the absorption of other minerals. Each nutrient moves into the root at its own characteristic rate, which is determined by such factors as its concentration both inside and outside the root and the ease with which it can penetrate cell membranes. Some of the inward movement of minerals, like that of water, is a result of passive diffusion along a concentration gradient; the mineral is in higher concentration in the soil solution than in the cells, and it simply moves from the region of its higher concentration to the region of its lower concentration. The gradient may be maintained by the removal of the substance from the root to other parts of the plant as fast as it enters or by the rapid utilization of the mineral in the synthesis of a different compound. In either case, the concentration of the ion in the cells of the epidermis and cortex remains lower than in the soil water.

Nitrogen is an example of a mineral that is quickly utilized in synthesis. The absorbed nitrate is reduced and built into organic compounds such as amino acids, amides, and other nitrogen-rich compounds. In this organic form, it is transported and stored; much of this storage is in vacuoles, where the concentration of the nitrogen compounds is often very high, much higher than in the cytoplasm itself. Clearly, the vacuolar membrane, or tonoplast, exerts a selective activity, secreting the compounds into the vacuole but preventing their escape from it. It is interesting to note that some of the soluble nitrogen-rich organic compounds manufactured from nitrate are amino acids of a sort not utilized in protein synthesis, and that others are compounds unique to the particular species of plant. The number of such soluble nitrogen compounds discovered grows every year. Obviously, nitrogen metabolism of plants is a complex phenomenon, and it is a mistake to think that nitrates are built directly into amino acids that are in turn promptly incorporated into protein.

Numerous experiments have shown that

Fig. 5.9. Pitcher plant (*Sarracenia*). [Courtesy Carolina Biological Supply Co.]

Fig. 5.10. Venus'-flytrap (*Dionaea*). [Courtesy Carolina Biological Supply Co.]

simple diffusion alone cannot account for all the absorption of mineral nutrients by roots. Plants can sometimes take in a mineral that is in higher concentration inside the root cells than in the soil solution and that therefore should, according to the rules of simple diffusion, move the other way. Furthermore, even when the concentration gradient favors inward movement, the rate of absorption is often greater than would be possible by passive diffusion alone. Active transport is clearly involved. The plant expends energy in the process of procuring the mineral nutrients essential to its continued existence. As will be evident throughout this book, active transport is the rule rather than the exception in most kinds of organisms, both plant and animal. Only rarely is simple diffusion the whole story when substances are moving across the membranes of living cells.

Insectivorous Green Plants

A few photosynthetic plants supplement their inorganic diet with organic compounds obtained by trapping and digesting insects and other small animals. Such plants can survive without capturing any prey, but, when they are successful, the nutrients thus obtained stimulate more rapid growth. Apparently it is the nitrogenous compounds of the animal's body that are of most benefit to the plant; insectivorous plants often grow in nitrogen-poor soils, particularly acid bogs and heavy volcanic clays, and their root systems are not extensive. The prey-capturing adaptations of these plants are interesting and worth examining here as examples of highly specialized leaves.

The pitcher plants (Fig. 5.9) have leaves modified to form a tube or sac, which is partly filled with water. The end of the leaf is further modified to form a hood, which partly covers the open mouth of the pitcher. Insects that fall into the sac are prevented from climbing out by numerous stiff downward-pointing hairs. The proteins of the trapped insects are digested by enzymes secreted into the water, and the

Fig. 5.11. Sundew (*Drosera*). Left: Several growing plants. Bottom right: Enlarged view of a leaf. Note the droplets of sticky fluid on the ends of the glandular hairs. [Courtesy Thomas Eisner, Cornell University.]

products of this digestion are absorbed by the inner surface of the leaf.

The leaf of the Venus'-flytrap (Fig. 5.10) has an expanded blade with a hinge down the middle. There is a row of long stiff teeth along the margin of each half of the blade. When an insect touches small sensitive hairs on the surface of the blade, the leaf quickly bends at the hinge and the two halves come together, with their marginal teeth interlocked. The trapped animal is then digested by enzymes secreted from glands on the leaf surface, and the resulting amino acids are absorbed. The rapid movement exhibited by the leaves of the Venus'-

flytrap is not yet fully understood, but probably involves changes in the turgor pressure of cells near the hinge.

The leaves of sundews (Fig. 5.11) show still another type of modification for carnivorous activity. They bear numerous hairlike tentacles, each with a gland at its tip. The gland secretes a sticky fluid in which small insects become trapped. The stimulus from a struggling trapped insect causes nearby tentacles to bend over the animal, further entangling it. As in the pitcher plants and Venus'-flytrap, the insect's proteins are digested by enzymes and the amino acids are then absorbed.

NUTRIENT REQUIREMENTS OF HETEROTROPHIC ORGANISMS

Heterotrophic organisms cannot manufacture their own high-energy compounds from low-energy inorganic raw materials. Yet they, like all living things, must extract from chemical bonds the energy necessary for both maintenance and growth. They must therefore obtain prefabricated high-energy organic nutrients. Heterotrophic plants may be *saprophytic* (living on dead organic matter) or *parasitic* (living on or in other organisms). Animals may be *herbivores* and eat green plants, thereby obtaining high-energy compounds directly from the organisms that first made them. Or they may be *carnivores* and eat the animals that ate the plants. Or they may be *omnivores,* eating both plant and animal material. Whether a heterotrophic organism is saprophytic or parasitic, or herbivorous, carnivorous, or omnivorous, it is clear that its energy-yielding nutrients came originally from green plants, which used radiant energy from the sun to make them.

Nutrients Required in Bulk

Carbohydrates, fats, and proteins are the main classes of compounds serving as energy sources for heterotrophic organisms. Of these, carbohydrates alone might seem at first glance to be sufficient. And, indeed, they alone would suffice if organic nutrients functioned only as an energy source. But organic nutrients also function in another very important way; they provide carbon skeletons and functional groups essential for the synthesis of new organic compounds. Carbohydrates alone cannot fulfill this second function; the various organic food materials are not fully interconvertible as raw materials for synthesis. For example, some animals (including rats and some moths, beetles, and cockroaches) that require linoleic acid, a common fatty acid, cannot synthesize enough for their needs, no matter how many other or-

ganic compounds are available to them. Severe disease symptoms or even death may result if such animals do not eat sufficient fat to provide presynthesized linoleic acid. For these animals, linoleic acid may be designated an essential fatty acid, i.e. one essential in their diet, since they cannot manufacture it themselves from carbohydrates or from proteins or even from other fatty acids. Most animals, however, can survive and grow with little or no fat in their diet; they can interconvert carbohydrate and fat, and may deposit much fat as a storage product in their bodies even when none is eaten.

Proteins, or the amino acids of which they are composed, must be included in the diet of most heterotrophic organisms, however. A diet including only carbohydrates and fats is usually soon fatal. One reason immediately comes to mind. Carbohydrates and fats lack the nitrogen necessary to form the amino acids that the organisms require. It is true that if heterotrophic organisms had the ability of green plants to combine inorganic nitrogen (usually nitrate) with carbon skeletons from carbohydrates to make amino acids, there might be no need for them to obtain organic nitrogen-containing nutrients. And, indeed, some kinds of heterotrophs have this ability. A few heterotrophic flagellated Protozoa can survive with ammonia (NH_3) as their only nitrogen source; in fact, some of them cannot use amino acids made available in the medium. Similarly, many bacteria can utilize ammonia as their sole source of nitrogen. Higher animals, however, must obtain dietary amino acids. This does not mean that they are totally incapable of utilizing inorganic nitrogen. It has been shown, in fact, that many, if not all, animals can use ammonia to a limited extent. But this limited use of inorganic nitrogen is far from sufficient to support the animal. Organic nitrogen is essential.

Suppose an animal were fed a diet containing only one kind of amino acid. Would this single source of organic nitrogen suffice? For most animals, the answer is no. A mixture of amino acids is necessary. Most animals have apparently lost the ability to synthesize certain amino acids and must get them in their diet. These are called the *essential amino acids*—a rather unfortunate term, since it seems to imply that the other amino acids commonly occurring in proteins are not essential; what is meant, of course, is that the designated amino acids are essential *in the diet,* whereas the others, which are also necessary for life, can be synthesized by the organism itself, either from ammonia and carbohydrate or from other amino acids or organic nitrogen compounds. Although the essential amino acids vary for different species of animals, and even for different stages in the life history of the same species, the basic pattern is similar for all. Eight amino acids are essential for almost all animals; the others may be essential for some, but not for all.

Since all the essential amino acids must be included in the diet of an animal, several different proteins should be eaten, because a single protein may not contain them all. For example, zein, the main protein in corn, is deficient in tryptophane, lysine, and cysteine, while egg albumin is low in leucine. It has been recommended that an average adult human being include at least 70 grams (about 1.85 ounces) of protein in his diet each day, of which at least half should be of animal origin. The proportions of the various amino acids in plant proteins are often quite different from those in animal proteins; hence plant proteins are not as reliable a source of essential amino acids for human beings. Kwashiorkor, a disease resulting from protein deficiency, is particularly common in children in countries where the diet consists primarily of plant material, as in Indonesia, where rice forms much of the diet, or parts of Africa, where corn is the principal staple. The disease is characterized by degeneration of the liver, severe anemia, and inflammation of the skin.

Current theory holds that present-day heterotrophs evolved originally from autotrophic ancestors. Presumably those ancestors, like modern autotrophs, could synthesize all necessary organic compounds. Concomitant with the later evolution of heterotrophic nutrition has apparently been a tendency to lose the capacity to synthesize certain important organic compounds. We have already mentioned essential fatty acids and essential amino acids as examples. Cholesterol is another such compound; all insects apparently require this or some other sterol in their diet, and dietary sterols are also necessary for many Protozoa, some snails, and various other invertebrates. Most vertebrates, however, synthesize enough sterol to meet their needs and do not require it in their diet. Choline, a compound that forms part of an important transmitter chemical in animal nervous systems, is still another example; relatively large amounts of it are necessary in the diet of many insects. Ordinarily, mammals can synthesize their own choline, but if their diet is very low in proteins (and particularly the amino acid methionine), which normally supply the raw materials for choline synthesis, dietary choline may become necessary. By far the best known to the general public is the class of essential compounds called vitamins.

Vitamins

Vitamins are organic compounds necessary in small quantities to given organisms that cannot synthesize them and must therefore obtain them prefabricated in the diet. Note that a compound which is a vitamin for species A may not be a vitamin for species B, because B may not have lost the ability to synthesize it. Vitamins are necessary in only very small quantities because they ordinarily function as coenzymes or as parts of coenzymes; you will recall that enzymes and coenzymes are catalysts that can be re-used many times, hence are not needed in large amounts.

The first recognition that certain diseases were connected with dietary deficiencies now identified as deprivation of vitamins came many years ago. In 1752 it was noticed that fresh fruits helped prevent scurvy, a painful disease, common among sailors long at sea; the symptoms are bleeding gums and loosening of teeth, anemia, delayed healing of wounds, and painful and swollen joints. Shortly before 1800, in an effort to control this debilitating disease, lime and lemon juice were made standard parts of British navy rations. But the full significance of the effect of citrus fruit (now known to contain vitamin C) on a disease was not realized.

Almost a century later, the Dutch government became concerned over the high incidence among servicemen in the East Indies of a crippling disease called beriberi, which is characterized by muscle atrophy, paralysis, mental confusion, and sometimes congestive heart failure. A team of investigators was sent to the East Indies to study the problem. At that time the work of such men as Pasteur and Koch had made scientists acutely aware of microorganisms (germs) as causative agents in disease, and it was logical that the research team should first direct its efforts toward discovering such a causative agent for beriberi. However, two years of work met with no success. Then Christiaan Eijkman, one of the members of the Dutch team, discovered that chickens fed primarily on polished rice dropped in the kitchen and dining area of the military quarters developed symptoms similar to those of human beriberi; because it was so cheap, such rice was the main food supplied to the servicemen. Eijkman found that if unpolished rice was added to the diet neither chickens nor men developed the disease. He showed later that the antiberiberi factor was water-soluble and could be extracted from rice polishings.

In 1906 F. G. Hopkins of Cambridge University, extending this type of investigation to other foods, demonstrated that, in addition to carbohydrates, fats, proteins, minerals, and water, normal foods contain minute traces of other substances essential to health. Hopkins

called such substances accessory factors. Then in 1911 Casimir Funk isolated and crystallized the antiberiberi factor, and, because it was chemically an amine, proposed that the name "vitamine" be used instead of accessory factor (the prefix *vit-* was supposed to indicate that it is essential for life). When it was found later that many accessory factors are not amines, some workers wanted to abandon Funk's term; a compromise resulted in abandoning only the final *e*, and the name became vitamin. We now call the antiberiberi factor vitamin B_1 or thiamine.

It is often exceedingly hard to demonstrate conclusively that a particular chemical compound is a vitamin. The quantities needed are so minute that it is difficult to be sure a diet supposedly free of a compound being tested does not contain trace amounts that would be sufficient to prevent symptoms from developing in an experimental animal. Elaborate purification techniques must be employed, but even these are not always successful. A list of compounds that may be vitamins for human beings is under investigation today, but it may be years before any certainty about them is reached. It is even more difficult to establish reliable minimum daily requirements for known vitamins. Such minimum requirements as have been supposedly established are still very much open to question. Little is known, for example, about how requirements alter with age or with changing health. Much research remains to be done. One thing, however, can be asserted with reasonable confidence; if a healthy person eats a varied diet including meats, fruits, and vegetables, as almost all Americans can afford to do, he will probably get all the vitamins he needs, despite numerous advertisments implying that he will not.

The relation between the pathological symptoms of vitamin deficiency and the actual biochemical function of the vitamin is often obscure. For example, we have already mentioned the symptoms of beriberi, a vitamin B_1–deficiency disease, but those symptoms give no indication that vitamin B_1 functions in the conversion of pyruvic acid into acetic acid and carbon dioxide. In fact, the exact biochemical roles of many vitamins are still unknown, despite extensive clinical information on the symptoms that a lack of them will cause.

Water-Soluble Vitamins. The vitamins in one group, collectively termed the water-soluble vitamins, function as coenzymes in metabolic reactions that take place in almost all animal cells. Some animals can synthesize one or more of these coenzymes, and for them, of course, such coenzymes are not vitamins and are not required in the diet.

The water-soluble group includes vitamin C and the vitamins of the so-called B complex. Vitamin C, now more commonly called ascorbic acid, its chemical name, is the previously mentioned factor in fruit that prevents scurvy. One of its most important known functions is its role in the formation of collagen fibers, which you will recall as the chief components of connective tissue. When the diet is severely deficient in ascorbic acid, collagen formation ceases and the most severe symptoms of scurvy result. Severe scurvy is rare among adults in this country, but occurs occasionally in infants; very mild cases, which are difficult to recognize, are more frequent. Since inclusion of citrus fruits or tomatoes in the diet provides an ample supply of ascorbic acid, supplements are usually necessary only for infants, pregnant women, and the seriously ill.

The B complex includes a large number of compounds, unrelated chemically, but somewhat similar in function and tending to occur together. Several of them act as components of coenzymes functioning in cellular respiration. For example, thiamine (vitamin B_1) is a principal part of the coenzyme that catalyzes the oxidation of pyruvic acid. Pantothenic acid is a component of coenzyme A, which, as we saw in the last chapter, plays an essential role in carrying the acetyl group into the Krebs cycle.

Nicotinamide, another B vitamin, is a major component of both DPN and TPN; commercial vitamin preparations often contain niacin, a compound that is converted into nicotinamide in the body. Riboflavin (vitamin B_2) is one of the hydrogen-carrier compounds in the critically important cytochrome system. Pyridoxine (vitamin B_6) is a component of a coenzyme involved in transaminations—reactions transferring amino groups from one compound to another. These metabolic functions of the B vitamins have not been enumerated here with the expectation that you will memorize them; the intention is only to show you why the vitamins are necessary to life. You are already aware of the central role played by the energy-releasing reactions of cellular respiration; now you can see why many of the vitamins, as essential catalysts in these reactions, are of prime importance in the diet of a heterotroph like man.

Some of the B vitamins, particularly vitamin B_{12} (cobalamin), a very important vitamin containing the element cobalt, seem to be involved in the formation of red blood cells. Vitamin B_{12} deficiency results in pernicious anemia, a chronic disease most common in older people. This vitamin, like several others (e.g. vitamin E, niacin, pantothenic acid, and folic acid), is usually synthesized by microorganisms in the digestive tract of mammals, including man, and may be absorbed from this source without having been present as such in the diet. This is an interesting example of the dependence of heterotrophs that have lost the ability to synthesize important compounds upon heterotrophs (in this instance microorganisms) that have not lost this ability. When human beings develop pernicious anemia, the problem is often not insufficient vitamin B_{12} in the intestine, but rather an inability to absorb it or an inability to convert it into an active form once absorbed.

Folic acid, another of the B vitamins, is apparently also involved in red blood cell formation, but its primary role is in the synthesis

Fig. 5.12. Folic acid–deficient chick. The two birds are both four weeks old. The one on the left was fed a folic acid–deficient diet, while the one on the right received a plentiful supply of the vitamin. [From the *Vitamin Manual*, The Upjohn Co., Kalamazoo, Mich.]

Fig. 5.13. Night blindness. Top: Normal individual's view of road. Bottom: Approximate view of road of vitamin A–deficient individual under same lighting conditions. He cannot see the road sign at all. [From the *Vitamin Manual*, The Upjohn Co., Kalamazoo, Mich.]

of raw materials for nucleoproteins, and it is thus essential for cell division (Fig. 5.12).

Fat-Soluble Vitamins. The compounds collectively known as the fat-soluble vitamins are apparently vitamins only for vertebrate animals. Though the same compounds, or very similar ones, occur in a great variety of other organisms, they apparently function differently in such organisms and are not dietary essentials. It is a common evolutionary pattern for compounds present in ancestral organisms to take on new functions in the course of evolution. In other words, natural selection, instead of giving rise to completely new compounds, frequently acts upon already existing compounds, giving them new functions.

The four principal fat-soluble vitamins are vitamins A, D, E, and K. Symptoms of vitamin A deficiency include retarded growth, excessive cornification (hardening by deposition of keratin, the chief component of claws, nails, and horns) of epithelia, and degeneration of columnar and cuboidal epithelia into stratified squamous epithelia. But the most conspicuous symptom is night blindness, a condition where vision in dim light is seriously impaired (Fig. 5.13). The explanation for this condition is that vitamin A is the chief component of the light-sensitive pigment in the rods of the eye. Deficiency of this vitamin is not common in the United States, because it can be synthesized in the animal body from the yellow pigment carotene, which you will recall is present in green and yellow vegetables and fruit; although carotene can be synthesized only by plants, it is abundant in such animal products as butter, cheese, milk, and egg yolk, and these foods provide a ready source of vitamin A precursor. An excess of vitamin A, as of some other vitamins, is decidedly harmful, and the indiscriminate use of vitamin preparations should be avoided.

Vitamin D is involved in calcium absorption and metabolism, and a deficiency in children results in the condition known as rickets, where the skeleton is deformed because the bones, lacking sufficient calcium, are very soft. Exposure to sunlight is the best preventive for rickets, because the ultraviolet radiation in sunlight acts on sterols in the skin to produce vitamin D. Rickets is therefore confined to the temperate zones, where people spend much time indoors and wear much clothing while outside; it is almost unknown in the tropics. The vitamin is present in egg yolk, milk, and fish oils.

Vitamin E is important in some animals in maintaining good muscle condition, normal liver function, and male fertility. It also has a variety of other effects that are not well understood. A deficiency of this·vitamin occurs rarely, if ever, in man.

Vitamin K is essential for the formation of one of the chemicals necessary for blood clotting. A deficiency results in slow blood clotting and, sometimes, in hemorrhages. Normally, enough vitamin K is synthesized by bacteria in the digestive tract of man, but a deficiency may develop if anything interferes with the absorption of fats and fat-soluble materials.

Table 5.2 lists the main vitamins for human beings and indicates deficiency symptoms and important food sources.

Evolutionary and genetic studies of loss of the ability to synthesize particular vitamins have been very rewarding in recent years. Current theories concerning the mode of action of genes hold that the genes exert their control over cellular functions by controlling the synthesis of enzymes. Mutation of a single gene, therefore, may result in loss of an enzyme necessary for the synthesis of a particular coenzyme. Consequently an organism showing such a mutant trait must obtain the coenzyme in its diet; for such an organism, the coenzyme in question has become a vitamin. Similarly, a mutation may result in loss of ability to synthesize a particular amino acid. For an organism showing this mutant characteristic, the amino acid in question has become an essential amino acid and must be included in the diet. Experimental organisms like bread mold can be exposed to mutation-producing X rays in the laboratory. The irradiated organisms can then be placed on a variety of nutrient media, each deficient in a different compound, and those organisms that have undergone mutations altering their nutritional requirements can be identified by determining on which media they can grow and on which they cannot. In this way, much can be learned about the genetic basis for the evolution of the kinds of nutritional requirements that characterize modern heterotrophs. Use of molds in many of these experiments is of special interest as an indication that at least some, and probably most, plants require many of the same coenzymes, particularly the water-soluble ones, as animals, even though they normally synthesize these substances for themselves.

Mineral Nutrition

Like the green plants, heterotrophs require certain minerals, which are usually absorbed as ions. Some of these are needed in relatively large quantity. Examples are sodium, chlorine, potassium, phosphorus, magnesium, and calcium, for which the minimum daily requirements for human beings vary from about 0.3 grams for magnesium to nearly 10 grams for sodium chloride. Other minerals are needed in much smaller amounts. Examples are iron, manganese, and iodine. And still other minerals, though essential to life, are needed only in trace amounts. Examples are copper, zinc, molybdenum, and cobalt. Some elements, like vanadium, barium, strontium, silicon, and nickel are necessary to a few species of animals, but have not been shown to be of more general importance. And others, like tin, aluminum, lead, and cadmium, occur in the bodies of many heterotrophic organisms, but no essential function is known for them.

The function of some of the minerals is obvious. Calcium is a major constituent of bones and teeth in vertebrates and plays a variety of other roles in most organisms. Phosphorus is a component of many high-energy organic compounds of critical importance. Iron is a constituent of the cytochromes and of hemoglobin. Sodium, chlorine, and potassium are important components of the body fluids, playing a role in osmotic phenomena and in such processes as nerve and muscle action. But the function of some of the minerals, particularly those needed only in trace amounts, is less obvious. Apparently, most of them act as components of coenzymes, or perhaps as cofactors helping to catalyze reactions without being actually incorporated into enzymes or coenzymes. Such minerals are comparable to vitamins, functioning in the same way. The only distinction, and an arbitrary one at that, is that vitamins are organic compounds and minerals are inorganic.

NUTRIENT PROCUREMENT BY HETEROTROPHIC PLANTS

It is a common error to think of all plants as autotrophic. There are many plants, in fact, that lack chlorophyll and are heterotrophic. The nutritional requirements of such plants resemble those of animals in that prefabricated organic compounds, necessary both as energy sources and as raw materials for synthesis, must be obtained from the surrounding environment.

The fungi constitute a large group of heterotrophic plants. Consider bread mold as an example of this group. The bread on which it grows is largely starch. But starch is a polysaccharide, whose very large and insoluble molecules cannot move across cell membranes. How can the mold obtain nourishment from such a source? Clearly something must be done to the starch before absorption can take place. The starch must be broken down to its constituent building-block compounds, the simple sugars, and these can then be absorbed. In short, the starch must be digested. Digestion is

TABLE 5.2

Some Vitamins Needed by Man

Vitamin	Some deficiency symptoms	Important sources
FAT-SOLUBLE		
Vitamin A (retinol)	Dry, brittle epithelia of skin, respiratory system, and urogenital tract; night blindness and malformed rods	Green and yellow vegetables and fruit, dairy products, egg yolk, fish-liver oil
Vitamin D (calciferol)	Rickets or osteomalacia (very low blood calcium level, soft bones, distorted skeleton, poor muscular development)	Egg yolk, milk, fish oils
Vitamin E (tocopherol)	Male sterility in rats (and perhaps other animals); muscular dystrophy in some animals; abnormal red blood cells in infants; abnormal eyes in embryos; death of rat and chicken embryos	Widely distributed in both plant and animal food, e.g. meat, egg yolk, green vegetables, seed oils
Vitamin K (phylloquinone, etc.)	Slow blood clotting and hemorrhage	Green vegetables
WATER-SOLUBLE		
Thiamine (B_1)	Beriberi (muscle atrophy, paralysis, mental confusion, congestive heart failure)	Whole-grain cereals, yeast, nuts, liver, pork
Riboflavin (B_2)	Vascularization of the cornea, conjunctivitis, and disturbances of vision; sores on the lip and tongue; disorders of liver and nerves in experimental animals	Milk, cheese, eggs, yeast, liver, wheat germ, leafy vegetables
Pyridoxine (B_6)	Convulsions, dermatitis, impairment of antibody synthesis	Whole grains, fresh meat, eggs, liver, fresh vegetables
Pantothenic acid	Impairment of adrenal cortex function, numbness and pain in toes and feet, impairment of antibody synthesis	Present in almost all foods, especially fresh vegetables and meat, whole grains, eggs
Biotin	Clinical symptoms in man are extremely rare, but can be produced by great excess of raw egg white in diet; symptoms are dermatitis, conjunctivitis	Present in many foods, including liver, yeast, fresh vegetables
Nicotinamide	Pellagra (dermatitis, diarrhea, irritability, abdominal pain, numbness, mental disturbance)	Meat, yeast, whole wheat
Folic acid	Anemia, impairment of antibody synthesis	Leafy vegetables, liver
Cobalamin (B_{12})	Pernicious anemia	Liver and other meats
Ascorbic acid (C)	Scurvy (bleeding gums, loose teeth, anemia, painful and swollen joints, delayed healing of wounds, emaciation)	Citrus fruits, tomatoes

nothing more than enzymatic hydrolysis, which, you will recall, involves the addition of water (see p. 34). In bread mold, the hydrolysis takes place outside the cell. Digestive enzymes synthesized inside the cells of the mold are released from the cells and hydrolyze the starch. The simple sugars that are the products of this digestion are then absorbed by the cells. Such digestion outside of cells is called *extracellular digestion.*

For other, more unusual, examples of nutrient procurement by fungi, consider the curious methods of certain predatory species. Some of these produce spherical knobs with sticky surfaces; nematode worms coming in contact with the knobs stick to them and are trapped (Fig. 5.14). Other species of predatory fungi form rings composed of three cells; when a worm enters the ring, the cells swell rapidly, constricting the ring and trapping the worm. Branches of the fungus then penetrate the worm's body and release digestive enzymes. Extracellular digestion takes place, and the products are absorbed.

Some higher flowering plants have lost most or all of their chlorophyll in the course of their evolution, and have become wholly or partly heterotrophic. Dodder, a highly specialized parasitic plant, is an example. It grows as a leafless yellow vine, twining around some other plant. Highly modified adventitious roots of the dodder penetrate into the stem of the host plant until they reach the vascular tissue of the host. There they absorb water, minerals, and organic nutrients. Dodder can be severely destructive to cultivated plants.

We have seen that most green plants do not procure organic compounds from the environment. It follows, of course, that these autotrophs do not carry out extracellular digestion. But they, like all other living things, must on occasion hydrolyze such compounds as polysaccharides, fats, and proteins into their constituent building-block compounds. If, for example, starch stored in one cell of a plant is to be moved to some other cell, it must first

be hydrolyzed, since the starch itself cannot move across the intervening membranes. Such hydrolysis reactions taking place within cells may be termed *intracellular digestion.* This kind of digestion is characteristic of almost all cells, both plant and animal.

NUTRIENT PROCUREMENT BY ANIMALS

Nutrient procurement by animals usually involves much more activity than it does in plants. Animals must often resort to elaborate methods of locating and trapping their food. Their incredibly varied feeding habits may be classified in any number of ways. We have already mentioned one possible classification, which distinguishes carnivores, herbivores, and omnivores, depending on whether the diet consists primarily of animals, plants, or both. Another possible criterion for classification is the size of the food. Thus we can recognize microphagous feeders, which strain microscopic organic materials from the surrounding water by an array of cilia, bristles, legs, nets, etc. And we can recognize macrophagous feeders, which subdivide larger masses of food by teeth, jaws, pincers, or gizzards, or solely by the action of enzymes. Smaller groups would include the sucking animals, adapted to extract fluid from plants or from animal prey, and those parasitic animals that are bathed in the nutrients of the host and absorb them directly through the body surface. Many characteristics of the animal as a whole can give clues to its methods of procurement. Thus speed and strength frequently characterize predators that overtake and overpower prey. Some very slow predators may stalk their prey, lure it, or trap it; often they are cryptically colored—i.e. they blend neatly with their background—and thus avoid betraying their presence.

Like the fungi already examined, most animals must digest their food before it can cross the membranes of their cells. Only rarely can

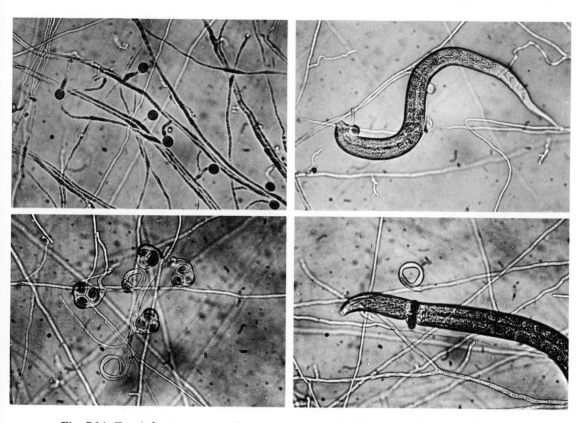

Fig. 5.14. Fungi that trap nematode worms. Top: *Dactylella drechsleri* has sticky knobs (left) which hold a worm that contacts them (right). Bottom: *Arthrobotrys dactyloides* has rings formed of three cells (left; several of the rings are shown closed here, so that the three cells can be seen plainly). When a worm enters the ring, the cells swell and constrict the ring, trapping the worm (right). [Courtesy David Pramer, *Science*, vol. 144, 1964. Copyright 1964 by the American Association for the Advancement of Science.]

they obtain as food such comparatively simple and diffusable compounds as glucose, glycerol, fatty acids, and amino acids; usually food material is in the form of polysaccharides, fats, proteins, etc., and must be hydrolyzed. Sometimes digestion is extracellular. In other instances, bulk food is taken into a cell by phagocytosis, or some similar process, and then digested in a food vacuole. Though the latter process is classified as intracellular digestion, it should be noted that the food material is separated from the rest of the cellular material by a membrane that it cannot cross until after digestion has occurred. Thus extracellular and intracellular digestion are alike in that digestion always precedes the actual absorption of complex foods across a membrane.

Although both the nutritional requirements and the basic processes of digestion are essentially similar in all animals, from single-celled Protozoa to man, the body plans of animals vary so greatly that the structures involved in food processing and the details of that processing are often different. We shall therefore briefly examine the digestive mechanisms of a variety of different animals.

Nutrient Procurement by Protozoa

Protozoa, being single-celled organisms, have a body plan that is obviously very different from that of other animals. We would therefore expect their adaptations for food procurement to be different from those of multicellular animals. And they do, in fact, show interesting differences. But the most interesting point, one with important biological implications, is that the similarities are often more striking than the differences.

Let us look first at *Amoeba,* an organism whose shape is constantly changing as its protoplasm flows along, pushing out new armlike projections and withdrawing others. When an amoeba is stimulated by nearby food, some of these armlike processes, called *pseudopodia,* may flow around the food until they have completely surrounded it. This is what we have called phagocytosis. The food is completely engulfed by the cytoplasm and is enclosed in a *food vacuole,* where it will be digested (see Fig. 3.14, p. 68). *Amoeba* is an example of a protozoan without specialized permanent di-

gestive structures, though its transitory food vacuoles are functional analogues of the digestive systems of higher animals.

The ciliates, of which *Paramecium* is an example, are another important group of Protozoa. They are characterized by innumerable cilia covering the surface of their bodies. Like all Protozoa, they are commonly regarded as unicellular. But it is a mistake to think of them as simple. Some of them, in fact, are among the most incredibly complex cells known—so complex that many biologists prefer not to regard them as single cells, but rather as acellular (i.e. as organisms whose bodies are not built of cells in the usual sense), for though they lack actual subdivision into recognizable cellular units, they show much of the internal specialization usually associated

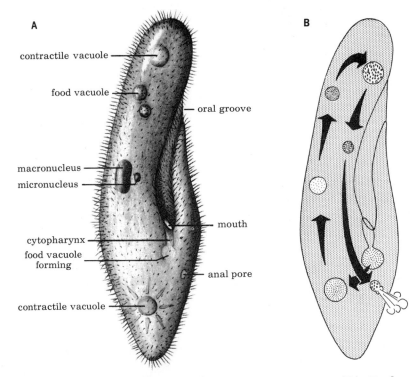

Fig. 5.15. *Paramecium.* (A) Drawing showing major structures. (B) Food vacuole forms at lower end of cytopharynx, then breaks off and moves toward anterior end of cell while enzymes are secreted into it; digestion takes place; and the products of digestion are absorbed into the general cytoplasm. Vacuole then moves posteriorly, attaches to anal pore, and expels digestive wastes. The vacuole undergoes several changes in size and appearance as it moves.

with multicellularity. Unlike *Amoeba, Paramecium* has a permanent structure, or organelle, that functions in feeding. It begins with an *oral groove*, which is a ciliated channel on one side of the cell (Fig. 5.15A). Food particles are swept into the oral groove by water currents produced by the beating cilia, and are carried down the groove into a *cytopharynx* by cilia lining the groove. As food accumulates at the lower end of the cytopharynx, a food vacuole forms around it (Fig. 5.15B). Eventually the vacuole breaks off and begins to move toward the anterior end of the cell. Digestive enzymes are secreted into the vacuole and digestion begins. As digestion proceeds, the products (simple sugars, amino acids, etc.) diffuse across the membrane of the vacuole into the cytoplasm, and the vacuole begins to move back toward the posterior end of the cell. When the vacuole reaches a tiny specialized region of the cell surface called the anal pore, it becomes attached to the surface and then ruptures, expelling to the outside any remaining bits of indigestible material. Not only does the food vacuole function as a digestive chamber, but by its movement it serves to distribute the products of digestion to all parts of the cell.

We have said that digestive enzymes are secreted into the food vacuoles of both *Amoeba* and *Paramecium*. But if these powerful enzymes are capable of hydrolyzing such compounds as polysaccharides, fats, proteins, and nucleic acids, and if the cell itself is composed of these kinds of compounds, how can the cell contain the digestive enzymes without being destroyed by them? A partial answer was given briefly in the chapter on cells; digestive enzymes are packaged in lysosomes, vesicles whose membrane apparently is both impermeable to the enzymes and capable of resisting their hydrolytic action. The digestive enzymes are presumably synthesized on the ribosomes of the endoplasmic reticulum and become surrounded by a membrane to form the lysosome. The origin of the membrane is unknown, but it may be derived from the endoplasmic reticu-

lum. When a food vacuole, sometimes also called a phagosome, is formed, a lysosome soon fuses with it (Fig. 5.16). Food materials and the digestive enzymes are mixed in the resulting composite vesicle, which is sometimes called a digestive vacuole. As already described, this vacuole circulates in the cytoplasm, the products of digestion are absorbed, and indigestible materials are eventually expelled from the cell.

Though the above description of lysosome activity is given in connection with digestion in Protozoa, it holds equally well for intracellular digestion in any animal cell. You will recall that lysosomes were in fact first discovered in rat liver cells. Here is only one example of the similarity between the basic processes of digestion in Protozoa and in higher animals.

Nutrient Procurement by Coelenterates

With the evolution of multicellularity came a corresponding evolution of cellular specialization resulting in a division of labor among cells. The coelenterates provide a comparatively simple example of this phenomenon. These radially symmetrical animals have a sacklike body composed of two principal layers of cells (Fig. 5.17), with traces of an obscure jellylike layer between them. The cells of the outer layer function as a protective and sensory epithelium, while those of the inner layer, or gastrodermis, act as a nutritive epithelium. Some cells of both layers are specialized as muscle fibrils, and others as nerves. The central cavity of this sacklike body functions as a digestive cavity. It has only one opening to the outside, which is surrounded by movable tentacles. A digestive cavity of this sort, having only one opening that must function as both mouth and anus, is called a *gastrovascular cavity.*

Coelenterates are strictly carnivorous. Embedded in their tentacles are numerous stinging structures called *nematocysts.* Each nema-

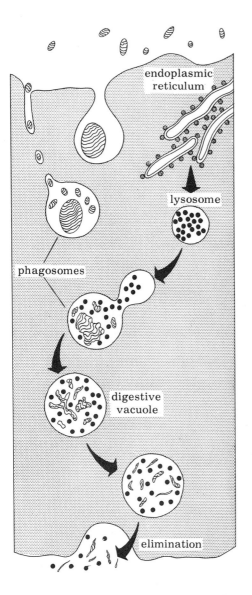

endoplasmic
reticulum

lysosome

phagosomes

digestive
vacuole

elimination

Fig. 5.16. The role of lysosomes in intracellular digestion. A lysosome containing digestive enzymes fuses with a food vacuole (phagosome). Digestion takes place within the composite structure thus formed (digestive vacuole), and the products of digestion are absorbed across the vacuolar membrane. The vacuole eventually fuses with the cell membrane and then ruptures, expelling indigestible wastes to the outside.

tocyst consists of a slender thread coiled within a capsule, with a tiny hairlike trigger penetrating to the outside. When appropriate prey comes in contact with the trigger, the nematocyst fires, the thread turns inside out, spines on its surface unfold, and it either penetrates the body of the prey or entangles the prey in sticky loops. The nematocysts also eject poisons, which have a paralyzing action on the prey. The tentacle then grasps the prey, and, if it continues to struggle, neighboring tentacles may also become involved. The tentacles draw the prey toward the mouth, which opens wide to receive it. Once the food is inside the gastrovascular cavity, digestive enzymes are secreted into the cavity by the gastrodermal cells, and extracellular digestion begins. This extracellular digestion, largely limited to the proteins in coelenterates, does not break down these substances completely to their constituent amino acids. As soon as the food has been reduced to small fragments, the gastrodermal cells engulf them by phagocytosis, and digestion is completed intracellularly in food vacuoles. Indigestible remains of the food are expelled from the gastrovascular cavity via the mouth.

If phagocytosis and intracellular digestion are going to take place anyway, we can ask what adaptive advantage the evolution of the additional process of extracellular digestion might have. Why should not coelenterates rely exclusively on intracellular digestion as the Protozoa do? The answer is obvious. Intracellular digestion severely limits the size of the food the organism can handle. Extracellular digestion enables it to utilize much larger pieces of food; even whole multicellular animals become possible prey. Extracellular digestion is the rule rather than the exception in multicellular animals.

We have seen, then, that coelenterates exhibit a variety of interesting evolutionary adaptations for prey capture and digestion and that, as a result of cellular specialization and division of labor, certain cells, those of the gastrodermis, carry out digestion for the whole organism.

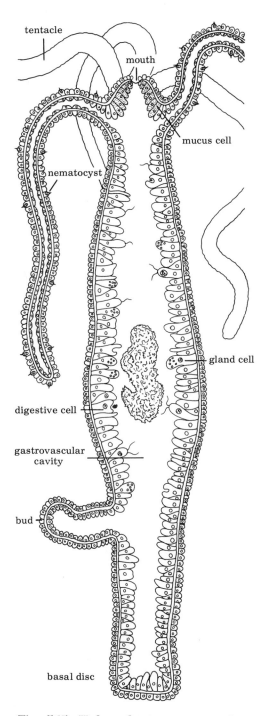

tentacle

mouth

mucus cell

nematocyst

gland cell

digestive cell

gastrovascular cavity

bud

basal disc

Fig. 5.17. Hydra, showing gastrovascular cavity with food material in it.

The products of digestion can be distributed from the gastrodermal digestive cells to cells specialized for other functions such as protection or movement or stimulus reception. Since the bodies of coelenterates are relatively small, and no cells are far removed from the gastrodermal layer, this distribution can be effected without any specialized transport system.

Nutrient Procurement by Flatworms

Unlike the radially symmetrical coelenterates, the flatworms are bilaterally symmetrical; they have distinct anterior (front) and posterior (rear) ends, and also distinct dorsal (upper) and ventral (lower) surfaces. Their bodies are composed of three well-formed tissue layers. Many flatworms are parasitic on other animals, but some are free-living, and it is to these free-living forms that we shall first direct attention, using planaria as an example (Fig. 5.18).

The mouth of planaria is located on the ventral surface near the middle of the animal, though in some flatworms it is farther forward on or near the head. The mouth opens into a muscular tubular *pharynx,* which can be protruded through the mouth directly onto prey. The pharynx leads into a gastrovascular cavity (i.e. a cavity with only one opening to the outside). This cavity, though functionally similar to that of the coelenterates, is far more branched, ramifying throughout the animal's body. This extensive branching of the digestive cavity explains why it is called a gastrovascular cavity; it functions in both digestion and transport of food to all parts of the body (*gastro-* refers to the stomach and *vascular* to a circulatory vessel). But the extensive branching has another important function; it greatly increases the total absorptive surface of the cavity. We saw with plants that as organisms increase in size, and particularly as their volume increases, the problem of sufficient absorptive surface becomes more acute. Many organisms have evolved greatly subdivided absorptive surfaces, thereby compacting much total surface area

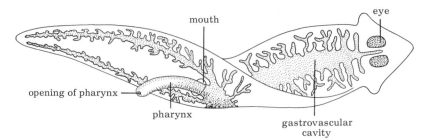

mouth

eye

opening of pharynx

pharynx

gastrovascular cavity

Fig. 5.18. Planaria, showing much-branched gastrovascular cavity and extruded pharynx.

into relatively little space. The root hairs of plants were one example, and the branched gastrovascular cavity of planaria is another; we shall encounter many other examples in this and later chapters.

Some extracellular digestion occurs in the gastrovascular cavity of planaria, but most of the food particles are engulfed by gastrodermal cells and digested intracellularly.

The members of one class of flatworms have become so highly specialized as parasites living in the digestive tracts of other animals that in the course of their evolution they have lost their own digestive systems. These are the tapeworms. They are constantly bathed by the products of the host's digestion and can absorb them without having to carry out any digestion themselves. Evolutionary adaptation can involve the loss of structures as well as their acquisition.

Animals with Complete Digestive Tracts

Animals above the level of coelenterates and flatworms have a complete digestive tract, i.e. one with two openings, a **mouth** and an **anus**. The advantages of such a system over a gastrovascular cavity are obvious. No longer must incoming food material and outgoing wastes pass through the same opening. Instead, food can be passed in one direction through a tubular system, which can be divided into a series of distinct sections or chambers, each specialized for a different function. As the food passes along this "assembly line," it is acted upon in a different way in each section. Some sections may be specialized for mechanical breakup of bulk food, some for temporary storage, some for enzymatic digestion, some for absorption of the products of digestion, some for reabsorption of water, some for storage of wastes, etc.

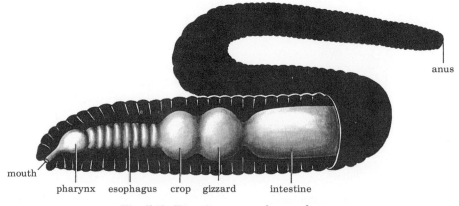

anus

mouth

pharynx   esophagus   crop   gizzard   intestine

Fig. 5.19. Digestive system of an earthworm.

The overall result is a much more efficient digestive system, as well as the potential for special evolutionary modifications fitting different animals for different modes of existence.

The digestive system of an earthworm is a good example of subdivision into specialized compartments (Fig. 5.19). Food, in the form of decaying organic matter mixed with soil, is drawn into the mouth by the sucking action of a muscular chamber called the **pharynx.** After passing from the mouth through a short passageway into the pharynx and then through a connecting passage called the **esophagus,** the food enters a relatively thin-walled **crop,** which functions as a storage chamber. Next, the food enters a compartment with thick muscular walls, the **gizzard,** where it is ground up by a churning action; the grinding is often facilitated by the presence of small stones. The pulverized food, suspended in water, now passes into the long **intestine,** where enzymatic digestion and absorption take place. Finally, in the rear of the intestine, some of the water involved in the digestive process is reabsorbed, and the indigestible residue is eliminated from the body through the anus.

Notice that earthworms utilize extracellular digestion. Cells of the intestinal lining secrete hydrolytic enzymes into the cavity of the intestine, and the end products of digestion, the simple building-block compounds, are absorbed. We have already seen that extracellular digestion is an adaptation for eating sizable pieces of food; the gizzard is obviously another such adaptation in earthworms. Mechanical breakup of bulk food is common among animals, and a variety of structures that serve this function have evolved. In our own case, food is torn and ground by the teeth. Many snails have a hard, toothed, pharyngeal plate, the radula, with which they rasp off small particles from larger pieces of food. Cockroaches and many other insects that feed on solid food have a chamber (proventriculus) that resembles the earthworm's gizzard except that its inner wall often bears several very hard

ridges and teeth. Note that the grinding or chewing device need not be in the first section of the digestive tract, as in our own case; in both earthworms and cockroaches, the grinding chamber comes after the crop, which corresponds functionally to our stomach, and mechanical breakup follows temporary storage instead of preceding it. The same arrangement exists even in some vertebrates; birds have a muscular gizzard, posterior to the less specialized part of the stomach (Fig. 5.20), in which hard food is ground with rocks and pebbles (often called grit). Why might a gizzard be adaptively superior to teeth in a flying animal like a bird?

It would be wrong, however, to imply that all large animals eat large pieces of food and have special masticating devices. They do not. For example, many animals are **filter feeders;** they strain small particles of organic matter from water. Clams and many other molluscs filter water through tiny pores in their gills; microscopic food particles are trapped in streams of mucus that flow along the gills and enter the mouth, kept moving by beating cilia. It is interesting that in such molluscs digestion is largely intracellular, as might be expected in animals that eat microscopic food.

Fig. 5.20. Digestive system of a bird. The chamber for mechanical breakup (gizzard) is located posterior to the stomach.

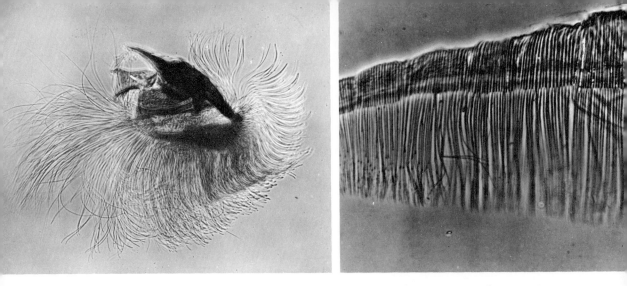

Fig. 5.21. Food brush and comb of mosquito larva. Left: Isolated food brush. Its motion causes water to flow into the mouth. Right: Much-enlarged portion of comb from the pharyngeal filter. It strains food particles from water. [Courtesy A. L. Burnett and Thomas Eisner, *Animal Adaptation,* Holt, Rinehart & Winston, 1964.]

The larvae of mosquitoes are also filter feeders. They eat bacteria and other small particles of organic matter in the water where they live. Two small hair-covered brushes (Fig. 5.21) near the mouth of the larva beat in a circular scooping motion, setting up water currents toward the mouth. The particles and water pass through the mouth and into the pharynx. Now, if the larva swallowed all the water, the salt and water balance of its body fluids would be seriously disturbed. The pharynx is specially adapted for eliminating water while filtering out food particles. Muscles in the wall of the pharynx contract, expelling the water through two small canals. Tiny combs in the canals strain out the food while the water passes through. The larva then swallows the resulting clump of food. Clams and mosquito larvae are only two of many possible examples of filter feeders. Current theory holds that the earliest vertebrates fed in this way. And even some of the largest present-day whales are filter feeders, straining small planktonic plants and animals from the vast quantities of water that they take into their mouths.

But let us return to the earthworm and examine the implications of another of the specialized compartments of its digestive tract, the crop. We have already said that this chamber functions in food storage. And the functional significance of food storage should be clear after a moment's thought. It enables the animal to take in large amounts of food in a short time, when it is available, and then to utilize this food over a considerable period of time. Such discontinuous feeding makes it possible for the animal to devote much of its time to activities other than feeding, such as searching for a mate, mating, egg laying, and, in some animals, care of young. Our own stomachs function as storage organs analogous to the earthworm's crop; they enable us to live well on only three or four meals a day, and to devote the rest of our time to other pursuits. A man can survive if his stomach is removed surgically, but he is unable to eat more than a few bites at a time and must therefore eat very frequently. It is not surprising that the vast majority of higher animals have evolved adaptations for discontinuous feeding, thereby gaining time for a behaviorally more varied existence.

We should not overlook the fact that discontinuous feeding is frequently also of adaptive advantage in the feeding process itself; it does more than merely free time for nonfeeding activities. For example, an animal's proper food may occur only in widely scattered locations; if it had to eat constantly to maintain its metabolic activity, it would be unable to spend time searching for a new food supply or capturing more prey when its original supply had been depleted. In short, it would have to live in an essentially unlimited and continuous source of food. Otherwise, it would soon die or become inactive. This is the case with tapeworms, nematode worms, and some other animals, which lack storage ability. It would be a mistake, however, to assume automatically that such animals are unsuccessful or poorly adapted; their long evolutionary history and their large numbers today testify to the contrary. They are simply adapted—successfully adapted—for a different way of life. Biological success is not measured by structural complexity or by the possession of any particular organ. The earthworm with its crop and the nematode worm without such an organ are both successful, each in its own way, and science can make no value judgments between them.

Different kinds of food-storage organs occur in different species of animals. In many birds,

an expanded region of the esophagus anterior to the stomach forms a thin-walled chamber, the crop, which is functionally analogous to the earthworm's crop (Fig. 5.20). Some birds also use the crop in carrying food to their young; they fill it with seeds, berries, fish, or whatever their food may be, and then fly to the nest, where they disgorge the food for their young. In many animals, storage organs take the form of blind sacs, or diverticula, branching off the digestive tract. A good example is seen in adult female mosquitoes, which have a very large diverticulum (Fig. 5.22) that opens off the anterior portion of the digestive tract and runs posteriorly, occupying much of the abdominal cavity. The female mosquito locates a suitable animal, pierces its skin with long needlelike mouthparts, and sucks blood until this diverticulum is filled. A single large blood meal may suffice to carry the female through the entire process of locating an egg-laying site and laying her eggs—a matter of four or five days.

The earthworm's food is digested in the intestine, after having passed through both the

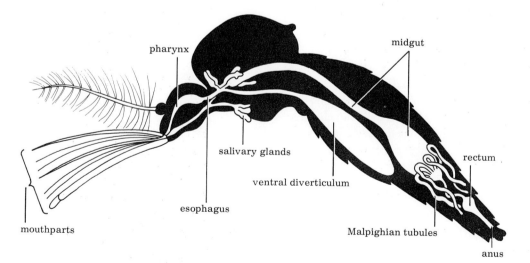

Fig. 5.22. Digestive system of adult female mosquito, showing very large diverticulum. The styletlike mouthparts, shown separated here, actually fit together to form an efficient piercing and sucking structure. [Modified from A. L. Burnett and Thomas Eisner, *Animal Adaptation*, Holt, Rinehart & Winston, 1964.]

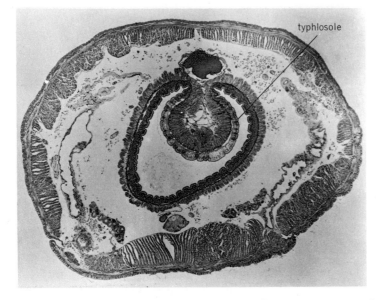

typhlosole

Fig. 5.23. Photograph of cross section of an earthworm in intestinal region. Note large dorsal fold (typhlosole). [Courtesy Thomas Eisner, Cornell University.]

crop and the gizzard. Enzymes are secreted into the intestine by glandular cells in its epithelial lining, and most of the digestion occurs extracellularly. The products are then absorbed. Here again we encounter the problem of surface area. The total interior surface of a digestive tract in the form of a round tube would be inadequate in relation to the total volume of an animal the size of an earthworm. But a cross section of the earthworm's intestine (Fig. 5.23) shows that it is not a round tube internally. A large dorsal fold projecting downward into the digestive cavity greatly increases the total absorptive area exposed to the food, without making the outer dimensions of the intestine prohibitively large. The fold is therefore functionally analogous to the root hairs of higher plants and to the branching of the gastrovascular cavity in planaria (though it does not, of course, function also as an internal transport route).

The Digestive System of Man and Other Vertebrates

Although an examination of the structure of man's digestive tract reveals little in the way of general principles that could not as easily be

seen in an earthworm, natural interest in ourselves and our own species prompts a more detailed examination of human systems.

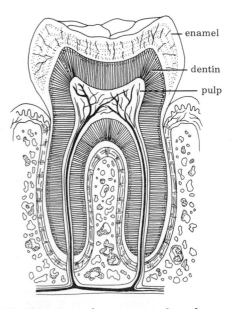

— enamel

— dentin

— pulp

Fig. 5.24. Internal structure of a human tooth. Blood vessels and nerves penetrate into the pulp, but not into the outer harder layers.

The Oral Cavity.   The first chamber of the digestive tract is, of course, the oral cavity. Located here are the teeth, which function in the mechanical breakup of food by both biting and chewing. The internal structure of a tooth is shown in Fig. 5.24. Human teeth are of several different types, each adapted to a different function (Fig. 5.25). In front are the

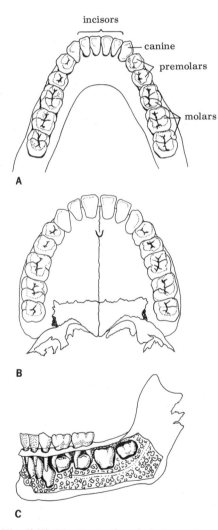

Fig. 5.25. Human teeth.   (A) Lower jaw of adult.   (B) Upper jaw of adult.   (C) Lower jaw of child, showing permanent teeth in gums below milk teeth.   [After Frank H. Netter, M.D., *The Ciba Collection of Medical Illustrations,* vol. 3, 1959.]

chisel-shaped *incisors,* four in the upper jaw and four in the lower, which are used for biting. Then come the more pointed *canine* teeth, one on each side in each jaw, which are specialized for tearing food. Behind each canine are two *premolars* and three *molars* in adults; these have flattened, ridged surfaces, and function in grinding, pounding, and crushing food. A child's first set of teeth does not include all those mentioned here; the first (or milk) teeth are lost as the child gets older, being replaced with the permanent teeth that have been growing in his gums (Fig. 5.25C).

The teeth of different species of vertebrates are specialized in a variety of ways and may be quite unlike those of man in number, structure, arrangement, and function. For example, the teeth of snakes are very thin and sharp (Fig. 5.26D) and usually curve backward. They function in capturing prey, but not in mechanical breakup; snakes do not chew their food, but swallow it whole. The teeth of carnivorous mammals, such as cats and dogs, are more pointed than those of man (Fig. 5.26A); the canines are long, and the premolars lack flat grinding surfaces, being more adapted to cutting and shearing (often the more posterior molars are lost). On the other hand, such herbivores as cows and horses have very large flat premolars and molars with complex ridges and cusps; the canines are often totally absent in such animals. Notice that sharp pointed teeth poorly adapted for chewing seem to characterize meat eaters like snakes, dogs, and cats, whereas broad flat teeth, well adapted for chewing, seem to characterize vegetarians. How can this difference be explained? Remember that plant cells are enclosed in a cellulose cell wall. Very few animals can digest cellulose; they must therefore break up the cell walls of the plant they eat if the cell contents are to be exposed to the action of digestive enzymes. Animal cells, like those in meat, do not have any such nondigestible armor and can be acted upon directly by digestive enzymes. Therefore chewing is not as essential

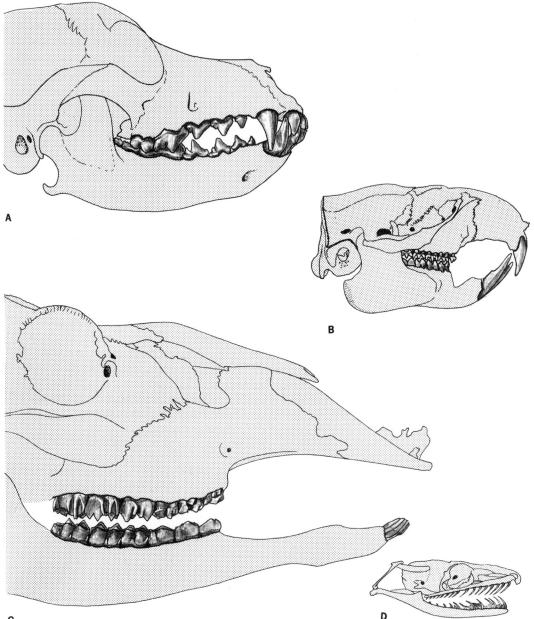

Fig. 5.26. **Variation of tooth structure and arrangement in different animals.** (A) Dog (carnivore): large canines, premolars and molars adapted for cutting and shearing. (B) Beaver (gnawing herbivore): few but very large incisors, no canines, premolars and molars with flat grinding surfaces. (C) Deer (grazing and browsing herbivore): six lower incisors (three on each side), but no upper incisors—these are functionally replaced by a horny gum; premolars and molars with very large grinding surfaces. Notice the large gap between the incisors and premolars. (D) Snake: thin, sharp, backward-curved teeth that have no chewing function (the snake skull is here shown disproportionately large in relation to the other three).

for carnivores as for herbivores. You have doubtless seen how dogs gulp down their food, while cows and horses spend much time chewing. But carnivores have other problems. They must capture and kill their prey, and for this, sharp teeth capable of piercing, cutting, and tearing are well adapted. Man, being an omnivore, has teeth that belong, functionally and structurally, somewhere in between the extremes of specialization attained by the teeth of carnivores and herbivores.

There are other functions of the oral cavity besides those associated with the teeth. It is here that food is tasted and smelled, activities of great importance in food selection. And it is here that food is mixed with saliva secreted by several sets of salivary glands. The saliva dissolves some of the food and acts as a lubricant, facilitating passage through the next portions of the digestive tract. The saliva of man also contains a starch-digesting enzyme, which initiates the process of enzymatic hydrolysis.

The muscular tongue manipulates the food during chewing and forms it into a mass, called a bolus, in preparation for swallowing; it then pushes the bolus backward through a cavity called the *pharynx* and into the *esophagus* (Fig. 5.27; see also Fig. 6.13, p. 215). The pharynx functions also as part of the respiratory passageway; the air and food passages cross here, in fact. Consequently, swallowing involves a complex set of reflexes that close off the opening into the nasal passages and trachea (windpipe), thereby forcing the food to move into the esophagus. As you know, these reflexes occasionally fail to occur in proper sequence and the food enters the wrong passageway, causing you to choke.

The Esophagus and the Stomach. The esophagus is a long tube running downward through the throat and thorax and connecting to the stomach in the upper portion of the abdominal cavity (Fig. 5.27). Food moves quickly through the esophagus, pushed along by waves of muscular contraction in a process

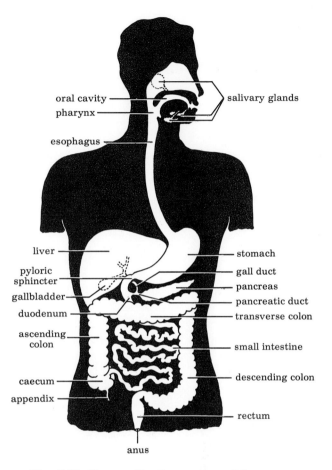

Fig. 5.27 **Human digestive system.** (The organs are slightly displaced, and the small intestine is greatly shortened.)

called *peristalsis.* Circular muscles in the wall of the esophagus just behind the food bolus contract, squeezing the food forward (Fig. 5.28). As the food moves, the muscles it passes also contract, so that a region of contraction follows the bolus and constantly pushes it forward, much as though you were to keep a ball moving through a soft rubber tube by giving the tube a series of squeezes, with your hand always just behind the ball.

At the junction between the esophagus and the stomach is a special ring of muscle called a *sphincter,* which, when it is contracted, closes the entrance to the stomach. It is normally

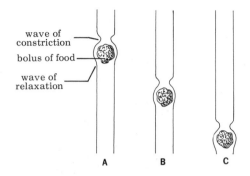

wave of
constriction

bolus of food

wave of
relaxation

A   B   C

Fig. 5.28. Peristalsis.   The wave of muscular
contraction pushes the bolus of food ahead
of it.

closed, thus preventing the contents of the
stomach from moving back into the esophagus
when the stomach moves during digestion.
It opens when a wave of peristaltic contraction
coming down the esophagus reaches it.

The stomach lies slightly to the left side in
the upper portion of the abdomen, just below
the lower ribs. It is a large muscular sac, which,
as we have already seen, functions as a storage
organ, making discontinuous feeding possible.
It has other functions too. Its thick walls are
composed of three layers: an inner mucus
membrane composed of connective tissue and
columnar epithelium with many glands, a thick
middle layer of smooth muscle, and an outer
layer of connective tisue. The muscle layer
contains fibers running around the stomach,
others running longitudinally, and still others
oriented diagonally. Thus the stomach is capable of a great variety of movements. When it
contains food, it is swept by powerful waves
of contraction, which churn the food, mixing
it and breaking the larger pieces. In this manner, the stomach supplements the action of the
teeth in mechanical breakup of food. The
glands of the stomach lining are of several
types. Some secrete mucus, which covers the
stomach lining—hence the name "*mucosa*" or
"mucus membrane" for the inner layer of the
stomach wall; others secrete *gastric*[2] *juice,* a
mixture of hydrochloric acid and digestive en-

zymes. Enzymatic digestion, then, is a third
important function of the stomach in man.

The Small Intestine.   The food leaves the
stomach as a soupy mixture. It passes through
the pyloric sphincter into the small intestine,
which is the portion of the digestive tract
where most of the digestion and absorption
takes place. The first section of the small intestine, attached to the stomach, is called the
duodenum (Fig. 5.27). It leads into a very
long coiled section lying lower in the abdominal cavity. The entire small intestine of an
adult man is about 23 feet long and an inch
in diameter.

The length of the small intestine shows interesting variations in different animals. The
intestine is usually very long and much coiled
in herbivores, much shorter in carnivores, and
of medium length in omnivores like man.
These differences, like those of the teeth, are
correlated with the difficulty of digesting plant
material because of the cellulose cell walls.
Even if the cellulose has been well broken up,

Fig. 5.29. Intestines of adult frog and tadpole.   The much-coiled intestine of the tadpole is much longer relative to the size of the
animal than the intestine of the adult frog.

[2] The adjective "gastric" and the prefix "gastro-"
always refer to the stomach.

it remains mixed with the digestible portions of the cells and tends to mask them from the digestive enzymes. This interference makes digestion and absorption of plant material much less efficient than that of animal material, with the result that a longer intestine is an adaptive advantage in extracting a maximum amount of nutrients from a herbivorous diet. A striking example of adaptation of the small intestine is seen in frogs, where the immature stage, or tadpole, is herbivorous and has a long coiled small intestine, while the adult is carnivorous and has a relatively much shorter one (Fig. 5.29).

Since the small intestine is the place where absorption of the products of digestion occurs, we would expect it to have special structural adaptations that increase its absorptive surface area. Clearly its great length plays a role here. But examination of its internal surface reveals other modifications that vastly increase the surface area over what it would be if the intestine were simply a smooth-walled tube. First, the mucosa lining the intestine is thrown into numerous folds and ridges (Figs. 5.30 and 5.31). Second, small fingerlike outgrowths, called *villi*, cover the entire surface of the mucosa. And third, the individual epithelial cells covering the folds and villi have a striated border of countless, closely packed, cylindrical

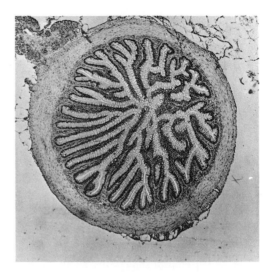

Fig. 5.31. Cross section of intestine of calico bass, showing extensive folding. [Courtesy Warren Andrew, *Textbook of Comparative Histology*, Oxford University Press, 1959.]

processes called *microvilli* (Fig. 5.32), revealed by the electron microscope. Thus the total internal surface of the small intestine, including folds, villi, and microvilli, is incredibly large.

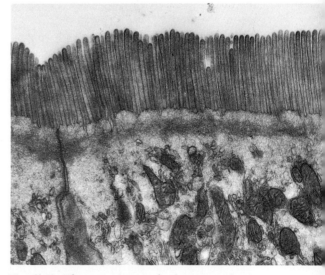

Fig. 5.32. Electron micrograph of portions of two epithelial cells from intestine of a hamster, showing numerous closely packed microvilli. × 23,300. [Courtesy E. W. Strauss, University of Colorado.]

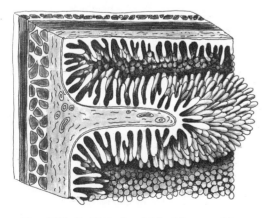

Fig. 5.30. Section of a fold of human intestine, showing many villi.

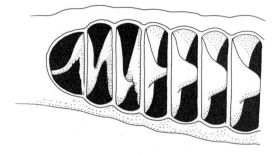

Fig. 5.33. Spiral valve of shark intestine. Food material must follow a winding course and is thus exposed to more surface area.

Some vertebrates show other adaptations for increasing absorptive surface area besides those seen in man. For instance, it is not unusual for special blind sacs, called **caeca,** to branch from the anterior end of the small intestine; in many fish such caeca are present in the pyloric region. Another example is the spiral valve of many primitive fish and of sharks. The spiral valve is an epithelial fold extending the length of the intestine. Like a carpenter's bit tightly enclosed in a tube, it forms a spiral within the intestine, to whose wall its base is attached (Fig. 5.33); hence food cannot move in a straight path, but must follow the spiral of the valve, thereby contacting much more epithelial surface than it could by moving straight through a tubular intestine of the same length.

The Large Intestine. In man, the junction between the small intestine and the large intestine (or colon) that follows it is usually in the lower right portion of the abdominal cavity. A blind sac, the **caecum,** projects from the large intestine near the point of juncture (Fig. 5.27). (Notice that most blind diverticula of the digestive tract are called caeca, even though their location and function may vary greatly. Thus the pyloric caeca of fish, mentioned above, are diverticula of the small intestine and often function in absorption, while the caecum of man is a diverticulum of

the large intestine and does not function in this way.) In man, there is a small fingerlike process, the **appendix,** at the tip of the caecum. As you know, the appendix frequently becomes infected and must be surgically removed.

The caecum of man is small and functionally unimportant, but in some mammals, particularly herbivorous ones, it is large and contains many microorganisms (bacteria and Protozoa) capable of digesting cellulose. Since the mammal cannot itself digest cellulose, it benefits from the action of the microbes. The caecum, however, is not located where the mammal can derive maximal benefit from the cellulose-digesting activity of the microbes in it. It is too far back on the digestive tract, behind the small intestine where most digestion and absorption takes place. Thus, even though horses have an enormous caecum, much coarse undigested plant material remains in their feces. A compensating adaptation has evolved in rabbits, which form two types of feces, one of them material from the caecum, which they promptly re-eat and expose to further digestion and absorption.

Ruminants, like the cow, also utilize microbial digestion, but the microorganisms are not held in a posterior caecum. Instead, such animals have four different stomachlike chambers (Fig. 5.34), of which the first three are thought to be expanded sections of the esophagus. The first of these chambers, called the **rumen,** is the largest. Vast numbers of bacteria and Protozoa live in it and in the second chamber, the reticulum. Swallowed food enters the rumen and reticulum, where the microbes begin digesting and fermenting it, breaking down not only protein, polysaccharides, and fats, but cellulose as well. The larger, coarser material is periodically regurgitated for further chewing; i.e. the animal "chews its cud." This rechewed material is again swallowed and mixed with the fermenting material in the rumen. Slowly the products of the microbial action and the microbes themselves move on into the true stomach and intestine, where the

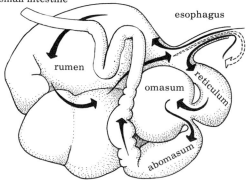

small intestine

esophagus

rumen

omasum

reticulum

abomasum

Fig. 5.34. The four "stomachs" of a ruminant. Food is swallowed initially into the rumen and reticulum (the drawing here shows it going only into the rumen), where it is fermented by microorganisms. It is then regurgitated as the cud for more chewing (white arrow) and then reswallowed, this time bypassing the rumen and moving quickly along a fold in the wall of the reticulum into the omasum and then into the abomasum, which is the true stomach.

more usual type of digestion and absorption takes place. Thus, by utilizing microbial digestion in the anterior portion of their digestive tracts rather than in a posterior caecum, ruminants derive maximal benefit from the microbial action. Much less undigested plant material remains in their feces than in the feces of horses. (It is worth noting—though the point has no direct bearing on digestion— that the microorganisms in the rumen can utilize ammonia and such comparatively simple organic compounds as urea as sources of nitrogen for synthesizing amino acids. Upon digesting the microorganisms, the ruminant obtains the amino acids, thus benefiting from the microbes' nitrogen metabolism. Modern agriculture often takes advantage of this microbial metabolism by supplying nitrogen in the form of cheap ammonium salts in cattle feed, rather than in the more expensive form of protein.)

Digestion of cellulose by symbiotic microorganisms is not limited to mammals. A variety of insects, notably the termites, feed on wood,

which they could not use as food were it not for intestinal microbes that can ferment the cellulose. A few species of wood-eating beetles do, however, themselves secrete cellulase, an enzyme that digests cellulose, and such beetles do not have to rely on intestinal microbes.

But let us return to our examination of the large intestine of man. From the caecum, the large intestine ascends on the right side to the mid-region of the abdominal cavity, then crosses to the left side, and descends again (Fig. 5.27). The three sections thus formed are frequently termed the ascending, transverse, and descending colons. One of the chief functions of the colon is reabsorption of much of the water used in the digestive process. If all the water in which enzymes are secreted into the digestive tract were lost with the feces, man would have a severe problem of desiccation. Occasionally the intestine becomes irritated, and peristalsis moves material through it too fast for sufficient water to be reabsorbed; this condition is known as diarrhea. Conversely, if material moves too slowly, excessive water is reabsorbed and constipation results. A good diet contains sufficient roughage (indigestible material, primarily cellulose) to provide the bulk needed to stimulate enough peristalsis in the large intestine to prevent constipation. A second function of the colon is the excretion of certain salts, such as those of calcium and iron, when their concentration in the blood is too high. The salts are excreted into the colon and are eliminated from the body in the feces. The large intestine also contains large numbers of bacteria, which live on the undigested food that reaches the colon. The significance of these bacteria in the life of a healthy person is not clearly understood. Approximately half the dry weight of the feces is made up of masses of these bacteria.

The last portion of the large intestine, the *rectum*, functions as a storage chamber for the feces until defecation. The feces are eliminated from the rectum through an opening called the anus.

Enzymatic Digestion in Man

Digestion by Saliva. Having traced the human digestive tract from mouth to anus, let us next consider the chemical changes that occur in a meal as it passes through this complex tubular system. We have said that enzymatic digestion starts in the mouth. The saliva contains an enzyme called *amylase*[3] (sometimes also called ptyalin) that begins the hydrolysis of starch. Amylase, however, does not completely hydrolyze starch to glucose. Instead, it splits the starch into units of maltose, a double sugar (Fig. 5.35), which must be further digested in the intestine. Why, we may well ask, can't the amylase split all the bonds between sugar units instead of splitting only every other one? So far as we know, there is no chemical difference between these bonds, and

[3] Note that the names of most enzymes end with the suffix *-ase,* which designates enzymes by international agreement. The first part of the name usually indicates the substrate upon which the enzyme acts; thus *amyl-* (from *amylum,* the Latin for starch) indicates that amylase acts upon starch.

it would seem logical that an enzyme capable of splitting one could also split the others. Biologists do not, as yet, have any satisfactory answer to our question. Perhaps the bonds between the simple-sugar building blocks are not really exactly alike. Or perhaps the enzyme and its substrate fit together in such a way that only every other linkage is in the proper spatial configuration to be broken. We have much to learn before we fully understand the amazing specificity exhibited by many enzymes.

Since the food remains in the mouth only a short time, the amylase has little opportunity to work there. Much of its action occurs inside each bolus after it is swallowed into the stomach. The acid of the stomach soon inactivates the enzyme, however, and salivary amylase actually digests only a small percentage of the starch in the food. In fact, the saliva of many mammals contains no amylase at all; dogs are an example. Can you think of reasons why there would have been little selection pressure for the evolution of such an enzyme in dogs and their relatives?

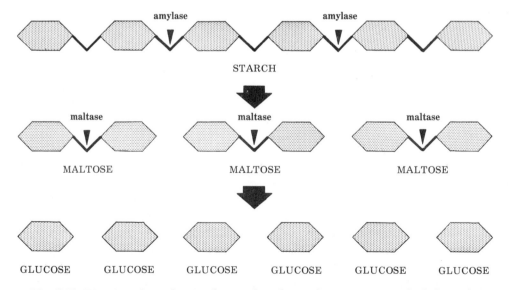

Fig. 5.35. Digestion of starch. Amylase in the saliva and pancreatic juice hydrolyzes the bonds between every other pair of glucose units, producing the double sugar maltose. Maltose is digested to glucose by maltase, secreted by intestinal glands.

Digestion in the Stomach. Once in the stomach, food is exposed to the action of gastric juice secreted by numerous gastric glands of the mucosa of the stomach wall. This juice contains much hydrochloric acid and several enzymes. The acid makes the contents of the stomach very acidic (pH of about 1.5–2.5). Note that advertisements for many patent medicines to the contrary, an acid stomach is both normal and necessary for proper function. The principal enzyme of the gastric juice is *pepsin,* which digests protein. Unlike most protein-digesting enzymes, pepsin will function only in an acid medium. Pepsin is characteristic of vertebrates; most invertebrates do not have any proteolytic enzymes that are active in strongly acid solutions. Some biologists have hypothesized that the evolution of pepsin is correlated with feeding on animals with bones, since bones disintegrate more easily in acid.

Pepsin does not hydrolyze protein all the way to its amino acid components. It splits the peptide bonds adjacent to only a few amino acids, particularly those adjacent to tyrosine and phenylalanine (Fig. 5.36). The specificity of proteolytic enzymes is more understandable than that of amylase, because proteins are composed of a variety of building-block compounds, not just one as in the case of starch. This means that the structural configuration around the various peptide bonds in a protein varies, depending on which two amino acids the bond joins. Consequently some bonds may fit on the active site of the enzyme and others may not. Pepsin, for example, seems to "fit" peptide bonds adjacent to amino acids whose R groups include a certain kind of ring structure (see Fig. 2.22, p. 38, for the structure of tyrosine).

Any discussion of protein digestion immediately raises one obvious problem. Why isn't the wall of the digestive tract digested by the proteolytic enzymes? After all, the wall of both the stomach and the intestine is composed mostly of protein. Two reasons can be given. First, the gastric glands do not actually secrete active pepsin. Instead, they secrete a precursor compound, pepsinogen, which has no proteolytic activity and which, so long as it is stored in the glands of the stomach wall, poses no threat to that wall. The pepsinogen is changed to active pepsin only after exposure to acid in the lumen (cavity) of the stomach. Second, the wall of the digestive tract is covered with mucus, which apparently shields the wall from the enzymes. Sometimes, however, this defense breaks down and the digestive enzymes begin to eat away a small portion of the lining; the resulting sore is known as an ulcer. Occasionally, an ulcer may be so severe that a hole develops in the wall of the digestive tract, allowing the contents of the tract to spill into the abdominal cavity. As you are probably aware, we have only a poor understanding of why and how ulcers first begin to develop. This means, of course, that we do not know all the reasons why the wall is not normally digested by the proteolytic enzymes. Presence or absence of sufficient mucus may not be the whole story. Much research remains to be done.

In addition to pepsin, the gastric juice of mammals contains another enzyme, *rennin,* that clumps milk proteins together, thus taking them out of solution and making them more susceptible to the proteolytic enzymes. As you might expect, few animals other than mammals, have such an enzyme. Rennin extracted from the stomachs of calves is often used commercially in the manufacture of some types of puddings and cheese. Note that, although rennin aids digestion, it is not, strictly speaking, a digestive enzyme, since it does not catalyze a hydrolysis reaction.

Digestion in the Small Intestine. It is in the next section of the digestive tract, the small intestine, that by far the most digestion takes place. When partially digested food passes from the stomach into the duodenum, its acidity stimulates the release of a large number of different digestive enzymes into the lumen of

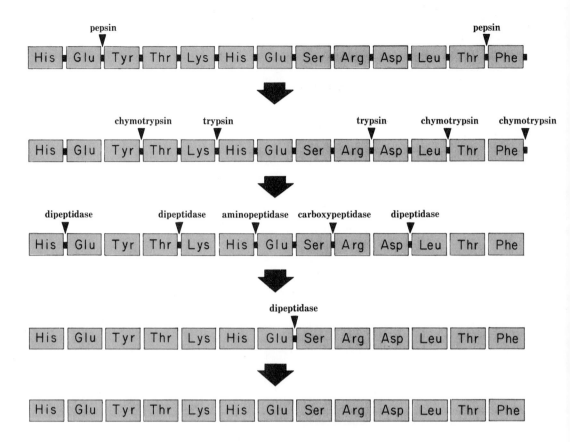

Fig. 5.36. Digestion of protein. Pepsin in the stomach hydrolyzes peptide bonds at the amino end of tyrosine (Tyr) and phenylalanine (Phe). Then the food moves into the intestine, where trypsin and chymotrypsin from the pancreas hydrolyze bonds adjacent to lysine and arginine and to tyrosine, phenylalanine, and leucine, respectively (chymotrypsin also hydrolyzes bonds adjacent to tryptophane and methionine when they are present). Pepsin, trypsin, and chymotrypsin hydrolyze only internal bonds, not bonds attaching terminal amino acids to the chains. Terminal bonds at the amino end of chains may be split by aminopeptidase and those at the carboxyl end by carboxypeptidase. Bonds between pairs of amino acids are split by dipeptidases, whereupon digestion is completed.

the intestine. These enzymes are secreted from two principal sources, the *pancreas* and the *intestinal glands.* The pancreas is a large glandular organ, lying just below the stomach (Fig. 5.27), which originates in the embryo as an outgrowth of the digestive tract; it retains a connection to the duodenum called the *pancreatic duct.* When food enters the duodenum, the pancreas secretes a mixture of enzymes, which flow through the pancreatic duct into the duodenum. Included in this mixture are enzymes that digest all three principal classes of foods—carbohydrates, fats, and proteins—as well as some that digest nucleic acids.

One of the pancreatic enzymes is *pancreatic amylase* (sometimes also called diastase or amylopsin), which, as its name implies, acts like salivary amylase, splitting starch into the double sugar maltose. It is far more important than salivary amylase, for it carries out most of the starch digestion.

Lipase is the fat-digesting enzyme of the pancreas. It splits molecules of fat into glycerol and fatty acids. Almost all fat digestion is catalyzed by this pancreatic enzyme. It has been reported that very small amounts of lipase are also secreted by the gastric glands of the stomach, but such secretion has not been fully substantiated and, in any case, is of no real importance.

Two of the proteolytic enzymes from the pancreas, *trypsin* and *chymotrypsin,* are active in an alkaline medium. Like pepsin, they are incapable of splitting all peptide linkages in a protein molecule. Each cleaves only the linkages adjacent to certain specific amino acids. Trypsin splits the peptide bonds adjacent to lysine and arginine; chymotrypsin, those adjacent to tyrosine, phenylalanine, tryptophane, methionine, and leucine (Fig. 5.36). Notice that chymotrypsin resembles pepsin in hydrolyzing bonds adjacent to tyrosine and phenylalanine. But this superficial resemblance is misleading. The two enzymes do not split the same bonds. Pepsin cleaves the bonds on the amino side of tyrosine and phenylalanine, while chymotrypsin cleaves those on the carboxyl side. This specificity, far from being unusual, is typical of most enzymes. Actually, the digestive enzymes are less specific than many others in that they will catalyze the reactions of several different substrates.

Like pepsin, both trypsin and chymotrypsin are secreted in inactive forms, called trypsinogen and chymotrypsinogen respectively. Trypsinogen is converted into active trypsin in the intestine by enterokinase, an enzyme secreted by intestinal glands. Chymotrypsinogen is converted into active chymotrypsin by the trypsin thus formed.

In summary, then, the action of pepsin in the stomach and of trypsin and chymotrypsin from the pancreas results in a splitting of proteins into fragments of varying lengths, but does not produce many free amino acids. These three enzymes are known as *endopeptidases,* i.e. enzymes that hydrolyze peptide bonds between amino acids located within the protein, not bonds linking terminal amino acids to the chain. Another class of enzymes, called *exopeptidases,* hydrolyze off the terminal amino acids, thereby completing the digestive process. There is a great variety of such enzymes, each highly specific in its action. One, for example (carboxypeptidase), hydrolyzes the linkage that binds the amino acid at the free carboxyl end of a chain. Another (aminopeptidase) hydrolyzes the linkage of the amino acid at the free amino end of a chain. Still others (dipeptidases) break apart pairs of amino acids; one breaks only the bond of a fragment consisting of glycine linked to leucine, another only the bond of a fragment consisting of two molecules of glycine linked together, and so on. It is these exopeptidases that complete the job begun by the endopeptidases. Most of them are secreted by intestinal glands, but some are produced in the pancreas.

The chemical action of the various proteolytic enzymes has been described at some length, not because it is important for you to remember in detail what bonds each enzyme hydrolyzes, but because the proteolytic mechanism provides a good example of enzyme specificity and of the way enzymes often work in teams. If we had simply said that proteins are digested by pepsin, trypsin, and a variety of other peptidases, you might have failed to appreciate the complexity, yet orderliness, that characterizes many of the seemingly simple functions of the body.

Just as certain enzymes from the intestinal glands complete the digestion of protein, other intestinal enzymes complete the digestion of carbohydrate begun by salivary and pancreatic amylase. These enzymes split double sugars into simple sugars. For example, maltase splits maltose, sucrase splits sucrose, and lactase splits lactose.

Bile. One more secretion should be mentioned in this discussion of human digestion. The *liver,* a critically important organ about which much will be said in later chapters, produces a fluid called bile, which aids in fat digestion. The liver is a very large organ occupying much of the space in the upper part of the abdomen. On its surface is a small storage organ, the *gallbladder* (Fig. 5.27). Bile, produced throughout the liver, is collected by a series of branching ducts and emptied into the gallbladder. When food enters the duodenum, the muscular wall of the gallbladder is stimulated to contract, and the bile is forced down the gall duct into the duodenum. Bile is not a digestive enzyme. It is not even a protein. It is a complex solution of bile salts, bile pigments, and cholesterol. The bile salts act as emulsifying agents, causing large fat droplets to be broken up into many tiny droplets suspended in water. This action is much like that of a good detergent. The many small fat droplets expose much more surface area to the digestive action of lipase than a few large droplets would. Bile salts apparently aid also in the absorption of fats. When insufficient bile salts are present in the intestine, both fat digestion and absorption are seriously impaired. The bile salts are reabsorbed by the large intestine, transported back to the liver, and used again.

The bile pigments and cholesterol play no perceptible role in digestion. The pigments are produced through the destruction of red blood cells in the liver; it is they that give the characteristic brown color to feces. The cholesterol, a relatively insoluble compound, sometimes causes trouble by becoming concentrated into hard gallstones, which may block the bile duct and interfere with the flow of bile.

REFERENCES

Anonymous, 1957. *Vitamin Manual.* Upjohn, Kalamazoo, Mich.

BEST, C. H., and N. B. TAYLOR, 1961. *The Physiological Basis of Medical Practice,* 7th ed. Williams & Wilkins, Baltimore. (See esp. Chapters 36–55.)

LLOYD, F. E., 1942. *The Carnivorous Plants.* Chronica Botanica, Waltham, Mass.

PROSSER, C. L., and F. A. BROWN, 1961. *Comparative Animal Physiology,* 2nd ed. Saunders, Philadelphia. (See esp. Chapters 4–5.)

STEWARD, F. C., ed., 1959–1963. *Plant Physiology,* vol. 2 (*Plants in Relation to Water and Solutes*) and vol. 3 (*Inorganic Nutrition of Plants*). Academic Press, New York.

STILES, W., 1961. *Trace Elements in Plants,* 3rd ed. Cambridge University Press, New York.

WINTON, F. R., and L. E. BAYLISS, 1962. *Human Physiology,* 5th ed. Little, Brown, Boston. (See esp. Chapters 5–7.)

SUGGESTED READING

CARLSON, A. J., V. JOHNSON, and H. M. CAVERT, 1961. *The Machinery of the Body,* 5th ed. University of Chicago Press, Chicago. (See esp. Chapters 7–8.)

D'AMOUR, F. E., 1961. *Basic Physiology.* University of Chicago Press, Chicago. (See esp. Chapters 11–13.)

DE DUVE, C., 1963. "The Lysosome," *Scientific American,* May. (Offprint 156.)

GALSTON, A. W., 1964. *The Life of the Green Plant,* 2nd ed. Prentice-Hall, Englewood Cliffs, N.J. (See esp. Chapter 3.)

GREULACH, V. A., and J. E. ADAMS, 1962. *Plants: An Introduction to Modern Botany.* Wiley, New York. (See esp. Chapters 8–11.)

MEYER, B. S., D. B. ANDERSON, and R. H. BÖHNING, 1960. *Introduction to Plant Physiology.* Van Nostrand, Princeton, N.J. (See esp. Chapters 6–7, 15.)

NEURATH, H., 1964. "Protein-Digesting Enzymes," *Scientific American,* December. (Offprint 198.)

PRAMER, D., 1964. "Nematode-Trapping Fungi," *Science,* vol. 144, pp. 382–388.

RAMSAY, J. A., 1957. *Physiological Approach to the Lower Animals.* Cambridge University Press, New York. (See esp. Chapter 1.)

RAY, P. M., 1963. *The Living Plant.* Holt, Rinehart & Winston, New York. (See esp. Chapters 4–5.)

SCHMIDT-NIELSEN, K., 1964. *Animal Psysiology,* 2nd ed. Prentice-Hall, Englewood Cliffs, N.J. (See esp. Chapter 1.)

SINNOTT, E. W., and K. S. WILSON, 1963. *Botany: Principles and Problems,* 6th ed. McGraw-Hill, New York. (See esp. Chapter 5.)

STEWARD, F. C., 1964. *Plants at Work.* Addison-Wesley, Reading, Mass. (See esp. Chapters 4, 9.)

CHAPTER

6

GAS EXCHANGE

WE HAVE SEEN HOW ENERGY-RICH NUTRIent compounds are procured by organisms, both autotrophic and heterotrophic. And we have examined the complex chemical reactions by which these compounds are broken down, releasing energy utilized in the synthesis of ATP, the energy currency. If nutrient materials are to be completely metabolized to carbon dioxide and water, molecular oxygen is essential. Thus one of the basic problems of life is the procurement of oxygen and the elimination of carbon dioxide.

It is true that a few unicellular organisms can subsist indefinitely in the total absence of oxygen, some even being killed when exposed to it. Other organisms can survive for limited periods under anaerobic conditions. But in these cases, the respiratory degradation of nutrients stops far short of completion, the end products usually being lactic acid or ethyl alcohol, which are relatively large molecules that still contain much chemical energy bound within them. Anaerobic respiration thus appears very wasteful in comparison with aerobic respiration; nevertheless, its importance in some cases should not be overlooked. By resorting to anaerobic metabolism, an organism (or part of an organism) may, for example, survive short periods of oxygen deprivation. For organisms capable of living anaerobically indefinitely, there are environments open for colonization that would otherwise be totally uninhabitable. Many bacteria, for example, are anaerobic and live in habitats where no other type of organism could survive. Nonetheless, aerobic rather than anaerobic respiration is the chief method of respiration in both plants and animals.

It is a common misconception that oxygen procurement is a problem faced only by animals, and that gas exchange in green plants consists exclusively of intake of carbon dioxide and release of oxygen. This is the exchange that takes place in association with photosynthesis, but the carbohydrate products of photosynthesis are of little value to the plant unless they can be respired to provide usable metabolic energy. Thus plants, like animals, are constantly taking in oxygen and releasing carbon dioxide as they carry out the process of cellular respiration. Both photosynthetic gas exchange and respiratory gas exchange are usually taking place when a green plant is exposed to bright light; since the rate of photosynthesis then greatly exceeds the rate of respiration, the *net* effect is one of uptake of carbon dioxide and release of oxygen. The reverse is true, of course, when the green plant is in the dark or when it has no leaves in winter.

THE PROBLEM

Gas exchange between a living cell and its environment always takes place by diffusion across the moist cell membrane. The gases that move across the membrane are in solution. In unicellular organisms and many small multicellular ones, particularly those that are aquatic, each cell is either in direct contact with the surrounding medium or only a few cells re-

moved from that medium. Thus exchange of oxygen and carbon dioxide is no serious problem, and these organisms have usually not evolved special respiratory devices.

Large body size, however, poses many complications in the gas-exchange process. And the evolution of specialized respiratory arrangements has been a prerequisite to the evolution of large size. Admittedly, some brown algae, the kelps, may grow to be 200–300 feet long and yet have no special gas-exchange mechanism other than direct diffusion between each cell and the surrounding water, but the large size of these plants is mostly in two dimensions (Fig. 6.1). The blades of even the longest kelps remain very thin; as a result, no cell is far from the surface, and the total gas-exchange area is fairly large in relation to the volume of the plant. The thicker stipe has

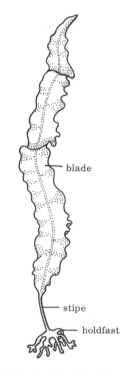

blade

stipe

holdfast

Fig. 6.1. A kelp (*Laminaria*), one of the large brown algae. [Modified from H. J. Fuller and O. Tippo, *College Botany*, Holt, 1949.]

numerous intercellular spaces filled with water that is continuous with the external medium.

When increase in body size involves three dimensions, as it generally does, the maintenance of a respiratory surface of adequate dimensions relative to the volume becomes a more complex problem, because area (a square function) increases much more slowly than volume (a cube function). The problem is most acute for the more active animals, whose rapid utilization of energy demands a large amount of oxygen per unit of volume. An additional complicating factor is that many organisms have evolved relatively impermeable skin and outer body coverings such as scales, feathers, and hair, which facilitate regulation of water and salt balance and also function as protective barriers between the fragile internal tissues and organs and the often hostile outer environment. The presence of these protective devices means that the gas-exchange surface must be confined to a restricted region of the body surface, making the problem of adequate exchange area even more critical.

Another complication brought on by large size in three dimensions is that many cells are deep within the organism, far from the gas-exchange surface. Diffusion alone is incapable of moving gases in adequate concentrations across the immense number of cells that may intervene between these more internal cells and the body surface, particularly in the case of the metabolically more active cells of animals. Some mechanism for conveying gases to every individual cell of the organism becomes essential.

The necessity that the moist membranes across which gas exchange occurs be in direct contact with the environmental medium also poses serious difficulties, especially for terrestrial organisms. The moist membranes must be exposed to the environment, but they must be exposed in such a way that the chances of desiccation are minimized. Further, a large, thin, moist surface is often very fragile and easily suffers mechanical damage. In general,

therefore, there has been a tendency toward the evolution of protective devices, particularly when the respiratory surfaces have been evaginated ones.

In general, specialized respiratory surfaces may be grouped into two large categories: those that are invaginations (inpockets) of the body surface and those that are evaginations (outpockets) (Fig. 6.2). Each of these categories embraces a diversity of form and detail, but the diversities become less bewildering if one bears in mind that each type of respiratory system represents merely one way of meeting the basic needs discussed above: a respiratory surface of adequate dimensions, means of keeping the surface moist, means of protecting the fragile surface from mechanical injury, and, for many organisms, methods of transporting gases between the area of exchange with the environment and the more internal cells.

SOLUTIONS IN TERRESTRIAL PLANTS

As indicated earlier, most primitively aquatic plants, notably the algae, carry out gas exchange across almost the entire body surface; but in response to the problems of desiccation and large three-dimensional size, more elaborate mechanisms have evolved in most terrestrial plants.

Leaves

Gas exchange associated with both photosynthesis and cellular respiration takes place at a particularly high rate in green leaves, organs strikingly adapted for this process. Recall that most of the visible outer surface of a leaf, covered as it is by a waxy cuticle, is more or less dry and impermeable, and hence ill suited for diffusion of gases. Exchange must therefore take place elsewhere. You had occasion to examine in some detail the anatomy of a green leaf while studying the photosynthetic process, and you will remember that the mesophyll parenchyma was packed very loosely, leaving large intercellular spaces (Fig. 6.3). A high percentage of the total surface of each mesophyll cell is exposed to the air in these spaces. The spaces are interconnected and are continuous with the external atmosphere by way of the *stomata,* which are openings in the epidermis. Gases can thus move easily between the surrounding atmosphere and the internal

spaces of the leaf. The actual gas exchange, by which we mean the diffusion of gases into and out of living cells, takes place across the thin moist membranes of the cells inside the leaf.

The green leaf clearly falls into our category of invaginated respiratory surfaces. It may be well at this point to examine in more detail the evolutionary adaptations that have enabled the leaf to fulfill the basic demands placed upon respiratory systems.

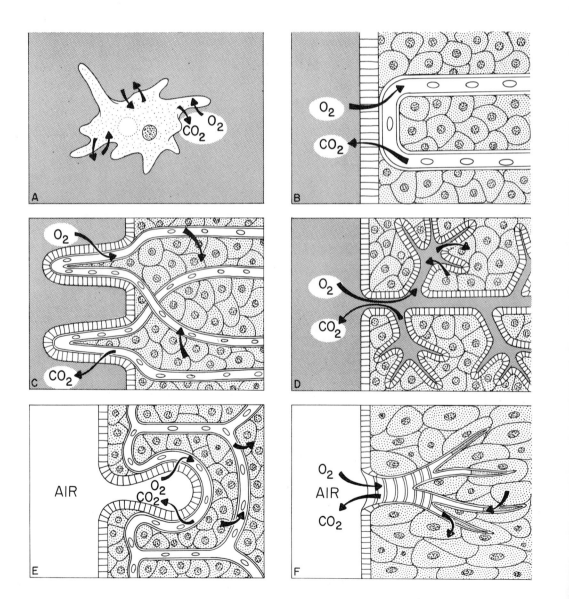

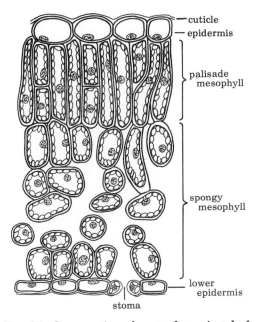

cuticle
epidermis

palisade
mesophyll

spongy
mesophyll

lower
epidermis

stoma

Fig. 6.3. Cross section of part of a privet leaf.

The surface area available for gas exchange in the leaf is very large; if the total area of cell membrane exposed to the intercellular spaces could be measured accurately, it would be found enormous by comparison with the total outer area of the leaf. The principle involved is a very elementary one: A chamber irregularly shaped and greatly subdivided by partial partitions will have far more wall space than a round or square one of equal volume.

The second problem, keeping the exchange surface moist, has also been solved. The exchange membranes are exposed to air only in internal spaces; the humidity within those intercellular spaces is nearly 100 percent, and

a thin film of water remains on the membranes of the mesophyll cells. Gases moving into the cell first dissolve in the film of water. The protective epidermal tissues and the layers of waxy cuticle on their outer surfaces act as barriers between the dry outside air and the moist inside air. But the barriers cannot be complete, or movement of gases between the outside and inside could not take place; thus, although the stomata are essential, in a sense they constitute weak links in the protective armor of the leaf. Here we see the sort of compromise that evolutionary adaptation has constantly had to make. Few characters, however beneficial, are free of possible deleterious effects. What determines the evolutionary fate of a character is not whether it is solely beneficial or solely harmful, but whether or not the beneficial effects outweigh the harmful ones. In this case, the advantages of stomata outweigh the danger of desiccation they pose; moreover, other adaptations have evolved that minimize the danger.

Each opening, or stoma, in the epidermis is bounded by two highly specialized epidermal cells called *guard cells,* which, unlike most other epidermal cells, contain chloroplasts (Fig. 6.4). These bean-shaped cells have cell walls of unequal thickness; the walls next to the stoma are considerably thicker than those on the side away from the stoma. When the guard cells contain much fluid and are turgid (usually in the light), the turgidity causes the thin outer wall of each cell to buckle outward, pulling the rest of the cell with it and opening the stoma. Gas exchange can now take place, and the leaf can obtain carbon

Fig. 6.2. Types of gas-exchange systems in animals. (A) Unicellular organisms exchange gases with the surrounding water directly across the general cell membrane. (B) Some multicellular animals use the general body surface as an exchange surface; the blood transports gases to and from the surface. (C) Many multicellular aquatic animals have specialized evaginated gas-exchange structures (gills). (D) A few aquatic animals, such as the sea cucumber, utilize invaginated exchange areas. (E) Most true air breathers have lungs, specialized invaginated areas that depend upon a blood transport system. (F) Land arthropods have tracheal systems, invaginated tubes that carry air directly to the tissues without the intervention of a blood transport system.

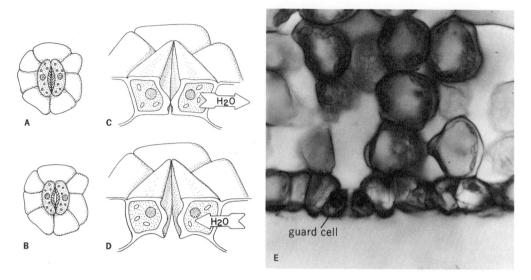

Fig. 6.4. Guard cells. Left: View from below, with stoma closed (A) and open (B). Middle: Median transverse section, with stoma closed (C) and open (D). For explanation of mechanism of guard-cell action, see text. (E) Photograph showing stoma and guard cells in lower epidermis of a privet leaf. × 828. [E: Courtesy Thomas Eisner, Cornell University.]

dioxide for photosynthesis. In the dark, the reverse usually occurs; the cells lose water and become flaccid, with the result that their thick inner walls close the stoma. That the stomata should be open during the day, when the air is usually drier, and should be closed ordinarily at night, when the air is often damper, may seem an inefficient way to combat desiccation. The fact is that the requirements of water conservation conflict with those of photosynthesis. Photosynthesis, without which the plant would perish, requires light. If the leaf is to perform photosynthesis at a high rate, it must take in a sufficient amount of carbon dioxide during the day, and for this the stomata must be open. Imperfect as the regulation of the stomata may be from the point of view of water conservation, it is better than none. Besides, although most plants lose enormous quantities of water by evaporation through the stomata every day in the process called *transpiration,* the humidity in the intercellular spaces of the leaf probably does not often drop appreciably, because the lost water is steadily replaced by water drawn up through the stem and distributed throughout the leaf by the many small veins. And transpiration itself has been utilized in the evolution of an effective transport mechanism, as we shall see in the next chapter. There is a "safety valve" in the system also. If the water loss by transpiration is too rapid and exceeds the capacity of the plant to supply more to the leaves, the leaf cells, including the guard cells, may become flaccid (i.e. wilted), whereupon the stomata close, preventing further water loss. This closing of the stomata as a result of wilt has the effect, however, of limiting the supply of carbon dioxide to that produced by cellular respiration; the rate of photosynthesis is therefore reduced until it is approximately equal to the rate of respiration. Respiration, in turn, is limited to using the oxygen released as a by-product of photosynthesis.

The mechanism whereby the rapid turgidity changes of the guard cells are effected is only poorly understood. One long-held theory was that when the guard cells are in light they carry out photosynthesis, producing sugar and other osmotically active materials and thereby reducing the concentration (though not necessarily the total amount) of their intracellular water. The result would be a tendency for water to move by osmosis into the guard cells, causing them to swell and open the stoma. In the dark, the concentration of sugar in the guard cells would decline and the concentration of water would rise, with the result that water would move out of the guard cells, which would then become flaccid and close the stoma. Many workers think, however, that this theory puts too great a demand on the photosynthetic capacity of the guard cells and that any stomatal movement caused solely by this mechanism would be much too slow. A later theory recognized that the starch metabolism of guard cells is unusual; the starch in these cells is converted into sugar in the light, whereas in most cells this conversion occurs mainly in the dark. It was suggested that the enzyme responsible for conversion of starch into sugar in the guard cells was particularly influenced by changes in pH, and that photosynthesis, by using up carbon dioxide, reduced the acidity in the guard cells and made the enzymes more active. Thus conversion of stored starch into sugar would augment photosynthetic production of sugar and bring about a more rapid osmotic change than would be possible with photosynthesis alone. But even this theory seems inadequate to account for the very rapid movements of guard cells that have often been observed, although the starch-sugar conversions, the pH changes, and the changes in sugar concentration definitely do occur and doubtless play some role in guard-cell movement. More recent theories have tended to supplement these factors by some sort of special energy-requiring mechanism, presumably driven by ATP. Much more research is needed before we really understand the surprisingly complex process whereby the plant regulates the size of the stomatal opening.

Before leaving the subject of stomata, let us note several other evolutionary adaptations associated with them. In most plants, the stomata are located primarily, if not exclusively in the lower epidermis—the side of the leaf that is usually turned away from the sun's rays, i.e. the side where the drying tendency is less severe. Further, the lower epidermis of many plants is covered with short hairs, which function in reducing direct air currents across the mouths of the stomata. Plant species adapted for life in particularly dry or particularly wet habitats often exhibit special adaptations of the stomata. In the oleander (*Nerium*), which lives in a very dry habitat, the stomata are located in deep-haired depressions in the lower epidermis, an adaptation that eliminates convection currents across the stomata (Fig. 6.5).

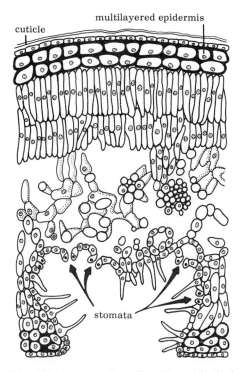

Fig. 6.5. Cross section of portion of leaf of oleander (*Nerium*). The stomata are located in deep hair-lined crypts in the lower surface of the leaf. Note also the other adaptations for living in very dry habitats, such as the multilayered epidermis and the very thick cuticle.

In the pondweed *Potamogeton,* which lives in a very wet habitat, the stomata are located in the very thin upper epidermis and not in the lower epidermis (Fig. 6.6). What is the adaptive significance of their placement?

The third problem of respiratory surfaces, danger of mechanical injury, is a relatively minor one for an internal exchange surface. The epidermis with its various hairs, spines, and other derivatives does, of course, function as a protective covering for the entire leaf. Internal transport of gases, the fourth problem, is apparently solved in leaves without any special adaptations; gases can reach each individual cell directly via the intercellular spaces.

Stems and Roots

Do not infer from this discussion that the leaves constitute the only gas-exchange areas of plants. We have simply chosen to examine these beautifully adapted organs in some detail in order to illustrate the types of problems and solutions characteristic of gas-exchange mechanisms.

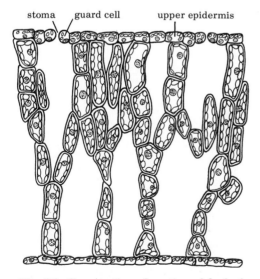

stoma   guard cell   upper epidermis

Fig. 6.6. Cross section of portion of leaf of pondweed (*Potamogeton*). The stomata are in the upper surface, and the mesophyll has very large intercellular air spaces. There are chloroplasts in the epidermal cells.

The relatively impervious layer of bark on many old stems would effectively cut off most of their oxygen supply if it were not for the development of numerous small areas of loosely arranged cells with many intercellular spaces between them through which gases can move freely. Each such loose group of cells is called a **lenticel** (Fig. 6.7). The spongy streaks that you always see in cork (an outer bark) are traces of the lenticels of the cork oak.

Roots also carry out gas exchange, though they usually possess no special adaptations for this function. Gases can diffuse readily across the moist membranes of root hairs and other epidermal cells (recall study of the roots as structures for nutrient procurement in the last chapter). For roots to obtain sufficient oxygen, however, the soil in which they grow must be well aerated. Different types of soils vary in their aeration characteristics, which depend on the amount of pore space, the affinity for water, and many other factors. Soils with very high percentages of clay particles, for example, have many pore spaces, but the tiny clay particles are so hydrophilic ("water-loving") and adsorb so much water during wet periods that the air spaces become filled with water, a condition known as waterlogging. Frequent waterlogging may so reduce the air content of the soil that many species of plants are stunted or cannot grow at all. In some poorly aerated soils, the circulation of gases between the pore spaces and the atmosphere above the soil is so slow that the air in the pore spaces becomes deficient in oxygen and often contains a harmfully high concentration of carbon dioxide. One of the benefits of hoeing, raking, plowing, or otherwise cultivating the soil is the increased air circulation they make possible.

There seems to be no need for special gas-transporting mechanisms in plants such as those that occur in animals, even though the most internal cells of a large stem or root are far removed from the surface of the plant. Two reasons for this are readily apparent. First, the metabolic rate of most plant cells is well below

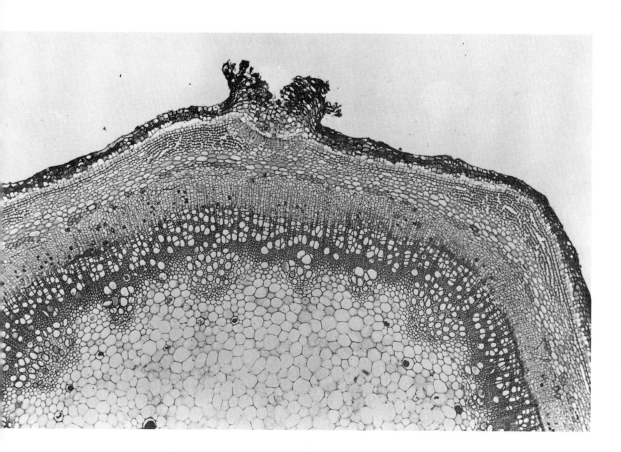

Fig. 6.7. Lenticel on stem of elderberry (*Sambucus*). × 44. [Courtesy Thomas Eisner, Cornell University.]

that of the cells of higher animals; hence their demand for oxygen and their production of carbon dioxide is much smaller. Second, most of the intercellular spaces in the tissues of land plants are filled with air, in contrast to the fluid-filled intercellular spaces of animal tissues. These air-filled spaces are interconnected to form an intercellular air-space system that opens to the outside through stomata and lenticels and that penetrates to the innermost parts of the plant body. Thus incoming gases can move in gaseous form directly to the internal parts of the plant from the environmental atmosphere without having to cross membranous barriers, and they do not have to diffuse long distances through water or cell fluids, since they do not go into solution until they reach the film of water on the surfaces of the individual cells. Since oxygen can diffuse some

300,000 times faster through air than through tissue fluids, the intercellular air-space system ensures that cells in the center of large stems or roots are adequately supplied. If the oxygen had to diffuse through fluid from the surface of a plant organ, it would penetrate less than one millimeter, and all the more internal cells would be deprived of oxygen and could not respire. Experiments show, in fact, that if the air-space system is blocked, as by waterlogging, the innermost cells soon start dying.

SOLUTIONS
IN AQUATIC ANIMALS

As we have already indicated, unicellular animals have no special gas-exchange devices, simple diffusion across their cell membranes being sufficient. Some of the smaller and simpler multicellular animals like jellyfish, hydra, and planaria show little further development, although their multipurpose gastrovascular cavities do facilitate the exposure of the more internal cells to environmental water (containing dissolved oxygen) drawn in through the mouth. No cell in these animals is far from the water medium. A few larger aquatic animals, particularly some of the marine segmented worms, lack special respiratory systems and utilize the skin of the general body surface, which is usually richly supplied with blood vessels. Most larger multicellular animals, however, have evolved true respiratory systems.

Gills

With a few exceptions, the respiratory systems of multicellular aquatic animals involve evaginated exchange surfaces, usually known as gills. Gills vary in complexity all the way from the simple bumplike skin gills of some starfish (Fig. 6.8), or the flaplike parapodia of many

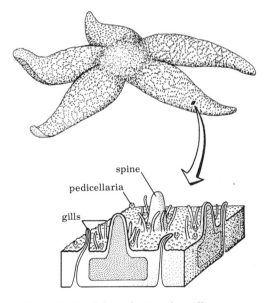

spine
pedicellaria
gills

Fig. 6.8. Starfish. The tiny skin gills are protected from damage by the spines and pedicellariae.

segmented marine worms (Fig. 6.9A), to the minutely subdivided gills of fish (Fig. 6.10). Such diverse animals as clams and lobsters, squids and salamanders, possess gills, these having evolved independently countless times during the history of animal life on earth.

Most gills, particularly those of very active animals, have such finely dissected surfaces that a few small gills may expose an immense total exchange surface to the water. Thus, although the gas-exchange surface takes up a very limited part of the animal, leaving the rest of the body free to evolve relatively impermeable protective coverings, the surface-to-volume ratio of the exchange surface remains high.

Another characteristic of most gills is that they contain a rich supply of blood vessels. Often the blood in these vessels is separated from the external water by only two cells: the single cell of the wall of the vessel and a cell of the gill surface. Sometimes even the vessel wall is eliminated, leaving only one cell between the blood and the water. Oxygen moves by diffusion from the water, across the intervening cells, and into the blood, where it is ordinarily picked up by a carrier pigment (the mechanism of transport by the blood will be discussed in the next chapter). The blood then transports the oxygen throughout the body to the individual cells. Carbon dioxide produced by cellular metabolism moves in the opposite direction, being transported to the gills and discharged into the surrounding water.

The fragile gills are easily damaged, and a variety of protective devices have evolved for them. Frequently, these devices are coverings, such as the carapace of lobsters or the operculum of fish (Fig. 6.10A), but sometimes they take other forms, as in the spines and pincers that surround the skin gills of starfish (Fig. 6.8).

Obtaining sufficient oxygen is a greater problem for aquatic animals than for air breathers, for two reasons. First, oxygen has a low solubility in water, constituting only about 0.5 per-

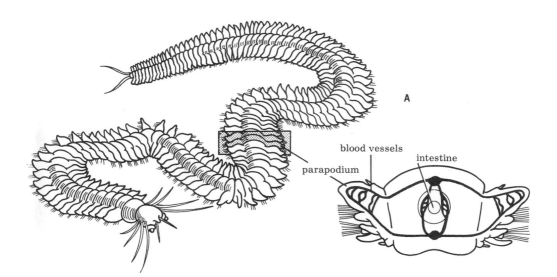

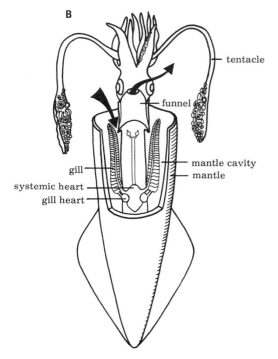

cent of sea water (the percentage is usually slightly higher in fresh water, but far more variable) compared with approximately 21 percent in air; second, the diffusion of oxygen is many thousands of times slower in water than in air. Most aquatic animals must therefore actively move water across the exchange surfaces. If the water remained still, the oxygen in the vicinity of the exchange surfaces would soon be depleted and would not be renewed by diffusion fast enough to sustain the animal. A fish moves water into the mouth, across the gill filaments, and out behind the operculum (see Fig. 6.10C). A lobster keeps water currents moving through small openings near the leg bases, into the gill chamber beneath the carapace, and out near the head.

Solutions Other Than Gills

Biology is a science of exceptions. Not all aquatic animals with special respiratory systems utilize evaginated gills. For example, sea cucumbers—relatives of starfish—have specialized invaginated systems called respiratory trees (Fig. 6.11). These long branched tubes are diverticula of the rectum; water is drawn into and expelled from the system by contractions of the rectum. This system is an elaboration of a simpler one used by a few animals, in which gas exchange takes place as water is alternately drawn in and expelled through the

Fig. 6.9. Gills of marine segmented worm and squid. (A) Marine segmented worm (*Nereis*), with cross section of one segment. The cross section shows that the flaplike parapodia on each segment are richly supplied with blood vessels. (B) Squid, with part of mantle cut away. Water flows into the mantle cavity at its open end when the mantle is relaxed. When the mantle contracts, its collar seals the opening and the water is forced out of the funnel. The jetlike expulsion of water when the mantle is contracted propels the animal backward with great force. [Modified from Ralph Buchsbaum, *Animals Without Backbones*, University of Chicago Press, 1948.]

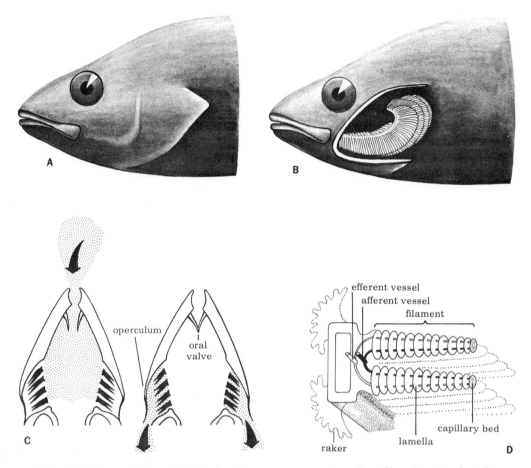

Fig. 6.10. Gills of fish. (A) Head with operculum covering the gills. (B) Head with operculum cut away and gills exposed. (C) Water is drawn through the mouth into the pharynx while the opercula are closed. Then the oral valves close as the oral cavity contracts; the water is forced across the gills (black structures) and out behind the now open opercula. (D) Structure of a gill. Each gill is composed of many filaments, each subdivided into numerous lamellae.

enlarged thin-walled posterior portion of the digestive tract.

Many insects that live in water are not fully aquatic because they must periodically come to the surface to breathe air. Of these, some exhibit highly interesting adaptations for obtaining oxygen. For example, there are beetles (*Dytiscus*) that store air under their hard shell-like forewings when they surface, then dive with this air bubble and breathe from it. You might think the oxygen in the bubble would very soon be depleted, but this is not

the case. Remember air contains high concentrations of other gases besides oxygen, and these gases are not used up. As a result, a gas bubble remains, and, as the partial pressure of oxygen in the bubble falls, there is a natural tendency for oxygen to diffuse into the bubble from the surrounding water, renewing the supply. In short, the bubble acts as a gill. In a few insects, this mechanism is so refined that their store of gases is permanent and they do not have to surface to renew it. These insects have thick layers of nonwettable hairs covering parts

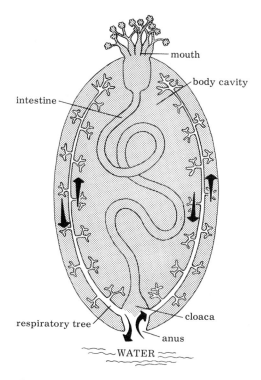

Fig. 6.11. Respiratory tree of sea cucumber.

of their bodies; the hairs hold the water away and maintain a film of air over the body surface.

SOLUTIONS IN TERRESTRIAL ANIMALS

A few land animals have evolved highly modified gill-type respiratory structures that function in air (e.g. the book lungs of spiders). But the hazards of desiccation for most such evaginated surfaces are considerable, and there are major structural problems associated with an array of filaments or a branched structure that is both sufficiently strong to maintain its shape against surface tension and gravity and sufficiently thin-walled to allow easy passage of gases. It is not surprising, therefore, that most terrestrial animals have evolved invaginated

respiratory systems. These invaginated systems are of two principal types, **lungs** and **tracheae.** In both, the air inside the system is kept moist, and the cells of the exchange surface are covered by a film of water in which gases can dissolve. Thus the process of gas exchange has remained essentially aquatic in land animals, as it has in the leaf.

Lungs

Lungs, which are invaginated gas-exchange organs limited to a particular region of the animal and dependent upon a blood transport system, are most typical of two unrelated animal groups, the land snails and the higher vertebrates, including some fish, most amphibians, and all reptiles, birds, and mammals. In their simplest forms, lungs are little more than chambers with slightly increased vascularization in their walls and with some sort of passageway leading to the outside. This simple type of lung is found, for example, in some snails that inhabit the lower levels of the ocean beach, where the necessity for air breathing is seldom pressing because oxygen is available from the water. From such a rudimentary beginning, the evolution of the lung has tended toward a greatly increased surface area, by subdivision of its inner surface into many small pockets or folds, and toward increased vascularization of its exchange surface. The latter tendency can be observed in almost diagrammatic simplicity in four closely related snails, called periwinkles, which inhabit successively higher levels of the ocean beach; the increase in vascularization of the lung (or mantle cavity) in these snails is precisely correlated with increased distance from the ocean and the concomitant increased necessity for air breathing.

It is not surprising that terrestrial vertebrates have lungs, but it may surprise you that some presently living relict species (species surviving from very ancient times) of fish have them also and, moreover, that many biologists are now convinced that the ancestral fish, from

which both modern fish and the land vertebrates evolved, had lungs that enabled them to
live in stagnant, poorly aerated water for long
periods of time when necessary. These primitive lungs were simple sacs that arose as ventral evaginations of the digestive tract in the
pharyngeal region behind the gills. A few salamanders still have such simple lungs, but in
most terrestrial vertebrates the inner surface
has become increasingly folded and subdivided, providing a far higher surface-to-volume

ratio for the exchange process. This evolutionary tendency reaches its culmination in mammals and birds, the two warm-blooded classes,
which must expend vast amounts of metabolic
energy to maintain their stable high body temperatures, and hence have exceedingly high
oxygen demands.

Let us look at the respiratory system of man
(Fig. 6.12) in some detail, as an example of
the mammalian type. Air is drawn in through
the *external nares,* or nostrils, and enters the

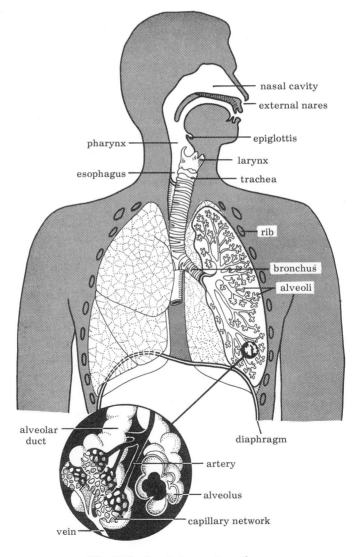

Fig. 6.12. Respiratory system of man.

nasal cavities, which function in warming and moistening the air, filtering out dust particles, and smelling. Bony ridges in the cavities, causing eddies in the air stream, help expose the air to these processes. The mucus layer on the epithelium of the nasal passages, and the cilia of many of the epithelial cells, increase the efficiency with which these processes occur; in addition, the mucus may have some bactericidal properties. Curiously, of the various functions mentioned, smelling is the primitive one; the external nares and the nasal passages originally had nothing to do with respiration, but evolved as smelling devices. Fish have nostrils but they do not breathe through them; they take in water for respiratory purposes through the mouth. Since smelling and feeding are so intimately related, it is not surprising that in fish, amphibians, and many reptiles there is little or no separation between the nasal cavity and the mouth cavity. It is in mammals that the separation has been most completely developed, a new "roof of the mouth" having evolved that consists of an anterior bony palate and a posterior soft palate (Fig. 6.13).

Even in mammals, however, the air and food passages ultimately join in a region known as the *pharynx.* During inhalation, air leaves the pharynx via a ventral opening, the *glottis,* which leads into the *larynx.* (We are here using the terms dorsal and ventral as though the human were standing on four legs like other mammals.) Since air enters the pharynx dorsally and exits ventrally, and since food enters ventrally and exits dorsally into the esophagus, it follows that the air and food passages not only join but actually cross in the pharynx. (This rather inefficient arrangement is the price we pay because natural selection modified the already existing smelling apparatus into respiratory passages instead of starting from scratch and building a totally new system. But this is typical of much evolution; the new is built from the old.) Elaborate mechanisms help ensure that when food is forced back into the pharynx it cannot enter the nasal

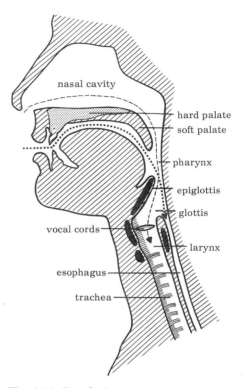

Fig. 6.13. **Detail of upper portion of human respiratory and digestive systems.** Dashed line, path of air. Dotted line, path of food. The two paths cross in the pharynx. [Modified from A. J. Carlson, V. Johnson, and H. M. Cavert, *The Machinery of the Body,* University of Chicago Press, 1961.]

cavity or the larynx, but must be swallowed into the esophagus. Without attempting to describe the whole complex action in detail, we can point out that the internal nares, which connect the nasal cavities with the pharynx, are closed by the soft palate and that the glottis is closed by a flap of tissue called the *epiglottis* when the larynx is raised against it during swallowing.

Having left the pharynx through the glottis, the air enters the larynx, a chamber surrounded by a complex of cartilages (commonly called the Adam's apple). In many animals, including man, the larynx functions as a voice box. It contains a pair of vocal cords—elastic ridges stretched across the laryngeal cavity that are vibrated by the passage of air currents between them; changes in the tension of the cords result in changes in the pitch of the sounds emitted.

The *trachea* is the air duct leading from the larynx into the thoracic cavity. Its epithelial lining is ciliated; the cilia beat in waves that carry foreign particles and mucus up the trachea away from the lungs. A series of C-shaped rings of cartilage are embedded in the walls of the trachea and prevent it from collapsing upon inhalation. At its lower end, it divides into two *bronchi,* tubes that lead toward the two lungs. (It is at the lower end of the trachea, where the bronchi branch away, that the voice box of birds, the syrinx, is located; birds have no vocal cords in their larynx.) Each bronchus branches and rebranches, and the bronchioles thus formed branch repeatedly in their turn, forming smaller and smaller ducts that ultimately terminate in tiny air pockets, each of which has a series of small chamberlike bulges in its walls termed *alveoli.* The total alveolar surface is enormous (about 1,000 square feet)—many times greater than the total area of the skin.

The walls of the alveoli are exceedingly thin, being usually only one cell thick, and each alveolus is surrounded by a dense bed of blood capillaries. The alveoli are the site of the actual gas exchange and may therefore be regarded as the primary functional units of the lungs. Oxygen entering an alveolus dissolves in the film of water on its wall and then moves by diffusion across the intervening cells to the blood. Experiments have demonstrated that both this movement and the reverse movement of carbon dioxide are cases of simple diffusion; no active transport across the cell barriers is involved. Oxygen is in higher concentration in the air of the alveolus than in the blood and carbon dioxide is in higher concentration in the blood than in the alveolus. Each gas simply moves from the region of its higher concentration to the region of its lower concentration, in accordance with the principles of diffusion that

you have already learned. There are actually very few instances where diffusion takes place within the body totally unaided by active transport, but it has been demonstrated that the body is incapable of active transport of oxygen in the lungs. As a result, when the partial pressure of oxygen in the atmosphere falls below normal, as at high altitudes, symptoms of oxygen deprivation rapidly develop, because passive transport is insufficient to meet oxygen demands.

Air is drawn into and expelled from the lungs by the mechanical process called *breathing.* In mammals this process generally involves muscular contractions of two regions, the *rib cage* and the *diaphragm.* The latter is a muscular partition separating the thoracic and abdominal cavities (Fig. 6.14). Inhalation (or inspiration) occurs whenever the volume of the thoracic cavity, in which the lungs lie, is increased; such an increase reduces the air pressure within the chest below the atmospheric pressure and draws air into the lungs. The increase in thoracic volume is accomplished by contractions of the rib muscles that draw the rib cage up and out, and by contraction, or downward pull, of the normally upward-arched diaphragm; the first mechanism is popularly

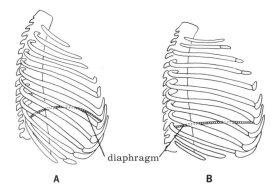

diaphragm

A   B

Fig. 6.14. The mechanics of human breathing. (A) Resting position. (B) Inhalation: The rib cage is raised up and out, and the diaphragm is pulled downward. Both of these motions increase the volume of the thoracic cavity, thereby reducing the pressure in the cavity and pulling air into the lungs.

called "chest breathing," while the second is called "abdominal breathing." Normal exhalation (or expiration) is a passive process; the muscles relax, allowing the rib cage to fall back to its resting position and the diaphragm to arch upward. This reduction of thoracic volume, combined with the elastic recoil of the lungs themselves, causes a rise in the pressure inside the lungs to a level above that of the outside atmosphere and drives out the air.

The air moved by a single normal breath—the tidal air—represents only a small fraction of the total capacity of the lungs. Additional air (complementary air) can be forcibly inhaled, and, similarly, forcible exhalation can expel additional air (reserve air). The total breathing capacity, or *vital capacity,* is thus the tidal air plus the complementary and reserve air; though it varies greatly from person to person, 4 liters is probably a rough approximation of the average. Trained athletes usually develop larger lungs, and, as would be expected, their vital capacity is usually substantially greater than normal. Even the vital capacity does not constitute the total capacity of the lungs; there is residual air that can be released only if the lung is collapsed, and, even beyond that, a minimal quantity of air always remains in any lung that has once been inflated.

In contrast to mammalian lungs, the lungs of birds (Fig. 6.15) can be ventilated almost completely at each breath. This is because there are usually numerous extensions beyond the lungs, called *air sacs,* that may extend into almost every part of the body, even replacing some of the bone marrow within the bones. On inspiration, the air moves completely through the lungs and into the air sacs; expiration drives the air back through the lungs. As you might predict, there are no alveoli in the lungs of birds. These dead-end chambers are replaced by tiny air capillaries that loop through the lung tissue and allow true circulation of the air. Muscle contractions, particularly during flight, put pressure on some of the air sacs and

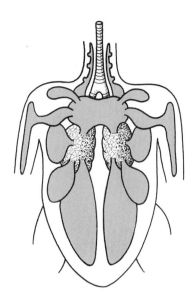

Fig. 6.15. Respiratory system of a bird. Attached to the lungs are many air sacs (black); some of the air sacs even penetrate into the marrow cavities of the wing bones.

probably increase the volume of air exposed to the exchange surfaces in the lungs per unit of time (no appreciable exchange takes place in the air sacs themselves). The air sacs, of course, are important adaptations for flight, allowing a low weight-to-size ratio, and, predictably, they are usually best developed in strong-flying species and very poorly developed in nonflying ones.

The mammalian and avian method of breathing is known as *negative-pressure breathing,* as contrasted with *positive-pressure breathing,* where air is forced into the lungs rather than drawn in. The latter method is used by adult frogs, for example. With the mouth closed and nostrils open, the frog lowers the floor of the mouth, thereby sucking air into the mouth cavity. Then it closes the nostrils and raises the mouth floor; this reduction in the volume of the mouth cavity exerts pressure on the imprisoned air and forces it into the lungs. (We should note in passing that a frog is an excellent example of an animal that utilizes a variety of gas-exchange mechanisms; the lungs are only occasionally filled, much exchange surface being provided by the thin membrane of the mouth cavity and the soft moist skin.)

Before leaving the subject of lungs and continuing our examination of respiratory systems in land animals, let us return to the hypothesis that the ancestral fish had lungs. The fate of the ancient lung is biologically a very interesting question, well worth pursuing here. A widely held theory has it that the primitively ventral lung evolved into the *swim bladder* of modern fish by gradually shifting to a dorsal position (Fig. 6.16). Its attachment to the pharynx also gradually shifted to a dorsal position, where it still is in some species, but in other modern species the connecting duct has been lost and there no longer is any direct entrance or exit to the swim bladder. The swim bladder enables the fish to remain at a given level in the water without sinking by adjusting its density to that of the surrounding water (as you might expect, bottom-dwelling fish seldom have swim bladders). The volume of gas in the bladder changes as the fish shifts from one water level to another level with a different pressure. If the fish swims upward, its swim bladder expands as a result of the reduced pressure, and to restore its normal density, the fish must remove gas from the swim bladder. If the fish swims downward, it must add gases to the swim bladder. The addition of gases to the swim bladder and their removal from it are accomplished by a region of specialized glandular cells (the gas gland) in the walls of the organ, with which many blood vessels are closely associated. Analysis of the gas in the swim bladder reveals a surprisingly high concentration of oxygen; perhaps the cells of the gas gland carry out active transport of oxygen against the concentration gradient, even though this feat apparently cannot be performed in the lungs. But there is still much we do not understand about the functioning of the swim bladder. For example, it is difficult to account for the high concentration of molecular nitrogen in the swim bladders

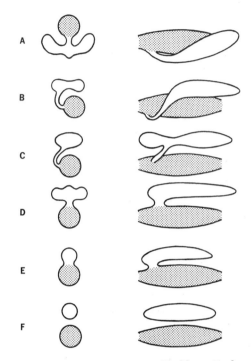

Fig. 6.16. Evolution of swim bladder. Each stage is shown in cross section (left) and longitudinal section (right), with the pharynx shaded. According to one theory, the swim bladder of modern fishes evolved from a primitive ventral lung (A). The lung may first have moved to a dorsal position while retaining a ventral attachment to the pharynx, as is still true in some living lungfish (B). The attachment to the pharynx may then have moved laterally (C) and finally become dorsal, as in the typical modern swim bladder (D and E). In some modern fishes, the connection to the pharynx has been lost entirely (F). [Modified from A. S. Romer, *The Vertebrate Body*, Saunders, 1949.]

of some fish, for active transport involves chemical reactions, but molecular nitrogen is chemically inactive in the bodies of animals. Only further research can provide an explanation.

Tracheal Systems

The second principal type of invaginated respiratory system evolved for air breathing is the tracheal system typical of most terrestrial arthropods, in which it has evolved independently many times. Here we find no localized respiratory organ and little or no significant transport of gases by the blood. Instead, the system is composed of many small tubes that ramify throughout the body (Fig. 6.17). These tubes, called *tracheae,* carry air directly to the individual cells, where diffusion across the cell membranes takes place. Air enters the tracheae by way of the *spiracles,* apertures in the body wall that can usually be opened and closed by valves (Fig. 6.18). Some of the larger insects actively ventilate their tracheal systems by muscular contraction, but most small insects and some fairly large ones apparently do not. Calculations have shown that the rate of diffusion of oxygen in air is rapid enough to maintain at the tracheal endings an oxygen concentration only slightly below that of the external atmosphere. This type of respiratory system, however, has doubtless been a factor in limiting the size attainable by insects, for which we may be thankful.

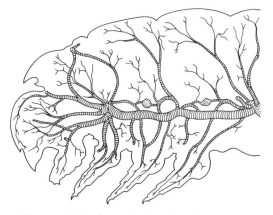

Fig. 6.17. Tracheae in head and thoracic segments of a caterpillar. Only the larger tracheae are shown. [Modified from R. E. Snodgrass, *Principles of Insect Morphology,* McGraw-Hill Book Co., 1935. Used by permission.]

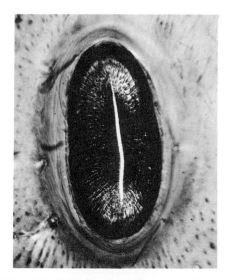

Fig. 6.18. Spiracle of grasshopper. The spiracles are usually located on the sides of the segments. The number varies in different kinds of insects. [Courtesy Warren Andrew, *Textbook of Comparative Histology,* Oxford University Press, 1959.]

REFERENCES

Best, C. H., and N. B. Taylor, 1961. *The Physiological Basis of Medical Practice,* 7th ed. Williams & Wilkins, Baltimore. (See esp. Chapters 30–33.)

Prosser, C. L., and F. A. Brown, 1961. *Comparative Animal Physiology,* 2nd ed. Saunders, Philadelphia. (See esp. Chapter 7.)

Winton, F. R., and L. E. Bayliss, 1962. *Human Physiology,* 5th ed. Little, Brown, Boston. (See esp. Chapter 4.)

SUGGESTED READING

CARLSON, A. J., V. JOHNSON, and H. M. CAVERT, 1961. *The Machinery of the Body,* 5th ed. University of Chicago Press, Chicago. (See esp. Chapter 6.)

CLEMENTS, J. A., 1962. "Surface Tension in the Lungs," *Scientific American,* December. (Offprint 142.)

D'AMOUR, F. E., 1961. *Basic Physiology.* University of Chicago Press, Chicago. (See esp. Chapter 10.)

RAMSAY, J. A., 1957. *Physiological Approach to the Lower Animals.* Cambridge University Press, New York. (See esp. Chapter 3.)

SCHMIDT-NIELSEN, K., 1964. *Animal Physiology,* 2nd ed. Prentice-Hall, Englewood Cliffs, N.J. (See esp. Chapter 2.)

WAGGONER, P. E., and I. ZELITCH, 1965. "Transpiration and the Stomata of Leaves," *Science,* vol. 150, pp. 1413–1420.

CHAPTER

7

INTERNAL TRANSPORT

EVERY LIVING CELL, WHETHER IT EXISTS alone as a single-celled organism or is a component of a multicellular one, must perform its own metabolic activities. It must synthesize its own ATP by cellular respiration (and/or photosynthesis) and carry out for itself those activities necessary for its growth and maintenance. It follows, then, that every cell must obtain the necessary raw materials to support its metabolism. It must obtain nutrients, and, if it utilizes aerobic respiration, it must obtain oxygen. Likewise, it must rid itself of metabolic wastes such as carbon dioxide and, in animals, nitrogenous compounds. In short, every cell must be exposed to a medium from which it can extract raw materials and into which it can dump wastes. In unicellular organisms and some of the structurally simpler multicellular ones, each cell is either in direct contact with the environmental medium or only a short distance from it. But in the larger and structurally more complex multicellular plants and animals, the more internal cells are far from the body surface and from the general environmental medium. We have already seen that in such organisms nutrient procurement, gas exchange, and waste expulsion take place in certain restricted regions of the body specialized for those functions. It follows that some mechanism is needed for transporting substances between the specialized systems of procurement, synthesis, or elimination and the individual living cells throughout the body.

ORGANISMS WITHOUT SPECIAL TRANSPORT SYSTEMS

Many of the smaller organisms and some bigger ones with large generally distributed surfaces for exchange of materials with the environment have no special transport systems. Some groups of aquatic organisms, particularly, tend to lack a special transport system. And plants, as a result of their lower metabolic rate associated with a lesser degree of activity, tend to be without one more often than animals. In bacteria, Protozoa, and unicellular algae (and within single living cells in general), diffusion plays an important role in the movement of materials. Since the individual particles of all substances within the cell exhibit random thermal agitation, they tend to become distributed throughout the cell if they are not prevented from doing so by specialized intracellular membranes. Diffusion is also important in movement of materials from cell to cell within the body of a multicellular organism; we have examined its part in the procurement of water by plant roots, for example. Such intercellular diffusion may be facilitated in plants by the plasmodesmata, which are tiny strands of protoplasm that penetrate the cell walls and interconnect the cytoplasmic contents of adjacent cells. We have also seen the importance in plants of diffusion of water along cell walls and of diffusion of gases through intercellular spaces.

But diffusion is a very slow process. If only diffusion were involved, it would take a long time for a substance to move from one cell to another, or even from one end of a single large cell to the other end. We should not be surprised, therefore, to find that even in unicellular and small multicellular organisms diffusion is supplemented by other transport mechanisms. We have seen, for example, that food vacuoles commonly move along a fairly precise path within the cell, thereby distributing the products of digestion to all parts of the cytoplasm. We have also seen that the endoplasmic reticulum may provide a specialized pathway for intracellular movement of some substances. And the cytoplasm itself is seldom motionless; it frequently exhibits rapid massive flow within the cell. The flowing cytoplasm of an active amoeba is an example. The cytoplasm of many plant cells undergoes a characteristic movement called cytoplasmic streaming, where the cytoplasm flows in definite currents along the surface of the cell vacuole (Fig. 7.1). Sometimes the streaming is restricted to local regions of the cell, while at other times most of the cytoplasm becomes involved and a general circulation results. The rate and direction of the flow may shift in response to a variety of factors, most of them not well understood. Increased temperature and physiological activity tend to accelerate the streaming. Such mass flow can transport substances from one part of a cell to another many times faster than simple diffusion.

Among multicellular plants, it is not only the very tiny ones that lack a specialized internal-transport system. Many algae, particu-

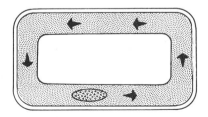

Fig. 7.1. Cytoplasmic streaming in a plant cell. The cytoplasm flows around the large central vacuole.

larly the brown and red algae, have large multicellular bodies, yet usually lack vascular tissue. As we have already seen, the cells of such plants are seldom far from the surrounding water or from water in intercellular spaces continuous with the external medium. Furthermore, nutrient and gas procurement is not limited to specialized restricted regions of the body, and photosynthesis is seldom localized in specific structures. Consequently each cell gets ample supplies locally, and long-distance transport is rarely necessary. Nevertheless, there is evidence that certain substances, particularly hormones, sometimes move over long distances surprisingly fast in some large non-vascular plants. The explanation for this is not clear, and more research is needed in this area.

Unlike plants, animals are usually adapted for active locomotion. This means that their metabolism is more rapid and less able to rely on such a slow process as diffusion, even when it is supplemented by the other intracellular processes mentioned above. Furthermore, because of their way of life, animals are much less likely than plants to have bodies that are large in one or two dimensions but flat and thin in the third. Consequently, very few even moderately large animals lack a circulatory system. There are exceptions to this rule, however. Some relatively large animals live an essentially sedentary life and can, like some large aquatic plants, keep one dimension thin. Large sea fans, a curious group of coelenterates, are an example of such plantlike animals. Tapeworms provide another example; they may be 75 feet long or more, but they are always flat and thin, and no cell is far from the food supply that bathes them in the host's digestive tract (see Fig. 22.18, p. 858).

In general, however, only very small animals lack a circulatory system. And even these frequently exhibit some adaptations for transport. Consider hydra as an example. Its body wall is basically only two cells thick, but even the cells of the inner layer are exposed directly to water containing dissolved oxygen, because such water is drawn into the gastrovascular cavity. It might seem at first glance that the cells in the tentacles would be far removed from the food supply, but closer examination shows that branches of the gastrovascular cavity penetrate into each tentacle and that food particles can be absorbed directly from this cavity by the tentacle cells. Planaria is another example. We have already seen that its gastrovascular cavity branches profusely, ramifying into all parts of the body and functioning as a primitive transport system. In short, though animals like hydra and planaria lack a true blood circulatory system, they do have compensatory adaptations that free them from complete dependence upon diffusion and intracellular transport.

VASCULAR PLANTS

As the term "vascular plants" implies, these plants are characterized by the presence of the two principal types of plant vascular tissue, xylem and phloem. Thanks to such specialized internal-transport tissues, they have been free to evolve bodies large in all dimensions and to develop far greater specialization of parts and more complete integration of function. Thus water and mineral uptake can be restricted primarily to the roots, while photosynthesis can be restricted largely to the leaves. In some very tall forest trees, the distance between the roots and the leaves may be enormous; yet the xylem and phloem form continuous pathways between them, and they can exchange materials with relative ease. Clearly, the successful exploitation of the land environment by plants was dependent upon the evolution of such a transport system.

Structure of Stems

Stems of plants serve many functions. Some contain chlorophyll and carry out photosynthesis. Others are highly specialized as storage organs; potato tubers, which are underground

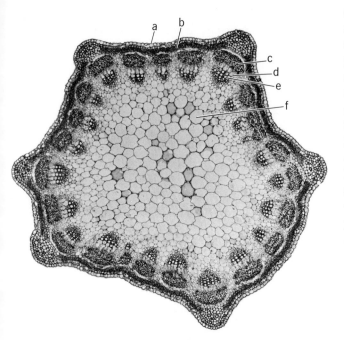

Fig. 7.2. Cross section of alfalfa (*Medicago*) stem. Alfalfa is a herbaceous dicot. (a) Epidermis; (b) cortex; (c) phloem fibers; (d) vascular phloem; (e) xylem; (f) pith. × 41. [Courtesy Thomas Eisner, Cornell University.]

stems, are an example. Here, however, we shall concentrate on stems as organs of transport and support, and examine in some detail the structural adaptations associated with these two important functions. Do not forget, just because we use stems as a basis for discussion of transport, that the vascular tissue of the stem is continuous with vascular tissue in the roots and in the leaves, and that internal transport in those organs is just as important as in stems.

Gross Anatomy. Let us first examine in cross section the stem of a herbaceous dicot like alfalfa (Fig. 7.2). ("Herbaceous" is a term usually applied to plants whose stems remain soft and succulent; the contrasting term is "woody.") The outer tissue layer of a herbaceous stem is epidermis. Next comes the cortex, which is frequently divided into an area of

collenchyma just beneath the epidermis and an area of parenchyma more internally. In some stems, an indistinct layer of endodermis lies just internal to the cortex, but endodermis is absent in most stems, being primarily a tissue of the roots. Internal to the cortex (or to the endodermis, when present) lies the vascular tissue, which may be arranged in a continuous hollow cylinder or in a series of discrete bundles, as in alfalfa. In either case, the phloem lies outside the xylem, with a layer of meristematic tissue, called *vascular cambium,* between them. The center of the stem is filled with pith, which is parenchyma tissue and functions as a storage area.

Notice that the arrangement of the tissues in the stele of a stem differs in several ways from that in a typical young root. First, the phloem and xylem form separate rings in the stem, the one outside the other, whereas the two tissues alternate in the young root. Second, stems characteristically have pith, whereas most dicot roots do not. A stele without pith, as in roots, is called a protostele (Fig. 7.3A). A stele in which the vascular tissue forms a cylindrical shell around a core of pith is called a siphonostele (Fig. 7.3B); if the hollow cylinder is broken into separate bundles, as in

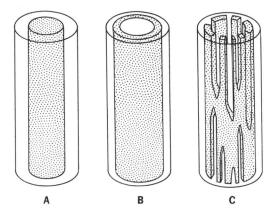

Fig. 7.3. Protostele (A), siphonostele (B), and dictyostele (C). [Modified from A. J. Eames and L. H. MacDaniels, *An Introduction to Plant Anatomy,* McGraw-Hill Book Co., 1947. Used by permission.]

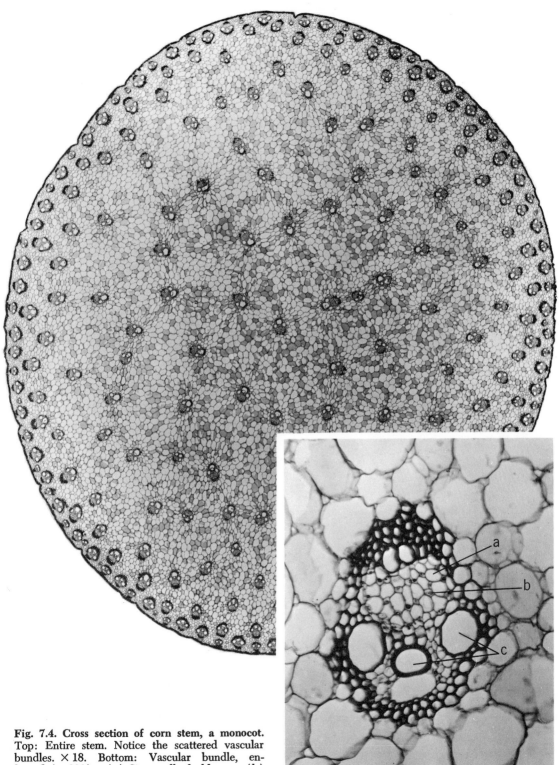

Fig. 7.4. Cross section of corn stem, a monocot.
Top: Entire stem. Notice the scattered vascular
bundles. ×18. Bottom: Vascular bundle, enlarged (×221). (a) Sieve cell of phloem; (b)
companion cell of phloem; (c) xylem vessels.
[Courtesy Thomas Eisner, Cornell University.]

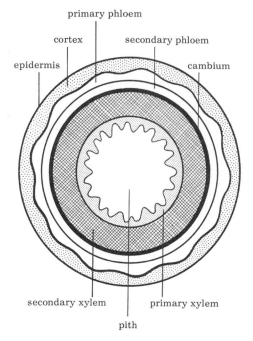

Fig. 7.5. Diagram of cross section of dicot stem after one year of secondary growth. [Modified from C. L. Wilson and W. E. Loomis, *Botany*, Dryden, 1957.]

alfalfa stems, the stele is called a dictyostele (Fig. 7.3C). The protostele is believed to be the ancestral type from which the others have evolved.

Stems of monocots are similar to those of herbaceous dicots. Their vascular tissue, however, always forms discrete bundles, never a continuous cylindrical shell, and the bundles are usually not arranged in a definite circle, as in dicots, but are more scattered through the stem (Fig. 7.4). This means that there is no clear distinction between cortex and pith in such stems. Most monocots lack cambium (palms and some lilies are exceptions).

The cambium of many herbaceous dicots never becomes active and never produces additional phloem or xylem cells. In such plants, all the vascular tissue is said to be *primary tissue* —tissue derived originally from the apical meristem as the stem (or root) grew in length. The apical meristem of a stem is, of course, in the bud, while that of the root is near the root tip. The new cells produced in the apical meristem soon begin to differentiate, some

Fig. 7.6. Cross sections of basswood (*Tilia*) stems at the end of one year, two years, and three years of growth. × 26. [Courtesy Thomas Eisner, Cornell University.]

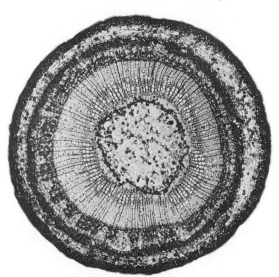

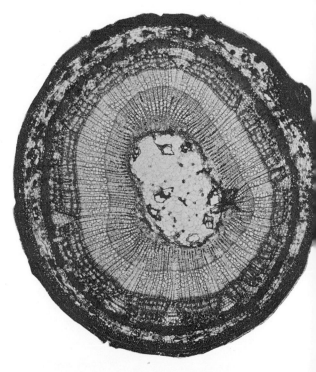

forming epidermis, some forming the fundamental tissues of the cortex and pith, and some forming the primary phloem, primary xylem, and cambium.

In some species of herbaceous plants, the cambium does become active, however. As the cambial cells divide, they give rise to new cells both to the inside and to the outside. Though the ratio varies, six to eight new cells are usually produced to the inside for every one produced to the outside. The new cells formed on the outer side of the cambium differentiate as *secondary phloem;* those formed on the inner side of the cambium differentiate as *secondary xylem.* Secondary vascular tissue, then, is tissue derived from the lateral meristem, the cambium, and is a result of growth in diameter rather than growth in length. As secondary phloem is produced by the cambium, it pushes the older, primary phloem farther and farther away from the cambium toward

the outside of the stem. Similarly, as secondary xylem is produced, it causes the cambium to be farther and farther removed from the primary xylem, which is left in the inner portion of the vascular cylinder. In a stem that has undergone secondary growth, therefore, the sequence of tissues in the stele (moving from the outside toward the center) is: primary phloem, secondary phloem, cambium, secondary xylem, primary xylem, pith (Fig. 7.5).

A cross section of a "woody" stem made early in its first year would not appear very different from that of a herbaceous stem; in the woody as in the herbaceous stem, the primary vascular tissue is arranged in a continuous ring (siphonostele) in some species and in discrete bundles (dictyostele) in others. Secondary growth, however, soon makes the rings continuous, and as this growth continues, the woody stem looks less and less like a herbaceous one (Fig. 7.6). The secondary xylem

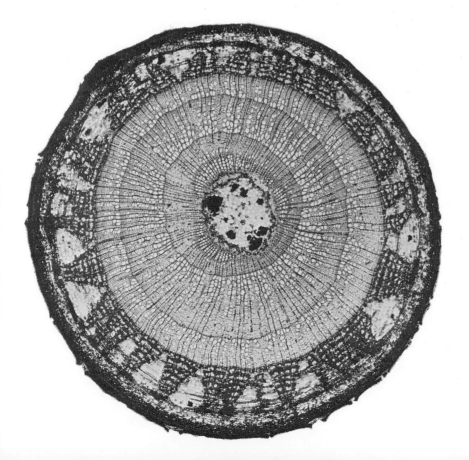

becomes thicker and thicker until almost the entire stem of an older plant is xylem tissue—commonly called wood.

Since new xylem cells produced early in the growing season, when conditions are best, grow larger than cells produced later in the season, a series of concentric annual rings are formed that are clearly visible in cross sections of the stem. Each such ring is made up of an inner area of spring wood with large cells and an outer area of summer wood with smaller cells (Fig. 7.7). A fairly accurate estimate of the age of a tree can be made by counting the annual rings. The width of the rings may vary depending upon such factors as the vigor of the tree and the climatic conditions during the growing season. Study of the rings of a

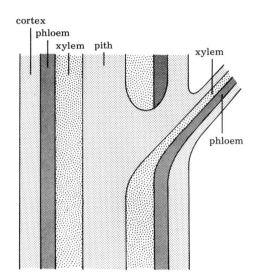

Fig. 7.8. **Diagram of leaf trace and gap.** At the point where the petiole of a leaf arises from the stem, the vascular tissue is diverted into the leaf as a leaf trace. This produces an interruption, or leaf gap, in the vascular cylinder just above the point where the leaf trace enters the base of the petiole. Because the vascular tissue in the veins of the leaves arises in this way, the phloem is usually in the lower part of each vein and the xylem is in the upper part. [Modified from A. J. Eames and L. H. MacDaniels, *An Introduction to Plant Anatomy,* McGraw-Hill Book Co., 1947. Used by permission.]

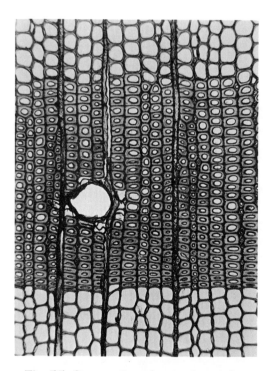

Fig. 7.7. **Cross section of part of secondary xylem (wood) of pine.** The smaller, thicker-walled cells are summer wood and the larger, thinner-walled cells are spring wood. A large resin duct can be seen in the summer wood. × 100. [Courtesy U.S. Forest Products Laboratory.]

large sample of very old trees can give a clue to the climate of an area in past ages. Since trees frequently live for many centuries, and some, like the huge redwoods and giant sequoias of California, may be as much as 3,000–4,000 years old, they can provide a valuable historical record. Tree-ring dating has even been used in archaeological studies; by matching the rings in wooden artifacts found among ancient ruins with cross sections of very old trees from the area, a reliable estimate of the age of the artifacts can be made.

In older trees, a variety of chemical and physical changes begin to occur in the older rings of xylem toward the center of the stem. The conducting cells become plugged, the parenchyma cells die, and pigments, resins, tannins, and gums are deposited. As these changes take place, the older xylem ceases to function in internal transport, but remains important as a strong supportive component of the tree. The rings in which these changes have occurred are known as *heartwood,* while the newer outer rings, which are still functional in transport, constitute the *sapwood.* A tree can continue to live after its heartwood has burned or rotted away, but it is much weakened and cannot withstand strong winds.

We have discussed changes in the aging woody stem internal to the cambium; now let us examine the portions of the stem outside the cambium. As woody stems (or roots) grow in diameter, a layer of cells outside the phloem takes on meristematic activity and becomes the *cork cambium.* As growth continues, the original epidermis and cortex flake off and are replaced by *cork cells* produced by cell division in the cork cambium. The layer of dead cork cells (periderm) constitutes the outer bark of the older stem or root. The inner bark is the phloem tissue. Since fewer phloem cells than xylem cells are produced by the vascular cambium, and the phloem cells have thinner walls that are easily crushed, and since the older phloem is pushed to the outside where it is periodically sloughed off, the phloem layer never becomes thick like the xylem, and annual growth rings are very difficult, if not impossible, to detect in it. Unlike the xylem, therefore, the phloem of an older woody plant does not function as an important supportive tissue, but its role in internal transport is very important, as we shall see.

In summary, then, the old woody stem of a tree has no epidermis or cortex. Its surface is covered by an outer bark of cork tissue. Beneath the cork cambium is the thin layer of phloem, or inner bark, and beneath this is the vascular cambium, which is usually only one cell thick. The rest of the stem is mostly secondary xylem, or wood, of which only the outer annual rings, or sapwood, still function in transport.

The Xylem.   Now let us examine the cellular makeup of the xylem. Xylem is a complex tissue containing several different types of cells. Two of these, the tracheids and the vessel cells, are important as conductive elements after they have matured. Actually, the cell walls are all that remains of a tracheid or vessel cell functioning in transport; the cellular contents, both cytoplasm and nucleus, have disintegrated. The main transport in the xylem occurs, then, in tubular remnants of cells, not in the living cells themselves.

Tracheids are elongate, tapering cells with heavily lignified secondary cell walls; the walls are particularly thick in summer wood and are important as supportive elements. Tracheids of the first-matured primary xylem are stretched during their development, and their secondary walls are usually in the form of rings or spirals (Fig. 7.9A–B). Those of secondary xylem arise after all lengthwise growth has ceased, and they are not stretched during their development; their secondary walls are more continuous, being interrupted only by numerous *pits* (Fig. 7.9C). The pits may occur anywhere on the cell wall, but they are often particularly numerous on the tapered ends of the cell where it abuts upon the next cell beyond it. Water and dissolved substances move from tracheid to tracheid through the pits.

The pits of tracheids, called *bordered pits,* are of rather intricate structure (Fig. 7.10B–D). At these pits, the secondary walls of two adjacent cells are interrupted and overhang the pit chamber, forming the pit borders. The primary walls and middle lamella are continuous through the pit and constitute the pit membrane, which, generally very thin and highly permeable to water and dissolved substances, offers little resistance to the movement of materials from one cell to the next. The bordered pits of conifers and a few other plants are particularly interesting in that the pit membrane, though very thin toward its edges, is thickened centrally to form a buttonlike *torus.* If the pressure in one of the cells becomes much greater

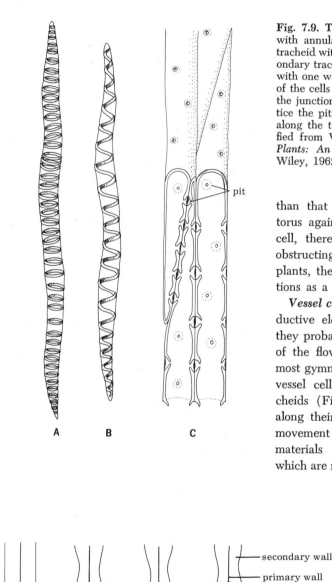

Fig. 7.9. Tracheids. (A) Primary tracheid with annular secondary walls. (B) Primary tracheid with spiral secondary walls. (C) Secondary tracheid (parts of four cells are shown, with one wall cut away from portions of three of the cells to expose their lumen and to show the junction between cells more clearly). Notice the pits, which are particularly abundant along the tapering ends of the cells. [Modified from V. A. Greulach and J. E. Adams, *Plants: An Introduction to Modern Botany,* Wiley, 1962.]

than that in the adjacent cell, it forces the torus against the pit borders of the adjacent cell, thereby blocking the pit aperture and obstructing the flow of materials. In such plants, the pit membrane with its torus functions as a valve between the cells.

Vessel cells are more highly specialized conductive elements than tracheids, from which they probably evolved. They are characteristic of the flowering plants and do not occur in most gymnosperms (conifers, etc.). In general, vessel cells are shorter and wider than tracheids (Fig. 7.11). They have bordered pits along their sides, through which some lateral movement of substances may take place, but materials move chiefly through their ends, which are more extensively perforated and may

secondary wall

primary wall

torus

pit membrane

pit border

pit aperture

pit chamber

Fig. 7.10. Diagrams of pit structure. (A) Simple pit pairs. The secondary walls are interrupted but do not overhang the pits. The primary walls of the two adjacent cells, and the middle lamella between them, are continuous through the pit and constitute the pit membrane. (B) Bordered pit pairs without torus. The secondary walls overhang the pit chamber. (C–D) Bordered pit pairs of pine, with torus. In (D) the torus of each pit pair has been pushed against the pit borders on one side; thus movement of materials through the pit is impeded.

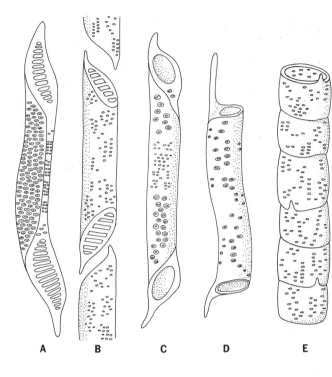

A   B   C   D   E

Fig. 7.11. Vessel cells. Five different types of vessel cells are shown—those thought to be the more primitive on the left and those thought to be the more advanced on the right. All traces of the end walls of the more advanced vessel cells have disappeared. [Modified in part from A. J. Eames and L. H. MacDaniels, *An Introduction to Plant Anatomy*, McGraw-Hill Book Co., 1947. Used by permission.]

even lack a wall altogether. Since the perforations lack both secondary and primary walls, material moving from one vessel cell to the next in a vertical sequence forms a continuous column. A vertical series of such vessel cells is called a *vessel*. There seems to have been an evolutionary trend for vessel cells to become shorter and wider, for the perforations of the end walls to become larger until no end walls remained, and for the ends to become less oblique and more nearly horizontal.

In addition to tracheids and vessel cells, xylem contains fiber cells and parenchyma cells. The fibers are elongate, very thick-walled cells that function as supportive elements. They apparently evolved from tracheids; numerous intermediate cell types still exist in some species. Like the conductive cells already discussed, they arise from elongate cells of the cambium (fusiform initials) (Fig. 7.12).

Some of the parenchyma cells of the xylem are scattered among the other cells, but many

Fig. 7.12. Cambium of black locust. This is a tangential section (a longitudinal section oriented at right angles to the radius of the stem). The elongate cells are fusiform initials, which give rise to tracheids and vessels, and the shorter cells arranged in groups are ray initials. [Courtesy A. J. Eames and L. H. MacDaniels, *An Introduction to Plant Anatomy*, McGraw-Hill Book Co., 1947. Used by permission.]

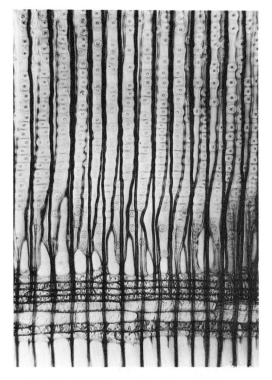

Fig. 7.13. Radial section of wood of pine.
Note the oblique junctions between successive
tracheids. Bordered pits are clearly visible.
Part of a ray about eight cells high is shown
in the lower quarter of the photograph. × 100.
[Courtesy U.S. Forest Products Laboratory.]

of them are grouped together to form **rays** that
run through the xylem in a radial direction
and function as pathways for lateral movement of materials and as storage areas (Fig.
7.6). A ray is usually only one or a few cells
wide (though in some species it may be many
cells wide) and as many as five to ten or more
cells high (Fig. 7.13). Ray cells arise from ray
initials in the cambium (Fig. 7.12).

The number, form, and distribution of tracheids, vessels, fibers, and parenchyma cells
vary from species to species, and cause the
woods of different species to differ in appearance and properties. The wood of pine, a
conifer, lacks vessels (Fig. 7.7) and is thus
very different from that of oak, which has
vessels (Fig. 7.14); oak wood, with its relatively few vessels, is, in turn, different from
elm wood or tulip-tree wood, both of which
are very porous and have numerous vessels.

The Phloem. Like xylem, phloem is a complex tissue. It contains supportive fibers and
also parenchyma; the phloem rays are continuous with the xylem rays. The principal
vertical conductive elements in phloem are the
sieve elements, which, in vertical series, form
a **sieve tube.** In their most advanced form,

Fig. 7.14. Cross sections of woods. White oak (left), tulip tree (middle), and American
elm (right). Note the differences in the number and size of vessels. [Oak and tulip tree:
Courtesy Thomas Eisner, Cornell University. Elm: Courtesy U.S. Forest Products Laboratory.]

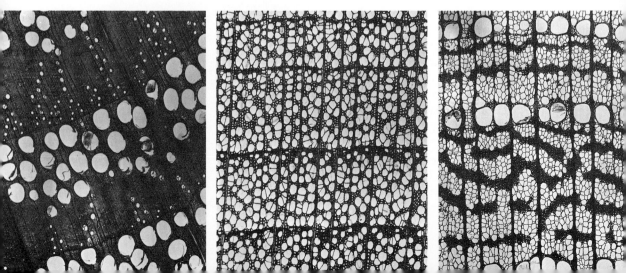

sieve elements are elongate cells with specialized areas on their end walls, called *sieve plates* (Fig. 7.15). As the name implies, a sieve plate is an area with numerous perforations or pores through which strands of protoplasm connect the contents of one cell with those of the next. Unlike the tracheids and vessels of the xylem, the sieve elements retain their cytoplasm at maturity, but their nucleus disintegrates.

The sieve elements of most flowering plants usually have one or more specialized, elongate, parenchymatous cells closely associated with them. These are called *companion cells,* and are derived from the same cambial cell as the associated sieve element. The cell walls of the sieve element and its companion cells are thin where they are in contact. Mature companion cells retain both their cytoplasm and their nucleus. There is abundant evidence that the sieve elements and their companion cells are closely associated not only in their origin and location but also in their physiology. Some biologists have suggested that the nucleus of the companion cell controls both its own cytoplasm and the cytoplasm of the adjoining sieve element after the nucleus of the latter has disintegrated. Such an association, they think, would help explain why the mature sieve element can continue to carry out many of the normal activities of a living cell, even though it has no nucleus of its own. A problem with this hypothesis is that the sieve cells of conifers and of a few primitive flowering plants lack companion cells and yet are fully active. There is evidence, however, that certain parenchyma cells are closely associated with the sieve cells in conifers, and they may function in the same way as companion cells. The most that can be said at this point is that there is clearly an intimate association between sieve elements and companion cells, but that the exact nature of the association and a full explanation for the activity of the sieve elements remain to be discovered.

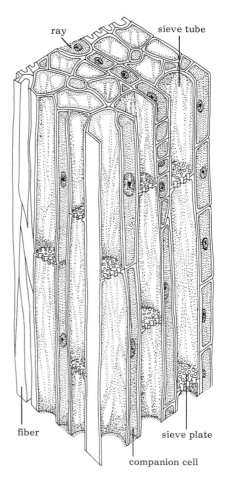

Fig. 7.15. Phloem. [Adapted from S. and O. Biddulph, "The Circulatory System of Plants," *Sci. Am.*, February, 1959. Copyright © 1959 by Scientific American, Inc. All rights reserved.]

The Ascent of Sap

Water, absorbed by the roots, moves upward throughout the plant body in the mature tracheids and vessels of the xylem. This much has been known for many years. That the upward movement of water is primarily in the xylem can easily be demonstrated by ringing experiments; if the cork, phloem, and cambium are removed from a ring around the trunk of a tree, the leaves will still remain turgid, even though they are connected only by xylem to the roots. But a complete explanation of this upward movement has eluded botanists for centuries. We shall here examine briefly some of the possible explanations, together with evidence both for and against them.

Any general explanation for the ascent of sap (water plus dissolved materials) in xylem must identify the forces capable of raising water to the tops of the tallest trees, which may be 300–400 feet high. A pressure of one atmosphere can support a column of water approximately 34 feet high at sea level (less than 34 feet at higher altitudes). It follows that a pressure of about 12 atmospheres would be needed to support a column 400 feet high. But the column must be more than supported; the water must be moved upward at a rate that may sometimes be as fast as 40 or more inches per minute, and this movement must take place in a system that offers frictional resistance to it. It has been calculated that an additional pressure of at least 18 atmospheres is necessary to overcome this resistance. Therefore, a total force of at least 30 atmospheres is necessary in the tallest trees, and any general theory of water movement in the xylem must account for forces of this magnitude. For example, the common idea that capillarity (the tendency of water to rise in a thin tube because of its tendency to flow along the walls of the tube) is responsible for the ascent of sap must be rejected, because the forces involved are far too small and the conditions in the closed tubes of the xylem are not conducive to capillarity.

The driving force might, of course, be at the base of the plant and push the water upward, or it might be at the top of the plant and pull the water up, or forces at both positions might be jointly involved. Each of these possibilities has had its advocates, and each has some evidence in its favor.

Root Pressure. Let us first consider the possibility of a force applied as a push from below. When the stems of certain species of plants are cut, sap flows from the surface of the stump for some time, and if a tube is attached to the stump, a column of water several feet high may rise in it. Similarly, when conditions are optimal for water absorption by the roots but the humidity is so high that little water is lost by evaporation, water under pressure may be forced out at the ends of the leaf veins, forming droplets along the edges of the leaves (Fig. 7.16). This process of water secretion is called *guttation.* When the water in the xylem is under pressure, as in these instances of bleeding and guttation, the pushing force involved is apparently in the roots, and is called *root pressure.*

The exact manner in which root pressure is built up is not fully understood. We have already seen that water moves from the soil, through the epidermis, cortex, endodermis, and pericycle of the root to the xylem, in which it then flows upward to the rest of the plant. Much of this movement across the tissues of the root is simple diffusion along a concentration gradient. But this cannot be the whole story. Water may be in much higher concentration in the xylem than in the protoplasm of the endodermal cells and yet continue to move from the endodermis into the xylem; if it were undergoing simple diffusion, it would go the other way. Furthermore, a tall column of water under positive pressure in the xylem would exert a strong downward hydrostatic force by virtue of its weight, and this force would tend to drive water out of the xylem in the roots. Clearly, then, some process other than simple diffusion must be involved if water is not only held in the stele of the root and prevented from diffusing out laterally, but is also continually secreted into the stele in sufficient quantity to build up a force capable of pushing the column upward. Activity by living cells is immediately suspected in a situation like this. And, indeed, if roots are killed, all root pressure disappears. Or if the roots are simply deprived of oxygen, the root pressure ceases, indicating that res-

Fig. 7.16. Guttation by a straw-berry leaf. [Courtesy J. Arthur Herrick, Kent State University.]

piratory production of ATP is necessary to provide the energy for the active inward secretion of water. Such secretion is perhaps one of the important functions of the living cells of the endodermis; they may function as an active barrier between the stele and the cortex of the root, secreting water into the stele against both the osmotic gradient and the hydrostatic force of the water column.

Next, we must ask if root pressure can reach the magnitude we have said is required. The answer is ambiguous. Some plants, particularly the conifers and their relatives, seem to be incapable of developing much root pressure at all. Attempts to measure the root pressure in those species of plants in which it does occur have rarely yielded values exceeding 1 or 2 atmospheres. However, Philip R. White of Jackson Memorial Laboratory, Bar Harbor, Maine, was able to show that isolated root tips of tomatoes growing in a tissue-culture medium can develop root pressures as high as 6–10 atmospheres.

The low values for root pressure revealed by most investigations are not the only reason for doubting that this pressure is the principal motive force for the ascent of sap. When a puncture is made in a xylem vessel during the summer, it is uncommon to find water under pressure; i.e. water is seldom forced out of the wound. Instead, one can often hear a short hissing sound as air is drawn into the vessel. Yet it is in summer that much of the upward movement of water occurs. Water under pressure is sometimes found in the xylem when the soil is very moist and the transpiration rate low, but under such conditions as these water moves only very slowly.

In short, root pressure is not the explanation we are seeking, though it may be involved in the ascent of sap in some plants some of the time. It may be particularly important in very young plants, and perhaps in a few species of trees in early spring.

The Cohesion Theory. What about the alternative hypothesis that the water is pulled up from above? According to this hypothesis, water lost by *transpiration* from the walls of parenchyma cells in the leaves (or other parts of the shoot) is replaced by water moving from the cell contents into the wall. This movement of water out of the leaf cells raises their osmotic concentration and, consequently, their suction pressure. These cells, therefore, take up water from adjoining cells, and they, in turn, withdraw water from cells adjacent to them. In this way, a gradient extends to the xylem in the veins of the leaf, and the parenchyma cells next to the xylem withdraw water from the column in the xylem. This removal of water from the top of the column pulls the column upward. Notice that this is not a matter of pulling the column up by air pressure or vacuum; the mechanism is not strictly analogous to your sucking up a liquid through a straw. Air pressure could raise water only about 34 feet, but we are dealing with a mechanism presumed to move a water column that may be hundreds of feet high. What is assumed here is a continuity between the water on the evaporating surfaces of the cell wall and the water in the xylem, and a continuity between the water at the top of the xylem and that in the roots. If this continuity of water all the way from leaf cell to root were broken by the entrance of air into the system, the damage would presumably be irreversible in most cases, and that particular xylem pathway would cease to function.

This theory of pull from above as a result primarily of transpiration (removal of water from the xylem for use in photosynthesis, growth, or other metabolic processes would also exert a pull) was stated in tentative form early in the eighteenth century by the English clergyman and pioneering botanist Stephen Hales. It was given a more complete formulation in 1894 by the Irish botanist H. H. Dixon and his physicist collaborator J. Joly. The whole theory depends upon water's having certain physical properties. Water molecules moving out of the top of the xylem must pull other water molecules behind them; there can be no break, no separation, between water molecules. In short, the validity of this theory depends upon the existence of great cohesive forces between the individual water molecules. And water does indeed exhibit great cohesive strength. In fact, you will recall, water molecules don't ordinarily exist as separate entities in the liquid phase (see Fig. 2.10, p. 27).

Measurements of surface-tension relationships, internal pressure, heats of vaporization, etc. lead to a predicted cohesive strength for water as high as 15,000 atmospheres. Actual experimental values are far lower and vary greatly depending on the experimental procedures and conditions. Values ranging from as low as 0.05 to as high as 300 atmospheres or more have been reported. We have already said that a pressure of 30 or more atmospheres would be necessary for ascent of sap in the tallest trees. How is the theory of Dixon and Joly affected by the great discrepancies in experimentally determined tensile strengths of water? If the lowest reported values are correct, the theory falls. If the reported values over 30 are more nearly correct, the theory remains tenable. No final decision can be made at present, but the majority of botanists believe that the tensile strength of water is probably high enough to support the theory.

Although there have been no experiments testing the theory under conditions duplicating those in very tall trees, some interesting ones have been made on a smaller scale. For example, Josef Böhm in Austria and E. Askenasy in Germany showed during the 1890's that if water (previously boiled to remove all dissolved air) is evaporated from the top of a thin tube whose walls are made of a material to which water molecules can adhere and whose lower end is immersed in mercury, a column of mercury can be pulled up the tube to a far greater height than a vacuum could pull it (Fig. 7.17). If the base of a cut branch is inserted tightly in the upper end of the tube and the leaves of the branch become the site of evaporation, similar results are obtained; the tension developed pulls the mercury to a height above the barometric height. The water molecules have adhered to each other (and to the walls of the tube) tightly enough to lift a heavy column of mercury. Such experiments support the theory of Dixon and Joly, commonly called the **cohesion theory** (or shoot-tension or transpiration theory). But these experiments are performed in air-tight systems. Is the xylem system equally air-tight? If negative pressure, or tension, really exists in the xylem vessels and tracheids, would not air readily penetrate the permeable walls of these dead passageways and disrupt the continuity of the water? The answer given by the proponents of the cohesion theory is "apparently not," but the reasons why not are unclear. Perhaps the wet walls of the vessels act as a

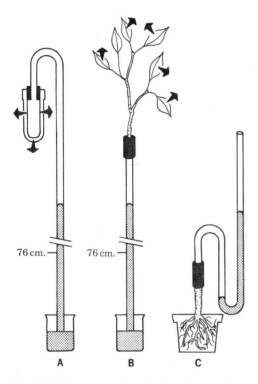

76 cm.

76 cm.

A   B   C

Fig. 7.17 Demonstrations of rise of water by pull from above (A, B) and root-pressure push from below (C). (A) Water is evaporated from a clay pot attached to the top of a thin tube whose lower end is in a beaker of mercury. The water in the tube rises and pulls a column of mercury to a point well above the 76 cm. to which a vacuum could pull it. (B) The same results are obtained when transpiration from the leaves of a shoot is substituted for evaporation from a clay pot. (C) In some plants, root pressure can raise a column of mercury. [Modified from V. A. Greulach and J. E. Adams, *Plants: An Introduction to Modern Botany*, Wiley, 1962.]

sufficient barrier to air because the water on the walls forms a film with a high surface tension, a film that even covers the minute pores in the bordered pits.

Support for the cohesion theory comes from other types of experiments also. In 1935 the German botanist Bruno Huber inserted small electric elements into the xylem and heated the sap. He then measured the time it took for the warmed sap to pass a thermocouple placed a short distance higher on the tree. He found that water begins to move in the upper parts of the tree earlier in the morning than it does in the lower parts of the trunk—an indication that the upward movement of the sap is initiated at the top of the tree, not at the bottom.

We saw earlier that one strong argument against the root-pressure theory of the ascent of sap is that water under pressure is seldom actually found in the xylem. We should now ask if, in agreement with the cohesion theory, water under tension is found. The answer is unclear. The conducting elements of the xylem sometimes seem to contain water under tension, but they frequently seem to contain no liquid at all! Instead, they seem to hold water vapor at very low pressure. As the thrice-repeated "seem" indicates, the matter has not been conclusively settled. There is much disagreement among botanists as to the reliability of the experiments and the data. Some think the experiments were performed in such a manner as to disrupt normal conditions in the highly sensitive xylem elements and that, consequently, the results obtained are artifacts of the procedure used rather than reliable indications of the xylem contents. Others are of the opinion that, even supposing the experimental procedures were adequate, the results can be interpreted in a variety of ways and hence are of minimal value. Here is an example of a frequently encountered difficulty—performing experiments on living organisms in such a way as to prevent the experiments themselves from changing the subjects being studied.

So far, then, the cohesion theory of the rise of sap has failed to gain complete acceptance. The majority of botanists seem to favor some form of the theory, while admitting modifications are needed. A few scientists reject it outright and suggest that a totally new theory must be advanced. Clearly, the rise of sap remains an intriguing problem for research. Perhaps a better explanation will have been found by the time you read this book, or perhaps the matter will still be unsettled twenty years hence. The course of scientific research is difficult to predict. Frequently, as in this case, the more we learn, the more unanswered questions we see before us. This is at once a challenging and a frustrating aspect of science; fortunately, the excitement and challenge outweigh the frustration for most scientists.

Even if the cohesion theory proves to be the correct explanation for the way sap is moved upward in the xylem once the system is established, it leaves unanswered the critical question how the system was first established, how the water got up there in the first place. The answer seems to be that the water, in a manner of speaking, grew there. The cambium produces a new layer of potential xylem cells every year. This layer lies just outside the previous year's xylem. The as yet undifferentiated and still living cells draw water laterally from the older xylem as they grow. These cells may, in fact, absorb so much water from the older xylem that their contents are under considerable positive presure early in the growing season, and if they are punctured, liquid may exude from them. As these cells mature, their end walls become more permeable and their contents can move more freely; a conductive system has been established. As the new spring leaves grow larger and the transpiration rate begins to rise, the liquid contents of the newly formed xylem elements may be pulled upward faster than the supply can be replenished from below. For this reason, the positive pressure of the early part of the growing season is lost, and tension develops in the column of liquid. Still

later, if the transpiration demands far exceed the rate of water absorption at the base of the tree, the liquid water under tension may give way to water vapor under very low pressure. The liquid column may be re-established when conditions are more favorable for absorption by the roots and less favorable for transpiration; the water could easily refill the xylem elements as long as no air leaked into the system while it was under negative pressure.

It must be stressed that this tentative explanation, combining action of living cells in immature xylem with the cohesion mechanism in mature xylem, has not been proved, as our examination of the problem of ascent of sap has shown, but its emphasis on the water-absorbing activities of the living cells of the newly differentiating xylem as the process that initially establishes each year's water columns seems reasonable. Once the columns have been established and mass flow has begun in the mature, and by now dead, xylem elements, activity of living cells is no longer necessary, and purely physical factors can maintain the columns (or their vapor replacements) and produce their movement. In contradiction to some theories, there is good evidence that the few living parenchyma cells in the mature xylem tissue do not act as pumps and are unimportant in the ascent of sap. Long sections of a stem can be killed by heat or poisons, and yet will continue to function in conduction.

Notice that if the water in the xylem really is under tension, the question how water moves into the xylem in the roots presents less difficulty. We said earlier that a water column under positive pressure would exert a downward hydrostatic force opposing the entrance of more water into the stele. But if the water in the xylem is under tension, it would exert no such downward force, but would, instead, exert a pull or suction tending to draw water from the soil, across the root tissues, and into the xylem. Little or no active inward secretion of water by the endodermis would be necessary in this case.

Translocation of Solutes

Translocation of Organic Solutes. Two principal classes of solutes are transported—or translocated, as plant physiologists generally call it—within the plant body: organic solutes and inorganic solutes. Let us consider the organic solutes first. We can conveniently divide these into two principal types, carbohydrates (usually transported as sucrose) and organic nitrogen compounds. (So little is known about the translocation of fats and related compounds in plants that we shall disregard them in this discussion.)

The classical picture of the translocation of solutes was that all upward movement was through the xylem and all downward movement through the phloem. About 1920, however, it was realized that this was not an accurate view. It became apparent that most of the movement of carbohydrates, whether up or down, was through the phloem. Most of the early work on the path of movement involved ringing experiments. It could be demonstrated that if all the bark (which includes, of course, the phloem) was removed from a ring around the trunk of a tree, the supply of carbohydrates to all parts of the plant below the ring was cut off, and those parts eventually died when they had depleted their stored reserves. Downward movement of carbohydrates was clearly through the phloem, not through the xylem, which had been left intact in these experiments. But it could also be demonstrated that if a branch was ringed a short distance behind the growing bud, the supply of carbohydrates moving to the bud was cut off. Again, the movement must have been in the phloem, but in this case the movement was upward. From numerous such experiments as these, most botanists came to regard it as a valid generalization that almost all carbohydrate movement is through the phloem.

But not all botanists accepted this view. Some workers, for example, have interpreted the high concentration of sugar in the xylem of such plants as the sugar maple in spring as an indication of upward movement of sucrose in the xylem. The reason for this high concentration of sugar has still not been established with certainty, but it has been argued that most of the sugar in the xylem is not actually moving vertically, but that starch stored in the parenchyma cells of the xylem is converted into sugar in early spring as a result of the temperature conditions at that time of year. Doubtless some of this sugar gets into the vessels and is carried upward in the water stream, but much of it probably moves laterally into the phloem and is transported in the sieve tubes.

Another objection has been that far too much carbohydrate moves within the plant body, and that it moves too rapidly, for the phloem to be the exclusive channel for this movement. After all, the total amount of functional phloem tissue in the trunk of a large tree is rather small. Surely, the argument has run, it is physically inconceivable that so much material should pass through so few sieve tubes, particularly since these tubes are not open pathways like xylem vessels. Numerous workers, however, among whom T. G. Mason and E. J. Maskell of the Cotton Research Station, Trinidad, are outstanding, have shown by careful ringing experiments that, hard to conceive as it is, the phloem is indeed the pathway of sugar movement, and that this movement is amazingly rapid. More recently, Susann and Orlin Biddulph of the State University of Washington have grown plants in an atmosphere containing carbon dioxide made from radioactive carbon. When a thin section is cut from the stem of such a plant and placed in contact with a photographic film, the resulting exposure shows that the radioactivity is restricted to the phloem; the sugar synthesized from the radioactive carbon has clearly traveled only in the phloem.

The situation is less clear with organic nitrogen compounds. It was formerly thought that nitrogen, absorbed by the roots primarily as nitrate, was carried upward in inorganic form through the xylem to the leaves, there to be used in synthesis of organic compounds, which were then transported through the phloem. This sequence probably holds true for some plants. There is now good evidence, however, that many species of plants promptly incorporate incoming nitrogen into organic compounds such as amides and amino acids in the roots. Opinion is divided on the question whether these organic nitrogen compounds move upward in the xylem or in the phloem. Probably they move to some extent in both, perhaps primarily in the xylem in some species and primarily in the phloem in other species. Physiological traits often vary widely from one species to another, and we should beware of making unjustified generalizations. We see in this case that the common statement that all upward transport of organic compounds is in the phloem and of all inorganic compounds in the xylem is simply not true for some plants. It may safely be said, however, that the upward transport of organic material is predominantly in the phloem and that almost all downward transport of this material is in that tissue.

Translocaton of Inorganic Solutes. Inorganic ions such as those of calcium, sulfur, and phosphorus are translocated upward from the roots to the leaves primarily through the xylem. Use of radioactive forms of these minerals indicates, however, that some are quite mobile in the plant, traveling rapidly back down the plant in the phloem, or moving out of the older leaves through the phloem and being transferred to the newer, more actively growing leaves. Phosphorus, for example, easily moves upward in the xylem and downward in the phloem, often circulating rapidly throughout the plant in this manner. If a plant is grown for a short time in a solution containing radioactive phosphorus, and the plant is then placed against a photographic plate, the younger leaves will be found to contain the greatest concentrations of radioactive phosphorus (Fig.

7.18). If the plant is then moved into a normal solution (one without the radioactive tracer), allowed to grow for a day or so, and again placed against a photographic plate, the resulting pictures will show that the radioactive phosphorus has moved from the leaves in which it was first concentrated to the new leaves just beginning to develop. Calcium, on the other hand, is not mobile in the phloem, and thus cannot move from old leaves to newer ones. Consequently plants must obtain a steady supply of new calcium from the soil, whereas they can easily survive with only intermittent feedings of phosphorus, since this element can shift from place to place within the plant and be re-used many times. Well-designed fertilization programs take into account such differences in the properties of the different mineral nutrients.

Theories of Phloem Function. We have said that most transport of organic solutes, both up and down, is through the phloem, and that most downward transport of minerals is also through the phloem. How phloem functions in this transport is a problem that has been under investigation for a very long time. Several hypotheses have been put forward, but it must be admitted that none is fully convincing.

There are several facts that any hypothesis about the transport mechanism in phloem must account for. (1) The movement is often rapid, much more rapid than simple diffusion alone could make it. In fact, it has been estimated that sugar moves through the phloem of the cotton plant more than 40,000 times faster than it diffuses in a liquid! (2) The speed of movement through the sieve tubes differs for different substances. (3) The direction of movement may be reversed periodically within a given sieve tube. (4) The directions of movement in neighboring sieve tubes may be opposite. (5) The movement takes place through sieve-tube cells that, unlike xylem, retain their cytoplasm (though the cytoplasm

Fig. 7.18. Movement of radioactive phosphorus in a growing plant. The plant was grown for one hour in a nutrient solution containing P^{32}. It was then removed to a nonradioactive solution. At the end of 6 hours (left), the P^{32} was particularly concentrated in the youngest leaves. By the end of 96 hours (right), much of the P^{32} had moved from the leaves in which it was formerly most concentrated to new leaves that had developed above them. (The darker the area, the more P^{32} it contains.) [Courtesy O. Biddulph *et al., Plant Physiol.,* vol. 31, 1958.]

is not exactly like that of most other cells). (6) Unlike the ends of xylem vessels, the ends of the individual sieve-tube cells are not broadly open, but are penetrated only by the tiny pores of the sieve plates. Clearly, we are here dealing with transport through active cells, not merely with movement through dead tubes by purely mechanical processes, as was the case with mature xylem.

One hypothesis is that materials are carried the length of each sieve cell by cytoplasmic streaming (Fig. 7.19). According to this hypothesis, materials diffusing into one end of a sieve cell through the sieve plate are picked up by the streaming cytoplasm and carried to the other end of the cell, where they diffuse across the sieve plates at that end and, upon entering the next cell in the tube, are again picked up by streaming cytoplasm. In this way,

by alternately streaming within cells and diffusing between cells, the materials would move long distances through the sieve tubes of the phloem. The diffusion across the sieve plates may, of course, involve active transport. It has been suggested in favor of this hypothesis that it can explain how two substances might simultaneously move in opposite directions through the same sieve tube, since cytoplasmic streaming frequently involves intracellular circulation, with some cytoplasm moving in one direction while other areas of cytoplasm, perhaps on the other side of the cell, move in the other direction. However, most claims that different substances can move simultaneously in opposite directions through the same sieve tube are unconvincing; in all probability, the observed movements in opposite directions actually occurred in two adjacent sieve tubes. In other

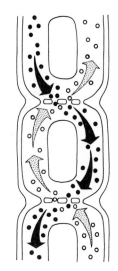

Fig. 7.19. The cytoplasmic-streaming hypothesis of translocation in the phloem. According to this hypothesis, it would be possible for two substances (white balls and black balls) to be moving in opposite directions at the same time through the same sieve tube. There is no evidence, however, that cytoplasmic streaming occurs in mature sieve cells.

words, one of the arguments used in support of the cytoplasmic-streaming hypothesis may well be irrelevant, since the phenomenon that this hypothesis is supposed to help explain may not actually exist. But this does not disprove the hypothesis. Other objections have been raised, however. One is that there is little, if any, evidence that cytoplasmic streaming occurs in mature sieve-tube cells. Here it may be countered that, sieve tubes being notoriously sensitive structures, the attempts to examine the cytoplasm of the sieve-tube cells may simply have caused the streaming to cease. A second objection is that measurements of the velocities of streaming in other cells, where the process does occur, yield values much lower than the known rates of solute movement through sieve tubes. At the present time, not many botanists accept the streaming hypothesis.

Another hypothesis is based on the knowledge that substances which lower the surface tension at interfaces spread rapidly along these interfaces. According to this hypothesis, substances move through the sieve cells by flowing along the intracellular interfaces—such interfaces as the vacuolar membrane and the various cytoplasmic membranes. The evidence, however, makes it doubtful that there is sufficient interface surface area in the sieve cells to account for the quantities of material known to be transported.

A third hypothesis assumes that, since the movement in the phloem is too fast to be simple diffusion, there must be some sort of activation of the solutes, producing what has been called activated diffusion. Most transport in the phloem is with the concentration gradient, as would be necessary in such a diffusion mechanism. However, phloem transport is not always with the concentration gradient, and, furthermore, there is no known activation mechanism such as the one postulated.

A fourth hypothesis, which invokes *pressure flow* or mass flow, is probably the one most widely held by botanists today. According to this hypothesis, there is a mass flow of water and solutes through the sieve tubes along a turgor-pressure gradient. Cells like those of the leaf contain high concentrations of such osmotically active substances as sugar. Much water therefore tends to diffuse into them, raising their turgor pressure. This pressure impinges upon the next cell and tends to force substances from the first cell into the second. Thus, under pressure, substances are forced en masse into the sieve-tube cells in the upper parts of the plant. This means that the upper portions of the sieve tubes are under pressure. But in storage organs or actively growing tissues, sugars are being used up; as sugars are removed from the sieve tubes in these regions, the osmotic concentrations in the tubes are lowered. They therefore tend to lose water, which results in a drop in their turgor pressure. We have, then, a sieve-tube system in which the contents in some portions of the plant are under considerable turgor pressure and the contents in other portions of the plant are under lower turgor pressure. The result is a mass flow of the contents of the sieve tubes from the regions under high pressure (usually in the leaves, but sometimes in storage organs when reserves are being mobilized for use, as in early spring) to the regions under lower pressure (usually actively growing regions or storage depots). The whole process is dependent upon massive uptake of water by cells at the one end, because of their high osmotic concentrations, and massive loss of water by cells at the other end, because their osmotic concentrations are lowered by their loss of sugar.

The chief objection to the mass-flow hypothesis is an obvious one. It seems to assume that material can flow with relative freedom from one sieve-tube cell to the next. But the openings in the sieve plates between successive sieve-tube cells are very tiny indeed. Furthermore, the cytoplasm of sieve-tube cells, particularly that in the vicinity of the sieve plates, seems to be rather viscous and should offer great resistance to mass flow. It has been argued, however, that the high viscosity results from the attempt to examine the cytoplasm; it is already known that when sieve cells are damaged the pores in the sieve plates quickly become plugged. It has been further suggested that movement through the sieve plates may be accelerated by some sort of electrical phenomenon. The most that can be said at present is that the mass-flow hypothesis is considered by many botanists to be the best so far proposed, but that there are major weaknesses in it.

Future research may supply the proof for one of the four hypotheses outlined here. Or it may produce new and different hypotheses. Or it may show that more than one mechanism is involved; perhaps some substances move in one manner and other substances move in a different manner. One intriguing line of re-

search now being pursued utilizes small insects called aphids. These animals have long stylet mouthparts that can penetrate through the bark of a stem and into a sieve tube, on whose contents they can then feed. Researchers have found that once an aphid has pierced a sieve tube, it is possible to anesthetize it with carbon dioxide, cut its body away, and leave the mouthparts in place in the stem. Contents from the pierced sieve tube will continue to exude from the mouthparts for days. In this way, sieve-tube contents can be obtained for analysis without causing the cell to react abnormally. Data less influenced by the experimental procedure may go a long way toward solving the vexing problem of how the phloem works.

It is interesting to note that some very large brown algae, called kelps, have evolved tissue closely resembling the phloem of the true vascular plants. In the light of our discussion of the respective functions of xylem and phloem, can you suggest reasons why the selection pressure for evolution of phloem in these brown algae should have been greater than for evolution of xylem?

CIRCULATION IN HIGHER ANIMALS

Upward transport in the xylem of plants, as we have seen, depends upon loss of water from the upper end of the system. Similarly, transport in the phloem is dependent upon loss of large quantities of materials from one end. Neither the xylem nor the phloem is therefore a circulatory system in the strict sense; there is no true circulation of materials through either of these systems alone, although substances may move from the xylem to the phloem, or the reverse, and circulate in this manner. Most higher animals, however, have a true circulatory system; blood is moved round and round through the body along a fairly definite path.

Animal circulatory systems usually include

some sort of pumping device called a **heart.**
There may be only one heart, as in our own
case, or a number of separate hearts, as in
earthworms, where five blood vessels on each
side of the animal pulsate, pumping blood from
the main dorsal longitudinal vessel into the
main ventral longitudinal vessel (Fig. 7.20).
Many insects have both a large general heart
and a series of smaller accessory hearts at the
bases of their legs and wings.

The one-way pumping action of the heart,
usually combined with a system of one-way
valves, moves the blood in a regular fashion
through the circuit. This circuit may be rigidly
encompassed in well-defined channels or vessels, in which case it is called a *closed circulatory system.* Or the circuit may have some
sections where definite vessels are absent and
the blood flows through large open spaces
known as sinuses; such a system is called an
open circulatory system. Closed circulatory
systems are characteristic of a great variety of
animals, including our old friends the earthworms and all vertebrates. Open circulatory
systems are characteristic of most molluscs
(snails, oysters, clams, etc.), all arthropods
(insects, spiders, crabs, crayfish, millipeds,
etc.), and a few worms.

The Insect Circulatory System

Since movement of the blood through an open
system is not as fast, orderly, or efficient
as through a closed system, it may seem surprising that such active animals as insects,
which must have relatively high metabolic
rates and precise internal regulation, should
have open circulatory systems. But you will
recall that insects do not rely on the blood to
carry oxygen to their tissues, this function having been taken over by the much-branched
tracheal system; consequently it is not vital for
insects that their blood flow very fast and in
a precise pathway. This is a good example of
the complex interrelationship between the various systems of a living creature.

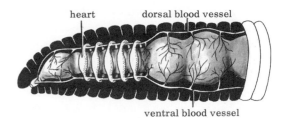

Fig. 7.20. Circulatory system of earthworm,
showing five hearts.

The circulatory systems of insects are even
more reduced than those of most other arthropods. Ordinarily, the only definite blood vessel
in an insect is a longitudinal vessel running
through the dorsal portion of the animal's
thorax and abdomen (Fig. 7.21). The posterior
portion of this vessel is pierced by a series of
openings, or ostia, each regulated by a valve
that will allow movement of blood only into
the vessel. This vessel acts as a heart. When
it contracts it forces blood out of its open
anterior end into the head region. When it relaxes again, blood is drawn into the rear portion of the heart through the ostia. Once outside the heart, the blood is no longer in vessels;
there are no veins, capillaries, or arteries, other
than the heart itself and the short so-called
artery that forms its anterior end. The blood
simply fills the spaces between the internal
organs of the insect, so that each organ is
bathed directly by blood.

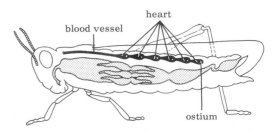

Fig. 7.21. Grasshopper, showing the dorsal
heart. Blood enters the rear portion of the
heart through the ostia and is pumped forward and out the end of the short vessel.

The action of the heart causes the blood to move sluggishly through the body spaces from the anterior end where it was released from the heart to the posterior end where it will again enter the heart. The movement of the blood is accelerated by the stirring and mixing action of the muscles of the body wall and gut during activity. Thus, when the animal is most active, as in running or flying, and its organs are in most need of rapid delivery of nutrients and removal of wastes, the blood moves with relative rapidity because of the activity itself. That insects are as successful as they are is proof enough that their open circulatory systems are sufficient for their needs.

The Human Circulatory System

Man, like all vertebrates, has a closed circulatory system, which consists basically of the heart and numerous arteries, capillaries, and veins. An *artery* is a blood vessel carrying blood away from the heart, while a *vein* is a vessel carrying blood back toward the heart. Note that, contrary to a common impression, the definitions of these two types of vessels are not based on the condition of the blood carried. Although it is true that the majority of arteries carry oxygenated blood and the majority of veins carry deoxygenated blood, oxygen content is not always a reliable way to distinguish them. *Capillaries* are tiny blood vessels that interconnect the arteries with the veins. It is across the thin walls of the capillaries that most of the exchange of materials between the blood and the other tissues takes place.

Since the constant beating of the heart is one of the most conspicuous aspects of the body's functioning, and since blood vessels can readily be seen through the skin on the wrist or the back of the hand and the pulse can be felt in the vessels of the wrist or neck, it may seem to you that the basic idea of circulation of blood via heart, arteries, and veins is perfectly obvious. Yet this seemingly simple notion was anything but obvious for centuries, even to highly educated men. For years the pumping action of the heart went unrecognized. And even after the idea of the heart as a pump prevailed, it was not understood that the blood circulates. It was thought that blood ebbed and flowed in the veins (arteries were thought to contain air, not blood) until it seeped into the tissues and was used up in the formation of new tissue or was lost in perspiration or urine. The blood steadily lost in this manner was thought to be replaced by new blood formed in the liver. A major turning point in the history of man's understanding of the functioning of his own body came with the work of the great English biologist William Harvey (1578–1657). In 1628 Harvey published a short book in Latin (which was the language of all scholarship at that time) entitled *Anatomical Dissertation Concerning the Motion of the Heart and Blood,* a work based on his extensive examinations of many different species of animals, from worms and insects to man. Here he clearly enunciated the idea of circulation of blood and outlined the basic components of the circulatory system as we know them today, even though he himself had never actually seen a capillary. Harvey's work not only improved knowledge of the circulatory system; it marked the beginning of the modern science of physiology, the attempt to understand bodily processes in terms of physics and chemistry.

The Circuit. Let us trace the movement of a drop of blood through the human circulatory system, beginning with blood returning to the heart from the legs or arms. Such blood enters the upper right chamber of the heart, called the *right atrium* (or auricle) (Figs. 7.22 and 7.23). This chamber then contracts, forcing the blood through a valve (the tricuspid valve) into the *right ventricle,* the lower right chamber of the heart. Now, this blood has just returned to the heart from its circulation through tissues, and consequently it contains

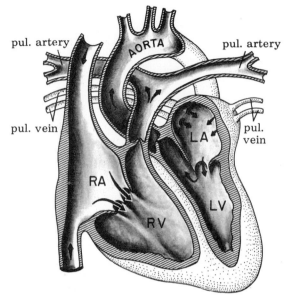

Fig. 7.22. The human heart. The arrows show direction of blood flow. RA, right atrium; RV, right ventricle; LA, left atrium; LV, left ventricle. [Modified from N. D. Millard and B. G. King, *Human Anatomy and Physiology*, Saunders, 1951.]

the *left atrium* (or auricle). When the left atrium contracts, it forces the blood through a valve (the bicuspid or mitral valve) into the *left ventricle,* which is the lower left chamber of the heart. The left ventricle, then, is a pump for recently oxygenated blood. When it contracts, it pushes the blood through a valve (the aortic semilunar valve) into a very large artery called the *aorta.*

After emerging from the anterior portion of the heart (the upper portion, in humans standing erect), the aorta forms a prominent arch and runs posteriorly along the middorsal wall of the thorax and abdomen (Fig. 7.23). Numerous branch arteries arise from the aorta along its length, and these arteries carry blood to all parts of the body. For example, the first branch of the aorta is the coronary artery, which carries

little oxygen and much carbon dioxide. It would be of little value to the body simply to pump this deoxygenated blood back out to the general body tissues. Instead, contraction of the right ventricle sends the blood through a valve (the pulmonary semilunar valve) into the *pulmonary artery,* which soon divides into two branches, one going to each lung. In the lungs, the pulmonary arteries branch into many small arteries, called arterioles, which connect with dense beds of capillaries lying in the walls of the alveoli. Here gas exchange takes place, carbon dioxide being discharged from the blood into the air in the alveoli and oxygen being picked up by the hemoglobin in the red cells of the blood. From the capillaries, the blood passes into small veins, which soon join to form large *pulmonary veins* running back toward the heart from the lungs. The four pulmonary veins (two from each lung) empty into the upper left chamber of the heart, called

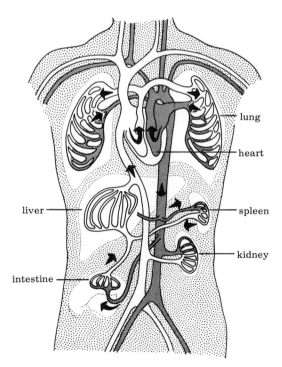

Fig. 7.23. Diagram of the human circulatory system. Dark vessels contain oxygenated blood; light vessels contain deoxygenated blood.

blood to the muscular wall of the heart itself. Other early branches of the aorta, which arise in the region of the aortic arch, are the arteries that supply the head, neck, and arms. As the aorta runs posteriorly, the arteries to the body wall, stomach, intestines, liver, pancreas, spleen, kidneys, legs, etc. arise from it. Each of these arteries, in turn, branches into smaller arteries, until eventually the smallest arterioles connect with the numerous tiny capillaries embedded in the tissues. Here oxygen, nutrients, hormones, and other substances move out of the blood into the tissues; such waste products as carbon dioxide and nitrogenous wastes are picked up by the blood, and substances to be transported, such as hormones secreted by the tissues, or nutrients from the intestine and liver, are also picked up. The blood then runs from the capillary bed into tiny veins, which fuse to form larger and larger veins, until eventually one or more large veins exit from the organ in question. These veins, in turn, empty into one of two very large veins that empty into the right atrium of the heart: the *anterior vena cava* (sometimes called the superior vena cava), which drains the head, neck, and arms, and the *posterior vena cava* (or inferior vena cava), which drains the rest of the body.

The blood now has completed the circuit. To recapitulate, it first entered the right side of the heart and was pumped to the lungs, where it picked up oxygen and gave up carbon dioxide, and then returned to the left side of the heart. This portion of the circulatory system is called the *pulmonary circulation* (Fig. 7.24). Note that in the pulmonary circuit the arteries carry deoxygenated blood and the veins carry oxygenated blood. From the left side of the heart, the blood was pumped into the aorta and its numerous branches, from which it moved into capillaries, and then into veins, and finally back in the anterior or posterior vena cava to the right side of the heart. This portion of the circulatory system is called the *systemic circulation*. The arteries of the systemic circulation carry oxygenated blood

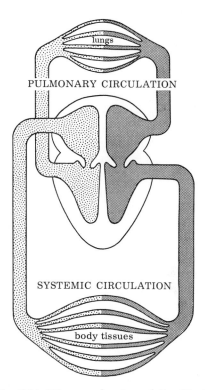

Fig. 7.24. Diagram showing relationship between the pulmonary and systemic circulations. Dark vessels contain oxygenated blood; light vessels contain deoxygenated blood.

and the veins carry deoxygenated blood—a reversal of their roles in pulmonary circulation.

The Heart. Let us now look more closely at the pumping device, the heart. We have seen that the human heart is a large four-chambered organ lying in the thoracic cavity just beneath the sternum (breastbone). It is, in effect, two hearts in one, since blood in the left side of a normal heart is completely separated from blood in the right side. This type of heart—four-chambered, with complete separation of sides—is characteristic of mammals and birds, the two groups of vertebrates commonly termed "warm-blooded." It stands to reason that animals like these, which maintain relatively constant, high body temperatures, regardless of fluctuations in the environmental temperature, should have high metabolic rates and very precise internal control mechanisms. Constant perfusion of the tissues with blood rich in oxygen is clearly essential to them. It would be highly disadvantageous to such animals if the oxygen-rich blood returning to the heart from the pulmonary circulation were mixed with the oxygen-poor blood returning from the systemic circulation.

The so-called "cold-blooded" animals, whose body temperature and metabolic rate fluctuate with the environmental temperature, do not need as highly efficient a circulatory system as mammals and birds. The hearts of primitive vertebrates apparently had only one atrium and one ventricle. Modern fish retain this type of heart (Fig. 7.25), but no mixing of oxygenated and deoxygenated blood occurs because blood aerated in the capillaries of the gills goes straight from the gills to the systemic circulation without first returning to the heart; in other words, most fish have only one basic circulation—blood goes from heart, to gills, to body tissues, and back to heart. But as the primitive lung evolved in lungfishes and amphibians, the division into two circulations, pulmonary and systemic, came into being, and with it the problem of the mixing of oxygen-rich and oxygen-poor blood in the heart. In

many of these animals, the single primitive atrium has been divided into two separate chambers, and partial division of the ventricle has also taken place in some cases. Complete division of the ventricle into two separate chambers is found in a few reptiles and, as we have seen, in all birds and mammals.

Even though the human heart is double, the two halves beat essentially in unison. Beating is an inherent capacity of the heart muscle. This muscle begins rhythmic contractions very early in the embryonic development of the individual, long before birth, and the contractions continue without pause throughout life. The heart of a resting adult pumps about 5 liters of blood each minute, which is approximately equal to the total amount of blood in the body. This does not mean, of course, that every individual drop of blood passes through the heart each minute; blood that happens to flow into one of the shorter circuits, such as one supplying the neck or chest, may return to the heart quickly and make several rounds per minute, while blood going to more distant parts of the body, such as the legs, may take several minutes to return to the heart of a resting person. During exercise, both the rate of contraction and the amount of blood pumped per beat increase greatly, and a given drop of blood

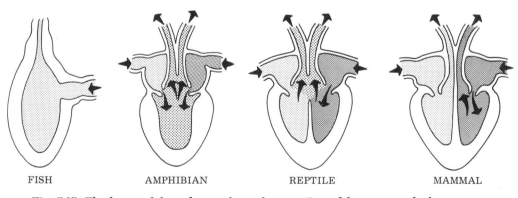

FISH   AMPHIBIAN   REPTILE   MAMMAL

Fig. 7.25. The hearts of four classes of vertebrates. From fish to mammal, there is increasing separation between the two sides of the heart, with consequent decrease in the amount of mixing between oxygenated and deoxygenated blood. [Based on P. C. Martin and E. L. Vincent, *Human Development*, © 1960, The Ronald Press Co., New York.]

may pass through the heart many times each minute.

That beating is inherent in the heart itself and not dependent upon stimulation from the central nervous system can easily be demonstrated by cutting all the nerve connections to the heart. Such a heart will continue to beat in a normal manner, although the rate of beat may change slightly. As you probably already know, the heart of a frog or turtle can continue to beat even after its complete removal from the animal's body, if it is placed in a solution with the proper osmotic concentration. Clearly, the initiation of the beat and the beat itself are intrinsic properties of the heart, but the rate of beat is partly regulated by stimulation from two sets of nerves.

The initiation of the heartbeat normally comes from a small mass of tissue on the wall of the right atrium near the point where the anterior vena cava empties into the atrium. This mass of tissue, called the sino-atrial node, or *S-A node,* is very unusual and very important. A second mass of *nodal tissue* called the atrio-ventricular node, or *A-V node,* is located in the lower part of the partition between the two atria. A bundle of nodal-tissue fibers runs from the A-V node into the walls of the two ventricles, branching to penetrate into all parts of the ventricular musculature. Nodal tissue, which is unique to the heart, has some of the properties of muscle and some of the properties of nerve; it can contract like muscle and it can transmit impulses like nerve. At regular intervals, a wave of contraction spreads from the S-A node across the walls of the atria. When this wave of contraction reaches the A-V node, the node is stimulated and excitatory impulses are rapidly transmitted from it to all parts of the ventricles via the bundle of branching fibers. These impulses stimulate the ventricles to contract as a unit. Notice that the atria contract a fraction of a second before the ventricles. Notice also that the atria do not contract as a unit; the wave of contraction begins at the S-A node and spreads across the

atria via the muscle fibers, so that the parts of the atria most distant from the S-A node contract slightly later than the parts closer to the S-A node. But the ventricles do contract as a unit, because the nodal fibers from the A-V node can transmit impulses very rapidly and stimulate the entire ventricular mass at essentially the same instant. It is easy to see why it should be adaptively more important for the ventricles to contract as a unit than for the atria to do so. After all, the ventricles must force blood through a long system of arteries, capillaries, and veins, and hence must exert great pressure on the blood. They can exert a greater force more efficiently if contraction occurs in all parts at once instead of moving across the chamber as a wave. The atria need not develop such great force because they push the blood only the short distance into the ventricles.

The alternation of systole (contraction) and diastole (relaxation) occurs at an average rate (pulse rate) of about 70 times per minute in a normal human being at rest; there is much individual variation. In the course of the beat, the heart emits several characteristic sounds, which can be heard easily if one places one's ear or a stethoscope against the chest. First, there is a long, low-pitched sound produced by the closing of the valves between the atria and the ventricles and by the contraction of the ventricles. Then there is a shorter, louder, more high-pitched sound produced by the closing of the valves between the ventricles and the arteries leading from them. Changes in these sounds often indicate to a physician that the heart is defective. A normal heart valve opens when the pressure in front of it is greater than the pressure behind it. For example, when the atria start contracting, they put pressure on the blood they contain, and as soon as this pressure is greater than the pressure in the ventricles, the tricuspid and bicuspid valves are forced open and the blood can flow into the ventricles. As soon as the atria begin to relax and the pressure in them falls below that in the ventricles, the valves snap shut. Similarly, when the ventricles contract and the pressure in them exceeds the pressure in the arteries leading from them, the semilunar valves open and the blood is forced into the arteries; as soon as the ventricles start to relax, the valves snap shut and prevent the blood in the arteries from flowing backward into the ventricles. The normal heart sounds indicate that all these valves are functioning properly. If, however, a valve has been damaged and cannnot shut completely, a hissing or murmuring sound can be heard as blood leaks backward through the damaged valve. This condition is called a heart murmur; it is a common result of rheumatic fever and some other diseases. The more extensive the damage to the valve and the greater the amount of leakage through it, the less efficient the heart action becomes and the more strain is placed upon the heart.

In the course of contraction, the heart muscle undergoes a series of electrical changes. These changes can be detected by electrodes attached to the skin and can be graphed by a device called an electrocardiograph. Abnormalities in the heart's action alter the pattern of the graph, or electrocardiogram. These alterations enable a trained physician to diagnose the abnormality.

Blood Pressure and Rate of Flow. When the left ventricle contracts, it forces blood under high pressure into the aorta, and blood surges forward in each of the arteries. The walls of the arteries are elastic and the pulse wave stretches them. During diastole, the relaxation phase of the heart cycle, the heart is not exerting pressure on the blood in the arteries and the pressure in them falls, but elastic recoil of the previously stretched artery walls maintains some pressure on the blood. There is thus a regular cycle of pressure in the larger arteries, the pressure reaching its high point during systole and its low point during diastole.

Both the systolic pressure and the diastolic pressure are important diagnostic indicators to the physician, as you know. Ordinarily these pressures are measured in the artery of the upper arm. The rubber cuff of a sphygmomanometer is attached around the arm, and then air is pumped into the cuff, which exerts more and more pressure on the arm, until finally all blood flow through the artery is blocked. A graduated column of mercury (a manometer) attached to the cuff indicates the pressure the cuff is exerting on the arm. Next, the bell of a stethoscope is placed against the artery just behind the cuff, and the air in the cuff is gradually released, with consequent reduction of pressure on the arm. When the pressure of the cuff has fallen to a value slightly lower than the maximum systolic pressure in the artery, a small stream of blood can squirt through the artery for an instant during each pulse, producing vibrations that can be heard through the stethoscope. The value shown on the column of mercury the instant before this sound is first detected is taken as the systolic pressure. In normal young adults at rest, this value averages about 120 mm. of mercury. As the pressure in the cuff is gradually lowered beneath this value, the sound produced as more and more blood surges through the artery at each systole becomes louder and louder. Eventually the pressure in the cuff drops to a value equal to that in the artery at diastole, and at this point the sound ceases; the flow of blood through the artery is now continuous. The value shown on the column of mercury at the instant the sound ceases is taken as the diastolic pressure. It averages about 80 mm. of mercury in a normal young adult at rest. The systolic and diastolic pressures are frequently written together as a fraction, e.g. 120/80.

The values obtained by the procedure just described are measurements of the blood pressure in the upper arm only. The values would not be the same for the lower arm or for the leg or for any other part of the body. The average blood pressure decreases continuously as

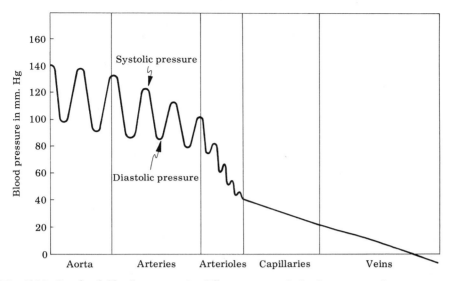

Fig. 7.26. Graph of blood pressure in different parts of the human circulatory system. In the arteries, there is considerable fluctuation between the systolic pressure and the diastolic pressure. This fluctuation diminishes in the arterioles and no longer occurs in the capillaries and veins. The most rapid fall in pressure is in the arterioles. Pressure in the veins near the heart may fall below zero.

the blood moves farther and farther away from the heart. Greatest in the part of the aorta close to the heart, it falls off steadily in the more distant parts of the aorta and it branches, falls even more rapidly in the arterioles and capillaries, then declines more slowly in the veins, reaching its lowest point in the veins nearest the heart, where its value may be as low as one atmosphere or even less (Fig. 7.26). The gradual decline of the blood pressure in successive parts of the circuit is the result of friction between the flowing blood and the walls of the vessels. Such a gradient of pressure is essential, of course, if the blood is to continue to flow; the fluid can only move from a region of higher pressure toward a region of lower pressure.

Several other changes also occur along the route of blood flow. First, the difference between systolic and diastolic pressures diminishes, until it disappears in the capillaries and veins. This means that the cyclic, surging type of flow characteristic in the arteries is replaced

by a constant rate of flow in the capillaries and veins. The change is due to the elasticity of the artery walls, which tends to damp out the fluctuations in the blood pressure. Second, the rate of flow tends to fall as the blood moves through the branching arteries and arterioles; the rate is lowest in the capillaries and increases again in the venules and veins. These changes in rate of flow result from changes in the total cross section of the vessel system. Linear rate of flow is inversely proportional to cross-sectional area. In other words, if a fluid is flowing through a tube that has a smaller cross section in some regions than in others, the fluid will move faster in these regions with the smaller cross sections and more slowly in the regions with the larger cross sections. The same rule applies if the tube is divided into many branches; the greater the effective cross section—i.e. the greater the total cross-sectional area of all the branches in any given region—the slower the flow. As the arteries branch, as they break up into arterioles, and as the arterioles break up

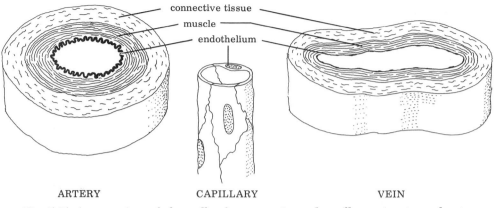

Fig. 7.27. A comparison of the walls of artery, vein, and capillary. Arteries and veins have the same three layers in their walls, but the walls of veins are much less rigid and they readily change shape when muscles press against them. Capillaries have walls composed only of a thin endothelium.

into capillaries, the total cross-sectional area keeps increasing, and the rate of flow becomes slower. As the capillaries unite to form venules and these join to form veins, the total cross-sectional area diminishes again, and the rate of flow increases.

Capillary Function. Very little, if any, exchange of materials between the blood and the other tissues occurs across the walls of the arteries or veins. The walls of these vessels are apparently impermeable to the substances in the blood and tissue fluid. Walls of arteries are composed of three layers: (1) an outer connective-tissue layer with elastic fibers, which give the vessels their characteristic elasticity; (2) a middle layer of smooth muscle, which can change the size of the vessels; and (3) an inner layer of connective tissue lined with simple squamous endothelium (Fig. 7.27). The two outer layers and the connective-tissue portion of the inner layer terminate at the ends of the arterioles, leaving the capillaries with walls composed of only the one-cell-thick endothelium. It is across these very thin walls of the capillaries that the exchange of materials takes place.

The capillaries are so numerous that they penetrate into all parts of every tissue; no cell is far removed from at least one capillary. One worker estimates that there are more than 1,500,000 capillaries per square inch in muscle tissue. The diameters of the capillaries are very small, being seldom much larger than those of the blood cells that must pass through them. The extensive branching and small diameters of individual capillaries are functionally important in several respects. They ensure not only that all portions of the tissues will be supplied with capillaries, but also that a very great capillary surface area will be available for the exchange process. It has been estimated that every cubic centimeter of blood actually contacts about 8 square feet of capillary surface each time it passes through a capillary bed! As we have seen, the branching also increases the total cross-sectional area of the system and thus makes blood flow more slowly in the capillaries than in the arteries or veins. This slower flow allows more time for the exchange process. Furthermore, the very small bore of the capillaries results in high frictional resistance to blood flow and causes a considerable drop in blood pressure in the capillary bed. This drop in blood pressure, which plays an extremely important role in the exchange process, deserves a more detailed examination here.

At the arteriole end of a representative capillary, the hydrostatic blood pressure averages about 35 mm. of mercury (Fig. 7.28). The pressure has fallen to about 15 by the time the blood reaches the venule end of the capillary. The hydrostatic pressure tends to force materials out of the capillaries into the surrounding tissue fluid. If this were the only force involved, there would be a steady loss from the blood

of both water and those dissolved substances that can readily cross the capillary walls. It can be demonstrated, however, that normally there is relatively little net loss of water from the blood in the capillaries. Clearly, some other force must act in opposition to the hydrostatic force. This other force derives from the difference in osmotic concentration between the blood and the tissue fluid. The blood contains a relatively high concentration of proteins, and these large molecules cannot easily pass through the capillary walls. The same kinds of proteins occur in the tissue fluids, but in much lower concentration. Because of the difference in protein concentration on the two sides of the capillary wall, the blood and tissue fluids will have different osmotic pressures. Normally, the osmotic pressure of the blood is about 25 mm. of mercury higher than that of the tissue fluid, with the result that water tends to move into the capillaries from the tissue fluid by osmosis. We have, then, a system in which hydrostatic pressure developed by the heart tends to force water out of the capillaries and osmotic pressure reflecting differences in protein concentration tends to force water into the capillaries. Obviously, the net movement of water will be determined by the relative magnitudes of these two opposing forces. Notice that at the arteriole end of our representative capillary the hydrostatic blood pressure is 35 and the osmotic pressure is 25. Subtracting one from the other, we find that there is a net pressure of 10 tending to force water out of the capillary. At approximately the midpoint of the capillary, the hydrostatic and osmotic pressures are equal (both being nearly 25) and there is no net movement of water. At the venule end of the capillary, the hydrostatic pressure has fallen to 15, while the osmotic pressure has not changed greatly (loss of water from the blood has, of course, slightly increased the concentration of protein in the blood and raised the osmotic pressure accordingly, but this change is relatively slight and can be ignored for our pur-

AT ARTERIOLE END
hydrostatic pressure > osmotic pressure

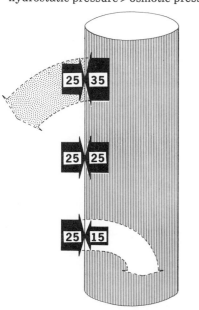

AT VENULE END
osmotic pressure > hydrostatic pressure

Fig. 7.28. Diagram of forces involved in exchange of materials across capillary walls. In this hypothetical capillary, the hydrostatic pressure of the blood (35) at the arteriole end exceeds the osmotic-pressure difference (25) and therefore materials move out of the capillary (gray arrow). At the venule end, the osmotic-pressure difference (25) exceeds the hydrostatic pressure of the blood (15) and materials enter the capillary (white arrow).

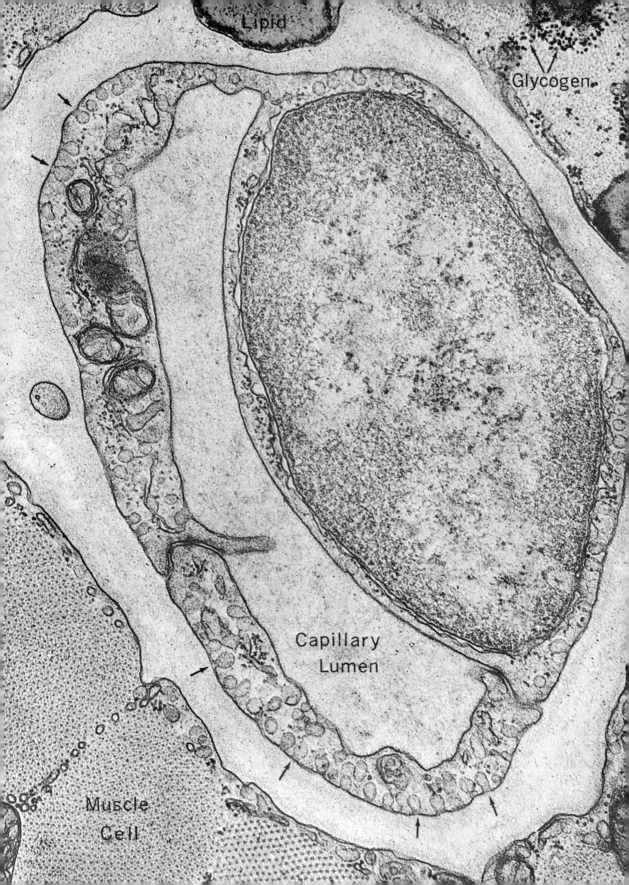

Lipid

Glycogen

Capillary
Lumen

Muscle
Cell

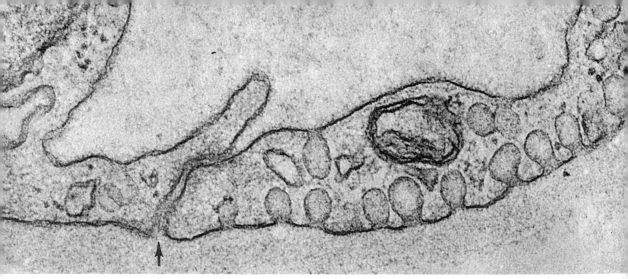

Fig. 7.29. Electron micrographs of cross section of capillary. Left: The two junctions between the two endothelial cells of which the wall of the capillary is composed are quite evident (the section shows the large nucleus of one of the cells). Numerous pinocytic vesicles (arrows) can be seen in the cytoplasm of the endothelial cells. These vesicles may play a very important role in movement of materials across the wall of the capillary. Above: Enlarged view of wall of a capillary, showing the space where two endothelial cells join (arrow) and numerous pinocytic vesicles apparently opening on the outer face of the cell. [Courtesy D. W. Fawcett, Harvard University.]

poses here). Therefore, there is now a net pressure of at least 10 tending to force water into the capillary. In summary, the balance between hydrostatic blood pressure and osmotic pressure is such as to force water out of the capillaries at the arteriole end and into the capillaries at the venule end.

The capillary walls are freely permeable to most of the smaller molecules dissolved in the blood plasma and tissue fluid, and these molecules tend to move with the water in which they are dissolved. Apparently, much of this movement is by bulk flow or filtration rather than by normal diffusion across cell membranes. There is considerable evidence suggesting that much of this filtration is through the intercellular spaces between the endothelial cells rather than across the cells themselves, although recent electron-microscope work suggests that transport may also take place in vacuoles or vesicles that pinch off from one side of an endothelial cell, migrate through the cytoplasm to the other side of the cell, and there release their contents (Fig. 7.29). Bulk flow or bulk transport in vesicles, if it actually

occurs, would help explain why the rates at which different dissolved substances move across capillary walls, as experimentally determined, are so similar to one another and bear so little relation to the rates predicted on the basis of their individual diffusion characteristics; the rate of movement of such substances would be determined by the rate of movement of the water in which they are dissolved.

There is, then, a net movement out of the capillaries at the arteriole end not just of water but of dissolved ions and nutrients as well. Similarly, there is a net movement into the capillaries at the venule end not only of water but also of waste materials from the tissues and of any special products synthesized by the tissues in question, such as hormones from the endocrine glands. In short, the blood in the capillaries first unloads materials for the tissues at the arteriole end and then picks up materials for transport at the venule end. In the process, there is normally very little net loss of water, and the blood volume is not appreciably altered.

The balance of hydrostatic and osmotic pressures in the capillaries is a very delicate one. Since it plays such an important role in the exchange of materials between the blood and the tissue fluid, any disturbance of it may have profound effects on the condition of the organism. For example, an increase in blood pressure would tend to increase loss of fluid from the blood, while a decrease in blood pressure would have the opposite effect. Such changes in blood pressure could be produced by any one or more of a variety of factors such as changes in rate or strength of heart action, increase or decrease in total blood volume, changes in the elasticity of the walls of the arteries, or increased dilation or constriction of capillaries.

The last-mentioned factor—degree of dilation or constriction of capillaries—is also important in determining the extent of the blood supply to any given tissue at a given time. The capillaries of the body are never fully open all at the same time; many capillaries are usually closed by constriction of rings of muscles at their bases. In a resting muscle, for example, only certain "thoroughfare" capillaries are generally open; but once the muscle becomes active, and its needs for oxygen and nutrients increase, the numerous smaller branch capillaries become dilated, and the local blood supply is greatly increased. Similarly, the capillaries in the wall of the intestine are extensively dilated following a large meal, when a major portion of the blood supply is channeled into this region where much absorption of digestive products is occurring. Increased dilation of skin capillaries often gives the skin a reddish hue, seen in blushing, while constriction of these same capillaries gives the skin a bleached, whitish look. A major form of heat loss from the body is by radiation from the blood in the superficial capillaries of the skin. Changes in dilation of these capillaries, by altering the amount of blood flow, are an important factor in helping to regulate heat loss.

Clearly, simultaneous dilation of a high percentage of the body's capillaries, such as those of the muscles, intestine, and skin, tends to lower the blood pressure in any given capillary, because the same amount of blood is now distributed in a greater total space. If all the capillaries were fully open at the same time, which never actually happens, they would contain all the blood in the body, and the blood pressure would fall to zero or below. When blood pressure falls because of extensive vasodilation or because of loss of blood by hemorrhage, the consequent increased absorption of tissue fluid by the capillaries increases the total blood volume (though not the total number of blood cells) and tends to compensate partially for the deficiency. At such times, the supply of circulating blood is also augmented by reserve blood previously stored in the *spleen.* This organ has large cavities, connected to its capillaries, in which blood is stored. Contractions of the smooth muscles in the walls of the spleen can expel this blood into the general circulation.

In addition to changes in hydrostatic blood pressure, changes in the relative concentrations of proteins in the blood and in the tissue fluids can also severely alter the balance of forces operating in the capillaries. Numerous experiments have been performed in which the protein concentration in the blood supply to a limb of a frog, cat, or dog was artificially regulated. As was predicted, increasing the protein concentration in the blood decreased loss of fluids from the blood and increased absorption from the tissue fluid. Conversely, decreasing the protein concentration in the blood increased loss of fluids from the blood and decreased reabsorption of fluid from the tissues, the result being an abnormal accumulation of fluid in the tissues, a condition known as edema.

The Lymphatic System. Let us suppose that in a particular tissue of a relatively healthy person there is a slight net loss of fluid from the blood to the tissue. Can the excess tissue fluid return to the blood by any other means than direct reabsorption into the blood capillaries? The answer is yes. Vertebrates have a special system of vessels that function in returning materials from the tissues to the blood. These vessels are called lymph vessels, and together they constitute the lymphatic system, which includes lymph veins and lymph capillaries, but no arteries. The lymph capillaries, which like the blood capillaries are distributed throughout most of the body, are closed at one end. Like blood capillaries, too, their walls are composed of a single layer of endothelium. Tissue fluid is absorbed into the lymph capillaries (whereupon it is called *lymph*) and slowly flows through the capillaries into small lymph veins, which unite to form larger and larger veins until finally two very large lymph ducts empty into veins of the blood circulatory system in the upper portion of the thorax near the heart.

We have indicated that the walls of lymph capillaries are structurally similar to those of blood capillaries, but their permeability characteristics are different. Lymph frequently contains a small concentration of proteins of the same types as those in the blood; these proteins can apparently move fairly easily across the walls of the lymph capillaries. Since the lymphatic system steadily carries small quantities of proteins from the tissue fluid to the blood, but the protein concentration in the tissue fluid does not normally decrease, our earlier assumption that blood proteins are not lost from the blood capillaries to the tissue fluid was evidently incorrect. There must normally be some very slight leakage of proteins from the blood capillaries, even though the walls of these capillaries are highly impermeable to proteins. The lymph vessels, whose walls are very permeable to proteins, return such proteins to the blood. The importance of this process in maintaining the normal osmotic balance between the blood and the tissue fluid is very great. Under certain conditions, major lymph vessels may become blocked, in which case the protein concentration in the tissue fluid rises

steadily and upsets the normal balance of forces operative in the capillaries. The difference in osmotic concentration between the blood and the tissue fluid steadily diminishes, which means that less and less fluid is reabsorbed by the blood capillaries. Severe edema (swelling caused by excessive fluid in the tissues) results.

Returning excess tissue fluid and proteins to the blood is only one function of the lymphatic system. There are many others. For example, much of the fat absorbed from the intestine is picked up by lymph vessels rather than by blood capillaries. Absorption of fats thus differs from the absorption of sugars and amino acids, which are picked up by blood capillaries. The lymph nodes, present in the lymphatic systems of mammals and some birds, but absent in most lower vertebrates, also perform some vital functions. They act as filters and are the sites of formation of certain types of white blood cells. Located along major lymph vessels, they are highly specialized areas composed of a meshwork of connective tissue that harbors many phagocytic cells. As the lymph trickles through this meshwork, it is filtered and such particles as dead cells, cell fragments, invading bacteria, etc. are destroyed by the phagocytic cells. Nondigestible particles such as dust and soot, which the phagocytic cells cannot destroy, are stored in the nodes. Since the nodes are particularly active during an infection, they often become swollen and sore; when one has a throat infection, for example, lymph nodes at the base of the jaw are frequently prominent.

Since the lymphatic system is not connected to the arterial portion of the blood circulatory system, it is obvious that lymph is not moved by hydrostatic pressure developed by the heart. In fact, as we have already seen, the pressure in the blood circulatory system itself has fallen so low by the time the blood reaches the veins that this pressure cannot fully account for movement of blood in the veins. Some mechanism other than pressure from the heart must operate in moving both blood in the veins and

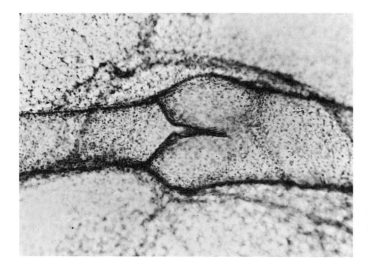

Fig. 7.30. Photograph of a valve in a lymph vessel. [Courtesy General Biological Supply House, Inc., Chicago.]

lymph in the lymph vessels. In both cases, the vessels involved have relatively thin, easily collapsible walls; the walls of both blood veins and lymph veins have the same three layers described for arteries, but the muscle layer is much less developed and there is more connective tissue. When nearby muscles contract as the organism moves, they put pressure on the veins and lymph vessels, compressing their walls and forcing the fluid in them forward. Note that the fluid can move only forward (i.e. in the direction toward the heart) because both veins and lymph vessels are equipped with numerous one-way valves (Fig. 7.30). The fluid is thus pushed along by local muscle contractions past one valve after another, being prevented by the valves at each step from flowing backward into the section whence it just came. As you doubtless already know, when you stand very still for a long period, your feet begin to swell and fatigue develops quickly; there is not enough muscle action in your legs to push the fluids upward against the pull of gravity. If you can manage, while standing, to keep moving your feet and legs, or regularly contracting and relaxing the leg muscles, the unpleasant symptoms will not be as pronounced.

The motions of the chest during breathing also aid in moving lymph and blood in veins. When the chest expands during inspiration, the pressure in the thorax falls. There is thus a pressure gradient from other parts of the body to the thorax, and blood and lymph tend to be drawn into the large vessels of the thorax and into the heart.

The above description of the mechanism of movement of lymph holds for all mammals, including man. Many of the other vertebrates differ, however, in that they have lymphatic hearts, which are pumping devices located along major lymph vessels. Most animals that have lymph hearts lack valves in their lymph vessels.

Blood

We have discussed at some length the routes followed by the circulating blood, the mechanism of circulation, and the process of exchange of certain materials with the tissue fluid. We should now examine the blood itself in more detail. It is one of the most important and unusual tissues in the animal body.

Composition of the Blood. In an earlier chapter, we classified blood as a type of connective tissue with a liquid matrix. The extracellular liquid matrix of blood is called *plasma.* Suspended in the plasma are the formed elements, which are of three major types in vertebrates: (1) the red blood cells or *erythrocytes,* (2) the white blood cells or *leukocytes,* and (3) the *platelets,* which are small disc-shaped bodies that probably arise as cell fragments. If whole blood, treated to prevent clotting, is left standing in a test tube, the formed elements will settle slowly to the bottom, leaving the fluid plasma above. The specific gravity of the formed elements does not greatly exceed that of the plasma, however, and the agitation associated with the normal circulation is sufficient to prevent separation within the circulatory system. Normally, the formed elements constitute about 40–50 percent of the volume of whole blood, while the plasma constitutes the other 50–60 percent.

The basic solvent of the plasma is, of course, water, which constitutes roughly 90 percent of the plasma. A great variety of substances are dissolved in the water; the relative concentrations of these vary with time and with the portion of the system under examination. For convenience, let us divide these solutes into six categories: (1) inorganic ions, (2) plasma proteins, (3) organic nutrients, (4) nitrogenous waste products, (5) special products being transported, and (6) dissolved gases.

1. The principal inorganic cations (positively charged ions) in the plasma are sodium (Na^+), calcium (Ca^{++}), potassium (K^+), and magnesium (Mg^{++}). The chief inorganic anions (negatively charged ions) are chloride (Cl^-), bicarbonate (HCO_3^-), phosphate (HPO_4^{--} and $H_2PO_4^-$), and sulfate (SO_4^{--}); of these, chloride and bicarbonate are by far the most abundant. Together, the inorganic ions and salts make up about 0.9 percent of the plasma of mammals by weight, of which amount more than half is sodium chloride, ordinary table salt. The concentrations of the individual ions remain relatively stable, being regulated by a variety of mechanisms, particularly the action of the kidneys and other excretory organs. This stability is essential to the normal function of the organism. For example, the total concentration of dissolved substances, particularly sodium chloride (NaCl) and sodium bicarbonate ($NaHCO_3$), determines the osmotic pressure of the plasma relative to the cells, and any appreciable shift in concentrations would upset the normal osmotic balance between the cells and the fluids that bathe them, causing severe disturbance or even death to the cells. Even if the total concentration of dissolved substances remains the same, shifts in the concentrations of particular ions can create serious disturbances. Nerves and muscles, for example, are highly sensitive to changes in the concentrations of K^+ and Ca^{++}. Similarly, the integrity of cell membranes is dependent upon proper balance of Ca^{++}, Mg^{++}, K^+, and Na^+ in the extracellular medium. The concentrations of certain ions are also very important in determining the pH of the body fluids, and even the slightest changes in this pH may kill the organism. The plasma is very slightly alkaline, having a pH of about 7.4.

2. The plasma proteins constitute 7–9 percent by weight of the plasma. Apparently these proteins, which are of three types termed fibrinogen, albumins, and globulins, are synthesized in the liver. We have already discussed their great importance in determining the osmotic pressure of the plasma and the influence they consequently have on the exchange of materials in the capillary beds and on the general water balance of the body. Later in this chapter, we shall examine their role in stabilizing the pH of the plasma. These proteins also play a central role in determining the viscosity of the plasma (viscosity is a measure of the internal friction of a fluid, i.e. the friction between molecules as they slide past each other). The heart can maintain normal blood pressure only if the viscosity of the blood is nearly normal. Injection of an isotonic salt solution into the circulatory system as an emergency measure following extensive hemorrhage can restore the blood volume to normal and

thus raise the blood pressure, but it cannot raise the pressure to the normal level because the saline solution has too low a viscosity.

In addition to the general functions mentioned above, plasma proteins have some more specific functions to be discussed later—e.g. those of fibrinogen and certain globulins in blood clotting and of gamma globulin in antibody reactions to infections.

3. Organic nutrients in the blood include glucose, fats, phospholipids, amino acids, lactic acid, etc. Some of these may have been picked up from the intestine; others may have entered the blood from storage areas such as the liver or the fat depots. Lactic acid is a product of glycolysis, especially in muscles, as we saw in an earlier chapter; it is transported by the blood to the liver, where some of it may be used in resynthesis of carbohydrates and some may be further oxidized to carbon dioxide and water. Another substance found in the plasma is cholesterol, of which some may be used as a nutrient and oxidized and some seems to have other functions not yet well understood.

4. The plasma also carries nitrogenous waste products from their sites of formation to such organs of excretion as the kidneys. In mammals, this waste is primarily in the form of urea; it usually also includes a small amount of ammonia and uric acid.

5. Among the special products carried by the plasma, the hormones are of particular significance. These substances, synthesized by the endocrine tissues, are very important regulatory chemicals to which much attention will be devoted in a later chapter.

6. Three principal gases are found dissolved in the plasma. One of these, nitrogen, which diffuses into the blood in the lungs, seems to be physiologically inert and can be disregarded here. The other two, oxygen and carbon dioxide, are of critical importance, and the details of their transport will be discussed more fully later in this chapter. Actually, in vertebrates most of the oxygen and much of the carbon dioxide are transported in the red blood cells rather than in the plasma, though small quantities are also present in the plasma.

Blood Clotting. Normally, the plasma of the circulating blood remains a liquid with its colloidal protein in the sol state. Under certain conditions, however, when a blood vessel has been ruptured or otherwise damaged, or when certain kinds of foreign substances have gained entrance into the circulating blood, or when the blood has been removed from the body, one of the plasma proteins, *fibrinogen,* is converted into the gel state and forms a hard lump or clot. In this way, a small hole in a vessel may be plugged, or a weakened place on the vessel wall may be strengthened.[1] Clearly, then, blood clotting is an evolutionary adaptation for emergency repair of the circulatory system and for preventing excessive blood loss. Clotting occurs in all vertebrates and in some invertebrates. An alternative adaptation serving the same basic function is seen in some invertebrates with powerful muscles that contract and close off the hole or damaged area.

It can be shown that clotting does not, as might seem plausible, result from exposure of the blood to air or from interference with its flow. If blood is carefully removed from a vessel without allowing it in any way to contact the damaged portion of the vessel, and if this blood is then put in an open dish lined with a nonwettable plastic, it will remain liquid for many hours. In this experiment, the blood is simultaneously exposed to air and prevented from flowing; yet it does not clot. Nor does it clot when it is held stationary in a portion of a blood vessel that has been tied off. Evidently, the factor or factors responsible for clotting must be sought elsewhere.

Since blood clotting occurs when a vessel is damaged, and since it occurs at the site of the damage, could it be that the damaged tissue releases some chemical that initiates the clotting process? If we prepare an extract from cells and add this to the liquid blood in the plastic-lined dish of the previous experiment, a clot will promptly start to form. We seem to be on the right track. But suppose we remove the blood from the vessel in the same careful way, preventing it from contacting damaged tissue, and put it in a glass dish instead of one lined with nonwettable plastic. In this case, the blood promptly clots even without the addition of tissue extract. Where does this leave us? Might there be some other source of the clot-initiating chemical we have postulated? If we allow fresh blood to contact glass while we watch it under a high-powered microscope, we can see that blood platelets tend to disintegrate upon contacting the glass. Perhaps the disintegrating platelets release the same clot-initiating chemical as is released by damaged tissues. Platelets seem to disintegrate much more readily upon contacting wettable foreign surfaces like glass than upon contacting nonwettable surfaces; this would explain why clotting did not occur in the dish lined with nonwettable plastic. It can be shown, finally, that platelets also disintegrate when they contact damaged tissue.

, The hypotheses suggested by the various experiments outlined here have been verified. It has been shown that both damaged tissues and disintegrating platelets release a group of substances called *thromboplastins* that initiate blood clotting. For reasons not well understood, thromboplastins are not effective, however, unless calcium ions are present. Some of the anticoagulants used in storing blood for later use in transfusions are chemicals that remove calcium ions from the blood and thus prevent clotting.

Why platelets disintegrate so readily upon contact with damaged tissue or wettable foreign surfaces has not been satisfactorily explained. In fact, the platelets themselves are not well understood. They seem to arise as fragments from certain large cells in the red bone marrow, though it is possible that they also arise in other parts of the body. Platelets occur in all mammals, but are absent from the blood of other vertebrates, which, however, have certain spindle-shaped cells that seem to play a similar role in blood clotting.

We have now mentioned three different substances essential for normal blood clotting: fibrinogen, thromboplastin, and calcium ions. But if we mix these three substances in a dish, no clotting occurs. Clearly something else must be involved. That something else seems to be one of the globulin proteins of the plasma, a protein called *prothrombin.* If prothrombin is added to our mixture of fibrinogen, thromboplastin, and calcium, a clot will form. It can be demonstrated, however, that prothrombin itself has no effect on clotting; it must first be converted into *thrombin,* which is the substance that converts fibrinogen into its gel form, called *fibrin,* of which the clot is formed. The function of thromboplastin is to convert prothrombin into thrombin; it is in this reaction that calcium ions participate. The thrombin then converts fibrinogen into fibrin. The fibrin fibers form a meshwork in which red and white blood cells are trapped (though these cells are not essential for clotting and can be removed without interfering with the process). The meshwork then begins to shrink, and, finally, a fluid called serum is squeezed out, leaving the hardened clot in place. The reactions can be summarized as follows:

$$(1) \quad \text{prothrombin} \xrightarrow[\text{Ca}^{++}]{\text{thromboplastin}} \text{thrombin}$$

$$(2) \quad \text{fibrinogen} \xrightarrow{\text{thrombin}} \text{fibrin}$$

These simplified summary equations show the relations between the essential substances. Actually, numerous other substances play roles in the clotting process, as accelerators, inhibitors, etc.

It would perhaps be well to clarify here the exact meanings of the three terms "whole blood," "blood plasma," and "blood serum," all of which occur frequently in references to medical procedures, particularly blood transfusions. Whole blood is blood just as it exists in the circulatory system, i.e. with none of its constituents removed. Blood plasma is whole blood minus the formed elements. Blood serum is plasma minus fibrinogen.

Erythrocytes and Their Function. Human erythrocytes or red blood cells are small, biconcave, disc-shaped cells (Fig. 7.31) that lack nuclei. Normally, there are roughly five million of them per cubic millimeter of blood (the number is slightly lower in women than in men). Though the number of red cells remains amazingly constant from day to day, there is continual destruction of some cells and formation of new ones. More than two million erythrocytes are destroyed every second, chiefly in the liver and the spleen, where they are engulfed by large phagocytic cells. There are also phagocytic cells in the lymph nodes, which destroy any erythrocytes that escape from the blood and get into the lymph. Though it is commonly supposed that the phagocytic cells of the liver and spleen destroy only old, worn-out red cells, this has not been proved.

The erythrocytes of adults are formed in the red bone marrow, which fills the interior of the ends of the long bones and the shafts of flat bones like those of the skull and ribs. Though the mature erythrocytes of mammals are devoid of nuclei, mitochondria, Golgi apparatus, etc., and therefore lack many of the characteristics of living cells, they arise from normally nucleated, rapidly dividing connective-tissue cells of the bone marrow. Toward the end of their development, they lose their nuclei and develop the red oxygen-carrying pigment called *hemoglobin.* They then enter the circulating blood. The developmental sequence in vertebrates other than mammals is somewhat different in that their mature erythrocytes retain nuclei. It has been suggested that the evolutionary loss of the nuclei in mammals has the adaptive advantage of leaving room for more hemoglobin in each cell. Extra hemoglobin might, in turn, be correlated with the high oxygen demand of the tissues of animals characterized by the high metabolic rates associated

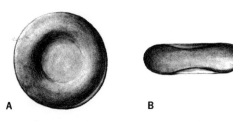

Fig. 7.31. Erythrocytes. The cells have a biconcave disclike shape. (A) Surface view. (B) Side view.

with homeothermy (warm-bloodedness); birds are also homeotherms, of course, but they retain nucleated erythrocytes. Analysis of the hemoglobin content of the red cells of a variety of vertebrates reveals that the cells of mammals, though they are smaller than those of many of the lower vertebrates, do, in fact, contain more hemoglobin.

Each human erythrocyte contains about 280 million molecules of hemoglobin. Each of these molecules is a combination of a globulin protein and four units of a complex iron-containing organic structure called heme (Fig. 7.32). The protein is a branched one, composed of four amino acid chains, each of which enfolds one of the heme groups. Hemoglobin is one of the proteins that was used in developing methods for analysis of protein structure. The sequence of amino acids in the four chains (which are actually of only two types occurring in pairs) has been determined by Gerhardt Braunitzer of the Max Planck Institute for Biochemistry in Munich, Germany, and by William H. Konigsberg and Robert J. Hill of the Rockefeller Institute in New York. Similar determinations for the hemoglobin of other vertebrates have revealed that there are many kinds of hemoglobin, differing from one another in the number and sequence of amino acids. As would be expected, the more closely related two animals are, the more similar their hemoglobins tend to be. For example, those of man and apes are much more alike than are those of man and fish. Not only do hemoglobins differ among species, but they also sometimes differ within a species. The hemoglobin of human embryos is slightly different from that of adults, for example; the fetal hemoglobin is replaced by adult hemoglobin shortly after birth. Some hereditary human blood diseases involve mutant genes that result in the change of one or two amino acids in the hemoglobin; even though each of the four chains includes about 140 amino acids, a change in only one of the 140 can severely alter the oxygen-transporting capacity of the molecule. Surprisingly, X-ray crystallographic studies of hemoglobin, as performed by Nobel Prize winner M. F. Perutz of Cambridge University, England, indicate that all hemoglobins have essentially the same three-dimensional structure, regardless of differences in amino acid sequence.

We have said that one hemoglobin molecule contains four heme groups, each with an iron atom at its center. Each of these iron atoms is capable, by virtue of its structural relationships within the hemoglobin molecule, of combining loosely with one molecule of oxygen (O_2). The compound resulting from the union

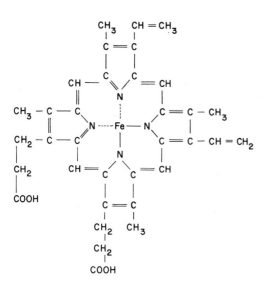

Fig. 7.32. **Structure of the heme group.**

of one molecule of hemoglobin (frequently abbreviated Hb) with four molecules of oxygen $(Hb + 4O_2)$ is called oxyhemoglobin. The addition of the oxygen to the hemoglobin slightly changes the orientation of the four amino acid chains, and this change in three-dimensional configuration causes oxyhemoglobin to appear redder than hemoglobin. It is on account of the oxyhemoglobin that arterial blood in the systemic circulation is more crimson than venous blood.

Though many invertebrates have hemoglobin, many others have a different oxygen-transporting pigment. The various alternative pigments are like hemoglobin in that they all contain a metal combined with protein. For example, many molluscs and arthropods have a pigment called hemocyanin, which contains copper instead of iron; when oxygenated, it is blue instead of red. Hemocyanin never occurs in cells; it is dissolved in the plasma of the animals that have it. Of the invertebrates that have hemoglobin, some have it in cells, like vertebrates, but many simply have it dissolved in the plasma. Though a hemoglobin molecule can function just as well in the plasma as in an erythrocyte, in animals with high metabolic rates there is a decided adaptive advantage for the pigment to be in cells; more pigment molecules can then be carried per unit volume of blood, and the oxygen-transporting capacity is correspondingly increased. If all the hemoglobin in the erythrocytes of a human being were in his plasma instead, the high concentration of protein would not only have a profound effect on the osmotic balance, but would make it impossible for the heart to force the blood through the vessels, for it would be as thick as syrup. Erythrocytes, then, are a convenient method of packaging large amounts of hemoglobin with relatively little disturbance of the viscosity and the osmotic concentration of the blood.

We have said that the combination of hemoglobin with oxygen is a loose one. Under certain conditions the combination will form, and under other conditions it will break down. Clearly, conditions in the lungs must favor formation of oxyhemoglobin and conditions in the capillary beds of the systemic circulation must favor release of oxygen and re-formation of hemoglobin. The critical condition in determining whether hemoglobin will load or unload oxygen is the partial pressure[1] of oxygen in the medium to which the hemoglobin is exposed. When the partial pressure of oxygen is high, the hemoglobin picks up oxygen; when the partial pressure of oxygen is low, the hemoglobin releases oxygen. This is simply another way of saying that hemoglobin loads oxygen when there is a relatively high percentage of oxygen in the surrounding medium, and that it unloads oxygen when the percentage is relatively low. There is, of course, a relatively high partial pressure of oxygen in the air in the alveoli of the lungs and a relatively low partial pressure of oxygen in the tissues serviced by the systemic circulation where the oxygen is being consumed in cellular respiration. Consequently hemoglobin tends to pick up oxygen in the capillaries of the lungs and to release oxygen in the capillaries of the systemic circulation.

Figure 7.33A shows a graph of the percentage of oxygen saturation of human hemoglobin at different partial pressures of oxygen; the lower the partial pressure, the greater the tendency for oxyhemoglobin to dissociate into hemoglobin and oxygen—hence the name "dissociation curve" for this graph. As you can see, the hemoglobin is about 98 percent saturated with oxygen at the partial pressure of oxygen typical of the lungs (108 mm.), while it is only about 58 percent saturated at the partial pressure of oxygen typical of the tissues at rest (32 mm.). The difference (40 percent) repre-

sents the approximate percentage of oxygen carried by hemoglobin that is actually released to the tissues. We see, then, that less than half the oxyhemoglobin releases its oxygen to the tissues and that venous blood still contains much oxygen. During exercise, the oxyhemoglobin releases more of its oxygen to the muscle tissues, so that the saturation of venous blood may fall as low as 28 percent. This extra release of oxygen probably results from the faster rate of utilization of O_2 by the tissues during exercise and from the far greater number of dilated capillaries in the muscle, which provide a much larger surface area for exchange of gases between the blood and the muscle tissues.

Notice that two different dissociation curves are given for human hemoglobin in Fig. 7.33A, one for the carbon dioxide concentration in arterial blood and one for the carbon dioxide concentration in venous blood. You can see that an increase in the concentration of CO_2 shifts the curve to the right, which means, on the one hand, that a higher partial pressure of oxygen is needed to load the hemoglobin and, on the other, that oxyhemoglobin releases oxygen more readily. Both these effects of higher

Fig. 7.33. Dissociation curves. (A) Adult human hemoglobin. Curves for both arterial and venous blood are shown. Of course, blood with the CO_2 content of arteries would never actually be found in any part of the circulatory system where the partial pressure of oxygen in the adjacent tissues is very low, and blood with the CO_2 content of veins would not be found where the pressure is very high; the curve characterizing the blood under the conditions in which it actually occurs in the body is called the physiological curve. (B) Hemoglobin of six different mammals compared. (C) Hemocyanin of blood of horseshoe crab at different temperatures. (D) Comparison of hemoglobin of two invertebrates, a fish, a reptile, a mammal, and a bird. [Modified in part from C. L. Prosser and F. A. Brown, *Comparative Animal Physiology*, Saunders, 1961; in part from K. Schmidt-Nielsen, *Animal Physiology*, © 1964, by permission of Prentice-Hall, Inc., Englewood Cliffs, N.J.]

[1] The partial pressure of a gas is the total pressure of the mixture of gases in which it occurs multiplied by the percentage of the total volume that it occupies. Thus, if the total pressure of all the atmospheric gases is about 760 mm. of mercury, and if oxygen is about 20 percent of this mixture, then the partial pressure of oxygen in the atmosphere is equal to 760 × 0.20, or 152 mm. of mercury.

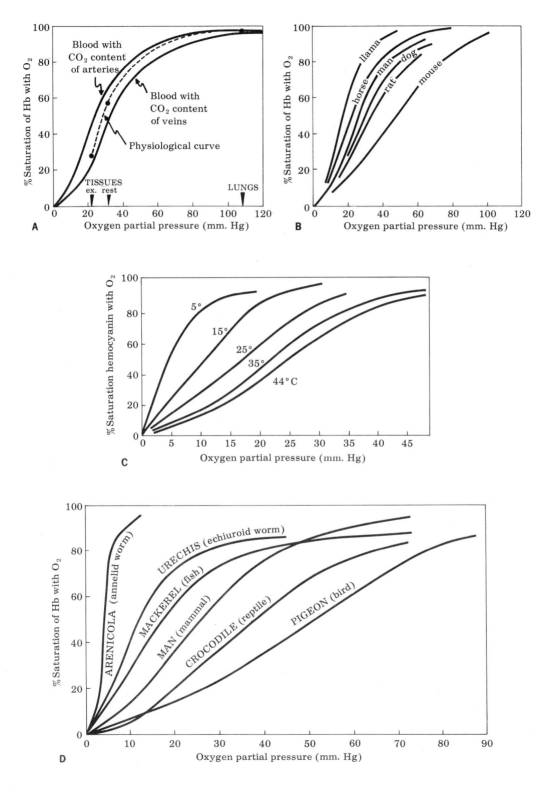

CO_2 concentration are physiologically important. The waste CO_2, picked up by the blood in the capillary bed of the tissues at the same time that it gives off O_2, facilitates the release of O_2. Conversely, release of CO_2 from the blood in the lungs shifts the dissociation curve back to the left and facilitates the pickup of O_2. It can be shown that the effect of CO_2 concentration on the affinity of hemoglobin for oxygen is actually a pH effect; increasing the CO_2 concentration makes the blood more acidic, and it is this increased acidity that reduces the affinity of hemoglobin for oxygen. The pH is not the only factor affecting the oxygen affinity of blood pigments. Temperature is another; as shown by Fig. 7.33C, the blood can pick up oxygen more easily from cold water than from warm water. We might expect this temperature effect to have considerable influence on the type of habitat a given species of animal can occupy.

Figures 7.33B and 7.33D show the dissociation curves for a variety of animals. As you can see, the hemoglobins of different animals differ significantly in their affinities for oxygen. Among mammals, the smaller species tend to have curves more to the right; i.e. their hemoglobin has a lower affinity for oxygen and therefore unloads it more readily. This tendency in small animals is probably correlated with the higher metabolic rates of their tissues, which have a higher rate of demand for oxygen. Similarly, the curves for birds, which have very high metabolic rates, as would be expected in such active animals, tend to be to the right of those for mammals. In general, the curves for cold-blooded animals (Fig. 7.33D) tend to be the left of those for warm-blooded animals; on account of their lower metabolic rates, the rate of demand for oxygen by their tissues is lower, and they have less need for oxyhemoglobin that dissociates very easily.

We have already mentioned that human fetal hemoglobin is slightly different chemically from adult hemoglobin. Figure 7.34 shows that fetal hemoglobin has a higher affinity for oxy-

gen than adult hemoglobin. The adaptive significance of this difference is readily apparent. The fetus gets its oxygen from the mother's blood, not directly from the air. If the hemoglobin of the fetus is to be able to take oxygen from the hemoglobin of the mother, it must have the greater affinity for oxygen; in other words, it must be able to compete successfully with the mother's hemoglobin.

The human fetus is an example of an organism that must get its oxygen from a medium in which the partial pressure of oxygen is lower than in the atmosphere we ordinarily breathe. Animals like the South American llama and vicuña live at very high altitudes in the mountains, where the partial pressure of oxygen is appreciably lower than it is nearer sea level (as you will know if you have ever experienced shortness of breath at high altitudes). It is not surprising, therefore, to find that these animals, like the human fetus, have hemoglobin with a higher affinity for oxygen than the average mammal; i.e. their dissociation curve is to the left of the average, meaning

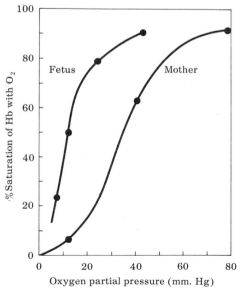

Fig. 7.34. Dissociation curves for fetal and maternal hemoglobin in the cow. Fetal hemoglobin has a higher affinity for oxygen than maternal hemoglobin.

that their hemoglobin loads more easily (Fig. 7.33B).

The llama and the vicuña have evolved a genetically determined type of hemoglobin that adapts them for life at high altitudes. But what of an animal such as a man, a sheep, a dog, or a rabbit that is moved to a high altitude? We know that eventually such an animal will become better acclimatized to its new environment and will no longer experience such severe shortness of breath as at first. Does its hemoglobin change? The answer is no. An individual animal's genes, and the hemoglobin they determine, are not changed simply by changing the environment; acclimatization involves other processes. Table 7.1 shows that acclimatized

TABLE 7.1

Percent of Blood by Volume
Occupied by Red Cells*

Animal	Altitude	% Cells
Man	Sea level	46.0
	17,600 feet	59.9
Sheep	Sea level	35.3
	15,420 feet	50.2
Dog	Sea level	34.6
	14,900 feet	50.0
Rabbit	Sea level	35
	17,500 feet	57
Vicuña	Sea level	29.8
	15,420 feet	31.9

* Data from C. L. Prosser and F. A. Brown, *Comparative Animal Physiology*, Saunders, 1961.

men, sheep, dogs, and rabbits at high altitudes have more erythrocytes per unit volume of blood than they normally have at sea level. This is apparently the result of at least two different reactions of the body to the decreased amount of oxygen reaching the tissues. First, erythrocytes stored in such areas as the spleen and skin capillaries are released into the general circulation. Second, in response to some as yet incompletely understood stimulus probably involving a hormone produced in the kidneys, the red bone marrow becomes more active and produces erythrocytes at a faster rate. Thus, through an increase in red cells, these animals partly compensate for the reduced percentage of saturation of the hemoglobin resulting from the lower partial pressure of oxygen at high altitudes. Notice, however, that the vicuña, which has hemoglobin adapted to high altitudes, shows little difference in red-cell count between sea level and high altitudes.

There are other gases besides oxygen that will also bind loosely to hemoglobin. One such gas, which binds even more readily than oxygen, is carbon monoxide (CO). This gas, common in coal gas used for heating and cooking, in the exhaust from automobiles, and in tobacco smoke, is a dangerous poison because even when its partial pressure in the air is relatively low such a high percentage of the hemoglobin may bind with it that not enough is left to carry sufficient oxygen to the tissues. Severe symptoms of asphyxiation (impairment of vision, hearing, and thought) or even death may thus result from exposure to carbon monoxide.

The blood not only transports oxygen from the lungs to the tissues, but it also has the very important function of transporting carbon dioxide in the reverse direction, from the tissues to the lungs. Some of this carbon dioxide is carried as gas dissolved in the plasma and some in loose combination with hemoglobin in the red cells, but most of it is carried as bicarbonate ions in the red cells and plasma. Relatively little of the CO_2 released from the tissue cells remains in the form of dissolved gas. Instead, it tends to combine with water to form carbonic acid (H_2CO_3):

$$CO_2 + H_2O \rightarrow H_2CO_3$$

This reaction takes place particularly fast within the erythrocytes because these cells contain an enzyme that accelerates the reaction.

But the blood must transport much CO_2, and if all of it were converted into carbonic acid and transported in this form, the pH of the blood would drop considerably. Now, cells are very sensitive to pH changes and can only live within a very narrow pH range. Any major increase in acidity (drop in pH) would clearly be very harmful to the organism.

Let us look at the problem of carbon dioxide transport more carefully. The difficulty arises because carbonic acid in the blood tends to dissociate into H^+ ions and HCO_3^- (bicarbonate) ions:

$$H_2CO_3 \rightarrow H^+ + HCO_3^-$$

It is the increase of free H^+ ions that increases the acidity of the solution. If the H^+ ions could somehow be combined tightly with something else, instead of being left in the solution as free ions, then the acidity would not increase so much. This is exactly what happens in the blood—and hemoglobin and other proteins play the critical role in the process. Much of the hemoglobin (Hb) is normally present as an almost completely ionized potassium salt (K^+Hb^-). Carbonic acid reacts with the potassium hemoglobin to form acid hemoglobin (HHb) and potassium bicarbonate ($KHCO_3$), which is usually completely ionized ($K^+HCO_3^-$):

$$H^+ + HCO_3^- + K^+ + Hb^- \rightarrow$$
$$K^+ + HCO_3^- + HHb$$

You might well question the advantage of exchanging carbonic acid for acid hemoglobin; after all, both are acids. But there is a big difference between them; acid hemoglobin is a much weaker acid than carbonic acid. Within the pH range of blood, very little of the acid hemoglobin is ionized. In other words, the reaction

$$HHb \rightarrow H^+ + Hb^-$$

which would release free hydrogen ions, does not occur at a significant rate. The reverse reaction

$$H^+ + Hb^- \rightarrow HHb$$

is much more likely. This means that the formation of acid hemoglobin removes free hydrogen ions from solution and prevents them from affecting the pH to any great extent. This is an example of the buffering action of proteins. A *buffer* is a substance that tends to prevent major shifts in pH by binding hydrogen ions when the solution begins to become more acidic and by releasing free hydrogen ions when the solution begins to become more alkaline. Hemoglobin is the principal buffer substance within the erythrocytes; it even indirectly buffers the plasma and increases its bicarbonate transporting capacity. The plasma proteins also act as buffers in the plasma. Transport of lactic acid, for example, involves buffering action by plasma proteins.

In summary, carbon dioxide released by the tissues and picked up by the blood reacts with water to form carbonic acid, most of which ionizes into hydrogen ions and bicarbonate ions. It is in the form of bicarbonate that most of the transport takes place, the excess hydrogen ions being bound to hemoglobin. In the lungs, the situation is reversed. Here the CO_2 pressure is less than in the blood, and the gradient therefore favors release of the CO_2 by a reversal of the chemical reactions outlined above.

Leukocytes and Their Functions. Human leukocytes or white blood cells are larger than the erythrocytes and have large, often irregularly shaped nuclei (Fig. 7.35). At least five different types can be distinguished on the basis of the shape of the nucleus and the density of granules in the cytoplasm. The granular types are formed in the red bone marrow, while the agranular or clear types are formed in such lymphoid tissues as those of the lymph nodes, spleen, tonsils, and adenoids, and of the thy-

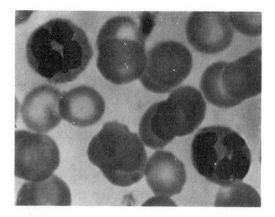

Fig. 7.35. Photograph of human blood. The cells without nuclei are erythrocytes. Those with large irregularly shaped nuclei are leukocytes. × 957. [Courtesy Thomas Eisner, Cornell University.]

mus. Leukocytes are not restricted to the blood, being even more abundant in the lymphatic system. And they are also found wandering free in loose connective tissues and occasionally in other tissues. They are capable of amoeboid movement, and can escape from the blood and lymph vessels by squeezing through the vessel walls at the points of contact between the endothelial cells. In essence, then, all connective tissues, including blood and lymph, form one continuous system so far as the leukocytes are concerned.

The leukocytes play a very important role in the body's defenses against disease and infection. Apparently, both damaged tissues and invading bacteria release chemicals that attract leukocytes. Some of the leukocytes act as phagocytes, engulfing and destroying bacteria and remnants of damaged tissue cells. In a severe infection, the leukocyte count in the blood and lymph increases enormously, and vast numbers of them may invade the infection area. The resulting mixture of dead tissue, bacterial cells, and living and dead leukocytes that accumulates at the site of the infection is commonly known as pus. Blood vessels in the infected area are generally more dilated than normal, with a consequent local increase in temperature and reddening known as an inflammation. Local swelling occurs because the blood vessels are frequently more permeable than normal and lose fluid to the tissues.

Phagocytosis is particularly important as a first defense against acute infections. Another type of defense, the production of antibodies, in which leukocytes also play a vital part, confers a degree of active immunity against the infection and is critical in fighting long-term chronic infections and in building resistance against further infection. But antibody manufacture takes time, and short-term infections are frequently brought under control by phagocytic leukocytes before significant quantities of antibody appear in the blood.

Though the leukocytes of other vertebrates may not be morphologically identical with those of human beings, and the corresponding cells of invertebrates differ even more, most animals have blood cells that serve a similar phagocytic function.

As we have indicated, only some of the leukocytes in vertebrates act as phagocytes; others are indirectly involved in the production of antibodies. The agranular (nongranular) leukocytes, particularly those of the type known as *lymphocytes,* seem to give rise to certain specialized cells called *plasma cells* that play a central role in immunologic reactions. Plasma cells respond to the presence of certain kinds of foreign substances called *antigens,* which are usually (but not always) proteins, by making *antibodies* that destroy or inactivate the antigens. Each type of antibody is usually very specific and will inactivate only the antigen that stimulated its synthesis. The antibodies are globulin proteins in the blood plasma. We shall discuss the topic of immunologic competency at greater length in a later chapter.

REFERENCES

BEST, C. H., and N. B. TAYLOR, 1961. *The Physiological Basis of Medical Practice*, 7th ed. Williams & Wilkins, Baltmore. (See esp. Chapters 1–29.)

BOLLARD, E. G., 1960. "Transport in the Xylem," *Annual Review of Plant Physiology*, vol. 11. Annual Reviews, Inc., Palo Alto, Calif.

PROSSER, C. L., and F. A. BROWN, 1961. *Comparative Animal Physiology*, 2nd ed. Saunders, Philadelphia. (See esp. Chapters 8, 13.)

STEWARD, F. C., ed., 1959. *Plant Physiology*, vol. 2. Academic Press, New York.

WINTON, F. R., and L. E. BAYLISS, 1962. *Human Physiology*, 5th ed. Little, Brown, Boston. (See esp. Chapters 1–3.)

ZIMMERMANN, M. H., 1960. "Transport in the Phloem," *Annual Review of Plant Physiology*, vol. 11. Annual Reviews, Inc., Palo Alto, Calif.

SUGGESTED READING

BALDWIN, E., 1964. *An Introduction to Comparative Biochemistry*, 4th ed. Cambridge University Press, New York. (See esp. Chapter 6.)

BIDDULPH, O., and S. BIDDULPH, 1959. "The Circulatory System of Plants," *Scientific American*, February. (Offprint 53.)

CARLSON, A. J., V. JOHNSON, and H. M. CAVERT, 1961. *The Machinery of the Body*, 5th ed. University of Chicago Press, Chicago. (See esp. Chapters 3–5.)

CRAFTS, A. S., 1961. *Translocation in Plants*. Holt, Rinehart & Winston, New York.

KILGOUR, F. G., 1952. "William Harvey," *Scientific American*, June.

MAYERSON, H. S., 1963. "The Lymphatic System," *Scientific American*, June. (Offprint 158.)

MEYER, B. S., D. B. ANDERSON, and R. H. BÖHNING, 1960. *Introduction to Plant Physiology*. Van Nostrand, Princeton, N.J. (See esp. Chapters 8, 17.)

PERUTZ, M. F., 1964. "The Hemoglobin Molecule," *Scientific American*, November. (Offprint 196.)

RAMSAY, J. A., 1957. *Physiological Approach to the Lower Animals*. Cambridge University Press, New York. (See esp. Chapter 2.)

RAY, P. M., 1963. *The Living Plant*. Holt, Rinehart & Winston, New York. (See esp. Chapter 6.)

SCHMIDT-NIELSEN, K., 1964. *Animal Physiology*, 2nd ed. Prentice-Hall, Englewood Cliffs, N.J. (See esp. Chapter 2.)

SCHOLANDER, P. F., 1963. "The Master Switch of Life," *Scientific American*, December. (Offprint 172.)

SINNOTT, E. W., and K. S. WILSON, 1963. *Botany: Principles and Problems*, 6th ed. McGraw-Hill, New York. (See esp. Chapter 7.)

STEWARD, F. C., 1964. *Plants at Work*. Addison-Wesley, Reading, Mass. (See esp. Chapter 10.)

WIGGERS, C. J., 1957. "The Heart," *Scientific American*, May. (Offprint 62.)

WOOD, W. B., 1951. "White Blood Cells vs. Bacteria," *Scientific American*, February. (Offprint 51.)

ZIMMERMANN, M. H., 1963. "How Sap Moves in Trees," *Scientific American*, March. (Offprint 154.)

ZWEIFACH, B. W., 1959. "The Microcirculation of the Blood," *Scientific American*, January. (Offprint 64.)

CHAPTER

8

REGULATION OF
BODY FLUIDS

EVIDENCE OF MANY TYPES HAS LED BIOLO-gists to the conclusion that life had its origin in the ancient seas. Of the major environmental media of the earth—sea water, fresh water, air—sea water exhibits by far the greatest stability. In such crucial characteristics as temperature, acidity, and salt concentration, the seas fluctuate remarkably little over immense spans of time, their vast bulk making any change very gradual and slow.

We have already seen that a living cell interacts constantly with its surrounding environmental medium. Such critical functions as nutrient procurement, gas exchange, metabolism —indeed life itself—are very closely dependent upon the properties of the surrounding medium. It is not surprising, therefore, that the protoplasm of the early cells had many characteristics in common with the sea water that bathed them, and that the life processes evolved a close dependence on the stable conditions existing in sea water. Similarly, it is not surprising that the evolution of complex multicellular marine animals involved the production of body fluids—tissue fluid, blood, etc.—

that could provide even the innermost body cells with a relatively nonfluctuating aquatic environment, and that the internal body fluids of those primitive marine animals resembled in many important ways the sea water that had been the cradle of life.

As the ages passed and evolution continued, the body fluids of different organisms evolved in different ways, just as did other characteristics. Comparison of the chemical makeup of the body fluids of a variety of present-day marine animals, for example, reveals many differences among them (see Table 8.1); even more noticeable differences are found if the comparison is extended to fresh-water and terrestrial animals, and very great differences indeed if it is extended to plants. We should

not make the mistake of exaggerating the similarities of these fluids. Nonetheless, it remains true that all these fluids have much in common, and that, as Ernest Baldwin of Cambridge University has said, "The conditions under which cell life is possible are very restricted indeed and have not changed substantially since life first began." The evolutionary development of the immense diversity now seen among living organisms has necessarily involved the concomitant evolution of mechanisms for maintaining within each organism a fluid environment with the properties necessary for the continued life of its cells. This basic principle was stated in a much-quoted form during the last century by the great French physiologist, Claude Bernard, as

TABLE 8.1

Concentrations of Ions in Sea Water and in Body Fluids (mM/l)*

	Na$^+$	K$^+$	Ca^{++}	Mg^{++}	Cl$^-$
Sea water	459.0	9.8	10.1	52.5	538.0
Marine invertebrates					
Jellyfish (*Aurelia*)	454.0	10.2	9.7	51.0	554.0
Sea urchin (*Echinus*)	444.0	9.6	9.9	50.2	522.0
Annelid worm (*Aphrodite*)	456.0	12.3	10.1	51.7	538.0
Lobster (*Homarus*)	472.0	10.0	15.6	6.8	470.0
Crab (*Carcinus*)	468.0	12.1	17.5	23.6	524.0
Fresh-water invertebrates					
Clam (*Anodonta*)	13.9	0.3	11.0	0.3	12.0
Crayfish (*Cambarus*)	146.0	3.9	8.1	4.3	139.0
Terrestrial animals					
Cockroach (*Periplaneta*)	161.0	7.9	4.0	5.6	144.0
Honeybee (*Apis*)	11.0	31.0	18.0	21.0	?
Japanese beetle (*Popillia*)	20.0	10.0	16.0	39.0	19.0
Chicken	154.0	6.0	5.6	2.3	122.0
Dog	150.0	4.4	5.3	1.8	106.0
Man	145.0	5.1	2.5	1.2	103.0

* Based on a larger table in C. L. Prosser and F. A. Brown, *Comparative Animal Physiology*, Saunders, 1961. (The abbreviation mM/l means millimoles per liter.)

follows: *"La fixité du milieu intérieur est la condition de la vie libre."* Freely translated, this statement says that the capacity of keeping the internal fluid environment constant is essential if organisms are to be able to live in a variety of environments.

THE EXTRACELLULAR FLUIDS OF PLANTS

Multicellular marine algae differ greatly from multicellular marine animals in the sort of fluid environment to which their cells are exposed. Roughly 50 percent of the water in the body of a complex animal is extracellular, being in the form of tissue fluid, lymph, or blood plasma. This extracellular body fluid, which bathes most of the cells, is separated from the environmental water by cellular barriers and has a characteristic composition, differing from both that of the intracellular fluid and that of the surrounding water. By contrast, most of the water content of a multicellular alga is intracellular. The water filling its intercellular spaces is essentially continuous with the environmental water and cannot be regarded as a separate or distinct fluid. The alga thus has no fluid that is fully analogous to the tissue fluid and blood of an animal. Hence, unlike the animal, which must regulate the composition of both intracellular and extracellular fluids, the alga must regulate the composition only of its intracellular fluids.

A similar contrast appears between an animal and a large vascular land plant. Such a plant obviously contains much extracellular fluid in the form of xylem sap and the water imbibed in its cell walls. But this fluid is not as fully distinct from the environmental water as are the tissue fluid and blood of an animal. You will recall that water can penetrate far into the cortex of a root by flowing along cell walls without having to cross any membranous barrier. Thus, much of the fluid that directly bathes the plant cells, even those far inside the

plant body, is essentially continuous with the environmental water and is therefore not fully analogous to animal tissue fluid, which is separated from the environmental medium by a membranous barrier. This means, of course, that the composition of much of the extracellular fluid of the plant cannot be as well regulated as the tissue fluid and blood of animals. Even the composition of the xylem sap, which is probably separated from external water by the membranous barrier of the endodermis, fluctuates widely, being dependent on such factors as the environmental conditions, the health of the plant, and the season of the year (Fig. 8.1).

We can easily understand why the inability of marine algal cells to regulate the composition of the fluid that bathes them poses no serious problem for the life of the cells; that fluid, after all, is essentially the same as sea water, which we have already said is the non-fluctuating medium in which life arose. (It is true that modern sea water has a composition quite different from that of the ancient seas, but the change was so very gradual that the organisms living in the seas had ample time in which to evolve with their evolving environment.) But what about a plant living in fresh water or on land? The fluids to which the internal cells of these plants are exposed will

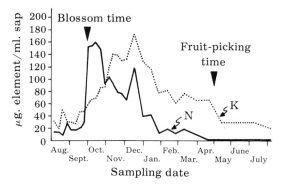

Fig. 8.1. Yearly fluctuations in nitrogen and potassium concentrations in xylem sap of apple trees in New Zealand. [Modified from E. G. Bollard, *J. Exp. Botany,* vol. 4, 1953.]

fluctuate much more than the tissue fluids of animals, and even their normal composition is one that would be quickly fatal to the internal cells of most higher animals. The reasons why plant cells seem to be able to withstand much greater fluctuations in the makeup of the fluids bathing them than can animal cells are complex and not yet well understood. But a partial explanation can be given. Animal cells are seriously affected by changes in the osmotic concentration of the extracellular body fluids, which, under normal conditions, are approximately isosmotic with the cells. If the osmotic concentration of those fluids rises, the cells lose water, and if it falls, the cells gain water. Such osmotic shifts often severely alter the physiology of the cells or even kill them. Unlike the animal cell, the cell of a land or fresh-water plant almost always exists in a medium that is much more dilute than the cell's contents.[1] In other words, the plant cell is decidedly hyperosmotic relative to the fluid that bathes it. In such a situation, an animal cell would take in so much water by osmosis that it would burst, unless it had some special mechanism for expelling the excess water. But the plant cell is surrounded by its cell wall, and as the cell takes in more water and becomes more turgid, the wall pressure becomes greater and resists further expansion. Eventually the wall pressure becomes as great as the opposing osmotic pressure, and then no further net gain of water by the cell is possible; i.e. the suction pressure has fallen to zero (see p. 72).

We see, then, that the plant cell can withstand rather pronounced changes in the osmotic concentration of the surrounding fluids as long as those fluids remain more dilute than the cell's contents, i.e. as long as the fluids remain appreciably hypoosmotic relative to the

cell. If the external fluids become decidedly hyperosmotic relative to the cell, the cell may lose so much water and shrink so grievously that it pulls away from its more rigid wall; such a cell is said to be plasmolyzed, and the phenomenon is called *plasmolysis* (Fig. 8.2). The presence of the cell wall in plants and its absence in animals thus makes the problem of salt and water balance quite different in these two types of cells.

To say that plants can tolerate much greater changes in the osmotic concentration of the fluids that bathe their cells than can animals is not to say that plants are unaffected by changes in the concentrations of individual ions in the surrounding medium. Such changes sometimes have pronounced effects on their health and growth. But the effects are usually attributable to an alteration in the chemical makeup of the plant, rather than to a disruption of its osmotic balance.

Land plants, like land animals, are frequently exposed to conditions that may cause excessive water loss by evaporation. We have already examined some of the adaptations whereby plants resist desiccation—cuticles on their exposed surfaces, regulation of stomatal openings by guard cells, stomata in deep hairlined pits in some plants living in very dry regions, etc. Some plants show little resistance to drought and quickly die when the soil moisture becomes deficient; many plants that

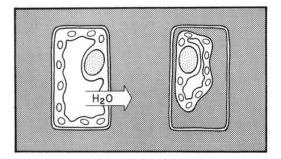

Fig. 8.2. Plasmolysis. A plant cell in a hyperosmotic medium will lose so much water (left) that, as it shrinks, it will pull away from its more rigid wall (right).

---

[1] There is evidence that vascular plants can exert some control over the osmotic concentration of the xylem sap, maintaining it well above that of the environmental fluid but below that of the cells; if the concentration of inorganic ions falls too low, the plant compensates by increasing the concentration of organic compounds in the sap.

grow only in the shade are in this category. Some plants are drought-resistant because their cells can be dehydrated without permanent injury; many mosses, lichens, and ferns are examples. Other plants can survive through long periods of drought because they store very large quantities of water and because they lose little by evaporation, thanks to very thick cuticles, few stomata, and a small surface-to-volume ratio; cacti and other succulent desert plants are good examples. Other plants are only moderately well equipped to withstand droughts; they frequently combine a limited ability to endure dehydration with some adaptations for preventing water loss and with large deep-penetrating root systems that increase absorptive capacity. Study of adaptations whereby plants withstand drought is an interesting field in its own right.

THE VERTEBRATE LIVER

As a first example of the problems involved in keeping the internal fluids of complex animals relatively constant in composition, consider the blood leaving the intestinal capillaries of your body shortly after you have eaten a meal. Digestion is actively taking place in the small intestine, and the products of digestion are moving in large quantities into the capillaries of the intestinal villi. This means that the blood leaving these capillaries contains high concentrations of such compounds as simple sugars and amino acids—concentrations considerably greater than those normally found in the blood in most parts of the circulatory system. But such a wholesale addition of these materials to the blood, if not controlled, would drastically alter the composition of the blood and other body fluids and make impossible the maintenance of a relatively nonfluctuating fluid environment for the cells.

Your body and the bodies of other vertebrates meet this difficulty through the function of a very important organ, the liver. Blood from

the intestine and stomach is collected in the *portal vein,* which does not empty into the vena cava as might be expected, but goes to the liver, where it breaks up into a network of capillaries (or, more precisely, sinuses) in the liver tissue (Fig. 8.3). The liver is one of only three places in your body where blood passes through a second set of capillaries before returning to the heart; other blood circuits involve only a single capillary bed.

The Liver's Role in Regulation of the Blood-Sugar Level. After a meal, the blood coming to the liver via the portal vein has a higher than normal concentration of glucose, and it also contains two other simple six-carbon sugars, fructose and galactose. Under these conditions, the liver removes most of the excess glucose, converting it into the insoluble polysaccharide, glycogen, which is the principal storage form of carbohydrate in animal cells; the liver also removes the fructose and most of the galactose, converts them into glucose, and then stores the glucose as glycogen. It is evident, therefore, that the blood leaving the liver via the **hepatic vein** (a vein that leads into the posterior vena cava) contains a concentration of glucose only slightly higher than

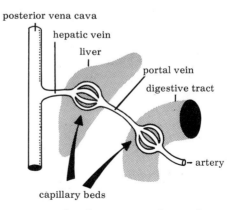

posterior vena cava

hepatic vein

liver

portal vein

digestive tract

artery

capillary beds

Fig. 8.3. The hepatic portal circulation. Blood from the intestinal capillaries is carried by the portal vein to a second bed of capillaries in the liver.

that normally found in the arteries, and that when this blood is mixed in the vena cava with blood from other parts of the body—blood that contains a lower concentration of sugar because it has given up glucose to the tissues through which it has passed—the blood entering the heart has the normal arterial glucose concentration. If the incoming supply of glucose exceeds all the body's immediate needs, and the liver has stored its full capacity of glycogen, the liver begins converting glucose into fat, which can then be stored in the various regions of adipose tissue throughout the body. Thus, in spite of the great quantities of sugar absorbed by the intestine, the blood-sugar level in most of the circulatory system is not greatly raised, only that in the short vessels between the intestine and liver being appreciably affected.

The whole process is reversed if you have not eaten recently and no sugar is being absorbed from the intestine. At such times, blood in the intestinal capillaries gives up glucose to the intestinal cells, just as blood in any capillary bed will give up nourishment to the surrounding tissues. This means that the blood reaching the liver via the portal vein is poor in glucose. Under these conditions, the liver converts some of its stored glycogen into glucose and adds it to the blood. The result is that blood leaving the liver in the hepatic vein has its normal glucose concentration, and that the blood entering the heart likewise has the normal blood-sugar level. We see, then, that the liver functions in helping maintain the blood-sugar concentration in a steady state.

The human liver is capable of storing enough glycogen to supply glucose to the blood for a period of about 24 hours. What happens if at the end of this period no new glucose has come to the liver from the intestine? A drop in the blood-sugar concentration to a level much below normal would soon be fatal; the brain cells are particularly sensitive to such a drop because they cannot store adequate amounts of glucose themselves or use fats or

amino acids as energy sources, and are thus wholly dependent on a regular supply of glucose from the blood. Under such conditions, the liver begins converting other substances, such as fats and amino acids, into glucose, and thereby maintains the normal blood-sugar level. Some other tissues of the body, particularly muscle, can store glucose as glycogen, but muscle glycogen apparently serves as a local fuel deposit only and is not generally available for maintaining the blood-glucose level.

The liver's activity in carbohydrate metabolism is regulated in a complex fashion by several hormones, as will be described in the chapter on hormonal control. An abnormal balance of these hormones may result in an unusually high blood-sugar level or an unusually low level. Either condition can be dangerous.

The Liver's Role in the Metabolism of Fats and Amino Acids. The liver's role in metabolism is not limited to carbohydrates. In addition to interconverting carbohydrates and fats, it also plays an important role in converting some of the incoming fats from the diet into the particular fats typical of the consuming animal's own body. You will recall, however, that much of the fat absorbed from the intestine enters the lymph system and hence is not carried directly to the liver. Once the fat gets into the bloodstream, it circulates freely through the body, and some of it is deposited directly in the adipose tissue without being processed by the liver.

Like the glucose, the amino acids absorbed by the villi of the intestine pass into the portal vein and thence to the liver. The liver removes many of these amino acids from the blood, temporarily storing small quantities and later gradually returning them to the blood, which carries them to other tissues for use in the synthesis of enzymes, hormones, or new protoplasm. But the usual diet contains far more amino acid than can be utilized in such syntheses. Since the animal body, unlike the plant, is capable of very little long-term storage of amino acids, proteins, or other nitrogenous compounds—those used as an energy source when supplies of carbohydrates and fats are exhausted are not stored products, but the actual structural material of the protoplasm of living cells—the excess amino acids must be converted into other substances such as glucose, glycogen, or fat. Such conversions take place by enzyme-catalyzed reactions in the liver.

You will recall that amino acids differ from carbohydrates and fats in always containing nitrogen in the form of an amino group (–NH$_2$). It is not surprising, therefore, that the first step in converting amino acids into these other substances is *deamination,* or the removal of the amino group. In the deamination reaction, the amino group is converted into *ammonia* (NH$_3$). The livers of some animals simply release this ammonia, which is a waste material, into the blood, and it is soon removed from the blood and from the body of the organism by excretory mechanisms. The livers of many other animals, including man, first combine the ammonia with carbon dioxide to form a more complex but less toxic nitrogenous compound called *urea* (Fig. 8.4), and then release the urea into the blood. The livers of still other animals convert the waste ammonia into a compound more complex than urea, called *uric acid,* and release this into the blood. In short, whether the nitrogenous waste product is ammonia, urea, uric acid, or some other compound, the liver dumps it into the blood, and it becomes necessary for another system of the body to prevent the wastes from reaching too high a concentration in the body fluids.

Notice that animals differ markedly from green plants in being unable to re-use much of the nitrogen from the amino acids they metabolize. Green plants can shift nitrogen-containing groups from one organic compound to another more freely than animals, and they can also utilize inorganic nitrogen to synthesize organic nitrogen-containing compounds. Hence excretion of nitrogenous wastes is esssentially an animal activity.

A Summary of the Liver's Functions. Over and over, as we have examined the physiology of vertebrate animals, we have mentioned some important role played by the liver. Before we leave the present discussion of this vital and versatile organ, let us compile a list of its functions. Though probably far from complete, the list may give some insight into the tremendous breadth and magnitude of the role of the liver in the maintenance of life. This organ

1. removes excess glucose from the blood and stores it as glycogen, and reconverts glycogen into glucose to maintain the blood-sugar level when the incoming supply is insufficient.

2. plays a major role in the interconversion of various nutrients, e.g. the conversion of carbohydrates into fats or the reverse, of incoming fats into fats more typical of the organism's own body, of amino acids into carbohydrates or fats.

3. deaminates amino acids, may convert the ammonia thus obtained into urea, uric acid, or some other compound, and releases the nitrogenous wastes into the blood.

4. detoxifies a great variety of injurious chemical compounds and is therefore one of the body's most important defenses against poisons.

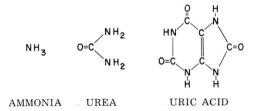

AMMONIA   UREA   URIC ACID

Fig. 8.4. Three important nitrogenous waste compounds.

5. manufactures many of the plasma proteins, including fibrinogen, prothrombin, albumin, and some globulin.
6. manufactures some plasma lipids, including cholesterol.
7. resynthesizes glycogen from some of the lactic acid produced by muscles during glycolysis.
8. stores various important substances such as vitamins and iron.
9. forms erythrocytes in the embryo.
10. destroys red blood cells.
11. excretes bile pigments.
12. synthesizes bile salts.

THE PROBLEM OF EXCRETION AND SALT AND WATER BALANCE IN ANIMALS

We have seen that animals need mechanisms for ridding their bodies of metabolic wastes—particularly nitrogenous ones, but many others as well. The process of releasing such useless substances is called excretion. In general, excretory mechanisms also serve a second very important function; they help regulate the water and salt balance of the organism. Our examination of excretion will be focused on both these aspects, which in most cases, indeed, are inextricably intertwined.

The Problem in Aquatic Animals

We have seen that the first nitrogenous waste formed by deamination of amino acids is ammonia. Now, ammonia is an exceedingly poisonous compound, and no organism can survive if its concentration in the body fluids gets very high. But the small, highly soluble molecules of ammonia readily diffuse across cell membranes, and there is no great difficulty in getting rid of them if an adequate supply of water is available. The water keeps the solution dilute while the ammonia is in the body, acts as a vehicle for the expulsion of the ammonia from

the body, and flushes the ammonia rapidly away from the vicinity of the animal. In view of the plentiful supply of water available to aquatic animals, it is not surprising that for many of these the characteristic nitrogenous excretory product is ammonia.

Marine Invertebrates. Many marine invertebrates lack special excretory systems, relying instead on release of wastes by diffusion across the general surface membranes. Such organisms seldom have any problem with water balance, since, as we have already said, they are essentially isosmotic with the surrounding sea water, and hence neither take in much excess water nor lose too much water. A variety of such organisms supplement the excretory process by phagocytic excretion; i.e. certain cells pick up solid particles of waste material by phagocytosis and then move to the outer body surface or to the surface of the digestive cavity, where the materials are released. In some cases, the phagocytic cells do not release the waste particles they have ingested, but go instead to some "storage" area, where they come to rest semipermanently. It is interesting that some animals with well-developed excretory systems, among them earthworms and man, also utilize phagocytic excretion, both the release and the storage variety, as a supplementary excretory device especially well suited to removal of particulate waste material.

Maintenance of the proper nonfluctuating internal fluid environment is relatively simple for marine invertebrates as long as they remain in the sea; it is quite a different matter when they move into hypoosmotic media such as the brackish water of estuaries or the fresh water of rivers and lakes. Many marine animals are incapable of moving into such habitats. Since their body fluids always lose salts until they have about the same salinity and osmotic concentration as the external fluids, and since their cells generally cannot tolerate much change in the makeup of the fluids bathing them, these animals soon die when they are put into brackish or fresh water. An example is the spider crab (*Maia*) (Fig. 8.5).

Some marine animals, however, have evolved adaptations that enable them to move into hypoosmotic media. The adaptations may be of an evasive character, as in oysters and clams, which simply close their shells and thereby exclude the external water during those parts of the tidal cycle when the water in the estuaries is most dilute. Or the tissues of the organisms may have become highly insensitive to changes in the osmotic concentration of the surrounding fluids. But by far the most important adaptations for survival in dilute media, and the ones that have played the principal role in the evolutionary movement of animals into fresh water, are those which enable animals to regulate the osmotic concentrations of their body fluids and keep them constant despite changes in the external medium. Such organisms are said to have the power of *osmoregulation*. Fresh-water animals generally have some mechanism whereby salt is removed from the surrounding water and secreted into the blood, a movement that is against the concentration gradient and hence must involve active transport. Obviously, such osmoregulation must also generally involve some mechanism for eliminating, or "bailing out," the excess water that will inevitably move into the organism by osmosis if the osmotic concentration of the body fluids is maintained at a higher level than the surrounding aquatic medium.

The shore crab (*Carcinus*) is an example of a marine invertebrate that has evolved a degree of osmoregulation enabling it to live in both sea water and brackish water (Fig. 8.5). In sea water, the crab's body fluids are in osmotic equilibrium, but in brackish water they are hyperosmotic relative to the surrounding medium. To maintain the internal fluids near their normal concentration in brackish water, the crab's gills remove salt from the surrounding water and actively secrete it into the blood, while the excretory organs eliminate the excess water that constantly pours in. The shore crab's excretory organs are not, however, very well adapted for life in brackish water, being incapable of producing urine that is more dilute than the blood; i.e. they cannot selectively remove salts from the urine and return them to the blood. Hence salts are constantly lost in the urine and must be replaced through active uptake by the gills.

Fresh-Water Animals. Once the ancestors of the modern fresh-water animals had made the transition to the fresh-water environment, presumably by way of the estuaries, there was no longer any great advantage to their descendants in continuing to maintain body fluids as concentrated as sea water, as long as they remained in their new environment. Such ex-

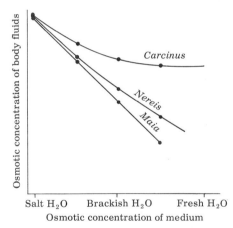

Fig. 8.5. **Variation of internal osmotic concentration with external osmotic concentration in three marine invertebrates.** The spider crab (*Maia*) has no osmoregulatory capacity, and the concentration of its body fluids falls in direct proportion to the fall in the concentration of the external medium. The clam worm (*Nereis*) has very slight osmoregulatory capacity; the concentration of its body fluids does not bear a straight-line relationship to the concentration of the external medium. The shore crab (*Carcinus*) has considerable osmoregulatory capability and can maintain relatively concentrated body fluids even in a very dilute external medium. [Modified from E. Baldwin, *An Introduction to Comparative Biochemistry*, Cambridge University Press, 1948.]

cessively hyperosmotic internal conditions simply aggravated the problem of obtaining enough salt (which involves energy expenditure, since active transport is necessary) and the problem of bailing out excess water. Thus it is not surprising that natural selection favored a reduction of the osmotic concentration of the body fluids within the bounds possible for the continuance of the life of the tissues, and that modern fresh-water animals, both invertebrate and vertebrate, have osmotic concentrations decidedly lower than sea water (Table 8.2). It seems to be incompatible with cellular existence, however, for the body fluids to be as dilute as fresh water, for no organisms are actually isosmotic with their fresh-water medium; the body fluids of fresh-water animals are typically hypoosmotic relative to sea water but hyperosmotic relative to fresh water.

Now, if fresh-water animals are hyperosmotic relative to the surrounding environmental medium, it follows that there will be a steady movement of water into the organism and a steady loss of salts from the organism to the surrounding water. At first glance, it might seem that the obvious evolutionary solution to this problem would have been the development of completely impermeable membranes covering the entire body, but further thought shows that this solution would have been impracticable, since a truly aquatic organism must maintain some permeable membranes exposed to the water for gas exchange. Because mammals that live in the water breathe air and hence need never expose permeable membranes to the water, they can maintain an impermeable barrier between their body fluids and the water in which they live. But fully aquatic animals cannot use the "method of evasion" exclusively, though they are using it as much as their gas-exchange requirements will allow when the respiratory membranes they need are restricted to a relatively small area and the rest of their body is covered with an impermeable cuticle. They must also utilize the so-called "method of correction," which involves possession of excretory organs that can pump out the water as fast as it floods in—preferably through the production of urine more dilute than the body fluids—and/or possession of special secretory cells somewhere on the body that can absorb salts from the environment and release them into the body. Both corrective measures—production of dilute urine and absorption of salts —entail movement of materials against concentration gradients and therefore necessitate

TABLE 8.2

Concentrations of Ions in the Blood of Fresh-Water Animals Compared with Sea Water and Fresh Water (mM/l)*

	Na$^+$	K$^+$	Ca^{++}	Mg^{++}	Cl$^-$
Sea water	459.0	9.8	10.1	52.5	538.0
Brown trout (*Salmo*)	149.3	5.1	?	?	140.5
Crayfish (*Cambarus*)	146.0	3.9	8.1	4.3	139.0
Clam (*Anodonta*)	13.9	0.3	11.0	0.3	12.0
Fresh water	0.65	0.01	2.00	0.21	0.48

* Based on a larger table in C. L. Prosser and F. A. Brown, *Comparative Animal Physiology,* Saunders, 1961. (The abbreviation mM/l means millimoles per liter.)

expenditure of energy in the doing of osmotic work.

An examination of the water and salt regulation typical of modern fresh-water bony fishes will provide a good example of the above-mentioned processes. The blood and tissue fluids of the fish are more concentrated than the environmental water (Table 8.2). The method of evasion is utilized to the extent that much of the body is covered by relatively impermeable skin and scales, and that the fish almost never drink. There is, however, a constant osmotic intake of water across the membranes of the gills and of the mouth, and a constant loss of salts across the same membranes. The method of correction is utilized in two ways; the excess water is eliminated in the form of very dilute and copious urine produced by the kidneys, and salts are actively absorbed by specialized cells in the gills (Fig. 8.6).

Marine Vertebrates. Curiously, bony fishes living in the sea have the reverse problem; they live in water, yet they steadily lose water to their environment and are in constant danger of dehydration. The explanation is that the ancestors of the bony fishes apparently lived in fresh water, not in the sea, and that when some of their descendants moved to the marine environment they retained their dilute body fluids. Thus marine bony fishes are hypo-osmotic relative to the surrounding water, and they have the problem of excessive water loss and excessive salt intake. Besides benefiting from the evasive adaptation of relatively impermeable skin and scales, they use two corrective measures; they drink almost continuously to compensate for the water loss, and they actively excrete salt in very concentrated form by means of specialized cells in the gills (Fig. 8.6). Most of the nitrogenous wastes are excreted as ammonia through the gills; hence only a small quantity of urine is produced by the kidneys, and little water need be lost in this manner. Apparently, fish kidneys have not

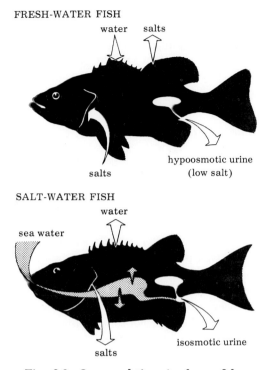

Fig. 8.6. **Osmoregulation in bony fishes.** Fresh-water fishes, which are hyperosmotic relative to the water in which they live, tend to take in excessive amounts of water and to lose too much salt. They compensate by seldom drinking, by actively absorbing salts through specialized cells on their gills, and by excreting copious dilute urine. Salt-water fishes, which are hypoosmotic relative to sea water, tend to lose too much water and to take in too much salt. They compensate by drinking constantly and by actively excreting salts across their gills. They cannot produce hyperosmotic urine; hence the kidneys are of little aid to marine fishes in osmoregulation.

evolved the capacity of producing concentrated urine, and they are consequently of no help in salt elimination.

The marine elasmobranch fishes (sharks and their relatives) probably also evolved from fresh-water ancestors, but they solved the osmotic problem in a very different way. Their blood contains about the same concentrations of salts as the blood of marine bony fishes, but their blood also contains high concentrations of urea. By conserving urea instead of excreting it, the marine elasmobranchs maintain in their blood a total osmotic concentration that is slightly greater than that of sea water. They, therefore, have no problem of water loss. Excess salt is excreted by special glandular cells in the rectum.

The Problem in Terrestrial Animals

We have already seen that one of the necessary conditions of animal life in fresh water is that as much of the body surface as possible have a relatively impermeable covering that aids in preventing excessive absorption of water. Therefore fresh-water animals had an important preadaptive advantage over primitively marine animals in colonizing the terrestrial environment. The evidence strongly supports the view that the movement to land was by way of fresh water, not directly from the sea.

On land, the greatest threat to life is desiccation. Water is lost by evaporation from the respiratory surfaces (lungs, tracheae, etc.), by evaporation from the general body surface, even though it is relatively waterproof, by elimination in the feces, and by excretion in the urine. The lost water must obviously be replaced if life is to continue. It is replaced by drinking, by eating foods containing water, and by the oxidation of nutrients (remember that water is one of the products of cellular respiration).

We saw that ammonia was a satisfactory nitrogenous excretory product for aquatic animals. It is far from satisfactory for terrestrial ones, because of the difficulty of getting rid of this highly toxic substance on land, where an unlimited water supply is not available. Amphibians and mammals, therefore, rapidly convert ammonia into urea, a compound that, though very soluble, is relatively nontoxic. Urea can remain in the body for some time before being excreted, and we can regard its production as an adaptation to the conditions of water shortage characteristic of terrestrial existence.

Although urea is a far more satisfactory excretory product than ammonia for land animals, it has the disadvantage of draining away some of the critically needed water, for, being highly soluble, it must be released from the body in an aqueous solution. If, however, uric acid, a very insoluble compound, is excreted instead of urea, almost no water need be lost. It is not surprising, therefore, that many terrestrial animals—most reptiles, birds, insects, and land snails—excrete uric acid. The excretion of this substance not only allows them to conserve water, but has another advantage, which may have been even more important in the evolution of uric acid metabolism. All these animals lay eggs that are enclosed within a relatively impermeable shell or membrane. If the embryos excreted ammonia, they would rapidly be poisoned, and if they produced urea, the concentration in the egg by the latter part of development would become decidedly harmful. Uric acid, on the other hand, is so insoluble that it can be precipitated in almost solid form and stored in the egg without exerting harmful toxic or osmotic effects. In the nitrogen metabolism of fully terrestrial animals, uric acid excretion is correlated with egg laying, while urea excretion is correlated with viviparity (giving birth to living young).

EXCRETORY MECHANISMS IN ANIMALS

Contractile Vacuoles

Special excretory structures are absent in many unicellular and simple multicellular animals. Nitrogenous wastes are simply excreted across the general cell membranes into the surrounding water. Some Protozoa (and a few sponge cells) do, however, have a special excretory organelle, the contractile vacuole (Fig. 8.7). Each vacuole goes through a regular cycle consisting of a stage in which it fills with liquid and becomes larger and larger, followed by a

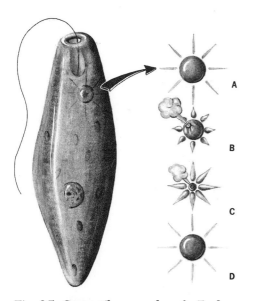

Fig. 8.7. Contractile vacuole of *Euglena.* *Euglena* is a unicellular organism with some animal-like and some plantlike characteristics. It swims by means of a long flagellum. It has chlorophyll. Its contractile vacuole removes the excess water that tends to move into the cell. The vacuole fills with water led into it by a system of radiating canals (A). When full, the vacuole contracts, expelling the water from the cell (B, C).

contraction stage in which the contents of the vacuole are ejected from the cell. Although there is now evidence that contractile vacuoles excrete some nitrogenous wastes, it seems clear

that their primary function is elimination of excess water. As could be predicted, they are much more common in fresh-water Protozoa than in marine forms, and their rate of contraction becomes slower as the osmotic pressure of the environmental medium increases.

Flame-Cell Systems (Protonephridia)

The beginnings of a tubular excretory system can be seen in the flatworms (planaria, flukes, tapeworms, etc.). These animals are relatively small and lack a functional body cavity; i.e. there is no major break in the tissue mass between the outer epithelium of the body and the gastrovascular cavity. There is no circulatory system. The body organization, more complex than in coelenterates such as hydra and jellyfish, is at the organ level instead of the tissue level, as the presence of excretory organs indicates.

Flatworm excretory systems usually consist of two or more longitudinal branching tubules running the length of the body (Fig. 8.8). In planaria and its relatives, the tubules open to the body surface through a number of tiny pores. In some other flatworms, such as the flukes, the tubules unite to form an enlarged bladder that opens to the outside. The critical portions of the systems are many small bulblike

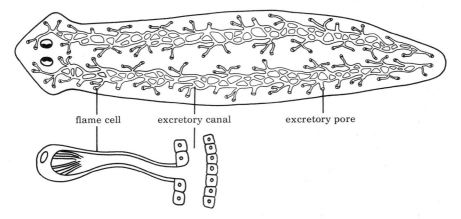

flame cell   excretory canal   excretory pore

Fig. 8.8. Flame-cell system of planaria. See text for explanation of its function. [Modified from R. Buchsbaum, *Animals Without Backbones,* University of Chicago Press, 1948.]

structures located at the ends of side branches of the tubules. Each bulb or photonephridium, has a hollow center into which a tuft of long cilia projects. The hollow centers of the bulbs are continuous with the cavities of the tubules. Water and some waste materials move from the tissue fluids into the bulbs. The constant undulating movement of the cilia creates a current that moves the collected liquid through the tubules to the excretory pores (nephridiopores), where it leaves the body. The motion of the tuft of cilia resembles the flickering of a flame, and for this reason this type of excretory system is often called a flame-cell system. Like the contractile vacuoles discussed earlier, flame-cell systems seem to function primarily in the regulation of water balance; most metabolic wastes of flatworms are excreted from the tissues into the gastrovascular cavity and eliminated from the body through the mouth.

Nephridia of Earthworms

Note that flame-cell systems are found in animals without circulatory systems, and that, as a result, they pick up substances only from the tissue fluids. In animals that have evolved closed circulatory systems, the blood vessels have become intimately associated with the excretory organs, making possible direct exchange of materials between the blood and the excretory system.

The earthworm is an example of an animal in which the circulatory system plays a critical role in excretion. The earthworm's body is composed of a series of segments internally partitioned from each other by membranes. In general, each of the compartments thus formed has its own pair of excretory organs, called nephridia, which open independently to the outside; the various nephridia are not connected to each other. A typical nephridium (Fig. 8.9) consists of an open ciliated funnel or nephrostome (which corresponds functionally to the bulb of a flame-cell system), a coiled

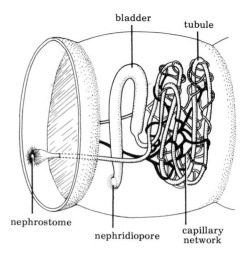

Fig. 8.9. **Nephridium of an earthworm.** The open nephrostome of each nephridium is located in the segment ahead of the one containing the rest of that nephridium. The tubule penetrates through the membranous partition between the two segments and is then thrown into a series of coils, with which a network of blood capillaries is closely associated. The tubule empties into a storage bladder that opens to the outside through a nephridiopore.

tubule running from the nephrostome, an enlarged bladder into which the tubule empties, and a nephridiopore through which materials are expelled from the bladder to the outside. Blood capillaries form a network around the coiled tubule. Materials move from the body fluids into the nephridium through the open nephrostome, but some materials are also picked up by the coiled tubule directly from the blood in the capillaries. There is probably also some reabsorption of materials from the tubule into the blood capillaries. The principal advance of this type of excretory system over the flame cell, then, is the association of blood vessels with the coiled tubule.

The Vertebrate Kidney

Structure of the Kidney. Like the nephridial system of earthworms, the excretory systems of vertebrates are closely associated with the closed circulatory system. When an efficient circulatory system can bring wastes to the excretory organs, the functional excretory units no longer have to be scattered throughout the body tissues, as in planaria. And the absence of internal segmentation of the body obviates the need for a series of individual excretory organs, as in earthworms. Higher vertebrates have typically evolved compact discrete organs, the kidneys, in which the functional units are massed. In man, the kidneys are located in the back of the abdominal cavity.

The functional units of the kidneys of higher vertebrates are called *nephrons.* Each nephron consists of a closed bulb called a **Bowman's capsule** (or renal capsule) and a fairly long coiled tube. The tubules of the various nephrons empty into collecting tubules, which in turn empty into the central cavity of the kidney, the pelvis. From the pelvis, a large duct leaves each kidney and runs posteriorly. In some animals (frogs, birds, etc.), these ducts empty into the **cloaca,** which is a common chamber through which pass materials from the digestive, excretory, and reproductive systems. In mammals, which have no cloaca, the ducts, called **ureters,** empty into the **urinary bladder.** This storage organ drains to the outside via another duct, the **urethra** (Fig. 8.10).

Blood capillaries and the capsules and tubules of the nephrons are intimately associated in the modern vertebrate kidney. No longer are materials picked up from the general body fluids; exchange of substances takes place almost exclusively between blood capillaries and nephrons. Blood reaches each kidney via a **renal artery,** a short vessel leading directly from the aorta to the kidney (Fig. 8.11). The renal artery enters the kidney at its median depression and then breaks up into many smaller branches that run through the inner portion of the kidney (the medulla) into the outer kidney layer (the cortex), where each of the many tiny branch arterioles penetrates into a cuplike depression in the wall of a Bowman's capsule. Within each capsule, the ar-

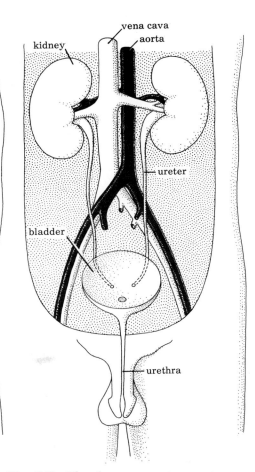

Fig. 8.10. The human excretory system. (The organs and vessels are shown larger relative to the body size than they actually are.)

teriole breaks up into a tuft of capillaries called the **glomerulus** (Fig. 8.12). Blood leaves the glomerulus via an arteriole formed by the rejoining of the glomerular capillaries. Having emerged from the capsule, the arteriole promptly divides again into many small capillaries that form a second dense network around the tubule of the nephron. Finally, these capillaries unite once more to form a small vein. The veins from the many nephrons then fuse to form the **renal vein,** which leads from the hilum of the kidney to the posterior vena cava. The kidney, you will note, is the

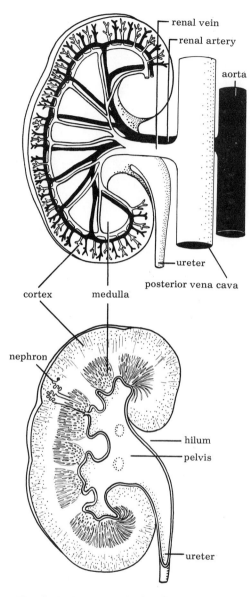

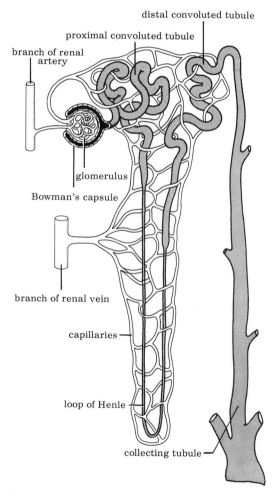

position to examine the mechanism of urine formation in the human kidney. In 1844 the German physiologist Carl Ludwig suggested that a glomerulus acts as a simple mechanical filter, that molecules small enough to pass through the capillary walls and through the thin membranous walls of the capsule filter from the blood into the nephron as a result of the high hydrostatic pressure in the glomerulus. If the filter theory is correct, the

Fig. 8.11. Sections of the human kidney. The top figure shows the blood circulation of the kidney. The bottom figure shows the large renal pelvis into which the collecting tubules of the nephrons empty.

second place where we have encountered blood circuits that involve two sets of capillaries.

The Formation of Urine. With the structural relationships in mind, we are now in a

Fig. 8.12. The human nephron. For description, see text. [Modified from H. W. Smith, *The Kidney,* Oxford University Press, 1951.]

liquid entering the lumen of the nephron should have basically the same percentage composition as blood, lacking only the formed elements and the plasma proteins, both of which are too large to filter through the membranes to any appreciable extent. Collection of capsular urine to check this prediction is a very difficult undertaking, one that, at best, can yield only minute quantities for analysis. In spite of the technical difficulties, A. N. Richards of the University of Pennsylvania was able to insert microscopic glass pipettes directly into a Bowman's capsule and to draw off small samples of glomerular filtrate. Analysis of these samples showed that the filtrate has essentially the same concentration of dissolved substances (glucose, urea, salts, amino acids, etc.) as blood plasma, just as had been predicted. Furthermore, it has been demonstrated that if the hydrostatic pressure in the glomerular capillaries is increased, the volume of the filtrate is increased proportionately, and that if the hydrostatic pressure is decreased, the filtrate volume declines proportionately. The experimental evidence also indicates that changes in filtrate volume are not accompanied by changes in the kidney's oxygen consumption, such as would occur if the kidney were performing work in moving materials from the blood to the capsule. All the evidence, therefore, supports Ludwig's theory that the cells of the glomerular capillaries and of the Bowman's capsules do not carry out active transport in the movement of materials from the glomeruli into the capsules, but that the work involved is performed by the beating heart as it drives the blood under high hydrostatic pressure into the glomeruli.

We have said that the filtrate closely resembles blood minus the cellular elements and the protein molecules. But if this filtrate were expelled from the body without modification, many very valuable, indeed essential, substances would be lost and the process would be wasteful in the extreme. If we consider water alone, it is overpowering to contemplate the

drinking that would be necessary to replace the 180 quarts of filtrate formed every day in the average person's kidneys! Selective reabsorption of most of the water and many of the dissolved materials is one of the functions of the tubules of the nephrons. In man, the filtrate passes first through the *proximal convoluted tubule,* then through the long *loop of Henle,* then through the *distal convoluted tubule,* and finally into the *collecting tubule* (Fig. 8.12). The Bowman's capsule and the proximal and distal convoluted tubules are in the kidney cortex layer, while most of the loop of Henle and the collecting tubule are in the kidney medulla. As the filtrate moves through the tubules, most of the water (about 99 percent) is reabsorbed by the tubules and returned to the blood in the capillary network surrounding the tubules. Thus the kidneys can produce concentrated urine, i.e. urine that is hyperosmotic relative to the blood plasma even though the initial filtrate was isosmotic.

To understand by what process the urine becomes concentrated, we must examine the loop of Henle (Fig. 8.13). Apparently the cells in the wall of the ascending limb of this loop actively pump sodium ions out of the tubule into the surrounding tissue fluid. Some, but not all, of this sodium passively diffuses back into the descending loop, so that there is, in effect, a cycling of some of the sodium from ascending limb to tissue fluid to descending limb to ascending limb to tissue fluid, etc. The result is that a sodium concentration gradient is maintained in the tissue fluid along the loop, with the concentration lowest in the outer part of the kidney cortex, where the convoluted tubules are located, and highest in the medulla, where the tips of the loops of Henle are located. The walls of the ascending limb of the loop must be impermeable to water since water does not diffuse out of the tubule as the sodium is pumped out. Consequently the net effect of passage of the filtrate through the loop of Henle is the removal from it of much sodium but very little water.

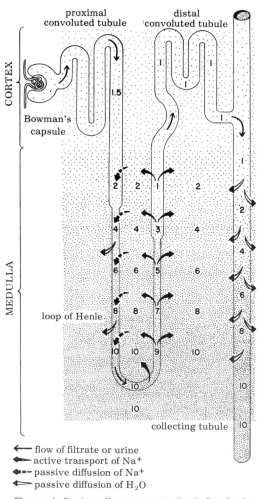

← flow of filtrate or urine
◄ active transport of Na⁺
◄-- passive diffusion of Na⁺
← passive diffusion of H₂O

Figures indicate sodium concentration in hundreds of millinormality.

Fig. 8.13. Production of concentrated urine by the human kidney. See text for a full discussion.

Hence the urine in the distal convoluted tubule is actually less, instead of more, concentrated than the initial filtrate. But now the urine flows into the collecting tubule, which runs from the cortex through the medulla to the renal pelvis, i.e. through a region of increasing sodium concentration in the tissue fluid. Since the walls of the collecting tubule are permeable to water, water moves by passive osmosis from the dilute urine in the tubule to

the surrounding hyperosmotic tissue fluid, until the final urine becomes essentially isosmotic with the highly concentrated tissue fluid in the inner region of the medulla. This final urine, then, is much more concentrated than the initial glomerular filtrate, and it is decidedly hyperosmotic relative to the blood plasma.[2]

As we indicated earlier, water is not the only substance reabsorbed by the tubules of the nephrons. In a normal healthy person, all the glucose, almost all the amino acid, and much of the salt are also reabsorbed and returned to the blood. Much of this reabsorption involves active transport, and thus energy expenditure by the tubule cells. (There is, in addition, passive reabsorption of a small amount of urea.) Our emphasis on the reabsorption of most of the substances in the filtrate might seem to imply that urine consists exclusively of a concentrated solution of urea and some uric acid (in human beings and a very few other mammals, a small amount of uric acid is formed by deamination of nuclear proteins). But urine generally is more than this. Most substances have what is called a kidney threshold level. If the concentration of such a substance in the blood exceeds its kidney threshold level, the excess is not reabsorbed from the filtrate by the tubules and appears in the urine. Glucose is an example of a substance with a high threshold value; ordinarily all glucose in the filtrate is reabsorbed because the threshold level for glucose is higher than the normal blood-glucose level. If, however, the blood-sugar level is abnormally high, as in diabetes, sugar appears in the urine. This elimination of excess sugar by the kidneys serves to emphasize again a point we have made many times in this chapter, that excretory organs do far more than just remove ni-

[2] The model for urine production discussed here and illustrated in Fig. 8.13 is called a countercurrent multiplier system, which is a system with a hairpin-loop structure that multiplies the effect of active transport, thus permitting production of higher concentration differences than might otherwise be possible.

trogenous wastes; they play a critical role in maintaining the relatively nonfluctuating internal fluid environment of the organism. In this case, when the liver and/or the peripheral tissues are not functioning properly and the blood-sugar level rises, the kidneys act as a second line of defense. The kidneys likewise help regulate the composition of the blood by keeping the relative concentrations of such inorganic ions as sodium, potassium, and chloride in the blood plasma at a nearly constant level. Whenever the concentration of an ion in the blood, and hence in the glomerular filtrate, exceeds its kidney threshold value, the excess in the filtrate is not reabsorbed but is released in the urine. The remarkably steady level of ionic concentration in the blood and the considerable variation noticeable in the urine suggest the extent of the regulation.

The movement of materials between the tubules and the capillaries surrounding them is not completely one-way. Many biologists once thought it was, but there is now evidence that some chemicals are actively removed from the blood by the tubules and deposited in the urine. This tubular excretion supplements glomerular excretion and increases the efficiency of the overall excretory regulation of blood composition.

The glomerular kidney, which probably arose first in ancestral marine vertebrates, doubtless played an important role in enabling the ancestors of the modern bony fishes to enter fresh water, a hypoosmotic medium relative to their body fluids.[3] We have seen that fresh-water fishes are constantly being flooded by osmotic water. The glomerular kidney is particularly well suited to pumping out excess water. Terrestrial vertebrates, on the other hand, have no need to excrete large quantities of water; their problem is the reverse, the conservation of water. It is not surprising, therefore, that in reptiles and birds the development

[3] It was formerly thought that the first vertebrates arose in fresh water, but now evidence seems to favor the view that they arose in the sea.

and activity of the glomeruli have declined. In these animals, much of the excretion of uric acid is tubular, not glomerular, excretion. Mammals, on the other hand, have not evolved reduced glomeruli, but have instead evolved longer tubules and more efficient water reabsorption. Like terrestrial vertebrates, modern marine fishes have a problem of water conservation, as we saw earlier in this chapter. They, too, often have reduced glomeruli; some species have even lost them completely and depend wholly on tubular excretion.

Special Excretory Adaptations of Vertebrates. The kidneys of vertebrates vary considerably in their capacity to produce concentrated urine. You will recall that marine fishes are incapable of producing urine more concentrated than their blood and that they must therefore excrete excess salt by another method, special cells on the gills. Similarly, marine birds (albatrosses, penguins, etc.) and sea turtles have not evolved very efficient kidneys and must excrete the excess salt in the water they drink by some other mechanism; these animals have special glands in their head, near the eye, that are capable of excreting salt in very concentrated solution.

Seals and some whales seldom drink; they get their water from the body fluids of the fish they eat, and thus benefit from the fishes' ability to excrete salt through the gills. A fish diet means much protein, however, and much urea to excrete. These animals have kidneys capable of excreting urine with a high urea concentration. Some whales eat marine invertebrates instead of fish, and accordingly take in much excess salt; apparently these species can produce urine with a high salt concentration.

Kangaroo rats living in deserts almost never drink; nor do they get water by eating succulent food. Most of their water is metabolic water obtained during the respiration of the dry grains they eat. They must, of course, conserve water extremely well; they are not active during the heat of the day, they do not sweat, they eliminate very dry feces, and they have extraordinarily efficient kidneys capable of producing extremely concentrated urine.

The human kidney is incapable of producing urine with a very high concentration of either salt or urea. And humans have no alternative excretory mechanism like those of marine fishes, birds, and turtles. As a result, a man adrift at sea is in serious danger, as you know. Drinking sea water aggravates his condition because he will excrete more water than he drinks, in the process of removing salt from his body. If he tries to get his water by eating fish, as seals do, he excretes much water in the process of removing urea. Man's kidneys are simply not adapted to life at sea or to life in very dry habitats.

Malpighian Tubules

Proceeding from flame-cell systems to earthworm nephridia to vertebrate kidneys, we have noticed an increasingly close interrelationship between the excretory structures and closed circulatory systems. In the flame-cell system, no circulatory system is involved. In the earthworm nephridium, blood capillaries are associated with the tubule but not with the nephrostome. And, finally, in the advanced vertebrate kidney, there are both tubule capillaries and glomerular capillaries, the glomerulus and renal capsule forming a compact interacting unit. We do not mean to imply that this sequence represents a true evolutionary progression; indeed the evidence indicates that the evolution of earthworms and the evolution of vertebrates had little to do with each other, and that the excretory systems of the two animal groups almost certainly evolved independently. Nonetheless, these systems do serve to emphasize the trend, seen in many animal groups, of increasing dependence of the excretory process on blood-capillary beds.

But we have said before and must say again

that in biology almost all generalizations have exceptions. Insects are a case in point here. The phylum to which this immense class of animals belongs probably evolved from an ancestral form similar to the ancestor of segmented worms like the earthworm. The evidence indicates that this ancestor had nephridia. Yet insects do not have nephridia, nor have their excretory organs evolved from nephridia. Recall that insects abandoned the closed circulatory system of their ancestors and evolved an open circulatory system instead. The absence of blood capillaries apparently led, in turn, to the evolutionary loss of nephridia, which are dependent upon capillaries. Consequently insects and many of their relatives evolved an entirely new excretory system, one that functions well in association with an open circulatory system.

The excretory organs of insects are called Malpighian tubules. They are diverticula of the digestive tract located at the junction between the midgut and the hindgut (Fig. 8.14). These blind sacs, variable in number, are bathed directly by the blood in the open sinuses of the animal's body. Fluid is secreted from the blood into the blind distal end of the Malpighian tubules. As the fluid moves through the proximal portion of the tubules, the nitrogenous material is precipitated as uric acid and much of the water and various salts are reabsorbed. The concentrated, but still fluid, urine next passes into the hindgut and then into the rectum. The rectum has very powerful water-reabsorptive capacities, and the urine and feces leave the rectum as very dry material.

The highly effective role played in water conservation by the insect rectum is similar to that of the cloaca of birds and some other vertebrates. In those animals, the urine must move through the posterior portion of the digestive tract, where it is subjected to the powerful reabsorptive action of the rectum; the uric acid is therefore eliminated as a nearly dry powder or hard mass.

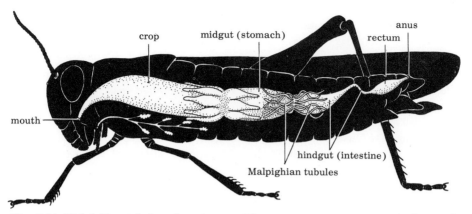

Fig. 8.14. Malpighian tubules of an insect. These excretory organs arise as diverticula of the digestive system at the junction between the midgut and hindgut.

The Cellular Basis of Active Transport of Salt

In our discussion of excretion and osmoregulation so far, we have paid little attention to events at the cellular level. We have indicated that active transport of some substances, particularly salts, is carried out by the cells in the walls of the kidney tubules and Malpighian tubules, by the osmoregulatory cells in the nasal glands of marine birds and turtles, and by the salt-secreting cells of the gills of bony fishes and of the rectal glands of elasmobranchs. But can we say any more than this? Is anything known about the active-transport process?

The Sodium-Potassium Pump. We have stated repeatedly that animals tend to maintain a nonfluctuating fluid environment for their cells, and that this fluid has approximately the same osmotic concentration as the cells, but these statements should not be understood to imply that the extracellular and intracellular fluids have the same ionic composition. On the contrary, their compositions are very different. All cells, plant and animal, tend to accumulate certain ions in much higher concentrations than are found in the surrounding fluids and to sta-

bilize their intracellular concentrations of other ions at levels far below those in the extracellular fluids. Certain algae, for example, accumulate amazingly high intracellular concentrations of a variety of ions, some of which seem to have little if any functional importance to the plant. And the vast majority of cells maintain an internal concentration of sodium ions far below that in the fluids bathing them, while at the same time accumulating potassium ions to a concentration many times that in the extracellular fluid.

Clearly, such discrepancies between the intracellular and extracellular concentrations of individual ions reflect properties of the cellular membranes. In part, the differential distribution of sodium and potassium ions may be explained by the different sizes of these ions relative to the pores in the cell membrane; the evidence indicates that the pores are large enough (hypothetically, about 3 angstroms in diameter) for hydrated potassium ions to move through them easily, but too small for the somewhat larger hydrated sodium ions to do so; the membrane is roughly 100 times more permeable to potassium than to sodium. This differential permeability alone is not enough, however, to explain how the cell so effectively maintains its composition distinct from that of the tissue fluid. It can be demonstrated that the unequal concentrations of most small ions on the two sides of the cellular membrane cannot be maintained under conditions that prevent the cell from carrying out energy-yielding chemical reactions such as cellular respiration. It can be inferred, therefore, that the cell must do work to accumulate some ions and expel others. In short, active transport across the membrane must be involved. We see, then, that active transport of such ions as sodium and potassium is not a phenomenon restricted to the cells of excretory and osmoregulatory organs, but that it is a general property of cells. Excretory and osmoregulatory cells have simply become highly specialized for this activity, and hence function not only in regulating their own intracellular composition but also in regulating the composition of the extracellular fluids for the whole animal.

Unfortunately, we have very little knowledge about the actual mechanism whereby sodium and potassium are actively transported across the cell membrane. One widely accepted model for this so-called sodium-potassium pump assumes that a carrier compound in the membrane is involved (Fig. 8.15). Let us look

briefly at this model. It is hypothesized that near the outer surface of the membrane the carrier compound exists in a form, X, in which it readily unites with potassium ions to form a new compound, KX. Since KX is in higher concentration near the outer surface of the membrane than near the inner surface, the molecules of this compound tend to diffuse passively across the membrane toward the inner surface. Once a molecule of KX reaches the inner surface of the membrane, it is assumed to dissociate, releasing the potassium ion into the interior of the cell. According to the model, the carrier molecule, X, is then immediately converted into another form, Y, by an energy-requiring reaction driven by ATP. In its new form, Y, the carrier molecule readily unites with sodium ions at the inner surface of the membrane to form a new compound, NaY. But NaY is in much higher concentration near the inner surface of the membrane where it is being synthesized than near the outer surface. Hence the molecules of NaY tend to diffuse passively across the membrane toward the outer surface. When such a molecule reaches the outer surface, it is assumed to dissociate, releasing the sodium ion into the fluid outside the cell. Y is then immediately reconverted into X by an enzyme-catalyzed reaction. The carrier molecule can now pick up another potassium ion to form KX and start the cycle over again. Thus the carrier molecule in its two forms, X and Y, constantly shuttles back and forth across the membrane, bringing potassium ions into the cell and taking sodium ions out. The energy that keeps the pump operating is provided by the ATP-driven conversion of X into Y at the inner surface of the membrane.

We must emphasize that this is only a hypothetical model of what happens in the membrane, and should not be taken as fact. Ion transport may actually proceed quite differently, and the mechanism by which the conversion of ATP into ADP is coupled with the

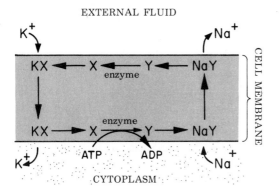

Fig. 8.15. Model of sodium-potassium pump. See text for explanation.

transport system may be completely unlike that hypothesized by the model. Much more research is needed on this subject. The most we can say at present is that somehow the cell maintains its low concentration of sodium ions and its high concentration of potassium ions, that the process utilizes energy derived from ATP, and that we can provisionally visualize the process by means of the model here described.

Now let us return to the epithelial cells involved in active transport in excretory and osmoregulatory organs. Most investigators believe that these cells utilize, at least in part, the same basic type of pump described above as characteristic of cells in general. But these specialized cells perform a particularly complex task. Consider the osmoregulatory cells in the gills of a marine fish; these cells must remove sodium from the blood and tissue fluid and actively secrete it into the surrounding sea water (chloride will follow passively to balance the electric charge). Or consider the cells in the walls of the ascending limb of the loop of Henle in a mammalian kidney; these cells must remove sodium from the urine and actively secrete it into the tissue fluid surrounding the nephron. In both instances, the cells are doing more than simply expelling sodium ions from their cytoplasm; they are picking up sodium ions on one side and expelling them on the other side. In other words, sodium ions are being moved completely across the cell barrier that separates the fish's tissue fluids from the sea water or that separates the contents of the mammalian nephron from the tissue fluid. This means that the membranes on the two sides of the cell must be functioning differently. It has been hypothesized that sodium ions can rather freely diffuse passively into the cell on one side, but that they are then actively expelled from the cell on the other side. Let us see how this hypothesis would apply to the osmoregulatory cells in the gill of a fresh-water fish, cells that must take in salt from the surrounding water and extrude it into the blood-derived tissue fluid. The pump would be active only at the tissue-fluid side of the cell, pumping sodium ions from the cell contents into the tissue fluid. This would lower the sodium concentration in the cell to a point below that in the environmental water, and if the membrane on the environmental side of the cell were permeable to sodium, sodium would tend to diffuse passively into the cell from the environmental water. In other words, sodium would diffuse passively into the cell from the environment on one side and then be actively secreted by the pump from the cell into the tissue fluid on the other side. In a marine fish, the situation would be reversed; the pump would be in the membrane on the side of the cell exposed to the sea water, and sodium would diffuse passively into the cell on the tissue-fluid side.

Structural Features of Osmoregulatory Cells. If the cells of excretory and osmoregulatory epithelia act as highly specialized ionic pumps, we can ask whether they exhibit any special structural features that might be associated with their function. The answer is yes. Electron micrographs of the secretory cells in the salt glands of marine birds and turtles, the rectal glands of elasmobranchs, the gills of salt-water and marine fishes, the gills of crustaceans, the osmoregulatory anal papillae of mosquito larvae, and the tubules of the mammalian nephron reveal that all such osmoregulatory cells possess extensive systems of smooth endoplasmic reticulum, dense populations of mitochondria containing large numbers of cristae, and, frequently, extensive deep infoldings of the cell membrane on the side of the cell where absorption is presumed to occur (Fig. 8.16). These distinctive structural features are believed to reflect the function of the cells. Further careful research aimed at a precise linking of the details of structure and function should greatly expand our knowledge in this field.

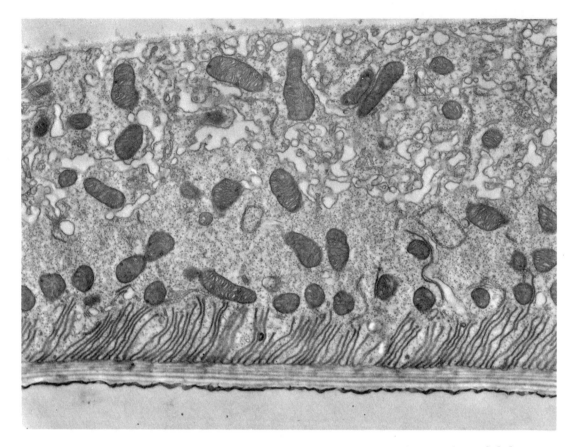

Fig. 8.16. Electron micrograph of section of anal papilla of mosquito larva. The epithelial cells of the papilla absorb salt from the fresh water in which the larva lives and secrete it into the blood. Note the large number of infoldings of the cell membrane near the outer (absorptive) surface of the cell (bottom of micrograph) and the numerous open vesicles on the secretory side of the cell (upper portion of micrograph). The vesicles may be directly connected to the secretory surface by the endoplasmic reticulum. Mitochondria are abundant in the cell. × 15,900. [Courtesy E. Copeland, *J. Cell Biol.*, vol. 23, 1964.]

REFERENCES

BEADLE, L. C., 1957. "Comparative Physiology: Osmotic and Ionic Regulation in Aquatic Animals," *Annual Review of Physiology*, vol. 19, pp. 329–358.

BEST, C. H., and N. B. TAYLOR, 1961. *The Physiological Basis of Medical Practice,* 7th ed. Williams & Wilkins, Baltimore. (See esp. Chapters 34–35.)

BLACK, V. S., 1951. "Osmotic Regulation in Teleost Fishes," *University of Toronto Studies: Biological Series,* vol. 59, pp. 53–89.

COLE, W. H., 1940. "The Composition of Fluids and Sera of Some Marine Animals and of the Sea Water in Which They Live," *Journal of General Physiology*, vol. 23, pp. 575–584.

DENISON, R. H., 1956. "A Review of the Habitat of the Earliest Vertebrates," *Fieldiana: Geology,* vol. 11, pp. 359–457.

EDNEY, E. B., 1957. *Water Relations of Terrestrial Arthropods.* Cambridge University Press, New York.

MAXIMOV, N. A., 1929. *The Plant in Relation to Water.* Allen & Unwin, London.

PROSSER, C. L., and F. A. BROWN, 1961. *Comparative Animal Physiology,* 2nd ed. Saunders, Philadelphia. (See esp. Chapters 2–3, 6.)

ROBERTSON, J. D., 1957. "The Habitat of the Early Vertebrates," *Biological Reviews,* vol. 32, pp. 156–187.

SCHMIDT-NIELSEN, B., 1958. "Urea Excretion in Mammals," *Physiological Reviews,* vol. 38, pp. 139–168.

SCHMIDT-NIELSEN, K., 1958. "Salt Glands in Marine Reptiles," *Nature,* vol. 182, pp. 783–785.

———, 1964. *Desert Animals: Physiological Problems of Heat and Water.* Oxford University Press, New York.

———, C. B. JORGENSEN, and H. OSAKI, 1958. "Extrarenal Salt Excretion in Birds," *American Journal of Physiology,* vol. 193, pp. 101–107.

WINTON, F. R., and L. E. BAYLISS, 1962. *Human Physiology,* 5th ed. Little, Brown, Boston. (See esp. Chapters 8–9.)

SUGGESTED READING

D'AMOUR, F. E., 1961. *Basic Physiology.* University of Chicago Press, Chicago. (See esp. Chapters 12, 14.)

BALDWIN, E., 1964. *An Introduction to Comparative Biochemistry,* 4th ed. Cambridge University Press, New York. (See esp. Chapters 1–5.)

CARLSON, A. J., V. JOHNSON, and H. M. CAVERT, 1961. *The Machinery of the Body,* 5th ed. University of Chicago Press, Chicago. (See esp. Chapters 8–9.)

RAMSAY, J. A., 1957. *Physiological Approach to the Lower Animals.* Cambridge University Press, New York. (See esp. Chapter 4.)

SCHMIDT-NIELSEN, B., 1965. "Comparative Morphology and Physiology of Excretion," *Ideas in Modern Biology,* ed. by J. A. Moore. Natural History Press, Garden City, N.Y.

SCHMIDT-NIELSEN, K., 1959. "Salt Glands," *Scientific American,* January.

———, 1959. "The Physiology of the Camel," *Scientific American,* December.

———, 1964. *Animal Physiology,* 2nd ed. Prentice-Hall, Englewood Cliffs, N.J. (See esp. Chapter 4.)

———, and B. SCHMIDT-NIELSEN, 1953. "The Desert Rat," *Scientific American,* July.

SMITH, H. W., 1953. "The Kidney," *Scientific American,* January. (Offprint 37.)

———, 1953. *From Fish to Philosopher.* Little, Brown, Boston. (Paperback edition by Doubleday Anchor Books, 1961.)

SOLOMON, A. K. "Pumps in the Living Cell," *Scientific American,* August. (Offprint 131.)

CHAPTER
9

CHEMICAL
CONTROL

How complex the life functions are, and how intricately they are interwoven, has emerged clearly from our study of various aspects of the biology of organisms—cellular structure, metabolism, nutrient procurement, gas exchange, internal transport, osmoregulation, and excretion. This complexity is not restricted to multicellular plants and animals, with their many cooperating cells, tissues, organs, and systems; it also characterizes unicellular organisms, which, as we have repeatedly seen, are far from simple. That living things function in an orderly fashion despite their immense complexity shows clearly that control mechanisms are at work. We have already examined the regulatory activities of the liver and excretory organs in maintaining a relatively constant fluid environment for the cells and tissues of higher animals. But coordination of these regulatory functions and all the myriad other functions of an organism depends upon special control mechanisms, of which we can recognize two principal types: chemical control mechanisms, which are found in all organisms, and nervous control mechanisms, which, in the strict sense, are found only in multicellular animals. This chapter will be concerned with the first of these—chemical control.

We have already seen that within any living cell vast numbers of different chemical reactions are occurring at any given instant. As a result, the chemical environment in every part of the cell is constantly changing slightly as some substances are synthesized and others are detroyed or removed. But any change in the chemical environment will affect subsequent chemical reactions and thereby exert some control over them. Whether the effect of one chemical reaction on another is slight or whether it is pronounced, the fact remains that each reaction will in some way influence all other reactions. This simple relationship constitutes the raw material for the evolution of more complex chemical regulatory mechanisms, and in this simple form much of the chemical regulation of all living cells still takes place.

Suppose that within a certain cell the following two reactions are occurring:

$$A + B \xrightarrow{\text{enzyme}} C + D \qquad (1)$$

$$X + Y \xrightarrow{\text{enzyme}} Z \qquad (2)$$

Suppose, further, that Z, the product of the second reaction, exerts a significant effect on the rate of the first reaction. If this effect is advantageous, natural selection might lead in time to cells with genetic systems that enhance the role of reaction 2 as a control mechanism for reaction 1, perhaps by producing more enzyme for reaction 2 and thereby causing it to proceed more readily, or by producing a slightly different form of the enzyme, which might speed up the reaction or lead to the synthesis of a compound Z_1 that is more effective as a control agent than the original compound Z. Or perhaps the newly evolved genetic systems have no effect on reaction 2, but change the enzyme of reaction 1 in ways that make it more susceptible to the regula-

tory action of Z. In what other ways could natural selection strengthen the influence of reaction 2 and its product Z as a chemical control mechanism?

We have thus far restricted our discussion of the relationship between Z and the reaction it regulates to the intracellular situation. Now let us suppose that Z is synthesized with particular ease by certain types of cells within the body of a multicellular organism and that reaction 1 proceeds most readily in other types of cells within the same organism. If Z is to play a major role in regulating reaction 1 in such an organism, it must be secreted (released) by the cells where it is produced and must reach and enter the cells in which reaction 1 is occurring. If this happens, intercellular control has been established; the product of one cell is regulating reactions in other cells. There is ample evidence that such intercellular interactions occur whenever two or more cells are in either direct or indirect contact. For example, the characteristics of a single cell growing on a culture medium in the laboratory are different from those of a cell from the same source grown next to another cell. It is true that some intercellular interaction involves mechanical, electrical, or other physical influences, but chemical influences are more important. It can be shown that cells separated from each other by a thin sheet of agar influence each other via chemicals that diffuse through the agar. Release of chemicals that affect other cells is characteristic of all cells. As we shall see in a later chapter, such intercellular chemical interactions play a critical role in the differentiation of cells and tissues within a developing embryo.

The multicellular organism, as we have noted repeatedly in other chapters, is characterized by division of labor between its parts. It is not unexpected, therefore, that evolution has led recurrently in such organisms to specialization of certain cells or tissues as producers of control chemicals. These chemicals often have important control functions in parts of the body far removed from their sites of synthesis. Transport between the sites of synthesis and the sites of action is frequently through the phloem of vascular plants and through the blood circulatory system in higher animals. Control chemicals produced in a regular fashion by tissues or organs specialized for that function and exerting their highly specific effects on other tissues of the body are usually called *hormones.* They are effective in very low concentrations, indicating that they probably function as coenzymes or parts of coenzymes, or that they influence the synthesis of enzymes or coenzymes, perhaps by regulating the activity of the genes that control the synthesis.

PLANT HORMONES

Plant hormones, at least those so far known, are produced most abundantly in the actively growing parts of the plant body, such as the apical meristems of the shoot and the root, young growing leaves, or developing seeds. The tissues in which these hormones are produced, frequently the meristematic tissues themselves, are specialized for hormone production, but they are not so highly specialized as to be concerned with little else, as is frequently the case with the most highly specialized hormone-producing tissues in animals. There are no separate hormone-producing organs in plants analogous to the endocrine glands of higher animals. Furthermore, plant hormones are almost exclusively involved in regulating growth patterns and are often called growth regulators, while animal hormones mediate a great variety of functions in addition to growth.

Work on plant hormones is one of the most active areas of modern botanical research, and our knowledge of this subject is growing rapidly. The following sections do not pretend to be complete in their coverage; they are intended, rather, as an introduction providing the background necessary for understanding advances as they occur. It is very likely that many exciting discoveries will have been made in the time between the writing and your reading of this book.

Auxins

One of the earliest-investigated and best-known groups of plant hormones, or growth regulators, includes those hormones collectively known as auxins. Auxins have an amazing variety of effects on different parts of the plant, but one of their most important effects, and the one most extensively studied, is their control of cell elongation in stems. Let us begin our discussion with an examination of this function of auxins.

Auxins and Phototropism of Shoots. Everyone is familiar with the strong tendency of many plants to turn toward the light. A potted plant in the living room bends toward a window; you turn the plant so that it will look nicer to people in the room, but discover that in a disconcertingly short time the shoot is again oriented toward the light of the window. Many housewives wage a running battle with their potted plants, turning them back toward the room every day or so. This phenomenon of responding to light by turning is called phototropism, from the Greek words for light and turning (other tropisms involve turning responses to other stimuli, as geotropism, a turning response to gravity, and hydrotropism, a turning response to water). In plant shoots, the phototropism is positive, a turning toward the stimulus; roots, on the other hand, exhibit negative phototropism, a turning away from a light stimulus.

One of the first to investigate the phototropism of plants was the incredibly versatile Charles Darwin. He, like many who followed him, performed his experiments on the hollow cylindrical sheath that encloses the first leaves of seedlings of grasses and their relatives. This sheath, called the *coleoptile*, grows principally by cell elongation, and it exhibits a very strong positive phototropic response. Darwin and his son Francis showed that if the tip of the coleoptile was covered by a tiny black cap, it failed to bend toward light coming to it from one side, while control coleoptiles with their tips exposed or covered with transparent caps bent, as expected, toward the light (Fig. 9.1). A black tube placed over the base of the coleoptile, but not covering the tip, failed to prevent bending. It seemed to be the tip of the coleoptile, therefore, that played the key role in the phototropic response. This was confirmed by experiments in which the Darwins cut off the tip and found that the coleoptile failed to bend, even though control coleoptiles damaged in other ways, but with their tips intact, bent normally. Clearly, it was the absence of the tip and not a reaction to wounding that blocked the phototropic response.

After experiments such as these, which showed, in the Darwins' own words that "the exclusion of light from the upper part of the cotyledons [i.e. coleoptiles] . . . prevents the lower part, though fully exposed to a lateral light, from becoming curved," they came to the conclusion, in 1880, that it is the tip of the coleoptile that detects the light and that "some influence is transmitted from the upper to the lower part, causing the latter to bend."

Nearly thirty years later, P. Boysen-Jensen in Denmark obtained the first clear evidence that the "influence" postulated by the Darwins was probably material rather than electrical or nervous. He removed the tips of oat coleoptiles (which made the coleoptiles stop growing), placed a thin layer of gelatin on the cut end of the stump, and then placed the tip on the gelatin. Thus the tip was separated from the rest of the coleoptile by a thin layer of gelatin (Fig. 9.2). The coleoptiles resumed grow-

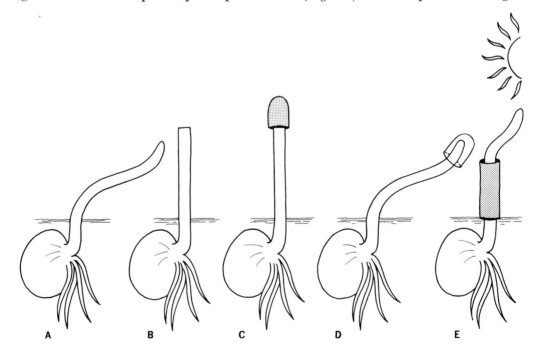

Fig. 9.1. Darwin's experiments on phototropism. (A) Coleoptile of canary grass bends toward the light. (B-C) The coleoptile does not bend if its tip is removed or is covered by an opaque cap. (D) The coleoptile does bend if its tip is covered by a transparent cap. (E) It also bends if its base is covered by an opaque tube.

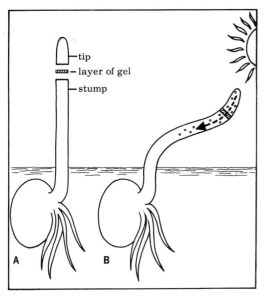

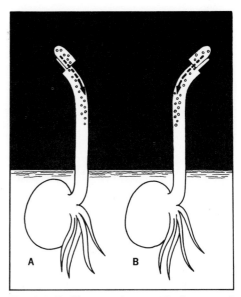

Fig. 9.2. Boysen-Jensen's experiment. When the top of an oat coleoptile is cut off, a layer of gelatin put on the end of the stump, and the tip replaced, the coleoptile will grow and turn toward the light.

Fig. 9.3. Paál's experiment. If the tip of a coleoptile is cut off and then replaced off center, the coleoptile will bend away from the side on which the tip rests, even in the dark.

ing. If the tip was then illuminated with a light from the side, the coleoptile base bent toward the light. The tip had received the light stimulus, and a message from the tip had moved across the gelatin barrier and induced bending in the base. Although this experiment did not completely rule out the possibility of an electrical or nervous message, it made such a possibility appear highly unlikely and strongly indicated that a diffusible chemical was involved.

That the tip could cause the base of the coleoptile to bend even in the dark was demonstrated by A. Paál in Hungary in 1918. He cut off the tip and then replaced it off center on the stump (Fig. 9.3). If he put the tip on the left side of the stump in the dark, the coleoptile bent to the right; if he put the tip on the right side, the coleoptile bent to the left. Apparently that part of the coleoptile directly under the replaced tip grew much faster than the part not under the tip. This asymmetric elongation of the coleoptile caused it to bend

away from the side undergoing the greatest elongation.

Experiments conclusively demonstrating that the growth stimulus moving downward from the tip is a chemical were reported in 1926 by Frits Went in Holland. He removed the tips from coleoptiles and placed these isolated tips, base down, on blocks of agar for about an hour (Fig. 9.4). (Agar is a gelatinlike material, made from seaweeds, that is frequently used as the base for laboratory culture media.) He then put the blocks of agar, minus the tips, on the cut ends of the coleoptile stumps. The stumps behaved as though their tips had been replaced; they resumed growth, responded to lateral light by bending toward it, and, if the agar blocks were put on off center, could be made to bend even in darkness. Plain agar blocks used as controls produced none of these effects. Apparently a growth-stimulating substance had diffused out of the tips and into the blocks of agar while the tips were sitting on the blocks. When the blocks containing the

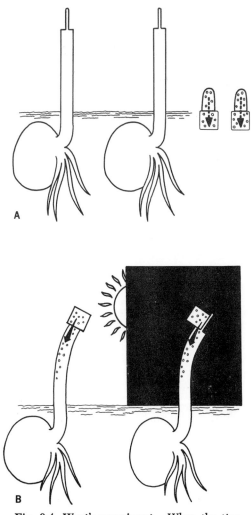

Fig. 9.4. Went's experiment. When the tips of coleoptiles are cut off and placed on blocks of agar for about an hour (A), and one of the blocks alone is then put on a stump (B, left), the stump will resume growing and will respond to light; if a block is placed off center on a stump in the dark (B, right), the stump will grow and will bend away from the side on which the block rests. Apparently a hormone has diffused from the tips into the blocks, and this hormone can then diffuse from the blocks into the stumps.

chemical were placed on the stumps, the chemical moved down into the stumps and stimulated elongation. This experiment ruled out the possibility that the stimulus was electrical or

nervous, because these types of stimuli cannot be stored in agar blocks. Professor Went named the diffusible hormone that must be involved auxin (from a Greek word meaning to grow). To this day, the identification of auxins is based on Went's experiment; if an agar block containing the substance in question causes a decapitated oat coleoptile to bend in the dark when the block is placed on one side of the cut end, the substance is an auxin.

Many different chemicals, some of them found naturally in plants and some synthesized only in the laboratory, have passed Went's test and are commonly called auxins. The one most often encountered and most investigated is *indoleacetic acid* (Fig. 9.5), which has been isolated from numerous natural sources.

The experiments we have discussed have shown, then, that the tip of the coleoptile releases auxin, which moves downward and stimulates cell elongation in the coleoptile. As the results obtained by Paál and Went suggest, there is normally little lateral movement of the auxin; the hormone reaches and stimulates only those cells directly under the point of release. But what about phototropism? It was this phenomenon we were discussing when we examined Darwin's experiments. Extensions of those experiments by Boysen-Jensen, Paál, and Went have revealed much about the more general problem of hormonal control of growth. What do these experiments say about the more specific problem of phototropic response? The superficial explanation of the phototropic response is fairly obvious. Light must somehow affect the amount of auxin released by the tip. When the light strikes the plant from one side, it must reduce the auxin supply on that side, but have little effect on the shaded side. Consequently the illuminated side of the plant grows more slowly than the shaded side, and this asymmetrical growth produces bending toward the slower-growing illuminated side.

We have called this a superficial explanation because we are still not certain how the tip detects the light, though carotenoid pigments

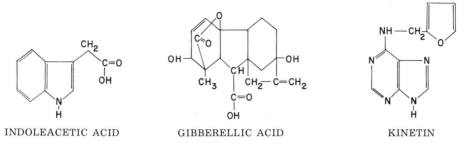

INDOLEACETIC ACID   GIBBERELLIC ACID   KINETIN

Fig. 9.5. Three important plant hormones.

are probably involved; nor do we know how the light, once detected, reduces the auxin supply on the illuminated side. Perhaps auxin on that side is destroyed, or perhaps the reactions that synthesize the auxin are blocked, or perhaps auxin somehow migrates from the illuminated side into the shaded side; the migration theory is the one most widely accepted at the present time. Whatever the mechanism may be by which light affects auxin supply, Went and numerous other workers have confirmed by careful measurements that there is indeed more auxin in the shaded side of a plant than in the illuminated side. Only further research can fully solve the intriguing problem of plant phototropism, which captured Darwin's interest so many years ago.

Auxins and Geotropism of Shoots. Auxin is involved in another plant tropism besides phototropism. If you lay a potted plant on its side and leave it for a few hours, you will find that the shoot has begun to bend upward (Fig. 9.6). This is a negative geotropic response; the shoot turns away from the pull of gravity. (How could you prove that the shoot is actually responding to gravity and not to some other stimulus such as light?) Herman Dolk in Holland showed that the concentration of auxin in the lower side of a horizontally placed shoot increases while the concentration in the upper side decreases. This unequal distribution of auxin stimulates the cells in the lower side to elongate faster than the cells in the upper side, and the shoot thus turns up-

ward as it grows. Again the external stimulus, in this case gravity, is apparently detected by the meristematic tissue in the shoot tip, but how it is detected and how this detection affects the auxin supply is unknown. It has been suggested that the meristematic cells may sense the pull of gravity by its effect on the distribution of cellular inclusions such as starch grains and other small bodies, which tend to respond to the pull of gravity and accumulate in the lower parts of the cell. How this gravitational effect on intracellular bodies could be translated into an effect on auxin supply is not yet clear.

Auxins and Geotropism of Roots. The effects of auxin discussed so far are consistent with each other. In both phototropic and geotropic turning by shoots, the side receiving the

Fig. 9.6. When a growing plant is left lying on its side, the shoot will bend upward and the roots will bend downward.

most auxin elongates faster than the other. But now let us look again at a plant placed on its side, and direct our attention to the roots instead of the shoot. We find that the roots, unlike the shoot, exhibit positive geotropism; they turn toward the pull of gravity (Fig. 9.6). If we examine the auxin distribution in the roots, we find that the hormone is produced in the growing root tip and secreted backward to the rest of the root, and that there is more auxin in the lower side of a horizontal root than in the upper side. In short, auxin distribution in the roots seems to be exactly analogous to that in the shoot. Why, then, does the root turn toward the pull of gravity while the shoot turns away from it? An obvious possibility is that auxin stimulates elongation in the shoot but inhibits it in the root. This explanation, obvious and easy as it seems, does not satisfy plant physiologists, because it is difficult to imagine that root cells are so different from stem cells that they respond in a diametrically opposite way to the same chemical. Further experiments have shown, in fact, that auxins do not always inhibit root elongation; in very low concentration, they stimulate root elongation. Thus we can offer another hypothesis to explain the positive geotropism of roots; perhaps roots normally contain so much auxin that any increase, such as occurs in the lower side of a horizontal root, raises the concentration to an inhibiting level.

It can be demonstrated that elongation of stems, too, can be inhibited if the concentration of auxin in them is raised to a very high level. The basic difference, then, between the reactions of root and shoot cells to auxin seems to be one of sensitivity. Root cells must be more sensitive to auxin, being stimulated to elongate at very low concentrations of the hormone and inhibited at higher concentrations (Fig. 9.7). Stem cells must be less sensitive, being stimulated by moderate concentrations of auxins and inhibited only by very high concentrations. An increase in auxin concentration above the normal moderate level thus inhibits root elongation but stimulates shoot elongation (provided the increase is not too great).

Auxins and Inhibition of Lateral Buds. Once we have recognized that the response curves to auxins of different plant organs may differ, i.e. that a stimulating concentration for one organ may be an inhibiting concentration for another, we are well equipped to understand another important function of auxin—its inhibiting effect on lateral buds in many plants. Auxin produced in the terminal bud moves downward in the shoot and inhibits development of the lateral buds, while at the same time stimulating elongation of the main stem. An examination of the graph in Fig. 9.7 shows how these two apparently opposite effects can occur at the same time; an auxin concentration that stimulates stem elongation is high enough to inhibit the more sensitive buds. The terminal bud thus exerts apical dominance over the rest of the shoot, ensuring that the plant's energy for growth will be funneled into the main stem and produce a tall plant with rela-

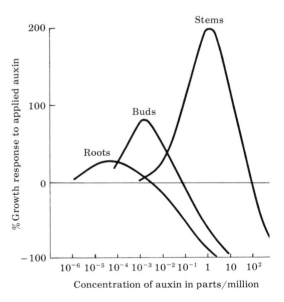

Fig. 9.7. Graph showing different sensitivities of roots, buds, and stems to auxins. [Redrawn from L. J. Audus, *Plant Growth Substances*, Leonard Hill, 1959.]

tively short lateral branches. Longer branches usually develop only from buds far enough below the terminal bud to be partly free of the apical dominance. If the terminal bud is removed, however, apical dominance is temporarily destroyed, and several of the upper lateral buds will begin to grow, producing branches whose terminal buds soon exert dominance over any buds below them (Fig. 9.8). Flower and shrub growers frequently pinch out the terminal buds of their plants one or more times each season in order to produce bushy well-branched plants with many flowering points instead of tall spindly ones bearing fewer flowers. This will not work for some plants, however, in which it is the young leaves, not the terminal buds, that exert control over the lateral buds.

Notice in Fig. 9.8 that once two or more branches have begun to develop, neither inhibits the other. Auxin secreted by the terminal bud of one branch cannot reach the terminal bud of the other branch and hence cannot slow its growth. The reason is that auxin can only move downward, never upward (Fig. 9.9). This movement in only one direction, for which no satisfactory explanation has been found, demonstrates that the transport cells like many (perhaps all) other cells are physiologically polarized; i.e. their ends differ from each other in some way.

The action of auxins in inhibiting growth of lateral buds has sometimes been used commercially to prevent sprouting of stored potatoes (which are stems, not roots). In former years, the buds (commonly called eyes) of potatoes usually began to grow during storage, frequently producing numerous long sprouts. The sprouting drained nutrients out of the potato tuber itself, often leaving only a shriveled remnant. Treatment with auxin made it possible to store potatoes for long periods, sometimes as long as three years, with relatively little loss. More recently, this use of auxins has declined, and another compound, maleic hydrazide, which is not an auxin, has been em-

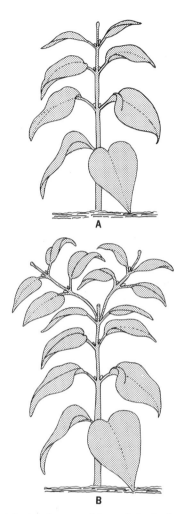

Fig. 9.8. Inhibition of lateral buds by the terminal bud. (A) As long as the terminal bud is present, it inhibits the lateral buds. (B) When the terminal bud is removed, several upper lateral buds begin to grow, and then the terminal buds of the new branches inhibit lateral buds below them.

ployed instead. This compound blocks cell division in plants and thus stops growth.

Auxins and Fruit Development. We have seen that auxins in certain concentrations will stimulate cell elongation in stems, buds, and roots, while the same hormones in higher concentrations will inhibit such growth. Which is

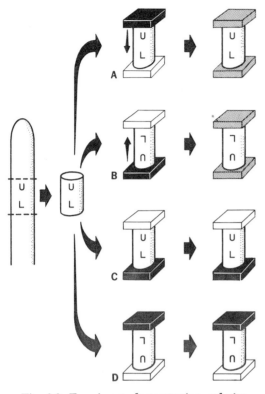

Fig. 9.9. Experiment demonstrating polarity of auxin movement. A segment is cut from a coleoptile (left). (A) An agar block containing auxin (black block) is placed on the upper end of the segment and a block without auxin (white block) is placed on the lower end. Some auxin moves from the one block, through the coleoptile segment, into the other block. (B) The same thing happens even if the whole preparation is inverted, indicating that the movement is not a response to gravity. (C) When the agar block containing auxin is put on the lower end of the coleoptile segment and the block without auxin is put on the upper end, no movement of auxin occurs, and inverting the group (D) makes no difference. Conclusion: Auxin can move in only one direction through a coleoptile, and that direction is determined by properties of the cells of the coleoptile itself, not by the pull of gravity.

the more important in the plant's development, the stimulatory or the inhibitory effect, depends for each organ on the particular concentration range to which that organ responds. One organ whose normal development depends on the stimulatory effect of auxins is the fruit. The fruit develops from the ovary or from the flower receptacle of the plant. Until the time of fertilization, growth of the ovary and receptacle is mostly limited to cell division without much accompanying cell enlargement; consequently the organ remains small. If fertilization does not occur, usually no fruit develops; instead, a weak layer of thin-walled cells, called an *abscission layer,* forms at the base of the flower stalk. This layer soon breaks, under any slight strain, and the withered flower with its ovary falls to the ground. If, on the other hand, fertilization does occur, no abscission layer forms, and the ovary at once begins to grow rapidly, mainly by enlargement of the numerous tiny cells formed earlier by cell division. It has been shown by many workers that this period of rapid growth by the ovary (and by the receptacle in some plants), as it develops into the fruit, is initiated by auxin released from the pollen grains that bring about the fertilization, and that the continued growth and development of the fruit depend upon stimulation by auxins produced by the seeds contained within it. It is these same auxins that prevent formation of an abscission layer at the base of the flower stalk.

Once the role of auxins in stimulating fruit development and in inhibiting abscission-layer formation was recognized, production of seedless fruit became a possibility. It was known that a few plants sometimes produce seedless fruit naturally, and it seemed likely that in these cases tissues of the ovary (or associated structures) themselves produced so much auxin that fertilization and the resulting development of seed became unnecessary for fruit growth. It was reasoned that if fertilization of plants that normally produce seeds, such as tomatoes, cucumbers, squash, and figs, could be prevented, and if auxins could be artificially supplied to take the place of those normally produced by the seeds, seedless fruits should develop. Experiments along these lines were tried, and in 1934 S. Yasuda in Japan produced seedless cucumbers and in 1936 F. G. Gustafson at the University of Michigan produced seedless tomatoes. Since that time, seedless fruits of many other plants have been produced. In some plants, however—notably most single-seeded fruits such as plums, cherries, and peaches—all attempts to produce seedless fruits have failed, for reasons as yet unknown. In other plants, such as strawberries and blackberries, seedless fruits have been produced, but the hard cases (derived from the ovaries) that normally cover the seeds have remained, so that a person eating the berry cannot tell whether it is seedless or not. To this writer, the failure of the breeders has its reassuring side; the idea of a strawberry without any crunch and without any pits to stick between one's teeth is somehow unsettling.

Treatment of fruit crops with auxins has other commercial applications. It is frequently used to supplement normal pollination in the setting of fruit, thereby ensuring a larger crop. In some cases, the size of the individual fruits can also be increased by auxin sprays. It has become common practice with many fruits to apply auxin sprays to orchards as the time of ripening approaches, thereby inhibiting abscission-layer formation and reducing preharvest fruit drop (fruit that drops to the ground is largely useless commercially; only fruit picked directly from the tree can be sold).

Auxins and Leaf Abscission. We have said that unfertilized flowers drop off the plant because a special layer of cells, the abscission layer, forms at the base of the flower stalk in the absence of high auxin production in the floral organs. And we have indicated that ripe-fruit drop is also a result of abscission-layer formation as auxin production by the mature seeds declines. Similarly, the shedding of leaves in autumn (or of diseased leaves at any time of year) by deciduous trees and shrubs usually (though not always) involves abscission-layer formation at the base of the petiole (Fig. 9.10) as a result of declining auxin production in the

Fig. 9.10. Photograph showing abscission layer at base of petiole of *Coleus* leaf. The arrow indicates the small cells of the abscission layer. [Courtesy Carolina Biological Supply Co.]

leaf blade. In each case, the actual break in the abscission layer can be initiated by any slight strain—as from a gentle wind—because the middle lamella between the cells has become soft and gelatinous (normally the middle lamella is strong and cements the cells firmly together). It is not yet clear whether abscission (leaf drop) is a result of reduced total concentration of auxins or whether changes in the relative concentration of auxins arriving at the abscission layer from its two sides (i.e. from the stem and from the leaf or fruit) are more important, although the latter seems more probable. Notice that unlike the previously discussed functions of auxins, their function in leaf and fruit abscission apparently does not involve stimulation or inhibition of cell enlargement.

We mentioned earlier that auxin sprays are frequently used in orchards to prevent pre-harvest fruit drop. Sprays of chemicals that are auxin antagonists are commonly applied to the leaves of cotton just before harvest. The antiauxins induce formation of abscission layers at the base of the leaves, causing the leaves to fall prematurely. This makes it easier for mechanical pickers to move through the fields and harvest the bolls.

Auxins and Cell Division. There is good reason to believe that, besides playing a part in cell elongation and abscission-layer formation auxins are involved in cell division. Apparently, it is auxin moving downward from the buds in early spring that stimulates renewed activity in the cambium, leading to production of new xylem and phloem tissue. As autumn approaches, auxin production by the buds and leaves declines, with the result that cambial activity also declines.

Auxins probably also initiate formation of lateral roots. Such roots usually have their origin in the layer of relatively undifferentiated cells called the pericycle (see Fig. 5.6, p. 163), which is located just internal to the endodermis. Most of the time, the cells of the pericycle show no meristematic activity. At intervals, however, a small group of cells in the pericycle changes into actively dividing meristematic tissue, giving rise to a new lateral root that bursts through the outer tissues of the main root and enters the soil. There is much evidence that the stimulus initiating this meristematic activity in the pericycle comes from auxins. Auxins can, in fact, be applied to the roots of plants to induce lateral branching. Unfortunately, the concentrations necessary to initiate formation of new lateral roots are high enough to inhibit root elongation; the result of auxin application, therefore, is a short bushy root system instead of a longer less bushy one. Someday, perhaps, methods will be devised for inducing long

bushy root systems, which would be the most advantageous.

It is in the development of adventitious roots from cuttings of such organs as stems or leaves that auxins (generally called "rooting hormones" in this context) have had one of their most important commercial uses. Cuttings from some plants, such as geraniums and willows, will readily root in water or soil without application of hormone, but many plants cannot be propagated in this manner. Application of auxins will frequently induce formation of roots in these cases, making it possible to propagate vegetatively many valuable strains of plants that might otherwise be lost.

Chemical Weed Control. The most extensively used of the modern weed killers, or herbicides, are 2,4-dichlorophenoxyacetic acid, usually abbreviated 2,4-D, and 2,4,5-trichlorophenoxyacetic acid, abbreviated 2,4,5-T. Both 2,4-D and 2,4,5-T have many of the properties of auxins, though they do not meet all the auxin tests. They have been used in vast quantities since the 1940's for control of broad-leaved weeds. Because they are selective in their action and, when used in proper concentrations, will not kill grasses or related monocots, they have been of enormous commercial value in sprays applied to kill broad-leaved weeds in lawns and pastures and in fields of corn, wheat, oats, or rice. Apparently these chemicals, which in low concentrations would have effects like those already described for auxins, kill plants when applied in higher concentrations by stimulating rapid, uncoordinated, and distorted growth of some body parts while seriously inhibiting the function of other body parts. The exact manner in which these effects are produced is not well understood. Even less well understood, unfortunately, is the basis of the selective action of these herbicides; we may hope that future research will explain why broad-leaved plants are so much more susceptible than grasses.

In recent years, a number of new herbicides even more selective than 2,4-D or 2,4,5-T have been developed and put into use; most of them are not auxins. The goal, of course, is the eventual discovery of herbicides so selective that man can kill at will any given species of weed with minimum disturbance to the other plants growing around it. Efforts to develop herbicides that will kill grasses but not broad-leaved plants have not, so far, been very successful.

Gibberellins

The Japanese have long been familiar with a disease of rice that they call "foolish-seedling disease." Afflicted plants grow unusually tall but seldom live to maturity. In 1926 a Japanese botanist, E. Kurosawa, found that all such plants are infected with a fungus named *Gibberella fujikuroi*. He showed that when the fungus was moved to healthy seedlings they developed the typical disease symptom of rapid stem elongation. Furthermore, he could produce the symptoms with an extract made from the fungus, and even with an extract made from culture media on which the fungus had grown. Clearly, some chemical was involved.

Several Japanese scientists worked on the problem of foolish-seedling disease during the 1930's. They succeeded in isolating and crystallizing a substance from *Gibberella* that produced typical disease symptoms when applied to rice plants. They even proposed a structural formula for the substance, which is called *gibberellin*, after the fungus in which it was first found. All of this work was reported in many papers, but for some reason botanists in the Western world paid little attention to it. Then came World War II and complete breakdown of communication with Japan. It was not until about 1950 that two groups of scientists, one in England and one in the United States, rediscovered the old papers

and began active investigations into the properties of gibberellins. Since that time, work on gibberellins has become widespread, hundreds of scientific papers on the subject being published every year. More than ten different substances that can be classed as gibberellins have been isolated from fungi and from higher plants; many more will doubtless be discovered in years to come. The gibberellin most often used in experimental work is called *gibberellic acid* (Fig. 9.5).

The most dramatic effect of gibberellins is their stimulation of rapid stem elongation in dwarf plants and other plants that normally undergo little stem elongation (Fig. 9.11). They have much less effect on most normally tall plants. An attractive hypothesis is that the dwarf varieties are genetically incapable of producing sufficient gibberellin, and that administration of extra quantities of the hormone simply makes up for the deficiency and allows the plants to grow more normally. Unfortunately for this hypothesis, all attempts so far have failed to show a higher concentration of gibberellins in normal plants than in dwarfs of the same species. Nevertheless, more research with more refined techniques is needed before the hypothesis is abandoned.

An obvious question arises at this point. If both auxins and gibberellins stimulate stem elongation, why not regard gibberellins as simply another group of auxins? Some workers have proposed doing just that. But there are several compelling reasons why gibberellins should be considered a separate class of hormones: (1) Gibberellins have a drastic effect on intact stems of dwarf plants, as we have seen, whereas auxins applied to an intact stem have no effect; auxins have an effect on elongation only after removal of the terminal bud. Apparently the intact stem contains as much auxin as can be effective, and any addition is simply surplus. Gibberellins probably function in conjunction with auxins, not as replacement for them. (2) Gibberellins

Fig. 9.11. Effect of gibberellic acid on cabbage. The plant at left is normal. The one at right was treated with gibberellic acid. [Courtesy S. H. Wittwer, Michigan State University.]

shoot and root characteristic of auxin-induced tropistic responses. (4) Gibberellins do not inhibit growth of lateral buds. (5) Nor do they prevent leaf abscission. (6) The effects of gibberellins on roots are the opposite of those of auxins; they seldom inhibit root elongation, but do inhibit formation of new roots. (7) Finally, gibberellins have certain effects on seeds and buds that are not characteristic of auxins; they will (a) often break seed and bud dormancy, (b) induce some biennials to flower during their first year of growth and not to wait until the second year, and (c) induce some plants to flower when the length of day is too short for them to flower normally. The actions of gibberellins in breaking dormancy and stimulating flowering will be discussed in more detail in later sections of this chapter.

Possible practical applications for gibberellins in agriculture are being extensively investigated. An obvious application would be to induce growth to greater height, e.g. in hay crops. Unfortunately, the tallness induced by gibberellins is usually offset by poorer leaf formation and overall spindliness, with the result that the total weight yield of the crop is little increased, if at all. Gibberellins do, however, have a beneficial effect on celery by inducing rapid growth, which produces tenderer stalks. They have also proved useful in accelerating seed germination in some plants in spring and in producing larger clusters of seedless grapes. Other important uses for these hormones will doubtless be found in the future.

Kinins

We have seen that both auxins and gibberellins play important roles in controlling cell enlargement. We have also seen that auxins are sometimes involved in stimulating the other basic aspect of growth, cell division. Gibberellins, too, may sometimes function in this way. But apparently neither auxins nor gibberellins are the major chemical control agents of cell division; each must work in conjunction with

produce no effect on decapitated coleoptiles when given the Went test for auxins, apparently because they cannot move freely out of the plant tissue in the tips into blocks of gelatin or agar. (3) Even more important, gibberellins cannot produce the bending movements of other substances whose function is more directly concerned with this process.

Much of the research on the chemical regulators of cell division in plants has depended on growing bits of plant tissue on sterile nutrient media in the laboratory. The development of superior methods of *tissue culture* has opened up whole new avenues of research that could never have been pursued without this technique. It can be anticipated that tissue culture will contribute greatly to discoveries in both plant and animal biology in the next few years.

Folke Skoog, Carlos O. Miller, and their associates at the University of Wisconsin developed methods of growing parenchyma tissue from tobacco plants on tissue-culture media. The cells formed a tumorlike mass of tissue called a callus, in which the constituent cells often grew to huge size. They did not, however, undergo complete cell division (sometimes the nuclei divided, but new cell walls did not form). The Wisconsin workers found that extracts made from old nucleic acids (the substances of which genes are composed) would cause the cells in the callus to divide, even though these cells possessed fully developed vacuoles, indicating that they were mature differentiated cells bearing little resemblance to normal meristematic cells. The compound responsible for providing the stimulus was eventually isolated and named *kinetin* (Fig. 9.5); it is a degradation product of nucleic acids and can be produced in the laboratory by subjecting nucleic acids to physical strain, as by high-speed centrifugation. The action of kinetin is enhanced when auxins are also present. Though kinetin itself may not be the actual control substance in normal living cells, there is abundant evidence that similar substances are involved. Skoog has applied the name *kinins* to the general class of control compounds that promote cell division—of which kinetin is one example.

F. C. Steward and his associates at Cornell University have also been much concerned with the chemical control systems that stimulate cell division. They have performed most of their experiments on bits of tissue cut from carrot roots and cultured on nutrient media. The cells are extracted from a point in the carrot root far enough from the cambium to ensure that they are mature cells that would ordinarily not divide again. When auxins are added to the media on which the carrot cells are cultured, some cell division occurs, but this soon ceases. Clearly, auxins alone are not enough to maintain the cells in a state of active division. Now, it has been known for some time that embryos developing within seeds seem to be stimulated by factors in the endosperm, the food-storage tissue of seeds. What would happen to the cultured carrot cells if endosperm were added to the media? Many seeds contain only a very small quantity of endosperm, which may be either solid or liquid, but the seeds of some plants, notably the coconut, contain relatively large amounts of liquid endosperm and constitute a good source of test material. Steward added coconut milk (the liquid endosperm) to his cultured carrot cells and found that the cells were returned to a state of active cell division; a mass of about 25,000 carrot cells could increase to 2.5 million or more. The coconut milk was particularly effective if auxin was present also.

Steward and his co-workers have devoted years of labor to isolating and identifying the components of coconut milk to determine which are responsible for stimulating cell division. The work is not yet complete, but enough factors have been isolated to show that no single substance is responsible by itself for the activity of coconut milk. This activity must involve at least four types of components: (1) auxins; (2) reduced nitrogen compounds such as amino acids; (3) certain types of alcohols that apparently create conditions in which the promoters of cell division can act; and (4) the kinins themselves, which are the actual promoters of cell division. The kinins have not all been identified as yet, but the evidence indicates that one of them is a derivative of urea, a compound previously thought to occur only in animals.

The picture of chemical control in the early stages of growth that emerges from studies of auxins, gibberellins, and kinins can be described briefly as follows: (1) Cell division, which is the first phase of growth, is probably inhibited by various substances, many of which are only poorly known; (2) cell division is stimulated by kinins and by other factors that enhance the activity of kinins; (3) it is the balance between the inhibitors and the kinins that determines whether a cell will divide or not; (4) control of cell enlargement, which is the second phase of growth, involves substances such as auxins and gibberellins.

Inhibitors

Growth inhibitors, which have effects opposite to those of auxins, gibberellins, and kinins, have already been mentioned several times in this chapter. Relatively little is known about them. A few have been isolated and identified, but the existence of many others has simply been inferred. The role of inhibitors in maintaining dormancy in the buds and seeds of some plants has attracted particular interest. It is believed that inhibitors block the activity of some buds and seeds in autumn, thus ensuring that they will not begin to grow during a few warm days, only to be killed by the rigors of the winter climate. The inhibitors are presumed either to break down gradually with time or to be destroyed by cold, so that the buds and seeds are free to become active in the next growing season. Many cases are also known where inhibitors in seeds must be leached out by water before the seeds can germinate. Such inhibitors constitute an important evolutionary adaptation in some desert plants. The seeds that fall to the ground will germinate only after long hard rains; light

showers that might provide enough moisture for germination by seeds not adapted for life in the desert do not leach out enough inhibitor to allow germination to begin in the desert-adapted seeds; thus no tender young seedlings are left to be killed by the dry conditions that would soon follow.

Chemical Control of Flowering

As you are doubtless aware, flowering is not a random process. Some plants flower early in the spring, others flower in midsummer, and still others, like chrysanthemums, flower in the fall. These simple facts have been known for centuries. But only since 1920 has anything been known of the control mechanisms involved, and the subject is still not well understood. This is an area of research in which major discoveries can be expected in the next few years.

Photoperiodism and Flowering. The intense modern interest in the flowering process dates from the work of W. W. Garner and H. A. Allard of the U.S. Department of Agriculture, working in Beltsville, Maryland. These two men found that a new mutant variety of tobacco, called Maryland Mammoth, grew unusually large (as much as 10 feet tall) but would not flower, thus making it unusable in breeding experiments. They propagated the new variety by cuttings and discovered that it would flower in the greenhouse in winter. Though flowering was not the subject Garner and Allard were originally investigating, they became interested in the question why Maryland Mammoth would flower in the greenhouse in winter but not in the fields in summer. Accordingly, they began a series of experiments that were to open the way to a whole new area of botanical research. This is but one of many examples that could be cited of important leads uncovered almost accidentally through research originally devoted to a different subject. It is the mark of the good scientist that he does not overlook such leads, but recognizes them when he finds them and pursues them, even though he might have to change the course of his research.

Garner and Allard realized that winter greenhouses and summer fields differ in temperature, moisture, light intensity, day length, etc. They began experiments that painstakingly eliminated one after another of these environmental factors until only one was left as the probable controlling factor in flowering—day length. They concluded that the short days of late autumn and early winter induced flowering in Maryland Mammoth tobacco. They could get the plants to bloom in summer if they shielded them from the light for a part of each day. Conversely, they could prevent blooming in the greenhouse in winter by extending the day length with electric lights.

Garner and Allard also experimented with Biloxi soybeans. They planted soybeans at two-week intervals from early May through July and found that all the plants flowered at the same time in September, even though their growing periods had differed by as much as 60 days. It was as though they were waiting for some signal from the environment. Garner and Allard were sure that the signal was short days.

Experiments with other species revealed that most plants can be placed in one of three groups: (1) short-day plants, which flower when the day length is below some critical value, usually in spring or fall (examples are chrysanthemum, poinsettia, dahlia, aster, cocklebur, goldenrod, ragweed, Maryland Mammoth tobacco, and Biloxi soybean); (2) long-day plants, which bloom when the day length exceeds some critical value, usually in summer (beet, clover, gladiolus, larkspur, black-eyed Susan); and (3) day-neutral plants, which are independent of day length and can bloom under conditions of either long or short days (dandelion, sunflower, carnation, pansy, tomato, corn, string bean). Notice that the difference between long-day and short-day

plants does not depend upon the actual day length at the time of flowering. A certain long-day plant might flower during 11½-hour days, and a certain short-day plant might flower during 15-hour days; in other words, the long-day plant can flower during shorter days than the short-day plant. The difference is that this particular long-day plant will flower only when the day length is *longer than* 11 hours, whereas this particular short-day plant will flower only when the day length is *shorter than* 15½ hours (Fig. 9.12). The critical day length is thus a minimum value for flowering by long-day plants and a maximum value for flowering by short-day plants. Garner and Allard called the phenomenon they had discovered *photoperiodism;* the term denotes a response by an organism to the duration and timing of the light and dark conditions.

Flowering Hormone. The critical question now becomes: How does day length exert its effect on flowering? It was suggested long ago that hormones might be involved, but the first convincing evidence for a floral hormone did not come until 1936, from the experiments of M. H. Chailakhian in Russia. Chailakhian removed the leaves from the upper half of chrysanthemums (which are short-day plants), while leaving the leaves on the lower half (Fig. 9.13). He then exposed the lower half to short days while simultaneously exposing the defoliated upper half to long days; the plants flowered. Next, he reversed the procedure, exposing the lower half to long days and the defoliated upper half to short days; the plants did not flower. He concluded that day length does not exert its effect directly on the flower buds, but that it causes the leaves to manufacture a hormone that moves from the leaves to the buds and induces flowering. This hypothetical hormone has been named *florigen.*

Further evidence for the existence of a moving stimulus, probably a hormone, has come from grafting experiments with cockle-

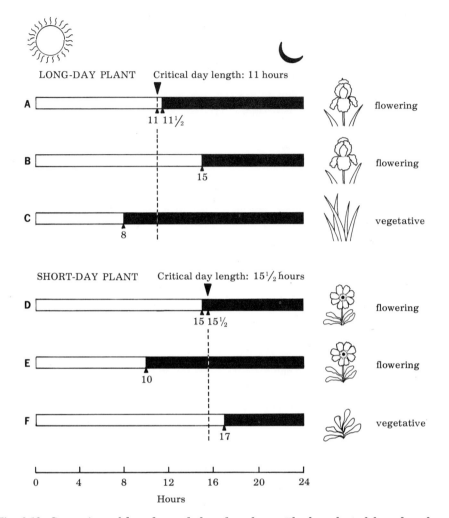

Fig. 9.12. Comparison of long-day and short-day plant. The hypothetical long-day plant has a rather short critical day length of 11 hours, and the hypothetical short-day plant has a rather long critical day length of 15½ hours. In other words, the critical day length for the long-day plant is shorter than that for the short-day plant. The difference is that the critical day length is a *minimum* value for the long-day plant and a *maximum* value for the short-day plant. Thus the long-day plant will flower when the day length is slightly *above* the critical value (A) or when it is much above the critical value (B), but will not flower when it is below the critical value (C). Conversely, the short-day plant will flower when the day length is slightly *below* the critical value (D) or when it is much below the critical value (E), but will not flower when it is above the critical value (F). (White bars indicate days and black bars nights.)

burs (which are short-day plants) (Fig. 9.14). If one plant is grafted onto another through a light-tight partition, and if the first plant is exposed to short days while the other is exposed to long days, the plant exposed to short days will flower, and soon thereafter the plant exposed to long days will also flower. Apparently a stimulus from the first plant moves through the graft and induces flowering in the second plant, even though the second

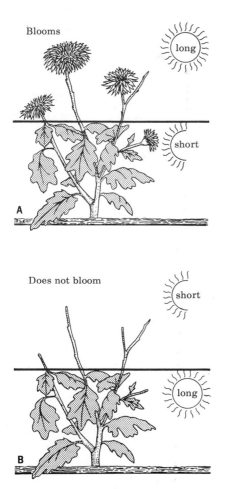

Blooms

long

short

A

Does not bloom

short

long

B

Fig. 9.13. Chailakhian's experiment. (A) He removed the leaves from the top half of a chrysanthemum (a short-day plant) and then exposed the top half of the plant to long days and the bottom half to short days. The plant flowered. (B) When he did the reverse experiment, the plant did not flower.

plant is exposed to the wrong photoperiod. Ringing experiments show that the stimulus is transported in the phloem.

Results different from those just described are obtained from experiments on Biloxi soybean plants (short-day plants) with two shoots. If one shoot (shoot X) is exposed to short days and the other (shoot Y) to long days, only shoot X blooms (Fig. 9.15). If, however, shoot Y is defoliated and exposed to long days, it will bloom when shoot X is simultaneously exposed to short days. Apparently when the leaves of shoot Y are exposed to long days they inhibit the action of florigen, perhaps by preventing transport of florigen to the bud of shoot Y, or by synthesizing an inhibitor chemical, or by destroying florigen. The last possibility seems the most probable. That the inhibiting action of the leaves occurs only when they are exposed to a noninducing photoperiod can be shown by leaving all leaves on the plant and exposing shoot X to short days while keeping shoot Y in the dark; both shoots will bloom.

An even more elegant demonstration of the inhibiting action of leaves exposed to a noninducing photoperiod comes from experiments on single leaves. If a light-tight barrier is placed across a leaf and the basal half of the leaf is exposed to a flower-inducing photoperiod while the distal half is exposed to a noninducing photoperiod, a nearby bud will flower. If the reverse experiment is run, with the basal half of the leaf exposed to a noninducing photoperiod and the distal half to an inducing photoperiod, the bud will either not flower or flower only weakly; apparently florigen produced under inducing conditions in the distal half of the leaf is destroyed as it passes through the basal half.

The explanation of flowering that emerges from the above experiments is that an inducing photoperiod (short days for short-day plants and long days for long-day plants) causes the leaves to produce florigen, which moves to the buds and stimulates development of the flower. A noninducing photoperiod (long days for short-day plants and short days for long-day plants) causes the leaves of many, but not all, plants to destroy florigen or to inhibit its action in some way. Under natural conditions, flower induction is triggered when, as the season changes, the day length passes a critical value and production of florigen exceeds its destruction.

This is a tidy explanation, but it still awaits

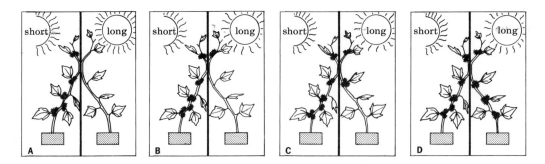

Fig. 9.14. Grafting experiment with cockleburs. The two plants are in separate light-tight chambers, but are connected by a graft. The plant exposed to an inducing photoperiod (short days) flowers (A), and shortly thereafter the other plant begins to flower near the graft (B). The flowering of the second plant slowly spreads (C), until the entire plant is in flower (D). (The flowers of the cocklebur are the burs.)

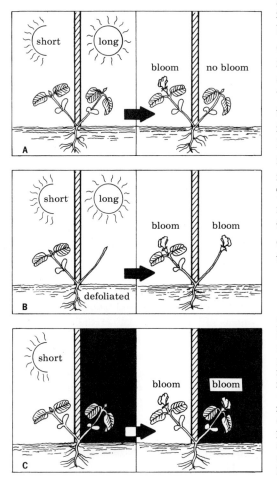

proof. All attempts to isolate and analyze a flower-inducing hormone have failed. It has been demonstrated that gibberellins will induce flowering in some long-day plants even in the absence of an inducing photoperiod. This effect, however, is largely limited to plants that "bolt" before flowering, i.e. to plants in which the stem elongates greatly in the transition from vegetative to reproductive states. It seems likely that the effect of gibberellins on flowering in such cases is an indirect and secondary result of a primary effect on stem elongation. There are also other reasons, which we cannot discuss here, for rejecting the possibility that gibberellins may be the true flower-inducing hormones, though they do not rule out the possibility that gibberellins and florigen

Fig. 9.15. Grafting experiments with soybeans. This is a short-day plant. (A) If one shoot is exposed to an inducing photoperiod and the other shoot is exposed to a noninducing photoperiod, only the first will flower if the leaves are left on both shoots. (B) If the leaves of the shoot exposed to the noninducing photoperiod are removed and the other shoot is exposed to an inducing photoperiod, both shoots will flower. (C) Both shoots will flower if the leaves are left intact and one shoot is exposed to an inducing photoperiod while the other is kept in the dark.

may work together to induce flowering. Both may be essential to the process.

Some scientists hold that there is no such thing as flower-inducing hormone or florigen, that the data so far obtained are consistent with the hypothesis of a diffusible inhibitor hormone rather than of a stimulating hormone. A variety of experiments, however, have yielded evidence that leads most botanists to continue favoring the florigen hypothesis over the inhibitor hypothesis. One such experiment was performed in 1945 by M. Stout of the U.S. Department of Agriculture. By grafting, Stout produced sugar beets (which are long-day plants) with three shoots. He exposed one shoot to long days, one to short days, and one to continual darkness (Fig. 9.16). The shoots exposed to long days and to darkness flowered, but the one exposed to short days did not. This indicates that a stimulus for flowering moved from the shoot exposed to long days into the shoot in darkness; there was no evidence for an inhibitor moving from the shoot exposed to short days into the shoot in darkness. In other experiments, A.-K. Khudari and K. C. Hamner of the University of California at Los Angeles showed that an en-

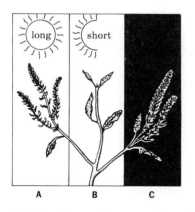

Fig. 9.16. Stout's experiment on a sugar-beet plant with three shoots. One shoot was exposed to an inducing photoperiod (long days), one to a noninducing photoperiod, and one to continual darkness. The first and third shoots (A and C) flowered, but the second (B) did not.

tire cocklebur plant could be induced to flower by exposing less than one square centimeter of leaf surface to a single inducing photoperiod. Other workers have shown that a single leaf may induce flowering not only in its own plant but also in several other plants grafted to it. It is difficult to understand how disinhibition of such a very small area could result in flowering if inhibitor was simultaneously being produced in all the other leaves. This sort of evidence makes the inhibitor hypothesis unappealing. The fact remains, however, that the florigen hypothesis will not rest on firm foundations until a flower-inducing hormone is actually isolated and identified. Perhaps this will have been accomplished by the time you read this book.

Detection of the Photoperiod. In our discussion so far, we have avoided asking one fundamental question: How do plants detect the photoperiod, how do they measure the relative lengths of the light and dark periods? Before we discuss current ideas about the detection process itself, let us find out more precisely what is the critical element in the photoperiod. If the critical element is day length, as the terms "long day" and "short day" imply, then we should be able to prevent a long-day plant from flowering at the proper season by shielding it from light for an hour or so during the middle of the day. But if this is done, nothing happens; the plant flowers normally. If, however, a short-day plant is illuminated by a bright light for a few minutes, or even seconds, in the middle of the night during the normal flowering season, it will not bloom. The same sort of experiment will induce flowering at the wrong season by a long-day plant (Fig. 9.17). It is clear, then, that the critical element of the photoperiod is actually the length of the night, not the length of the day. Our terminology would be more accurate if, instead of speaking of long-day and short-day plants, we spoke of short-night and long-night plants. Having established this,

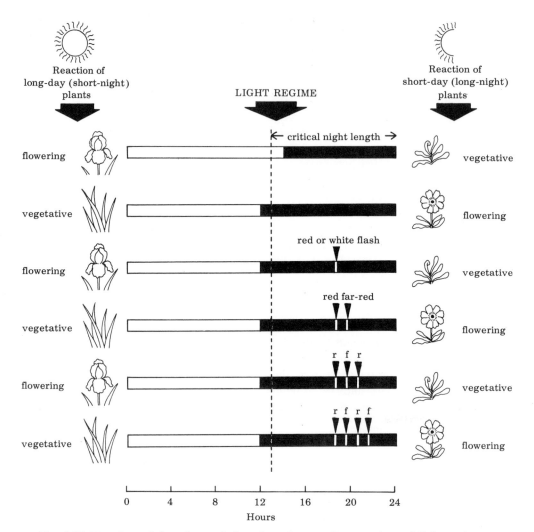

Fig. 9.17. Reactions of long-day and short-day plants under a variety of light regimes.
White bars are days; black bars are nights. Long-day (short-night) plants flower when the
night is shorter than the critical value, or when a longer night is interrupted by an intense
red or white flash or by a series of flashes of which the last is red or white. Short-day (long-
night) plants give the reverse responses.

we must rephrase our question and ask: How
does the plant detect and measure the dark
period?

Since interrupting the dark period prevents
flowering by a short-day (long-night) plant
and induces flowering by a long-day (short-
night) plant, the light itself must be detected
by the plant. What wavelengths of light are
involved? H. A. Borthwick, S. B. Hendricks,

and their associates of the U.S. Department of
Agriculture, Beltsville, Maryland, began investigating this question in 1944. They exposed Biloxi soybeans to light of different
wavelengths, and found that red light (wavelength about 6,600 angstroms) is by far the
most effective in inhibiting flowering in these
short-day plants; the same red light is very
effective in inducing flowering by long-day

plants. Later it was found that far-red light (wavelength about 7,300 angstroms), which is invisible to the human eye, has effects exactly contrary to those of red light; it induces flowering in short-day plants and inhibits flowering in long-day plants. Not only do red and far-red light have opposite effects, but each reverses the effect of prior exposure to the other (Fig. 9.17). A short-day (long-night) plant will not flower if its long night is interrupted by a bright flash of red light; if, however, the red flash is followed by a far-red flash, the plant flowers normally. Almost any number of successive flashes can be used, the final effect depending solely on whether the last flash was red or far-red.

The fact that red and far-red light can reverse each other led Borthwick and Hendricks to conclude that a single receptor pigment is involved and that this pigment exists in two forms: one that absorbs red light (R form) and one that absorbs far-red light (F form). They called this pigment *phytochrome.* It has since been shown to be a protein. When R-phytochrome absorbs red light, it is rapidly converted into F-phytochrome. Conversely, absorption of far-red light by F-phytochrome rapidly converts it into R-phytochrome. The R form is apparently the more stable of the two; in darkness, F-phytochrome is slowly converted metabolically into R-phytochrome. We can summarize these conversions as follows:

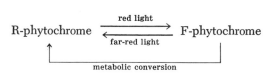

When phytochrome is exposed to both red and far-red simultaneously, the red light dominates and the pigment is converted into the F form. Sunlight or light from ordinary electric lamps contains both red and far-red wavelengths; hence, during the day, the phytochrome exists predominantly in the F form. During the night, the F-phytochrome is slowly converted metabolically into R-phytochrome. The pigment thus gives the plant a way of sensing whether it is day or night.

We began this part of our discussion with the question: How does the plant detect and measure the dark period? We have answered the first half of the question; the plant possesses a sensitive pigment, phytochrome, that responds to presence or absence of light. But what about the crucial second half of the question? It is, after all, the measuring of the dark period that is fundamental to control of flowering. Unfortunately, we have no clear answer to this part of the question. The most obvious hypothesis would be that the metabolic conversion of F-phytochrome into R-phytochrome in the dark proceeds so slowly that the amount of conversion occuring between two light periods provides a measure of the length of the intervening dark period. In other words, the system would work like an hourglass. Light would convert all the pigment into F-phytochrome. Then during the following dark period the amount of F-phytochrome converted into R-phytochrome before the next light period would tell the plant how long the dark period had lasted. This would explain why a burst of bright red or white light in the middle of the night would inhibit flowering in short-day (long-night) plants; the burst of light would reset the hourglass by rapidly converting all R-phytochrome into F-phytochrome, with the result that the plant would measure two short nights, one before and one after the light burst, instead of the single long night necessary for flowering. The hourglass hypothesis would also explain why this effect of a burst of red or white light would be canceled if followed immediately by a burst of far-red light; the far-red light would rapidly reconvert F-phytochrome into R-phytochrome (light conversion is much more rapid than metabolic conversion), so that at the end of the night a high proportion of the phytochrome would be in the R form, indicating to the plant that the night had been long.

This is an attractive and simple hypothesis, but unfortunately the evidence is against it. The hypothesis requires that metabolic conversion be slow enough not to be complete before the end of a long night. Available evidence indicates, however, that metabolic conversion, though much slower than light conversion, is much faster than the hourglass hypothesis requires. Furthermore, the rate of metabolic conversion would be temperature-dependent, but all evidence indicates that the plant's measure of time is not influenced by temperature. The mechanism whereby the plant measures the length of the dark period is apparently tied to a phenomenon, now believed to occur in all living cells, involving persistent and regular rhythms in function, rhythms that must be dependent on some internal time-measuring system, or "internal clock." Biological time measurement is an exciting area of modern research, and we shall discuss it at more length in a later chapter. For the moment we shall simply say that phytochrome enables the plant to sense whether it is in light or darkness, but the actual measuring of the time lapse between the moment the plant senses onset of darkness and the moment it senses the next exposure to light must depend upon an internal clock.

Once the phytochrome mechanism and the internal-clock mechanism have together indicated to the plant that the photoperiod is appropriate to flowering, the leaves must begin synthesizing florigen, which is then transported in the phloem to the buds. How phytochrome is actually coupled to florigen synthesis is unknown, but apparently it is the F-phytochrome that is important in developmental processes. It is now known that the phytochrome mechanism is also coupled to other functions besides flowering. For example, germination of some types of seeds involves exposure to red light, which is sensed by phytochrome. Many other reactions, including gibberellin-controlled stem elongation, expansion of new leaves, breaking of dormancy in

spring, formation of plastids in cells, and leaf abscission, also involve this pigment. An example of a reaction to light that does not involve phytochrome is provided by phototropism; here it is blue light, apparently absorbed by carotenoids, that is most effective.

The control of flowering is a dynamic and exciting field where much remains to be learned. It is worth studying a phenomenon like flowering not only because it is interesting in itself, but also because from such study we often gain new ideas and understanding about other biological phenomena as well. Anything we learn about one aspect of life increases our understanding of all aspects of life.

HORMONES IN INVERTEBRATE ANIMALS

Much interest in the hormones of invertebrate animals has developed in recent years. Hormonal mechanisms have been found in a variety of invertebrates, including arthropods, annelid worms, molluscs, and echinoderms. It seems likely that hormonal control is a general phenomenon in both plants and animals, and that the list of animals in which such control is demonstrated will become steadily longer. At present, however, our knowledge of the hormones of invertebrates is extremely rudimentary. The arthropods, particularly the insects, have been most extensively studied, and our discussion here will be limited to these animals. We shall not attempt to mention all the insect hormones now known, much less to enumerate those known in other invertebrates. The intent is simply to give you a quick introduction to the subject of hormonal control in invertebrates, and to give you some insight into the potential value of research in this field from the standpoint of increasing our understanding of developmental processes in general.

Although most known hormones of insects, including the three discussed below, regulate growth and development, the idea that they are restricted to regulation of these processes is no longer tenable. In 1963 a hormone was discovered in cockroaches that regulates the blood-sugar level. This was an important discovery because it indicated that hormones are involved in homeostatic regulation of body fluids in insects just as they are in vertebrates. Many more such hormones, regulating such conditions as salt and water balance and the concentration of other metabolites in the blood, will probably be discovered in the near future.

Much of the early work on insect hormones was done in the 1930's in England by V. B. Wigglesworth. Wigglesworth was studying the metamorphosis of insects. Now, insects show a pattern of growth different from that of vertebrates. Their body is encased in a hard outer covering, or exoskeleton, that severely limits size increase. The insect's tissues grow until they exert considerable pressure against the inner surface of the exoskeleton; further growth is impossible unless the exoskeleton is shed. This is exactly what happens. The insect periodically molts its old exoskeleton and develops a new larger one in its place. Wigglesworth was interested in the mechanisms that control this molting.

Most of his experiments were performed on a bloodsucking bug from South America named *Rhodnius*. This bug goes through five immature or nymphal stages, each separated by a molt, before it becomes an adult. During each nymphal stage, the bug must obtain a blood meal, which engorges and stretches the abdomen. This repletion apparently stimulates release of hormones that cause molting at the end of a precise time interval following the meal. For example, the last molt (from fifth nymphal stage to adult) occurs about 28 days after the blood meal. Wigglesworth showed that if *Rhodnius* is decapitated during the first few days after the blood meal, molting does not occur, even though the animal may continue to live for several months. Decapitation more than eight days after the blood meal does not interfere with molting; a headless

adult is produced. If, however, the circulatory systems of a bug decapitated shortly after a blood meal and of a bug decapitated eight days later are joined, both bugs molt into adults. Clearly, some stimulus passes via the blood from the one insect to the other and induces molting. That stimulus must be a hormone, whose secretion by the head begins about eight days after a blood meal.

Later Wigglesworth showed that the *brain hormone* functions by stimulating glands in the insect's prothorax (the part of the body immediately behind the head, to which the first pair of legs is attached). The prothoracic glands, in turn, secrete a hormone that induces molting. This same hormone, often called *ecdysone* (from the Greek *ekdysis* meaning a getting out or shedding) or molting hormone, has been shown to be involved in many other growth and development processes also. Apparently ecdysone, acting directly on the nuclei or genes of several types of cells, stimulates these cells to produce certain types of proteins, to grow, and to divide. This hormone promises to become an important tool in explaining how factors outside the cell nucleus interact with the genes and thereby exert an influence on development. This interaction is fundamental to life; we know that genes and environmental influences act together to produce a complex, highly specialized organism from a single initial cell.

Wigglesworth became interested in the control factors that determine when a molt will result in an adult and when it will result in another immature stage. This is a particularly important question in insects like flies, beetles, and moths, which undergo a radical change from immature to adult characteristics—i.e. which undergo the complete metamorphosis that produces a fly from a grub or a moth from a caterpillar. Wigglesworth found that a third hormone is involved. This hormone, called *juvenile hormone,* is produced by a pair of glands (corpora allata) located just behind the brain and closely associated with it. When juvenile hormone is present in high concentration at the time of molting, another immature stage follows the molt (Fig. 9.18). The pupal stage, which is the changeover stage between the last larval stage and the adult in insects like flies and moths, results from a low concentration of juvenile hormone. Juvenile hormone is absent in the pupa, and when it molts an

adult results. Removal of the corpora allata from insects in the first or second immature stage results in pupation at the next molt, followed by a molt that results in a midget adult. Conversely, implantation of active corpora allata into insects about to undergo their final molt results in another immature stage instead of an adult; in this way, several extra immature growth stages can be inserted into the insect's developmental sequence. These can be followed by pupation and a molt producing an unusually large adult when juvenile hormone is finally eliminated. The interactions, as now understood, between brain hormone, ecdysone, and juvenile hormone in molting are shown in Fig. 9.18.

Notice that the nervous system of insects is intimately involved in endocrine function. Of the three hormones we have discussed, one is secreted by the brain itself, one is secreted by glands closely associated with the brain, and secretion of the third is directly controlled by brain hormone. This intimate association between the nervous system and endocrine function, and the consequent lack of clear distinction between the two control systems, generally holds true for invertebrates.

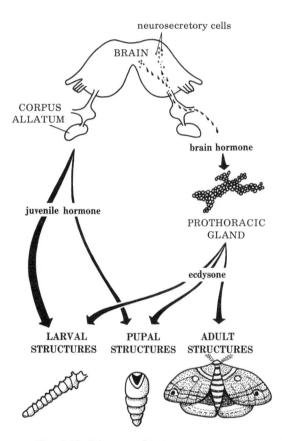

Fig. 9.18. Diagram showing interactions of juvenile hormone, brain hormone, and molting hormone (ecdysone) in *Cecropia* silkworm. If much juvenile hormone is present when the insect molts, it will molt into another larval stage. If a low concentration of juvenile hormone is present, the larva will molt into a pupa. If no juvenile hormone is present, the pupa will molt into an adult. [Modified from H. A. Schneiderman and L. I. Gilbert, *Science*, vol. 143, 1964. Copyright 1964 by the American Association for the Advancement of Science.]

HORMONES IN VERTEBRATE ANIMALS

It is not our purpose here to enumerate all known vertebrate hormones and their attributes. Instead, as in our discussion of plant hormones, we shall try to give you some insight into the way the diverse functions of a complex organism are regulated and indicate what is currently known of chemical control in vertebrates. Since far more is known about hormones in mammals, especially man, than about those of any other group of animals, it is the mammalian hormonal system that we shall emphasize here (Fig. 9.19; Table 9.1).

We have already said that hormones are specific chemical messengers that exert effects

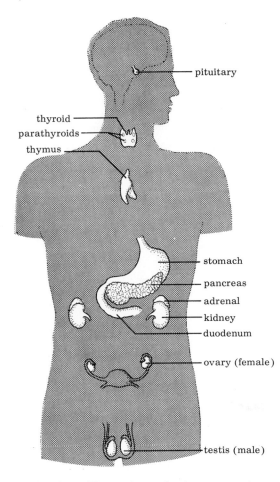

- pituitary

thyroid
parathyroids
thymus

- stomach
- pancreas
- adrenal
- kidney
- duodenum

- ovary (female)

- testis (male)

Fig. 9.19. The major endocrine organs in man.

involved. In fact, endocrine glands are frequently called the ductless glands.

Hormonal Control of Digestion

Let us first examine a hormonal control system in which production of the hormone is not restricted to a discrete organ specialized for just that function, i.e. a system in which production of hormone is at a more primitive evolutionary stage than in true endocrine glands. The example we shall use is the chemical control system for secretion of gastric fluid by glands in the wall of the stomach.

The famous Russian physiologist Ivan P. Pavlov (1849–1936) showed in a series of now classic experiments that secretion of saliva is under nervous control. Training dogs to associate the sound of a bell with food, he demonstrated that they salivated upon hearing the bell, even if they could not see, smell, or taste food. Pavlov was also interested in the control of gastric secretion, which in 1902 he showed to be at least partly under nervous control. For this demonstration, the esophagus of a dog was bisected surgically and both of the cut ends were led to the outside through an incision in the dog's neck. The food the dog ate did not reach its stomach then, but was collected as it emerged from the cut end of the esophagus. When dogs were sham-fed in this manner, gastric juice was secreted in their stomachs. If, however, the nerves to the stomach were cut, sham feeding did not cause gastric flow. It was clear, therefore, that nervous stimulation of the stomach wall can trigger gastric secretion before food actually reaches the stomach. But this secretion was only about one fourth as great as normal. Evidently some other factor was also involved. Pavlov showed that if he inserted partly digested food into the cut end of the esophagus leading to the stomach, without allowing the dog to see, smell, or taste it, better than half the normal gastric flow began as soon as the food reached the stomach; cutting the nervous

at points some distance removed from their sites of production. Hormones may, of course, diffuse from one place to another, but, as would be expected in animals with well-developed circulatory systems, most of their transport in mammals is by the blood. The tissues and organs that produce and release hormones are termed *endocrine* tissues and endocrine organs. The use of the word "endocrine" —i.e. secreting internally—is meant to convey that the hormones are secreted directly into the blood in the capillaries supplying the endocrine tissues and that no special ducts or tubes are

TABLE 9.1

Important Mammalian Hormones

Source	Hormone	Principal effects
Pyloric mucosa of stomach	Gastrin	Stimulates secretion of gastric juice
Mucosa of duodenum	Secretin	Stimulates secretion of pancreatic juice
	Cholecystokinin	Stimulates release of bile by gallbladder
	Enterogastrone	Inhibits secretion of gastric juice
Damaged tissues	Histamine	Increases capillary permeability
Pancreas	Insulin	Stimulates glycogen formation and storage; stimulates carbohydrate oxidation; inhibits formation of new glucose
	Glucagon	Stimulates conversion of glycogen into glucose
Kidney plus blood	Hypertensin	Stimulates vasoconstriction, causing rise in blood pressure
Thymus	Thymic hormone	Stimulates immunologic competence in lymphoid tissues
Testes	Testosterone	Stimulates development and maintenance of male secondary sexual characteristics and behavior
Ovaries	Estrogens	Stimulate development and maintenance of female secondary sexual characteristics and behavior
	Progesterone	Stimulates female secondary sexual characteristics and behavior, and maintains pregnancy
Thyroid	Thyroxin	Stimulates oxidative metabolism
Parathyroids	Parathormone	Regulates calcium-phosphate metabolism

TABLE 9.1 (*Cont.*)

Important Mammalian Hormones

Source	Hormone	Principal effects
Adrenal medulla	Adrenalin	Stimulates syndrome of reactions commonly termed "fight or flight"
	Noradrenalin	Stimulates reactions similar to those produced by adrenalin, but causes more vasoconstriction and is less effective in conversion of glycogen into glucose
Adrenal cortex	Glucocorticoids (corticosterone, cortisone, hydrocortisone, etc.)	Stimulate formation (largely from noncarbohydrate sources) and storage of glycogen; help maintain normal blood-sugar level
	Mineralocorticoids (aldosterone, deoxycorticosterone, etc.)	Regulate sodium-potassium metabolism
	Cortical sex hormones (adrenosterone, etc.)	Stimulate secondary sexual characteristics, particularly those of the male
Anterior pituitary	Growth hormone	Stimulates growth
	Thyrotrophic hormone	Stimulates the thyroid
	Adrenocorticotrophic hormone (ACTH)	Stimulates the adrenal cortex
	Follicle-stimulating hormone (FSH)	Stimulates growth of ovarian follicles and of seminiferous tubules of the testes
	Luteinizing hormone (LH)	Stimulates conversion of follicles into copora lutea; stimulates secretion of sex hormones by ovaries and testes
	Prolactin	Stimulates milk secretion by mammary glands
Intermediate lobe of pituitary	Melanocyte-stimulating hormone	Controls cutaneous pigmentation
Posterior pituitary	Oxytocin	Stimulates contraction of uterine muscles; stimulates release of milk by mammary glands
	Vasopressin	Stimulates increased water reabsorption by kidneys; stimulates constriction of blood vessels (and other smooth muscle)

connections of the stomach did not change the results of this experiment. Apparently, then, this second phase of gastric secretion was not under nervous control.

Pavlov began a series of experiments designed to determine the control mechanisms involved in the second phase of gastric secretion. His earlier experiments, as we have seen, had demonstrated that food in the stomach somehow leads to release of gastric juice. Is the mere physical presence of food sufficient to stimulate this release? Pavlov's experiments showed that the answer is no. If a piece of fresh meat was inserted directly into the stomach without allowing the dog to sense the food, there was no secretion of gastric juice. Furthermore, stimulation of the stomach wall with a glass rod, with sand, or with other mechanical devices resulted in very little secretion. If, however, a piece of partly digested meat was inserted directly into the stomach, secretion promptly began. Apparently, compounds released from the partly digested meat triggered the secretion. The conclusion to be drawn was that, under normal conditions, the gastric flow of the first phase, triggered by nervous stimulation, initiates digestion, and this, in turn, releases from the food compounds that trigger the second phase of gastric secretion, which makes possible the continuation of gastric digestion after nervous stimulation has ceased.

The next question was: How do the substances from partly digested meat stimulate release of gastric juice? An obvious possibility was that they might act by direct stimulation of the gastric glands. This was ruled out, however, when Pavlov divided the stomach surgically into two chambers and showed that partly digested meat in one chamber stimulated release of gastric juice in both chambers, even when the stomach had been completely isolated from nervous control. Direct contact between the meat substances and the glands was thus not necessary to induce secretion, even though nervous stimulation was not involved. Perhaps the substances from the partly

digested meat were absorbed and carried to the gastric glands by the blood. This, too, was ruled out when it was shown that injection of the meat substances directly into the blood caused relatively little secretory response, and that, furthermore, little or no absorption occurred in the stomach.

At least one other good possibility remained. Perhaps the meat substances triggered release of a hormone into the blood, and this hormone, in turn, stimulated the gastric glands to begin secreting. J. S. Edkins at St. Bartholomew's Hospital, London, showed in 1905 that, if a piece of mucosa stripped from the pyloric region of the stomach wall was ground up in the presence of meat substances and an extract was prepared from it, injection of the extract stimulated gastric secretion. Edkins concluded that the meat substances stimulated the mucosa of the pyloric region of the stomach to release a hormone, which he called *gastrin*. He believed that the gastrin was carried by the blood to the gastric glands and stimulated them to secrete gastric juice. Numerous later experiments have tended to confirm Edkins' conclusions. For example, when the circulatory systems of two dogs are interconnected, and partly digested food is placed in the stomach of one of the dogs, the gastric glands of both dogs begin secreting gastric juice; presumably, gastrin from the one dog is carried by the blood to the other dog and stimulates its gastric glands.

It has since been shown that fats stimulate the wall of the duodenum to release another hormone, *enterogastrone*, which inhibits secretion of gastric juice. This is one reason why a diet heavy in milk and oils is often recommended for patients with stomach ulcers, which are irritated by gastric juice. It is possible that injections of enterogastrone will eventually be useful in treatment of ulcers. Under normal conditions, the amount of secretion of gastric juice is probably determined by the balance between gastrin and enterogastrone. We see, then, that in animals, as in plants, functions are frequently controlled by a delicate interplay between stimulators and inhibitors.

W. M. Bayliss and E. H. Starling of University College, London, showed in 1902 that secretion of pancreatic juice is also under control of a hormone. This hormone, called *secretin*, is released by the mucosal cells of the small intestine when they are stimulated by the acidity of food coming from the stomach. Another hormone, cholecystokinin, released by the small intestine under stimulation by acids and fats, stimulates release of bile from the gallbladder.

Histamine

Damaged tissues release a substance called histamine, which relaxes the muscles in the walls of blood vessels and makes the vessels more permeable than they are normally. This increased permeability probably facilitates movement of white blood cells and antibodies into the damaged area and helps prevent and fight infection. The release of histamine can have deleterious consequences, however—particularly in allergies. In hay fever, for example, antigen-antibody reactions occur in the nasal mucosa; these reactions damage the mucosa and cause it to release histamine. The histamine makes the walls of the blood vessels in the mucosa more permeable, which results in a copious flow of fluids both from the vessels themselves and from the mucosal glands. Histamine also causes constriction of the walls of the bronchioles, which may at times be so severe as to make breathing difficult, as in the condition known as asthma. Excessive release of histamines can sometimes be slowed by use of drugs commonly called antihistamines.

It can be debated whether histamine should be considered a true hormone. But whatever one calls it, this substance is an example of a chemical that is released locally and exerts its major effect locally. There is increasing evidence that many other such local control chemicals exist; how important they will prove to be

we can only guess in our present state of ignorance.

The Pancreas as an Endocrine Organ

Diabetes (or, more precisely, diabetes mellitus), a disease in which much sugar is excreted in the urine, has been known for centuries, but its causes did not begin to be understood until the latter half of the nineteenth century. In 1889 two German physicians, Johann von Mering and Oscar Minkowski, who were interested in the role of the pancreas as a producer of digestive enzymes, surgically removed the pancreas from a dog. A short time later, it was noticed that the dog's urine was attracting an unusual number of ants. Analysis showed that the urine contained a high concentration of sugar. Furthermore, the dog soon developed other symptoms strikingly like those of human diabetes. Von Mering and Minkowski removed the pancreas from other dogs, and diabetes invariably developed. To eliminate the possibility that the extensive damage resulting from so severe an operation might be the causal factor, they performed operations in which all the damage usually associated with the operation was produced, but the pancreas was not actually removed. These dogs did not develop symptoms of diabetes. Clearly, the onset of diabetes was directly correlated with extirpation of the pancreas. But operations in which the pancreatic duct was destroyed without producing the disease made it clear also that diabetes was not correlated with absence of the pancreatic digestive enzymes. The conclusion to be drawn was that the pancreas functioned not only in digestion, but in some other way as well.

Mounting evidence pointed to secretion by the pancreas of some substance that prevents diabetes in the normal animal, but all attempts at proof failed. Feeding bits of pancreas to diabetic dogs had no effect; if the pancreas contained a control chemical—a hormone—it was destroyed by digestive enzymes. Repeated efforts by numerous investigators to show that injection of an extract made from the pancreas would alter diabetic symptoms failed. The reason for these failures was soon realized; grinding pancreatic tissue to produce the extracts mixed the hormone with the pancreatic digestive enzymes, which destroyed the hormone. But how could this be avoided?

It was known that the pancreas is a compound organ, i.e. that it contains several types of cells, which apparently function independently. There are the cells involved in production and release of digestive enzymes, and there are other quite different cells, called *islet cells* or islets of Langerhans. It seemed likely that the hormone so many people were searching for was produced by the islet cells. In a critical experiment that supported this hypothesis and opened the way for isolation of the hormone, it was shown that tying off the pancreatic duct resulted in atrophy of most of the pancreas but not in development of diabetes. Examination of the atrophied pancreas revealed that it was the enzyme-producing portion that had atrophied, while the islet cells had remained essentially intact. The hormone that prevented diabetes must have come from this portion of the pancreas.

The hormone, *insulin,* was finally isolated in 1922 by F. G. Banting and C. H. Best, working in the laboratory of J. J. R. MacLeod at the University of Toronto. They tied off the pancreatic ducts of a number of dogs, waited until the enzyme-producing tissue had atrophied, removed the degenerated pancreas and froze and macerated it in an isosmotic medium (freezing prevents any remaining digestive enzymes from acting), filtered the solution, and quickly injected the filtered material into diabetic dogs. The dogs showed marked improvement. Banting and Best also obtained good results with extracts prepared from the pancreases of embryonic animals; since the islet cells develop in the embryo sooner than the enzyme-producing cells, there are no enzymes to destroy the insulin during the extraction

procedure. Banting and MacLeod received the Nobel Prize in 1923 for this important work.

Banting and Best followed a procedure considered standard for demonstrating that a particular organ or tissue has an endocrine function. Let us outline the essential criteria of that standard procedure: (1) Removal or destruction of the organ in question should result in predictable symptoms presumed to be associated with absence of the hormone. (2) Administration of material prepared from the organ in question should relieve the symptoms. (3) It should be demonstrated that the hormone is present in both the organ and the blood, and the hormone should be extractable from each. Fortunately, administration of extracts of suspected organs has not always been as difficult as with the pancreas before Banting and Best solved the problem.

Insulin was crystallized by J. J. Abel of Johns Hopkins University in 1926. And as we have already seen, it was the first protein for which the complete amino acid sequence was determined (by F. Sanger in 1954; see p. 40). Someday, perhaps, methods will be devised for synthesizing insulin in the laboratory. In the meantime, however, millions of people who would once have been doomed to invalidism and premature death will continue to lead relatively normal lives thanks to injections of insulin extracted from natural sources.[1]

We have repeatedly mentioned high concentrations of sugar in the urine as a major symptom of diabetes. How is insulin related to this symptom? Before attempting to answer this question, we must examine the symptom further. The presence of sugar in the urine of a diabetic does not necessarily indicate that the kidneys are functioning improperly. Instead, it indicates that the blood-sugar concentration is higher than normal and that the kidneys are removing part of the excess. We must there-

[1] In recent years, a variety of drugs (e.g. certain sulfonylurea and biguanide compounds) have been found to have antidiabetic activity when administered orally. A major effect of some of these is to stimulate increased insulin production.

fore look for reasons for the high concentration of glucose in the blood. You will recall that the liver plays a critical role in regulating blood-sugar levels. When blood coming to the liver via the portal vein from the intestines contains a higher than normal concentration of sugar, the liver removes much of the excess and stores it as glycogen, with the result that blood leaving the liver via the hepatic vein contains approximately the normal concentration of sugar. Conversely, when blood coming to the liver is low in sugar, the liver converts some of its stored glycogen into glucose and adds this to the blood, so that, again, blood leaving the liver contains a normal concentration of sugar. Other parts of the body, particularly the muscles, are also important elements in this regulatory system; e.g. when the blood-sugar concentration rises after a carbohydrate meal, part of the excess glucose is stored as glycogen in the muscles, and the rate of oxidation of carbohydrate in the muscles may also increase under these conditions.

This brief outline of the interplay between liver, blood, and muscles suggests several possible ways in which insulin could act to lower blood-sugar levels. The insulin might act primarily on the liver, inducing it to remove more sugar from the blood for storage as glycogen and inhibiting it from converting glycogen into glucose. Or the insulin might act primarily on the muscles by increasing glycogen production (either by facilitating absorption of glucose from the blood by the muscle cells or by accelerating the enzymatic conversion of glucose into glycogen) or by stimulating more rapid oxidation of carbohydrate by cellular respiration. Some biologists are advocates of the liver as the principal site of insulin's action, and other biologists are equally strong advocates of the muscles. The majority of investigators, however, seem to think that an either-or choice is not necessary, that insulin probably plays an important role in both the liver and the muscles. If this is true, insulin probably functions in at least three ways to reduce the concentration of glucose in the blood: (1) It stimulates (probably by altering membrane permeabilities) both the liver and the muscles to remove glucose from the blood and to store it as glycogen; (2) it inhibits the liver from producing glucose from glycogen or other stored materials; and (3) it stimulates the muscles (and perhaps also the liver) to oxidize carbohydrates at a more rapid rate.

Too much insulin in the system, as from an overactive pancreas or from administration of excessive insulin to a diabetic, can produce a severe reaction called insulin shock. The blood-sugar level falls so low that the brain, which has few stored food reserves of its own, becomes overly irritable; convulsions may result, followed by unconsciousness and often death. A naturally occurring excess of insulin is, however, extremely rare. Far more common is a deficiency of insulin, and it is this that we call diabetes. The liver and muscles do not convert enough glucose into glycogen, the liver produces too much new glucose, and utilization of carbohydrate in cellular respiration is impaired. The blood-sugar level rises above normal, and part of the excess glucose begins to appear in the urine. More water must be excreted as a vehicle for this glucose, and the diabetic thus tends to become dehydrated. The glycogen reserves become depleted as more and more glucose is poured into the blood and lost in the urine; yet the body still lacks sufficient energy, because of the impairment of carbohydrate metabolism. As a result, the body begins to metabolize its reserves of proteins and fats, particularly the latter. The diabetic consequently becomes emaciated and weak and is easily subject to infections. As if this were not enough, the excessive but incomplete metabolism of fats releases toxic substances that seriously disturb the delicately balanced pH of the body, and these substances often have a major part in the eventual fatal outcome of the untreated disease.

The pancreas secretes another hormone besides insulin. This hormone, called *glucagon,* is produced in certain islet cells called alpha cells, while insulin is produced in the beta islet cells. Glucagon, which is not as well understood as insulin, seems to have the opposite effect; it causes an increase in blood-glucose concentration. Several hormones produced by the adrenal glands also cause a rise in the blood-sugar level, and hormones from the pituitary may do so also. Again we see that the normal functioning of an organism depends on a delicate balance between opposing control systems; if either of the opposing factors is disturbed and the proper balance is destroyed, abnormalities result, and in severe cases these abnormalities may lead to disease or even death.

The Kidneys as Endocrine Organs

It has long been known that kidney malfunction is commonly associated with high blood pressure (or hypertension, as it is known technically). But it was not until 1934 that H. Goldblatt and his associates at Western Reserve University showed that constriction of the renal arteries consistently causes pronounced and permanent hypertension. They fastened tiny screw clamps on the renal arteries of dogs. By means of the screw adjustment, they could restrict the blood flow to the kidneys to any desired amount. The dogs consistently developed hypertension to the extent predicted on the basis of the restriction in blood flow. It was later shown that when blood flow is restricted the kidney cortex secretes a protein (renin) that reacts with a protein in the blood to form a hormone called *hypertensin* (or angiotonin). Hypertensin is a vasoconstrictor; i.e. it stimulates the smooth muscles in the walls of small blood vessels to contract, thereby constricting the vessels. Vasoconstriction, in turn, causes the blood pressure to rise, both because the constricted vessels offer more resistance to flow and because the heart compensates for the lessened flow by increased output. The higher blood pressure can force

more blood through the partly blocked renal arteries into the glomeruli of the kidneys. Thus the kidneys have a way of compensating for the reduced blood flow caused by constrictions or other obstructions in their arteries.

Since both the kidneys and the blood contribute materials necessary to the production of hypertensin, it is difficult to specify the endocrine organ in this case. However the question is decided, the fact remains that hypertensin may prove to be a critical causal element in the onset of hypertension, a very frequent and dangerous pathologic condition in our society. The exact role of hypertensin in naturally occurring cases of hypertension has not yet been determined; it is almost certainly far more complex than this brief account might seem to indicate.

The Thymus as an Endocrine Organ

Recent experiments have shown, at long last, that one of the functions of the long-enigmatic thymus, a gland in the neck region that is particularly prominent in young animals, is production of a hormone important in stimulating immunologic competence in the plasma cells of the spleen, lymph nodes, and other lymphoid tissues during early stages of development. The hormone itself has not been isolated at the time of this writing, but it is the object of a concentrated search and will doubtless be isolated soon. The thymus and its hormone will be discussed at more length in another chapter.

The Thyroid

The endocrine organs examined so far—stomach, duodenum, pancreas, kidneys, and thymus—and the gonads, which will be discussed later, all have other major functions in addition to hormone secretion. They are multipurpose organs; each is an important component in both the endocrine system and some other system. There are, however, some endocrine organs whose only known function is hormone secretion. They represent the highest degree of specialization for endocrine function. These endocrine glands are the thyroid, the parathyroids, the adrenals, and the pituitary. We shall consider each in turn.

Most vertebrates have two thyroid glands located in the neck; in man the two have fused to form a single gland (Fig. 9.19). There is good evidence that the vertebrate thyroids evolved from ventral pouches of the pharynx. These pouches probably functioned originally as channels in which food particles were strained from water currents flowing into the mouth and out through the gill slits. In the vertebrates, however, the developing pouches soon lost all connection to the pharynx and became both structurally and functionally independent of the digestive system. This is but one example of a common evolutionary occurrence—the evolution of a functionally new structure from an ancestral structure with an apparently unrelated function.

Years ago, a condition known as goiter, in which the thyroid may become so enlarged that the whole neck looks swollen and deformed (Fig. 9.20), was very common in some areas of the world, such as the Swiss Alps and the Great Lakes region of the United States. Goiter was often associated with a group of other symptoms, including dry and puffy skin, loss of hair, obesity, a slower than normal heartbeat, physical lethargy, and mental dullness. No cause for this condition was known. Then in 1883 a Swiss surgeon, who believed that the thyroid had no important function, removed the gland from a number of his patients. Most of these patients developed all the symptoms usually associated with goiter. The results suggested that the normal thyroid must secrete some chemical that prevents these symptoms. The curious fact that patients with no thyroid and patients with the excessively large thyroid of a goiter showed the same complex of symptoms could be explained if the malformed gland of the goiter was, despite its large size, secreting too little hormone. By the 1890's, patients with goiters or the other symptoms of hypothyroidism[2] were being successfully treated with injections of thyroid extract or with bits of sheep thyroid in their diet. But nothing more specific was known as yet about the hypothetical thyroid hormone itself. True, a German chemist, E. Baumann, discovered in 1896 that the thyroid contains iodine, an element previously unknown in the body. But little attention was paid to his discovery.

In 1905 David Marine of Western Reserve University noticed that many people in Cleveland had goiters. A high percentage of the dogs also had goiters. Even many of the trout in the streams had goiters. Marine wondered if the goiters might be caused by an insufficiency of iodine in the food and water. When he administered tiny traces of iodine in water to his experimental animals, their goiters and other symptoms disappeared. In 1916 Marine tried his treatment on approximately 2,500 schoolchildren in Akron, Ohio. He fed these children

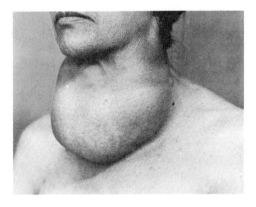

Fig. 9.20. A particularly large goiter. Most goiters are much smaller. [Courtesy A. J. Carlson, V. Johnson, and H. M. Cavert, *The Machinery of the Body*, University of Chicago Press, 1961.]

[2] The prefix *hypo-* means less than the ordinary, while the prefix *hyper-* means more than the ordinary. Thus hypothyroidism means less than normal thyroid activity, and hyperthyroidism means more than normal thyroid activity.

iodized salt. Another 2,500 children used as controls were fed un-iodized salt. At the end of a specified period, he found only two cases of goiter among the children who had eaten iodized salt, whereas there were 250 cases among the controls. Though it took years to convince a skeptical public, use of iodized salt finally became widespread, and hypothyroidism caused by insufficient iodine in the soil and water now seldom occurs. Hypothyroidism caused by malfunction of the thyroid gland itself is treated by administration of the thyroid hormone, which is called *thyroxin.*

Hypothyroidism is particularly serious when it occurs in newborn children. Such children, called cretins, are pitiable creatures of grotesque development. They are dwarflike, and they never mature sexually. They have very low intelligence, seldom achieving a mental age of more than four or five years at the most. Prevention of cretinism by early administration of thyroxin to babies showing deficiency symptoms is surely one of the triumphs of modern medicine.

The various symptoms of hypothyroidism all result from a slowing down of the oxidative energy-releasing reactions of the body. Thyroxin must therefore speed up the metabolism in some manner. Hyperthyroidism, the opposite of hypothyroidism, produces symptoms that you might predict: a higher than normal body temperature, profuse perspiration, high blood pressure, loss of weight, irritability, and muscular weakness. It also produces one very characteristic symptom that you might not predict, because it lacks an obvious connection to a higher than normal metabolic rate; this symptom is exophthalmia, a condition in which the eyeballs protrude in a startling manner (Fig. 9.21). Hyperthyroidism has been treated by removal of part of the gland or by partial destruction with radiation, but these methods are not very satisfactory. More recently, several drugs that inhibit the thyroid have been discovered, and their use is supplanting the older surgical procedures.

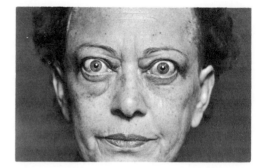

Fig. 9.21. Exophthalmia. [Courtesy A. J. Carlson, V. Johnson, and H. M. Cavert, *The Machinery of the Body,* University of Chicago Press, 1961.]

Thyroxin was isolated in 1914 and synthesized in the laboratory in 1927. It proved to be an amino acid that contains four atoms of iodine (Fig. 9.22). In the last few years, another thyroid compound, identical to thyroxin except that it contains only three atoms of iodine, has been found even more active than thyroxin. It is possible that thyroxin is normally converted into this compound just before it exerts its effect on the tissues. Unfortunately, we do not know how thyroxin acts to speed up metabolism. Many theories have been proposed, but none have been proved.

The Parathyroids

The parathyroid glands in man are small pea-like organs, usually four in number, located on the surface of the thyroid (Fig. 9.23). They were long thought to be part of the thyroid or to be functionally associated with it. Now, however, we know that their close proximity

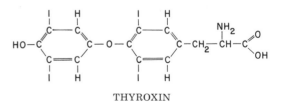

THYROXIN

Fig. 9.22. Structural formula of thyroxin.

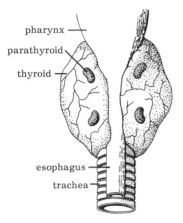

pharynx
parathyroid
thyroid
esophagus
trachea

Fig. 9.23. Posterior view of thyroid and parathyroid glands.

to the thyroid is misleading; both developmentally and functionally, they are totally separate from the thyroid.

The parathyroid hormone, often called *parathormone*, functions in regulating the calcium-phosphate balance between the blood and the other tissues. Consequently it is an important element in maintaining the relative constancy of the internal fluid environment of the body, a subject discussed at length in an earlier chapter (we have already seen that such hormones as insulin and glucagon are also important in this regard). Parathormone increases the concentration of calcium in the blood and decreases the concentration of phosphate. It does this by acting on at least three different organs: the kidneys, the intestine, and the bones. It inhibits excretion of calcium by the kidneys and intestines, and it stimulates release of calcium into the blood from the bones (which contain more than 98 percent of the body's calcium and 66 percent of its phosphate). But calcium in bone is bonded with phosphate, and breakdown of bone releases phosphate as well as calcium. Parathormone compensates for this release of phosphate into the blood by stimulating excretion of this material by the kidneys. Actually, it overcompensates, causing more phosphate to be excreted than is added to the blood from

bone; the result is that the concentration of phosphate in the blood drops as the secretion of parathormone increases.

Naturally occurring hypoparathyroidism is very rare, but the parathyroids are sometimes accidentally removed during surgery on the thyroid. The result is a rise in the phosphate concentration in the blood and a drop in the calcium concentration (as more calcium is excreted by the kidneys and intestines and more is incorporated into bone). This change in the fluid environment of the cells produces serious disturbances, particularly of muscles and nerves. These tissues become very irritable, and respond even to very minor stimuli with tremors, cramps, and convulsions. Complete absence of parathormone is usually soon fatal unless very large quantities of calcium are included in the diet. Injections of parathormone are effective in preventing the symptoms.

Hyperparathyroidism sometimes occurs naturally when the glands become enlarged or develop tumors. The most obvious symptom of this condition is bones that are weak and easily bent or fractured, because of excessive withdrawal of calcium from the bones.

The Adrenals

The two adrenal glands, as their name implies (*ad-* means near and *renal* refers to the kidney), lie very near the kidneys (Fig. 9.19). Each adrenal in mammals is actually a double gland, composed of an inner corelike *medulla* and an outer barklike *cortex.* The medulla and cortex arise in the embryo from different tissues, and their mature functions are unrelated. In fact, they remain as two separate pairs of glands in adult fish and amphibians. Reptiles, birds, and mammals have evolved a close spatial relationship between the two sets of glands (in reptiles and birds, the tissues of the two are actually intermingled, instead of being separated into distinct cortex and medulla, as in most mammals), but they remain functionally distinct. We shall therefore discuss the two component parts of the mammalian adrenals separately.

The Adrenal Medulla. The adrenal medulla secretes two hormones, *adrenalin* (often also called epinephrine) and *noradrenalin* (norepinephrine), whose functions are very similar but not identical. Both hormones have been isolated, identified, and synthesized in the laboratory (Fig. 9.24). They can be shown to produce a great variety of effects on the body. For example, adrenalin causes rise in blood pressure, acceleration of heartbeat, increased conversion of glycogen into glucose and release of glucose into the blood by the liver, release of reserve erythrocytes into the blood from the spleen, vasodilation and increased blood flow in skeletal and heart muscle, resistance to fatigue, vasoconstriction and decreased blood flow in the smooth muscle of the digestive tract, inhibition of intestinal peristalsis, erection of hairs, production of "gooseflesh," and dilation of the pupils. At first glance, this list may seem to include a curious assortment of seemingly unrelated effects, but a more careful examination shows that these reactions occur together in response to stress, variously caused by physical exertion, pain, fear, anger, or other heightened emotional states. They have sometimes been called "fight-or-flight" reactions. It has been suggested, therefore, that adrenalin functions to mobilize the resources of the body in emergencies (by such reactions as those that together increase the supply of glucose and oxygen carried by the blood to the skeletal and heart muscles) and to inhibit those functions not immediately important during the emergency (such as digestion, which might otherwise compete with the skeletal muscles for oxygen).

This seems a reasonable theory and much evidence supports it, but the importance of adrenalin from the adrenal medulla in producing the fight-or-flight reactions can be seriously questioned on a number of grounds. For example, complete removal of the adrenal medullae causes little noticeable change in an animal; the animal still shows normal fight-or-flight reactions to appropriate stimuli. As we shall see in the next chapter, the portion of the nervous system called the sympathetic system stimulates the same fight-or-flight reactions as adrenalin, and most of the available evidence indicates that the sympathetic system is far more important in an animal's response to emergencies. Why vertebrates evolved hormonal and nervous control mechanisms that seem to duplicate each other remains an intriguing question.

The Adrenal Cortex. A person can live normally without the adrenal medullae, but not without the cortices. These are essential for life, and their removal is soon fatal. Death is preceded by a severe fall in the concentration of sodium and chloride in the blood and tissue fluids, a rise in the concentration of potassium in these fluids, loss of water from the blood resulting in diminished total blood volume and lowered blood pressure, impairment of kidney function with accompanying rise in concentration of certain metabolic wastes in the blood, impairment of carbohydrate metabolism with a marked decrease in both blood-glucose concentration and stored glycogen, loss of weight, general muscular weakness, and a peculiar browning of the skin. These same symptoms are seen in varying degrees in indi-

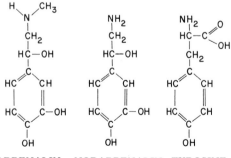

ADRENALIN   NORADRENALIN   TYROSINE

Fig. 9.24. Structural formulas of adrenalin and noradrenalin, and of tyrosine, the amino acid from which they are derived.

viduals whose adrenal cortices are insufficiently active. The condition is known as Addison's disease.

Whereas a great variety of effects are attributable to the one hormone adrenalin (and to some extent noradrenalin) from the medulla, the numerous symptoms of adrenal cortical insufficiency listed above are not related to a single hormone. The adrenal cortex is, in fact, an amazing endocrine factory, producing so many different hormones that we still have no idea of the total number. At least forty different cortical hormonelike substances (of which only about ten are very active) have already been isolated and identified, but after all these have been removed from the cortex the residue still shows activity, indicating that more hormones remain to be isolated. All the cortical hormones are chemically extremely similar; all are steroids, often differing from each other by only one or two atoms of hydrogen or oxygen (Fig. 9.25). Yet these differences, minor as

they may appear to us, give the various hormones strikingly different properties. The chemical specificity displayed in many life functions never ceases to amaze even experienced professional biologists.

Note that these hormones are chemically quite unlike the other hormones we have discussed. In mammals, only the hormones of the adrenal cortex and those of the gonads and other reproductive structures are steroids. All the hormones of other endocrine organs, as far as we know, are amino acids (or, like adrenalin, compounds derived from amino acids), short polypeptide chains, or proteins. Our understanding of the role of steroids in the chemistry of life is still very limited, but what we have learned so far strongly suggests that for years to come steroid research will be a highly rewarding field, both for its contribution to our understanding of the basic processes of life and for its potential practical uses in medicine, agriculture, and industry.

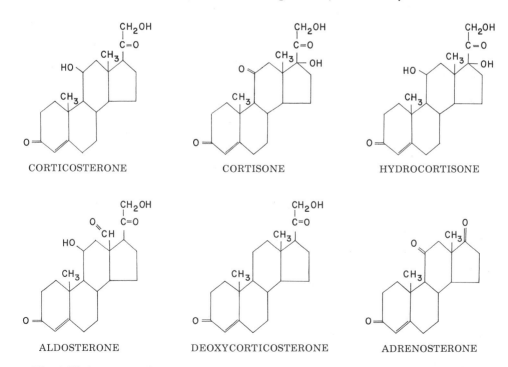

Fig. 9.25. Some steroids secreted by the adrenal cortex. Very slight differences in side chains can result in markedly different properties.

It is beyond the scope of this book to deal with all the known cortical hormones individually. We shall simply try here to give you some insight into the immense importance of this group of compounds. The cortical hormones may be grouped into three categories on the basis of their functions: (1) those that act primarily in regulating carbohydrate and protein metabolism, (2) those that act primarily in regulating salt and water balance, and (3) those that function primarily as sex hormones.

Hormones in the first category (e.g. corticosterone, cortisone, hydrocortisone) stimulate conversion of amino acids into carbohydrate and formation of glycogen by the liver. They also stimulate formation of reserve glycogen in the tissues. When administered to a person with Addison's disease, they restore the blood-sugar level to normal. They thus act as antagonists to insulin.

Hormones in the second category are apparently the most important of the cortical hormones for survival; regular injections of these hormones will enable an animal whose adrenals have been removed to live in an almost normal condition. These hormones (e.g. aldosterone, deoxycorticosterone) stimulate the cells of the convoluted tubules of the kidneys to decrease reabsorption of potassium and increase reabsorption of sodium, which leads also to increased reabsorption of chloride and water. The reabsorption of these substances, in turn, causes a rise in blood volume and blood pressure. It is clear, then, that these cortical hormones, together with insulin, glucagon, parathormone, and adrenalin, are important elements in the intricate regulation of the body's internal fluid environment. As we shall see, some hormones from the pituitary are also involved in this regulation. Our discussion of regulation of body fluids in Chapter 8 was far from complete because we ignored the hormones.

Hormones in the third category (e.g. adrenosterone) are very similar both chemically and functionally to the sex hormones produced by the gonads. They stimulate development of such secondary sexual characteristics in the male as growth of the beard, deepening of the voice, and maturation of the genital organs. Although there are both male and female cortical sex hormones, the male hormones greatly predominate. Consequently, when tumors of the adrenal cortex increase secretion of these hormones to a level far above normal in a female, she begins to develop masculine characteristics such as hair on chest and face, a deeper voice, and more masculine musculature, while her feminine characteristics such as breast development and menstruation are suppressed. Cortical tumors in young children lead to precocious masculine sexual development.

The similarity between the hormones of the adrenal cortex and those of the gonads may stem from the similar embryological origin of the two sets of glands. They begin their development in the embryo side by side in the same ridge of tissue.

The medical use of some of these hormones, particularly *cortisone*, has an interesting history. Much of the early work on cortical hormones was done by E. C. Kendall of the Mayo Foundation. He isolated the first few granules of hormone in 1934, and continued his efforts at isolation, identification, and synthesis in the following years. He was eventually able to isolate a series of different hormones, of which one, cortisone, apparently had remarkable ability to increase a test animal's resistance to exposure, cold, poisons, and other physiological stresses. This effect of cortisone roused great interest, and a major effort was made to devise a method of synthesizing it, so that there would be enough to try on human subjects. Finally, in 1948, after years of tedious and discouraging effort, scientists at the Merck laboratories succeeded in synthesizing the hormone. The first test of cortisone as a therapeutic agent for human beings was performed at the Mayo Clinic on a young woman suffering from severe rheumatoid arthritis. All previous attempts to relieve her symptoms had failed, and she could now hardly move. But by the third day after injections of cortisone were begun she could move easily, and by the eighth day all her symptoms were essentially gone. If the injections were stopped, however, the symptoms promptly returned. Trials of cortisone on other arthritic patients yielded similar results.

Next, various investigators began trying cortisone on a host of diseases, many of them unrelated. And most of these investigators reported dramatic relief of symptoms, though seldom any actual cures. For example, all pneumonia symptoms of a boy with severe lobar pneumonia disappeared within 24 hours after administration of hormone (in this case the hormone used was not actually cortisone but a pituitary hormone, ACTH, that stimulates release of cortisone by the adrenal cortex). But the bacteria that cause pneumonia remained in large numbers in his body. Similarly, all disease symptoms of patients with tuberculosis disappeared several days after treatment with hormone was begun, but tuberculosis bacteria still swarmed in their bodies. In each case, disease symptoms would immediately return if treatment was suspended.

You can imagine the excitement such results stirred among doctors (and in the newspapers). It was hoped that ways would be found to produce actual cures with the hormones, but, even if that proved impossible, relief of symptoms for everything from rheumatism to chronic alcoholism and from asthma to cancer with a single drug seemed to signal the beginning of a new era in medicine. It was thought that cortisone helps the body withstand stress conditions, and that it is stress that opens the body to disease symptoms. Administration of extra cortisone would thus give the body greater ability to withstand stress, thereby minimizing its susceptibility to the damaging disease symptoms normally elicited by infections with pathogenic microorganisms or by metabolic disturbances.

Cortisone and related hormones may to some extent actually function in this manner. They may indeed be involved in the body's reaction to stress, and stress may well play a fundamental role in disease. But, unfortunately, cortisone has not proved to be the panacea first envisioned. When administered in large doses or over a long period of time, it frequently causes side effects as bad as or worse than the condition being treated: high blood pressure, excessive growth of hair, mental aberrations ranging from moodiness or mild anxiety to psychoses such as paranoia, delayed wound healing, lowered resistance to certain infections such as poliomyelitis and tuberculosis, peptic ulcers, brittle bones that are easily fractured, etc. The hormone is now most frequently used to give partial relief from the symptoms of arthritis and other diseases of connective tissues (it apparently causes changes in the collagenous fibers of such tissues). It is also sometimes used to treat severe allergic diseases, particularly asthma, and some types of lymphatic diseases. And it is used for temporary relief of severe symptoms in emergency situations. In every case, however, the physician must weigh the possible harmful side effects against the hoped-for symptomatic relief before he decides to use the hormone. And he seldom prescribes enough to give full symptomatic relief, preferring to have the patient endure mild symptoms in order to minimize harmful side effects. He may try, for example, to give an old lady some relief from her rheumatism without at the same time making her bones so brittle that they will break the next time she falls. If her pains persist and she demands more treatment, he must try to decide whether it is better to refuse her pleas or to yield and increase the risk of a broken hip.

The dilemma presented by cortisone serves as an extreme example of a general problem faced by physicians every day; most drugs— and other treatments, for that matter—have potential harmful side effects (though they are usually far less numerous than those of cortisone). The physician must therefore always balance possible good against possible harm, and he must always remember that even the safest drugs are dangerous when used in excessive quantity or at the wrong time. The body is, after all, a finely tuned machine, with interactions between its parts so intricate that we still know little about them. We cannot expect to subject it to chemicals that almost always affect more different functions than we know of without risking damage to the machine. Medicine has a long way to go before it can eliminate a very large element of guesswork from its practice, but it has come a long way too, and the future looks encouraging as the increasing tempo of biological discovery provides the basis for new medical applications.

The Pituitary

The pituitary (also called the hypophysis) is a small gland lying just below the brain. Like the adrenals, the pituitary is a double gland (Fig. 9.26). Its anterior lobe develops in the embryo as an outgrowth from the roof of the mouth; its posterior lobe develops as an outgrowth from the lower part of the brain. The two lobes eventually contact each other as they grow, and the anterior lobe partly wraps itself around the posterior lobe. In time, the anterior

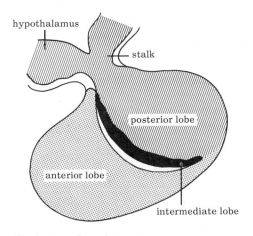

hypothalamus

stalk

posterior lobe

anterior lobe

intermediate lobe

Fig. 9.26. The pituitary gland.

lobe loses its original connection with the mouth, but the posterior lobe retains its stalk-like connection with a part of the brain called the *hypothalamus.* Despite their intimate spatial relationship, the two lobes remain fully distinct functionally, and we shall consider them separately here.

The Anterior Pituitary. The anterior pituitary (also called the adenohypophysis) is an immensely important organ that produces a number of different hormones of far-reaching effect. There are at least six of them, and more will probably be found.

One of these hormones, called lactogenic hormone or *prolactin,* stimulates milk production by the female mammary glands shortly after birth of a baby. In the absence of this hormone, milk secretion soon ceases.

Another of these hormones, *growth hormone* (also called somatotrophic hormone, STH), plays a critical role in the normal processes of growth. If the supply of this hormone is seriously deficient in a child, growth will be stunted and the child will be a midget. Oversupply of the hormone in a child results in a giant. (The tallest pituitary giant ever reported reached a height of 9 feet 5 inches.) Both pituitary midgets and pituitary giants have relatively normal body proportions, and their appearance is not unattractive. If, however, oversecretion of growth hormone begins during adult life, only certain bones, such as those of the face, fingers, and toes, can resume growth. The result is a condition known as acromegaly, characterized by disproportionately large hands and feet and distorted features—a greatly enlarged and protruding jaw, enlarged cheekbones and eyebrow ridges, and a thickened nose.

There is some evidence that growth hormone may also interact in some way with insulin and glucagon from the pancreas, and may thus play a role in diabetes. Under certain conditions, the pituitary seems to be involved in the onset of diabetes, but the role of pituitary hormones in this disease is poorly understood. It was formerly thought that a separate pituitary hormone (called diabetogenic hormone) played a critical role in diabetes, either by antagonizing the action of insulin and aiding glucagon or by directly affecting the secretion of these hormones by the pancreas. The evidence now indicates that no separate diabetogenic hormone exists and, furthermore, that the role of the pituitary in diabetes may be to a large extent indirect through its action in stimulating the adrenal cortex. There is evidence, however, that animals whose pituitary has been removed show a hypersensitivity to insulin that cannot be explained simply on the basis of hypofunction of other glands in the absence of pituitary hormones. The pituitary must also have some other role in carbohydrate metabolism, but what that role is only further research can determine.

One of the most important functions of the anterior pituitary is its secretion of hormones that exert controlling action on other endocrine organs. These hormones are *thyrotrophic hormone,* which stimulates the thyroid, *adrenocorticotrophic hormone* (frequently abbreviated ACTH), which stimulates the adrenal cortex, and at least two *gonadotrophic hormones* (follicle-stimulating hormone, abbreviated FSH, and leuteinizing hormone, abbreviated LH), which act on the gonads. Proper growth and development of these endocrine glands depend upon adequate secretion of the appropriate trophic hormone from the pituitary; if the pituitary is removed or becomes inactive, these organs atrophy and function at very low levels. It is easy to understand why the pituitary is often called the "master gland" of the endocrine system.

The interaction between the anterior pituitary and the other endocrine glands over which it exerts control is an example of feedback, a type of interaction very common in living systems. Thyrotrophic hormone, released by the pituitary when the concentration of thyroxin in the blood is low, stimulates increased production of thyroxin by the thyroid, but the resulting rise in concentration of thyroxin in the blood inhibits secretion of more thyrotrophic hormone by the pituitary. In other words, the pituitary responds to a low thyroxin level in the blood by sending a chemical messenger that stimulates increased activity by the thyroid. But once the thyroid becomes more active, the increased amount of thyroxin produced tells the pituitary that release of thyrotrophic hormone can now be reduced. There is thus a feedback of information from the thyroid to the pituitary. The pituitary exerts control over the thyroid, and the thyroid, in turn, exerts some control over the pituitary. Each sends chemical messengers to the other. But note that the message from the pituitary to the thyroid is a stimulating one, while the return message from the thyroid to the pituitary is an inhibiting one. The feedback is negative, as it is in most normally-functioning biological feedback systems (in many instances, positive feedback would lead to constant acceleration and runaway activity; such a process is, in fact, observable in some diseases). The pituitary tends to speed up the system, and the thyroid tends to slow it down. The interaction between the two opposing forces produces a delicately balanced system.

The interaction between the pituitary and the adrenal cortex or the gonads is similar to that outlined for the thyroid. The pituitary responds to low levels of cortical hormones by secreting more ACTH and to low levels of sex hormones by secreting more gonadotrophic hormone. The resulting rise in concentration of cortical hormones or of sex hormones inhibits further secretion by the pituitary.

But the delicately balanced feedback interaction between the pituitary and other endocrine glands clearly cannot be the whole control story. What other factors regulate the regulator? Suppose, for example, an animal faces a situation that puts it under stress and its adrenals release more cortisone. Or suppose it encounters an attractive potential mate and its gonads secrete more sex hormone. How did its perception of the stressful stimulus or of the sexual stimulus affect its endocrine glands? Its perception of the stimulus involved its nervous system, but there are no nervous connections to the anterior pituitary or to the endocrine cells in the adrenal cortex or the gonads. Somehow information must move from the nervous system to the endocrine system, but it cannot do so by way of nervous connections (except in the case of the posterior pituitary and the adrenal medulla, to be discussed later). Might the nervous system itself secrete chemical messengers that stimulate the endocrines? Most biologists believe that it does, and neurosecretory activity is currently an object of intensive research.

Let us return to our two hypothetical examples—an animal facing either stress or a mate (one might argue that the two are not very different, but that is a subject for some other book). In either situation, it turns out that the hypothalamus is one of the parts of the brain most involved. Now, the hypothalamus is located just above the pituitary. Perhaps this spatial relationship reflects a less obvious functional relationship. There is no direct physical connection between the hypothalamus and the anterior pituitary, but there is an unusual connection between their blood supplies. Arteries to the hypothalamus break up into capillaries, and these capillaries eventually join to form several veins leading away from the hypothalamus. But unlike most veins, these do not run directly into a larger branch of the venous system; instead, they pass downward into the anterior pituitary and there break up into a second capillary bed. We have encountered two other places in the body where the circulation depends on two beds of capillaries arranged in sequence—the kidney nephrons, where one bed forms the glomerulus and the other envelops the tubules, and the hepatic portal system, where one bed is in the wall of the intestine and the other is in

the liver. In both places, the special type of circulation reflects an important functional arrangement. In the hepatic portal system, for example, many substances picked up by the blood in the first capillary bed are removed from the blood in the second capillary bed. Might the portal system linking the hypothalamus and the anterior pituitary function in a similar fashion? Might the hypothalamus, when stimulated appropriately, release hormonelike substances into the blood, substances that, carried directly to the anterior pituitary, could stimulate it to greater activity? The answer seems to be yes, and the relationship between the body's two principal control systems—nervous and endocrine—thus becomes much easier to understand. It is apparently by sending such substances (often called neurohumors) to the anterior pituitary, the "master gland," that the nervous system can stimulate the endocrine system. Thus our hypothetical animal would detect a sexual object with his sense organs; a nervous impulse would be transmitted from the sense organs to the hypothalamus of the brain; the hypothalamus would release neurohumors into the blood; the neurohumors would stimulate the anterior pituitary to increase its secretion of gonadotrophic hormones; the gonadotrophic hormones would stimulate the gonads to secrete more sex hormone; and the sex hormones would help prepare the animal physiologically to react appropriately to the stimulus.

Notice that this model assigns an endocrine function to the nervous system; the nervous system is viewed as a source of hormones. The distinction between the two control systems thus becomes somewhat blurred. As we shall see in our discussion of the posterior pituitary below, and of the nervous system in the next chapter, there are many other reasons why no sharp distinction between the two systems can be made, and why it is reasonable to regard nervous and chemical control as aspects of the same coordinating system.

The Posterior Pituitary. Two hormones released by the posterior pituitary (also called neurohypophysis) were isolated, identified, and synthesized by Vincent du Vigneaud of the Cornell University Medical College in the early 1950's. This was the first time that polypeptide chains of specific amino acid sequence had been synthesized in the laboratory. Du Vigneaud received the Nobel Prize in 1955 for this pioneering work.

As Fig. 9.27 shows, these two hormones, called *oxytocin* and *vasopressin*,[3] are chemically very similar. Each contains eight amino acids (counting cystine as a single amino acid). Six of these occur in both compounds. Yet the two amino acids that are different cause the two hormones to have very different properties. Oxytocin acts mainly on the muscles of the uterus, causing them to contract. It is probably involved in childbirth. Vasopressin causes constriction of the arterioles, with a consequent marked rise in blood pressure. It also stimulates the kidney tubules to reabsorb

[3] Oxytocin and vasopressin are also known as pitocin and pitressin respectively. A mixture of the two is sometimes called pituitrin.

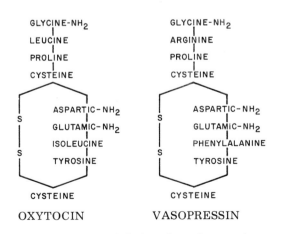

OXYTOCIN   VASOPRESSIN

Fig. 9.27. Structural formulas of oxytocin and vasopressin. (Cysteine is the name for half a unit of cystine.)

more water; this function, doubtless the more important under normal conditions, was once thought to be performed by a separate hormone, to which the name "antidiuretic hormone" was applied.

We said earlier that the posterior pituitary originates as an outgrowth of the hypothalamus of the brain. Even in the adult it retains a stalklike connection with the hypothalamus (Fig. 9.26). Nerves pass down this stalk from the hypothalamus to the posterior pituitary, and impulses traveling along these nerves control the release of oxytocin and vasopressin from the posterior pituitary. Is this a case where secretion of hormone by an endocrine gland is controlled by direct innervation? Not quite. There is now good evidence that the hormones do not originate in the posterior pituitary. Apparently oxytocin and vasopressin are produced in the hypothalamus and flow along the nerves to the posterior pituitary, where they are stored. The storage organ releases the hormones when stimulated to do so by nervous impulses from the hypothalamus. If water is withheld from an experimental animal until intense thirst develops, it can be shown by staining that the downward flow of hormone along the nerves becomes very pronounced. The increased osmotic concentration of the blood, resulting from desiccation, has apparently stimulated the hypothalamus to increase its secretion of vasopressin, which can then stimulate the kidneys to conserve water by increasing reabsorption. Cutting the stalk between the hypothalamus and the posterior pituitary results in an accumulation of dark-staining material (presumably the hormone) at the cut end of the stalk, and stops release of the hormone by the posterior pituitary. It seems clear, then, that the hypothalamus, not the posterior pituitary, is the true endocrine organ in this case. Once again a rigid distinction between nervous system and endocrine system becomes meaningless. Secretion of hormones is a function of some nervous tissue.

Hormonal Control of Vertebrate Reproduction

Reproduction is the central theme of life. All the other aspects of living discussed in this book—nutrient procurement, gas exchange, internal transport, waste excretion, osmoregulation, growth, hormonal and nervous control, and behavior—can be viewed, in a sense, as processes that enable organisms to survive to reproduce. It has been said that "the hen is the egg's way of producing another egg," and the idea is equally applicable to man; we are, in a way, elaborate devices for producing eggs and sperms, for bringing them together in the process of fertilization, and for giving birth to young. We shall not attempt here to discuss all aspects of animal reproduction; such fundamental topics as genetics, differentiation, and growth will be the subjects of later chapters. This section will be concerned only with the physiology of vertebrate (particularly mammalian) reproduction as an example of the complex interplay between a variety of different control mechanisms.

The Process of Sexual Reproduction. Sexual reproduction in higher animals always involves the union of two parental cells, an egg and a sperm. Occasionally both of the uniting *gametes* are produced by the same individual. Such a process, known as self-fertilization, is most common among internal parasites such as tapeworms, whose chances of locating another individual for cross-fertilization are often poor. However, most animals utilize cross-fertilization, even when, as in earthworms, each individual is hermaphroditic (i.e. possesses both male and female sexual organs). Sexual reproduction among vertebrates always involves cross-fertilization, and it will be exclusively with this type of reproduction that we shall be concerned here.

Sexual reproduction, as we have said, depends upon the bringing together of an egg cell and a sperm cell, which then unite in the process of fertilization to form the first cell of the new individual. There are two basic ways in which egg cells and sperm cells are brought together: external fertilization, where both types of gametes are shed into the surrounding medium and the sperm cells swim or are carried by water currents to the egg cells; and internal fertilization, where the egg cells are retained within the reproductive tract of the female until after they have been fertilized by sperms inserted into the female by the male.

External fertilization is limited essentially to animals living in aquatic environments, because the flagellated sperm cells must have fluid in which to swim and the egg cells, in the absence of a protective coat or shell, which would prevent the sperms from penetrating and fertilizing them, would become desiccated on land. Almost all aquatic invertebrates, most fishes (but not sharks), and many amphibians utilize external fertilization. As you would expect, shedding eggs and sperms into the water of a lake or stream is an uncertain method of fertilization; many of the sperms never locate an egg and many eggs are never fertilized, even if both types of gametes are shed at the same time and in the same place, as is usually the case. Consequently animals utilizing external fertilization generally release vast numbers of eggs and sperms at one time. And they often go through elaborate behavioral sequences (in which hormonal control is very important) that ensure concurrence in both time and space in the release of gametes by the two sexes.

Most land animals, both invertebrate and vertebrate, utilize internal fertilization. In effect, the sperm cells are provided with the sort of fluid environment that is no longer available to them outside the animals' bodies. Thus the sperms remain aquatic and swim through the film of fluid always present on the walls of the female reproductive tract. Once fertilized, the egg is either enclosed in a protective shell and released by the female or held within the female's body until the embryonic stages of development have been completed. Internal fertilization requires, of course, very close physiological and behavioral synchronization of the sexes, and this synchronization involves extensive hormonal control. Internal fertilization has usually also involved the evolution of accessory sex organs used in transferring sperms from the body of the male to that of the female in the process of copulation.

Let us summarize briefly the characteristic reproductive methods employed by the major classes of vertebrates. Fish, being aquatic, almost always utilize external fertilization and thus, of course, lay eggs with no shell. Although they usually go through elaborate behavioral rituals that help synchronize the release of gametes, huge numbers of eggs and sperms are released at each mating and the wastage of gametes is enormous. Amphibians (frogs, salamanders, etc.) evolved from fish, and they too generally utilize external fertilization; they must therefore return to the water or to a very moist place on land to lay their eggs. Some salamanders have evolved a behavioral sequence in which the male releases a membranous packet containing sperms that the female picks up with her cloaca. These amphibians have thus evolved a primitive type of internal fertilization, and some of them can mate on land, but their eggs must still be laid in very moist places.

The reptiles, modern representatives of which are snakes, lizards, and turtles, evolved from ancestral amphibians. They were the first vertebrates to be fully emancipated from the ancestral dependence on the aquatic environment for reproduction. As would be expected, they utilize internal fertilization, and they lay eggs enclosed in tough membranes and shells. Since internal fertilization entails much less wastage of eggs than external fertilization, only a few egg cells are released during each reproductive season. Birds evolved from one group of ancient reptiles, and they too employ internal fertilization and lay eggs with shells.

The eggs of land vertebrates such as reptiles and birds have four different membranes in addition to the shell. These are the *amnion*, the *allantois*, the *yolk sac*, and the *chorion* (Fig. 9.28). The embryo lies in a fluid-filled chamber enclosed by the amnion; evolution of the amnion has thus made it possible for the embryo to develop in an aquatic medium even though the egg as a whole may be laid on dry land. The allantois functions as a receptacle for the urinary wastes of the developing embryo, and its blood vessels, which lie near the shell, function in gas exchange. The yolk sac, as its name indicates, encloses the yolk, which is food material used by the developing embryo. The chorion is an outer membrane surrounding the embryo and the other membranes.

Mammals evolved from reptiles, but not from the same reptiles that gave rise to birds. Like reptiles and birds, mammals utilize internal fertilization, but (with a few rare exceptions) no shell is deposited around the fertilized egg and it is not laid. Instead, the early embryo with its membranes becomes implanted in a specialized chamber of the female genital tract, and there embryonic development is completed. The young animal is then born alive. The remainder of our discussion here will be concerned with mammalian reproduction.

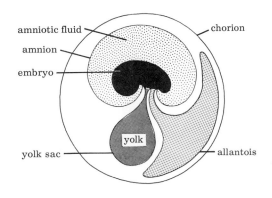

Fig. 9.28. The embryonic membranes in a bird's egg.

The Genital System of the Human Male.
Before discussing the hormonal control of
human reproduction, let us look quickly at
the structure of the genital system.

The male gonads are the *testes*, which are
oval-shaped glandular organs that form in the
dorsal portion of the abdominal cavity from
the same embryonic tissue that gives rise to
the ovaries in females. In the human male, the
testes descend about the time of birth from
their points of origin into the *scrotal sac*, which
is a pouch whose cavity is initially continuous
with the abdominal cavity via a passageway
called the *inguinal canal*. After the testes have
descended through the inguinal canal into the
scrotum, the canal is slowly plugged by
growth of connective tissue, so that the scrotal
and abdominal cavities are no longer continuous. Sometimes the inguinal canal fails to
close properly. And even when it does close,
it remains a point of weakness and is easily
broken open again when subjected to excessive strain, as when a man lifts a heavy object.
The opening resulting from insufficient closure
or from later rupture is known as an inguinal
hernia; it is the most common type of hernia
in human males. If the hernia is large, it must
be repaired surgically to prevent a loop of the
intestine from slipping through the opening
into the scrotal sac, where the intestine may
become caught so tightly that its blood supply
is cut off and gangrene results. Inguinal hernia
is largely a human hazard attributable to two-
legged stance, which places much strain on the
lower abdomen; such hernias are very in-
frequent in mammals that walk on four legs.

Each testis is composed of two different
functional components: the *seminiferous tubules,* in which the sperm cells are produced,
and the *interstitial cells,* which secrete male
sex hormone. The seminiferous tubules of the
human are not functional at temperatures as
high as that characteristic of the abdominal
cavity; if the testes fail to descend, the
germinal epithelium of the tubules eventually
degenerates. If, however, the testes descend

normally into the scrotal sac, where the temperature is approximately three degrees cooler,
the germinal epithelium of the seminiferous
tubules becomes functional at the time of
puberty. Mature sperm cells pass from the
seminiferous tubules via many tiny ducts into
a much-coiled tube, the *epididymis*, which
lies on the surface of the testis (Fig. 9.29).
The sperms are stored in the epididymis until
they are released during copulation.

A long sperm duct, or *vas deferens*, runs
from each epididymis through the inguinal
canal and into the abdominal cavity, where it
loops over the bladder and joins with the *urethra* just beyond the point where the urethra
arises from the bladder. The urethra, in turn,
passes through the *penis* and empties to the
outside. Notice, then, that the urethra in the
mammalian male is a common passageway
used by both the excretory and reproductive
systems; urine passes through it during excretion and semen passes through it during sexual
activity. In more primitive vertebrates, the
relationship between the excretory and reproductive systems is even closer. In frogs, for

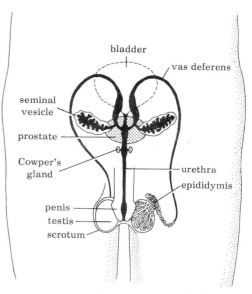

Fig. 9.29. Reproductive system of the human
male.

example, sperm cells pass from the testes into the kidneys and down the excretory ducts to the cloaca; the reproductive system has no separate vasa deferentia. In the vertebrates, there has been an evolutionary trend toward increasing liberation of the reproductive system from its ancestral dependence on the excretory system. There is far more separation in mammalian males than in fish or frogs, but the two systems still share the urethra and thus do not have separate openings to the outside. As we shall see, only in mammalian females has complete separation arisen.

As sperms pass through the vasa deferentia and urethra, seminal fluid is added to them to form *semen,* which is a mixture of seminal fluid and sperm cells. The seminal fluid is secreted by three sets of glands: (1) the *seminal vesicles,* which empty into the vasa deferentia just before these join with the urethra; (2) the *prostate,* which empties into the urethra near its junction with the vasa deferentia; and (3) the *Cowper's glands,* which empty into the urethra at the base of the penis (Fig. 9.29). Seminal fluid has a variety of functions: It serves as a vehicle for transport of sperms; it lubricates the passages through which the sperms must travel; as an effectively buffered fluid, it helps protect the sperms from the harmful effects of the acids in the female genital tract; and it contains much sugar (mostly fructose), which the active sperms can use as a source of energy. The tiny sperm cells can store very little food themselves and hence depend on an external source of nutrients for use in the cellular respiration that provides them with the ATP necessary to keep their flagella active. The base of a sperm flagellum is an amazing power plant, packed with mitochondria, in which energy can be extracted from the sugar absorbed from the seminal fluid.

During sexual excitement, the arteries leading into the penis dilate and the veins from the penis constrict in response to stimulation by nerves of the autonomic system. Much blood is pumped under considerable pressure through the arteries into the spaces in the spongy erectile tissue of which the penis is largely composed. The engorgement of the penis by blood under high arterial pressure causes the penis to increase greatly in size and to become hard and erect, thus preparing it for insertion into the female vagina during copulation. Note that erection of the penis does not involve activity of skeletal muscles but is entirely a vasomotor phenomenon.

When the penis is sufficiently stimulated by friction during copulation, nervous reflexes involving pathways of the sympathetic system cause waves of contraction in the smooth muscles of the walls of the epididymides, vasa deferentia, seminal glands, and urethra. These contractions move sperms from the epididymides down the vasa deferentia, combine seminal fluid from the various glands with the sperms, and expel the semen from the urethra. An average of about 100 million sperm cells in about 3.5 ml. of semen are released during one ejaculation by a human male.

Hormonal Control of Sexual Development in the Male. No sperms and very little male sex hormone are produced by the testes before puberty. The onset of puberty is apparently triggered by increased release of gonadotrophic hormones by the anterior pituitary, and this activity of the pituitary is itself stimulated by chemicals secreted by the hypothalamus and carried to the pituitary by blood in the portal system that links these two organs. As we have seen, two different gonadotrophic hormones are secreted by the anterior pituitary: *FSH,* which stimulates maturation of the seminiferous tubules, and *LH,* which stimulates maturation of the interstitial cells and induces them to begin secretion of the male sex hormone, *testosterone* (Fig. 9.34).

Once testosterone appears in appreciable quantity in the system, it stimulates the complex of changes in the secondary sexual characteristics normally associated with puberty; growth of the beard, growth of pubic hair, deepening of the voice, maturation of the seminal vesicles and the prostate gland, development of larger and stronger muscles, etc. If the testes are removed (castration) before puberty, these changes in the secondary sexual characteristics never occur. If castration is performed after puberty, there is some retrogression of the adult sexual characteristics, but they do not disappear entirely. Castration after puberty abolishes the sex urge in many animals, but not in man, where psychological factors are of much greater importance than in other animals.

The Genital System of the Human Female. The female gonads are the *ovaries,* which are located in the lower part of the abdominal cavity, where they are held in place by large ligaments. Like the testes, the ovaries have the two main functions of producing gametes (in this case, egg cells) and secreting sex hormones. At the time of birth, a girl's ovaries already contain a huge number of primordial egg cells, estimates of which range from 100,000 to 1,000,000. Since, during the approximately 30 years of her reproductive life, a woman ovulates about 13 times per year, producing one mature egg cell, or ovum, each time, it follows that only about 390 primordial egg cells ever mature and leave the ovaries. The rest eventually degenerate, and none can be found in the ovaries of women past about the age of 50.

Each primordial egg cell is enclosed within a cellular jacket called a *follicle.* The egg cell fills most of the space in the small immature follicle. In the process of maturation, however, the follicle grows bigger relative to the egg cell and develops a large cavity filled with a granular fluid (Fig. 9.30); the egg cell, embedded in a mass of follicular epithelial cells, protrudes into the cavity. A ripe follicle bulges from the surface of the ovary; when ovulation occurs, its outer wall ruptures and both the liquid and the detached mature ovum

are expelled. In the human, only one ovum is normally released at each ovulation. There is no apparent regularity as to which ovary will ovulate at any given period.

A ripe egg is released from the ovary into the abdominal cavity. From there, it is usually promptly drawn into the large funnel-shaped end of one of the *oviducts* (or Fallopian tubes), which partly surround the ovaries but are not continuous with them (Fig. 9.31). Cilia lining the funnel of the oviduct produce currents that help move the egg into the oviduct. If sperms are present, the egg is fertilized while it is still in the upper third of the oviduct (Fig. 9.32).

Each oviduct empties directly into the upper end of the *uterus* (or womb). This organ, which is about the size of a fist, lies in the lower portion of the abdominal cavity just behind the bladder. It has very thick muscular walls and a mucous lining containing many blood vessels. If an egg is fertilized as it moves down the oviduct, it becomes implanted in the wall of the uterus, and there the embryo develops until time of birth. A method of birth control under extensive investigation at present involves insertion of a plastic ring or spiral into the uterus. Such intra-uterine rings seem to be very effective in preventing pregnancy, but it is not yet clear whether they do so by interfering with fertilization of the egg or by preventing implantation in the uterus.

At its lower end, the uterus connects with a muscular tube, the *vagina,* which leads to the outside. The vagina acts as the receptacle for the male penis during copulation. The great elasticity of its walls makes possible not only the reception of the penis but the passage of the baby during childbirth.

The uterus and vagina do not lie in a straight line, as Fig. 9.31 might seem to indicate. Instead, the uterus projects forward nearly at a right angle to the vagina, as shown in Fig. 9.32. The *cervix,* a muscular ring of tissue at the mouth of the uterus, protrudes into the vagina. The cervix is often torn during

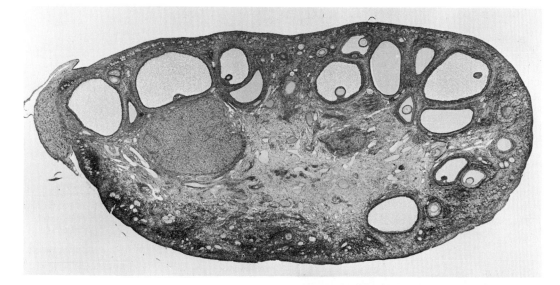

Fig. 9.30. Photographs of sections of cat ovary. Top: Follicles of different sizes are shown in a section of the entire ovary. The more mature follicles have a large cavity, with the egg cell embedded in a pedestal of epithelial cells that projects into the cavity. Bottom: Enlarged view of a nearly mature follicle with its egg cell. [Courtesy Thomas Eisner, Cornell University.]

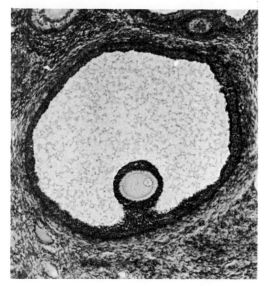

childbirth, and the scar tissue that results frequently acts as a focal point for development of cervical cancer, one of the most common types of cancer in women. Most modern obstetricians urge repair of the damage to the cervix during the year following childbirth and an examination each year thereafter; this procedure can greatly reduce the danger of cancer.

Devices that block the mouth of the uterus by covering the cervix are widely used in birth control. One such device, the diaphragm, is a shallow rubber cup with a spring around its rim. It is inserted into the vagina and positioned so that it covers the entire cervical region. It is very effective in preventing sperms from entering the uterus, particularly if it is used in conjunction with spermicidal jellies or creams.

The opening of the vagina in young human females is partly closed by a thin membrane called the **hymen**. Traditionally, the hymen has been regarded as the symbol of virginity, to be destroyed the first time sexual intercourse takes place. Frequently, however, the membrane is ruptured during childhood, by disease or by a fall or as a result of strenuous physical exercise. If it has escaped such damage, many physicians urge that it be destroyed surgically

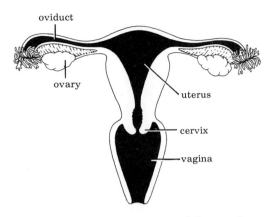

Fig. 9.31. Reproductive tract of human female, anterior view.

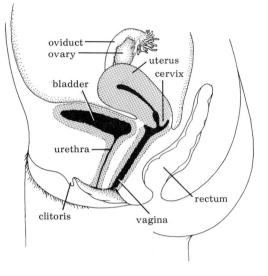

Fig. 9.32. Reproductive tract of human female, lateral view.

at the time of the premarital physical examination in order to avoid the risk of infection or of excessive pain or bleeding on the wedding night.

The external female genitalia are collectively termed the *vulva.* The vulvar region is bounded by two folds of skin that enclose the vestibule. The vagina opens into the rear portion of the vestibule, and the urethra opens into the mid-portion of the vestibule. Note, then, that in the adult mammalian female there is no interconnection between the excretory and reproductive systems, and that the urethra carries only excretory materials. During embryonic development, the vagina does open into the urethra, but as development proceeds, the junction moves posteriorly until the vagina acquires its own opening to the exterior and the old interconnection disappears.

In the anterior portion of the vestibule, in front of the opening of the urethra, is a small erectile organ, the *clitoris,* which forms from the same embryonic tissue that gives rise to the penis in the male. Like the penis, it becomes engorged with blood during sexual excitement and is a major site of stimulation during copulation.

Hormonal Control of the Female Reproductive Cycle. As in the male, puberty in the fe-

male begins when the hypothalamus stimulates the anterior pituitary to release increased amounts of FSH and LH. These gonadotrophic hormones cause maturation of the ovaries, which then begin secreting the female sex hormones, *estrogen* and *progesterone.* The sex hormones, particularly estrogen, stimulate development of the female secondary sexual characteristics: growth of pubic hair, broadening of the pelvis, development of the breasts, increase in the size of the uterus and vagina, some change in voice quality, and the onset of *menstrual cycles.* We shall be particularly concerned here with the menstrual cycles as an example of the complex interplay between several hormones and between the endocrine and nervous systems.

Rhythmic variations in the secretion of gonadotrophic hormones in the females of most species of mammals lead to what are known as *estrous cycles*—rhythmic variations in the condition of the reproductive tract and in the sex urge. The females of most species will accept the male in copulation only during those brief periods of the cycle near the time of ovulation when the uterine lining is thickest and the sex urge is at its height. During such periods, the female is said to be "in heat" or in estrus. Many mammals have only one or a few estrous periods each year, but some, like rats, mice, and their relatives, may have them as often as every five days. If fertilization does not occur during the heat period, the thickened lining of the uterus is gradually reabsorbed by the female's body; ordinarily, no bleeding is associated with this process.

The reproductive cycle in humans and other higher primates differs in several important ways from that of other mammals. There is not so pronounced a heat period, the female being to some degree receptive to the male during most parts of the cycle. And the thickened lining of the uterus is not completely reabsorbed if no fertilization occurs; instead, part of the lining is sloughed off during a period of bleeding known as menstruation. Human menstrual cycles average about 28 days; so there are approximately 13 of them each year. This is an extremely rough average, however, extensive variation occurring from

person to person and from period to period in the same person.

Let us trace the sequence of events in the menstrual cycle. It is customary in medical practice to consider the first day of menstruation as the first one of the cycle. From a biological point of view, however, it is more appropriate to regard the end of the period of bleeding as the beginning of the cycle. At this point, the uterine lining is thin and there are no ripe follicles in the ovaries. The first event in the new cycle is an increase in secretion of FSH by the anterior pituitary as a result of stimulation by the hypothalamus (Fig. 9.33). FSH (the initials, you will recall, stand for follicle-stimulating hormone) stimulates growth of follicles in the ovaries. One of the follicles soon gains ascendancy, and the other follicles cease growing. If there is also a small amount of LH in the system to act synergistically with the FSH, the growing follicles begin secreting the first of the two female sex hormones, estrogen. The estrogen, in turn, stimulates the lining of the uterus to thicken. This follicular or

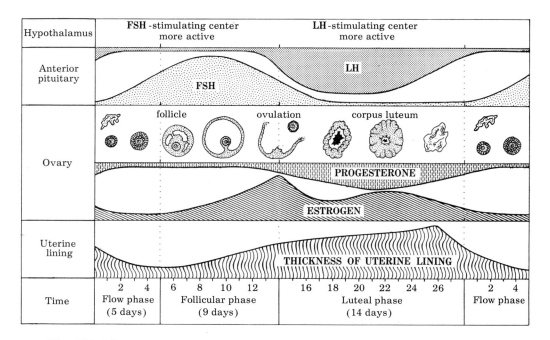

Fig. 9.33. The sequence of events in the human menstrual cycle. See text for description.

growth phase of the cycle lasts, on the average, about nine to ten days after cessation of the previous menstrual flow.

As the follicles grow under the influence of FSH from the pituitary, they produce more and more estrogen. This increase in the level of estrogen in the blood exerts an inhibitory effect on the FSH-stimulating center in the hypothalamus, the result of which is a drop in the secretion of FSH by the anterior pituitary. Here we have an example of the principle of negative feedback discussed earlier. But the increasing concentration of estrogen in the blood apparently stimulates the LH-stimulating center in the hypothalamus, with the result that, as the secretion of FSH by the pituitary declines, secretion of LH by the pituitary rises. When the concentration of LH in the system has reached a critical level, the ascendant follicle—by this time mature and bulging from the surface of the ovary—ovulates. The mechanism of ovulation is unknown. It is frequently stated that the pressure of the follicular fluid causes the wall to burst, but there is much evidence that, on the contrary, this pressure may actually decline slightly just before ovulation. Ovulation marks the end of the follicular or growth phase of the menstrual cycle.

Following ovulation, LH (leuteinizing hormone) induces changes in the follicular cells converting the old follicle into a yellowish mass of cells rich in blood vessels. This new structure formed from the ruptured follicle under the influence of LH is called the *corpus luteum* (Latin, for yellow body). The corpus luteum continues secreting estrogen, though not as much as was secreted by the follicle just prior to ovulation. But the corpus luteum also secretes a second female sex hormone, *progesterone* (Fig. 9.34), often called the luteal hormone.[4]

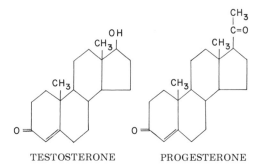

Fig. 9.34. **The structural formulas of male sex hormone (testosterone) and female sex hormone (progesterone).** Differing in only one side group, these two steroids have amazingly different effects on the body.

Progesterone functions in preparing the uterus to receive the embryo. Acting on the uterine lining, which has already become much thicker under the stimulation of estrogen during the follicular phase, it causes maturation of the complex system of glands in the lining. The luteal phase of the menstrual cycle is, in fact, sometimes called the secretory phase, though this name is a little misleading, since there is also some glandular activity in the uterine lining during the latter part of the follicular phase. Repeated experiments have shown that implantation of a fertilized ovum in the uterus cannot occur in the absence of the changes in the uterine lining produced by

---

[4] There is evidence that in rats LH is responsible for the conversion of the follicle into the corpus luteum, but that a third pituitary gonadotrophin is necessary for maintenance of the corpus luteum in

secretory condition once it is formed. This leuteotrophic gonadotrophin has been identified as prolactin, a hormone involved in stimulation of milk secretion by the breasts following parturition. Repeated efforts to show that prolactin is necessary for maintenance of active corpora lutea in other mammals (including guinea pigs, rabbits, sheep, goats, pigs, and monkeys) have, however, been unsuccessful. Furthermore, in 1964 D. T. Armstrong, at Harvard University, and his associates showed that only LH was necessary to induce secretion of progesterone by cow luteal tissue in tissue cultures, and about the same time William Hansel and his associates at Cornell University showed that LH alone induces progesterone secretion in the living cow. Though the matter is far from settled, the current evidence seems to support the view that in most mammals (probably including human beings) FSH and LH are the only important gonadotrophic hormones, and that LH not only controls ovulation and the conversion of the old follicle into the corpus luteum but also stimulates the corpus luteum to secrete progesterone.

progesterone. Progesterone is, in a very real sense, the hormone of pregnancy.

In addition, progesterone inhibits the FSH-stimulating center in the hypothalamus, and thus prevents a rise in FSH secretion by the pituitary, which would trigger the start of a new cycle. Consequently, as long as progesterone is present in quantity in the system, there is little follicular growth. This FSH-inhibiting effect of progesterone is, of course, an important element in regulating the duration of the menstrual cycle. It is also the basis for the action of birth-control pills. These pills contain synthetic compounds similar to progesterone and estrogen. Taken daily, they inhibit secretion of FSH (and LH) and thus prevent follicular growth and ovulation and, consequently, conception.

If no fertilization occurs during a normal cycle, the continued high levels of progesterone begin to exert negative feedback action on the LH-stimulating center in the hypothalamus, with the result that secretion of LH by the pituitary falls. But LH is necessary for maintenance of the functioning corpus luteum. Hence, when the level of LH in the system has fallen appreciably, the corpus luteum begins to atrophy and ceases secreting progesterone.[5] When this happens, the thickened lining of the uterus can no longer be maintained, and reabsorption of part of the lining begins. Unlike most mammals, humans and other higher primates cannot reabsorb all the extra tissue laid down during the follicular and luteal phases of the cycle; part of it must be sloughed off during the flow phase, which lasts about four or five days. Absence of sex hormone, resulting from atrophy of the corpus luteum, frees the FSH-stimulating center in the hypothalamus from inhibition and allows it to stimulate the pituitary to increase secretion of FSH, which triggers the follicular growth

marking the beginning of a new cycle. The sequence of events in a normal menstrual cycle is depicted diagrammatically in Fig. 9.33. The hormonal interactions are shown in Fig. 9.35.

During the flow phase, particularly its first few days, the old corpus luteum has ceased secreting estrogen and progesterone and the follicles of the new cycle have not yet begun secreting significant amounts of estrogen. As a result, the woman's body must function temporarily in the absence of female sex hormone. But since the time of puberty, her body has been accustomed to functioning most of the time in the presence of sex hormone, and when those hormones are withdrawn at the end of the luteal phase of each menstrual cycle, there are frequently symptoms of physiological and psychological disturbance, including irritability, depression, and sometimes nausea. In addition, strong contractions of the uterus often cause abdominal cramps.

Emotional stress sometimes also accompanies the *menopause,* a period lasting a year or two at the end of a woman's reproductive life. The menopause usually comes between the ages of 45 and 50. It is apparently attributable both to cessation of secretion of LH by the pituitary as a result of declining activity of the LH-stimulating center in the hypothalamus, and to declining sensitivity of the ovaries to the stimulatory activity of gonadotrophins. In the absence of LH, secretory activity in the ovaries falls off; neither estrogen nor progesterone can be produced in significant quantities. Consequently, no cyclic thickening of the uterine lining occurs, and hence no menstruation. Since the cells and tissues of the woman's body have been accustomed to the presence of female sex hormone for about 30 years, the withdrawal of those hormones during menopause may cause physiological and psychological disturbances until a new physiological balance has been established.

We have seen that ovulation in human beings occurs roughly midway in the menstrual

---

[5] Some workers have suggested that the uterus may secrete a substance that contributes to the atrophy of the corpus luteum, but the evidence on this point is still inconclusive.

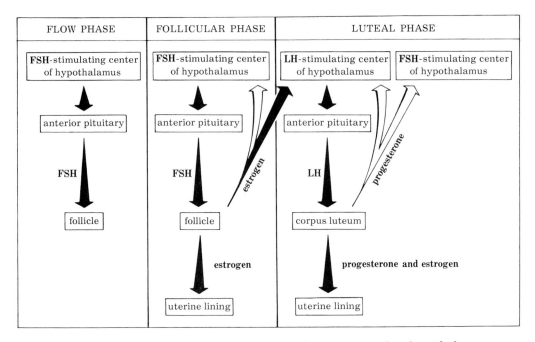

Fig. 9.35. Diagram of hormonal interactions during human menstrual cycle. Black arrows indicate stimulation and white arrows inhibition.

cycle. This ovulation is spontaneous; it does not depend upon a copulatory stimulus. In some mammals, like rabbits and cats, however, ovulation is reflex-controlled; the nervous stimulation of copulation is necessary for the hypothalamus to trigger the release of LH by the pituitary that will lead to ovulation. In such reflex ovulators, it is possible to predict with great precision just when ovulation will occur; in the rabbit, for example, it occurs about 10½ hours after copulation. Such precision is not possible with spontaneous ovulators like humans. Yet predictions of the time of ovulation are important in the practice of the so-called rhythm method of birth control.

The rhythm method is based on the premise that fertilization can take place only during a very short period in each menstrual cycle. Copulation without risk of pregnancy should be possible during all other parts of the cycle. Present evidence indicates that human egg cells begin to deteriorate about 12 hours (maximum 24 hours) after ovulation and can no

longer be fertilized after that time. In other words, fertilization can occur only if fertile sperms are in the upper third of the oviduct during the 12 to 24 hours immediately following ovulation; conception is not possible during the other 27 days of a 28-day cycle. Immediately, the question of the fertile life of sperms in the female reproductive tract becomes pertinent. We have said that one ejaculation releases about 100 million sperm cells into the vagina. Conditions in the vagina are very inhospitable to sperms, and vast numbers of sperm cells are killed before they have a chance to pass the cervix. Millions of others die or become infertile in the uterus and oviducts, and millions more go up the wrong oviduct or never find their way into an oviduct at all. The journey to the upper portion of the oviducts is an extremely long and hazardous one for so tiny an object as a sperm cell. There is good evidence that movement of sperms from the vagina to the upper portion of the oviduct does not depend solely on the sperm's own swimming motions; movements of the female genital tract may actually carry the sperms part of the way to their destination. Current evidence indicates that, in the female genital tract, human sperm cells remain fertile only about 48 hours or less after their release. The time may be much longer in some other animals. William A. Wimsatt of Cornell University has shown that some bats mate in the fall but do not ovulate until after hibernation in the spring; the sperms must therefore remain fertile for several months. And in some invertebrates, such as bees and ants, fertile sperms may actually be stored in the body of the female for years, so that one mating suffices to provide a queen honeybee with enough sperms to last her throughout her reproductive life, during which time she produces thousands of offspring.

Since the fertile life of the egg cell lasts at most one day and that of the sperm cell at most two days, there is a period of about three days during which copulation can result in conception (the day when the egg is fertile and the two preceding days). But which three days? It is our inability to answer this question precisely that makes the rhythm method of birth control unreliable. We know that the three days come about midway through the menstrual cycle, but we cannot accurately predict how long a given cycle will be and therefore cannot determine its midpoint. Many women have very irregular cycles that vary by as much as 8–15 days or more. Even women whose cycles are very regular will have some that vary by as much as four or five days during the course of a year. Sickness or emotional upset frequently delays ovulation and prolongs the cycle by altering the hypothalamic control of LH secretion. There is good evidence that the least variable part of the cycle is the luteal phase, the interval between ovulation and the onset of the next menstrual flow. This phase apparently averages between 14 and 15 days, and when a cycle is unusually short or long, it is primarily the duration of the follicular phase

that has changed. But the fact that the duration of the luteal phase is relatively stable is of little help in predicting the day of ovulation; we have no way of knowing beforehand when the next menstrual flow will begin, and therefore cannot count back 14 or 15 days to determine the ovulation date.

Hormonal Control of Pregnancy. Our discussion so far has assumed that conception did not occur and that each cycle was terminated by a menstrual flow. Let us now assume that the egg cell is fertilized at some time during the 12 hours after ovulation. Only one of the millions of sperm cells released into the vagina actually penetrates the egg cell and fertilizes it. As soon as that one cell has fertilized the egg, the outer membrane of the egg changes in consistency and becomes impenetrable to the other sperm cells, which soon die. The fertilized egg, or *zygote,* moves down the oviduct, probably carried by fluid whose movement is caused by contractions of the circular muscles in the walls of the oviduct. The rate of movement is partly controlled by estrogen. During the days of transit, cell divisions begin and an embryo is formed.

The human embryo becomes implanted in the wall of the uterus 8–10 days after fertilization. During the interval between fertilization and implantation, the embryo is nourished by its limited supply of yolk and by materials secreted by the glands of the female genital tract. The delay before implantation varies from species to species; e.g. it is about 20–22 days in sheep, 35 days in cows, and as long as 56 days in horses. In a few species, there is a much longer delay, during which development of the embryo proceeds very slowly or even ceases; among mammals with delayed implantation are brown bears (about five months), pine martens (six months), American badgers (two months), and armadillos (14 weeks).

After implantation in the uterine lining, the embryonic membranes form the *umbilical cord,* through which blood vessels contributed by the allantois run to a large structure, the *placenta,* formed from the embryonic membranes (primarily the chorion) and from the adjacent uterine tissue (Fig. 9.36). Within the placenta, the blood vessels of the embryo and those of the mother lie very close together, but they are not joined and there is no mixing of maternal and fetal blood. Exchange of materials takes place in the placenta by diffusion between the blood of the mother and that of the embryo; nutritive substances and oxygen move from the mother to the embryo, and urinary wastes and carbon dioxide move from the embryo to the mother.

We saw earlier that progesterone is essential for maintenance of the uterine lining during implantation and pregnancy. But we saw also that in a normal menstrual cycle the high level of progesterone exerts negative feedback action on the hypothalamus, with a consequent decrease in LH secretion by the pituitary and eventual atrophy of the corpus luteum. The atrophy of the corpus luteum cuts off the supply of progesterone, with the result that menstruation occurs. Clearly this sequence of events cannot take place after conception, or the uterine lining with the implanted embryo would be sloughed off and lost. It can be shown that when conception occurs, the corpus

luteum does not atrophy but lasts through most of the term of pregnancy. How can we explain this? Apparently the chorionic portion of the placenta secretes a hormone very similar to LH. This gonadotrophin takes the place of LH from the pituitary and preserves the corpus luteum, which continues to secrete progesterone and thus sustains the pregnancy.

So much chorionic gonadotrophin is produced in a pregnant woman that much of it is excreted in the urine. Many commonly used tests for pregnancy are based on this phenomenon. Urine from the subject is injected into a test animal such as a rat, rabbit, or frog. If chorionic gonadotrophin is in the urine, it induces development of corpora lutea and changes in the vagina of female rats 72 to 96 hours after injection. The rabbit test is faster; pregnancy urine induces corpora lutea formation within 24 hours after injection. And frog tests are even faster; pregnancy urine induces ovulation by females and release of sperms by males within 6–8 hours after injection.

Although the corpus luteum is essential during early pregnancy, it can be shown that in humans it is no longer necessary after about the first two months. Removal of the ovaries after this time does not terminate the pregnancy, evidently because both estrogen and progesterone, which can still be detected in the urine after excision of the ovaries, are produced by another organ. Apparently, the placenta begins to secrete these hormones early in pregnancy, and once this secretion has reached a sufficiently high level the placenta itself can maintain the pregnancy in the absence of progesterone from the corpus luteum. This is not true of the rabbit, where removal of the ovaries just a few days before the end of pregnancy invariably results in abortion unless progesterone is artificially administered.

Hormonal Control of Parturition and Lactation. Much research is needed to clarify the complex interactions of hormones that control the birth process (parturition). Current theory

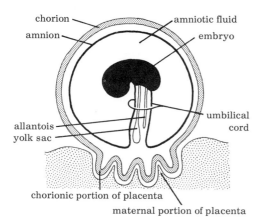

Fig. 9.36. Diagram of human embryonic membranes and placenta.

holds that one important factor in parturition is a shift in the balance of estrogen and progesterone. It is known that estrogen stimulates contractions of the uterine muscles and that progesterone severely inhibits muscular contraction. It is also known that secretion of estrogen by the placenta rises sharply just prior to parturition. It seems reasonable to assume, therefore, that during most of pregnancy progesterone blocks contraction of the uterine muscles, but that the rise of estrogen concentration late in pregnancy overcomes this progesterone block and stimulates the onset of the contractions that eventually expel the fetus from the uterus. Since oxytocin, secreted by the posterior pituitary (and perhaps also by the placenta), is known to have a powerful stimulatory effect on uterine contractility, it seems likely that this hormone acts in conjunction with estrogen in inducing labor.

Another hormone important in parturition is *relaxin,* which is secreted during pregnancy by the ovaries and the placenta. This hormone loosens the connections between the bones of the pelvis, thereby enlarging the birth canal and facilitating parturition. Relaxin may also aid in dilation of the cervix. The activity of relaxin is enhanced by estrogens.

Like the hormonal control of parturition, that of milk secretion is complicated and not completely understood. Growth and development of the mammary glands seem to be controlled by a complex interaction between estrogen, progesterone, growth hormone, prolactin, and some of the adrenocorticosteroids. Initiation and maintenance of lactation by mature mammary glands following parturition seem to be controlled primarily by prolactin and growth hormone; the process may be aided by ACTH and thyrotrophic hormone. These hormones apparently become effective in inducing lactation when the high levels of sex hormones, which inhibit lactation, disappear at the time of parturition.

The actual release of milk from the mammary glands involves both neural and hormonal mechanisms. The stimulus of suckling, or, in conditioned cows, of seeing the calf or hearing rattling milk pails, causes nervous stimulation of that part of the hypothalamus that secretes the oxytocin stored in the posterior pituitary. This stimulation induces increased release of oxytocin, which in turn induces constriction of the many tiny chambers in which the milk is stored in the mammary glands. The constriction forces the milk into ducts that lead to the nipple. Adrenalin inhibits this milk-ejection process.

Knowledge of the mechanism of mammalian reproduction is part of a sound general education. Yet the purpose of this rather lengthy discussion has been not so much to present the sequence of events in an essential physiological process as to illustrate the intricate chemical regulation of such a process. The hormonal control of reproduction typifies the interaction of a multiplicity of factors in determining the eventual outcome of bodily activities.

REFERENCES

Audus, L. J., 1959. *Plant Growth Substances*, 2nd ed. Leonard Hill, London.

Best, C. H., and N. B. Taylor, 1961. *The Physiological Basis of Medical Practice*, 7th ed. Williams & Wilkins, Baltimore. (See esp. Chapters 56–60.)

Gorbman, A., ed. 1959. *Comparative Endocrinology*. Wiley, New York.

———, and A. A. Bern, 1962. *A Textbook of Comparative Endocrinology*. Wiley, New York.

Meyer, B. S., D. B. Anderson and R. H. Böhning, 1960. *Introduction to Plant Physiology*. Van Nostrand, Princeton, N.J. (See esp. Chapters 22–24.)

PINCUS, G., and K. V. THIMANN, eds., 1948–1964. *The Hormones* (4 vols.). Academic Press, New York.

PROSSER, C. L., and F. A. BROWN, 1961. *Comparative Animal Physiology*, 2nd ed. Saunders, Philadelphia. (See esp. Chapter 20.)

SCHARRER, E., and B. SCHARRER, 1963. *Neuroendocrinology*. Columbia University Press, New York.

SWEENEY, B. M., 1963. "Biological Clocks in Plants," *Annual Review of Plant Physiology*, vol. 14. Annual Reviews, Inc., Palo Alto, Calif.

TURNER, C. D., 1966. *General Endocrinology*, 4th ed. Saunders, Philadelphia.

YOUNG, W. C., ed., 1961. *Sex and Internal Secretions* (2 vols.), 3rd ed. Williams & Wilkins, Baltimore.

ZEEVAART, J. A. D., 1962. "Physiology of Flowering," *Science*, vol. 137, pp. 723–731.

SUGGESTED READING

BECK, S. D., 1960. "Insects and the Length of Day," *Scientific American*, February.

BORTHWICK, H. A., and S. B. HENDRICKS, 1960. "Photoperiodism in Plants," *Science*, vol. 132, pp. 1223–1228.

BUTLER, W. L., and R. J. DOWNS, 1960. "Light and Plant Development," *Scientific American*, December. (Offprint 107.)

CSAPO, A., 1958. "Progesterone," *Scientific American*, April. (Offprint 163.)

DAVIDSON, E. H., 1965. "Hormones and Genes," *Scientific American*, June. (Offprint 1013.)

FIESER, L. F., 1955. "Steroids," *Scientific American*, January. (Offprint 8.)

GALSTON, A. W., 1964. *The Life of the Green Plant*, 2nd ed. Prentice-Hall, Englewood Cliffs, N.J. (See esp. Chapters 4–5.)

GRAY, G. W., 1950. "Cortisone and ACTH," *Scientific American*, March. (Offprint 14.)

GREULACH, V. A., and J. E. ADAMS, 1962. *Plants: An Introduction to Modern Botany*. Wiley, New York. (See esp. Chapter 12.)

HILLMAN, W. S., 1962. *The Physiology of Flowering*. Holt, Rinehart & Winston, New York.

JACOBS, W. P., 1955. "What Makes Leaves Fall?" *Scientific American*, November. (Offprint 116.)

KOLLER, D., 1959. "Germination," *Scientific American*, April. (Offprint 117.)

LERNER, A. B., 1961. "Hormones and Skin Color," *Scientific American*, July.

LEVEY, R. H., 1964. "The Thymus Hormone," *Scientific American*, July. (Offprint 188.)

LI, C. H., 1963. "The ACTH Molecule," *Scientific American*, July. (Offprint 160.)

NAYLOR, A. W., 1952. "The Control of Flowering," *Scientific American*, May. (Offprint 113.)

RASMUSSEN, H., 1961. "The Parathyroid Hormone," *Scientific American*, April. (Offprint 86.)

SALISBURY, F. B., 1957. "Plant Growth Substance," *Scientific American*, April. (Offprint 110.)

———, 1963. *The Flowering Process*. Pergamon Press, Oxford.

———, and R. V. PARKE, 1964. *Vascular Plants: Form and Function*. Wadsworth, Belmont, Calif. (See esp. Chapters 8, 14–18.)

SCHNEIDERMAN, H. A., and L. I. GILBERT, 1964. "Control of Growth and Development in Insects," *Science*, vol. 143, pp. 325–333.

STEWARD, F. C., 1963. "The Control of Growth in Plant Cells," *Scientific American*, October. (Offprint 167.)

———, 1964. *Plants at Work*. Addison-Wesley, Reading, Mass. (See esp. Chapter 11.)

WENT, F. W., 1962. "Plant Growth and Plant Hormones," in *This Is Life*, ed. by W. H. Johnson and W. C. Steere. Holt, Rinehart & Winston, New York.

WILKINS, L., 1960. "The Thyroid Gland," *Scientific American*, March.

WILLIAMS, C. M., 1950. "The Metamorphosis of Insects," *Scientific American*, April. (Offprint 49.)

WURTMAN, R. J., and J. AXELROD, 1965. "The Pineal Gland," *Scientific American*, July. (Offprint 1015.)

CHAPTER
10

NERVOUS CONTROL

WE SAW IN THE LAST CHAPTER THAT there is an intimate relationship between endocrine and nervous control systems in multicellular animals. Together, these systems make possible the integrated control so typical of animal behavior. Although plants, as we have seen, are far from passive, being complex dynamic organisms that grow, change, react to external stimuli, and move—indeed it is no exaggeration to say that plants behave—there is a fundamental difference in the type of behavior exhibited by them and by animals. And this difference is not exclusively one of a sedentary versus a mobile way of life, though this dichotomy doubtless played an important role in the early evolutionary divergence of these organisms. Perhaps the single characteristic that most readily distinguishes the behavior of animals from that of plants is speed. In general, the movements and other behavior patterns of animals are much faster than those of plants. Much of the behavior of plants is dependent on variations in growth rates or changes in the turgidity of cells, both of which are inherently rather slow ways to bring about movement. Animals, on the other hand, do not rely on such processes as growth to produce their movements; they have evolved tissues specialized for production of rapid movement, notably the muscles. Correlated with this fundamental difference in the speed of movement —a result of the very different ways the movement is produced—are basic differences in the control systems involved.

Hormonal control is a relatively slow process. Even when a hormone is transported via phloem or bloodstream, there is an appreciable delay between the release of the hormone and its arrival at the target organ. Response to the stimulus that induced secretion of the hormone is therefore not immediate; there is a lag of seconds or often of minutes. Given the inherent slowness of the mechanisms whereby plants move, however, the delay involved in chemical control is insignificant, and this type of control mechanism is fully sufficient. Slow chemical control is also sufficient for animals when instantaneous response is not needed, as in control of digestion, salt and water balance, metabolism, and growth. But when rapid response is required, as in the movements produced by skeletal muscles, chemical control is not sufficient. It is here that nervous control is essential. A nerve impulse can move several hundred feet per second, thus reducing the interval between stimulus and response to milliseconds. Evolution of nerve and muscle tissues, then, was basic to the evolution of active multicellular animals as we know them today.

EVOLUTION OF NERVOUS SYSTEMS

Irritability.   Irritability—the capacity to respond to stimuli—is a universal characteristic of protoplasm. Any manifestation of irritability —any reaction to stimulus—ordinarily involves three principal components: (1) reception of a stimulus, (2) conduction of a signal, and (3) response by an effector.

A stimulus is an environmental change of some sort; hence it always involves energy. Any change in the environment is potentially a stimulus, but whether it actually becomes a stimulus depends on many things. First, of course, protoplasm must be present, or the change has no opportunity to act as a stimulus. But, in addition, the protoplasm must be capable of detecting the change, or the change cannot function as a stimulus. Many environmental changes never function directly as stimuli, so far as we know, because no protoplasm can detect them; examples are radio and TV radiations. Human beings can use radio and TV radiations in communication because they have learned to convert these undetectable energy changes into detectable ones—sound vibrations and light—which function as the actual stimuli.

Conduction of a signal, the second component in a reaction to stimulus, is a capacity inherent in the nature of protoplasm itself. If a stimulus can produce a change in protoplasm at some point (i.e. if it can be received), neighboring regions of protoplasm will almost surely be influenced to some extent; the initial change will spread. This spread may be limited and slow, or it may be extensive and rapid. It is this tendency for protoplasmic changes to spread from the point of origin, for changes at one point to induce changes at neighboring points, that was the raw material for evolution of nervous conduction.

The response, the third component, is the action prompted by receipt of a stimulus. What different organisms do upon receiving the same stimulus may be very different. And what a single organism does upon receiving the same stimulus on two different occasions may also be different. Thus the response depends more on the characteristics of the organism than on the characteristics of the stimulus. The response is not produced directly by the stimulus—the way the breaking of a vase is by hitting it with a hammer.

In unicellular organisms, all three components of a reaction to stimulus—stimulus reception, signal conduction, and response—obviously occur within the protoplasm of a single cell; any conduction is simply from one part of the cell to another. Most often, this conduction is brought about by the natural slow conductivity of the cytoplasm or of the plasma membrane. Similarly, stimulus reception is often general and nonlocalized. Some unicellular (or better, acellular) organisms show more specialization, however. In ciliate Protozoa, for example, the bases of the cilia are interconnected by a system of fibrils that may function as a coordination network (Fig. 10.1). A specialized region of the cell (motorium) has been found to serve as a coordinating and relay center for impulses traveling along these fibrils; removal of this region or cutting of the fibrils disrupts the normally coordinated movement of the cilia. Similarly, many Protozoa possess organelles specialized for stimulus reception, such as eyespots and sensory bristles. And they frequently have specialized effector organelles such as cilia, flagella, and contractile fibrils. Clearly, even at the acellular level of complexity, specialized structures have evolved for sensory reception, conduction, and rapid response.

Sponges are primitive multicellular animals that lack a special intercellular communications system. Slow conduction occurs along each individual cell, and the impulses may slowly spread to adjacent cells, but rapid spread of impulses over greater distances within the organism is impossible. In general, plants, too, exhibit this sort of intercellular impulse transmission; stimulation of one plant cell causes an impulse to move slowly along the cell membrane, until it stimulates a similar impulse in an adjoining cell.

Simple Nervous Pathways. It is to the higher animals that we must look for the elaborative evolution of specialized conductile tissue. All animal groups above the level of the

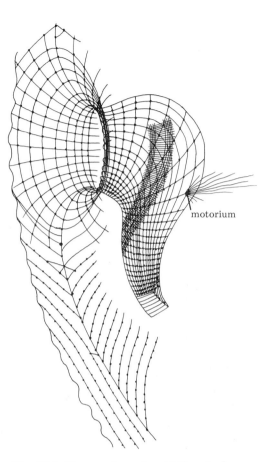

motorium

Fig. 10.1. Neuromotor system of the cytopharyngeal area of *Paramecium.* The fibrils interconnect the basal bodies of cilia (shown here as dots). The motorium apparently functions as a coordinating center. [Modified from L. H. Hyman, *The Invertebrates,* vol. 1, McGraw-Hill Book Co., 1940, used by permission. After E. E. Lund, 1935.]

sponges have some form of nervous system, though in some groups it is very primitive. In the tentacles of some coelenterates, we see the simplest possible type of true nervous pathway—a pathway composed of only two specialized cells, a receptor-conductor cell and an effector cell (Fig. 10.2A). Such a pathway allows little flexibility of behavior because there are no alternative pathways for the impulse to travel, and because the lack of interconnection between this pathway and other parts of the

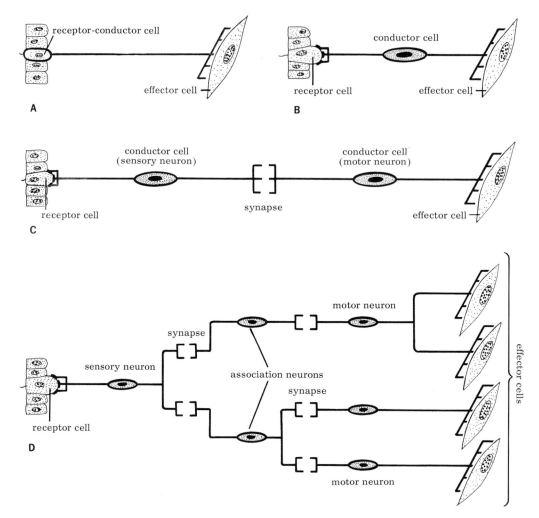

Fig. 10.2. Representative nervous pathways. (A) Pathway in which the receptor cell (which also functions as a conductor cell) is in direct contact with the effector cell. Such short pathways are extremely rare. (B) Pathway in which separate cells perform the three roles of receptor, conductor, and effector. Pathways with only one conductor cell (neuron) are rare. (C) Pathway with separate sensory and motor neurons. (D) The more usual type of pathway, in which association neurons are interposed between the sensory and motor neurons and in which the impulse may follow alternative routes.

nervous system precludes central control. Most nervous pathways, even in coelenterates, comprise at least three separate cells. In some cases, these three cells represent the three components of reaction to stimulus; there is a receptor cell specialized for reception of a particular kind of stimulus, a conductor cell specialized for transmission of impulses over long distances, and an effector cell (frequently a muscle cell) specialized for giving a response (Fig. 10.2B). In other cases, three-cell pathways include a first cell specialized for both reception and conduction, a second cell specialized for conduction, and an effector cell. More complex pathways may involve any number of additional conductor cells interposed between the receptor cell and the effector cell (Fig. 10.2C, D). Once the pathways include several conductor cells, flexibility of response becomes possible because more than one route is usually open to the impulse coming from the receptor; any one of several alternative effectors may be activated, or all of the possible effectors may be activated. In general, the more conductor cells in the circuitry, the more flexible the response.

As shown in the diagrammatic representations of conductor cells in Fig. 10.2, the typical nerve cell, or **neuron**, consists of an enlarged region, the **cell body**, which contains the nucleus, and one or more long processes, or **nerve fibers**, which extend from the cell body and may measure as much as 6 feet or more. Long as the neurons sometimes are, the average diameter of their cell bodies is less than 0.1 mm. and their long fibers are commonly only a few thousandths of a millimeter in diameter. Neurons leading from receptor cells are called **sensory neurons**, those leading to effector cells are called **motor neurons**, and those lying between the sensory and motor neurons are called **association neurons** (or internuncials or intercalary neurons). Notice that the neurons in a nervous pathway do not actually contact each other; their fibers come very close to each other but a tiny gap remains between them (except in a few very special cases). A junction of this sort between adjacent neurons is called a **synapse**.

Nerve Nets and Radial Systems. An organized nervous system is seen in its simplest form in coelenterates of the hydra type, which have reached the level of separate receptor, conductor, and effector cells. The conductor cells do not, however, form definite pathways, but interlace to form a diffuse **nerve net** running throughout the body (Fig. 10.3). There is apparently no central control of any sort. Conduction is slow, and the impulse can move in either direction along the fibers. An impulse simply spreads from the region of initial stimu-

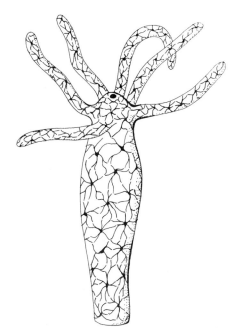

Fig. 10.3. **Nerve-net system of hydra.** There is no central nervous system. (The gaps between the fibers of adjacent nerve cells are not as wide as shown here.)

lation to adjacent regions, becoming less intense as it spreads. The stronger the initial stimulus, the farther the impulses will spread. Reactions are mostly limited to local contractions. Such a system, lacking the potential for central coordination of complex reactions, can produce only a limited behavioral repertoire. It is not surprising that the behavior of hydra is relatively simple; what is surprising is that it should be as complex as it is. The nerve net seems to function better than we might have predicted, but its capacities are nonetheless severely limited.

Some other coelenterates, such as jellyfish, have a somewhat more complex nervous system than hydra. Here there is some degree of centralization in the form of two nerve rings in the "bell" portion of the body. The other nerve cells tend to funnel into these rings, and conduction from one side of the animal to the other is thus much more rapid than would be possible with the randomly oriented pathways of a simple nerve net. This greater degree of coordination is reflected in the swimming movements of jellyfish, which consist in contraction of the whole bell in a rhythmic coordinated fashion.

Apparently, radial symmetry, like that of coelenterates, severely restricts the evolutionary potential for extensive centralization of nervous systems. Even relatively advanced radial animals such as echinoderms, whose nervous systems are characterized by central nerve rings, unidirectional conduction, well-coordinated stimulus-response patterns, and probably some learning ability, exhibit behavior that is simple compared with that of many bilaterally symmetrical animals. It is to these that we must turn if we are to understand the major trends in the evolution of nervous· systems.

Evolutionary Trends in Bilateral Nervous Systems. The major trends in the evolution of nervous systems in bilaterally symmetrical animals can be detected even in the lowly flatworms. Let us summarize these trends briefly: (1) increasing centralization of the nervous system by formation of major longitudinal nerve cords (the *central nervous system*) through which most pathways between receptors and effectors must pass and in or near which most neuron cell bodies come to lie; (2) increasing complexity of nervous pathways within the central nervous system by interpolation of large numbers of association neurons, with a concomitantly increased flexibility of response; (3) increasing segregation within the central nervous system of cells performing different functions, with eventual formation of distinct functional areas and structures; (4) increasing dominance of the front end of the longitudinal cords, leading to formation of a *brain,* which becomes more and more dominant; (5) limitation of conduction along nervous pathways to one direction only, with a resulting distinction between sensory fibers leading toward the central nervous system (afferent fibers) and motor fibers leading away from the central nervous system (efferent fibers); (6) increasing number and complexity of sense organs.

These trends are not yet very distinct in the most primitive flatworms (those thought to be most like the ancient ancestral forms); such flatworms have only a nerve net much like that of hydra. Some slightly more advanced flatworms (less like the ancestral forms) show the beginnings of a condensation of major longitudinal cords within their nerve nets (Fig. 10.4A); there are often as many as eight of these cords, located ventrally, dorsally, and laterally (Fig. 10.4B). Still more advanced flatworms show a reduction in the number of longitudinal cords (Figs. 10.4C, D), the most advanced representatives having only two, both located ventrally. Despite this evolution of a central nervous system in the most advanced flatworms, these animals retain an extensive nerve-net system located just beneath the muscular layer of the body wall. There are, however, definite afferent and efferent pathways connecting the nerve net with the cords.

Those flatworms with the most primitive development of longitudinal cords show very little evidence of any special structure at the anterior end that could be called a brain (Fig. 10.4A); biologists have, however, charitably labeled as a brain the tiny swellings present there. Flatworms at more advanced stages show a much better developed brain (Fig. 10.4E), though even this brain exerts only limited dominance over the rest of the central nervous system. One of the principal functions of such a brain is serving as a relay station between the sense organs and the cords. The sense organs tend to be most concentrated at the anterior end of the animal. It may seem "natural" to us for an animal's brain to be in its head (i.e. at the anterior end of its body), but, if we lay our preconceptions aside, we can see that this arrangement should not be taken for granted, that there must be an evolutionary and functional explanation for its almost uni-

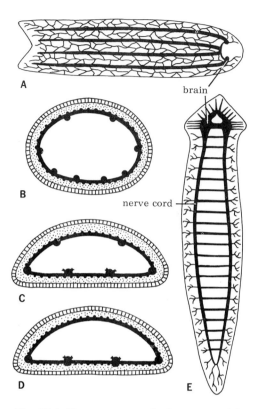

Fig. 10.4. Nervous systems in flatworms. (A) Submuscular plexus of *Amphiscolops*. This is essentially a nerve net, but several longitudinal cords are present within it; the so-called "brain" is only a very tiny thickening at the anterior end of these cords. (B) Cross section of a somewhat more advanced flatworm with eight well-developed cords: a dorsal pair, a lateral pair, a ventrolateral pair, and a ventral pair. (C–D) There are fewer cords in (C), and still fewer in (D). (E) Ventral nerve plate of planaria, with two cords and a moderately developed brain. [Modified in part from L. H. Hyman, *The Invertebrates,* vol. 2, McGraw-Hill Book Co., 1951, and in part from R. Buchsbaum, *Animals Without Backbones,* University of Chicago Press, 1948. Used by permission.]

versal occurrence. That explanation almost certainly lies in the animal's direction of movement. The anterior end is usually the part of a bilateral animal that first encounters new stimuli as the animal moves. Natural selection has therefore favored development of a particularly high concentration of sense organs in

this region, which, in turn, has led to enlargement of the anterior ends of the longitudinal nerve cords.

The most primitive version of the brain was probably almost exclusively concerned with funneling impulses from the sense organs into the cords. Then, because of the adaptive advantage of shortening the pathway these impulses have to follow before reaching the main coordination areas of the central nervous system, natural selection must have favored grouping those areas toward the anterior ends of the cords. Thus the brain came to be more than a sensory funneling area; as coordination became more concentrated in it, it became more and more dominant over the rest of the central nervous system. This dominance is at a rudimentary level in flatworms; it has its greatest development in mammals, especially man.

The evolutionary trends whose beginnings can be seen so clearly in flatworms, where intermediate stages between a simple nerve-net system and a centralized system can be studied in living animals, have their most extensive development in the vertebrates and, among invertebrates, in the annelids and arthropods. In all these animals, there is a high degree of centralization, and the old nerve net (which is presumed to be the ancestral system) is represented only by vestiges in a few parts of the body where sluggish movements—e.g. the peristaltic contractions of the mammalian intestine—are controlled by slow diffuse conduction.

In annelids and arthropods, the central nervous system is a longitudinal cord in which the cell bodies of the neurons form masses called *ganglia* and the fibers, gathered into huge bundles, function as through-conducting systems. Thus in primitive annelids and arthropods, there is a prominent ganglionic mass in each body segment, with the ganglia connected by bundles of fibers running between the segments (Fig. 10.5); almost all the cell bodies are located in ganglia. The brain is

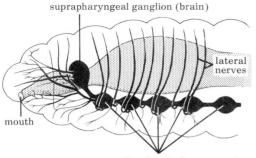

Fig. 10.5. Anterior portion of earthworm nervous system. The two parts of the double ventral nerve cord separate at the anterior end and encircle the pharynx. The ring of nervous tissue thus formed consists of the paired suprapharyngeal ganglia, the paired subpharyngeal ganglia, and the cords connecting them. The suprapharyngeal ganglia are customarily regarded as the brain, but they are only slightly larger than the segmental ganglia of the ventral nerve cord. [Modified from T. I. Storer and R. L. Usinger, *General Zoology*, McGraw-Hill Book Co., 1957. Used by permission.]

simply another ganglion located in the animal's head. It is little if any larger than the segmental ganglia; its dominance over the other ganglia is noticeable, but limited in comparison to that of the vertebrate brain. More advanced arthropods, particularly some of the insects, show more concentration of coordination in the front end; abdominal ganglia have frequently moved forward and fused with the third thoracic ganglion, or all the abdominal and thoracic ganglia have fused into a single large thoracic ganglionic mass. The brain, however, has remained relatively small, and has continued to share many vital coordinating functions with the thoracic ganglia. The persistence of thoracic ganglia in insects is probably correlated with at least two important functional arrangements of their bodies: the attachment of both their legs and wings on the thorax, which makes a concentration of motor coordinating centers in the thorax advantageous; and the location of many of their sense organs on their legs or thorax rather

than on their head (e.g. taste receptors are on the feet of flies and some other insects, and the ears, when present, are often on the sides of the thorax).

The central nervous system (spinal cord plus brain) of vertebrates differs in several important ways from those of annelids and arthropods: (1) The vertebrate spinal cord is single; it is located dorsally; and it forms in the embryo as a tube with a hollow central canal, a remnant of which survives in the adult (see Fig. 10.10). The cords of annelids and arthropods, on the other hand, are double (two cords lying side by side and often partly fused); they are located ventrally, and they are always solid. (2) The vertebrate spinal cord is not so obviously organized into a series of alternating ganglia and connecting tracts (ancestral vertebrates did not have internally segmented bodies like those of many annelids and ancestral arthropods). There is a general separation between areas containing cell bodies and areas containing fibers running lengthwise through the cord, but this separation occurs throughout the length of the cord, the central area of the cord (gray matter) containing mostly cell bodies and the peripheral area of the cord (white matter) containing mostly fibers (see Fig. 10.10). (3) Although many coordinating functions in vertebrates are still performed by the spinal cord, there has been extensive development of a brain, and this brain exerts far more dominance over the entire nervous system than the brain of any annelid or arthropod. The vertebrate brain, in short, is the master control center for **all bodily** functions.

NERVOUS PATHWAYS IN VERTEBRATES

Far more is known about the structure and general function of the nervous system of vertebrates than about that of any other group of animals (though, as we shall see later, more is probably known about the mechanism of neuron function in certain invertebrates). For this reason, and because of our natural interest in the system that more than any other makes man man, we shall use vertebrates as our models in discussing basic nervous pathways.

Neurons of Vertebrates

Vertebrate neurons may have one, two, or more fibers. When a neuron has more than one fiber, those fibers are usually of two different types: *dendrites,* which receive excitation from other cells and conduct impulses toward the cell body; and *axons,* which conduct impulses away from the cell body (Fig. 10.6). Dendrites are usually rather short, and there are often many of them per neuron; they frequently branch profusely, and their numerous short side branches may give them a spiny appearance; when stained, they ordinarily show many dark granules. There is usually only one axon per neuron (very rarely there are two), and it is frequently longer than the dendrites; it may branch extensively, but does not have a spiny appearance and does not show dark granules when stained. These and other histological differences are a more reliable basis for distinguishing dendrites from axons than conduction toward or away from the cell body. However, the most fundamental distinction between dendrites and axons is that dendrites receive excitation from other cells whereas axons generally do not, and that axons can stimulate other cells whereas dendrites cannot.

Nerve fibers are not differentiated into dendrites or axons in coelenterates, where, as we have seen, impulses can move in any direction in the nerve net. And there is little histological distinction between fibers in flatworms or the other lower invertebrates. The fibers of many of the higher invertebrates (e.g. molluscs, annelids, and arthropods) are usually differentiated into dendrites and axons, though their histological characteristics may be some-

what different from those of vertebrate fibers.

Vertebrate axons are usually enveloped in a sheath (or neurilemma) formed by special cells, the **Schwann cells,** that almost completely encircle the axons (Fig. 10.7). The Schwann cells play a role in the nutrition of the nerve fibers, and they provide a conduit within which damaged fibers can grow from the cell body back to their proper target tissues. Many axons, though not all, are also enveloped in a *myelin sheath* lying between most of the Schwann-cell cytoplasm and the axon. The myelin sheath is interrupted at regular intervals; the interruptions are called *nodes* (Fig. 10.6). The myelin, which contains much fatty material, functions in speeding up the transmission of impulses in the axons it envelops. A long-held belief that the sheath was secreted by either the Schwann cells or the axons themselves was disproved by Betty Ben Geren-Uzman and J. David Robertson of the Harvard Medical School, whose work also contributed greatly to our understanding of the cell membrane. They showed by electron microscopy that the sheath is not a secretion product, but a tightly packed spiral of the cell membrane of the Schwann cells (Figs. 10.8, 10.9). The nodes in the myelin sheath are simply the points at which one Schwann cell ends and another begins.

Reflex Arcs

A reflex arc is a simple neural pathway linking a receptor and an effector. Such arcs are important functional units of the nervous system. The reflexes they produce, which are responses to specific stimuli, are usually rapid and relatively automatic.

The simplest reflex arcs in vertebrates involve only two neurons, sensory and motor. A classic example of such an arc is the one in the knee-jerk reflex, commonly checked by physicians during physical examinations (Fig. 10.10). In this reflex, the receptors are stretch receptors, which are spindles formed by an

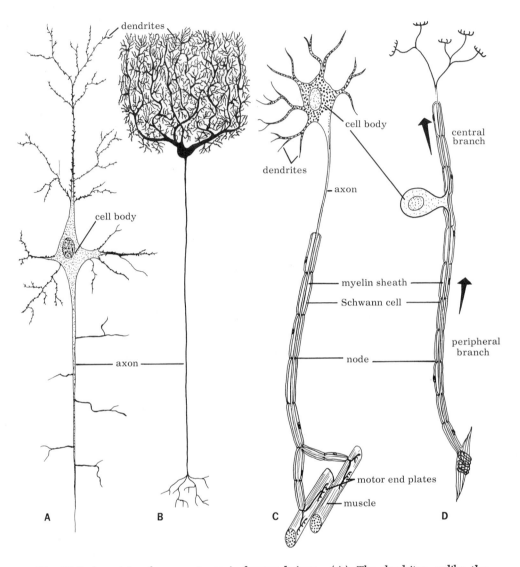

Fig. 10.6. A variety of neuron types in human beings. (A) The dendrites, unlike the axon, often have a spiny look. (B) The dendrites of certain brain cells branch profusely, giving the cell a treelike appearance. (C) Motor neurons have long axons that run from the central nervous system to the effector (in this case muscle); these axons are frequently, but not always, myelinated. Note the presence of many dark granules in the cell body and dendrites. (D) A sensory neuron. There is only one fiber, which branches a short distance from the cell body, one branch (peripheral) running between the receptor site and the dorsal-root ganglion in which the cell body is located, and the other branch (central) running from the ganglion into the spinal cord or brain. Except for its terminal portions, the entire fiber is structurally and functionally of the axon type, even though the peripheral branch conducts impulses toward the cell body. A sensory neuron thus has no true dendrites, although the peripheral branch is often called a dendrite because of the direction in which it conducts impulses. [Modified from many sources, including Ranson and Clark, 1959, Gardner, 1963, Peele, 1961, and others.]

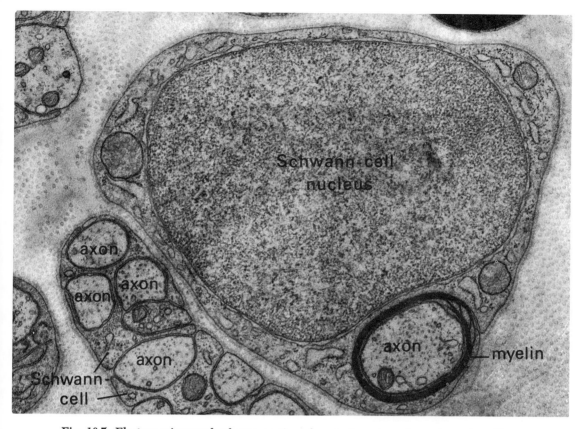

Fig. 10.7. Electron micrograph of cross section of part of a nerve of a guinea pig. The axons of the neurons are enveloped by Schwann cells. The axon at lower right has a myelin sheath, which develops from an invaginated coiled portion of the Schwann-cell membrane. Note the large nucleus of the Schwann cell. Several unmyelinated axons are enveloped by a single Schwann cell at lower left. The numerous small circular structures in the spaces between the Schwann cells (as in extreme lower right corner) are cross sections of collagen fibrils. × 31,000. [From W. Bloom and D. W. Fawcett, *A Textbook of Histology*, Saunders, 1962. Courtesy H. deF. Webster, Harvard University.]

intimate association between the terminal branches of a fiber of a sensory neuron and a specialized portion of a tendon or muscle. The sensory neuron is a very long one, running all the way from the stretch receptor in the knee to the spinal cord. The cell body of the sensory neuron is located in a *dorsal-root ganglion* (or spinal ganglion), which lies just outside the spinal cord near its dorsal surface. The axon of the sensory neuron leaves the dorsal-root ganglion and enters the cord dorsally, where it synapses with the dendrites or cell body of a motor neuron within the gray matter of the

spinal cord. The axon of the motor neuron then exits ventrally from the spinal cord and runs all the way to the effector cells, which in this case are muscle fibers in the leg. Thus, when the physician taps the tendon in the knee and a stretch receptor is stimulated, impulses travel up a sensory neuron to the spinal cord and back down a motor neuron to the leg, where they stimulate muscle fibers, which contract, causing the leg to jerk. A minimum of three cells are involved in this reflex arc: a receptor-sensory neuron, a motor neuron, and an effector cell.

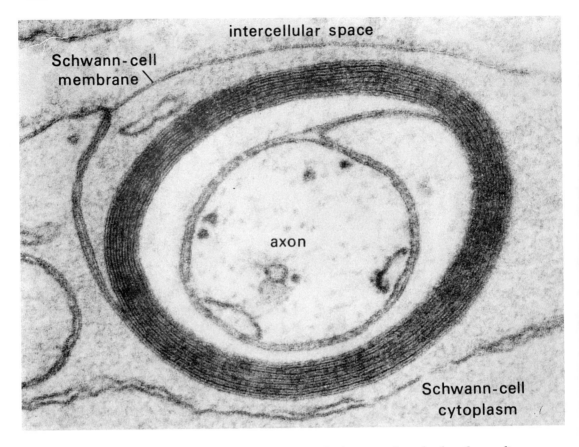

Fig. 10.8. Myelin sheath. This electron micrograph shows conclusively that the myelin sheath is a coil of the Schwann-cell membrane. × 128,000. [Courtesy J. David Robertson, *Ann. N.Y. Acad. Sci.*, vol. 94, 1961.]

Using this very simple reflex as a model, we can make several generalizations about all spinal reflex arcs: (1) There is never more than one sensory neuron, which, however, may be exceedingly long (consider a sensory neuron in an elephant running all the way from its foot to the spinal cord). (2) The cell body of a sensory neuron is always outside the spinal cord in a dorsal-root ganglion. (3) The axons of sensory neurons always enter the spinal cord dorsally. (4) The axons of motor neurons always leave the spinal cord ventrally. (Remember that the terms "dorsal" and "ventral" as used here refer to the usual vertebrate standing on four legs; in man the dorsal be-

comes the posterior side, and the ventral becomes the anterior side.)

So far, we have not used the term "nerve" in our discussions of neural pathways. A **nerve** is a compound structure consisting of a number of neuron fibers bound together. Although there may be thousands of fibers in a single nerve, each is insulated from all the others and conducts impulses independently of the others. A nerve, therefore, is much like a telephone cable containing many functionally separate telephone wires; the many independent communications pathways have been packaged together for structural convenience. Thus the sensory and motor neurons of the knee-jerk

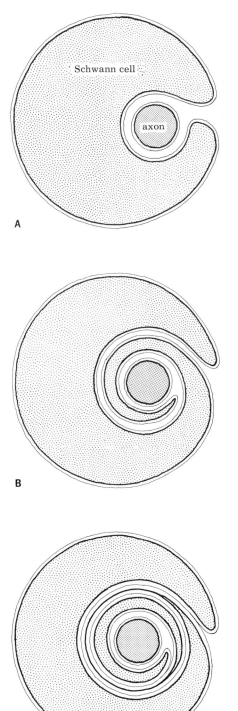

A

B

C

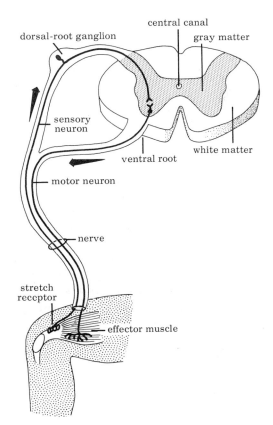

Fig. 10.9. Development of the myelin sheath. Initially the unmyelinated axon lies in an inpocketed area of the Schwann cell (A). The inpocketed area begins to coil (B), and the membrane is wound ever more tightly around the axon (C).

Fig. 10.10. Diagram of the knee-jerk reflex arc. Impulses from the stretch receptor travel along the sensory neuron to the spinal cord. The cell body of the sensory neuron is located in a dorsal-root ganglion lying just outside the cord. The sensory axon enters the cord dorsally and synapses with a motor neuron in the gray matter of the cord. The motor neuron leaves the cord ventrally and carries impulses to the effector muscle.

reflex run through the same nerve, even though they carry impulses in opposite directions. A nerve containing both sensory and motor fibers is called a mixed nerve. All the nerves connected to the spinal cord are mixed nerves. There are 31 pairs of such spinal nerves in man, all of which branch repeatedly, giving rise to smaller nerves that innervate most parts of the body below the head. Some nerves connect directly to the brain rather than to the spinal cord; in man there are 12 pairs of these cranial nerves, some purely motor, some purely sensory, and some mixed.

We have so far described reflexes in their simplest possible form. Now, however, we should re-examine them in their far more typical complexity. First, we must note that very few reflexes involve only two neurons. At least one association neuron is usually interposed between the axon of the sensory neuron and the dendrites of the motor neuron (Fig. 10.11), and it is common for many association neu-

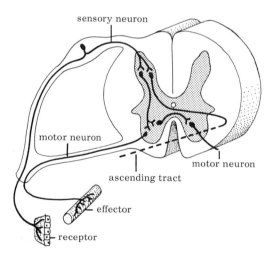

Fig. 10.11. Diagram of a reflex arc with association neurons. The sensory neuron synapses with several association neurons in the gray matter of the cord. Some of these association neurons may synapse directly with motor neurons on the same side, but some cross to the other side of the cord and there synapse with other motor neurons and with additional association neurons that run in ascending tracts through the cord to the brain.

rons to be involved even in relatively simple reflex arcs. Second, we should emphasize that reflex arcs always interconnect with other neural pathways. For example, there are always interconnections with pathways leading to the brain, and the brain can send impulses that modify the reflexes. If you know the doctor is going to strike your knee, you can be ready for him, and consciously either partly inhibit the reflex or augment it. In this case, the interconnections of the knee-jerk reflex with pathways to the brain enable you to become aware of what is happening and to modify the movement deliberately. In many other cases, in reflexes involving internal organs, for example, you may never become aware of what is happening and remain unconscious of the fact that your brain plays a part in the reflexes.

Let us suppose you decide to try to inhibit the knee-jerk reflex. What do you do? You send many excitatory impulses to those leg muscles that oppose, or antagonize, the extensor muscles. Thus, when your knee is struck and impulses are sent by way of the knee-jerk reflex arc to the extensor muscles, those muscles cannot bring about much jerk (extension) of the leg; there are too many other muscles pulling against them. But you can do more than this. You can send inhibitory impulses to the motor neurons of the extensor muscles themselves. In other words, you can make it more difficult to stimulate the motor neurons to those muscles. This is an important point; impulses are not all excitatory. It is an interaction between excitatory and inhibitory impulses that makes possible the precisely integrated control exerted by the nervous system, just as similar interactions are fundamental to the function of the endocrine control system. Thus the knee-jerk reflex really has two components: stimulation of motor neurons leading to extensor muscles in the leg, and inhibition of motor neurons leading to flexor muscles in the leg, so that extensor muscles contract and flexor muscles at the same time partly relax.

Consider for a moment another spinal reflex. You are walking barefoot and you step on a thorn with your right foot. Impulses from pain receptors in your foot immediately ascend along sensory neurons to the spinal cord, pass along association neurons in the cord, and descend along motor neurons to the muscles of your leg. Some of these descending impulses are excitatory to flexor muscles and others are inhibitory to extensor muscles. The result is that the flexor muscles contract, the extensor muscles partly relax, and your foot is quickly raised off the thorn. But if you raise your right foot, your left foot must bear the entire weight of your body. The association neurons carrying impulses from the pain receptors in your right foot do not synapse only with motor neurons leading to your right leg; some of them cross over to the left side of the spinal cord and synapse with motor neurons leading to your left leg. Excitatory impulses are sent to the extensor muscles of the left leg and inhibitory impulses are sent to the flexor muscles, with the result that the left leg remains firmly planted on the ground as the right leg is raised off the thorn. But balancing on one leg involves muscles in the sides of the leg in addition to those most concerned with extending and flexing it; the association neurons in the cord also synapse with neurons to these other muscles, sending impulses that bring them into the proper functional relationship to the extensors and flexors as you throw your weight onto that leg. Now, we have already said that the association neurons of any reflex arc will synapse with other neurons leading to the brain. Some of these neurons carry impulses to parts of the brain that are concerned with conscious activity, and you become aware of what is happening. Other neurons carry impulses to a part of the brain concerned with your general state of awareness, and you become more alert and "wide-awake." And still other neurons carry impulses to the part of the brain called the cerebellum, telling it, in effect, what motor activities have been

initiated. As the muscles of the legs start responding to the stimuli reaching them, stretch receptors in those muscles send impulses along sensory pathways to the spinal cord and up to the cerebellum, telling it how the muscles are actually responding. The cerebellum apparently compares the information from these two sources, and if there is a discrepancy between what has been ordered and what is actually happening, it sends impulses to parts of the brain that function in modifying muscular activity.

We could continue adding layers of complexity almost indefinitely; we have mentioned here only a few of the many pathways stimulated by impulses coming to the cord from the pain receptors in your foot. Evidently, a "simple reflex" is not really simple; even apparently automatic reflexes may involve intricate and complex coordinating mechanisms. Our discussion may suggest how the linking together of sufficient numbers of neural pathways can result in the many far more complex behavior patterns exhibited by animals.

The Autonomic Nervous System

We have seen that the peripheral portions (i.e. the portions outside the central nervous system) of many reflex arcs include one sensory neuron and one motor neuron. Such arcs are called somatic reflex arcs. They usually innervate skeletal muscle, and they involve, at least potentially, some conscious control of the reflex or an awareness that the reflex has occurred. However, there are other pathways exiting from the central nervous system that ordinarily are not under the control of the will and that usually function without our being aware of them. These are the pathways of the autonomic nervous system (ANS). They innervate the heart, some glands, and the smooth muscle in the walls of the digestive tract, respiratory system, excretory system, reproductive system, and blood vessels. Autonomic pathways differ structurally from somatic pathways in having two motor neurons instead of one. In most cases, the second motor neuron of an autonomic arc is unmyelinated and hence conducts impulses much more slowly than the single myelinated motor neuron of a somatic reflex arc.

The autonomic nervous system is separated into two parts, both structurally and functionally. These are called the *sympathetic* and the *parasympathetic* systems (Fig. 10.12). The cell bodies of the first motor neurons of the sympathetic system lie in the thoracic and lumbar portions of the spinal cord. The axons of these neurons exit ventrally from the cord and run to ganglia lying near the cord, where they synapse with second motor neurons whose cell bodies lie in the ganglia. Thus the synapse between the first and second motor neurons occurs in a ganglion that is at a distance from the target organ, and the axon of the second motor neuron is quite long.

Two principal structural differences distinguish the parasympathetic system from the sympathetic system. First, the cell bodies of the first motor neurons of the parasympathetic system lie in the brain and in the sacral region of the spinal cord. Second, the synapses between first and second motor neurons of the parasympathetic system occur in the immediate vicinity of the target organs, or even inside those organs; the axon of the second motor neuron is thus relatively short.

Most internal organs are innervated by both sympathetic and parasympathetic fibers, with the two systems functioning in opposition to each other. Thus if the sympathetic system excites a particular organ, the parasympathetic system usually inhibits that organ, and vice versa. In general, the sympathetic system produces the same effects as the hormones of the adrenal medulla, i.e. those effects we have termed the "fight-or-flight" responses. Present evidence suggests that this nervous mechanism is far more important than the endocrine mechanism in preparing an animal for emergency situations. You can easily figure out for yourself the effects produced by the parasympathetic system by simply reversing the fight-or-flight responses. The condition of an organ innervated by the autonomic nervous system is determined at any given moment by the relative amounts of stimulation coming to it via each of the two parts of the autonomic nervous system.

Reflex Control of Breathing and Heartbeat

For two examples of reflex control at a somewhat more complex level than the reflexes already discussed, let us look briefly at the nervous control of breathing, which involves somatic reflex arcs, and of heartbeat, which involves autonomic control.

Fig. 10.12. The autonomic nervous system. Of the 12 cranial and 31 spinal nerves, 4 cranial nerves (see shaded area of brain where they emerge, at upper right) and about half of the spinal nerves (see shaded vertebrae at which they emerge from the cord) contribute neurons to the autonomic nervous system, which innervates internal organs.

The ANS is customarily divided into two components: the sympathetic and the parasympathetic systems. The pathways of both usually have two motor (efferent) neurons; a first (presynaptic) neuron exits from the central nervous system and synapses with a second (postsynaptic) neuron that innervates the target organ. The presynaptic neurons of the sympathetic system exit from the thoracic and upper lumbar regions of the spinal cord, and synapse with the postsynaptic neurons in a series of small ganglia lying near the cord or in larger ganglia in the abdominal cavity; the postsynaptic neurons then run from the ganglia to the target organs. The presynaptic neurons of the parasympathetic system exit from the medulla of the brain and from the sacral region of the spinal cord. These are very long neurons that run all the way to the target organ, where they synapse with short postsynaptic neurons. Most, but not all, internal organs are innervated by both the sympathetic and the parasympathetic systems.

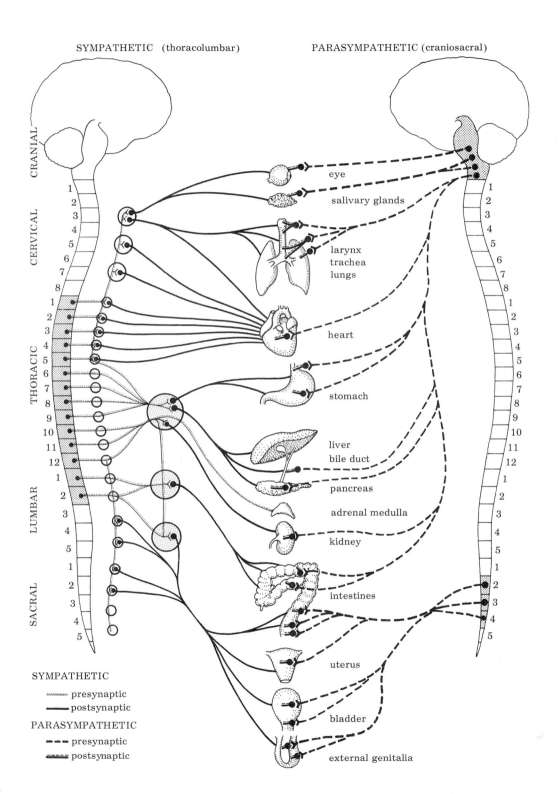

SYMPATHETIC (thoracolumbar)

PARASYMPATHETIC (craniosacral)

Control of Breathing. We saw in Chapter 6 that the effectors for the breathing movements are the muscles of the rib cage and diaphragm. These are skeletal muscles, and they can be controlled voluntarily to some extent. Ordinarily, however, the breathing movements occur automatically. The control center for these automatic movements is in a portion of the brain called the medulla oblongata, which is the portion of the brain to which the spinal cord attaches. When the breathing center in the medulla sends impulses to the muscles of the rib cage and diaphragm, those muscles contract, moving the rib cage up and out and pulling the diaphragm downward (see Fig. 6.14, p. 216). This increases the volume and lowers the pressure in the thorax, with the result that air is drawn into the lungs. As the lungs expand, however, stretch receptors in their walls are stimulated, and they send impulses to the breathing center in the medulla (Fig. 10.13). These im-

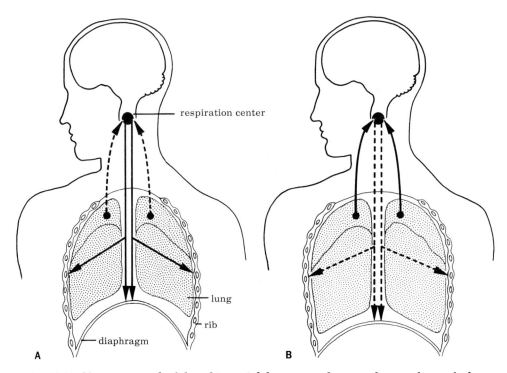

Fig. 10.13. **Nervous control of breathing.** Solid arrows indicate pathways along which many impulses are moving; dashed arrows indicate pathways that are not carrying many impulses. (A) Excitatory impulses from the respiration center in the medulla of the brain go by motor neurons to the rib muscles and diaphragm. The muscles thus stimulated contract, moving the rib cage up and out and pulling the diaphragm downward. This increases the volume of the thoracic cavity and pulls air into the lungs in the process of inspiration. (B) When the chest is expanded and the lungs are full of air, stretch receptors in the lungs are stimulated. These receptors send inhibitory impulses along sensory neurons to the respiration center and cause it to send fewer impulses to the rib muscles and diaphragm. When the muscles cease receiving excitatory impulses from the respiration center, they relax, thereby reducing the volume of the thoracic cavity and expelling air from the lungs in the process of expiration. [Modified from G. G. Simpson, C. S. Pittendrigh, and L. H. Tiffany, *Life: An Introduction to Biology.* Copyright, © 1957, by Harcourt, Brace & World, Inc., and reproduced with their permission.]

pulses inhibit the breathing center, and it sends fewer excitatory impulses to the muscles, with the result that the muscles relax and expiration occurs. But when the muscles have relaxed, the stretch receptors are no longer stimulated and send fewer inhibitory impulses to the breathing center. The breathing center, now free of inhibition, begins sending excitatory impulses to the muscles of the rib cage and diaphragm, and inspiration occurs again. The interaction of the breathing center in the medulla with the stretch receptors in the lungs —another example of negative feedback—thus results in the alternation of inspiration and expiration of the typical breathing cycle.

You ordinarily perform the rhythmic alternation of inspiration and expiration without any conscious effort—in fact, without even being aware of it; the activity is automatic. It is clear, then, that somatic reflexes such as this cannot be distinguished from autonomic reflexes simply on the basis of whether the reflex is performed consciously or not. The difference lies in the potential for conscious control of the effectors involved in the reflex. In this case, the effectors are skeletal muscles, and you can exert some conscious control over them if you choose to do so. For example, you can make other parts of your brain send inhibitory impulses to the breathing center in the medulla, blocking the sending of excitatory impulses to the muscles used in breathing. In other words, you can voluntarily hold your breath. But, as you know, you cannot hold your breath indefinitely; your conscious control of the breathing cycle is limited. This is because carbon dioxide in the blood acts as a powerful stimulant to the breathing center in the medulla. The longer you hold your breath, the higher the concentration of CO_2 in the blood rises, until eventually its excitatory effect on the breathing center surpasses the inhibitory effect of your conscious effort to cease breathing. When this happens, you must breathe again, despite your efforts not to do so. It is this same excitatory action of increased CO_2 concentra-

tion in the blood that causes the breathing center to accelerate the breathing rate during exercise.

It may seem strange that the index by which the breathing center determines when accelerated breathing is necessary should be the concentration of the waste product CO_2 rather than decreased concentration of oxygen, but the effect is the same as though O_2 concentration were the determinant factor, for CO_2 production by the cells of the body is proportional to their consumption of oxygen; thus increased concentration of CO_2 reliably reflects decreased concentration of O_2. This reliance of the breathing mechanism on CO_2 concentration does, however, create some curious problems in the artificial situations to which civilized man is increasingly subjecting himself. For example, if the ventilating system of a space ship failed to supply enough oxygen but removed CO_2 so fast that a concentration sufficient to stimulate the breathing center could not build up, the astronauts might actually black out from oxygen deprivation without ever having begun rapid breathing, because their breathing centers would not "know" that an increased breathing rate was necessary.

Control of Rate of Heartbeat. The nervous control of the rate of heartbeat provides a good example of autonomic control. Here the effector, which is heart muscle, is not potentially under conscious control (though you may consciously alter its rate of contraction indirectly, as by deliberately working yourself into an emotional or excited state). As we saw in Chapter 7, nervous impulses are not necessary for the initiation of the heartbeat, such initiation being under the direct control of the S-A node in the wall of the heart itself. But the rhythm of the S-A node can be modified by impulses coming to it via two sets of nerves— a set of sympathetic nerves, which exert an excitatory effect on the S-A node, and a set of parasympathetic nerves, which exert an inhibitory effect. Although the sympathetic nerves to the heart issue from the central nervous system in the thoracic region of the spinal cord, the impulses they carry originate in an accelerating center in the medulla of the brain (Fig. 10.14). Similarly, the impulses carried by the parasympathetic nerves to the heart originate in an inhibiting center in the medulla of the brain. When the right atrium is stretched by an unusual amount of blood, as during exercise, stretch receptors in its walls send excitatory impulses to the accelerating center in the medulla, which thereupon sends more impulses to the S-A node, thus causing the heart to beat faster. The accelerating center may also be stimulated to greater activity by impulses coming to it from receptors in an artery of the neck; these receptors are stimulated by an increased concentration of CO_2 in the blood. As the rate of heartbeat increases, the blood pressure increases. Pressure receptors in the aorta detect this increased blood pressure and send impulses to the inhibiting center in the medulla, causing it to send more inhibitory impulses to the S-A node, whereupon the rate of heartbeat becomes slower. The actual rate of heartbeat partly depends, then, on the relative activity of the accelerating and inhibiting centers in the medulla, and the ac-

tivity of these centers partly depends, in turn, on the relative amount of excitation they receive from the stretch receptors in the atrium and the chemoreceptors in the neck artery, on the one hand, and from the pressure receptors in the aorta, on the other. We say "partly," because the two centers in the medulla are also significantly influenced by impulses from other parts of the brain. For example, a man sees a shapely girl and his pulse quickens;

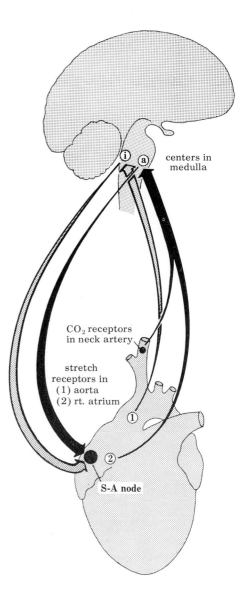

Fig. 10.14. Nervous control of rate of heartbeat. Black arrows indicate pathways concerned with acceleration of the heartbeat, and stippled arrows indicate pathways concerned with slowing the heartbeat. When the heart is engorged with blood, stretch receptors (2) in the wall of the right atrium send impulses to the accelerating center (a) in the medulla; this center may also receive impulses from CO_2 receptors in one of the neck arteries (the carotid). The impulses from the stretch receptors and CO_2 receptors stimulate the accelerating center to send excitatory impulses to the S-A node, thereby causing the heart to beat faster. But as the blood pressure rises, pressure receptors (1) in the wall of the aorta begin sending impulses to the inhibiting center (i) in the medulla, stimulating it to send inhibitory impulses to the S-A node, with the effect of slowing the heartbeat.

impulses from his visual sense organs have been relayed through higher centers of the brain to the accelerating center in the medulla, and the familiar response has ensued.

TRANSMISSION OF NERVOUS IMPULSES

We have repeatedly mentioned the transmission of impulses along neural pathways, and have indicated that this transmission may be as fast as 100–300 feet per second. We have said that in higher animals impulses generally move in a specified direction along the dendrites and axons of a neuron, and that transmission across synapses is also directional, being from the terminal portion of an axon to the dendrites or cell body of the next neuron in the sequence. We have not, however, explained what an impulse is or how it is transmitted. It is to this fundamental topic that we must now turn our attention. Actually, transmission along a neural pathway involves two very different components: transmission along nerve cells and transmission across the synaptic gaps between cells. We shall discuss these two aspects of transmission separately.

Transmission Along Neurons

General Features of the Nerve Impulse. Nerves will respond to a great variety of stimuli, such as a mild electric shock, a pinch, or an abrupt change of pH. Electrical stimuli are the most frequently used in laboratory experiments, for a number of reasons: The intensity and duration of such stimuli can be precisely measured; an electrical stimulus can be terminated almost instantaneously; and mild electrical stimuli do little if any damage to nerve cells.

Let us suppose that we are working with an isolated nerve fiber. We have touched two electrodes to the surface of the fiber at points several centimeters apart. These electrodes are connected to recording equipment, which enables us to detect any electrical changes that may occur at the points on the nerve fiber with which the electrodes are in contact. Now we apply an extremely mild electrical stimulus to the nerve fiber. Nothing happens; our recording equipment shows no change. We next apply a slightly more intense stimulus; still there is no change. We further increase the intensity of the stimulus and try again. This time our equipment tells us that an electrical change occurred at the point in contact with the first electrode and that a fraction of a second later a similar electrical change occurred at the point in contact with the second electrode. We have succeeded in stimulating the nerve fiber, and a wave of electrical change has moved down the fiber from the point of stimulation, passing first one electrode and then the other. Let us suppose that our recording equipment has enabled us to measure the intensity of this electrical change. We next apply a still more intense stimulus. Again we record a wave of electrical change moving down the fiber, but the intensity and speed of this electrical change are the same as those recorded from the previous stimulation. Again we increase the intensity of the stimulus, but again the recorded change shows the same intensity and speed.

We have learned several important facts from this experiment. (1) A nervous impulse can be detected as a wave of electrical change moving along a nerve fiber. (2) A potential stimulus must be above a critical intensity (and duration) if it is actually to stimulate a nerve fiber; this critical intensity is known as the *threshold* value, and it differs for different nerve fibers. (3) Increasing the intensity of the stimulus above the threshold value does not alter the intensity or speed of the nervous impulse produced; i.e. the nerve fiber fires maximally or not at all, a type of reaction commonly called an *all-or-none response.*

Immediately, an important question comes

to mind. If a nerve fiber exhibits the all-or-none property with respect to intensity of impulse and speed of transmission, how do animals normally detect the intensity of a stimulus? They do this in several ways. First, a nerve fiber does not exhibit an all-or-none response with respect to frequency. The more intense the stimulus, the more frequent are the impulses moving along the fiber (up to a maximum value, of course). Second, because different fibers have different thresholds, a more intense stimulus ordinarily stimulates more nerve fibers; individual fibers exhibit all-or-none properties, but nerves (which are composed of many fibers) do not. Apparently the brain interprets both a greater frequency of impulses coming to it via individual fibers and a greater number of stimulated fibers as indicating greater intensity of the stimulus.

The Nature of the Impulse. When it was discovered over a century ago that a nerve impulse involves electrical changes, scientists assumed that the impulse was a simple electric current flowing through a nerve, just as other currents flow through wires. It was soon shown, however, that this is not the case. The speed of electricity is far greater than the speed of a nerve impulse. Furthermore, the cytoplasmic core of nerve fibers offers so much resistance to simple electric currents that they die out after moving only a few millimeters through a nerve. The fact is that any resistance at all, however low, would cause a simple electric current to diminish in strength as it moved. Yet if we measure a nerve impulse at various points along the fiber, we find that it remains the same; its strength does not decrease with distance. It has further been observed that crushing or poisoning a nerve fiber may destroy its ability to transmit nerve impulses without appreciably altering its electrical conductivity. In short, evidence of many sorts forces us to the conclusion that neural transmission depends on activity by the living cell, activity that almost certainly involves chemical pro-

cesses. According to this view, the impulse is not an electric current but an electrochemical change propagated along the nerve fiber.

The basic outlines of the modern theory of nerve action were proposed in 1902 by Julius Bernstein of the University of Halle in Germany. It was known by that time that the concentrations of certain ions are very different inside nerve cells and in the surrounding fluids, the concentration of sodium being very low inside the cell and the concentration of potassium and negative organic ions being very high (we saw in Chapter 8 that this is true to some extent of most cells). It had also been shown that the unequal distribution of ions results in an electric potential difference across the cell membrane in the resting state, the inside being negatively charged relative to the outside (Fig. 10.15A). Bernstein suggested that the permeability of the nerve-cell membrane varies for various ions, and that it is the great selectivity of this membrane that maintains the separation of ions and the resulting electric potential. He further suggested that during the passage of an impulse the selectivity of the membrane is momentarily destroyed. As a result, the ions can move freely, and the electric potential difference across the membrane falls to zero. In other words, the membrane is momentarily unable to maintain a separation of charge (Fig. 10.15B). The rush of ions across the membrane at one point momentarily destroys its selectivity at adjacent points, causing ions to move there also. And this transfer of ions, in turn, destroys the selectivity of the membrane at the next points (Fig. 10.15C–E). In this manner, each successive point along the membrane becomes depolarized as it is altered by the depolarization of the preceding point. According to Bernstein's theory, then, the nerve impulse is a wave of depolarization moving along the membrane of the neuron. The effect is much like that of falling tenpins; when the bowling ball hits the first pin, that pin falls and strikes the next pin, which falls and hits the pin be-

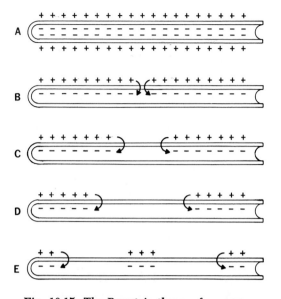

Fig. 10.15. The Bernstein theory of propagation of a nerve impulse. (A) The resting nerve fiber is polarized, with the inside negative relative to the outside. (B) If the fiber is stimulated at a point along its length, ions can move across the membrane at that point, destroying the original polarity. (C–D) Waves of depolarization move along the fiber in both directions as the rush of ions across the membrane at each successive point causes changes in the permeability of the membrane at the next point. (E) Repolarization begins at the point where the stimulus was administered and moves along the fiber behind the wave of depolarization; as soon as a portion of the fiber has been repolarized, it can respond to a new stimulus. – More recent research has necessitated one change in this theory. Rather than depolarization, momentary polarization reversal is believed to occur.

hind it, etc. If one is skillful or lucky, hitting one pin with the ball will cause all the other pins to fall in succession. In a nerve fiber, stimulation at only one point produces depolarization at that point and initiates the wave of depolarization.

Bernstein's membrane theory was widely accepted by biologists, but for many years little experimental evidence either for or against it could be obtained. Nerve fibers were simply too small for accurate measurements of the changes taking place inside them during im-

pulse transmission. Then in 1933 J. Z. Young, at that time at Oxford University, discovered that squids (relatives of octopuses) possess several giant nerve fibers, which may be as much as a millimeter in diameter. These fibers run in the body wall of the squid (Fig. 10.16) and innervate muscles that enable the animal to propel itself backward at very high speed by explosively expelling water from its mantle cavity through a funnel near its head. The great size of these fibers makes them conduct impulses very rapidly. In general, the greater the diameter of a nerve fiber, the faster it conducts; conductance per unit length increases as the square of the diameter. Fibers larger than normal, though rarely as large as those of the squid, are also found in many other invertebrates in parts of the body where very rapid conduction is important; vertebrates

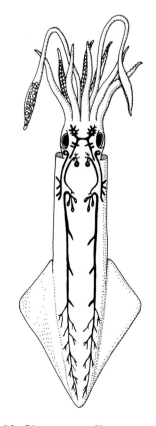

Fig. 10.16. Giant nerve fibers of a squid.

have evolved myelinated fibers as an alternative adaptation for increasing conduction speed. Use of the giant nerve fibers of the squid, which finally made it possible for biologists to study in detail the events that transpire during conduction, opened a whole new era of discovery in the important field of neurophysiology. The central role of the squid in this research explains why so many experiments on nerve function were performed at marine biological stations like those at Woods Hole, Massachusetts, and Plymouth, England.

In 1939 H. J. Curtis and K. S. Cole at Woods Hole and A. L. Hodgkin and A. F. Huxley at Plymouth developed a technique for inserting into a squid nerve fiber a very thin microelectrode consisting of a glass tube filled with salt solution or metal. The microelectrode was inserted into one end of the fiber and pushed down it a distance of 1–3 cm. (Fig. 10.17). Great care was taken to prevent the microelectrode from scraping the membrane and thus damaging its conductance properties. With this technique, it could be shown that the electric potential across the nerve membrane did indeed change during the passage of an impulse, just as Bernstein had predicted. But one thing was wrong; the potential changed too much. For an instant, the inside of the nerve actually became positive relative to the outside. The membrane did not simply become depolarized; it actually reversed its polarization momentarily. Clearly, then, stimulation does not destroy the selectivity of the membrane, as Bernstein thought; if it did, the result would be simple depolarization, as shown in Fig. 10.15. Instead, it must radically alter this selectivity. In other words, the stimulated point on the membrane remains selective, but its selectivity is different; it must initially allow far more positive sodium ions to enter the cell than it allows other ions to leave. With this slight modification, proposed in 1947 by A. L. Hodgkin and B. Katz, the Bernstein membrane theory of neural transmission has stood the test of extensive experimentation and is the theory generally held today.

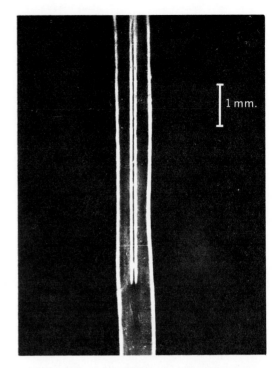

Fig. 10.17. Photograph of a giant axon of a squid with a glass-tube microelectrode inside it. [Courtesy A. L. Hodgkin, *J. Physiol.* (*London*), vol. 131, 1956.]

Let us summarize the current understanding of the sequence of events during impulse transmission. The membrane of the resting neuron is polarized, with the inside negative relative to the outside. The concentration of sodium ions is much higher outside, and the concentration of potassium ions is much higher inside. Stimulation causes the membrane to undergo an initial great increase in permeability to sodium ions. Sodium ions rush across the membrane into the cell, both because of their natural tendency to diffuse from regions of their higher concentration to regions of their lower concentration and because they are attracted by the negative charge inside the cell. The inward flux of sodium is so great, however, and so much sodium moves into the cell, that for a moment the inside actually becomes positively charged relative to the outside. A fraction of a second later, the membrane becomes highly permeable to potassium ions, which rush out of the cell because their concentration is higher inside than outside and because they are repelled by the momentary high positive charge inside the cell. This exit of positively charged potassium ions restores the electric charge inside the cell to its original negativity. In short, the inside surface of the membrane is initially negative; it becomes positive when sodium ions flood inward and then becomes negative again when potassium ions rush outward. It is this rapid cycle of changes, occurring at successive points in sequence, that constitutes the nerve impulse as it flows along a neuron. As Bernstein suggested, the impulse is propagated along the neuron because the cycle of changes at each point alters the permeability of the membrane at the adjacent point and initiates a similar cycle there.

The modified Bernstein theory of neural transmission explains why the nerve impulse, unlike a simple electric current moving through a wire, does not decrease in strength as it moves along the fiber. The impulse is constantly being regenerated; the polarization reversal at each successive point is a new event, equal in magnitude to the similar events at the preceding points. An electric current is generated by a battery or dynamo and is simply carried passively by the wire, but a nerve impulse derives its energy from the path along which it travels, being generated anew at each successive point along the fiber.

According to the membrane theory of conduction, myelinated fibers transmit impulses faster than nonmyelinated fibers because the wave of momentary polarization reversal jumps from node to node along such a fiber instead of moving smoothly along the entire surface of the fiber.

The Sodium-Potassium Pump. At this point, we encounter the really perplexing part of nerve activity. If impulse transmission involves inward flow of sodium followed by outward flow of potassium, how does the neuron re-establish its original ionic balance? In other words, how does it get rid of the sodium and

regain the potassium, so that the initial low concentration of sodium and high concentration of potassium inside the cell will be restored? If the initial ionic distribution were not restored, the neuron would eventually lose its ability to transmit impulses, but we know for a fact that a normal neuron can continue to transmit impulses indefinitely, with only a very brief refractory period (on the order of 0.5–2 milliseconds) after each impulse.

Since expelling the sodium means making it move against its concentration gradient and against the electrostatic gradient, and since regaining the lost potassium means making it move against its concentration gradient, some form of active transport across the membrane must be involved. It has been theorized that there exists in the membrane of the neuron a so-called sodium-potassium exchange pump of the same basic sort as that discussed in Chapter 8. We saw there that many cells actively extrude sodium and take in potassium; the neuron, then, is a type of cell that has evolved an extraordinarily effective version of the ionic pump so widely found in other cells. The development of such a pump, combined with the evolution of extreme susceptibility to induction of membrane-permeability changes by external stimuli, has been the basis for the neuron's high degree of specialization for impulse conduction.

Let us review briefly the model of the sodium-potassium exchange pump discussed in Chapter 8 and see how this model applies to nerve cells. According to this model (see Fig. 8.15, p. 292), a carrier substance, X, is assumed to combine with potassium ions (K^+) at the outer surface of the membrane, forming a new compound KX. KX then diffuses passively across the membrane following its own concentration gradient. At the inner surface of the membrane, KX dissociates, releasing potassium into the cell. X is immediately converted into another form, Y, by an energy-requiring reaction. Y combines with sodium ions (Na^+) at the inner surface of the membrane, forming a new compound NaY, which diffuses passively back across the membrane to the outer surface along its own concentration gradient. At the outer surface, NaY dissociates, releasing sodium to the outside. Y is then immediately converted by an enzyme-catalyzed reaction back into X, which can pick up a new load of potassium and start the process over again. Thus the carrier substance in its two forms constantly moves back and forth across the membrane, bringing potassium into the cell and taking sodium out. The whole process is kept going by an expenditure of metabolic energy at the inner surface of the membrane.

This pumping model explains how the cell can maintain its low concentration of sodium ions and its high concentration of potassium ions. But an important question remains: If the pump simply exchanges positive sodium ions for positive potassium ions, i.e. if it is electrically neutral, how does it give rise to a potential difference across the membrane? At first glance, this model seems to provide no way to establish a separation of charge, positive to the outside and negative to the inside. Two facts must be kept in mind, however. First, inside the cell there is a high concentration of negative organic ions, which cannot cross the membrane. Second, the membrane of the resting cell is more permeable to potassium than to sodium. Therefore, even if there were always an exact one-to-one exchange of sodium for potassium—and there is good evidence that this need not be true—potassium would leak back out of the cell down its concentration gradient faster than sodium would leak back into the cell down its concentration gradient. This excess of outward-leaking positive potassium ions over inward-leaking positive sodium ions would result in a net outward movement of positively charged ions. There could be no correspondingly large outward movement of negatively charged ions, since the organic ions, which account for most of the negative charge inside the cell, cannot cross the membrane. Thus a separation of charge is established.

But what stops the buildup of polarization at the normal resting level? Why doesn't the unequal leakage of potassium and sodium cause the polarization to rise indefinitely? As the working of the pump causes the concentration gradient for sodium ions to become steeper and steeper, the net inward diffusion of these ions eventually comes to equal the outward pumping. Similarly, as the concentration of potassium ions inside the cell falls, and as the negativity inside the cell rises, outward leakage of potassium ions becomes slower, and passive inward diffusion (caused by electrical attraction between the positive potassium ions and the negative cell contents) rises. In time, the net passive outflow of potassium falls to the point where it equals the active inflow. When net passive diffusion of both sodium and potassium has reached the point where it exactly balances the effects of the sodium-potassium pump, a steady state has been reached and the resting polarization is established (Fig. 10.18).

Perhaps the mechanism whereby the membrane becomes polarized can best be understood by means of a hypothetical example. Suppose that for each 0.1 square millimeter of cell membrane the pump extrudes 10,000 sodium ions and brings in 10,000 potassium ions each millionth of a second. This exchange in itself would be electrically neutral. But the cell membrane is far more permeable to K^+ ions than to Na^+ ions. Suppose, therefore, that in the same millionth of a second 2,000 K^+ ions leak back out of the cell but only one Na^+ ion leaks in. The net effect would be a loss of 1,999 positive ions from the cell (Table 10.1). But the net loss of charge would not be as great as this figure seems to indicate, because many of the lost K^+ ions would probably be accompanied by negative chloride ions. The loss of Cl^- ions, however, would be less than that of K^+ ions, because Cl^- ions make up only a small fraction of the cell's negative charge, most of this charge being in the form of negative organic ions, and because the concentration gradient favors retention of chloride.

OUTSIDE CELL MEMBRANE INSIDE

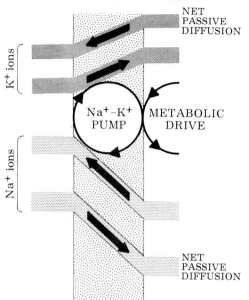

Fig. 10.18. The sodium-potassium pump. When the system is at equilibrium, the net passive diffusion of K^+ ions out of the cell equals the inward movement of K^+ ions through the metabolically driven pump, and the net passive diffusion of Na^+ ions into the cell equals the outward movement of Na^+ ions through the pump. [Modified from J. C. Eccles, *The Physiology of Nerve Cells,* Johns Hopkins Press, 1957.]

TABLE 10.1

Exchange of Ions Between a Hypothetical Neuron and the Surrounding Fluid During a Millionth of a Second

Na^+ pumped out of cell	10,000
K^+ pumped into cell	10,000
K^+ leaked out of cell	2,000
Na^+ leaked into cell	1
Net loss of positive ions	1,999
Cl^- leaked out of cell	1,990
Net loss of positive charge	9

The loss of positive charge would therefore always slightly exceed the loss of negative charge. For example, if 1,990 of the K^+ ions that leak out of the cell during our hypothetical millionth of a second are accompanied by Cl^- ions, there would still be a net loss of 9 positive charges. If the same thing happened in each of several succeeding millionths of a second, there would soon be an appreciable separation of charge, the inside being negative relative to the outside. The membrane of the neuron would thus become polarized and ready to function. Note again that the whole process depends on three interacting factors: the metabolically driven sodium-potassium pump, the greater leakage of potassium ions than of sodium ions, and the inability of the negative organic ions to leave the cell.

The above discussion of the sodium-potassium pump may have given the impression that movement of massive quantities of ions is involved. Actually, studies with radioactive ions have shown that only small quantities of sodium and potassium move at each impulse. A neuron whose pump has been poisoned can therefore maintain a sufficient ionic concentration gradient for some time and conduct many impulses before it becomes nonfunctional. At each successive impulse, the membrane undergoes a rapid cycle of permeability changes that allow first sodium and then potassium to move passively down their concentration gradients across the membrane. Roughly equivalent quantities of Na^+ and K^+ ions are exchanged at each such cycle, so that the membrane's polarization is partly restored at the end of each cycle. But with the pump not functioning, the sodium that enters at each impulse remains in the cell and the lost potassium is not regained. Eventually, therefore, the concentration of sodium in the cell becomes so high and the concentration of potassium becomes so low that there is not enough outward leakage of potassium to establish sufficient polarization and the neuron can no longer function unless the pump becomes active again.

It has actually been shown that the protoplasm inside the fiber is not essential for impulse transmission. If the protoplasm is removed and replaced with an isosmotic solution
of a potassium salt, the resulting preparation
may carry as many as 300,000 impulses before
it ceases to function. Clearly, simple ionic concentration gradients across the membrane provide the immediate source of energy for the
impulse. The role of the rest of the protoplasm
of the living cell is to supply the metabolic
energy necessary to drive the sodium-potassium pump and maintain the cell in functional
condition. This energy is doubtless supplied in
the form of ATP. It can be shown that the
pump will not work when ATP is absent;
substances that block ATP utilization act as
poisons to the pump. Furthermore, there is an
ATP-splitting enzyme in the membrane that
is activated by sodium and potassium and inhibited by substances that interfere with
sodium-potassium transport.

Transmission Across Synapses

The Nature of Synaptic Transmission. We
have said that the axon of one neuron synapses
with the dendrites or cell body of other neurons. Since the terminal portion of an axon
usually branches repeatedly, a single axon may
synapse with many other neurons, and it usually synapses at numerous points with each of
these neurons (Fig. 10.19). Each tiny branch
of an axon ends with a small swelling called
a *synaptic knob,* whose membrane is separated
from the postsynaptic membrane of the adjoining cell by a space of about 20 millimicrons.
Many scientists once thought that transmission
across this gap was electrical, but the evidence
now strongly supports the view that most
synaptic transmission is by a diffusible chemical (in a few unusual synapses, where the
membranes may be in direct contact or separated by a cleft even narrower than 20 millimicrons, transmission may be electrical).

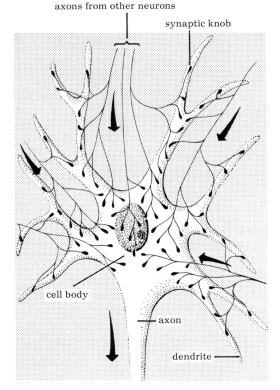

axons from other neurons

synaptic knob

cell body

axon

dendrite

Fig. 10.19. Synapses on a motor neuron.
Many different axons, each of which branches
repeatedly, synapse on the dendrites and cell
body of a single motor neuron. Each branch
of an axon terminates in a swelling called a
synaptic knob.

The electron microscope has revealed that
each synaptic knob contains numerous tiny
synaptic vesicles (Fig. 10.20). Apparently
these vesicles contain molecules of the transmitter chemical. It seems probable that an impulse traveling along an axon reaches the synaptic knob and somehow causes vesicles lying
near the membrane to discharge their contents
into the synaptic cleft. The discharged vesicles
then move away from the membrane and probably become refilled with transmitter substance
in some unknown manner. The transmitter
molecules released into the cleft diffuse across
it and alter the membrane potential of the
adjoining nerve cell. The fact that transmission
depends on diffusion—an inherently slow

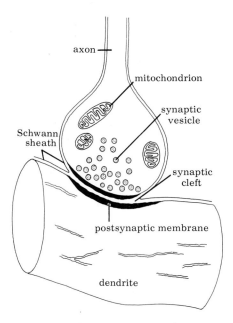

axon

mitochondrion

synaptic vesicle

Schwann sheath

synaptic cleft

postsynaptic membrane

dendrite

Fig. 10.20. The synapse. Each synaptic knob at the end of an axon encloses numerous synaptic vesicles containing transmitter substance. When vesicles release this substance into the synaptic cleft, the substance diffuses across the cleft and alters the polarization of the postsynaptic membrane of the dendrite or cell body of the next cell.

process—means that, even though the cleft is very narrow, synaptic transmission is much slower than transmission along the neurons. For this reason, the time it takes an impulse to traverse a neural pathway is always longer than would be calculated on the basis of the length of the pathway and the speed of transmission along the fibers. In general, the more synapses in a neural pathway, the slower the average speed of transmission per unit distance along the pathway.

It is the synapses that make transmission of impulses along the neural pathways of higher animals one-way. A neuron can conduct impulses in both directions. If, for example, we stimulate an axon at a point between its base and its terminus, an impulse will move in both directions along the axon from the point of stimulation. But the impulse moving back toward the cell body and dendrites will die

when it reaches the end of the cell; it cannot bridge the gap to the next cell. Only the ends of axons can secrete transmitter substances.

For synapses between neurons outside the central nervous system, the transmitter chemical is almost certainly *acetylcholine.* This chemical is released by the vesicles in the synaptic knobs of axons, diffuses across the synaptic cleft, exerts its effect on the postsynaptic membrane of the dendrite or cell body of the next cell, and is then promptly destroyed by an enzyme called *cholinesterase.* This destruction is of critical importance. If the acetylcholine were not destroyed, it would continue its stimulatory action indefinitely and all control would be lost. In fact, many insecticides are cholinesterase inhibitors. They block destruction of acetylcholine, with the result that the animal's nervous system soon runs wild; the insect goes into uncontrollable tremors and spasms, and death results.

There is good evidence that acetylcholine is one of a number of transmitter substances inside the central nervous system, but only a few of the others have been identified with certainty. There may actually be many such substances, and their identification will almost certainly greatly aid our understanding of how the central nervous system functions.

The Action of Transmitter Substances. Let us now examine more closely the effects of transmitter substances on postsynaptic membranes. When such a substance has diffused across the synaptic cleft, how does it affect the polarization of the postsynaptic membrane of the dendrite or cell body of the next neuron? Let us suppose, first, that we are dealing with an excitatory transmitter substance. Apparently, such a substance slightly increases the permeability of the postsynaptic membrane to sodium ions. The resulting increased inward flow of sodium ions along their concentration gradient slightly decreases the polarization of the neuron; i.e. the inside becomes less negative relative to the outside (Fig. 10.21). If the

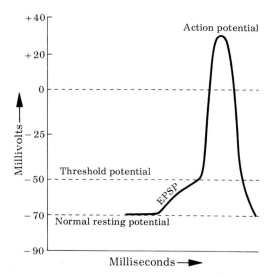

Fig. 10.21. Initiation of an impulse by an excitatory transmitter substance. The transmitter substance slightly reduces the polarization of the postsynaptic membrane (i.e. makes the inner surface of the membrane less strongly negative), thereby creating what is called an excitatory postsynaptic potential (EPSP). If the EPSP reaches the threshold level, an impulse is triggered; a sudden inrush of sodium ions causes the inside of the cell to become positive (the action potential). A fraction of a second later, potassium ions rush out of the cell, and the inside of the cell again becomes negative. [Modified from J. C. Eccles, *Science*, vol. 145, 1964. Copyright 1964 by the American Association for the Advancement of Science.]

decrease is sufficiently great, it may spread to the base of the cell's axon and there trigger a nerve impulse, which will move down the axon to the next synapse. What happens, in effect, is that excitatory transmitter substances produce a short circuit in the postsynaptic membrane potential, and this triggers the nerve impulse.

Synapses are points of resistance in the nervous pathways, and some impulses reaching the synapses are not transmitted to the next neurons. In such a case, not enough transmitter substance is released to depolarize the postsynaptic membrane sufficiently; hence no impulse is triggered. Ordinarily, excitatory im-

pulses must arrive at more than one synapse on the cell within a short space of time if the cell is to be sufficiently depolarized to trigger an impulse. These cooperating synapses may all be located at the terminals of branches of a single axon, or they may be at the terminals of the axons of several different neurons. The transmitter molecules from each individual synapse cause slight depolarization; acting together, they produce enough depolarization to pass the critical level and trigger an impulse. This additive phenomenon is called **summation.** Summation may be temporal as well as spatial; if new subthreshold impulses arrive before the effects of previous subthreshold impulses have disappeared, the effects may cumulate and trigger an impulse in the postsynaptic cell. In other words, the first subthreshold stimulus has facilitated the postsynaptic membrane and made it easier for the second subthreshold stimulus to induce an impulse.

The thresholds for different neurons differ; i.e. the critical levels of depolarization at which they will fire differ. Depending on its threshold, a given neuron may fire an impulse when stimulated by only a few incoming axons or it may not fire unless stimulated by many incoming axons. The difference in thresholds at different synapses plays an extremely important role in determining the routes impulses will follow through the nervous system. Synapses, in effect, are the regulatory valves of the nervous system. It has been suggested that learning may involve a reduction of the threshold at certain synapses as a result of their use. Later impulses would thus encounter less synaptic resistance if they followed the same pathways that earlier impulses had followed.

The transmitter substances we have discussed so far reduce the polarization of the postsynaptic membrane; i.e. they produce an excitatory postsynaptic potential leading to production of a new impulse. The transmitter substances released by the axons of some neurons, however, have an opposite effect—an inhibitory one. They increase the polarization of the postsynaptic membrane and thus make the neuron harder to fire; i.e. they produce an inhibitory postsynaptic potential. Apparently these substances produce their inhibitory effects by making the postsynaptic membrane more permeable to potassium or to chloride or both. If more potassium ions leave the cell or if more chloride ions enter the cell or if both these ionic movements occur, the membrane becomes more polarized; i.e. the inside of the cell becomes more negative relative to the outside. More than the usual number of excitatory impulses would be needed to reduce the polarization of such an inhibited neuron to the threshold level for triggering an impulse. (Not all neural inhibition is caused by hyperpolarization of the postsynaptic membrane; there is evidence that presynaptic inhibition also sometimes occurs, presumably because either the synthesis or the release of transmitter substance is inhibited in some way.)

How synaptic transmitter substances exert their effects on the permeability of the postsynaptic membrane is still a matter of speculation. It has been hypothesized that inhibitory transmitters open channels through the membrane large enough for the passage of potassium and chloride ions but too small for the larger sodium ions,[1] and that excitatory transmitters open larger channels through which sodium ions can pass. It seems unlikely that channels of such precise size could be created anew through the whole thickness of the membrane and maintained for a thousandth of a second every time a burst of transmitter substance is released into the synaptic cleft. Models of the synapse have therefore assumed that the postsynaptic membrane normally contains pores of two different sizes built into its

structure, but that these pores are plugged in some manner in the normal resting neuron (Fig. 10.22). The function of transmitter substances would thus be to displace the plugs momentarily. Inhibitory transmitters would selectively unplug the smaller channels, permitting free outflow of potassium ions and free inflow of chloride ions for an instant. Excitatory transmitters would selectively unplug the larger channels, permitting free inflow of sodium ions for an instant. Though this model helps us think about the mechanism of syn-

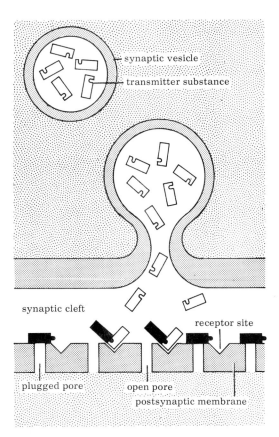

Fig. 10.22. Model of excitatory synapse. The synaptic vesicle releases molecules of transmitter substance into the cleft. These molecules diffuse across the cleft and react with receptor sites adjacent to pores in the postsynaptic membrane; in doing so they remove the plugs from the pores, with the result that ions can pass through the pores.

[1] The ions with which we are concerned here are hydrated ions—ions that have a shell of water bound to them. Because the shell of water around sodium ions is considerably thicker than that around potassium ions, hydrated sodium ions are larger than hydrated potassium ions.

aptic transmission, it may or may not approximate the actual mechanism; how close it comes to the facts, only further research can establish.

Transmission Between the Motor Axon and the Effector

Just as there is a gap at the synapses between successive neurons in a neural pathway, there is a gap between the terminus of an axon and the effector it innervates.[2] When the effector is skeletal muscle, the gap is usually contained within a specialized structure, the *motor end plate* (or neuromuscular junction), formed from the end of the axon and the adjacent portion of the muscle surface (Fig. 10.23). Transmission across this gap is via transmitter chemicals. In somatic endings in vertebrates, the transmitter substance is apparently acetylcholine, which produces a similar effect on the membrane of muscle cells as on the postsynaptic membrane in synapses between neurons. Much less is known about the transmitter substances at the motor end plates of invertebrates; it is clear, however, that other substances besides acetylcholine are important. For example, it is known that acetylcholine is not the transmitter substance at the neuromuscular junctions of insects; drugs that interfere with acetylcholine transmission have no effect on insect neuromuscular junctions, even when administered in massive doses. All efforts to identify the actual transmitter substance have failed.

Parasympathetic motor fibers of vertebrates release acetylcholine at their junctions with effectors, just as somatic motor fibers do. But many sympathetic motor fibers release a different substance, which seems to be *noradrenaline,* a substance also produced as a hormone by the adrenal medulla. The fact that para-

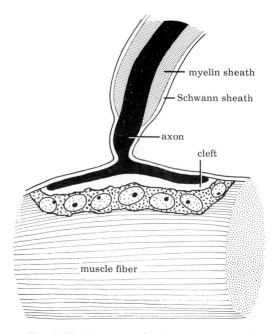

Fig. 10.23. Neuromuscular junction. The end of the axon and the specialized adjacent portion of the muscle fiber together constitute the motor end plate. As in a synapse between two neurons, there is a cleft between the two cells.

sympathetic and sympathetic neuro-effector junctions often employ different transmitter chemicals helps explain why these two components of the autonomic nervous system produce different responses by effectors.

We have said several times that the sympathetic nervous system and the hormones of the adrenal medulla have amazingly similar effects on the body, both eliciting the so-called "fight-or-flight" syndrome of responses. It now becomes clear why their effects are so similar; they release the same chemicals, and the reason they do apparently lies in a fascinating functional and evolutionary relationship between them. We have said that autonomic pathways typically include two motor neurons. There is one exception to this rule. The sympathetic pathway to the adrenal medulla has only one motor neuron (see Fig. 10.12). Apparently the adrenal medulla forms from presumptive nervous tissue (i.e. tissue destined

---

[2] Some biologists apply the term "synapse" to both the gap between two neurons and the gap between the end of an axon and an effector cell. Other biologists restrict "synapse" to gaps between neurons; we shall follow this usage.

to become nerve) in the embryo, and is actually itself the highly specialized second motor neuron of this sympathetic pathway. In other words, evolution has converted what once was a motor neuron of the sympathetic nervous system into an endocrine gland specialized for secretion in quantity of the same substances that all second motor neurons of the sympathetic system secrete.

Here, then, is another example of the close interrelationship between the nervous system and the endocrine system—one that our entire examination of the mechanism of transmission at synapses and at neuro-effector junctions should have helped clarify for you. Neurosecretory activity like that of the hypothalamus in its interaction with the pituitary, and like that of the insect brain, which produces the hormone that regulates the prothoracic gland, is not an unusual or isolated phenomenon. Neurosecretion is fundamental to nerve action. Impulse transmission across all gaps in neural pathways depends upon it. It is not surprising, therefore, that natural selection has caused parts of the nervous system to become highly specialized for secretion in quantity of regulatory chemicals, which, when carried by the blood, may exert profound effects on distant parts of the body. In short, it is not surprising that evolution has sometimes given nervous tissue endocrine functions, and has given chemicals secreted by nervous tissue the properties of hormones.[3]

SENSORY RECEPTION

Virtually the entire body of a unicellular organism is directly exposed to environmental stimuli. Even in such organisms, however, certain regions of the cell may be specialized for stimulus reception. As animals became larger and more complex, and as many of their body cells lost all direct contact with the outside world, natural selection apparently placed a premium on increasing specialization of certain cells for stimulus reception. For higher animals, these specialized receptor cells came to be the body's principal means of gaining information about the surrounding environment. They are the first elements in the reflex arcs whose structure and function we have been discussing in this chapter.

Receptors are either portions of nerve cells, as in the case of many sensory endings in the skin, or specialized cells in intimate contact with nerve cells, as in the case of the taste cells of the tongue. In general, each type of receptor is responsive to a particular kind of stimulus; some are stimulated by stretching, others by heat or cold, others by certain kinds of chemicals, others by vibrations, and still others by light. Most receptors will not respond to stimuli of types other than those for which they are specialized. Each type of receptor functions as a transducer, converting one form of energy into another, i.e. converting the energy that constitutes the particular stimulus to which it is attuned into the electrochemical energy of the nerve impulse.

The traditional view is that man has five senses: touch, taste, smell, vision, and hearing. The expression "a sixth sense" is often used to describe an uncanny faculty for obtaining information that does not depend on the senses of the average man. But the expression is meaningless from a biological point of view; every man has not only a sixth sense, but a seventh, eighth, ninth, tenth, etc., sense as well. In short, the traditional five senses are only a few of many senses with which all human beings are endowed. We shall examine some of these senses here, in preparation for a discussion of the mechanisms by which information input to animal nervous systems occurs.

[3] The evolutionary origin of the nervous system might have been the reverse of this process. Elongation of secretory cells to form neurons might have been favored by natural selection because by such means a stimulus could cause release of hormones right at a distant target organ and, as a result, more precise control could be achieved with less hormone.

Sensory Receptors of the Skin, Skeletal Muscles, and Viscera

Types of Receptors. There are numerous types of sensory receptors in the skin (Fig. 10.24). (See also Fig. 3.48, p. 105, which shows some of these receptors *in situ*.) These receptors are concerned with at least five different senses, although the traditional classification mentioned above recognized only one

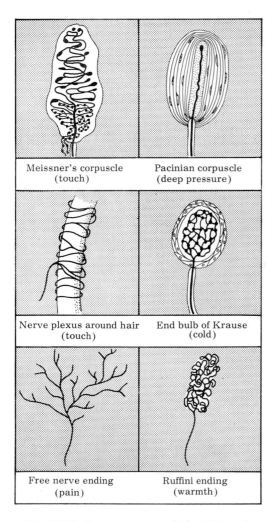

Meissner's corpuscle (touch)	Pacinian corpuscle (deep pressure)
Nerve plexus around hair (touch)	End bulb of Krause (cold)
Free nerve ending (pain)	Ruffini ending (warmth)

Fig. 10.24. Some receptors of the skin and the senses with which they have been thought to be associated. Recent evidence has cast doubt on the associations here indicated.

—touch. These five senses are touch, pressure, heat, cold, and pain. Some of the skin receptors, particularly those concerned with pain, are simply the unmyelinated terminal branches of neurons. Others are nets of fibers surrounding the bases of hairs; these fibers, which are particularly important in the sense of touch, are stimulated by the slightest displacement of the tiny hairs that are present on most parts of the body. Other skin receptors are more complex, consisting of nerve endings surrounded by a capsule of specialized connective-tissue cells.

The relative abundance of the different types of receptors differs greatly; e.g. pain receptors are nearly 27 times more abundant than cold receptors, and cold receptors are nearly 10 times more abundant than heat receptors. The receptors are not distributed evenly over the entire surface of the body; e.g. touch receptors are much more numerous in the fingertips than in the skin of the back, as might be expected in view of the normal functions of those two parts of the body. You can easily survey for yourself the distribution of different skin receptors on various parts of the body by using a very fine stiff bristle for touch, a thin needle to test for pain, and a very finely pointed sliver of ice to test for cold.

Unlike the receptors in the skin, which function in receiving information from the outside environment, some other receptors that are widely dispersed over the body function primarily in receiving information about the condition of the body itself. Though the senses these receptors mediate are not included in the traditional classification of five senses, they are of immense importance in the life of the individual. Among these receptors are the stretch receptors (proprioceptors) in the muscles and tendons (Fig. 10.25), which we mentioned earlier when discussing the knee-jerk reflex. They are sensitive to the changing tensions of muscles and tendons, and send impulses to the central nervous system informing it of the position and movements of the various receptors send the same sort of message to the central nervous system; in each case the message consists of waves of electrochemical change moving along neurons, the intensity of the stimulus being signaled by the frequency of impulses along individual neurons and by the number of parallel neurons stimulated. How, then, do these messages, which, qualitatively, are essentially identical, produce the entirely different sensations of touch and cold? The difference lies neither in the receptors nor in the messages they send, but in the destinations of the messages in the brain. The sensation is not in any way an inherent property of the stimulus or of the neural message; it is a creation of your own brain.

Each type of receptor sends impulses to a particular part of the brain; cold receptors send impulses to cold centers in the brain, touch receptors send impulses to touch centers, and pain receptors send impulses to pain centers. You experience the sensation of cold whenever excitatory impulses arrive at the cold center, and you experience the sensation of pain whenever excitatory impulses arrive at the pain center. It doesn't matter where the impulses originate or what stimulus initiates the impulses. It only matters what brain center is stimulated.

Normally, of course, impulses from a given receptor go to the appropriate brain center because of the way the nerve circuitry is organized. But the circuitry can be changed experimentally. Thus if the fibers leading from one of your touch receptors and from one of your cold receptors were cut, and if they were rerouted so that impulses from the touch receptor would go to the cold center in the brain and vice versa, every time you were touched and a touch receptor fired, you would experience the sensation of cold, and every time a cold object stimulated a cold receptor to fire, you would experience the sensation of touch. In other words, you would experience a sensation "inappropriate" to the stimulus, because the impulses would be going to the

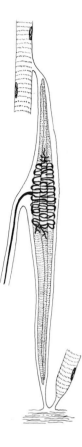

Fig. 10.25. A stretch receptor in skeletal muscle. The branches of a sensory nerve fiber are intimately associated with several specialized muscle fibers in a region where the muscle fibers have few cross striations. The entire apparatus is called a neuromuscular spindle.

parts of the body. Other dispersed receptors include those of the so-called visceral senses, located in the internal organs. Examples of them are the previously mentioned receptors in the neck artery that are sensitive to carbon dioxide concentrations in the blood and the receptors in the aorta that are sensitive to blood pressure. The firing of such visceral receptors seldom results in sensation (i.e. we are not aware of their action); the responses to their stimulation are usually mediated by the autonomic system. Sometimes, however, stimulation of visceral receptors produces conscious sensations, such as thirst, hunger, and nausea.

Sensations. The sensations you experience when touch receptors are stimulated are very different from those you experience when cold receptors are stimulated. Yet both types of wrong brain centers. But note that this inappropriateness would not change the quality of the sensation; the sensations would be the normal ones of touch and cold, even though they were in response to the wrong stimuli. The sensation is simply your brain's interpretation of incoming stimuli, and depends upon the part of the brain stimulated. Someone has dramatically emphasized this point by suggesting that if nerve fibers from your eyes could be crossed with nerve fibers from your ears, you would hear lightning and see thunder.

It is also the brain that is responsible for the localization of the sensation. Each part of the body has its own sensory area in the brain. Thus fibers from your big toe run to the big-toe center in your brain, fibers from your ankle run to the ankle center, fibers from the thumb run to the thumb center, etc. Again, it is the part of the brain to which the impulses go, not the stimulus or the receptor or the message itself, that determines localization of the sensation. If the fibers from the pain receptors in your big toe were crossed with those from your thumb, and if your big toe were then pricked with a needle, you would experience a sensation of pain in your thumb and would promptly examine your thumb for the cause of the trouble. In other words, the pain sensation is a creation of your brain, and it exists only in your brain, but it is referred by the brain to some other part of the body, where it then seems to you to exist.

Let us cite an actual experiment that makes this point with particular force. A group of scientists cut and crossed the fibers from pain receptors in the right and left rear feet of a white rat. They then made a small wound on the bottom of the right rear foot. Each time the rat put its weight on this foot the pain receptors there fired. But the impulses from these receptors were carried by the altered nerve circuitry to the part of the brain specialized as the sensory area for the left rear foot. The rat's brain, therefore, interpreted the signals as coming from the left rear foot, and

the animal began to walk on three legs, keeping the left rear foot raised off the ground. This, of course, only intensified the stimulation of the pain receptors in the wounded right foot, because now that foot had to bear more weight than before. Presumably the rat thereupon experienced an even more intense sensation of pain in the left foot, and it raised that foot higher and higher, all to no avail. No matter how long an experiment such as this was continued, the rat never learned that raising its right foot would alleviate the pain. Its central nervous system continued to interpret the pain as coming from the left foot. A human being in such a situation would eventually learn to raise the right foot; it would still seem to him that the pain was in the left foot, but he could consciously interpret pain in the left foot as a signal to raise the right foot. He could, in other words, alter his reflexes by an effort of will. Higher brain centers would in time dominate the control of his response to pain stimuli.

Another dramatic illustration of the fact that both the quality and the localization of sensation are determined exclusively by the brain is provided by the phenomenon of so-called "phantom-limb" pains. People who have had an arm or a leg amputated sometimes complain of pains in the limb that isn't there. Apparently the stumps of the nerve fibers that formerly ran from the amputated limb to the brain become irritated in some manner and send impulses to the brain. Since those impulses go to the sensory area of the brain concerned with the amputated limb, the impulses are interpreted by the brain as coming from the lost limb. The fact that the person knows his left arm, for example, is missing doesn't alter the fact that the sensation he experiences is one of pain in the left arm. His sensation is presumably of the same type as the one you experience when you feel pain in your left arm, even though you still have your left arm and he does not have his.

Notice that in our discussion of the experiment with white rats we said that "presumably" the rat experienced a sensation of pain. The word "presumably" is very important here. We cannot be sure whether the rat experienced any sensation at all, much less what sort of sensation. Remember, sensation is a conscious experience. Nervous function that does not involve consciousness centers in the brain can produce automatic reactions to stimuli, as in the case of autonomic pathways, but it cannot produce sensation. No sensation is experienced when a receptor in an artery is stimulated by a high concentration of carbon dioxide in the blood, but the body responds to this stimulation. We have no way of knowing whether a rat has any such thing as consciousness; hence we cannot know whether it experiences sensation. We know that it responds to stimuli, and we know that many of its responses are ones we tend subjectively to identify with consciousness, but this is not the same thing as an objective proof of consciousness. Indeed, many scientists have insisted that since we cannot prove consciousness exists in other animals, we should assume that it is absent. To many biologists, however, particularly in recent years, it has seemed more consistent with the known facts about nervous systems and behavior to assume that other higher vertebrates besides man are capable of some conscious activity. But no biologist would attribute to other animals the same degree of consciousness or the same type of consciousness as man's; other animals have brains that differ markedly from that of man, and these structural differences surely reflect functional differences. Thus, even if a rat has some degree of conscious awareness and can experience a true sensation of pain, that sensation is very likely qualitatively different from the human sensation of pain.

Sensations may well differ qualitatively even from one human being to another. That is why we said that the person experiencing phantom-limb pains in his left arm presumably experiences sensations of the same type as those you experience in your left arm. When two persons talk about pain in the left arm, we can be reasonably certain that their sensations are similar, because their nervous systems are similar, but we cannot be certain that the sensations are identical. The two persons have learned to apply the same words and descriptions to their individual sensations, but the possibility of qualitative differences remains and can never be ruled out. We might show that the two stimuli are identical and that the receptors are identical and that the neural messages are identical, but these do not determine the sensation.

Mechanism of Receptor Function. We have repeatedly stated that stimuli, which are environmental changes of some sort, cause receptors to initiate impulses that travel along neurons to the central nervous system, but we have yet to explain how stimuli cause receptors to initiate impulses.

We have said that excitatory transmitter substances at synapses induce impulses in the postsynaptic neuron by reducing the polarization of the membrane of that neuron to a critical level. Might a similar process be involved in the case of sensory receptors? Might the stimulus somehow cause sufficient depolarization of the membrane of the receptor cell to cause it to initiate an impulse? This possibility has received much attention during the last fifteen years or so, and the answer to our questions seems to be yes. Bernhard Katz of University College, London, demonstrated in 1950 that the stretching of a muscle spindle produces a local depolarization of the receptor cell. When the depolarization, called the *generator potential*, reaches a threshold level, it triggers the firing of an impulse in the nerve fiber (Fig. 10.26). The generator potential increases in direct relation to the increase in the energy of the stimulus, and the frequency of the triggered impulses increases with the intensity of the generator potential and with the rate at which it increases. The output

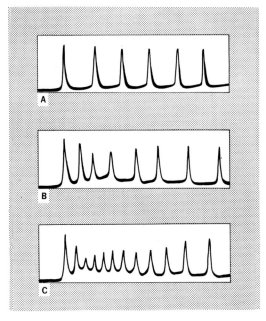

Fig. 10.26. Relationship of impulse pattern to intensity of stimulation of a stretch receptor. (A) A neuromuscular spindle is stretched slightly. This produces a generator potential (shown here as an upward shift in the base line) that triggers a series of impulses. (B) The same neuromuscular spindle is stretched more. The generator potential (base line) rises higher, and the frequency of the impulses increases. (C) The spindle is stretched still more. The generator potential rises even higher, and the frequency of the triggered impulses again increases. Thus the frequency of impulses is seen to be a function of the intensity of the generator potential, which in turn is a function of the strength of the stimulus. [Redrawn from B. Katz, J. Physiol. (London), vol. 111, 1950.]

from the receptor thus conveys a measure of the strength of the stimulus.

The characteristics of the generator potential explain why we are unable to distinguish between a constant stimulus and an intermittent stimulus of very high frequency. We are usually more aware of this inability as it affects vision—the fact that a rapidly flickering light gives us the same sensation as a constant light makes moving pictures and television possible —but it also affects our other senses. A sound

turned on and off at a very rapid rate would register as a constant sound. An intermittent stimulus applied hundreds of times a second to a pain receptor would cause a sensation of constant pain. Figure 10.27 helps show why this phenomenon of "flicker fusion" occurs. Stimulation of a receptor cell produces a sus-

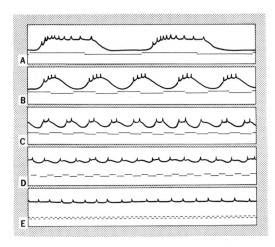

Fig. 10.27. Relationship of impulse pattern to frequency of stimulation. The broken horizontal lines in the lower portion of each box indicate when the eye of a horseshoe crab is exposed to light (raised line) and when the light is off (lowered line). (A) The light is alternately turned on for a long interval and then off for a long interval; when the light is on, a generator potential is maintained (the base line of the curve is raised) and a series of impulses (spikes) are triggered, but when the light is off the generator potential falls and no impulses are triggered. The fluctuations in the generator potential and the impulses it triggers signal to the brain that the stimulus is an intermittent one. (B) The light flickers at a faster rate, but there is still time for the generator potential to fall between bursts of light. (C) The flicker is faster, and the generator potential cannot fall all the way to the resting level between bursts of light; but it falls enough to cause a fluctuation in the impulse pattern. (D) The light flickers even faster, and the generator potential falls only slightly between bursts of light; the impulse pattern is thus much more regular. (E) The light flickers so rapidly that there is no appreciable drop in the generator potential between bursts of light, and the impulse pattern does not fluctuate; hence the animal cannot detect the fact that the stimulus is an intermittent rather than a constant one. [Courtesy W. H. Miller et al., Rockefeller University.]

tained local depolarization. As long as this depolarization (the generator potential) continues above the threshold value, impulses will be generated. If intermittent stimuli are applied only a few times a second, the generator potential will fall between successive stimulations and rise again with each stimulus. These fluctuations in the generator potential give rise to isolated bursts of impulses, and we can therefore detect that the stimulation is not constant. If, however, the intermittent stimuli are applied in very rapid succession, the generator potential does not have time to fall between stimulations and the spacing between impulses becomes more uniform, with the result that we cannot tell when one stimulation has ended and another begun and hence cannot detect that the stimulus is not constant.

The basic question of sensory reception is, of course: How does the stimulus produce the generator potential? Since the generator potential is the result of partial depolarization of the cell membrane (i.e. a reduction of the negativity at the inner surface of the membrane), we would predict, reasoning from the analogy of synaptic stimulation, that the membrane becomes more permeable to sodium ions, which thus flow inward. The question then becomes: How does the stimulus increase the permeability of the membrane to sodium ions? For the present, at least, only tentative answers can be given. Since different receptors are stimulated by different stimuli, the mechanism may well vary. In the case of vision, light energy is known to cause chemical changes in receptor pigments, and these are presumed to initiate chemical reactions that produce some sort of transmitter substance, which in turn depolarizes the membrane in about the same way as synaptic excitatory transmitter substances. In the case of stretch receptors and pressure receptors, mechanical distortion of the membrane is thought to produce the permeability changes directly. Perhaps the membrane of the receptor cell is breached by tiny channels built into its structure, as is thought

to be true of postsynaptic membranes. Mechanical distortion might somehow unplug the channels and allow sodium ions to leak inward, or distortion might increase the size of channels that are otherwise too small for the passage of sodium ions. The direct relationship between strength of stimulus and magnitude of generator potential could be explained by assuming that stronger stimuli distort a greater area of membrane, thereby opening more channels and allowing more ions to pass through the membrane. Much more research will be needed to determine whether this model contains any elements of truth.

The Senses of Taste and Smell

The receptors of taste and smell are chemoreceptors; i.e. they are sensitive to solutions of certain types of chemicals. These two senses are much alike, and when we speak of a taste sensation we are often referring to a compound sensation produced by stimulation of both taste and smell receptors. One reason why hot foods often have more "taste" than cold foods is that they vaporize more, the vapors passing from the mouth upward into the nasal passages and there stimulating smell receptors. And one reason why we cannot "taste" foods well when we have a cold is that, the nasal passages being inflamed and coated with mucus, the smell receptors are essentially nonfunctional. In other words, much of what we call taste is really smell. Conversely, some vapors entering our nostrils pass across the smell receptors and down into the mouth, where they stimulate taste receptors. In each case, taste and smell, chemicals must go into solution in the film of liquid coating the membranes of receptor cells before they can be detected. The major functional difference is that taste receptors are specialized for detection of chemicals present in quantity in the mouth itself, while smell receptors are more specialized for detecting vapors coming to the organism from distant sources; they are thus much more sensitive than taste receptors, as much as 3,000 times more in some cases.

Taste. The receptor cells for taste are located in *taste buds* (Fig. 10.28) on the upper surface of the tongue and, to a lesser extent, on the surface of the pharynx and larynx. The receptor cells themselves are not neurons, but are specialized cells with hairlike processes on their outer ends (Fig. 10.29). The ends of nerve fibers lie very close to these receptor cells, and when a receptor cell is stimulated, it generates impulses in the fibers.

There are apparently four basic taste senses: sweet, sour, salt, and bitter. The receptors for these four basic tastes have their areas of greatest concentration on different parts of the tongue—sweet and salt on the front, bitter on the back, and sour on the sides (Fig. 10.29). A few substances stimulate only one of the four types of receptors, but most stimulate two, three, or four types in varying degrees.

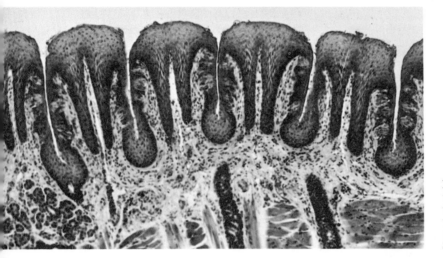

Fig. 10.28. Photograph of section of rabbit tongue. The taste buds are located in the walls of the deep narrow pits. [Courtesy General Biological Supply House, Inc., Chicago.]

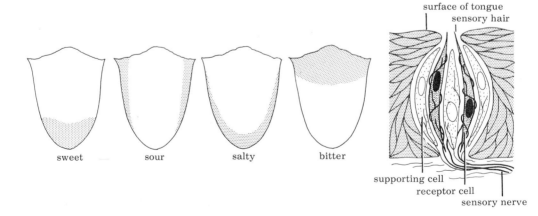

Fig. 10.29. Distribution and structure of taste buds. The receptors for the four different taste senses are on different parts of the tongue. Each taste bud contains two specialized types of cells: supporting cells and receptor cells; the latter bear sensory hairs that are exposed on the tongue surface. The ends of sensory neurons are closely associated with the receptor cells.

The sensations we experience are thus produced by a blending of the four basic sensations in different relative intensities. To illustrate, let us rate the intensity of stimulation of each of the basic tastes on a scale from 1 to 8, with 1 designating little or no stimulation, 8 designating maximal stimulation, and the numbers in between designating intermediate intensities. Substance A might stimulate sweet receptors at an intensity of 6, sour receptors at an intensity of 2, salt receptors at an intensity of 4, and bitter receptors at an intensity of 3. Consequently we could describe the taste of A by the formula 6243. Another substance, B, might also stimulate all four sets of receptors, but at different intensities, as represented by the formula 5274. In other words, A and B stimulate the same sets of receptors, but the taste sensations we experience in response to them are totally different, because the relative intensities at which they stimulate the receptors for each of the four basic tastes are different. If we remember also the immense role played by smell in producing "taste" sensations, we can begin to understand how a relatively small number of independent taste senses can mediate so many different taste sensations.

It was said earlier that the sensations experienced by different people in response to the same stimuli may not be the same. This statement can readily be substantiated for taste. The same substance can give rise to sensations of sweet in one person, if it stimulates his sweet receptors primarily, to sensations of bitter in a second person, if it stimulates his bitter receptors primarily, and to no sensation at all in a third, if it fails to stimulate any of his receptors. It is possible for someone to have particularly sensitive sweet receptors and unusually insensitive sour receptors; such a person might not like sugary food, because it would stimulate his sweet receptors excessively and arouse a sickeningly sweet sensation, but he might be very fond of lemon candy so sour that most people would reject it, because his sour receptors, being unusually insensitive, would not be much stimulated by this candy. Thus a given substance might very well have the taste formula 6254 for one person and the formula 4345 for another person. Although psychological factors play a large role in determining which foods people like and which they don't, it is also true that the different reactions of two persons to the same food may be, at least in part, the result of real biological differences between them. The sense of taste thus provides a particularly forceful illustration of the fact that sensations are not an inherent property of the stimulus but reside exclusively in the nervous system itself.

Smell. The receptor cells for the sense of smell (olfaction) in man are located in two clefts in the upper part of the nasal passages (Fig. 10.30A). Unlike the receptor cells of taste, the olfactory receptors are true nerve cells. The cell bodies of most of these neurons lie embedded in the epithelial layer of the walls of the olfactory area of the nasal chamber (Fig. 10.30B). Dendrites run from the cell bodies to the surface of the epithelium, where they bear a cluster of hairlike filaments, which apparently function as the receptor sites.

Many attempts have been made to identify a group of primary odors from which all more complicated odors can be derived. The olfactory sense has not, however, proved as easily analyzable as taste, where the four basic components were identified years ago. As far back as 1895, a system was devised in which all odors were explained in terms of nine basic odors. It soon became clear, however, that this system did not reduce odors to their fundamental components. For example, although most sense receptors exposed to a constant and unchanging stimulus for a long period of time become adapted to the stimulus (i.e. they cease responding to it or respond only weakly), it was shown that when the olfactory receptors became adapted to one odor and were then

suddenly exposed to another odor presumed to
be in the same one of the nine classes, they
frequently responded well. The inference was
that different receptors must be involved and
that the odors were not really made up of the
same basic components. Many other classifications of fundamental odors were proposed during the next sixty years, but most proved to be
just as unsatisfactory. In the 1950's, however,
John E. Amoore, who later joined the U.S.
Department of Agriculture, proposed a system
that seemed to go a long way toward giving
us a consistent and meaningful theory of olfaction.

Chemical analysis of substances that smell
much alike frequently reveals that they are
not at all similar chemically. This fact confused
scientists for many years, because it seemed
reasonable to expect substances capable of
stimulating the same receptors to have similar
functional groups. Amoore, while still an
undergraduate at Oxford University, worked
out the theoretical basis for a new theory of
odor that explained why chemically similar
substances often do not have a similar smell.
Noting the great dissimilarities in chemical
structure of substances that smelled alike, he
decided that there must be some other basic
similarity in the apparently dissimilar molecules. It had been suggested in 1949 by R. W.
Moncrieff of Scotland, who argued from the
generally accepted importance of spatial configuration in enzyme-substrate reactions and
antigen-antibody reactions, that the size and
shape of a molecule might be more important
than its chemical structure in determining
which smell receptors it can stimulate. Amoore
examined the size and shape of approximately
600 organic compounds for which the odors
had been well described, and thought that the
evidence supported Moncrieff's hypothesis. In
1952 he published a stereochemical theory of
olfaction in which all odors are described in
terms of seven basic primary odors: camphora-
ceous, musky, floral, pepperminty, ethereal
(like ether), pungent, and putrid. He gave a

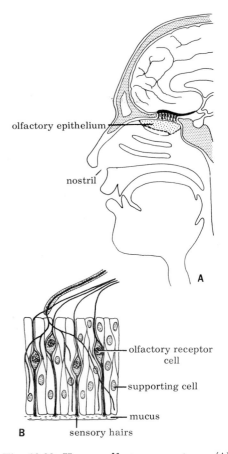

Fig. 10.30. Human olfactory receptors. (A)
The receptors are located in two clefts in the
upper part of the nasal passages. (B) The
cell bodies of most of the receptor cells are
located in the olfactory epithelium. Long axons
run from the cell bodies to the brain.

detailed description of the size and shape a
substance must have to stimulate the receptors
for each of these primary odors. Thus, according to Amoore, camphoraceous-smelling molecules are roughly spherical with a diameter of
approximately 7 angstroms; musky-smelling
molecules are disc-shaped and about 10 angstroms in diameter; floral-smelling molecules
are in the form of a disc with a flexible elongate
side group attached; ethereal-smelling molecules are thin and rod-shaped; pepperminty-
smelling molecules have a wedge shape; etc.
The receptor sites on the sensory cells must

have shapes into which such molecules can fit, just as a key fits into a lock. Amoore thought the receptor cells must be of seven types, each with receptor sites appropriate to one of the classes of molecules. A molecule could stimulate more than one kind of receptor cell if one part of the molecule could fit into one type of receptor site and another part into a different type of receptor site.

The results of research on Amoore's theory since 1952 have been ambiguous. Amoore and his co-workers at Georgetown University have reported that they can synthesize molecules of certain shapes, predict what odor they will have, and then show (using panels of trained smellers) that the odor is indeed the one predicted. They have also reported that they have been able to design and synthesize molecules totally unlike one another in chemical structure, but with similar sizes and shapes, and to show that even trained odor testers cannot tell them apart. Other researchers, however, have not been able fully to duplicate Amoore's results. Moreover, several physical chemists have claimed that the shapes of some compounds Amoore considered similar are actually not similar at all. For the present, then, the stereochemical theory of odor must be considered interesting but unproved.

Before leaving our discussion of the olfactory sense, we should emphasize that this, like all senses, may be very different in other species of animals. It is well known that many animals have a far more acute sense of smell than man, that most mammals, for example, depend much more on olfaction than man does. Some moths have incredibly sensitive smell receptors, the males being capable of detecting the females at a distance of several miles. If the sense of smell depends on a limited number of primary odors, it seems entirely possible that these are not the same in all animals. Mammals and moths, for instance, are so different in their other characteristics that one would expect their smell receptors to function differently also.

The Sense of Vision

All cells are sensitive in some way to radiation —not only radiation in the visible part of the spectrum (see Fig. 4.2, p. 116), but radiation in the infrared (i.e. heat) and ultraviolet portions as well. Cells are, in fact, particularly sensitive to ultraviolet radiation, which can be severely destructive to protoplasm. However, it is radiation of those wavelengths we know as visible light that are most widely useful to organisms. A vast array of plants and animals have independently evolved structures specialized for their sensitivity to these wavelengths, which are peculiarly suited to serve as carriers of information to the organism—information frequently coming from very distant sources. Longer wavelengths, such as those of the infrared and radio portions of the electromagnetic spectrum do not have enough energy to produce quickly the kinds of chemical reactions upon which many biological functions, including vision, photosynthesis, and phytochrome conversions, depend. Shorter wavelengths, such as those of the ultraviolet, X-ray, and gamma-ray portions of the spectrum, have so much energy that they are destructive to many of the kinds of molecules of which organisms are composed. It is no accident, therefore, that so many unrelated organisms have convergently evolved specialized mechanisms for utilizing the same narrow band of wavelengths as a source of information about their environment.

Light Receptors of Animals. Almost all animals respond to light stimuli. Even Protozoa react quickly to changes in light intensity, often moving away from brightly lit areas. In fact, the single cells of many Protozoa have a special region that serves as a sensitive detector of light. This region contains a pigment that undergoes chemical changes when exposed to light energy. These changes "tell" the protozoan that light is present. Most multicellular animals have evolved specialized light receptor cells, but the basic mechanism of detection is the same as in protozoans; light energy produces changes in a light-sensitive pigment. This pigment is usually a protein to which a portion of a carotenoid molecule is attached. Carotenoids, you will recall, are yellow light-sensitive pigments in plants. Animals obtain the carotenoid in their diet as a vitamin (vitamin A), since it can be synthesized only by plants.

The light receptors of many invertebrates do not function as eyes, in the usual sense of that word. They do not form images, but simply indicate to the animal whether or not light is present and, frequently, whether the intensity of the light is increasing or decreasing. Some of these receptors give the animal no clue to the direction in which the light source lies, and the animal responds by essentially random movements. However, many light receptors are structurally arranged in such fashion that direction becomes an additional type of information detectable by the animal. The eye spots of planaria (see Fig. 5.18, p. 182) are an example; the sensory cells in these organs are stimulated primarily by light coming from above and slightly to the front. Receptor organs capable of detecting in which direction a light source lies frequently contain numerous sensory cells oriented at different angles; light coming from different directions will stimulate different cells. These more complex eyes can often also detect movement, because light from a moving object stimulates different cells in succession. Still more complex eyes commonly include a lens capable of concentrating light on the receptor cells, thereby increasing the sensitivity of the eye to light of weak intensity. Lenses also greatly increase the ability to detect direction and movement by focusing the light from each source onto only a few receptor cells.

Lenses, which doubtless evolved initially as structures for concentrating the incident light, made possible the later evolution of image-forming eyes in some molluscs, most arthro-

pods, and most vertebrates, and perhaps in a few worms. We can easily imagine the steps in the evolutionary development of image-forming eyes from relatively simple lensed eyes. Such simple eyes presumably enabled the animal to detect the direction and movement of objects, but not their shapes. With the development, through natural selection, of better lenses that focused light more precisely and thus made possible increased discrimination of light intensity, direction, and movement, vague images—no more than patterns of light and dark—must have formed on the bed of receptor cells located behind the lens. Natural selection would have favored those individuals whose eyes formed the best images and whose central nervous system could best translate these images into information leading to appropriate responses (it is obvious that unless the nervous system was able to interpret the patterns of impulses, or images, coming to it from the receptor cells, these images would have been useless). Over long spans of time, the image-forming capabilities of the species must slowly have improved. Since increased information about objects in the environment is clearly highly advantageous to most active free-moving animals, we may suppose that the selection pressure for improved image formation was a strong one.

The independent evolution of image-forming eyes by different groups of animals has resulted in two quite different basic types of eyes: *camera-type eyes,* such as those of molluscs and vertebrates, and *compound eyes,* such as those of insects and crustaceans. A camera-type eye utilizes a single lens system to focus light on a surface containing many receptor cells packed close together; the receptor surface, called the *retina,* thus functions in a manner analogous to a piece of film. The light pattern focused on the retina produces differential stimulation of different receptor cells, just as a light pattern focused on a piece of film produces different amounts of chemical reaction at different points on the film.

A compound eye, on the other hand, utilizes many closely packed lenses, each associated with only a few sensory cells (Fig. 10.31). Each lens with its associated receptor cells forms a functional unit called an ommatidium (Fig. 10.32). Image formation depends upon the light pattern falling on the surface of the compound eye; this light pattern determines which ommatidia will be stimulated and at what intensity. Thus there is no structure strictly analogous to the retina of a camera eye, the critical surface being the outer surface of the compound eye itself, composed of the closely packed individual lenses. Since each ommatidium points in a slightly different direction, each is stimulated by light coming from different points in the surrounding area. The insect's brain must integrate the messages coming to it from many ommatidia to produce (presumably) an image that represents the sum of many separate much smaller images.

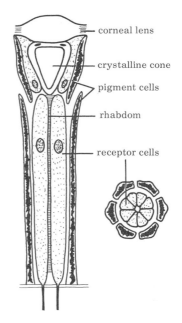

Fig. 10.32. Longitudinal section and cross section of an ommatidium from an insect compound eye. The lens and crystalline cone focus incoming light rays into the rhabdom, which distributes the light into the eight receptor cells surrounding it. The pigment cells prevent passage of light from one ommatidium to another. [Redrawn from R. E. Snodgrass, *Principles of Insect Morphology*, McGraw-Hill Book Co., 1935. Used by permission.]

Fig. 10.31. Photograph of head of a horsefly, showing compound eye. [Courtesy Thomas Eisner, Cornell University.]

It is commonly said that the mosaic nature of the stimuli coming to an insect's brain from its compound eyes must result in a rather crude image sensation that retains its mosaic characteristics. This is, indeed, the kind of image produced if the outer surface of a compound eye is detached and a photograph is taken through it. But we should be very wary of extrapolating from the nature of the receptor organ to the nature of the animal's sensations (if, indeed, we can even apply the word "sensation" to an animal that may have no conscious awareness in the human sense). We have repeatedly emphasized the overriding importance of the brain as the source of sensation, and we have no way of knowing what the insect's brain does with the information coming to it from the compound eye. It certainly does not function simply like the camera we use to take a picture through the insect's eye. Furthermore, we have good evidence that the receptor cells of the eye itself modify incoming information before sending it to the brain. In other words, eyes do not function in so simple a manner as models based on cameras or mosaics would imply. They do not just convert a pattern of light input into a matching pattern of electrochemical energy in the form of nerve impulses sent to the brain. For example, certain cells inhibit or facilitate the propagation of impulses along other sensory cells. Stimulation of one ommatidium influences the pattern of impulses sent to the brain by neighboring ommatidia, just as stimulation of receptor cells in one part of the retina of a camera-type eye influences the pattern of impulses conveyed by nerve fibers from other parts of the retina. Such information-modifying functions of the eye strengthen differences in neural activity originating from differently lighted parts of the eye, with the result that contrast is heightened and contours become sharper. Thus the photograph we take through the eye of an insect certainly does not represent the modified information pattern actually transmitted to the insect's brain. When the modified information pattern reaches the brain, it is further modified by the intricate interactions of the nerve cells there. The result is almost certainly a clearer image than we would predict on the basis of the structure of the receptor organ alone. It is entirely possible that an insect has much clearer vision (perhaps totally unlike a mosaic) than is commonly supposed.

Structure of the Human Eye. The adult human eye is globe-shaped and has a diameter of approximately one inch (Fig. 10.33). It is encased in a tough but elastic coat of connective tissue, the *sclera.* The anterior portion of the sclera, called the *cornea,* is transparent and more strongly curved, and functions as the first element in the light-focusing system of

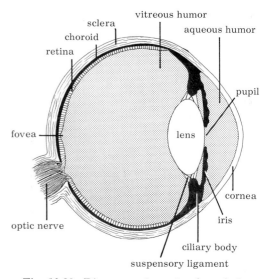

Fig. 10.33. Diagrammatic section through the human eye.

the eye. Just inside the sclera is a layer of darkly pigmented tissue, the *choroid,* through which many blood vessels run; the choroid is important both as the structure providing a blood supply to the rest of the eye and as a light-absorbing layer that (like the black inner surface of a camera) helps prevent internally reflected light from blurring the image. Just behind the junction between the main part of the sclera and the cornea, the choroid becomes thicker and has smooth muscles embedded in it; this portion of the choroid is called the *ciliary body.* At a point anterior to the ciliary body, the choroid leaves the surface of the eyeball and extends into the cavity of the eye as a ring of pigmented tissue, the *iris.* The iris contains smooth muscle fibers arranged in both circular and radial directions; when the circular muscle fibers contract, the opening in the center of the iris, called the *pupil,* is reduced; when the radial muscles contract, the pupil is dilated. The iris thus regulates the size of the opening admitting light (the pupil) in about the same way as the diaphragm of a camera regulates the lens aperture.

The *lens,* which functions as the second element in the light-focusing system, is suspended just behind the pupil by a *suspensory ligament* attached to the ciliary body. The lens and its suspensory ligament thus divide the cavity of the eyeball into two chambers, each filled with transparent fluid or semifluid material. The material in the chamber between the cornea and the lens is watery and is called the aqueous humor. The material in the chamber behind the lens is viscous and gelatinous; it is called the vitreous humor.

The *retina,* which contains the receptor cells for the sense of vision, is a thin tissue covering the inner surface of the choroid. It is composed of several layers of cells. The receptor cells are of two different types, called *rod cells* (Fig. 10.34) and *cone cells.* The rod cells are more abundant toward the periphery of the retina. They are exceedingly sensitive and enable us to see in light too dim to stimulate cone cells. They cannot detect colors, however, and the images to which they give rise are coarse and poorly defined. The cones, which are more abundant in the central portion of the retina, are used for vision in bright light. They give rise to detailed well-defined images, and they enable us to detect color. The rods and cones synapse in the retina with short sensory neurons, which themselves synapse in the retina with longer neurons whose axons, bundled together as the optic nerve, run to the visual centers in the brain.

The presence of several sets of synapses in the retina enables the eye to modify extensively the information transmitted from the receptor cells to the brain. That the information pattern leaving the eye via the optic nerve is quite different from the information pattern entering the eye has been shown, for example, by J. Y. Lettvin and his co-workers at the Massachusetts Institute of Technology. They have identified four different sets of fibers running to the brain in the optic nerve of frogs. The fibers in one set (the "sustained-contrast detectors") respond only to edges, i.e. boundaries between

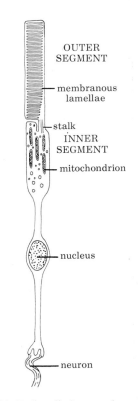

OUTER SEGMENT

— membranous lamellae

— stalk
INNER SEGMENT

— mitochondrion

— nucleus

— neuron

Fig. 10.34. Rod cell from a human retina. The outer segment and the stalk connecting it to the inner segment develop as a highly specialized cilium (electron microscopy reveals that a basal body—not shown here—is located at the inner end of the stalk, and that the nine peripheral fibrils characteristic of all cilia run from it through the stalk into the outer segment; as is true of most cilia that have lost their motile properties, the two central fibrils of motile cilia are absent). The visual pigment is located in the numerous membranous lamellae of the outer segment.

areas of different brightness; they presumably provide the frog with something like an outline drawing of its surroundings. Fibers of the second set ("moving-edge detectors") also respond to boundaries of brightness, but only if they are moving. Fibers of the third set ("net-dimming detectors") respond to sudden reductions in illumination over a large part of the visual field; they presumably warn the frog when a larger animal, perhaps a predator, is approaching. Fibers of the fourth set ("net-convexity detectors") respond only to small dark objects, particularly moving ones; they probably function as the frog's "bug detectors." These four types of information—about edges, moving edges, sudden dimming, and moving small objects—are apparently the only components of the total incoming information that are filtered through the visual receptors and sent to the brain. From them, the brain must construct whatever sort of "sensation" or "image" the frog experiences about its visual surroundings.

Analogous processing of information doubtless occurs in the eyes of all higher organisms. D. H. Hubel and T. N. Wiesel of Harvard University, working on cats, whose eyes are presumably more like those of human beings than are those of frogs, have shown that incoming visual information is extensively modified as it enters the cerebral cortex. Such findings help explain why there are frequently major discrepancies between the images actually focused on the retina and the subjective sensations in our brains.

Function of Rods and Cones. Both rods and cones contain light-sensitive pigments. The pigment in rods (called rhodopsin) is converted into a slightly different form when struck by photons of light and is regenerated to its original form in the dark. Apparently it takes one photon to convert one molecule of rhodopsin. This light-driven chemical reaction must act in some manner to produce a generator potential across the membrane of the rod cell. The rod-cell membrane seems to be exceedingly sensitive to the photochemical reaction; available evidence indicates that conversion of one molecule of rhodopsin by one photon produces a generator potential sufficient to cause impulse induction. The impulses going to the brain from the rods signal that light is present, but they convey no information concerning color.

The mechanism of cone vision is much more complex, and our understanding of color perception is still elementary. Recent evidence, from experiments performed at Johns Hopkins University, Harvard University, and the University of Pennsylvania, indicates that there are three functional types of cones, each containing a different pigment. Each of the three pigments is sensitive to wavelengths of light covering a broad band of the visible spectrum, but each has its maximum absorption in a different portion of that spectrum (Fig. 10.35). Thus the three pigments[4] can be designated as blue-absorbing, green-absorbing, and red-absorbing. This evidence for a three-color, three-receptor mechanism of cone reception agrees with a theory of color vision long supported by psychological experiments.

Yet electrophysiological experiments on the neurons whose fibers make up the optic nerve have repeatedly indicated that the information code transmitted to the brain along each neuron involves only two elements, not three. Most optic neurons are specialized to fire during exposure of the eye to light of certain wavelengths, but they also fire when exposure to other wavelengths ceases. In other words, a given neuron gives an "on" response to light of certain colors and an "off" response to light of other colors. Thus the code by which information is transmitted from the eye to the brain along each neuron involves two elements: "on" and "off." Somehow the three-color information at the level of the cones must be translated in the retina into two-color "on-off" signals. The evidence now seems to indicate that each of the neurons whose axons lead to the brain synapses with pathways coming from at least two of the three types of cones. Some of these synapses are excitatory and others are inhibitory. Thus one neuron may receive excitatory impulses from green cones and inhibitory impulses from red cones; it would therefore give "on" signals in response to impulses from green cones and "off" signals in response to impulses from red cones. An-

---

[4] Named cyanolabe, chlorolabe, and erythrolabe respectively.

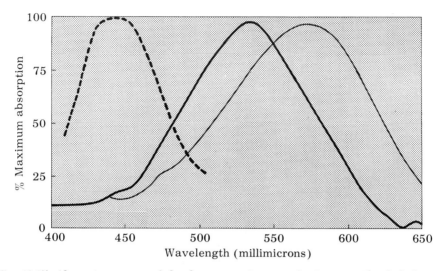

Fig. 10.35. Absorption spectra of the three cone pigments of primates. The dashed curve is for the blue-absorbing pigment; the heavy solid curve is for the green-absorbing pigment; and the light solid curve is for the red-absorbing pigment (which actually has its maximum sensitivity in the yellow region of the spectrum). [After E. F. MacNichol.]

other neuron may give "on" signals in response to impulses from red cones and "off" signals in response to impulses from blue cones. And still other neurons may give "blue-on, green-off" responses, or "red-on, green-off" responses, etc. Whether a given neuron fires during illumination or whether it fires immediately after illumination ceases (i.e. whether it signals "on" or "off") depends on the relative number of excitatory and inhibitory impulses it receives per unit time. In summary, each individual nerve fiber transmits information concerning only two of the three basic colors, but because different fibers carry information about different pairs of basic colors, the brain receives information concerning the relative intensity of illumination of the eye by each of the three basic colors. The brain then integrates this information in some unknown manner to produce multicolor sensations.

Human beings are so accustomed to their own color vision that they tend to assume other animals see colors in the same way. Man and other primates are, however, rather unusual among mammals in possessing color vision; most mammals see only in shades of gray. A bull doesn't really react to the color red; he reacts to the movement of the matador's cape. The cape could be almost any color without significantly altering the results. Apparently many fishes and reptiles and most birds do have color vision; it is curious that in this characteristic man bears a greater resemblance to these animals, to which he is only distantly related, than to the other mammals, to which he is more closely related.

Insects, too, often have color vision—a very important attribute for the ones that feed on flowers. Many of them, however, do not have the same visible spectrum as man. Their eyes cannot always detect light of the longest wavelengths seen by man; hence a room in which there is only pure red light will be in total darkness to many insects. But these insects can see light of wavelengths in the near end of the ultraviolet band, which human beings cannot see. We have no way of knowing, of course, what sort of color sensation an insect experiences when it sees ultraviolet light, but we do know that it can distinguish these wavelengths as a color distinct from the other colors in its visible spectrum.

Refraction and Accommodation. Since the pattern of illumination of retinal receptor cells is fundamental to image formation, high-resolution image vision depends on precise focusing of incoming light beams on the retina, just as clear high-resolution photography depends on precise focusing of incoming light on the film. If focusing is not good, the image is blurred. The object of focusing is to bring together at one point on the receptor surface all rays of light originating from a single point source. Suppose, for example, that you are looking at the face of another person. If you are to experience a clear image of that face, all light rays reflected from each point on the face must be brought together at a single point on your retina; thus all rays reflected from the point of the chin must be brought together at one point on your retina, all rays from the tip of the nose must be brought together at another point on your retina, all rays from the center of the forehead must be brought together at still another point on your retina, etc. In short, the projection of a true image of the observed object onto your retina requires a lens system capable of bending incoming rays of light and focusing them on the retina (Fig. 10.36), just as the lens system of a

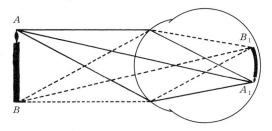

Fig. 10.36. Image formation on the retina. Incoming light rays from each point on the object being viewed are bent by the cornea in such a manner that they come together at a single point on the retina. Thus an image of the object is projected on the retina. Note, however, that the image is inverted.

movie projector focuses onto the screen light that has come from the film.

The lens system of the human eye has two principal components, the cornea and the lens. It is actually the cornea, not the lens, that does most of the bending of incoming light rays. The great importance of the lens stems from the fact that it is the alterable part of the system; it makes possible adjustments in the focus depending upon whether the object being viewed is close or distant. Let us consider for a moment the differences between focusing light coming from close objects and focusing light coming from distant objects. Light rays reflected from a given point travel away from that point in all directions (Fig. 10.37). The cornea of an eye located near the point source (position 1) will be struck by many light rays, some of which will be traveling at strongly divergent angles from each other. If, however, the cornea is located farther away from the point source (position 2), many of the most divergent light rays, which would have struck it at position 1, will miss it entirely, and the rays that do strike it will be traveling at only very slight angles to each other. If the cornea is 20 feet or more from the point source, the rays of light that strike it can be considered for all practical purposes as traveling parallel to each other. From these facts it follows that if all the divergent rays of light from a near object are to be brought into focus on the retina, they must be strongly bent by the lens system; much less bending is necessary to bring into focus the essentially parallel rays coming from a distant object.

Most *refraction* (bending) of light from distant objects is performed by the cornea. But the cornea cannot refract the strongly divergent light from near objects sufficiently to bring the image into clear focus on the retina. It is here that the lens becomes important. The lens can produce enough refraction in addition to that produced by the cornea to bring the image into focus. The lens is an elastic biconvex structure. It is attached, you

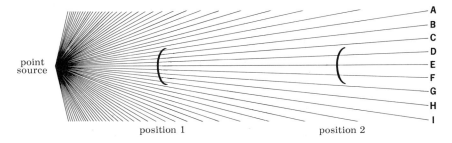

Fig. 10.37. Difference in degree of divergence of incoming light rays from near and far sources. Light rays from a point source travel outward in all directions. A cornea near the point source (position 1) will thus be struck by many strongly divergent light rays (rays A through I). A cornea farther away (position 2) will be missed by the most divergent rays (A–C and G–I) and will be struck by rays traveling at much smaller angles to each other (D–F). If the cornea is 20 or more feet from the point source, the light rays reaching it will be traveling almost parallel to each other.

will recall, to the ciliary body by the suspensory ligament. When the eye is viewing distant objects (i.e. objects more than 20 feet away), a considerable tension on the suspensory ligament stretches the lens, which is thus flattened and becomes less convex. Now, the less convex a lens is, the less refractive power it has. Hence, when the lens is maximally stretched, it exerts very little influence on incoming light rays; under these circumstances, refraction is primarily a function of the cornea. When, however, the eye is viewing a near object, the tension on the suspensory ligament is partly relaxed, and the front surface of the lens bulges outward as a result of its natural elasticity. In other words, the reduced tension on the lens allows it to become more convex, which means that its refractive power increases. Tension on the lens is relaxed just enough for its refractive power to reach the point where it adequately supplements the refractive power of the cornea, and the image is brought into clear focus on the retina. The nearer the viewed object is to the eye, the more the tension on the lens is relaxed. This process of correcting the focus of images of near objects by changes in the shape of the lens is called *accommodation.*

Accommodation depends upon the action of the smooth muscles in the ciliary body. These muscles are arranged in such a fashion that when they contract they pull the points of attachment of the suspensory ligament forward closer to the iris. The ligament consequently forms a circle with a smaller radius than before and, the tension on it being thus reduced, allows the curvature of the lens to increase. Note that accommodation for near vision depends upon a muscular contraction that *reduces* tension, and that adjustment for distant vision depends upon a muscular relaxation that *increases* tension. Ordinarily, muscular contractions increase tension and muscular relaxations reduce tension. That the organization of the ciliary body should reverse this usual relationship provides a very interesting example of biological adaptation. Men spend far more time viewing objects more than 20 feet away than viewing near objects (this has become less true since men became civilized and began to read and write, a relatively recent phenomenon). An arrangement whereby muscular contraction produces the tension on the lens necessary for distant vision would have required that the muscles be contracted most of the time. Under the existing arrangement, however, according to which relaxation produces the tension, there is less energy expenditure and less strain on the muscles themselves.

We have repeatedly compared the human eye to a camera, and there are indeed many striking similarities between them. But the focusing mechanisms are not similar, as we have just shown. The shape of a camera lens cannot be changed; hence focusing is accomplished by changing the distance between the lens and the film. The same arrangement is found in some animals with camera-type eyes. Fish, which lack ciliary muscles, have, instead, muscles that can move the whole lens forward and backward within the eye. And some molluscs change the length of the entire eyeball, thereby changing the distance between the cornea and the retina.

Structural defects in the shape of the eye are quite common in human beings. Figure 10.38 shows how overly short eyeballs result in farsightedness (hypermetropia) because the

distance between the lens system (cornea plus lens) and the retina is not sufficient for the strongly divergent rays from near objects to be brought into proper focus on the retina. The figure also shows how overly long eyes result in nearsightedness (myopia) because the cornea brings together the nearly parallel rays from distant sources at a point far in front of the retina, but brings together the more divergent rays from near sources at a point closer to the retina. Another common condition, astigmatism, stems from unequal curvature of the cornea; it can be corrected with a lens ground unequally to compensate for the defects of the cornea.

The Sense of Hearing

Receptors of the sense of hearing are specialized for the detection of vibrations, whether those vibrations come initially to the animal

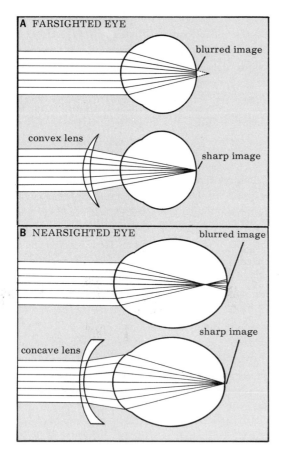

Fig. 10.38. Farsighted and nearsighted eyes. (A) The farsighted eye is so short that the focal point would be behind the retina; i.e. the cornea and lens cannot bend the light rays enough to bring them together on the retina. Since rays from a distant source are almost parallel, they need less bending than the divergent rays from a near source; hence the person can see distant objects more clearly. Farsightedness is corrected by a convex lens (one that is thicker in the center than at the edges). Such a lens bends the incoming light rays before they reach the cornea, thus aiding the cornea in bringing them together on the retina. (B) The nearsighted eye is so long that the focal point is in front of the retina and the rays have started to diverge again by the time they reach the retina, thus producing a blurred image. The strongly divergent rays from a near source require more bending; the focal point for them is therefore nearer the retina than is the focal point for the almost parallel rays from a distant source. Hence the person can see near objects more clearly. Nearsightedness is corrected by a concave lens (one that is thinner in the center than at the edges). Such a lens spreads the incoming parallel rays from a distant source, thus making them strike the cornea at divergent angles just as the rays from a near source would do.

via gases, solids, or liquids. The human ear is sensitive to vibrations of an amazing range of frequencies—from about 16 to 20,000 cycles per second in young people (some children can even hear frequencies as high as 40,000 cycles per second, but our ability to hear high frequencies declines steadily as we grow older). Some other animals can hear much higher frequencies; dogs respond to whistles at 30,000 cycles, which few human beings can hear, and bats and some moths can hear frequencies of 100,000 cycles or higher. Like smell and vision, hearing enables an animal to gain information from distant parts of its environment. It is not surprising, therefore, that sound is an important medium of communication.

Structure of the Human Ear. The human ear (Fig. 10.39A) is divided into three parts: the *outer ear,* the *middle ear,* and the *inner ear.* The outer ear consists of the ear flap, or pinna, and the auditory canal. At the inner end of the auditory canal is the *tympanic membrane,* more commonly called the eardrum.

On the other side of the tympanic membrane is the chamber of the middle ear. This chamber is connected to the pharynx via the *Eustachian tube,* which functions as a duct making possible the equalization of air pressure between the outer and middle ear. When you ascend a high hill, the reduced pressure at the higher altitude results in a lower pressure in the auditory canal than in the middle-ear chamber, and the tympanic membrane is stretched outward. The pressure is equalized when air escapes from the middle ear through the Eustachian tube into the pharynx. When you descend quickly from a high altitude, the reverse process occurs. As you know, passage of air through the Eustachian tube is facilitated by swallowing, yawning, or coughing. Three small bones[5] arranged in sequence ex-

tend across the chamber of the middle ear from the tympanic membrane to a membrane called the *oval window.* Another membrane, the *round window,* lies just below the oval window in the wall of the middle-ear chamber.

On the inner side of the oval and round windows is the inner ear, a complicated labyrinth of interconnected fluid-filled chambers and canals. The upper group of chambers and canals is concerned with the senses of static and dynamic equilibrium and will be discussed later. The lower portion of the inner ear consists of a long tube coiled like a snail shell. This is the *cochlea,* which is the organ of hearing. Inside the cochlea are three canals (Fig. 10.39B–D): the vestibular canal, which begins at the oval window; the tympanic canal, which connects with the vestibular canal and ends at the round window; and the cochlear canal, which lies between the other two. All three canals are filled with fluid. The sensory portion of the cochlea, called the *organ of Corti,* projects into the cochlear canal from the *basilar membrane,* which forms the lower boundary of the cochlear canal. The organ of Corti consists of a layer of epithelium on which lie rows of specialized receptor cells bearing sensory hairs at their apexes. Dendrites of sensory neurons terminate on the surfaces of the hair cells. Overhanging the hair cells is a gelatinous structure, the *tectorial membrane,* into which the hairs project. When vibrations of the basilar membrane cause the sensory hairs to move up and down against the less movable tectorial membrane, the deformations of the hairs thus produced apparently give rise to a generator potential in the hair cells, and these cells, in turn, stimulate the sensory neurons.

Reception of Vibratory Stimuli. Let us now trace briefly the steps involved in the reception of vibratory stimuli by the ear. Vi-

---

[5] These are the malleus, incus, and stapes, also commonly known respectively as the hammer, anvil, and stirrup. Only the stapes is present in the ear of amphibians, reptiles, and birds. The malleus and incus of mammals evolved from bones that are parts of the jaws in these other vertebrates.

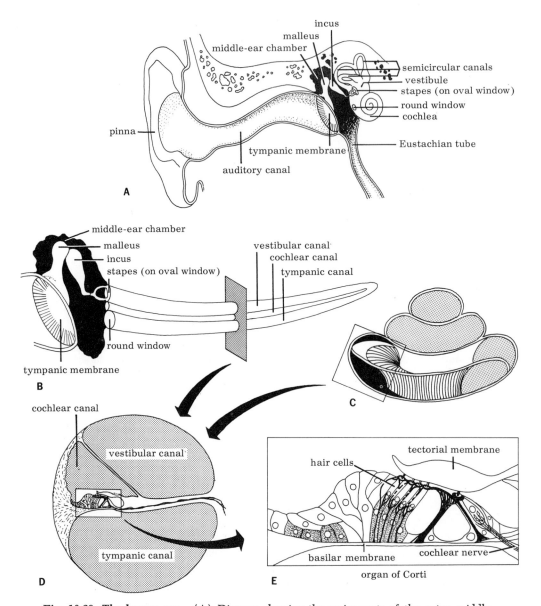

Fig. 10.39. The human ear. (A) Diagram showing the major parts of the outer, middle, and inner ear (see text for description). (B) Diagram of the relationship between the middle ear and the cochlea, which has here been uncoiled to show its canal system more clearly. (C) A section through the cochlea in its normal coiled state. (D) Enlarged cross section through one unit of the coil, showing the relationship between the vestibular, cochlear, and tympanic canals and the location of the organ of Corti. (E) Enlarged diagram of the organ of Corti, which rests on the basilar membrane separating the cochlear and tympanic canals. When the basilar membrane vibrates and moves the sensory hair cells up and down, the hairs rub against the tectorial membrane overhanging them. The resulting deformation of the hairs produces a generator potential in the hair cells, and this triggers impulses in sensory neurons running from the organ of Corti to the brain.

brations in the air pass down the auditory canal of the outer ear and strike the tympanic membrane, causing it to vibrate at the same frequency as the impinging air waves. These vibrations are transmitted across the cavity of the middle ear to the oval window by the three small middle-ear bones. These bones are arranged in such a manner that they constitute a lever system that diminishes the amplitude of the vibrations but increases their force. Furthermore, since the area of the tympanic membrane is nearly 30 times greater than that of the oval window, the pressure transmitted from the tympanic membrane is brought to bear on a much smaller area. Thus the result of transmission across the middle ear is the transformation of small pressures on the surface of the tympanic membrane into pressures as much as 22 times greater on the oval window. This increase in the force of incoming stimuli is very important in enabling us to detect very faint sounds—vibrations that, unmodified, would be insufficient to stimulate the receptor cells.

Vibrations of the eardrum, then, cause movements of the middle-ear bones, which in turn produce movements of the membrane of the oval window. These movements in their turn produce movements of the fluid in the canals of the cochlea. Each time the membrane of the oval window is bent inward by the piston-like action of the bone attached to it, fluid is pushed from the vestibular canal to the tympanic canal, with the result that the membrane of the round window bulges outward; when the membrane of the oval window then oscillates outward, fluid moves in the opposite direction and the membrane of the round window bulges inward. (Note that the immense resistance of fluids to compression would make movements of the oval window and fluid impossible if it were not for the presence of the movable round window, which acts as a pressure-release valve.)

The movements of the fluid in the cochlea are at the same frequencies as those of the air that entered the outer ear. The pressure waves in the fluid of the cochlea cause the basilar membrane to move up and down and rub the hairs of the hair cells against the tectorial membrane, thus deforming them. Stimulated through this deformation, the hair cells then stimulate the sensory neurons, which carry impulses to the auditory centers in the brain.

The Characteristics of Sounds. We can ordinarily distinguish three characteristics of the sounds we hear: pitch, volume (intensity), and tone quality. A satisfactory theory of hearing must be able to explain all three.

Pitch is a function of frequency; low-frequency vibrations stimulate a sensation of low pitch, and high-frequency vibrations stimulate a sensation of high pitch (remember that the sensation of pitch is not a property of the vibratory stimuli, but an interpretation of frequency produced by the brain). Apparently, low-frequency vibrations stimulate hair cells near the apex of the cochlea; high-frequency vibrations, hair cells near the base of the cochlea; and intermediate frequencies, hair cells of correspondingly intermediate regions of the cochlea. Thus the hair cells, like the keys of a piano graduated from low pitch to high pitch, are arranged in sequence, from those stimulated by low frequencies at the apex to those stimulated by high frequencies at the base. The neurons from each region along the length of the cochlea lead to slightly different areas in the brain. The pitch sensation we experience depends upon which of these areas of the brain is stimulated.

Volume is a function of the amplitude of vibrations. Thus very intense vibrations cause the fluid of the cochlea to oscillate at greater amplitude, and the correspondingly greater amplitude of oscillation of the basilar membrane produces more intense stimulation of the hair cells. The result is the transmission of more impulses to the brain per unit time. The brain interprets this increased stimulation as loudness.

If a violin, a piano, and a clarinet all play a note at the same pitch and volume, each will sound different. We call this difference tone quality. It is apparently the result of stimulation of hair cells in other regions of the cochlea besides the main region stimulated. We call the secondary vibrations that produce such stimulation harmonics or overtones. Different instruments (and different voices) produce different patterns of harmonics. Tone quality is thus the interpretation put by the brain on the pattern of hair cells stimulated.

Not all animals with an acute sense of hearing detect all three of the characteristics of sound that are important to man. Many insects, for example, have well-developed sound receptors, usually involving hair cells, but all available evidence indicates that they cannot detect pitch or tone quality. Insects are, however, more responsive than human beings to changes in the intensity and in the rhythm (duration and pattern) of bursts of sound. Sound is an exceedingly important medium of communication for both insects and men, but the relative importance of the various components of sound as vehicles of information is not the same for the two groups of animals.

The Senses of Static and Dynamic Equilibrium

The upper portion of the labyrinth of the inner ear is composed of three *semicircular canals* and a large vestibule that connects them to the cochlea (Fig. 10.40). Inside the vestibule are two chambers, the *utriculus* and the *sacculus.* Each contains a bed of sensory hair cells, upon which rest crystals of calcium carbonate. Changes in the position of the head cause these crystals, called otoliths, to exert more pull on some hair cells than on others (Fig. 10.41), thereby stimulating them more. The relative strength of the pulls signals to the cerebellum of the brain what the position of the head is at any given moment. This sense

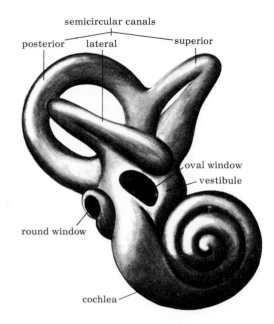

Fig. 10.40. **Labyrinth of right human ear.** [Modified from *Sobotta-Figge: Atlas of Human Anatomy,* 8th English ed., Hafner Publishing Co., New York.]

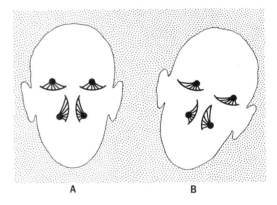

Fig. 10.41. **Function of the organs of static equilibrium.** Crystals of calcium carbonate (otoliths) rest on sensory hair cells in the utriculi and sacculi. Changes in the position of the head relative to gravity displace the crystals, thereby altering the pattern of push or pull they exert on the hair cells. This, in turn, alters the pattern of impulses sent to the brain.

of position is called the sense of static equilibrium.

Similar sensory devices are found in some other animals besides vertebrates. For example, crayfish and lobsters have equilibrium organs that consist of sand grains resting on beds of hair cells. When the animal molts, it loses the lining of the equilibrium organ, and with it the sand grains. Normally the animal shovels new sand grains into the organs when molting has been completed. If a crayfish is kept in a tank containing iron filings instead of sand, it will replace the lost sand with filings. If a strong magnet is then held near the crayfish, it will orient to the magnet as though it were the pull of gravity. The crayfish can thus be made to swim upside down; the experiment causes the animal's organs of equilibrium to signal to the central nervous system that "down" is "up."

The semicircular canals are concerned with the sense of dynamic equilibrium. Each of the three canals is oriented in a different plane of three-dimensional space (Fig. 10.40). At the base of each canal is a small chamber containing a tuft of sensory hair cells. When the head is moved or rotated in any direction, the fluid in the canals lags behind because of its inertia. As you know, the same thing happens if you move a glass of water; the water tends to lag and thus rises to a higher level on the back side of the glass and falls to a lower level on the front side (if the glass is very full, or if you move the glass very suddenly, the water may lag so much that it will spill over the edge). If you measured the pressure exerted by the water on the sides of the glass, you would find that when you move the glass the water exerts increased pressure on the back side. The same thing happens in the semicircular canals. When the head moves (or, more precisely, when the velocity—speed and direction—of its movement changes), the fluid in the canals lags and thus exerts increased pressure on the hair cells. This pressure stimulates the hair cells to initiate impulses to the cerebellum of the brain. The brain, by integrating the different amounts of stimulation coming to it from each of the three canals, can then determine very precisely the direction and the speed of the movement.

Lateral-Line Systems

Terrestrial vertebrates lack a sensory system that is of great importance to fishes. This is the lateral-line system, which consists of a series of grooves on the head and sides. Clusters of sensory hair cells lie at intervals in the grooves. Apparently the sensory cells are stimulated when pressure waves or currents in the water bend the hairs. This sensory system is important in enabling the fish to measure its progress through the water during locomotion, in informing it of localized water disturbances, and in "distant touch"—the detection of moving objects, such as predators or prey, or of stationary objects that reflect water movements produced by the fish itself. Fish also frequently stimulate the lateral-line system of other individuals by fanning water against the receptors with their tails during courtship or combat.

The lateral-line system is important from an evolutionary point of view because it is thought that the sensory hair apparatus of hearing and equilibrium in terrestrial vertebrates evolved from elements of the ancestral lateral-line system. Both the senses of hearing and of dynamic equilibrium in terrestrial vertebrates are based, as we have seen, on detection by hair cells of pressure currents in liquids, just as is the lateral-line sense of fishes. Hearing on land has involved the evolution of structures capable of converting weak pressure waves in air into stronger pressure waves in liquid. No such conversion is necessary in fishes, and, in fact, it is difficult to say if they hear in the strict sense. Their ear is entirely internal and is primarily an organ of equilibrium. But fishes certainly detect pressure waves easily, and some can even detect pitch (i.e. discriminate between different frequencies), but is this a hearing sense or a lateral-line sense? This question is probably meaningless; the animal detects the stimulus and can respond to it, and that is what is biologically important.

THE BRAIN

We said in the first part of this chapter that the brains of invertebrate animals are much smaller in relation to the size of their bodies than are those of vertebrates, and that their dominance over the rest of the central nervous system is usually less pronounced. The brains of many invertebrates, such as earthworms and insects, consist of a ring of nervous tissue encircling the anterior portion of the digestive tract (see Fig. 10.5). Frequently the two small ganglia lying on the upper side of the digestive tract are the only parts of this ring to which the name "brain" is given. Whether the entire ring is considered the brain or whether only the upper ganglia are given that distinction, the fact remains that such a brain is usually not much larger than the other ganglia of the longitudinal ventral nerve cords.

Some interesting experiments with earthworms have shed light on the interrelationship between the brain and ventral cords of these animals. Earthworms were put in the long arm of a simple T-maze or Y-maze. When the worms, moving down the passage, came to the fork, they received a mild electric shock if they turned left, but if they turned right they came to a moist chamber containing food. After many trials in the maze, the earthworms learned to turn right in the majority of cases. Then the heads of half the trained worms were tied off and amputated (with care taken to prevent infection or excessive bleeding). The other worms were kept as controls. After enough time had elapsed for the experimental worms to recover from the operation, they were again put in the maze. They ran the maze almost as well as when they had their heads! A memory of their earlier training

had apparently been stored in the ventral nerve cord, and when the head was removed, the cords took complete command. Eventually some of the worms regenerated heads, and they then lost their ability to run the maze and had to be trained all over again. Apparently the new head, which had no memory of the earlier training, took dominance over the nervous system and suppressed the memory in the cords. Such experiments as this seem to indicate that the earthworm's brain, when present, has a limited dominance over the cords, but that the cords share enough of the brain's most basic functions for the animal to survive and behave almost normally without the brain.

The brains of the most primitive vertebrates are not much more dominant than those of invertebrates, but they do show the beginnings of the evolutionary trends that have made extensive brain development one of the most prominent characteristics of vertebrates. The immense importance of the vertebrate brain makes it worthy of more extensive treatment than we can give it here. The following is a brief introduction to a few of the most important aspects of this subject.

Evolution of the Vertebrate Brain

The most primitive vertebrate brains and the partly developed brains of embryos consist of three irregular swellings at the anterior end of the longitudinal nerve cord. These three regions undergo much modification in adults of more advanced vertebrates, developing specially thickened areas in their walls and distinctive outgrowths in other places. Despite these changes, however, the original three divisions of the brain can still be recognized even in the most advanced vertebrates, including man. The three divisions are the *forebrain,* the *midbrain,* and the *hindbrain* (Fig 10.42). The central canal of the spinal cord extends into the brain as a series of hollow compartments, or ventricles; these, like the

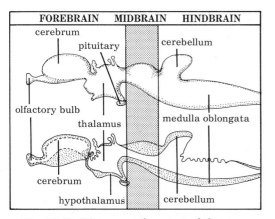

Fig. 10.42. Diagram of the principal divisions of the vertebrate brain. Top: Lateral view. Bottom: Longitudinal section. [Modified from A. S. Romer, *The Vertebrate Body*, Saunders, 1962.]

canal, are filled with cerebrospinal fluid. Both the brain and the spinal cord are wrapped in three protective membranes known as *meninges*.[6] The spaces between the three meninges are filled with cerebrospinal fluid, which provides a cushion that prevents damage to the nervous tissues by the bones in which they are encased.

Very early in its evolution, the brain underwent modifications that set the stage for later evolutionary trends. Briefly, the modifications were these: (1) The ventral portion, or *medulla,* of the hindbrain became specialized as a control center for some autonomic and somatic pathways concerned with visceral functions (recall our discussions of respiration and heartbeat) and as a connecting tract between the spinal cord and the more anterior parts of the brain, while the anterior dorsal portion of the hindbrain became much enlarged as the *cerebellum,* a structure concerned with balance, equilibrium, and muscular coordination (see p. 371). (2) The dorsal part of the midbrain became specialized

[6] The three meninges are: the pia mater, which lies on the surface of the brain and spinal cord; the dura mater, a tough membrane on the inner surface of the skull and vertebrae; and the arachnoid, a very fragile membrane lying between the other two.

as the *optic lobes,* visual centers associated with the optic nerves. (3) The forebrain became divided into an anterior portion consisting of the *cerebrum,* with its prominent olfactory bulbs, and a posterior portion consisting of the *thalamus* and *hypothalamus.* Later evolution has made few changes in the hindbrain, though the cerebellum has become larger and more complex in many animals. The really major evolutionary change has been the steady increase in size and importance of the cerebrum, with a corresponding decrease in relative size and importance of the midbrain (Fig. 10.43).

The ancestral cerebrum was only a pair of small smooth swellings concerned almost exclusively with the sense of smell. It has justifiably been called a "smell brain." As in the spinal cord, the gray matter (cell bodies and synapses) was mostly internal. The synapses functioned only as relays between the olfactory bulbs and more posterior parts of the brain; little, if any, correlation occurred in the cerebrum. The cerebrums of modern fishes are still little more than this, although the areas of gray matter are more massive. In amphibians, which evolved from ancestral fish, there was an expansion of the gray matter and a multiplication of synapses between neurons. No longer was the cerebrum only a relay station; it now functioned as a correlation center between impulses coming to it from the smell receptors and impulses sent to it by other sensory areas of the brain. Slowly this gray matter moved outward from its initially internal position, until it came to lie on the surface of the cerebrum. We call this surface layer the *cerebral cortex* (cortex means bark). In amphibians and many reptiles, it is concerned largely (but not exclusively) with the sense of smell.

But in certain advanced reptiles, a new structure, the *neocortex* (or *neopallium*), arose at a point on the anterior surface of the cerebrum. Mammals, which evolved from reptiles of this type, show the greatest development

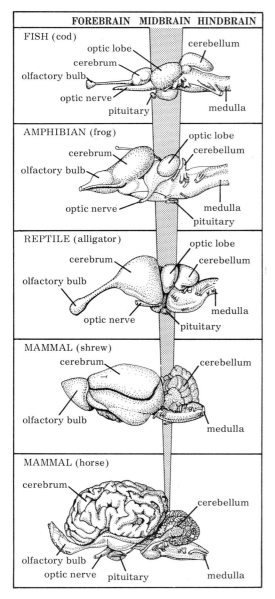

FOREBRAIN	MIDBRAIN	HINDBRAIN

FISH (cod)

optic lobe

cerebellum

cerebrum

olfactory bulb

optic nerve

pituitary

medulla

AMPHIBIAN (frog)

optic lobe

cerebellum

cerebrum

olfactory bulb

optic nerve

medulla

pituitary

REPTILE (alligator)

optic lobe

cerebrum

cerebellum

olfactory bulb

medulla

optic nerve

pituitary

MAMMAL (shrew)

cerebrum

cerebellum

olfactory bulb

medulla

MAMMAL (horse)

cerebrum

cerebellum

olfactory bulb

optic nerve   pituitary   medulla

Fig. 10.43. Evolutionary change in relative size of midbrain and forebrain in vertebrates. In the sequence from fish through amphibian, reptile, and primitive mammal (shrew) to advanced mammal (horse), the relative size of the midbrain markedly decreases, while the forebrain expands enormously. [Modified in part from A. S. Romer, *The Vertebrate Body,* Saunders, 1962; and in part from G. G. Simpson, C. S. Pittendrigh, and L. H. Tiffany, *Life: An Introduction to Biology,* copyright, © 1957, by Harcourt, Brace & World, Inc. Used by permission of the publishers.]

of the neocortex. Even in primitive mammals, the neocortex has expanded to form a surface layer covering most of the forebrain. This does not mean that the old cortex of the ancestral smell brain has been reduced; as you know, the sense of smell remains of prime importance in most mammals. Furthermore, the so-called "smell brain" of higher vertebrates performs many important functions that have nothing to do with smell; e.g. it plays a role in control of emotions. The old cortex has simply been pushed to an internal position by the immense increase in relative size of the neocortex, which is a major coordinating center for sensory and motor functions involving all senses and all parts of the body.

As the neocortex continued to expand, both by relative increase in its total size and by folding, which increased its surface area, it became more and more dominant over the other parts of the brain. The midbrain had been the chief control center in the earliest vertebrates. Then the thalamus portion of the forebrain became a major coordinating center, first sharing these functions with the midbrain and later dominating it. Finally, with the rise of the neocortex and its preempting of many control functions from both the midbrain and thalamus, the midbrain was left as a small connecting link between the hindbrain and the forebrain; it remains a control center for a few local reflex mechanisms and some of the simpler visual functions; it also apparently plays a minor role in control of emotions.

We have repeatedly said that the neurons from different sensory receptors lead to different parts of the brain. These parts can be located and mapped by carefully following the paths of nerve fibers in dissections and by sectioning and staining. The results thus obtained can be checked by electrical techniques; sensory receptors are stimulated, and recordings made from the brain tell us which area of the brain receives the incoming impulses. Similar research approaches allow mapping of the motor centers. As has been shown by mapping the brains of various mammals, the proportion of the total area of the cerebrum devoted to sensory and motor functions differs greatly from one species to another (Fig. 10.44). In general, the larger and the more convoluted the cerebral cortices, the smaller the proportion devoted exclusively to sensory and motor activities. Man represents the extreme example of this trend; the so-called associative areas constitute by far the largest proportion of his cerebral cortices. It is, of course, precisely this characteristic, with its behavioral consequences, that most clearly distinguishes man from other animals.

Like the mammals, birds are very advanced vertebrates, and like the mammals, they evolved from reptiles. But the reptiles from which they descended, unlike the ones that gave rise to the mammals, had not evolved a primitive neocortex. From their earliest stages, therefore, the brains of birds were different from those of mammals. Modern birds have relatively large cerebrums that are clearly important coordination centers having little to do with the sense of smell, which is very poorly developed in most birds. But the evolutionary expansion of the avian cerebrum took place in a completely different way from that discussed above for mammals. In the absence of an incipient neocortex, another more internal portion of the cerebrum increased in size and became the dominant part of the brain. This part remained relatively small in all other vertebrates. It has been suggested that the different origins of the dominant portions of the cerebrums of birds and mammals may partially explain the differences in their behavior, birds being more dependent on innate or "wired-in" behavior and less able to modify their behavior by learning than mammals.

The Mammalian Forebrain

Our information about the function of the various parts of the brain, acquired through experiments utilizing electrical stimulation and

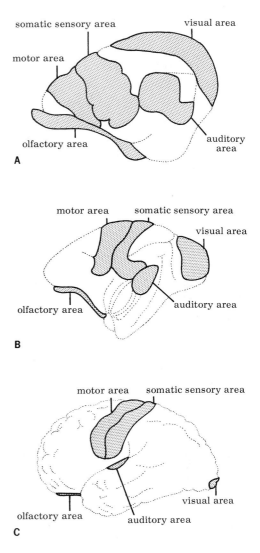

Fig. 10.44. Proportion of cerebral cortex devoted to sensory and motor functions in three mammals. (A) Cat. Sensory and motor areas constitute a major portion of the cortex. (B) Monkey. The proportion of cortex devoted to association areas is much greater than in the cat. (C) Man. The sensory and motor areas occupy a relatively small percentage of the cortex, most of the cortical area being devoted to association. [Modified in part from J. E. Rose and C. N. Woolsey, *Electroencephalog. and Clin. Neurophysiol.*, vol. 1, 1949; and in part from W. Penfield and L. Roberts, *Speech and Brain Mechanisms*, © 1959 by Princeton University Press and used with their permission.]

recording, has reference particularly to such animals as rats, cats, monkeys, and chimpanzees, on which the experiments were performed. But about the human brain, too, a considerable body of information has accumulated, most of it derived from electrical stimulation during brain surgery and from observation of the effects of tumors and of accidental damage or destruction of parts of the brain. We cannot hope to summarize the whole fund of current knowledge here, but a few comments must be made about the forebrain, which plays so vital a part in all our lives.

The Thalamus. The thalamus (Fig. 10.45) is a major sensory-integration center in lower vertebrates, and although in man many of the more complex aspects of sensory integration have been taken over by the cerebrum, the thalamus continues to be an important element in such integration.

The thalamus also contains part of an extremely important neural formation known as the *reticular system,* which is a completely interconnected feltwork of neurons that runs through the brain stem of the medulla and midbrain as well as the thalamus. Every sensory pathway traveling to the higher centers of the brain sends side branches to the reticular system, and every descending motor pathway does so too. In short, the reticular system receives "wire taps" from all incoming and outgoing communication channels of the brain. There are also pathways leading from the reticular system to a great variety of areas in the cortex, brain stem, and spinal cord. Probes of the reticular system by means of microelectrodes have revealed that many of its neurons are "unspecific" in the sense that the same neuron may respond to stimulation of pain receptors in the foot, touch receptors on the hand, sound receptors in the ear, light receptors in the eye, etc. Apparently a major function of this curious part of the brain is activation of the rest of the brain upon receipt of stimuli. It acts as an arousal system, much as

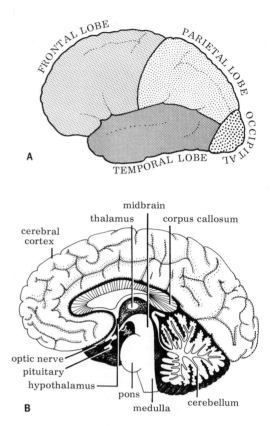

Fig. 10.45. The human brain. (A) Diagram of the cerebral cortex showing its four main lobes. (B) Sagittal section (a vertical longitudinal section through the midline) showing major parts of the brain. [Modified from S. W. Ranson and S. L. Clark, *The Anatomy of the Nervous System,* Saunders, 1959.]

an alarm clock arouses you in the morning. In fact, the alarm clock wakes you only if it stimulates the reticular system sufficiently. Direct stimulation of the cortex does not awaken the brain; it must be called into action by the reticular system. The more stimulation the reticular system receives from its "wire taps," the more arousal signals it sends to the rest of the brain. One reason why it is much easier to fall asleep when the bedroom is dark and quiet is that there are fewer incoming stimuli to trigger your arousal system.

But relatively indiscriminate arousal is not the only important function of the reticular system. Apparently it also monitors all incoming stimuli, compares them with one another, and then magnifies some and suppresses others. Remember that at any given instant stimulation is coming into your central nervous system from receptors all over your body; touch receptors are being stimulated by your clothes, pressure receptors are being stimulated in your feet if you are standing (or somewhere else if you are sitting), hundreds of different vibrations are stimulating the hair cells of the cochlea, and light from literally thousands of objects is bombarding your rods and cones. You are aware of only a few of these stimulations at any given moment. If you were aware of all of them at once and tried to respond to them, you would become completely disorganized—literally go haywire. The reticular system, then, is an indispensable filter that lets only a few of the major inputs reach the higher centers of the brain and elicit reactions.

Not only does the reticular system filter out some stimuli at the level of the brain itself, but it also sends inhibitory impulses down the spinal cord to block some incoming impulses before they ever reach the brain. Thus if you are watching something intently, you may be completely unaware of a touch, or of whether you are warm or cold. And you may also be completely unaware of all objects in your visual field except the one upon which you are concentrating. Or if you are extremely absorbed in what you are doing, you may be unaware that you have suffered a serious injury; soldiers in battle are often surprised to find that, hours before, they received wounds that would have caused them excruciating pain under normal circumstances—yet they never felt any pain at all.

The reticular system can do more than modify and even block incoming sensory impulses; it can similarly modify outgoing motor impulses both at the level of the brain and at the level of the spinal cord, thereby increasing the magnitude of some muscular responses and decreasing that of others.

The Hypothalamus. Extensive research on the hypothalamus, the part of the brain stem just ventral to the thalamus, has led to the conclusion that it is the most important control center for the visceral functions of the body. Stimulation of the hypothalamus with microelectrodes has made it possible to locate centers that control hunger, thirst, body temperature, water balance, blood pressure, reproductive behavior, pleasure, hostility, pain, etc. It is possible to fit experimental animals with electrodes has made it possible to locate control centers and then, by turning the electricity on or off, to make the animal feel hungry or sated, cold or hot, angry or benign. Cats wired in this way may be friendly one moment and in a rage, with fur on end, eyes wide, and claws out, the next moment, depending upon whether their rage center is being stimulated or not. Rats with electrodes in their pleasure centers will spend much of the time pressing levers that turn on the current; the sensation is apparently one they cannot resist. Cats that have just eaten a large meal will resume gulping food as soon as stimulation to their hunger centers is turned on. Often these various centers may be only a few millimeters apart; e.g. stimulation can sometimes be shifted from extreme pleasure to extreme pain or fright by moving the electrode only 0.02 inch.

The Cerebral Cortex. Because the cerebral cortex has been identified with intellectual capacity, we sometimes tend to think of it as synonymous with the brain. But we have seen that other parts of the brain play a critical role in almost all our activities. The cortex has, in fact, been viewed by some workers as an organ of elaboration and refinement of functions that, in its absence, could be performed to some extent by other parts of the brain. This certainly seems to be true in lower vertebrates. A frog whose entire cerebrum has been removed shows almost no behavioral changes and can see as well as before. A decorticated rat shows no obvious motor defects, and, though its ability to distinguish complex visual patterns is impaired, it can tell light from dark and can respond to movement. A cat without its cerebral cortices can move around sluggishly, swallow, react appropriately to pain stimuli, say miaow, and even purr, but it has the appearance of an automaton, seeming to be essentially unconscious. Monkeys and human beings, on the other hand, are severely debilitated by loss of their cerebral cortices; monkeys retain only a very crude ability to detect light and they are badly paralyzed, while human beings become totally blind and extensively paralyzed and, though they can carry out such vegetative functions as breathing and swallowing, they usually soon die. It seems, then, that no bodily processes vital to life are controlled exclusively by the cortex, but that, in the course of the cortex's evolution from the simple olfactory forebrain of the primitive vertebrate, new connections were established with the older parts of the brain stem, each part coming to have its own piece of the cortex

to assist it in its functions. Gradually, however, more and more of the function of some of the older parts was transferred to the cortex until, as in human vision, the role of the cortex became predominant or even essential.

We said earlier that the percentage of the cortex taken up by purely motor and sensory areas is smaller in man than in other animals (see Fig. 10.44). Probing with electrodes shows, however, that within these limited areas each part of the body is represented by its own control center. These centers are not arranged in random fashion, but form a regular pattern. For example, the point on the cortex that controls the thumb is adjacent to the point that controls the first finger, and this is adjacent to the point that controls the second finger, etc.; all points for finger control are near the points controlling the palm and the wrist. Thus, if we map the surface of the somatic sensory area of the cortex (Fig. 10.46), we obtain on the right side a picture of the entire left side of the body, and on the left side

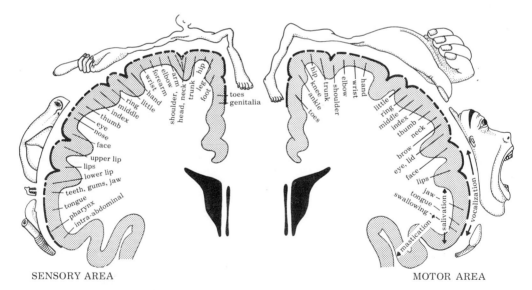

SENSORY AREA   MOTOR AREA

Fig. 10.46. Function maps of the surface of the somatic sensory area (left) and motor area (right) of the cerebral cortex of man. Note that the area of cortex devoted to each body part is proportional to the importance of the sensory or motor activities of that part, not to its size; hence the face and hand are especially prominent. [Modified from W. Penfield and T. Rasmussen, *The Cerebral Cortex of Man*, Macmillan, 1950.]

a picture of the entire right side of the body (we do not know why the fiber tracts running between the brain and the spinal cord cross to the opposite side, so that the left brain controls the right side of the body and the right brain the left side). We obtain similar pictures if we map the surface of the motor area of the cortex. These pictures, however, are not faithful reproductions of the bodily proportions; they are distorted and grotesque because the area of the cortex devoted to each part of the body is proportional not to the size of the part but to its sensory or motor capabilities. Thus, in man, little motor area is devoted to muscles of the back, but an enormous area is devoted to the muscles of the hand and of the mouth, two of man's most active parts. The motor area for the hands is larger than their sensory area, whereas the sensory area for the lips is larger than their motor area. As you might expect, allocation of brain area is different in different animals and reflects the special characteristics of each; the snout of a pig is represented by a large area of the cortex, and the skin around the nostrils of a horse has nearly as much cortical area as all the rest of the body put together.

If we can map man's sensory and motor areas, can we likewise map the association areas so prominent in the human cortex? This is more difficult, but progress is being made. Wilder Penfield of the Montreal Neurological Institute has located three speech areas on the cortex (Fig. 10.47). Curiously enough, these are almost always restricted to the left hemisphere in the normal brain; most functions are symmetrically represented in the two hemispheres, but speech seems to be an exception. When we say that these three areas are speech areas, we do not mean that they control the muscular motions involved in talking; such motions are controlled by motor areas. The speech areas are concerned with the thought processes underlying speech. For example, when Penfield stimulated one point in the speech area of a certain patient, showed him

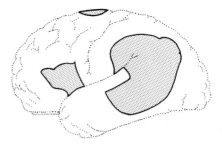

Fig. 10.47. The three speech areas of the human cortex. In most cases, the speech areas occur only in the left hemisphere. [Redrawn from W. Penfield and L. Roberts, *Speech and Brain Mechanisms*, © 1959 by Princeton University Press and used with their permission.]

a picture of a foot, and asked him to name it, the patient said he knew what it was—it "is what you put in your shoes"—but he simply couldn't think of the word. As soon as stimulation by the electrode ceased he said "foot." Another patient under stimulation could not name a comb, but when asked what he does with it, he said, "I comb my hair." Even after saying this, he still could not think of the word "comb" when shown a picture of one and asked to name it.

Most of Penfield's mapping of cortical areas in the brain was done during operations on patients suffering from severe epilepsy. Epileptics periodically suffer seizures varying in severity from a momentary tingling or sense of numbness in part of the body to general muscular convulsions and unconsciousness. Epilepsy usually results from injuries to the cortex. An epileptic attack occurs when spontaneous and uncontrolled discharges spread from the damaged region into the surrounding healthy tissue. If the discharges spread only a short distance, the attack is mild. If they spread over the entire brain, a catastrophically severe seizure results. Penfield and others developed techniques for cutting away a flap of bone from the roof of the patient's skull, stimulating the exposed brain surface with electrodes to locate the diseased region and also to determine the areas essential to proper speech, sensory, or motor function, which should not be removed, and then excising the diseased region. Such operations are performed while the patient is under only local anesthesia and is fully conscious (this is possible because, interestingly enough, there are no pain receptors in the brain itself). During the mapping phase of the operation, the surgeon stimulates various parts of the brain while the patient, who cannot see the surgeon and does not know when stimulation is on or off, talks with an observer who asks him questions and records his responses.

Brain surgery, particularly on patients suffering from severe epilepsy or other types of brain damage, has not only allowed mapping of motor, sensory, and speech areas, but has also made possible investigations of memory storage. When Penfield stimulated certain regions of the temporal lobes of the cerebral cortices (Fig. 10.45A), he sometimes caused patients to experience remarkably detailed recollections of past events, events that frequently had not been remembered for many years. For example, one patient relived an episode from her childhood. Another heard her small son playing in the yard, accompanied by sounds of automobiles, barking dogs, and all the other usual neighborhood noises. Another watched a scene from a play she had not seen in years. Another heard Christmas carols being sung in the church in her home town in Holland. Another saw himself with his cousins and two young ladies at their home in South Africa (an event that had occurred many years before), and he cried out, "Yes, Doctor! Yes, Doctor! Now I hear people laughing—my friends—in South Africa." When he later discussed this experience with Penfield, he could not remember what the laughter was about. Penfield says, "Doubtless he would have discovered that also, if the strip of experience had begun earlier, or if the surgeon had continued the stimulation a little longer."

Still another patient was certain the doctors were playing a record of a song in the operating room; she could not be convinced that there was really no phonograph—the memory was not a memory to her, it was reality. This attitude, in fact, was a general one. Penfield says, "The patients have never looked upon an experiential response as a remembering. Instead of that it is a hearing-again and seeing-again—a living-through of past time." There is evidence that under these circumstances the brain plays back the stored data at the same speed as the events actually happened. If the stimulation that gave the woman the experience of listening to the phonograph record was stopped and then almost instantly begun again, the record always went back and started at the beginning; it would not resume playing where it had left off when the stimulation ceased. Memories of similar "realness" and detail have sometimes been elicited by hypnosis. A classical case is that of an elderly bricklayer who, when hypnotized, described in detail the bumps on the individual bricks in a wall he had laid in his twenties and had not seen for years; the wall was checked and the bumps the bricklayer described were there!

Penfield himself has summarized his work on electrically stimulated memory and some of its implications in the following graphic words:

The experiential responses of the flash-back variety were, for the most part, quite unimportant moments in the patient's life: standing on a street corner, hearing a mother call her child, taking part in a conversation, listening to a little boy as he played in the yard. If these unimportant minutes of time were preserved in the ganglionic recordings of these patients, why should it be thought that any experience in the stream of consciousness drops out of the ganglionic record?

When, by chance, the neurosurgeon's electrode activates past experience, that experience unfolds progressively, moment by moment. This is a little like the performance of a wire recorder or a strip of cinematographic film on which are registered all those things of which the individual was once aware—the things he selected for his attention in that interval of time. Absent from it are the sensations he ignored, the talk he did not heed.

Time's strip of film runs forward, never backward, even when resurrected from the past. It seems to proceed again at time's own unchanged pace. It would seem, once one section of the strip has come alive, that the response is protected by a functional all-or-nothing principle. A regulating inhibitory mechanism must guard against activation of other portions of the film. As long as the electrode is held in place, the experience of a former day goes forward. There is no holding it still, no turning back, no crossing with other periods. When the electrode is withdrawn, it stops as suddenly as it began.

A particular strip can sometimes be repeated by interrupting the stimulation and then shortly reapplying it at the same or a nearby point. In that case it begins at the same moment of time on each occasion. The threshold of evocation of that particular response has apparently been lowered for a time by the first stimulus. . . .

The thread of time remains with us in the form of a succession of "abiding" facilitations. This thread travels through ganglion cells and synaptic junctions. It runs through the waking hours of each man, from childhood to the grave. On the thread of time are strung, like pearls in unending succession, the "meaningful" patterns that can still recall the vanished content of a former awareness.

No man can voluntarily reactivate the record. Perhaps, if he could, he might become hopelessly confused. Man's voluntary recollection must be achieved through other mechanisms. And yet the recorded patterns are useful to him, even after passage of many years. They can still be appropriately selected by some scanning process and activated with amazing promptness for the purposes of comparative interpretation. It is, it seems to me, in this mechanism of recall and comparison and interpretation that the interpretative cortex of the temporal lobes plays its specialized role.[7]

[7] Reprinted by permission of the publishers from Wilder Penfield and Lamar Roberts, *Speech and Brain Mechanisms,* © 1959 by Princeton University Press, pp. 53–55.

Present evidence indicates that complex memories like those studied by Penfield, which involve the simultaneous presence of many different sensory qualities, are not stored in one place as a single memory. Instead, the visual component is stored in one place, the auditory component in another place, the smell component in a third place, etc.; each such sensory component is apparently stored in the same general part of the brain as that used in its recognition. (Actually, in the normal brain, each of these component memory traces is stored in duplicate, once in each half of the cortex; this duplication does not occur if all cross connections between the two hemispheres are severed.) These different memory traces must be interconnected and synchronized, so that the so-called memory areas in the temporal lobes can act as playback mechanisms, recombining the component sensory modalities to create the integrated memory sensation.

What is memory? We cannot say as yet. We assume it is a neuronal circuit facilitated by prior use, probably as a result of some sort of change in the synapses that interconnect the neurons participating in that memory trace. Presumably, the more impulses are sent along a given memory trace, the easier it becomes for later impulses to travel the same circuit. Facilitation induced by repeated use of a circuit would help explain why practice improves performance. It might also help explain the common experience of college students who find that material that seemed extremely difficult during a cramming session at night seems clear and simple the following morning; the periodic spontaneous neuronal firings that are known to occur during sleep may well tend to follow the circuits facilitated by the study session and thus further facilitate them.

If our memory stores far more detail than we normally suspect (as the data from hypnosis and from experiments such as Penfield's suggest), if our permanent record of past events is far more complete than our normal conscious recollection of them, a fantastic amount of information must be stored in each human brain. How? We do not know. We do not even know whether every detail really is stored, whether the bricklayer actually has in his brain a memory of the surface detail of every brick he used in his 40-year career. But despite our ignorance, we can make a few calculations that help us understand the problems involved in memory storage. John Von Neumann has calculated that if the brain keeps a complete record of all electrochemical signals generated in all sensory receptors during a lifetime of 60 years, and if a record of the electrochemical activity of the approximately 10 billion neurons in the brain is also stored somehow, then the storage load must be about 2.8×10^{20} bits[8] of information. Reasoning from computer technology, we assume that storage of one bit requires one on-off switch. Von Neumann's calculations lead to the conclusion that every neuron must have a memory capacity equivalent to 30 billion on-off switches! But if the individual neurons actually had such a capacity, they could not be the basic storage elements because, by definition, a basic storage element may store only one bit of information.

Fortunately for our calculations, the anatomical and physiological evidence indicates that the whole neuron need not be the basic storage element. If memory resides in the strength of synapses, and if, as some workers claim, the dendrites and cell body of each neuron in the brain receive an average of 1,000 synapses, then 1,000 times as many storage elements are available as there would be if the whole neurons were the basic elements. But if Von Neumann's calculations are correct, the individual synapses would still need a storage capacity of 30 million bits; hence they could not be the basic storage elements we are searching for. Recently it has been suggested that the many tiny glial cells packed in the

spaces between the neurons may play a role in neural function. It was formerly thought that these cells function only in "housekeeping" chores, helping to maintain the proper metabolic condition of the neurons. Now, however, there is evidence that they interact electrochemically with the neurons. Perhaps changes in the electrochemical activity of these cells, which crowd to within a millionth of an inch of the neurons, participate in memory storage by altering the conductivity of the neuronal dendrites. If this is so, the storage capacity of the brain would be many times greater than calculations based only on the number of neurons and synapses show.

Many scientists have questioned whether it is necessary to assume storage of every electrical event, as Von Neumann did. The fact that the experiential recall stimulated by a neurosurgeon is incredibly detailed does not mean that every sensory detail is included. Indeed, it seems highly unlikely that this is so. Psychological tests indicate that a person can take in and deal consciously with only about 25 bits of information per second, even under the most favorable conditions. Most of the rest of the incoming stimulation is suppressed (we have already discussed the role of the reticular system in such suppression). Furthermore, the rate of 25 bits per second occurs only during a small fraction of the time, when the person is maximally alert; certainly such a rate is not maintained during sleep, for example. If we use figures based on considerations such as these, rather than Von Neumann's extreme figure of 2.8×10^{20} bits, the calculated storage capacity of the brain (taking into account numbers of neurons, synapses, and glial cells) comes well within the requirements placed upon it. This does not mean that we really know how memory is stored. Our model may prove seriously flawed. And even if it is basically correct, it still does not explain the physicochemical changes necessary for information storage.

We would expect that stimulation, if it is to

---

[8] A "bit" is the smallest unit of information utilized in information theory. It corresponds to the result of a choice between two equally probable events.

produce a memory, must cause chemical changes in the neurons. Recently it has been found that neuronal activity does, in fact, increase the amount of the nucleic acid RNA in the nerve cells. Furthermore, the RNA content of nerve cells is among the highest of any cells in the body. It has been shown in genetic studies in recent years that nucleic acids are complex polymers capable of encoding in their structure an enormous amount of information; it is in nucleic acids that all the information of heredity is stored. The intriguing possibility thus arises that the facilitation of nerve circuits that establishes memory traces involves encoding information in the RNA of the nerve cells.[9] Much more research is needed to answer our many questions about memory and thought. It will be an exciting search.

Our knowledge of how the brain functions is still in its infancy; there is a very long way to go. But progress is being made at an ever accelerating pace, and the day can be foreseen when man will understand his own understanding, when the "higher faculties" that set man apart can be explained in physicochemical terms. And with this understanding will come, inevitably, increased power to control the functioning of men's minds (power that is already much further developed in its potential than most people realize). The use man makes of this knowledge may well determine, more than any other factor, what the future of our species will be. The day may come when the problems associated with the ability to control men's brains will outweigh the problems associated with the harnessing of nuclear energy.

REFERENCES

BEST, C. H., and N. B. TAYLOR, 1961. *The Physiological Basis of Medical Practice*, 7th ed. Williams & Wilkins, Baltimore. (See esp. Chapters 61–79.)

BLOOM, W., and D. W. FAWCETT, 1962. *A Textbook of Histology*, 8th ed. Saunders, Philadelphia. (See esp. Chapters 9, 32–33.)

BUCHANAN, A. R., 1961. *Functional Neuro-Anatomy*, 4th ed. Lea & Febiger, Philadelphia.

ECCLES, J. C., 1957. *The Physiology of Nerve Cells*. Johns Hopkins Press, Baltimore.

————, 1964. "Ionic Mechanism of Postsynaptic Inhibition," *Science*, vol. 145, pp. 1140–1147.

FESSARD, A., R. W. GERARD, J. KONORSKI, and J. F. DELAFRESNAYE, eds., 1961. *Brain Mechanisms and Learning*. Thomas, Springfield, Ill.

GARDNER, E., 1963. *Fundamentals of Neurology*, 4th ed. Saunders, Philadelphia.

HUXLEY, A. F., 1964. "Excitation and Conduction in Nerve: Quantitative Analysis," *Science*, vol. 145, pp. 1154–1159.

MAGOUN, H. W., 1963. *The Waking Brain*, 2nd ed. Thomas, Springfield, Ill.

NACHMANSOHN, D., 1959. *Chemical and Molecular Basis of Nerve Activity*. Academic Press, New York.

PEELE, T. L., 1961. *The Neuroanatomic Basis for Clinical Neurology*, 2nd ed. McGraw-Hill, New York.

PENFIELD, W., and H. JASPER, 1954. *Epilepsy and the Functional Anatomy of the Human Brain*. Little, Brown, Boston.

PENFIELD, W., and T. RASMUSSEN, 1950. *The Cerebral Cortex of Man*. Macmillan, New York.

PENFIELD, W., and L. ROBERTS, 1959. *Speech and Brain Mechanisms*. Princeton University Press, Princeton, N.J.

[9] During the months just before this book went to press, much excitement was generated by studies that seem to indicate that the effects of learning can be transferred by extracting RNA (or perhaps some other chemical) from the brains of conditioned rats and injecting it into naïve rats. Evidence that drugs that stimulate synthesis of RNA may improve memory was also presented. At this writing, it is still too early to evaluate the reliability of these claims.

PROSSER, C. L., and F. A. BROWN, 1961. *Comparative Animal Physiology*, 2nd ed. Saunders, Philadelphia. (See esp. Chapters 10–12, 21.)

RANSON, S. W., and S. L. CLARK, 1959. *The Anatomy of the Nervous System*, 10th ed. Saunders, Philadelphia.

ROSENBLITH, W. A., ed., 1961. *Sensory Communication*. Wiley, New York.

RUCH, T. C., H. D. PATTON, J. W. WOODBURY,

and A. L. TOWE, 1961. *Neurophysiology*. Saunders, Philadelphia.

RUSSELL, W. R., 1959. *Brain, Memory, Learning*. Oxford University Press, New York.

WALLS, G. L., 1942. *The Vertebrate Eye and Its Adaptive Radiation*. Cranbrook Institute of Science, Bloomfield Hills, Mich.

YOUNG, J. Z., 1957. *The Life of Mammals*. Oxford University Press, New York. (See esp. Chapters 17–28.)

SUGGESTED READING

AMOORE, J. E., J. W. JOHNSTON, and M. RUBIN, 1964. "The Stereochemical Theory of Odor," *Scientific American*, February. (Offprint 297.)

BENZINGER, T. H., 1961. "The Human Thermostat," *Scientific American*, January. (Offprint 129.)

BEST, C. H., and N. B. TAYLOR, 1958. *The Living Body*, 4th ed. Holt, Rinehart & Winston, New York. (See esp. Chapters 11–13.)

BOYCOTT, B. B., 1965. "Learning in the Octopus," *Scientific American*, March. (Offprint 1006.)

CARLSON, A. J., V. JOHNSON, and H. M. CAVERT, 1961. *The Machinery of the Body*, 5th ed. University of Chicago Press, Chicago. (See esp. Chapters 10–12.)

DETHIER, V. G., and E. STELLAR, 1964. *Animal Behavior*, 2nd ed. Prentice-Hall, Englewood Cliffs, N.J. (See esp. Chapters 1–5.)

ECCLES, J. C., 1958. "The Physiology of Imagination," *Scientific American*, September. (Offprint 65.)

———, 1965. "The Synapse," *Scientific American*, January. (Offprint 1001.)

FENDER, D. H., 1964. "Control Mechanisms of the Eye," *Scientific American*, July. (Offprint 187.)

FISHER, A. E., 1964. "Chemical Stimulation of the Brain," *Scientific American*, June. (Offprint 485.)

FRENCH, J. D., 1957. "The Reticular Formation," *Scientific American*, May. (Offprint 66.)

GRAY, G. W., 1948. "The Great Ravelled Knot," *Scientific American*, October. (Offprint 13.)

HAAGEN-SMIT, A. J., 1952. "Smell and Taste," *Scientific American*, March. (Offprint 404.)

HELD, R., 1965. "Plasticity in Sensory-Motor Systems," *Scientific American*, November. (Offprint 494.)

HODGKIN, A. L., 1964. "The Ionic Basis of Nervous Conduction," *Science*, vol. 145, pp. 1148–1154.

HUBEL, D. H., 1963. "The Visual Cortex of the Brain," *Scientific American*, November. (Offprint 168.)

HYDER, H., 1961. "Satellite Cells in the Nervous System," *Scientific American*, December. (Offprint 134.)

KATZ, B., 1961. "How Cells Communicate," *Scientific American*, September. (Offprint 98.)

KENNEDY, D., 1963. "Inhibition in Visual Systems," *Scientific American*, July. (Offprint 162.)

KEYNES, R. D., 1958. "The Nerve Impulse and the Squid," *Scientific American*, December. (Offprint 58.)

KOLERS, P. A., 1964. "The Illusion of Movement," *Scientific American*, October. (Offprint 487.)

LAND, E. H., 1959. "Experiments in Color Vision," *Scientific American*, May. (Offprint 223.)

LOEWENSTEIN, W. R., 1960. "Biological Transducers," *Scientific American*, August. (Offprint 70.)

MACNICHOL, E. F., 1964. "Three-Pigment Color Vision," *Scientific American*, December. (Offprint 197.)

MELZACK, R., 1961. "The Perception of Pain," *Scientific American*, February. (Offprint 457.)

MILLER, W. H., F. RATLIFF, and H. K. HARTLINE, 1961. "How Cells Receive Stimuli," *Scientific American*, September. (Offprint 99.)

MUNTZ, W. R. A., 1964. "Vision in Frogs," *Scientific American*, March. (Offprint 179.)

OLDS, J., 1956. "Pleasure Centers in the Brain," *Scientific American*, October. (Offprint 30.)

PRITCHARD, R. M., 1961. "Stabilized Images on the Retina," *Scientific American*, June. (Offprint 466.)

RAMSAY, J. A., 1957. *Physiological Approach to the Lower Animals*. Cambridge University Press, New York. (See esp. Chapters 5–8.)

ROBERTSON, J. D., 1962. "The Membrane of the Living Cell," *Scientific American,* April. (Offprint 151.)

RUSTON, W. A. H., 1962. "Visual Pigments in Man," *Scientific American,* November. (Offprint 139.)

SCHMIDT-NIELSEN, K., 1964. *Animal Physiology,* 2nd ed. Prentice-Hall, Englewood Cliffs, N.J. (See esp. Chapters 6–7.)

SNIDER, R. S., 1958. "The Cerebellum," *Scientific American,* August. (Offprint 38.)

SPERRY, R. W., 1959. "The Growth of Nerve Circuits," *Scientific American,* November. (Offprint 72.)

———, 1964. "The Great Cerebral Commissure," *Scientific American,* January. (Offprint 174.)

VON BÉKÉSY, G., 1957. "The Ear," *Scientific American,* August. (Offprint 44.)

WALD, G., 1950. "Eye and Camera," *Scientific American,* August. (Offprint 46.)

WALLACH, H., 1963. "The Perception of Neutral Colors," *Scientific American,* January. (Offprint 474.)

WOOLDRIDGE, D. E., 1963. *The Machinery of the Brain.* McGraw-Hill, New York.

CHAPTER

11

EFFECTORS

WE DISCUSSED THE SENSORY AND CON-
ductor components of reflex arcs at some
length in the last chapter. The last components
in those arcs, the effectors, are the subject of
this chapter. The effectors, unlike the sensory
receptors and conductor cells, are not themselves parts of the nervous system; they are
the parts of the organism that do things, that
carry out the organism's response to stimuli.
Their activity may be controlled by the nervous
system, but this is not always so; there are
numerous effector systems not under nervous
control, among them the effector systems of
plants, many (though not all) glands of animals, nematocysts of coelenterates, and the
pigment cells of many animals.

The response of an organism to stimulation
may not involve movement of the organism
in the usual sense (though molecular movement is a characteristic of any response). Examples of effector actions that can occur
without gross movement of the organism include secretion from glands, changes in the
size of pigment cells or in the distribution of
pigment within the cells with resulting changes

in an animal's color, and light production by fireflies and by other luminescent organisms. But the responses usually most obvious to us involve motion. It is these that constitute most of what we call behavior. And it is with the effectors that produce motion that we shall be especially concerned in this chapter.

EFFECTORS OF NONMUSCULAR MOVEMENT

Movements Produced by Differential Growth or by Turgor Changes in Plants. We do not ordinarily think of plants as actively moving organisms. Yet there are, in fact, many instances when plants actively move. We examined some of these in our discussion of phototropic and geotropic movements. In these cases, no specialized effector cells were involved, the slow movements being produced by differential growth rates under the control of hormones. All the cells of the elongating tissues were, in a sense, the effectors of this movement.

But plants are frequently capable of other movements in addition to growth responses: Some leaves droop or fold at night and expand again in the morning; the flowers of many plants open and close in a regular fashion at different times of day; the leaves of sensitive plants (*Mimosa*) fold and droop within a few seconds after being touched, and the response may even spread rapidly to untouched leaves; the leaves of the Venus'-flytrap rapidly close around insects that have landed on them; the seed pods of some plants snap open at maturity, vigorously expelling their seeds. All these movements are far too rapid to depend on differential growth changes. Clearly some other mechanism must be involved. That mechanism is turgor-pressure change. Leaves droop when certain of their cells lose so much water that they are no longer turgid and no longer give rigidity to the leaf. Flowers fold when specially sensitive cells arranged in rows

along the petals lose their turgidity, and they open again when these cells regain their turgidity. Rapid changes in turgidity in special effector cells located along the hinge of the leaf of the Venus'-flytrap are responsible for that plant's curious behavior. Similarly, rapid turgidity changes in specialized effector cells at the bases of the leaflets and petioles of the sensitive plant are responsible for this plant's response to a touch or other mechanical stimulus; spread of stimulation from the point of actual disturbance is apparently brought about by a chemical messenger moving through the phloem.

Cytoplasmic Streaming. Cytoplasmic streaming is another type of movement in plant cells, as yet only poorly understood. A similar streaming process is responsible for the amoeboid movement characteristic of many protozoans, slime molds, human leukocytes, etc. As we saw in an earlier chapter, an amoeba moves as its cytoplasm flows into new armlike projections of the cell called *pseudopodia.* For years scientists have sought explanations for this movement in the hope of gaining insight into some fundamental properties of protoplasm, particularly contractile properties. But a definitive explanation has not yet emerged. Several competing theories have been proposed. All such theories must start from observations that the forward streaming is restricted to a central core of the cytoplasm, the *endoplasm* (Fig. 11.1). When the endoplasm reaches the advancing end of the pseudopodium, it spreads peripherally, forming a stiffer nonmoving layer, the *ectoplasm.* There is continuing conversion of ectoplasm into endoplasm at the rear of the advancing cell, and conversion of endoplasm into ectoplasm at the front. Endoplasm generated at the rear slides forward over the lower layer of stationary ectoplasm, which rests on the substratum, and then becomes converted into ectoplasm, while the rearmost ectoplasm is simultaneously being converted into endoplasm and becoming

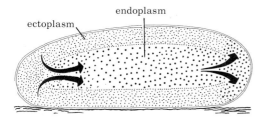

ectoplasm

endoplasm

Fig. 11.1. Amoeboid movement. The endoplasmic core slides forward between the layers of ectoplasm. The lower layer of ectoplasm rests on the substratum and is stationary. As the core moves forward, ectoplasm at the rear of the cell is converted into endoplasm, while endoplasm at the front of the cell is converted into ectoplasm.

mobile once more. The resulting movement of the cell is much like that of a bulldozer on its caterpillar track.

One theory has it that the endoplasm is essentially a sol while the ectoplasm is a gel. According to this theory, the ectoplasmic gel near the rear of the cell contracts, squeezing the endoplasmic sol forward. But recent experiments have shown that the core of the endoplasm is not really a sol, although its outermost part is. Apparently a core of endoplasmic gel moves forward within a tube of ectoplasmic gel, the core and the tube being separated by a shear zone of sol between them. This finding has led to a theory that the core is not squeezed forward from behind but is pulled forward by a contraction of the core itself at the front, where it is moving outward to become ectoplasm. Still another theory contends that the motive force is exerted neither as a push from the back nor as a pull from the front, but as some sort of ratchet mechanism along the sol interface between the gel core and the gel tube. Which, if any, of these three theories is correct remains for future research to show. It seems likely that, as is often the case, a combination of elements from several theories will prove to be closest to the truth; there is no reason, for example, why contraction at the front or back (or both) could not function in combination with a ratchetlike

mechanism at the interface to propel the endoplasm forward.

Movement by Cilia and Flagella. Another type of nonmuscular movement exhibited by some plant cells and some animal cells is that produced by the beating of cilia or flagella. Many bacteria, Protozoa, and primitive algae move in this way, and the sperm cells of all animals and of some multicellular plants (large algae, mosses, ferns, etc.) swim by means of cilia or flagella to the egg cells to bring about fertilization. Even some small multicellular animals use cilia in their movements, and most multicellular animals possess ciliated epithelia that function in moving small particles along the epithelial surface, as in the human trachea.

The most common type of motion of a cilium is a power stroke, much like the power stroke of a human swimmer, in which the stalk is extended fairly rigidly and swept back by bending at its base (Fig. 11.2). The recovery stroke brings the cilium forward again, as a wave of bending moves along the stalk from its base; at no time during the recovery stroke is much surface opposed to the water in the direction of movement. Flagella, being much longer than cilia, are capable of more varied movements, but most of these are variants on the basic stroke described here.

Cilia and flagella have the same basic structure (described on p. 84). Within the stalk of each are eleven fibrils, nine usually double ones arranged in a circle near the periphery of the stalk and two single ones lying in the

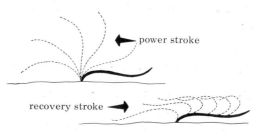

power stroke

recovery stroke

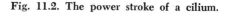

Animal moves to right.

Fig. 11.2. The power stroke of a cilium.

center of the stalk (see Fig. 3.29). It has been suggested that five of the outer filaments on one side contract simultaneously along their whole length, thus pulling the stalk through the power stroke. The four filaments on the other side of the stalk would then contract slowly, with the contraction beginning at the base and moving along each filament toward its apex; this would produce the recovery stroke. According to this theory, the two central filaments act as pathways along which the stimulus for the power stroke can be transmitted to the contractile filaments. The basal body is apparently the originator of the motive stimulus; if its connection to the filaments is broken, motion of the stalk no longer occurs.

THE EVOLUTION AND STRUCTURAL ARRANGEMENTS OF MUSCULAR EFFECTORS

The most obvious effectors in all multicellular animals except sponges are the muscles, tissues composed of specialized contractile cells. All protoplasm possesses some ability to contract, and we have seen that an elaboration of this ability may play an important role in amoeboid movement, as it clearly does in the action of cilia and flagella with their specialized contractile filaments. It is not strange, then, that as multicellular animals became larger and more complex, and as division of labor among their cells and tissues increased, they evolved elongate cells specialized for contraction, which became the principal effectors of movement in higher animals.

Animals with Hydrostatic Skeletons

The first multicellular animals (disregarding the sponges) were doubtless small, perhaps on the order of one millimeter in length. They probably swam by means of cilia. Even today, the smallest flatworms and the tiny larvae of

many coelenterates depend primarily on cilia as their locomotory effectors. But cilia are effective as locomotory structures only in very small organisms. As animals evolved larger size, they evolved contractile tissues that first supplemented and then supplanted the cilia as the chief effectors of locomotion. Though coelenterates have only very primitive contractile fibers, which do not constitute distinct tissues, rhythmic contractions of such fibers in the bell of a jellyfish enable it to swim weakly, and contractions of other fibers enable a jellyfish or a hydra to move its tentacles. The hydra is even able to move by turning somersaults (Fig. 11.3), a type of movement that is rather surprising in an animal with such primitive nerve and muscle cells.

The musculature of the body wall in the most primitive flatworms is only feebly developed and can produce only minor changes of shape. But in more advanced flatworms, like planaria, the muscle fibers are organized in longitudinal and circular layers. The fibers in these two layers are antagonistic to each other; i.e. they produce opposite actions. Contraction of the longitudinal muscles shortens the animal, and, since body volume remains constant because the semifluid body contents resist compression, this contraction also produces a compensating increase in the diameter of the animal. Conversely, contraction of the circular muscles reduces the diameter and increases the length of the animal.

Waves of contraction of the longitudinal muscles of the lower surface of a flatworm (or a higher animal like a snail) can move points on the lower surface forward a fraction of a

Fig. 11.3. Somersaulting locomotion of hydra.

millimeter; these points may then grip the substrate and, as the wave of contraction passes posteriorly, act as anchors toward which more posterior parts of the lower surface are drawn. In this way, the animal can glide along in a slow manner that may be described as snail-like. This type of locomotion makes little use of the circular muscles or of the hydrostatic properties of the body contents. A more rapid type of locomotion that makes more use of the circular muscles and of the fluid or partly fluid noncompressible body contents, or *hydrostatic skeleton,* is the looping movement characteristic of some worms and particularly well exemplified by leeches (Fig. 11.4). The leech attaches the posterior end of its body to the substrate by means of a sucker, extends its body forward by contraction of the circular muscles, attaches the front end by its sucker, and then detaches the posterior end and draws it forward by contraction of the longitudinal muscles. Notice that this type of locomotion is possible only because the force of the muscular

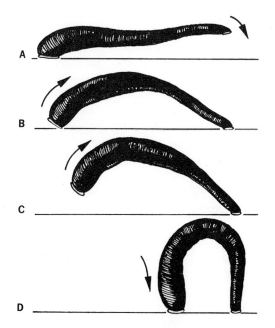

Fig. 11.4. Looping locomotion of a leech. The movement of the well-known "inchworm" is of the same type.

contractions can be applied against the non-compressible body contents.

The relatively soft internal tissues of solid-bodied animals like flatworms can function as a hydrostatic skeleton to some extent. But full exploitation of powerful contractions of the longitudinal and circular muscles of the body wall requires a more effective skeleton than this. More active wormlike animals have evolved a variety of body cavities located between the body wall and the digestive tract. These cavities are filled with fluid and provide a more effective hydrostatic skeleton. However, in those animals in which the fluid-filled cavity extends for most of the length of the body as a single chamber, agile movements involving precise control are still not possible, because changes in the fluid pressure are freely transmitted to all parts of the body and the animal thus cannot perform simultaneously a variety of localized movements.

The most complete exploitation of the potentialities of hydrostatic skeletons is seen in certain annelid worms, such as earthworms. Here the body cavity is partitioned into a series of separate fluid-filled chambers. Correlated with this *segmentation* of the body cavity is a similar segmentation of the musculature; the fact that each segment of the body has its own circular and longitudinal muscles makes possible effective use of the compartmented hydrostatic skeleton. Such segmentation carries with it, of course, a necessity for some degree of segmental organization of the nervous system and for serial repetition of other organs such as the nephridia. Present evidence indicates that annelid-type segmentation evolved as an adaptation for burrowing; the compartmented hydrostatic skeleton aids movement by peristaltic waves, which can develop considerable thrust against the substrate and push aside the particles of which it is composed. Though there are many unsegmented worms that burrow by peristaltic wave motions, none of them can develop as much thrust or burrow so continuously and effectively as segmented worms.

The bodies of worms that utilize peristaltic locomotory waves always have a nearly round cross section, because such waves involve contraction of well-developed circular muscles. Worms that move by other mechanisms commonly have less well developed circular muscles and are often flatter, thus presenting a greater surface area to the ground and increasing their locomotory efficiency. Round worms are less well adapted to creeping along the surface of the substrate than more flattened worms, but their round bodies are well suited to burrowing through the ground, where their entire body surface is in contact with the substrate.

Many marine annelids possess paired lateral flaps on each segment. These flaps, called parapodia (see Fig. 6.9A, p. 211), may have evolved first as devices for producing respiratory and feeding currents inside the tubes in which many rather sedentary annelids live. Or they may have evolved as adaptations for movement over an ocean bottom littered with objects that made simpler forms of movement difficult. Or they may simply have evolved as gills. Actually, the evolution of parapodia probably involved two or more of these functions. But whatever their original function, the parapodia of various species serve all three of the functions mentioned here. Let us concentrate, however, on those annelids in which the parapodia are particularly well adapted as locomotory appendages. Such worms exhibit striking modifications of the body-wall musculature. No longer can all the muscles be grouped conveniently into longitudinal and circular layers, though these layers are still present. Many large muscles run at odd angles and clearly function in moving the parapodia. But these muscles are not arranged in such fashion as to act effectively against the resistance of the hydrostatic skeleton. What, then, do they pull against? In part, they pull against the force of other muscles that do act against the hydrostatic skeleton. But in part, also, they pull against the body wall, which in

these annelids has a cuticle that is much tougher and less pliable than that of the earthworm. The cuticle is so tough, in fact, that locomotion by peristaltic contractions is not characteristic of these worms, because their girth is fixed and there can be little alternating swelling and constriction. Many of these worms lack such complete internal segmentation as characterizes earthworms and their relatives, though they retain segmentation of the musculature of the body wall. It is usually held that it was from ancestral annelid worms of this general type that the arthropods evolved.

Animals with Hard Jointed Skeletons

Exoskeletons Versus Endoskeletons. The arthropods and the vertebrates are much the most mobile of the multicellular animals. Both groups possess paired locomotory appendages —legs and sometimes wings. Neither depends on a hydrostatic skeleton as the mechanical resistance against which their muscles act; each has evolved, instead, a hard jointed skeleton, with most of the skeletal muscles so arranged that one end is attached to one section of the skeleton and the other end to a different section (Fig. 11.5). Thus, when the muscle contracts, it causes the skeletal joint between its two points of attachment to bend. In many ways, then, the skeletal and muscular systems of arthropods and vertebrates show striking functional similarities. But these two great groups of animals evolved (if we read the evidence correctly) from entirely different ancestral stocks. The vertebrates did not evolve from annelids, nor, in all probability, from ancestors closely related to annelids. The arthropods and the vertebrates represent, in fact, the highly successful products of two very different evolutionary lines. It is not surprising, therefore, that an examination of the bases of their striking similarities reveals impressive differences. The two groups of animals have evolved many similar adaptations to the same

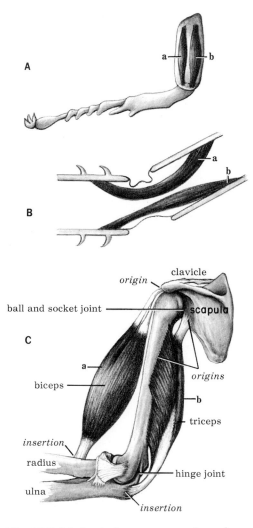

Fig. 11.5. **Mechanical arrangement of muscle and skeleton in human arm and insect legs.** When the biceps (muscle **a**) of the human arm (C) contracts, the arm is flexed (bent) at the elbow. The triceps (muscle **b**) has the opposite action; when it contracts, the lower arm is extended. The comparable muscles (**a** and **b**) in the insect leg of (A) have the same action, even though the muscles are inside the skeleton, because the fulcrum of the joint is distal to the insertions of the muscles. However, muscles **a** and **b** in the insect leg of (B) have reverse actions: **a** is an extensor and **b** is a flexor. Thus, although the muscles in both (B) and (C) span the joint, the actions of those in (B) are the reverse of the ones in the same position in (C) because the muscles of (B) are inside the skeleton while those of (C) are outside.

functional problems, but they have arrived at those adaptations in entirely different ways.

The most obvious difference between the skeletal systems of arthropods and vertebrates is that the arthropods have an *exoskeleton*—a hard body covering with all muscles and organs located inside it—whereas vertebrates have an *endoskeleton*—a framework embedded within the organism, with the muscles outside. Both types of skeletons function not only as structures against which muscles can pull, but in other ways as well. They are important, of course, in providing shape and structural support for large animals, particularly animals living on land where the buoyancy of water is not available for support, just as the rigid xylem is a critical factor in enabling land plants to attain large size. Exoskeletons, which are composed of noncellular material secreted by the epidermis, function also as a protective armor for the softer body parts and as a waxy barrier preventing excessive water loss by terrestrial arthropods. The rib cage of the vertebrate endoskeleton protects the organs of the thorax, and the skull and vertebral column protect the brain and spinal cord.

Exoskeletons obviously impose difficulties in overall growth, and periodic molting of the exoskeleton and deposition of a new one are necessary to permit size increase. Further, the mechanics of an exoskeletal system are such as to impose limitations on the possible size of animals that have them. The immense bulk that would be required in an exoskeleton sufficiently strong to support an insect as large as a man would pose insuperable mechanical problems. This is certainly one reason why arthropods, as varied and successful a group as they are, have never even approached the sizes of many vertebrates. In small animals, however, exoskeletons and endoskeletons are about equally effective, and in very small ones exoskeletons are probably superior.

The Vertebrate Skeletal and Muscular Systems. Vertebrate skeletons are composed pri-

posed almost entirely of cartilage. Cartilage is the primary component of the skeletons of embryos of all vertebrates; it is progressively replaced by bone as development proceeds. In the adult skeletons of most higher vertebrates, cartilage is retained wherever firmness combined with flexibility is needed, as at the ends of ribs, on the articulating surfaces in skeletal joints, in the walls of larynx and trachea, in the external ear, and in the nose.

Some bones are partly "spongy," consisting of a network of hardened bars with the spaces between them filled with marrow. Other bones are more compact, their hard parts appearing as an almost continuous mass with only microscopic cavities in them. The shafts of typical long bones, like those of the upper arm and thigh, consist of compact bone surrounding a large central marrow cavity. In adults, the marrow in the cavities of the shafts of long bones is primarily of the yellow fatty variety, while the marrow in the flat bones of the ribs and skull and in the ends of long bones is primarily of the red variety and is active in the production of blood cells. There is no sharp distinction between the two types of marrow, however, and they may grade into each other. Even the most characteristic red marrow contains about 70 percent fat.

Compact bone is composed of structural units called *Haversian systems* (Fig. 11.6). Each such unit is irregularly cylindrical and is composed of concentrically arranged layers of hard inorganic matrix surrounding a microscopic central Haversian canal. Blood vessels and nerves pass through this canal. The scattered irregularly shaped bone cells lie in small cavities located along the interfaces between adjoining concentric layers of the hard matrix. Exchange of materials between the bone cells and the blood vessels in the Haversian canals is by way of radiating canalicules that penetrate and cross the layers of hard matrix.

Vertebrate skeletons are customarily divided into two components: the axial skeleton, which is the main longitudinal portion, composed of

Fig. 11.6. Photograph of cross section of bone, showing Haversian systems. Each Haversian system is seen as a nearly round area. The light circular core of each system is the Haversian canal, through which blood vessels pass. Around the Haversian canal is a series of concentrically arranged hard lamellae. The elongate dark areas located between the lamellae are cavities, called lacunae, in which the bone cells are located. The numerous very thin dark lines running radially from the central canal across the lamellae to the lacunae are canalicules through which tissue fluid can diffuse. × 300. [Courtesy Thomas Eisner, Cornell University.]

marily of bone and/or cartilage, two types of connective tissue mentioned earlier (see p. 101). Cartilage is firm, but not as hard or as brittle as bone. The skeletons of some adult vertebrates, such as sharks and rays, are comthe skull and the vertebral column with its associated rib cage, and the appendicular skeleton, which includes the bones of the paired appendages (fins, legs, wings) and their associated pectoral and pelvic girdles (Fig. 11.7). Some bones are joined together by immovable joints or sutures, as in the case of the numerous small bones that together constitute the skull. But many others are held together at movable joints by *ligaments.* Skeletal muscles, attached to the bones by means of *tendons,* produce their effects by bending the skeleton at these movable joints. The force causing the bending is always exerted as a pull by contracting muscles; muscles cannot actively push. Reversal of the direction in which a joint is bent must be accomplished by contraction of a different set of muscles.

If a given muscle is attached to two bones with one or more joints between them, contraction of the muscle generally causes movement of only one of the two bones, the other being held relatively rigid by other muscles. The end of the muscle attached to the essentially stationary bone—generally the proximal end in limb muscles—is called the *origin,* and the end of the muscle attached to the bone that moves—generally the distal end in limb muscles—is called the *insertion* (see Fig. 11.5C). The movable bones behave like a lever system with the fulcrum at the joint. A single muscle sometimes has multiple origins and/or insertions, which may be on the same or on different bones. The action resulting from contraction of any specific muscle depends primarily on the exact positions of its origins and insertions and on the type of joint between them.

Actually, under normal circumstances, muscles do not contract singly. The nervous system does not send impulses to one muscle without sending impulses to other nearby muscles. Thus the various muscles operate in antagonistic groups; if one group of muscles is strongly contracted, an antagonistic group is exerting an opposing pull, and these stretched muscles

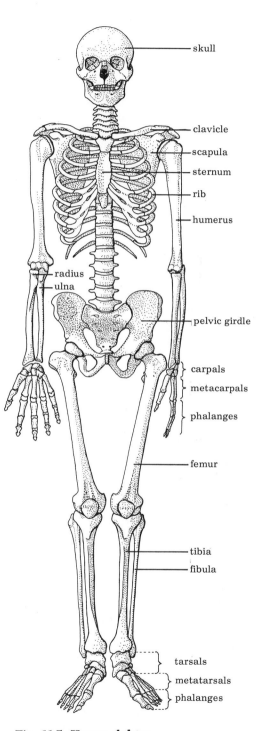

Fig. 11.7. **Human skeleton.**

are ready to reverse the direction of the movement. In addition, other muscles (synergists) serve to guide and limit the principal movement. To understand fully the action of a muscle, therefore, it is necessary to know, in addition to its own origins and insertions, the positions, actions, and relations of its antagonists and synergists. What compounds the difficulty of obtaining a complete functional picture is that we tend to identify and study the muscles individually, although they usually act in complex coordinated sequences, producing motions that are the result of integration of numerous component motor patterns. Even the simplest action, e.g. taking a step, involves a complicated pattern of activity by a large number of muscles.

The various types of skeletal joints and the numerous muscle-joint arrangements exemplify the basic mechanical principles of pulleys, levers, braces of various types, etc., and make a fascinating subject of study for those who are interested in engineering and mechanics, but they are beyond the scope of this book.

The Types of Muscle. Three different types of muscle tissue are recognized in vertebrates: *smooth muscle* (also called visceral muscle), *skeletal muscle* (also called voluntary or striated muscle), and heart or *cardiac muscle.*

Smooth muscle forms the muscle layers in the walls of the digestive tract, bladder, various ducts, and other internal organs. It is also the muscle present in the walls of arteries and veins. The individual smooth-muscle cells—or fibers, as they are commonly called—are thin, elongate, and usually pointed at their ends (Fig. 11.8A). Each has a single nucleus. The cells are not striated. These fibers interlace to form sheets of muscle tissue rather than bundles. Smooth muscle is innervated by the autonomic nervous system.

Skeletal muscle produces the movements of the limbs, trunk, face, jaws, eyeballs, etc. It is by far the most abundant tissue in the verte-

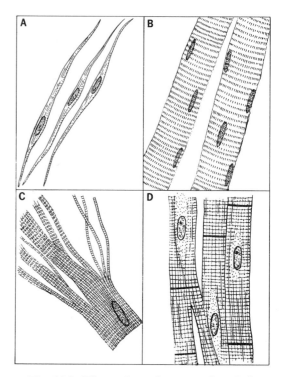

Fig. 11.8. Fibers of vertebrate muscle. (A) Three smooth-muscle fibers. (B) Portions of two skeletal-muscle fibers. Each has many nuclei and is crossed by alternating light and dark bands, or striations. (C) Part of a skeletal-muscle fiber teased apart to show its constituent myofibrils. (D) Cardiac muscle. The dark black lines, called intercalated discs, are now known to be the places where one cell ends and the next begins.

brate body. Most of what we commonly call "meat" is skeletal muscle. Each skeletal-muscle fiber is roughly cylindrical, contains many nuclei (i.e. it is coenocytic), and is crossed by alternating light and dark bands called *striations* (Fig. 11.8B). The fibers are usually bound together by connective tissue into bundles rather than sheets; these bundles, in turn, are bound together by connective tissue to form muscles. A muscle is, then, a composite structure composed of many bundles of muscle fibers, just as a nerve is composed of many nerve fibers bound together. Skeletal muscle is innervated by the somatic nervous system.

Cardiac muscle, the tissue of which the heart is composed, shows some characteristics of skeletal muscle and some characteristics of smooth muscle. Its fibers, like those of skeletal muscle, are striated and contain numerous nuclei. But like smooth muscle, it is innervated by the autonomic nervous system, and its activity is more like that of smooth muscle. Until only a few years ago, it was thought that cardiac muscle differed from both skeletal muscle and smooth muscle in lacking distinct fibers. Ordinary microscopes showed no separation into individual cells, and it was assumed that the entire heart was one large branching syncytium, i.e. a single mass of cytoplasm containing many nuclei. Recent studies with the electron microscope, however, have revealed that there are, in fact, separate fibers in cardiac muscle, but that the adjacent surfaces of these cells are so tightly appressed against each other and so complexly interdigitated that they had not previously been recognized as cellular junctions. The sites of these junctions had been visible under light microscopes as dark-colored discs (Fig. 11.8D), but they had been variously interpreted as special contraction bands, as nutritive structures, and as structures for intracellular conduction.

The descriptions of the muscle types given above do not apply in all respects to the muscles of invertebrate animals. For example, all the muscles of insects are striated, even those in the walls of their internal organs; many other invertebrates possess only smooth muscles. In general, striated muscle contracts faster than smooth muscle, but cannot remain contracted as long. Some invertebrates have evolved arrangements that take advantage of this difference, enabling them to perform the same action in two different ways. Thus scallops, which swim by opening and closing their shells in a flapping motion, have two sets of shell-closing muscle fibers: a striated set, whose fast action is used in swimming, and a smooth set, whose slower but longer-lasting action is used for keeping the shells closed when the scallop is at rest.

THE PHYSIOLOGY OF MUSCLE ACTIVITY

In vertebrates, skeletal muscle is primarily concerned with effecting adjustments to the organism's external environment, while smooth muscle is responsible for movements in response to internal changes. These differences in action are reflected in differences in their physiological characteristics. Cells of skeletal muscle are innervated by only one nerve fiber; they contract when stimulated by nerve impulses and relax when no such impulses are reaching them. Smooth-muscle cells, by contrast, are usually innervated by two nerve fibers, one from the sympathetic system and one from the parasympathetic system; they contract in response to impulses from one of the two kinds of fiber and relax in response to impulses from the other. Skeletal muscles cannot function normally in the absence of nervous connections and actually degenerate when deprived of their innervation, but smooth muscle (like cardiac muscle) can often contract without any nervous stimulation, as is commonly the case in peristaltic contractions of the intestine, for example. The action of skeletal muscle is more rapid, but smooth muscle can remain contracted longer. Skeletal muscle is more sensitive to electrical stimuli than smooth muscle, but the latter is more sensitive to chemical stimuli. Skeletal muscle has a definite resting length, whereas smooth muscle does not; yet smooth muscle contracts more readily in response to stretching.

More is known at present about the processes involved in contraction of skeletal muscle than of smooth muscle. Consequently most of the discussion below will be restricted to skeletal muscle.

The General Features of Muscle Contraction

Stimulation. Like the membrane of a resting neuron, that of a resting muscle fiber is polarized. Apparently the same sort of sodium-potassium pump is operative here as in nerve. A stimulatory transmitter substance released by a nerve axon at the neuromuscular junction apparently causes a momentary reduction of this polarization. If the reduction reaches the threshold level, there is a sudden inrush of sodium ions followed by an outflow of potassium ions. These events cause the same sort of change in potential as is seen when a neuron is stimulated; the inside of the muscle fiber becomes slightly positive relative to the outside for an instant, but then becomes negative again as potassium ions move outward. In some manner not yet understood, this change in electrical potential, which is propagated over the entire surface of the fiber and probably also into its interior via membranous subcellular components, triggers the contraction process. All impulses arriving at skeletal-muscle fibers of vertebrates are excitatory, since these fibers are singly innervated; but the striated-muscle fibers of some invertebrates, such as crustaceans, are doubly innervated, and the impulses arriving at the muscle fibers via one of the two types of nerve fibers are inhibitory, probably causing hyperpolarization of the fiber membrane, just as inhibitory synapses between neurons often cause hyperpolarization of the postsynaptic neuronal membranes.

Since individual muscle fibers resemble individual nerve cells in their manner of stimulation and in firing only if an impinging stimulus is of threshold intensity, duration, and rate, we can ask whether they also exhibit the all-or-none property. The answer seems to be yes for vertebrates. If we administer to an excised vertebrate muscle fiber a stimulus above the threshold value, we obtain the same degree of contraction whatever the value of

the stimulus, provided, of course, that it is not so strong as to damage the cell.

Contraction of a Whole Muscle. You know, of course, that you can use the same muscles to perform tasks as different as lifting a pencil or lifting a 20-pound weight. Clearly, an individual muscle can give graded responses depending upon the strength of the stimulation reaching it. We can demonstrate this in the laboratory by removing a leg muscle from a frog and attaching it to a device that will measure the extent of contraction of the muscle when it is stimulated. If we administer a stimulus barely above threshold intensity, the muscle gives a very weak twitch (Fig. 11.9). If this is followed after a few seconds' delay by a slightly stronger stimulus, the muscle gives a slightly stronger twitch. We can keep increasing the strength of the stimulus and getting a stronger contraction from the muscle until we reach a point where further increases in the stimulus do not increase the strength of the response. The muscle has reached its maximal response.

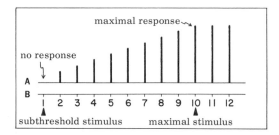

Fig. 11.9. **Response of a muscle to stimuli of various intensities.** Line B indicates the intensities at which stimuli were administered, and A shows by the height of the black bars the strength of muscle response. Stimulus 1 was very weak and elicited no response; i.e. it was subthreshold. Stimulus 2 was somewhat stronger and proved to be above threshold, for the muscle contracted. Each stimulus from 3 to 10 was slightly stronger than the preceding one, and each elicited a correspondingly stronger muscle contraction. Stimuli 11 and 12 were stronger than 10, but the muscle gave no greater response, indicating that 10 had elicited a maximal response.

How do we explain these results if muscle fibers give all-or-none responses? One possible explanation is that the threshold values of the different muscle fibers of which a muscle is composed are not the same. Furthermore, different muscle fibers may be innervated by different nerve fibers, and these nerve fibers may not all fire at the same time. Thus, although single fibers give an all-or-none response to stimuli, an increase in the strength of the stimulus above the threshold level may elicit a greater response from the whole muscle by stimulating more muscle fibers. Ultimately, however, all the fibers will be stimulated to respond and the muscle will thus have reached a maximal response; increasing the intensity of the stimulus to supramaximal levels will not increase the response, as there are no more fibers to stimulate. It must be stressed that the description given here applies only to vertebrate skeletal muscles. The striated muscles of invertebrates seldom exhibit the all-or-none property; the strength of their contraction is proportional to the frequency of stimulation.

In the experiment described in the preceding paragraph, we were careful to allow an appreciable time delay between stimuli. Thus each response was induced by a single brief stimulus, and the muscle had sufficient time to relax fully before it was stimulated again. Such a muscular response is called a *simple twitch.* Let us examine its characteristics. Suppose that an isolated frog muscle has been attached to a kymograph apparatus (Fig. 11.10) in such a manner that every time the muscle is stimulated by an electric shock it moves a lever that writes on the revolving drum of the kymograph. The stronger the contraction of the muscle, the higher it will pull the lever. If a single adequate stimulus is administered to this muscle, there is a brief interval during which no contraction occurs; this is the *latent period,* the interval between stimulation of the muscle and the commencement of the shortening process. Actually, the true latent period of a muscle usually varies between 0.0025 and

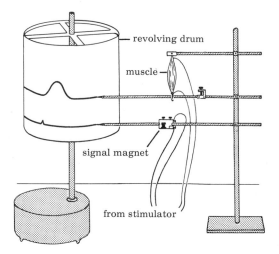

Fig. 11.10. Kymograph apparatus for studying muscle contraction. The drum of the kymograph, which is covered with paper, revolves at a constant speed. The muscle is mounted in such a way that when it contracts it raises a stylus that writes on the revolving drum. Wires lead from a stimulator to the muscle and also to a signal magnet that can deflect a second stylus. At the moment when a stimulus is sent to the muscle, the signal stylus is deflected, producing a blip in the trace it is drawing on the revolving drum; one such blip is shown on the trace in this picture. This blip shows us exactly when the stimulus was administered. The stimulus causes the muscle to contract, raising the stylus to which it is attached and producing a corresponding rise in the trace the stylus is drawing on the revolving drum. As the muscle relaxes, the stylus is lowered and the trace it is drawing falls. Thus the trace drawn on the kymograph drum gives us a record of the contraction pattern of the muscle.

0.004 second and could hardly be detected with a kymograph, even a very sensitive one (the latent period shown in Fig. 11.11 has been exaggerated). The latent period is followed by the **contraction period,** and this is followed immediately by a **relaxation period.** These three periods comprise a single simple twitch of the muscle.

Now let us suppose that a series of very frequent stimuli is applied to the muscle. In this case, the muscle will not have completely relaxed after contracting in response to one stim-

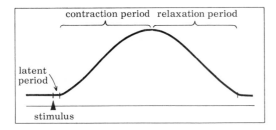

Fig. 11.11. Kymograph record of a simple twitch. For description, see text.

ulus when the next stimulus arrives. When this happens, a contraction is elicited that is greater than either stimulus alone would produce (Fig. 11.12). There has been a *summation* of contractions, the second adding to the first. If the initial stimulus was submaximal, the summation may be due in part to recruitment of additional muscle fibers by the second stimulus. But this is not the whole story; summation can occur even if the individual stimuli are of maximal intensity, i.e. even if all fibers in the muscle are activated by each stimulus. Some change in the physiological condition of the muscle fibers during activity must account for the increased strength of contraction. Our earlier statement that individual muscle fibers give an all-or-none response must therefore be slightly qualified. Each fiber will respond maximally to a single isolated stimulus if that stimulus is above the threshold level, but the fiber may respond in a slightly stronger manner if it is given a rapid series of stimuli, because its initial contraction produces chemical changes that make it more irritable. These chemical changes may be in part due to the increase in temperature resulting from the work of contraction.

When stimuli are given with extreme rapidity, the muscle cannot relax at all between successive stimuli. Consequently the individual contractions become indistinguishable and fuse into a single sustained contraction known as *tetanus* (do not confuse this normal muscular response with the bacterial infection known also as lockjaw). For the reasons given in the

explanation of summation, of which tetanus is a form, a tetanic contraction is greater than a maximal simple twitch of the same muscle. Normally, a high percentage of our actions involve tetanic contractions rather than simple twitches, because a volley of nerve impulses is sent to the muscle. If, however, a tetanic contraction is maintained too long, the muscle will begin to fatigue, and the strength of its contraction will fall even though the stimuli continue at the same intensity. Fatigue is probably due in part to an accumulation of lactic acid, in part to depletion of stored energy reserves, and in part to other chemical changes.

Normally, the muscles of the body are never completely relaxed, but are kept in a state of partial contraction called muscle tone or *tonus*. Tonus is maintained by alternate contraction

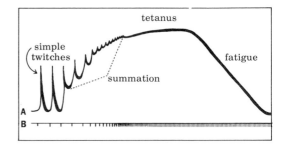

Fig. 11.12. Kymograph record showing summation and tetanus. When the stimuli (line B) are widely spaced, the muscle has time to relax fully before the next stimulus arrives, and simple twitches result (the drum is revolving much more slowly than in Fig. 11.11, so that each simple twitch is recorded as a sharp spike on the trace). As the frequency of the stimuli increases, the muscle does not have time to relax fully from one contraction before the next stimulus arrives and causes it to contract again. The result is summation—contractions that are stronger (and hence produce a taller spike in the trace) than any single simple twitch. If the stimuli are very frequent, the muscle may not relax at all between successive stimulations; the resulting strong sustained contraction is called tetanus. If the very frequent stimulation continues, however, the muscle may fatigue and be unable to maintain the contraction.

of different groups of muscle fibers, so that no single fiber has a chance to fatigue.

The Molecular Basis of Contraction

It has been known for many years that when a muscle contracts it releases heat. Now, if a contracting muscle can perform work and if it releases heat in the process, an energy supply in the form of ATP must be involved. And the energy of the ATP must come from oxidation of food materials such as glycogen and glucose. It is in the muscles, in fact, that a high percentage of the oxidative phosphorylation in an animal's body occurs. Much of the early work on cellular respiration was performed on muscle tissue.

Very little ATP is actually stored in the muscles. A few muscular twitches can quickly exhaust the supply. But there is a supply of stored high-energy phosphate in muscles. In vertebrates and some invertebrates, particularly echinoderms, this supply is in the form of *creatine phosphate,* a compound formed by linkage of a phosphate group to creatine by a high-energy bond. Many invertebrates utilize a similar compound, arginine phosphate. These two compounds—creatine phosphate and arginine phosphate—are called *phosphagens.* Apparently the phosphagens cannot supply energy directly to the contraction mechanism of muscle, but they can pass their high-energy phosphate groups to ADP to form ATP, and the ATP can then act as the direct energy source for contraction. Enough high-energy phosphate is stored in the muscle to enable it to contract strongly during the several seconds' delay necessary before the machinery of cellular respiration can be speeded up and larger quantities of new high-energy phosphate synthesized.

If the demands on the muscles are not great, much of the energy used to replenish the supply of phosphagens and ATP may come from the complete oxidation of carbohydrate to carbon dioxide and water via glycolysis and the Krebs citric acid cycle. During the unavoidable delay before adjustments of the respiratory and circulatory systems increase the oxygen supply to the active muscles, some of the oxygen for the aerobic respiration may come from oxymyoglobin. *Myoglobin* is a compound in muscles that is chemically similar to hemoglobin. It forms a loose combination with oxygen while the oxygen supply is plentiful and stores the oxygen until the demand for it increases.

But during violent muscular activity, as when you are exercising strenuously or lifting a very heavy object, the energy demands of the muscles may be greater than can be met by complete respiration alone, because sufficient oxygen cannot be gotten to the tissues fast enough after the oxymyoglobin has been used up. Under such circumstances, lactic acid fermentation occurs. The muscles obtain the extra energy they need from anaerobic processes, and lactic acid accumulates in them. The muscles thus incur what physiologists call an *oxygen debt,* and when the violent activity is over they continue using large quantities of oxygen as they reconvert the lactic acid into pyruvic acid and oxidize some of it, utilizing the energy thus obtained to resynthesize glycogen from the rest of the lactic acid. In this manner, the oxygen debt is paid off, and the lactic acid is removed. This is why you continue to breathe hard or to pant for some time after you have stopped the violent activity that initiated the process.

If ATP is the immediate source of energy for muscle contraction, how is the ATP coupled to the contraction process and what is that process? Analysis of muscle shows that the major components of its contractile parts are two proteins called *actin* and *myosin.* V. A. Engelhardt and M. N. Ljubimova of the Academy of Sciences in Moscow demonstrated in 1939 that myosin can function as an enzyme that catalyzes removal of the terminal phosphate group from ATP. This is, of course, precisely the energy-liberating reaction we would expect to find coupled to the contraction process. Might myosin function in the intact muscle both as one of the contractile elements and as the enzyme that makes energy available for contraction? The answer seems to be yes. Here seems to be an excellent example of the dual functions of which some (and perhaps all) proteins are capable; they can function simultaneously as structural elements and as enzymes.

Evidence for the dual function of myosin in muscle contractions comes from experiments performed by Albert Szent-Györgyi, now of the Institute for Muscle Research, Woods Hole, Massachusetts. Szent-Györgyi showed that if actin and myosin are separately extracted from muscle, purified, and put into solution together, they will combine spontaneously to form a loose complex known as actomyosin. If the actomyosin complex is then precipitated and artificial fibers are prepared from it, the fibers will contract when exposed to ATP. Neither actin nor myosin alone will contract. Clearly, then, the actomyosin complex is a contractile material. Clearly, also, the complex (actually its myosin component) can itself liberate from ATP the energy necessary for its own contraction, since in this experiment no other possible enzyme is present.

Szent-Györgyi also performed other experiments in which he tied fresh muscles to frames at their natural lengths and soaked them in cold glycerine for several hours; he then removed the muscles from the glycerine and washed them thoroughly. This procedure killed the muscles and removed from them almost everything but the actin and myosin (and a third protein tropomyosin). If this dead actomyosin remnant was then warmed in a dilute solution, it would contract upon exposure to ATP. We could enumerate still other experiments that yield similar results, but the important point has been made: The essential elements for contraction are actomyosin and ATP in a salt solution of suitable ionic concentra-

tion. No other components of the muscle are necessary.

If actomyosin really is the contractile component of muscle, we must ask how it contracts. One possible way a protein complex of this sort could shorten would be for it to fold more tightly. This was the hypothesis put forward by many workers. More recently, however, anatomical studies have shown that it is probably incorrect. Let us turn, then, from the physiological evidence to the anatomical evidence.

We have seen that a skeletal muscle is composed of numerous muscle fibers bound together by connective tissue. Examination of these fibers under very high magnification reveals that they, in turn, are composed of numerous long thin *myofibrils,* each about a micron in diameter (Fig. 11.8C). Between the myofibrils are large numbers of mitochondria —subcellular components that we would expect to find in abundance in cells that have a high energy requirement. The myofibrils show the same pattern of cross striations as the fibers of which they are a part (Fig. 11.13). There is an alternation of fairly wide light and dark bands, which have been called *I-bands* and *A-bands* respectively. In the middle of each dark A-band is a region that is lighter than the rest of the A-band but darker than the I-bands —the *H-zone.* In the middle of the light I-band is a very dark thin line called the *Z-line.* Might these striations so characteristic of skeletal muscle be a structural reflection of the functional contractile units? A variety of evidence indicates that the answer is yes. Chemical analysis shows that myosin is concentrated in the A-bands and that actin is concentrated in the I-bands. Furthermore, A. F. Huxley of Cambridge University showed in 1954 that the relative widths of the bands change as the fiber contracts; the I-bands and H-zones become narrower but the A-bands remain the same, with the result that the A-bands are moved closer together.

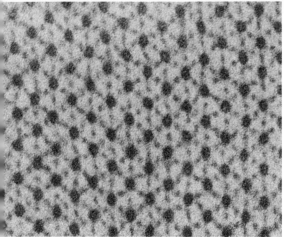

Fig. 11.13. Electron micrograph of skeletal muscle from a rabbit. The myofibrils run diagonally across the micrograph from upper left to lower right; each looks like a ribbon crossed by alternating light and dark bands. The wide light bands are called I-bands; there is a narrow dark Z-line in the middle of each I-band. The wide dark bands are A-bands, each of which has a lighter H-zone across its middle. × 24,360. [Courtesy H. E. Huxley, Cambridge University.]

Fig. 11.14. Electron micrograph of cross section of insect flight muscle. The thick myosin filaments and the thin actin filaments form a very orderly pattern. × 400,000. [Courtesy H. E. Huxley, Cambridge University.]

At about the time A. F. Huxley was performing his experiments under a high-power light microscope, H. E. Huxley (no kin to A. F.) of University College, London, developed a new technique for viewing muscle with the electron microscope. He found that within each myofibril there are two types of filaments, thick ones and thin ones (Fig. 11.14), arranged in a very precise pattern. The two types of filaments are interdigitated with each other, with the thick ones located exclusively in the A-bands and the thin ones primarily in the I-bands but extending some distance into the A-bands. This explains the different appearances of the A-bands, I-bands, and H-zones. Each dark A-band is precisely the length of one region of thick filaments; it is darkest near its borders, where the thick and thin filaments overlap, and lighter in its mid-region or H-zone, where only the thick filaments are present (Fig. 11.15). Each light I-band corresponds to a region where only the thin filaments are present. The Z-line is interpreted as a membranous structure to which the thin

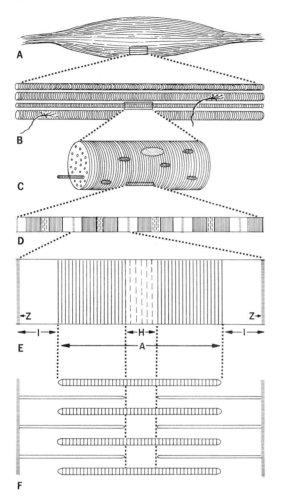

Fig. 11.15. The component parts of skeletal muscle. (A) A whole muscle. (B) A small part of the muscle magnified to show the muscle cells, or fibers. (C) Part of a fiber much magnified. (D) A myofibril removed from a fiber. (E) A small portion of the myofibril much magnified to show the pattern of striations. (F) The myosin and actin filaments that give rise to the pattern of light and dark bands. The dark A-band corresponds to the length of the thick myosin filaments; the H-zone is the region where only the thick filaments occur, while the darker ends of the A-band are regions where thick and thin filaments overlap. The light I-band corresponds to regions where only thin actin filaments occur. [Adapted from H. E. Huxley, "The Contraction of Muscle," *Sci. Am.*, November, 1958. Copyright © 1958 by Scientific American, Inc. All rights reserved.]

filaments are anchored at their mid-points; it may function to hold the filaments in proper register, and it may also function as the structure against which the filaments exert their pull during contraction.

The observations of the two Huxleys led each of them independently to propose a new theory of muscle contraction: that instead of folding, the filaments telescope together by sliding past each other (Fig. 11.16). If the filaments slide together, the zone of overlap between thick and thin filaments would increase until the thin filaments from the I-bands on the two sides of an A-band might actually meet; this sliding together would reduce the width of the H-zone and even obliterate it entirely if the thin filaments met. The sliding together would also pull the Z-lines closer together and greatly reduce the width of the I-bands. But it would not change the width of the A-bands, since these correspond to the full length of the thick filaments, which remains the same. Thus the sliding theory accounts for the changes that have been observed to occur.

Numerous electron micrographs of muscle fibers in various degrees of contraction have tended to support the sliding-filament theory.

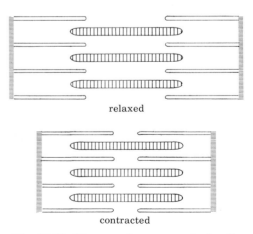

Fig. 11.16. Diagram of arrangement of actin and myosin filaments in relaxed and contracted muscle.

The more contracted the muscle, the more telescoped are the filaments. Tending to discredit the older folding theory is the observation that the lengths of the individual filaments do not change appreciably unless the contraction is so great that filaments meet and crumple.

If the sliding-filament theory is the one most widely accepted today, what explanation is given for the sliding? What is the mechanism that brings it about? Here the evidence is less clear. Analysis shows that the thick filaments are composed of myosin and the thin filaments of actin. We have already seen that myosin and actin must unite to form the actomyosin complex before they possess contractile properties. Some sort of connection must exist, then, between the thick myosin filaments and the thin actin filaments. Electron micrographs do indeed show what appear to be small cross bridges between the filaments (Fig. 11.17A). The evidence suggests that they are portions of the myosin molecules. H. E. Huxley has proposed that they act as hooks or levers that enable the myosin filaments to pull the actin filaments (Fig. 11.17B). His hypothesis is that the cross bridges are movable and that they bend toward the actin, hook onto it at specialized receptor sites, and then bend in the other direction, pulling the actin with them; they would then let go, bend in the first direction again, hook onto the actin at a new active site, and again pull. In other words, the sliding together of the filaments would be effected by a ratchet mechanism.

Huxley assumes that each oscillation of a cross bridge would require the energy of one ATP molecule. On the basis of the characteristic rate of contraction of the rabbit muscle he used in his studies and the number of cross bridges counted per unit length, he has calculated that each bridge would have to go through from 50 to 100 cycles of activity per second. This would mean that 50 to 100 molecules of ATP would be used up per cross

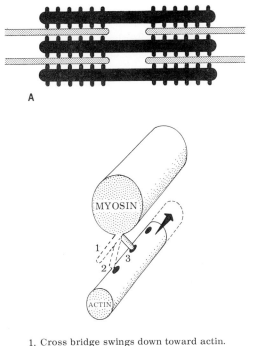

1. Cross bridge swings down toward actin.
2. Hooks onto active site.
3. Contracts, pulling actin inward.

B

Fig. 11.17. Model of the function of cross bridges between myosin and actin filaments. (A) The cross bridges are thought to be part of the thick myosin filaments. (B) Movement of the cross bridges pulls the actin filaments in a ratchetlike mechanism.

bridge per second. If the total number of cross bridges in the muscle fiber is estimated, and if this figure is used to estimate the total ATP consumption by the fiber per second, the resulting figure is compatible with the known rate at which myosin can catalyze the removal of terminal phosphate groups from ATP.

Although the remarkably precise arrangement of filaments found in striated-muscle cells has not been found in other types of muscle cells, the evidence seems to suggest that such cells contract by essentially the same mechanism. Actomyosin can be extracted from these other muscles, and the electron microscope often reveals some filaments within them. Furthermore, a contractile protein very similar to actomyosin has been isolated from slime molds, and another one has been found associated with the flagella of sperm cells. Moreover, when smooth-muscle cells, amoeboid cells, and sperm cells are subjected to the same glycerin treatment that Szent-Györgyi gave striated-muscle cells, the resulting dead remnants can split ATP and move in their characteristic manner; the remnants of the smooth-muscle cells and the amoeboid cells contract, and the remnant of the flagella of the sperm cells lashes vigorously (it has been shown that ATP splitting by flagella occurs only in the nine outer filaments). In other words, all these cells —striated- and smooth-muscle cells, amoeboid cells, and flagellated cells—possess either acto-myosin or a similar contractile protein, and in each type of cell the contractile protein contracts when exposed to ATP, whose energy-releasing breakdown the contractile protein itself catalyzes. It would be surprising, therefore, if the mechanism of the contraction were not basically the same in all these motile cells.

Perhaps the difference between striated-muscle cells and other motile cells lies in the degree of order superimposed on the actin and myosin molecules. Each thick filament of striated muscle is composed of many myosin molecules, each probably contributing one cross bridge. Similarly, each thin filament consists of many actin molecules. It seems possible that the actin and myosin molecules of some contractile and amoeboid cells are grouped together in smaller, differently arranged filaments or are not grouped into filaments at all, but this need not mean that the individual molecules do not slide over each other during contraction. The sliding may simply be at the level of individual molecules, or small groups of them, rather than at the level of large clumps of molecules.

Clearly, much more research is needed before we can speak with any certainty about the mechanism of muscle contraction, of amoeboid movement, or of flagellar movement. But the last few years have seen exciting advances, and the future looks promising. It will be interesting to see if our current surmise that the underlying mechanisms of these three types of movement are the same proves to be correct. A single mechanism for all three would be one more striking example of the unity in diversity so typical of the living world.

REFERENCES

Bloom, W., and D. W. Fawcett, 1962. *A Textbook of Histology*, 8th ed. Saunders, Philadelphia. (See esp. Chapters 6–8.)

Chapman, G., 1958. "The Hydrostatic Skeleton of Invertebrates," *Biological Reviews*, vol. 33, pp. 338–371.

Clark, R. B., 1963. "The Evolution of the Celom and Metameric Segmentation," *The Lower Metazoa*, ed. by E. C. Dougherty. University of California Press, Berkeley.

Gray, J., 1953. *How Animals Move*. Cambridge University Press, New York.

Howell, A. B., 1944. *Speed in Animals: Their Specialization for Running and Leaping*. University of Chicago Press, Chicago.

Hoyle, G., 1957. *Comparative Physiology of the Nervous Control of Muscular Contraction* (Cambridge Monographs in Experimental Biology, no. 8.) Cambridge University Press, New York.

Huxley, A. F., and H. E. Huxley, eds., 1964. "A Discussion of the Physical and Chemical Basis of Muscular Contraction," *Proceedings of the Royal Society* (*London*), series B, vol. 160, pp. 433–542.

Prosser, C. L., and F. A. Brown, 1961. *Comparative Animal Physiology*, 2nd ed. Saunders, Philadelphia. (See esp. Chapters 14–19.)

Rivera, J. A., 1962. *Cilia, Ciliated Epithelium, and Ciliary Activity*. Pergamon, Oxford.

RUCH, T. C., H. D. PATTON, J. W. WOODBURY, and A. L. TOWE, 1961. *Neurophysiology.* Saunders, Philadelphia. (See esp. Chapter 4.)

WINTON, F. R., and L. E. BAYLISS, 1962. *Human Physiology,* 5th ed. Little, Brown, Boston. (See esp. Chapter 16.)

YOUNG, J. Z., 1957. *The Life of Mammals.* Oxford University Press, New York. (See esp. Chapters 4–9.)

ZENKEVICH, L. A., 1945. "The Evolution of Animal Locomotion," *Journal of Morphology,* vol. 77, pp. 1–52.

SUGGESTED READING

ALLEN, R. D., 1962. "Amoeboid Movement," *Scientific American,* February. (Offprint 182.)

CARLSON, A. J., V. JOHNSON, and H. M. CAVERT, 1961. *The Machinery of the Body,* 5th ed. University of Chicago Press, Chicago. (See esp. Chapter 10.)

HAYASHI, T., 1961. "How Cells Move," *Scientific American,* September. (Offprint 97.)

HUXLEY, H. E., 1958. "The Contraction of Muscle," *Scientific American,* November. (Offprint 19.)

———, 1965. "The Mechanism of Muscular Contraction," *Scientific American,* December. (Offprint 1026.)

LISSMANN, H. W., 1963. "Electric Location by Fishes," *Scientific American,* March. (Offprint 152.)

McELROY, W. D., and H. H. SELIGER, 1962. "Biological Luminescence," *Scientific American,* December. (Offprint 141.)

PORTER, K. R., and C. FANZINI-ARMSTRONG, 1965. "The Sarcoplasmic Reticulum," *Scientific American,* March. (Offprint 1007.)

ROSENBLUTH, J., 1965. "Smooth Muscle: An Ultrastructural Basis for the Dynamics of Its Contraction," *Science,* vol. 148, pp. 1337–1339.

SATIR, P., 1961. "Cilia," *Scientific American,* February. (Offprint 79.)

SMITH, D. S., 1965. "The Flight Muscles of Insects," *Scientific American,* June. (Offprint 1014.)

CHAPTER

12

ANIMAL BEHAVIOR

WHAT ANIMALS DO AND HOW THEY DO IT constitutes one of their outstanding attributes: behavior—an outcome, as we saw in the preceding chapters, of the functions and interactions of control and effector mechanisms. Inclusion of a chapter on behavior in this book on biological science is based on a firm conviction that the behavior of animals is just as valid a part of biology as are anatomy and physiology. Biology is the study of life, and surely behavior is one of the most fundamental characteristics of life in animals. Admittedly, many aspects of the study of behavior are customarily classified as psychology, and psychology, in turn, is frequently grouped with the social sciences rather than with the biological sciences. But demarcations between allied disciplines are bound to be arbitrary and must not be allowed to interfere with the search for knowledge. One of the most invigorating and productive developments in the recent history of science has been the ever increasing tendency for the traditional physical and biological sciences to blend together, so that it is now often difficult to classify a scientist as a chemist or a biologist. A similar interfusion of the biological and social sciences has begun and will almost certainly gather momentum. This change in our outlook, which will surely benefit research in both areas, is one to be welcomed and nourished.

Having pleaded for increased interplay between the biological and the social sciences, particularly psychology, we must now admit that the subject of animal behavior is such an enormous one that even a superficial treatment of all its many aspects, as they have been elucidated by both psychologists and biologists, is far beyond the scope of this book. Accordingly, only a few aspects of behavior, primarily those most directly related to the other topics discussed in this book and those most often studied by scientists trained in biology, will be mentioned here. You are urged to pursue the subject further by consulting a good psychology text.

THE NATURE OF BEHAVIOR

Behavior is a highly complex subject that demands the application of the most refined techniques of neurophysiology, endocrinology, effector physiology, anatomy, ecology, evolutionary biology, mathematical analysis, etc. It is, in short, a synthetic study, which depends for its own advances upon advances in a great variety of other disciplines. It is not surprising, therefore, that rigorous scientific investigation of behavior is a relatively recent development and that our knowledge of this crucial subject is still in its infancy.

Even the mere detailed description of the behavior of an animal is a difficult task—not only because it requires incredibly careful observation over a long period of time, but also because our language lacks adequate words with which to convey accurately what has been seen. Almost all our words have some sort of human connotation, imply some type of human motivation and purpose. But such mo-

tivation and purpose may have no relevance to the behavior of other animals, and we must constantly guard against unwarranted attribution of human characteristics to other species. Anthropomorphic or teleological[1] thinking has no place in a scientific study of animal behavior. Some persons feel so strongly about this that they try to avoid all words that betray a human bias; the result is often almost unreadable prose—and still such attempts usually fail because less common words embodying the human point of view are simply being substituted for the more familiar ones. An attempt has been made in this book to avoid the most obviously and blatantly anthropomorphic or teleological expressions. But the book has been written in English, and English (like all human languages), having developed around human activities and human interpretations, inevitably reflects these, often with a strong cast of supernaturalism. Such being the limitations of language, no attempt has been made to perform the hopeless task of scrubbing our text clean of all words or expressions that might imply human or supernatural purposiveness to someone. You are cautioned, therefore, to recognize the pitfalls inherent in any application of human-oriented language to the activities of other animals, or even to such topics as physiology or evolution.

Tropisms, Taxes, and Reflexes

Occam's Razor and Morgan's Canon. For centuries, men have observed the behavior of animals and have explained this behavior in terms of their own experience. Observing insects fly away at the approach of a man, they

---

[1] Anthropomorphism is the attributing of human characteristics to nonhuman beings and things. Teleology is the doctrine that the processes of nature are purposive and directed toward some goal. Another idea that can confuse scientific thinking about behavior is the so-called vitalist doctrine, which holds that life processes are not exclusively determined by the laws of the physical universe but involve some nonphysical "vital force."

have said that the insects see the man, are afraid of him, and fly away in order to avoid him. Observing earthworms squirm when pierced by fishhooks, they have said that the hooks hurt the worms, causing them to writhe in pain. Observing adult birds feeding their young, they have said that the birds love their babies and want to feed and protect them. But such descriptions are unacceptable; we have no evidence that being afraid, feeling pain, loving, wanting to do something, as those descriptions apply to human beings, are meaningful when applied to insects, earthworms, or birds. Such interpretations are projections to animals of the sensations human beings would experience in similar circumstances, but as was emphasized in our discussion of the nervous system, sensations are products of the brain and depend upon conscious awareness. Insects and earthworms have brains so different from man's that extrapolations from one to the other must be made only with great caution. It is more than unlikely that insects and earthworms experience conscious awareness in the human sense, if, indeed, they experience it in any sense. The same arguments apply, though with slightly less force, to comparisons between birds and men.

What, then, can we say about the insects that fly away and the earthworms that squirm on the fishhooks and the birds that feed their young? There is a centuries-old principle of logic called Occam's razor that says if several different explanations are all compatible with the evidence at hand, the simplest should be considered the most probable, or to put it another way, explanations should be no more complicated than necessary. Application of this principle to our examples helps eliminate the excessively anthropomorphic interpretations first considered, in favor of simpler explanations of the observed behavior. The insect receives visual stimuli from an approaching man, impulses travel along reflex circuits and stimulate the muscles of flight, and the insect flies away. This description is compatible with our observations, and it is undeniably simpler than one that assumes that the insect consciously experiences a sensation of fear and consciously decides to fly away. "Fear" and "decide" are words that should not be applied to insects to describe their behavior. The same is true of the earthworm; "pain" may be a meaningless word when applied to such an animal. The hook certainly stimulates receptors that initiate impulses along nerve circuits, and these impulses result in squirming, but we have no basis for assuming that any conscious awareness is involved, no basis for saying that the worm feels pain. Squirming, as a reflex response to stimulation of sensory receptors by fishhooks or other objects, has an obvious adaptive advantage; it might help the worm avoid further physical damage. No conscious awareness or volition need be associated with such an adaptive response. Even the more complex behavior of a mother bird feeding her young can be explained in terms of responses to stimuli within the context of the physiological condition of the bird at the time; no "love" or "desire" need be assumed.

Application of Occam's razor to the study of animal behavior was strongly urged by C. Lloyd Morgan of Bristol, England, who said in 1893: "In no case may we interpret an action as the outcome of the exercise of a higher psychical faculty, if it can be interpreted as the outcome of the exercise of one which stands lower in the psychological scale." In other words, we should interpret the behavior of other animals in terms of the simplest neural mechanisms that can explain the observed actions. This principle, often called Morgan's canon, rules out invoking conscious thought, deliberate decision, purposive determination, or foresight as explanations of animal behavior. It prohibits anecdotal descriptions and anthropomorphic interpretations.

Jacques Loeb and "Animal Tropisms." The rebellion begun by Morgan against the old anthropomorphic approach to animal behavior

found a strong supporter in the German physiologist Jacques Loeb, who from 1891 worked
in the United States. Loeb was intrigued by
the discoveries being made at the time in the
study of plant tropisms. These discoveries reduced plant behavior to a very low "psychical"
level indeed. The plant turns because unequal
stimulation on opposite sides produces certain
physicochemical changes that result in the
turning response. Loeb set out to show that
animal behavior rests on a similar basis, that
"animal tropisms" are the elements of which
more complex behavioral responses are composed.

Numerous experiments showed that in some
cases animals orient so that the critical stimulus
registers equally on their left and on their right
side. Thus it can be demonstrated that grayling
butterflies, which escape from predators by
flying toward the sun, thereby causing the
predators to be partly blinded, orient to the
sun by turning to that position in which both
eyes are equally stimulated. If one eye is experimentally blinded, the butterfly flies in
circles; it cannot orient toward the sun because
it cannot achieve equal stimulation of the two
eyes. Similarly, planarians will move toward a
light by orienting in such a manner that both
eyes are equally stimulated. If two equally
bright lights a short distance apart are placed
near a planarian, the animal will orient toward
a point midway between the two lights, thus
attaining equal stimulation of the two eyes
(Fig. 12.1). Admittedly, these oriented behaviors bear a superficial resemblance to plant
tropisms, but the underlying mechanisms depend upon nervous reflexes rather than hor-
monally controlled differential growth patterns,
and Loeb's designation of them as "animal
tropisms" is seldom adopted today; the term
"tropism" is reserved for plants, and simple
continuously oriented movements in animals
are called *taxes* (the singular is taxis).

Criticism of Loeb's Theory. Loeb, in pursuing his theory of "animal tropisms," put great

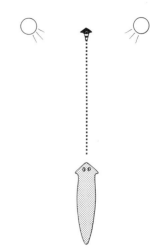

Fig. 12.1. Phototaxis of a planarian. Two
equally bright lights are located at equal distances from the worm. The animal moves toward a point midway between the two lights.

stress on the factor crucial in plant tropisms:
the relative amount of stimulation on different
sides of the organism. But taxes of this type are
of limited occurrence. Many taxes do not depend upon a comparison within the animal's
central nervous system of the incoming stimuli
from two sides. We have seen that orientation
of the grayling butterfly toward the sun depends upon both eyes, but male graylings can
orient toward a female and follow her in flight
even if one eye has been blinded. Similarly, a
dragonfly with only one eye can orient toward
and pursue its prey. Clearly, these taxes involve different mechanisms from those of the
taxes previously considered.

And responses of animals to simple stimuli
need not involve any orientation relative to the
stimulus. As an example, let us examine the
tendency of paramecians to congregate at a
fairly precise distance from a bubble of carbon
dioxide (Fig. 12.2). There is no evidence that
the animals actually swim toward the bubble,
but when in the course of their random swimming movements they chance to enter a region
where the CO_2 has made the water mildly
acidic, they swim more slowly than when they
are not in such a region. As a result, they

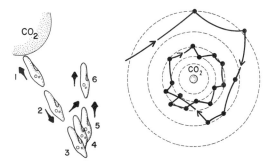

Fig. 12.2. Response of *Paramecium* to a bubble of CO_2. Left: A paramecian encounters a bubble of CO_2 (1), backs away (2), turns through an angle of about 30 degrees (3–5), and swims forward again (6). Right: The paramecian tends to remain at a rather precise distance from the bubble through a combination of avoidance reactions when it is too close to the bubble and slower swimming when it is in mildly acidic regions. See text for fuller explanation. [Redrawn from N. Tinbergen, *The Study of Instinct*, Oxford University Press, 1951, after Jennings.]

gradually collect in the region of mild acidity, even though there is no oriented response involved. But they do not congregate in the more strongly acidic zone immediately surrounding the bubble of CO_2; the region of congregation is farther away from the bubble. Whenever a paramecian moves too close to the bubble, it reacts to the stronger acidity (lower pH) by stopping, swimming backward, turning through an angle of roughly 30 degrees, and proceeding forward again; the direction of the turn is not related to the stimulation by the acid. If the paramecian again gets too close to the CO_2 bubble while swimming along its new course, it repeats the sequence of movements just described, turning through another 30-degree angle. Such behavior, sometimes called trial-and-error behavior, keeps the animal away from the zone of excessive acidity, but the orientation of the forward swimming movements is not controlled by the pH stimulus. True taxes play little part in the trial-and-eror avoidance of the zone of high acidity immediately adjacent to the bubble of CO_2 and the slower random swimming in the region of

mild acidity that together result in a congregation of paramecians where conditions are optimum. Presumably the adaptive value of this behavior is related to the fact that the decay bacteria upon which paramecians frequently feed generally lower the pH of the water surrounding them; it is therefore advantageous to the paramecians to be near regions of lowered pH, but not so near as to be damaged themselves.

Such simple behavior as a paramecian's response to a bubble of CO_2 is not dependent upon taxes, as we have just seen. This fact and the fact that most taxes involve several reflexes, because the whole body is usually oriented in response to the stimulus, indicate that although taxes are extremely interesting behavior patterns, of great importance in the lives of lower animals, they hardly qualify as the fundamental units upon which all behavior is built. Should we then regard reflexes as the fundamental behavioral units? In a sense, the answer is yes. Reflexes are certainly more general and more fundamental than taxes, particularly the limited type of taxis recognized by Loeb. And it is true that there is no difference in kind between simple reflexes and more complex reactions; every possible intermediate stage exists between the simplest of reflex pathways and the most complicated of neural pathways. In a sense, even the most complex behavior could be viewed as the result of an intricate interaction among many enormously complex reflexes. But such a use of the term "reflex" is rather unproductive; we cannot study complex behavior in the same way that we can study simpler reflexes. And applying the term "reflex" in such a broad manner simply makes it synonymous with "behavior," which doesn't help us at all. It is customary, therefore, to restrict the term "reflex" to relatively simple and essentially automatic responses to stimuli and to designate more complicated behavior patterns by other terms.

The more complicated behavior patterns, which cannot profitably be interpreted simply as reflexes or taxes, predominate in higher animals, particularly the vertebrates. The behavior of the most primitive invertebrate animals may well be based primarily on reflexes and taxes, but an evolutionary trend toward lesser importance of these components in the overall behavior is noticeable in the worms, and is even more pronounced in the insects (Fig. 12.3). In the higher mammals, taxes, as they are usually understood, are almost nonexistent, and simple reflexes, though still important, constitute only a very small portion of the total behavioral repertoire. It is a mistake, therefore, to try to explain the behavior of such animals in terms as simple as those proposed by Loeb.

And it is also a mistake to try to apply Morgan's canon too rigidly to the complex behavior patterns of higher animals, particularly the mammals. Morgan's canon freed the study of animal behavior from the stranglehold of the uncritical anthropomorphic approach of earlier times and enabled it to develop as a valid branch of science. But on the debit side, overzealous application of the canon led workers to underestimate the capabilities of the complex central nervous systems in higher animals. Horses and dogs, for example, have large well-developed brains with the same parts as human brains. It is therefore a mistaken application of Occam's razor to insist on interpreting all the behavior of these animals in terms of simple stimulus-bound and automatic responses, as Morgan's canon would have us do. It is actually simpler to assume that the brains of horses and dogs function more or less like human brains, and that these animals can think. Obviously, they don't think exactly the way men do; their nervous systems are structurally different from those of men, and this fact is reflected in their characteristically different behavior. Scientists studying higher animals must, therefore, perform the exceedingly difficult task of describing and explaining animal behavior in a way that avoids anthropomorphism on the one hand and misapplication of Morgan's canon on the other.

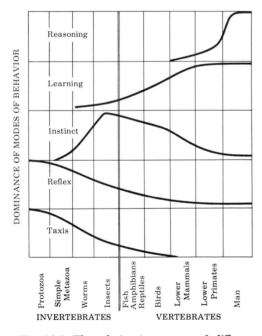

Fig. 12.3. The relative importance of different modes of behavior in various groups of animals. Taxes and simple reflexes are very important in many invertebrates, but relatively unimportant in vertebrates. More complex instinctive behavior is important in the more advanced invertebrates and in most vertebrates. Learning is more prominent in vertebrates than in invertebrates. [Modified from V. G. Dethier and E. Stellar, *Animal Behavior*, © 1964. By permission of Prentice-Hall, Inc., Englewood Cliffs, N.J.]

Inheritance and Learning in Behavior

Nature Versus Nurture. During much of the first half of this century, a controversy raged over the relative importance of inheritance and learning in animal behavior. Some psychologists, particularly some members of the "white rat" school in America, went so far as to deny that inheritance plays any significant role in behavior. Such a view seemed preposterous to biologists, familiar as they were with the nervous and effector systems of animals. Clearly, nervous pathways and effectors are inherited, and an animal can exhibit only those behavior patterns for which it has the appropriate neural and effector mechanisms. Furthermore, learning itself depends upon inherited neural pathways; if the necessary connections are lacking, no amount of experience can establish a given behavior pattern. But if some psychologists went to extremes in their emphasis on learning, many biologists studying animal behavior went to equal extremes in the other direction. They greatly exaggerated the role of inheritance by claiming that it determines even the precise details of complex behavior patterns, and they unreasonably ignored the obvious importance of learning.

Fortunately, much of the furor of this old "nature versus nurture" controversy has now subsided, and both psychologists and biologists increasingly recognize that inheritance and learning are both fundamental in determining the behavior of higher animals and that the contributions of these two elements are inextricably intertwined in most behavior patterns. As in so many instances in the history of science, insistence on an either-or approach proved unproductive; often, as here, neither of the two alternatives in an either-or proposition fits all the facts.

One way of viewing the interaction of inheritance and learning in animal behavior is to regard inheritance as determining the limits within which a particular type of behavior can be modified and to regard learning as determining, within those limits, the precise nature of the behavior. In some cases, as in the simplest reflexes, the limits imposed by inheritance leave little room for modification by learning; the available neural pathways and effectors rather rigidly determine the response to a given stimulus. In other cases, the inherited limits may be so wide that learning plays the major role in determining the behavior elicited by a given stimulus.

A dramatic example of the interaction between inheritance and learning is that of the song of the European Chaffinch. W. H. Thorpe of Cambridge University raised Chaffinches in isolation and found that such birds gave recognizable Chaffinch calls but were unable to sing a normal Chaffinch song. One might immediately conclude from this that the call is inherited but that the song is not. The matter is more complicated, however. Thorpe demonstrated that young Chaffinches raised in isolation and permitted to hear a recording of a Chaffinch song when about six months old would quickly learn to sing properly. But young Chaffinches permitted to hear recordings of songs of other species that sing similar songs did not ordinarily learn to sing those other songs. Apparently Chaffinches must learn to sing by hearing other Chaffinches, but they inherit ability to recognize and respond to the songs of their own species. This conclusion was reinforced by experiments in which Thorpe played Chaffinch songs backward to his young birds; they responded to these, even though to our ears such a recording sounds completely unlike a typical Chaffinch song. Here, then, is an example in which the inherited limits ordinarily preclude an animal's learning something uncharacteristic of its species. The songs of individual Chaffinches differ slightly, and the differences are probably due, in part, to learning, but these differences are minor compared to those between the songs of closely related species.

Clearly, to ask whether Chaffinch song is inherited or learned is to ask a meaningless question. The either-or choice is not applicable to this situation. The song is neither wholly inherited nor wholly learned; it is both inherited and learned. Chaffinches inherit the neural and muscular mechanisms responsible for Chaffinch song, and they inherit, apparently, the ability to recognize a Chaffinch song when they hear it, and they inherit severe limits on the type of song they can learn, but the experience of hearing another Chaffinch sing is necessary to trigger their inherited singing abilities into action, and in this sense their song is learned.

Human speech clearly involves a much

greater learning component than Chaffinch songs. Human languages differ from one another much more than they do, and the inherited limits for human language must be far less restrictive. But this does not mean that inheritance plays no role in human speech. The fact that all efforts to train apes to speak have failed is evidence enough that human speech depends upon human genes.[2] The relative roles of inheritance and learning are very different in human speech and in Chaffinch song, but for the one as for the other, a simple either-or choice is unrealistic. It is meaningful and useful to ask questions concerning the respective roles of inheritance and learning in any specific behavior pattern (though precise answers to these questions are often difficult to obtain), but it is not meaningful or useful to insist that either is sufficient without the other.

In general, the inherited limits within which behavior patterns can be modified by learning are much narrower in the invertebrates than in the vertebrates, and narrower in the so-called lower vertebrates (fish, amphibians, reptiles, and birds) than in the mammals. These differences are, in part, responsible for the old nature versus nurture controversy; psychologists, particularly those who adopted the most extreme views in favor of learning, worked largely on mammals, while zoologists working on animal behavior—ethologists, as they frequently call themselves—worked mostly on insects, fishes, and birds. It is not surprising that the psychologists tended to overgeneralize from the learning abilities that impressed them in their mammalian subjects, while the ethologists tended to overemphasize the numerous apparently instinctive behavior patterns they observed in their insect, fish, and bird subjects.

The difference of opinion was not, however, wholly due to actual differences in the animals

studied; it also stemmed from the biases with which the investigators approached their study of behavior. Most psychologists of the "learning only" school were trained in the social sciences and were interested predominantly in the learning process. They thus tended to concentrate on learning and to ignore the other elements in animal behavior. They frequently viewed their animal subjects (usually white rats) more as convenient objects for laboratory experimentation, which might yield information applicable to human beings, than as creatures interesting in their own right. They seldom thought in terms of genetics, evolution, or adaptation, and they rarely concerned themselves with the behavior of wild animals under natural conditions. Thus their experiments, though they yielded immense amounts of important data about certain aspects of mammalian behavior, were weakened by lack of reference to natural situations, based as they were on inbred and frequently abnormal animals living under highly artificial conditions. Ethologists of the "instinct only" school, on the other hand, were trained as zoologists and were interested in animals as animals, and only incidentally in what their behavior might reveal about human behavior. They were usually most concerned with behavior as a phenomenon of evolutionary adaptation; hence they tended to focus their attention on inherited components and to ignore the role of learning, a process in which they had little interest. They concerned themselves with the function of behavior patterns in the life of individual animals under natural conditions, with the biological significance of these behavior patterns for the survival of the species, with the gross causation of behavior patterns (particularly the roles of external stimuli and of internal physiological condition), and with the evolutionary derivation of the behavior. Their studies yielded much new information about the behavior of many species, and shed fresh light on the importance of behavior as an adaptive characteristic of animals and on the evolution

---

[2] Apes have sometimes learned to imitate the sound of a few simple words, but they are unable to put words together in a meaningful way.

of behavior, but these zoologists usually dealt with so many variables at once and utilized so few rigorously controlled experiments that they often failed to differentiate between the more subtle behavorial determinants and to detect the contributions of learning to many behavior patterns that at first sight appear wholly instinctive. The recent tendency for psychologists and ethologists to pay more attention to each other's methods and results, so that both groups remain aware of the interaction of inheritance and learning, and both are more conscious of the limitations of their own approach and more willing to adopt new methods, promises to contribute greatly to future progress in this important field of science.

To say that the inherited limits of behavior patterns in insects or birds tend to be narrower than those of higher mammals is not to say that the limits of all insect or avian behavior are narrower than the limits of all mammalian behavior. In any animal, the limits for different behavior patterns are different; each animal, whether insect, bird, or mammal, has some behavioral traits that are rather rigidly determined by inheritance, with very little possibility of modification by learning, and other behavioral traits capable of much modification. Such a difference can be observed in Herring Gulls. The adult birds nesting in colonies learn to recognize their own young about five days after they hatch; thereafter, if young of the same age from another nest are substituted for their own, the adults will not accept them and will neglect or even kill them. Yet these same gulls show amazingly little aptitude for learning to recognize their own eggs (at least in this context). They can be given substitute eggs quite different in color, pattern, shape, or size and will accept them without hesitation. These gulls, then, exhibit great aptitude for learning to recognize individual young so alike in appearance that human beings can tell them apart only with great difficulty, if at all, but they show very little aptitude for learning to recognize eggs so different that human be-

ings can distinguish them at a glance. From an evolutionary point of view, this difference is readily understandable; there must have been far more selection pressure for evolution of recognition of young, which might stray from their own nest under normal circumstances, than for recognition of individual eggs, which in nature surely seldom wander from nest to nest.

Another example of the difference in inherited limits on learning between two behavior patterns of the same animal is that of orientation and hunting in the digger wasp *Philanthus*. A female wasp quickly learns to recognize the location of her nest with great precision by means of landmarks, but the hunting behavior of the same wasp shows little modifiability. When, therefore, we say that the inherited limits of behavior patterns tend to be narrower in insects, fish, or birds than in higher mammals, we mean that, overall, the behavior of these groups is less modifiable than mammalian behavior, but we are not saying anything about specific behavior patterns.

Difficulties in Studying Learning. It is probably impossible to separate completely what is inherited and what is learned in any behavior pattern. Behavior is not a simple combination of these two elements, but is the outcome of a fusion between them. So far as the part played by learning can be distinguished, however, the learning process is one well worth studying.

Before we examine some commonly recognized categories of learning, we should mention several factors that complicate its study First, it is often difficult to determine whether improvement in the performance of a behavior pattern is due to experience or simply to greater maturity or to a different physiological condition. For example, observations that young birds just leaving the nest cannot fly well, but improve rapidly over the next few days, have led to the widespread belief that the birds must learn to fly and that they improve with practice. But, as repeated experiments have demonstrated, when young birds are reared in narrow tubes or other devices that prevent them from flapping their wings and are released at an age when they normally would have "learned" to fly, they are able to fly as well as control birds raised under normal conditions. In other words, it is not practice that causes the flight of a newly fledged bird to improve; it is greater maturity. Numerous other examples could be cited of improvement that appears to be a result of learning but is really a result of maturation. The fact that injections of hormones often cause behavior patterns to change in ways previously thought to be produced only by learning experiences is a further demonstration that one must be exceedingly careful to rule out physiological changes as a possible cause for a particular behavioral change before asserting that it is due to learning.

A second complication in studying the learning ability of animals is that an animal may readily learn something in one context and be completely incapable of learning it in some other context. Thus one may erroneously conclude that the animal cannot learn it when, in fact, the negative results are simply a product of the experimental situation used. As an example, let us consider the behavior of a female of the digger wasp *Ammophila*. This wasp digs two or three burrows, provisions each with a caterpillar she has paralyzed, and lays an egg in each. After the eggs have hatched and the larvae have begun to consume the caterpillars, she spends several days provisioning the burrows with additional caterpillars before she closes them and leaves them forever. G. P. Baerends, then of the University of Leiden in the Netherlands, investigated the factors that determine how much food will be brought to each burrow. He showed that the wasp inspects all her burrows early in the morning and then spends the rest of the day provisioning the one that contained the least food. If, after observing which burrow the

wasp has chosen for provisioning that day, one experimentally adds food to that burrow, the wasp's behavior is unchanged; she continues trying to stuff more caterpillars into the already overflowing burrow. If an experimenter were unaware of the inspection visit, and performed an experiment of this type during the late morning, he might well conclude that the wasp instinctively spends a full day provisioning each burrow and that she is incapable of learning by observation of the burrow how much food is needed. Here, then, is a situation where the wasp can learn by inspection in the context of the first visit of the day, but cannot learn the same thing in the context of later visits that day.

A third difficulty in determining what an animal can learn is that a particular behavior can often be learned only during a rather limited critical period in its life. If the animal does not encounter the necessary learning situation during the critical period, it may never learn the behavior in question. Exposure to the learning situation before or after the critical period may be ineffective in producing learning. For example, during his studies of the development of Chaffinch song. Thorpe demonstrated that young Chaffinches must hear a Chaffinch song during a certain period in their development; if they do not hear it during this period, they never learn to sing properly, despite frequent later exposure to singing Chaffinches. Critical periods are seldom so rigid in human beings, but there is abundant evidence that various types of learning ability are greatest at certain ages. For example, children between the ages of two and ten can learn languages far more easily than adults.

A fourth difficulty is that one cannot always tell immediately whether or not learning has occurred. There may be considerable delay between exposure to the learning situation and the performance of a behavior pattern that shows effects of learning. For example, if young Chaffinches only a few weeks old are allowed to hear a tape recording of a singing adult for a few days and are then raised in isolation, they will sing a nearly normal Chaffinch song when they first begin to sing the following spring. Exposure to the song during their first summer, long before they themselves are old enough to sing, results in learning, but the proof does not come until many months later.

A fifth difficulty arises in any attempt to compare the learning capabilities of different species. Superficially similar learning in different species may actually involve different underlying mechanisms and fulfill entirely different functions in the lives of the animals, as might be deduced from the differences in their nervous systems. Thus, as shown by T. C. Schnierla of Columbia University, rats and ants can learn to run the same maze, but they do this in very different ways. Furthermore, whereas mastery of the maze tends to improve the performance of rats when they are subsequently placed in new mazes, it actually seems to hinder the performance of ants in new mazes. In other words, rats not only learn the particular maze but can also generalize to some extent from this experience and thus develop increased competence at maze running in general, whereas ants learn only the particular maze and this achievement makes their behavior in new mazes less flexible.

Despite the obvious dangers of the comparative approach, many papers have been published purporting to measure the relative intelligence of animals as different, say, as fish, pigeons, rats, and monkeys by exposing them to the same problem-solving situation, usually one in which the animal must choose between two visual stimuli that differ in shape, color, or position. Results from such experiments are highly suspect as measures of intelligence, however, because animals as different as these have entirely different modes of life and are likely to have evolved radically different levels of response to any given type of stimulus, depending upon its importance in their lives under natural conditions. Their abilities to dis-

criminate visually between the stimuli may also be different. Such an experiment is thus usually less a measure of differences in intelligence than simply a measure of differences in response to the particular stimuli in the particular context of the experiment. Because of the bias of the experimenter, experiments of this sort are commonly set up in a context that is biologically most meaningful to mammals, and hence the mammals are found to be the most "intelligent"; if the experiment were set up in a context biologically most meaningful to fish, quite different results might be obtained. This does not mean that one cannot establish a definition of intelligence consistent with its application to human beings and test animals for this characteristic; it simply means that the test should be adapted to the animal in question and that the biological implications of the results should be considered in their interpretation. It is certainly true that from the point of view of their total behavior mammals surpass other vertebrates in learning potential.

Types of Learning. There are many different classifications of learning, but we shall restrict our discussion here to some of the categories recognized by one of the most commonly used systems. All forms of learning are, by definition, considered to involve relatively enduring changes in behavior due to experience rather than maturation. More transient changes, such as those due to sensory adaptation, fatigue, fluctuations in physiological condition, and differences in motivation, are not considered to be learning.

One of the simplest types of learning is *habituation.* It is a gradual decline in response to "insignificant" stimuli upon repeated exposure to them without any *reinforcement* (reward or punishment). In effect, it is a learning to ignore stimuli that are unimportant in the life of the animal. Its relative durableness distinguishes it from sensory adaptation or fatigue.

A second type of learning is *conditioning—*

the associating, as a result of reinforcement, of a response with a stimulus with which it was not previously associated. The simplest form of conditioning is seen in the conditioned reflex. Conditioned reflexes were first studied scientifically by the great Russian physiologist Ivan Pavlov. Pavlov rang a bell each time he fed meat to a group of dogs, and eventually the salivary reflex of the dogs became conditioned to the auditory stimulus of the ringing bell. Pavlov could then ring the bell and the dogs would salivate even if they could not see, smell, or taste meat. A new reflex had been established, presumably by facilitation of neural pathways previously unused; a stimulus had elicited a reflex response that it had never elicited before the training. The new stimulus (sound of ringing bell) had apparently been associated in the dogs' nervous systems with the original stimulus (sight, smell, or taste of meat), and the same response was now given to both.

Conditioning is not restricted to behavior patterns as simple as reflexes. Animals may be conditioned to perform such reflex activities as running, pushing levers, opening doors, and performing complicated tricks. For example, conditioning is the basis for much of the training of domesticated animals such as cats, dogs, and horses; the animals learn to associate stimuli such as whistles or spoken commands with responses not normally elicited by such stimuli. Conditioning is often used in testing the sensory capabilities of animals. To determine, for example, how sensitive a dog's hearing is to sounds of different frequencies, one can condition a dog to respond in a certain way to sounds of a particular frequency, say 1,200 cycles per second, and to respond in a different way to sounds of all other frequencies. By then exposing the dog to sounds of frequencies differing only slightly from 1,200 cycles, and noting the responses, the experimenter can determine the smallest differences in frequency to which the dog is sensitive. (It has been found that dogs can discriminate between

sounds differing by as little as two cycles per second.) Conditioning, whether simple or complex, is most easily accomplished if the new and original stimuli to be associated occur at the same time and place, if distracting stimuli are held to a minimum, if the associated stimuli are repeated together many times, and if reinforcement is provided, usually in the form of a reward of some sort for "correct" associations and/or punishment for "incorrect" associations.

A third type of learning is called **trial-and-error learning.** An animal does something. If the result is rewarding, it may do the same thing again. If the result is not rewarding, or is disagreeable, it may, after several trials, learn not to do the same thing any more. This is, of course, an extremely common type of learning with which we are all personally familiar. We learned as children not to touch hot stoves because we tried it and were burned. We learned to eat candy by trying it and liking the taste. We learned to play games like baseball or tennis by trying the various actions involved and profiting from our mistakes and successes. Trial-and-error learning is a fundamental type of learning in all bilaterally symmetrical animals; however, it is much more effective in higher animals than in such animals as worms, which generally require repeated trials before they learn. Much psychological research has been devoted to studying the sorts of influences that speed up or slow down trial-and-error learning, as in the running of mazes by experimental animals.

A fourth type of learning is called **imprinting.** It is characterized by an extremely short critical period, which, in all cases so far known, occurs early in the animal's life. The concept of imprinting was first formulated in 1935 by the great Austrian zoologist Konrad Lorenz, who is one of the fathers of modern ethology. He was studying, at the time, birds such as geese, chickens, and partridges whose young, being precocial, are able to move around and feed themselves soon after hatching. He found that the young of such species will follow the first moving object they see and will form a strong and lasting attachment to it, particularly if the object emits a sound. In effect, they adopt this object as their parent. Ordinarily the first moving vocal object such a young bird sees is its mother, and imprinting on her has obvious survival value. But under experimental conditions, the young bird may be imprinted on a toy train or a box pulled around by a string (particularly if the box contains a loudly ticking clock or some other sound-producing device), or even on a dog, cat, or human being. Once the critical period, usually only about 36 hours, has passed and the young birds have been imprinted on such surrogate mothers, they cannot be imprinted on any other object, including their true mother. This kind of imprinting is called social imprinting; it has obvious importance not only in establishing a bond between the young and their mother under natural conditions, but also in establishing proper species recognition and interaction. More recently, Eckhard H. Hess of the University of Chicago has described what he calls food imprinting, which he says, functions in establishing a strong food preference by the third day of life in chicks. Some workers have suggested that there is a third type of imprinting, called environmental imprinting, but its existence has not yet been conclusively demonstrated; it is said to involve imprinting on the kind of situation the young animal experiences during its early life.

Imprinting is an interesting example of the interaction of inheritance and learning; inheritance determines the critical period, the class of objects to which the response may be directed, the tendency to respond promptly and strongly to the first object in that class to which the animal is exposed, and the near irrevocability of the attachment once it is formed, while learning establishes the tie between the animal and the particular object upon which the imprinting occurs.

There is a fifth type of learning that is sometimes recognized—*insight learning.* It is most prevalent in the higher primates, particularly man. Some workers prefer to call it reasoning, and to distinguish it from learning as such. Essentially, insight is the ability to respond correctly the first time to a situation different from any previously encountered. The animal is able to apply its prior learning in other situations to the new situation and, in effect, solve the new problem mentally without the necessity of overt trial and error (Fig. 12.4). It is important to distinguish insight from simple *generalization,* which is a characteristic feature of most learning. A dog conditioned to salivate upon hearing a sound of 1,200 cycles per second will also salivate to some extent if it hears sounds of 1,000 or 1,400 cycles. Or a pigeon trained to peck a red button to receive food may peck an orange one if a red one is not available. These are examples of generalization, the ability of an animal conditioned to one stimulus to respond in the same way to

Fig. 12.4. Lack of insight in a raccoon. Tied to stake A, the animal cannot quite reach the food dish as long as its leash is looped around stake B. In this situation, a man or a chimpanzee would immediately turn, walk around stake B, and go to the food; they would do this without any previous trial-and-error experience of such a situation. But the raccoon will not perform the task correctly at first. It must find the solution by trial and error, though once it has done so it will learn very quickly. [Modified from *High School Biology,* Rand McNally, 1963. Used by permission of the Biological Sciences Curriculum Study.]

other similar stimuli. In simple generalizations, the new stimuli differ very little from previously experienced ones; in examples of insight, they differ much more. Insight is the ability to respond correctly to new stimuli that may be qualitatively as well as quantitatively different from previous ones. And insight often requires the mental putting together of several elements originally learned separately. For example, a hungry chimpanzee, released in a room with various boxes scattered around the floor and with a bunch of bananas hanging from the ceiling above the animal's reach, will often survey the situation for a short time and then begin gathering the boxes and piling them on top of each other under the bunch of bananas. He can then climb on top of the boxes and reach the bananas.

Many other more restricted types of learning are recognized by some scientists, including such complicated processes as concept formation, principle learning, and symbolism. These, as you would expect, are for the most part limited to higher mammals, particularly primates. It is beyond the scope of this book to discuss all such forms of learning.

Motivation

Motivation can be defined as the internal state of an animal that is the immediate cause of its behavior. All forms of learning are dependent upon adequate motivation in the animal; so, too, is the performance of learned or inherited behavior patterns. But to say that behavior is dependent upon motivation is to say no more than that behavior depends upon its causes. It is when we try to say something more meaningful, more precise, about motivation that we encounter difficulty.

Students of behavior often speak of motivation in terms of drives or tendencies. They say that an animal experiences hunger drives, thirst drives, sex drives, attack drives, escape drives, etc.[3] But what determines these drives

or tendencies? This is not an easy question, and we are far from being able to give a complete answer to it. Obviously no one factor can be said to determine a drive; many factors must interact in intricate ways. In gross terms, however, we can say that all of the following play important roles in higher animals: the general health of the animal, hormones, integrative activity of the central nervous system, sensory stimuli, and previous experience that led to learning.

Clearly, the relative contributions of these different elements vary with the behavior pattern in question. Thus hormones and learning are of little significance in simple behavior like the knee-jerk reflex, where sensory stimuli are the predominating causal elements, but hormones are of enormous importance in the reproductive behavior of cows, which will not receive the bull in copulation when the level of their sex hormones is low. Similarly, the relative contributions of the different motivational elements vary in different animal species, even when they are performing analogous behavior patterns. Thus the relative contribution of hormones to the sex drive is considerably less in primates, particularly man, than in rats, dogs, or cows, while the relative contributions of sensory stimuli, activity of the cerebral cortex, and learning are greater.

All available evidence points to the hypothalamus as the part of the brain that acts as the principal controller of behavioral drives in higher vertebrates. Located here are the excitatory and inhibitory centers for the various drives. Arousal of a particular drive must re-

---

[3] Much caution is necessary when one uses such terminology. To ascribe all the complex behavior involved, for example, in finding, capturing, and eating food to activation by a single "hunger drive" seems to imply that all the diverse components of this behavior depend on the same underlying physiological mechanisms. But they do not. The concept of a unitary drive such as hunger may be useful for descriptive purposes, but as an explanation of behavior it may easily lead to sterile theorizing and formulation of the wrong questions, questions that do not lend themselves to investigation by scientific methods.

sult from activation of its hypothalamic excitatory centers as a consequence of the action upon those centers of hormones, incoming impulses from sensory receptors, and impulses from the cerebral cortex and from other parts of the brain. Similarly, reduction or satiation of a drive must result from activation of its hypothalamic inhibitory centers and from reduced stimulation of its excitatory centers.

You will have noticed in our discussion of the various forms of learning that repeated references were made to reinforcement, the rewarding of the animal for some responses and/or punishing for others. Psychologists have conducted innumerable experiments designed to measure the relative effectiveness of positive reinforcement (reward for correct responses), negative reinforcement (punishment for wrong responses), and both together in eliciting rapid learning (this last is usually most effective). Let us consider positive reinforcement for a moment. The fact that it facilitates learning implies that behavior can be goal-directed. By this we do not mean that the animal consciously decides on a goal and then strives to attain it; we mean simply that motivated behavior is biologically functional and adaptive, that it tends to lead to the fulfillment of biological needs of the animal. This is true of both learned and instinctive behavior. For example, when the hypothalamic excitatory centers for hunger become activated, usually as a result of such influences as a low glucose concentration in the blood, the strength of the animal's hunger drive rises, or, to put it another way, behavior of a sort that may result in feeding becomes more highly motivated. This behavior may include both learned and instinctive components, and it may involve many sorts of activities. Thus the animal may first become restless; it may begin to move around in what appears to be a rather random manner. But then its activities may become more obviously coordinated into some form of "searching" behavior. If this behavior results

in the finding of food, the food may then be eaten, which may entail a variety of motor patterns such as tearing, chewing, and swallowing. Once the food has been eaten, the animal's behavior may well undergo radical changes; searching activities may cease, and some completely different behavior, such as courtship, or nest building, or preening, or sleeping, may begin. We can say, then, that if the behavior caused by one drive results in attainment of its biological goal, the strength of that drive is then diminished, and the animal's next behavior pattern will be determined by whatever other drives are now strongest. Attainment of a goal tends to satiate the corresponding drive and leave the animal free to respond to other drives. But attainment of the goal also acts as positive reinforcement to the successful behavior pattern. Thus, if the behavior is of a sort that can be modified by learning, the animal will be more likely to perform similar activities when the drive is again high than to perform activities that did not lead to goal attainment.

Sometimes the goal of motivated behavior is less obvious than in feeding. Feeding or drinking supplies materials necessary to the continued existence of the organism; hence such behavior clearly contributes to maintenance of stability in the organism. Similarly, escape from pain plainly contributes to maintenance of stability because pain functions as a warning to the animal that the stimuli involved may well be harmful. But what about mating, or nest building, or care of the young? Such behavior patterns involve strong drives, and they obviously contribute to continuation of the species. But can they be said to contribute to maintenance of stability in the individual organism? We must apparently answer in the affirmative. Such behavior seems to fulfill biological needs built into the animal's nervous system; if those needs are not met, they apparently constitute a source of internal instability. Behavior, like the other regulatory mechanisms of organisms already studied, seems to function, then, in maintaining homeostasis, an equilibrium among the animal's various physiological functions and between the animal and its environment. Under natural conditions, anything that contributes to homeostasis constitutes a positive reinforcement, and anything that contributes to instability constitutes a negative reinforcement.

The Concept of Releasers

We have repeatedly spoken of behavior patterns as occurring in response to stimuli detected by the sensory receptors. This is true of both instinctive and learned behavior. Let us now consider for a moment the role of the stimulus that triggers a behavior pattern. And let us here restrict ourselves to behavior patterns that are primarily innate, since these are generally easier to analyze and have been studied extensively by ethologists.

When we examined the provisioning behavior of a female *Ammophila* digger wasp, we saw that that behavior is not much altered by the stimuli the female encounters on her provisioning visits to her burrow following the early-morning inspection visit. She surely sees and feels and smells the extra caterpillars put in the burrow by an experimenter, but her provisioning behavior remains unchanged. It is as though the behavior, once triggered by the proper stimulus during the inspection visit, must run its course regardless of later stimuli. Or consider the case of male *Aedes* mosquitoes attracted to a tuning fork producing a sound similar in pitch to that of a female mosquito in flight (Fig. 12.5). The males can surely detect by sight and smell that a tuning fork is different from a female mosquito, yet the sound continues to attract them. Similarly, males of some species of insects will attempt to copulate with bits of paper on which female scent has been placed, even though they can

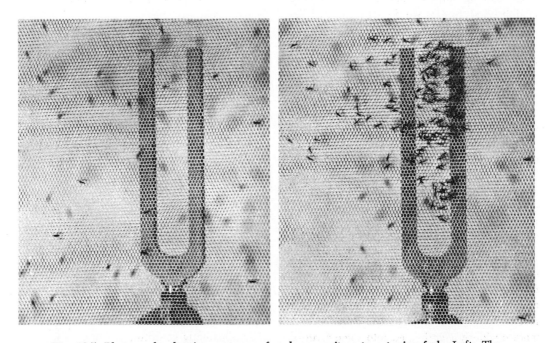

Fig. 12.5. Photographs showing response of male mosquitoes to a tuning fork. Left: The fork is silent. Right: The fork is vibrating and its sound is attracting males. [Courtesy E. R. Willis, Illinois State Normal University.]

certainly see and feel the difference between the paper and a female insect. Observations of this type lead to the conclusion that an animal responds at any given time only to a limited number of the stimuli its receptors are detecting. In a somewhat less rigid way, the same is true of human beings. A man driving an automobile along a highway sees hundreds, or perhaps thousands, of objects every minute —trees, telephone poles, houses, grass, clouds, etc.—but (one devoutly hopes) he does not respond to all of them. His driving behavior is determined largely by certain limited classes of stimuli, including the visual stimuli that indicate the width and curvature of the road, the visual stimuli from oncoming automobiles, and the auditory stimuli from automobile horns. Furthermore, a careful analysis would doubtless show that a driver responds to only a few of the clues that could provide him with information about road conditions; in other words, he ignores not only irrelevant stimuli but many relevant ones as well.

From an evolutionary standpoint, it is readily understandable that animals should be prompted to action by only a few of the many stimuli they encounter. An animal cannot possibly respond to all the stimuli impinging upon its receptors. It must be selective. In the case of instinctive behavior, natural selection seems to have led to the evolution of special behavioral sensitivity to a few stimuli that under natural conditions would be reliable clues to the situation in which an animal finds itself. Thus the condition of a wasp's burrow at the time of the inspection visit would normally be a reliable clue; under natural circumstances, extra caterpillars seldom materialize in the burrow by another agency than the wasp's. Similarly, tuning forks and bits of paper specially impregnated with the scent of a female insect are not common in the insect cosmos. In short, the animal's seemingly blind, rigid response to certain stimuli to the exclusion of others is biologically functional and adaptive most of the time; it is only when

an unpredictable factor like man intervenes that things go wrong.

Ethologists have called the stimuli that are particularly effective in triggering behavior *releasing stimuli* (or sign stimuli), and they have termed the structures or actions or sounds, etc., that give rise to the releasing stimuli *releasers.* According to their conception, the intensity of releasing stimulation necessary to trigger a behavior pattern is inversely proportional to the animal's motivation (or specific-action potential) to perform the behavior in question. The motivation, in turn, is determined by such factors as hormones, influences from various neural centers like the cerebral cortex, previous learning experience, and recent sensory stimulation, as we have already seen. The animal must possess neural mechanisms that are selectively sensitive to the releasing stimuli; it is these *releasing mechanisms,* as they are called, that initiate the behavior when they are activated by the releasing stimuli appropriate to them.

In summary, then, the ethologists' model holds that a certain part of the animal's environment may act as a releaser, i.e., as a source of stimuli to which a releasing mechanism in the animal is sensitive; if motivation is sufficiently high, the releasing mechanism then activates the neural pathways necessary for performance of the appropriate behavior pattern. It should be emphasized that the term "releasing mechanism," as currently used, is not meant to apply to any particular part of the nervous system or to any particular type of neural function; indeed, the releasing mechanisms for different behavior patterns may well have entirely different neurological bases. The term is simply a nonspecific designation for neural mechanisms selectively sensitive to certain stimuli—the releasing stimuli—and functioning in the coupling of these stimuli to behavior patterns regularly associated with them.

Let us examine some of the actual behavior patterns the analysis of which has contributed to the ethologists' view of behavior. N. Tinbergen and his associates at Oxford University studied fighting between male stickleback fish in spring. In the spring, the throat and belly of the males become intensely red. It seemed probable, therefore, that the red color was an important stimulus. The investigators presented their subjects with a series of models, some quite like actual male sticklebacks except that they lacked the red coloration, and some showing little resemblance to actual sticklebacks except that they were red on the lower surface (Fig. 12.6). The male fish attacked the red-bellied models, despite their un-fishlike appearance, much more vigorously than they did the fishlike ones that lacked red. Surely the sticklebacks could see the other characteristics of the models, but they reacted essentially only to the releasing stimuli from the red belly. David Lack observed a similar reaction in European Robins. He showed that a male Robin would threaten a bundle of red feathers more readily than it would a whole mounted young Robin lacking a red breast (Fig. 12.7). The red breast was apparently such a strong releaser that its effect outbalanced that of the obviously un-birdlike features of the tuft of feathers.

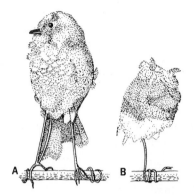

Fig. 12.7. Models of European Robin. The mounted young Robin at left with a dull-brown breast was attacked much less than the tuft of red feathers at right. [Redrawn from N. Tinbergen, *The Study of Instinct*, Oxford University Press, 1951, after Lack.]

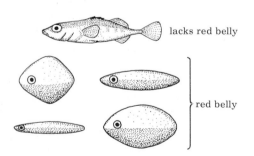

lacks red belly

red belly

Fig. 12.6. Models of male stickleback. The realistically shaped model lacking the red belly was attacked by male sticklebacks much less frequently than the oddly shaped models with red bellies. [Modified from N. Tinbergen, *The Study of Instinct*, Oxford University Press, 1951.]

Fig. 12.8. Difference in response by a hen to her chick's visual and vocal distress signals. Top: The hen ignores the chick if she cannot hear its calls, even though its actions are clearly visible. Bottom: Distress calls elicit vigorous reaction from the hen even when she cannot see the chick. [Modified from N. Tinbergen, *The Study of Instinct*, Oxford University Press, 1951.]

ANIMAL COMMUNICATION

Communication between members of a single species (and, less commonly, between members of different species) is an important aspect of animal behavior. The ability to communicate is not restricted to species that live in societies, such as bees, ants, termites, and human beings; animals that live in less complex social groupings also communicate, and even the least social of animals must communicate with other individuals at certain critical times, such as the time of mating. The highly varied methods of communication animals have evolved utilize particularly the senses of hearing, sight, and smell. A brief examination of some of these methods will not only aid in understanding a subject that is in itself fascinating, but will also illuminate some of the most fundamental principles of animal behavior.

Communication by Sound

Being vocal animals ourselves, we are very familiar with the use of sound as a medium of communication. No other species has a sound language that even approaches the complexity and refinement of human spoken languages. But many other species can communicate an amazing amount of information via sound, information upon which both the life of the individual and the continued existence of the species may depend.

Sound Communication in Insects. We have already mentioned two examples of sound communication: Male *Aedes* mosquitoes are attracted by the buzzing sound produced by the female's wings during flight (or by devices such as tuning forks that emit sounds of a similar pitch), and hen chickens respond in a characteristic fashion to the distress calls of their chicks. Let us return to the first of these examples. The head of a male mosquito bears two antennae, each covered with long hairs.

Fig. 12.9. Oystercatcher reacting to giant egg. She chooses it instead of her own egg (foreground) or a Herring Gull's egg (left). [Redrawn from N. Tinbergen, *The Study of Instinct*, Oxford University Press, 1951.]

G. H. Brückner of the University of Rostock, Germany, studied a situation in which a sound acts as a releasing stimulus while associated visual stimuli have little if any effect. He showed that a hen reacts to her chick's distress calls, but not to its distress actions (Fig. 12.8). A chick fastened to a peg under a soundproof glass dome can struggle agitatedly in full view of the hen without eliciting any reaction from her, but the hen reacts vigorously if she hears the chick's call, even if the chick is hidden from view.

It has been shown repeatedly that once the releasing stimuli for a particular behavior pattern have been carefully analyzed, it is often possible to design releasers that are even more effective than the natural one. For example, N. Tinbergen showed that the size of Oystercatcher eggs is important in determining the releasing properties of the eggs for the adult birds. An adult Oystercatcher provided with normal Oystercatcher eggs and with larger eggs of other species will usually react preferentially to the largest egg, even if she cannot possibly hatch it (Fig. 12.9).

When sound waves of certain frequencies strike the antennae, these are caused to vibrate in unison. The vibrations stimulate sensory cells packed tightly into a small segment at the base of each antenna. The male responds to such stimulation by homing in on the source of the sound, thus locating the female and copulating with her. A striking demonstration of the adaptiveness of this communication system is that during the first 24 hours of the adult life of the male, when he is not yet sexually competent, the antennal hairs lie close to the shaft (Fig. 12.10, left) and thus make him nearly deaf. Only after he becomes fully developed sexually do the hairs stand erect (Fig. 12.10, right), enabling the antennae to receive sound stimuli from the female. Thus the male does not waste energy responding to females before he is sexually competent, but once he becomes competent he has a built-in system for locating a mate without random searching. Furthermore, his built-in receptor system is species-specific; it is stimulated by sounds of the frequency characteristic of females of his own species, not by the frequencies characteristic of other species of mosquitoes. Hence the sound produced by the female's wings functions both as a mating call and as a species recognition signal.

Many other insects utilize sound in a similar way. For example, male crickets utilize calls produced by rasping together specialized parts of their wings. These calls function in species recognition, in attracting females and stimulating their reproductive behavior, and in warning away other males. So species-specific are the calls of crickets that in several cases closely related species can best be told apart by human beings on the basis of the calls; the species may be almost indistinguishable on an anatomical basis, but have distinctly different calls.

Sound Communication in Frogs. The calls of frogs serve functions similar to those of cricket calls, and like these they are very species-specific. The male frogs attract females to their territory by calling. In one experiment, C. M. Bogert of the American Museum of Natural History recorded the call of male toads. He then captured 24 female toads and released them in the dark in the vicinity of a loudspeaker over which he was playing the recorded male call. Thirty minutes later, he turned on the lights and determined the position of each female. Nineteen of the females had moved nearer the loudspeaker, four had moved farther away, and one had escaped. Eighteen of the nineteen females that had moved toward the speaker were physiologically ready to lay eggs; of the four females that moved away from the speaker, three had already laid their eggs and the other was not yet of reproductive age. In a control experiment, Bogert showed that 24 females released in the dark near a silent speaker had scattered randomly in all directions by the time the lights were turned on 30 minutes later. This demonstration that females ready for mating are strongly attracted by the male's vocalizations while other females are not serves to emphasize that the effectiveness of a releasing stimulus depends, among other things, on the condition of the recipient of the stimulus; the call of the male frog is an effective releaser for movement by the female toward the male only if the female's reproductive drive is high, largely as a result of a high level of sex hormones.

Bird Songs. Everyone has heard the buzzing of mosquitoes, the calling of crickets and frogs, and the barking, roaring, purring, grunting, etc. of various mammals, but perhaps no other form of animal sound (with the exception of human speech) has received so much attention as has the singing of birds. It has been celebrated in poetry, copied in musical compositions, mimicked by whistlers, adored by lovers, and enthusiastically welcomed by those impatient for spring. The popular "explanation" for bird song is simple. The bird is happy and sings with joy, welcoming the

Fig. 12.10. Photographs of head of male mosquito. Left: A very young male with the antennal hairs recumbent against the shaft. Right: Mature male with the antennal hairs erect. [Courtesy A. L. Burnett and Thomas Eisner, *Animal Adaptation,* Holt, Rinehart & Winston, 1964.]

morning and the spring and expressing love for his mate. Probably few other biological phenomena have been so enshrouded in anthropomorphic fancies. But biologists must cast a skeptical eye on such admittedly appealing interpretations and insist upon an objective analysis. The interpretation that emerges from such an analysis is rather different from the popular one. Bird song functions primarily as a species recognition signal, as a display that attracts females to the male and contributes to the synchronization of their reproductive drives (increasing sexual motivation and decreasing attack and escape motivations), and as a display important in defense of territory. In its defensive function, a bird's singing is certainly no indication of "happiness" or "joy"; if such human-oriented concepts could properly be applied to birds, which they cannot, the

singing would more accurately be taken as an indication of combativeness.

The role of singing in the establishment and defense of territories is an especially interesting one. A territory may be defined as an area defended by one member of a species against intrusion by other members of the same species (and occasionally against members of other species). A male bird chooses an unoccupied area and begins to sing vigorously within it, thus warning away other males. The boundaries between the territories of two males are regularly patrolled, and the two may sing loudly at each other across the border. Though there is often much shifting of the boundaries during early spring as more and more males arrive and begin competing for territories, the boundaries usually become fairly well stabilized and each male knows where they are. During the period when the boundaries are being established, it is often the males that can sing loudest and most vigorously that successfully retain large territories or even expand their territories at the expense of other males that sing less loudly and vigorously.

Experiments performed on thrushes by William C. Dilger of Cornell University illustrate especially well the role of singing in territorial defense. Dilger set up a loudspeaker in the territory of a male Wood Thrush, and placed a stuffed thrush near it. Wires led from the loudspeaker to a tape recorder in a blind in which Dilger could sit. When Dilger played a recording of a singing male Wood Thrush, the male bird in whose territory the loudspeaker was located responded as though another male had entered its territory. If the volume at which the recording was played was very low, the defending male attacked the stuffed bird. If the volume was high, the defending bird retreated. By alternately turning the volume up and down, Dilger could make the defending male move alternately toward or away from the stuffed bird and loudspeaker, almost as one might work a yo-yo. So precisely was he able to control the defending bird's movements by this method that he could make it teeter on one leg, its conflicting attack and escape drives almost exactly balancing each other.

Notice that agonistic (hostile) encounters between individuals of the same species may often be resolved by vocal and/or visual displays without any physical combat. It is, in fact, rather rare that individuals of the same species engage in combat serious enough to cause significant damage. The adaptive importance of this is obvious. Physical damage to one or both of the combatants is biologically deleterious to the species as well as to the individuals. Agonistic encounters between individuals of the same species occur frequently, and if they often led to serious physical damage, the future of the species would not be bright. It is not surprising, therefore, that most animals

have evolved other methods of resolving conflicts. Those other methods usually involve displays by which the combatants convey to each other the intensity of their attack motivation. The individual showing the higher attack motivation is ordinarily the winner. The animals can, in effect, tell without fighting which would be the probable winner if they were to fight; hence an actual fight is unnecessary. In our example, the vigor and loudness with which male Wood Thrushes sing convey to other Wood Thrushes very precise information concerning the motivational states of the singers. A singing duel can, therefore, resolve a boundary dispute without fighting.

Dilger's experiments also illustrate the importance of song in species recognition. Several other species of thrushes breed in the area where the experiments on Wood Thrushes were conducted. Some of these species look much like Wood Thrushes; they have brown backs and spotted breasts. Dilger showed that male Wood Thrushes would attack models of any of these species set up in their territories, provided the models were silent. They would even attack models of other species unrelated to thrushes if these happened to be brown with spotted breasts. If, however, the models were set up on a loudspeaker and Dilger played a recording of the song appropriate to the model, the Wood Thrush would pay the models of other species little attention. In other words, the male Wood Thrush apparently could not distinguish visually (in this context) between the various brown thrushlike birds with spotted breasts, and responded to all, if they remained silent, as though they were invading members of its own species. But the Wood Thrush could distinguish between the songs of the other species and that of its own species, and would not attack a model "singing" the song of some other species, even if it was brown and had a spotted breast. Auditory stimuli were thus shown to be far more important than visual stimuli in species recognition by thrushes. This is frequently the case among birds living in dense woods and thickets, where vision is obstructed; visual displays are often more important for birds living in more open habitats.

Sound Communication by Dolphins.

Much attention has recently been devoted to sound communication in whales, particularly the small ones called dolphins. There is evidence that these intelligent creatures can produce a great variety of sounds that convey many types of information. One investigator even believes that dolphins have an intelligence approaching that of human beings and that they have a language far more extensive and advanced than that of any other animal except man. He goes so far as to claim that within a decade or two man will be able to hold simple conversations with dolphins. The majority of scientists do not share this expectation, but none would deny the desirability of more intensive research on dolphin communication.

Echolocation.

Not only do dolphins use sound in communication, but they also use it in navigating and in locating food. They emit frequent high-pitched whistling sounds, and apparently determine the location of objects in the water by detecting the echoes produced when these sounds strike the objects. It has been shown, for example, that dolphins can swim through a tank of turbid water, easily avoiding all submerged obstacles. That this behavior involves echolocations, sometimes called sonar, instead of vision can be demonstrated by submerging rigid sheets of clear plastic. The dolphins easily avoid these also. And they can swim rapidly through an obstacle course while blindfolded. Dolphins can also quickly and unerringly locate food thrown into murky water or chase and capture live fish while blindfolded; this too involves echolocation.

Echolocation is by no means restricted to dolphins. It is probable that many marine organisms use it to some extent. And it has definitely been demonstrated in Oilbirds and in many bats. The Central American Oilbirds (*Steatornis caripensis*) live in deep caves, coming out to feed at night. They fly rapidly through the near total darkness of the caves without bumping into walls or columns. They accomplish this by emitting a steady stream of clicking sounds and detecting the echoes from obstacles. If their ears are plugged, they cannot fly through a dark cave, but can do so if some light is provided, an indication that they are capable of using both auditory and visual cues.

Echolocation by bats is probably the most widely known example of sonar navigation. In 1793 the great Italian naturalist Lazzaro Spallanzani observed that captive bats released in a completely dark room could fly about without hitting the walls or the furniture. Thinking that the bats might have extremely acute vision and be able to see by light not detectable by himself, Spallanzani put black hoods over their heads and found that they could no longer avoid obstacles. This seemed to indicate that vision was indeed important in obstacle avoidance. However, in later experiments Spallanzani removed the eyes from several bats and found that they could navigate well, but that if he plugged their ears they could not. It seemed likely, therefore, that bats use sound cues. But what sound? Flying bats seem remarkably silent. The clicks of Oilbirds can be detected by the human ear, but no such sounds can be heard from bats.

It was not until 1938 that Donald R. Griffin of Harvard University solved the mystery. He showed that flying bats produce a great variety of vocalizations, some of them at frequencies as high as 100,000 cycles per second. The problem had been that these sounds are too high-pitched for the human ear to detect. When picked up by a sensitive microphone and transformed to lower frequencies, these sounds can be heard by us as a series of short clicks. The extremely high frequencies of the sounds and their correspondingly very short wavelengths are particularly well suited for echolocation because they can be reflected from smaller objects and they spread less widely and are less diffuse than sounds of longer wavelengths. They thus permit more sensitive detection and more precise localization of objects. For example, some bats can avoid wires that are only 0.2 mm. in diameter. Similarly, they can locate and catch very small insects. Bats have a remarkable ability to detect the echoes of their own clicks, even in the midst of an enormous amount of noise. All attempts to confuse them by exposing them to intense vibrations while they are flying have failed. It is biologically important, of course, that they be able to analyze sounds and eliminate noise. They often fly in flocks of thousands, and it is essential that each bat be able to distinguish the echoes of its own sounds from those of all the other bats.

Echolocation is not, strictly speaking, a form of communication, since only one individual is involved. The sounds used by bats in echolocation have, however, come to have some interesting interspecies communication properties, to the disadvantage of the bats themselves. The bats that use echolocation feed on insects, which they capture in flight. Among these insects are a number of species of moths. Some of these moths have evolved simple ears capable of detecting the high-pitched clicks of the bats. When such a moth hears an approaching bat, it begins evasive tactics and often escapes. It has recently been discovered that some moths produce high-pitched sounds of their own, which, in some manner as yet not understood, seem to interfere with the bat's ability to locate the moth. We see, then, that there is constant interplay in the evolution of interacting species; in this example, the evolution of more effective echolocation by bats has resulted in greater selection pressure for improved ears and evasive tactics in moths, and these adaptive changes, in turn, may be expected to affect the selection pressure acting on the bat's echolocation system.

Communication by Chemicals

Since most communication between human beings involves auditory or visual signals, we tend to think of these as inherently the most appropriate methods of communication in animals. And biologists studying behavior have understandably focused much of their attention on animals such as birds that, like man, rely strongly on their auditory and visual senses. Such animals are generally easier for us to study than those more dependent on olfaction, because we can more readily detect the stimuli to which they respond. But we should not let the limitations of our own senses prevent us from recognizing that the olfactory sense is immensely important in the lives of many animals and constitutes a basis for effective communication.

Many animals secrete substances that influence the behavior of members of the same species. Such substances are called *pheromones* (or sometimes ectohormones). Most pheromones can be classified in one or the other of two groups: those that act as releasers, triggering a more or less immediate and reversible behavioral change in the recipient, and those that act as primers, initiating more profound physiological changes in the recipient but not necessarily triggering any immediate behavioral reaction.

Releaser Pheromones. We have seen how a male mosquito is attracted to the female by the sound produced by her beating wings. Many insects, and also other types of animals, utilize chemical sex attractants instead of mating calls. For example, female silkworm moths release a sex attractant so powerful that males are attracted to a single female from distances of two miles or more, even though each female releases less than 0.00000001 gram (0.01 microgram) of the attractant chemical. The males must be able to detect and respond to incredibly minute amounts of the attractant, perhaps even single molecules. The chemical acts as a releaser to which the male moth responds by flying upwind, thus moving toward the female. Only in the immediate vicinity of the female is the concentration of pheromone sufficient to establish a gradient; when the male comes into this region, he stops flying upwind and follows the gradient instead, thus locating the female. It can be shown that the male responds only to the chemical releaser, not to visual stimuli, in this behavior; he will be attracted to a female in a gauze cage even if he cannot see her, but he will not be attracted to a female clearly visible in a tightly sealed glass cage from which none of the pheromone can escape. Sex-attractant pheromones are known to occur also in cockroaches, queen honeybees, and many other insects. The chemical nature of only a few of these is known at present. This is a field of biological investigation in which research has just begun.

Another class of releaser pheromones is the trail substances of ants (Fig. 12.11). A foraging ant returning to the nest from a food source

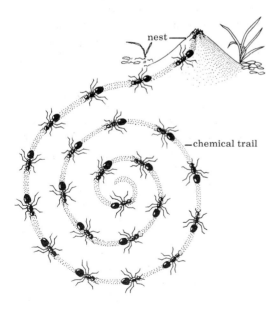

Fig. 12.11. Ants following a spiral path of trail substance laid down by an experimenter.

intermittently touches the tip of her abdomen to the ground and secretes a tiny amount of trail substance. Other worker ants can follow the trail to the food source; these ants also will lay trail substance as they return with food to the nest. The better the source of food, the more ants are attracted to the trail, which thus grows stronger. Workers that do not find food do not lay trail; hence when the food has been consumed no more trail is laid and, since the trail pheromone is very volatile, the trail disappears within a few minutes. It has been demonstrated that trail substances are species-specific; no two species have been found to secrete the same substance. This specificity is, of course, biologically adaptive, because it ensures that workers will not mistakenly follow trails of other ant species that may cross their own.

Other releaser pheromones of ants include alarm substances and death substances. The latter provide a particularly good example of the extent to which much insect behavior is stimulus-bound and rigidly stereotyped. Certain long-chain fatty acids and their esters released from a dead and decomposing ant act as pheromones that stimulate worker ants to pick up the carcass and carry it to a refuse pile outside the nest. When living ants are experimentally painted with these substances, workers pick them up and dump them on the refuse pile. The hapless victims of the experimenter promptly return to the nest, only to be thrown back on the refuse pile, again and again. The workers can surely see and feel that the object they are carrying is struggling in a most undead manner, but they disregard the evidence from all their other senses and respond only to the death pheromone and continue to treat the painted ant as a carcass to be taken to the refuse pile.

Our examples have been drawn from insects, but releaser pheromones are by no means restricted to them. There is abundant evidence that pheromones are common in mammals, most of which, as you know, rely much more on olfaction than does man. Male mammals can often tell by smell when the female is in heat, because she secretes certain pheromones at that time. Besides playing a part in sexual recognition and reproduction, mammalian pheromones are often important in marking territories and home ranges. You are familiar with the way dogs and many other mammals use their urine as a marking substance.

Primer Pheromones. Primer pheromones produce relatively long-term alterations in the physiological condition of the recipient and thus change the effects that later stimuli will have on the recipient's behavior. They do not necessarily produce any immediate behavioral change. For example, W. K. Whitten of the Australian National University has shown that the estrous cycles of female mice in a laboratory colony can be initiated and synchronized by the odor of a male mouse, even if the male cannot be seen or heard. And Helen Bruce of the National Institute for Medical Research in London has found that the pregnancy of a newly impregnated female mouse will be blocked by the odor of a strange male mouse. The blockage will not occur if the olfactory bulbs of the female mouse's brain are removed. The pheromone from the strange male probably exerts its effect by inhibiting in some manner the secretion of the pituitary gonadotrophins necessary for development of the corpus luteum.

In 1955 S. van der Lee and L. M. Boot in the Netherlands found that crowding of female mice results in disturbance and even blockage of estrous cycles; pheromones are probably involved because removal of the olfactory bulbs restores the cycles to normal. It seems likely, therefore, that pheromones help regulate population density.

Another type of primer pheromone is seen in social insects such as ants, bees, and termites. These pheromones are ingested rather than simply smelled, and they play an impor-

tant role in caste determination. For example, termite queens and kings secrete substances that prevent the workers from developing reproductive capabilities. The number of soldiers in a termite colony is regulated by similar pheromones secreted by the fully developed soldiers.

Communication by Visual Displays

Displays in Reproductive Behavior. A display may be defined as a behavior that has evolved specifically as a signal. According to this definition, a song or a call is a display. Many animals have also evolved a variety of often complex actions that function as signals when seen by other individuals; such displays frequently include vocal elements. For example, at mating time in the spring many male Prairie Chickens assemble on a courting stage, usually a small knoll or open grassy area. Each male then begins to shuffle his feet and run back and forth with wings drooped, neck erect, and bill pointed straight down, while at the same time making deep pumping noises. The females congregate on the periphery of the courting stage and watch the displaying males for a while. Finally each female chooses one of the males for her mate (among most birds the female does the choosing).

Other examples may often be observed. Most people have seen a male pigeon strutting, with tail spread and dragging on the ground, neck fluffed, and wings lowered, or they have noticed that courting songbirds in spring go through odd and seemingly senseless antics (more than one kindhearted person has felt sorry for the poor "demented" bird). Watch, if you have the opportunity, a flock of ducks on a pond in early spring. You may see a male give a loud whistle and raise both his head and his tail as high in the air as he can get them, while also raising his wings (Fig. 12.12B), or you may see him raise his stern in the air, dip his head in the water, and then

Fig. 12.12. Displays of a male Mallard. (A) Normal swimming posture. (B) The "Head-up-tail-up" display. (C) Part of the "Down-up" display. (D) The "Grunt-whistle" display. These are all courtship displays. [Adapted from K. Z. Lorenz, "The Evolution of Behavior," *Sci. Am.*, December, 1958. Copyright © 1958 by Scientific American, Inc. All rights reserved.]

abruptly raise it and whistle (Fig. 12.12C), or you may see him put his bill in the water and then quickly flick his head to the side, toss an arc of droplets into the air while arching his body upward, and follow this acrobatic feat with a whistle and a grunt (Fig. 12.12D). Such antics may seem senseless to a casual observer in the park on a Sunday afternoon, but biologically they are far from senseless; they function in synchronizing the sexual physiology of the male and female and in making the female more receptive to the male. They also assure that the female will choose a male of her own species as her mate; the males of each species—there may be more than one on the same pond—give somewhat different displays. Special structures or bright patches of color are often elaborately exposed during the displays (Fig. 12.13), and these clearly evolved in association with the displays as part of the signal system.

The flashing lights of fireflies are an example of another, rather different, type of visual signal system. Females are attracted to the males by the flashing. The pattern of the flashes differs from species to species, and thus acts as a species-recognition signal.

Complex behavior patterns are often composed of several separate activities occurring in sequence, with each activity serving as the

Fig. 12.13. A male bird of paradise giving a courtship display. Many of the movements are concerned with exhibiting the elaborate plume feathers and the color pattern of the body, which have important signal functions. [Redrawn from A. J. Meyerriecks, *Courtship in Animals*, Heath, 1963. Used by permission of the Biological Sciences Curriculum Study.]

initiator of the next. The mating behavior of the three-spined stickleback provides a good example. In spring, the male fish has bright red underparts, and the female's abdomen is swollen by the large number of eggs it contains. Tinbergen and his associates have shown that the female is attracted by the male's red belly and that the male is stimulated by the sight of the female's swollen abdomen. When a female swims into the territory of a male in reproductive condition, she often adopts an unusual head-up posture (Fig. 12.14). The combination of her swollen abdomen and courting posture acts as a releaser for the male to swim toward her in a curious zigzag fashion. The combination of the male's red belly and zigzag dance acts as a releaser for the female to swim toward the male in the head-up posture. Her approach acts as a releaser for the male to turn and swim rapidly toward the nest that he has already constructed. This, in turn, stimulates the female to follow him, which stimulates the male to make a series of rapid thrusts with his snout into the nest entrance and then to turn on his side and raise his dorsal spines. This "showing-of-the-nest-entrance" behavior of the male acts as the releaser for the female to enter the nest. Her occupation of the nest, in turn, stimulates the male to thrust his snout against her rump in a series of quick rhythmic trembling movements. This induces the female to spawn. It can be shown that without the stimulus of the male's tremble-thrusts, the female is incapable of spawning; the stimulus can be effectively duplicated, however, by prodding her with a glass rod or other hard object. Once the female has spawned, the fresh eggs stimulate the male to fertilize them.

Most of the links in the chain of reactions in stickleback courtship depend on displays

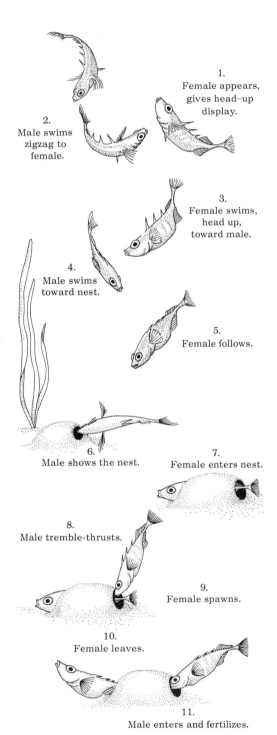

1. Female appears, gives head-up display.

2. Male swims zigzag to female.

3. Female swims, head up, toward male.

4. Male swims toward nest.

5. Female follows.

6. Male shows the nest.

7. Female enters nest.

8. Male tremble-thrusts.

9. Female spawns.

10. Female leaves.

11. Male enters and fertilizes.

Fig. 12.14. Courtship behavior in the three-spined stickleback. See text for full description. [Modified from N. Tinbergen, *The Study of Instinct,* Oxford University Press, 1951.]

that provide visual releasing stimuli. Though the sequence described here is the usual one followed, it is not absolutely rigid and variations do occur. If, however, the sequence or the way in which the displays are performed is altered too much, the final acts—spawning and fertilization—will not occur. Since the mating behavior of each species of stickleback differs in certain critical elements, it is unlikely that a male of one species and a female of another will get through enough of the ritual for spawning and fertilization to occur. This elaborate behavior functions, therefore, both in bringing together and synchronizing the two sexes in the mating act and in avoiding errors of mating.

Displays in Agonistic Behavior. The examples of visual displays so far cited have been drawn from reproductive behavior, but visual displays are also of great importance in many other aspects of an animal's life. You are familiar, for example, with the way a dog wags his tail as a greeting display and with the way he tucks his tail between his legs as a display of appeasement. And you have surely seen two dogs or cats displaying in an antagonistic encounter, with hackles raised, teeth bared, ears laid back, body raised as high off the ground as possible, and movements stiff-legged and exaggerated. Or you have seen the loser of such an encounter giving appeasement displays—fur sleeked, tail tucked under, head down and often turned away from the antagonist, legs bent. Such visual displays function like vocalizations in similar situations; they communicate the current balance between the individual's attack and escape motivation.

Analogous agonistic displays can be observed in many animals. As in dogs, a high attack motivation is often conveyed by directing the face straight at the antagonist and spreading and raising the body, making it look as large as possible. Appeasement displays usually involve making the body appear as small as possible and turning the face away

from the antagonist or exposing to the antagonist the appeaser's most vulnerable spot; such appeasement displays tend to inhibit further attack by the antagonist. Compare the agonistic displays of the Black-headed Gull, as shown in Fig. 12.15, with those you have seen in dogs or cats.

Communication in Honeybees

A last example of communication should be mentioned. This is the amazing ability of scout honeybees to inform the workers in the hive of the quality of a food source and its direction and distance from the hive. This communication depends on displays that utilize auditory, visual, chemical, and tactile elements.

The work of Karl von Frisch of the University of Munich, Germany, on the language of bees is a biological classic. Von Frisch had long been interested in the ability of bees to distinguish between different colors and scents. In the course of his experiments, he would set up in the vicinity of a hive a table with sheets of paper on which he had smeared honey. He would then have to wait—sometimes for several hours—for the bees to find the honey. He noticed that when one bee finally discovered the feeding place, many others appeared at the table within a short time. It seemed likely that the first bee had somehow informed the others of the existence of the new feeding place. In order to see what happens in the hive when a scout bee returns from a new food supply, von Frisch set up an observation hive with glass sides. When a bee landed at the new feeding place and began to feed, von Frisch daubed a spot of paint on her thorax so that he could recognize her when she returned to the hive. He discovered that the returning bee first feeds several other bees and then performs a dance on the surface of the honeycomb. The dance consists of circling first to the right, then to the left, and repeating this pattern over and over with great vigor (Fig. 12.16A). Von Frisch named this the round

A Long Call   **B** Upright   **C** Choking   **D** Facing Away

Fig. 12.15. Agonistic displays of Black-headed Gull. (A) The first response given by a male on his territory when another male approaches is the "Long Call," in which the body is tilted downward, the wing butts are lifted, the head is thrust forward, and a characteristic call is given. (B) If the other male continues to approach, the defending bird may move to meet the intruder at the boundary of his territory, where he gives the "Upright" display, lifting his still-folded wings, stretching his neck upward, and pointing his bill downward. (C) If the intruder performs counterthreat displays, the defender may then adopt the "Choking" posture, tilting his body head down in an almost vertical position and moving his head in a series of quick up-and-down jerks. (D) "Facing Away" is an appeasement display in which a gull turns his head so that the other bird cannot see the beak and eyes or the black facial mask. [Adapted from N. Tinbergen, "The Evolution of Behavior in Gulls," *Sci. Am.,* December, 1960. Copyright © 1960 by Scientific American, Inc. All rights reserved.]

dance. The dance excites other bees in the vicinity of the dancer, and they begin to follow her, with their antennae held close to her.

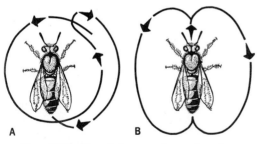

Fig. 12.16. Round dance and wagging dance of scout honeybee. (A) In the round dance, the bee circles first one way and then the other, over and over again. The dance tells other bees that there is a source of food near the hive. (B) In the wagging dance, the scout runs forward in a straight line while wagging her abdomen, circles, runs forward again, circles in the other direction, and runs forward again. The orientation of the run indicates the direction from the hive of the food source, and the number of turns per unit time indicates the distance. [Redrawn from K. von Frisch, *Bees: Their Vision, Chemical Senses, and Language.* Copyright 1950, Cornell University. Used by permission of Cornell University Press.]

Suddenly, however, they turn away one by one and leave the hive; a short time later they appear at the feeding place. Apparently the round dance is a display that informs the other bees of the existence of the food supply.

Von Frisch wanted to know exactly what sorts of information the round dance conveys. He fed several bees at a dish containing sugar water scented with honey that he had located 10 meters west of the hive. He also put out dishes of sugar water to the north, south, and east of the hive. Other bees began appearing in approximately equal numbers at all four dishes a few minutes after the bees that had been fed at the west dish began performing a round dance in the hive. There was no evidence that the round dance indicated direction, and other similar experiments brought no evidence that it indicated distance. It seemed simply to say, "Fly out and seek in the neighborhood of the hive." Von Frisch did find, however, that if each of the dishes of sugar water was scented with a different flower, the other bees came in significantly greater numbers to the dish that the dancer had visited. He showed that these bees determined what scent to search for in two ways; they smelled the body of the dancer by holding their antennae near her, and they detected the odor in the droplets of material she fed to them.

Even though von Frisch had demonstrated that the round dance indicates neither direction nor distance, he began to suspect that at times bees are able to communicate this type of information, presumably in some other way. In 1944 he performed the following experiment. He set up two dishes of sugar water, one at 10 meters from the hive and the other at 300 meters. Each was scented with lavender oil. He then fed a few bees at the dish 10 meters from the hive; shortly thereafter, numerous bees appeared at this dish but only a few appeared at the distant dish. When he reversed the procedure and fed forager bees at the dish 300 meters from the hive, other bees appeared in large numbers at this dish but only a few appeared at the nearer dish. Distance was clearly being communicated in some manner. When von Frisch observed the dances of the forager bees returning from the two dishes, he saw immediately that they were entirely different. The foragers from the dish 10 meters from the hive danced the familiar round dance, but the foragers from the dish 300 meters away danced a different dance, one that von Frisch named the wagging dance (Fig. 12.16B). The bee runs a short distance in a straight line while wagging her abdomen from side to side very rapidly, then circles, runs forward again, circles in the other direction, and runs forward again. She repeats this dance many times. Von Frisch found that there is a relationship between the distance of the food source and the number of turns per unit time in this wagging dance (Fig. 12.17). He naturally concluded that the number of turns tells the other bees the distance to the food. However, recent investigations by A. M. Wenner at the University of California at Santa Barbara and by Harald Esch of the University of Munich suggest that sounds made by the bee during the dance may be more important than the movements in communicating distance.

Von Frisch found, furthermore, that the location of the food relative to the position of

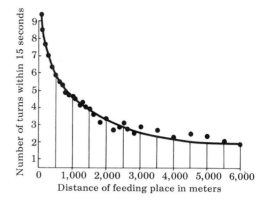

Fig. 12.17. Graph showing relationship between distance of food source and number of turns per unit time in the wagging dance. The number of turns decreases with distance. [Modified from K. von Frisch, *Bees: Their Vision, Chemical Senses, and Language.* Copyright 1950, Cornell University. Used by permission of Cornell University Press.]

the sun is indicated by the direction of the straight portion of the wagging dance. In the dark hive, a run straight up the vertical comb means that the food lies in the direction of the sun; a run straight down the vertical comb means the food lies in the opposite direction from the sun; a run at an angle indicates that the food is to be found at that angle to the sun (e.g. a run 30 degrees to the right of vertical indicates that the feeding place is 30 degrees to the right of the sun). In other words, bees use the force of gravity as a symbol for the sun when inside the dark hive. When, however, they perform the wagging dance on a horizontal surface outside, they abandon the symbolism and orient the dance relative to the sun itself.

It can be shown that bees can detect the sun's position and orient themselves by it even if they cannot see the sun itself but only a small patch of blue sky, because their compound eyes are able to analyze the polarization of the light reflected from the particles in the atmosphere. Since the plane of polarization of light from any point in the sky is related in a fixed manner to the position of the sun and to the position of the observer, the bees' detection of this plane of polarization can indicate to them where the sun is, and thus enables them to continue foraging on cloudy days as long as one small patch of blue sky remains visible.

THE EVOLUTION OF BEHAVIOR

Implicit throughout this discussion has been the assumption that behavior is a biological attribute, one to be investigated like anatomy or physiology and subject to the same kinds of evolutionary processes. The corollary assumptions—that behavior is adaptive and that natural selection brings about an increase in well-adapted and a decrease in poorly adapted behavior patterns in the population—are basic to the elucidation of many types of behavior. The following example will serve to show that behavior patterns, like anatomical or physiological characteristics, can be understood in terms of their adaptive roles.

Black-headed Gulls always remove broken eggshells from their nest after the young have hatched. Tinbergen and his associates at Oxford were interested in discovering the biological significance of this behavior pattern. They found that it is not limited to the time of hatching; it can be elicited by placing shells or other conspicuous objects in the nest at any time during the breeding season. It seemed that the more conspicuous the object was, and the more like real eggshell, the greater was its releaser potential. These observations made the investigators suspect defense against visual predators. They constructed artificial nests in which they placed eggs and other conspicuous objects; in the control nests, they put only eggs. Upon later examination, they found that many more of the nests containing conspicuous objects had been robbed of their eggs, primarily by Carrion Crows and Herring Gulls. They also found that nests containing washed whole eggs were robbed less often than nests containing unwashed shell fragments. In this case, olfactory predators, primarily hedgehogs and foxes, were the culprits. These experiments demonstrated that, on the average, gulls that remove broken eggshells and other conspicuous objects from their nests will successfully raise more young than gulls that do not. The value of this behavior pattern in raising offspring must have constituted an effective selection pressure favoring its evolution.

If behavior patterns evolve and can be studied in terms of the selection pressures that produce them, it follows that we should be able to make reasonable conjectures concerning the ancestral behavior patterns from which newer behavior patterns have arisen, just as we can make inferences about the ancestral structures from which our hands or other structures have evolved. And we should be able to study the genetics of behavior just as we study the genetics of other characters. Both of these approaches to behavior have been much used in recent years.

The Derivation of Behavior Patterns

Evidence from Comparison of Species. One fruitful way of studying the evolutionary derivation of behavior is to compare the behavior patterns of a number of related species. Because these patterns often represent different stages of development of the same basic behavior, they may give a clue to the ancestral condition. Let us look at several examples.

There are certain species of flies (family Empididae) in which the males always present the females with a silken balloon before mating. This is a curious bit of behavior, and we could hardly guess what selection pressures brought it about, and from what ancestral beginnings, were it not for the fact that there are other species of empidid flies still living today that exhibit various stages of development of this courtship pattern. In many species of empidid flies where the male does not give anything to the female when courting her, she sometimes captures and devours him. In other slightly more advanced species, the male captures prey, and presents this to the female, and then mates with her while she is occupied with eating the prey. The selection pressure for this behavior seems easy to explain. Males that divert the females' attention by giving them prey succeed in mating and escaping more frequently than those that do not. The male of still more advanced species captures prey, wraps it in a ball of silk, and presents this to the female. Presumably the fact that the female is occupied longer in opening the balloon and eating the prey gives the male more time to accomplish copulation. In still more advanced species, the male encloses only a tiny prey or fragments of prey in the balloon, and the female does not actually eat the prey. In other words, at this stage in the evolution of the courtship behavior, the balloon has replaced the prey as the important element, becoming part of a display that functions in making the female more receptive to the male. We can understand, therefore, how in still more advanced species an empty balloon or even some other bright object such as a rose petal can suffice. By examining a whole group of species in this way, we can get a reasonably good idea of the derivation of behavior that would otherwise seem odd and enigmatic, and we can identify the probable selection pressures involved.

Another good example is the evolution of nest building in the parrot genus *Agapornis*, which has been studied by William C. Dilger, whose experiments with Wood Thrushes we mentioned earlier. These small African parrots are unusual in building nests; most parrots simply lay their eggs on the bare floor of a cavity in a tree and do not build any nest. The various species of *Agapornis* exhibit a variety of stages in the evolution of nest-building behavior. Females of the most primitive living species use their very sharp bills to cut small irregular bits of bark, leaf, wood fiber, or paper. They thrust these small

pieces of material amidst their feathers at any point on the body. When a number of pieces are lodged among their feathers, they will fly to the nest cavity and unload them. The nest they make from this material is only a simple pad. Females of a somewhat more advanced species cut long regular strips of material and tuck the ends of these into the feathers of their rumps (Fig. 12.18). They fly to the nest cavity with three or four such strips dangling in the air behind them. They construct more elaborate nests with a deep cup for reception of the eggs. Females of the most advanced species no longer tuck nesting material amidst their feathers, but carry it to the cavity one piece at a time in their bills. This means that they can carry sticks and other stronger material and hence can construct very elaborate roofed nests with two chambers and a passageway. We have, then, what appears to be an evolutionary sequence involving (1) a trend from carrying material tucked all over the body, to carrying it only in the rump feathers, and finally to carrying it in the bill; (2) a trend from cutting small irregular pieces, to cutting long regular ones, and finally to using twigs in addition to the strips; (3) a trend toward increasing complexity of the nests from a simple pad, to a well-formed cup, and finally to an elaborate roofed structure. If the more advanced species were the only ones still living today, we would have little hope of understanding the evolution of nest-building behavior in these parrots. But the fact that more primitive species are still extant enables us to make comparative studies that help us not only to understand how this particular behavior evolved but also to get new insight into the ways in which animal behavior in general evolves.

Dilger has also used the carrying behavior of *Agapornis* to demonstrate the importance of genetics in behavior. He has succeeded in hybridizing the species that carries strips tucked in the rump feathers with the species that carries material in the bill. The hybrids

Fig. 12.18. Photograph of female *Agapornis roseicollis* tucking strips of paper in her rump feathers. She cut each strip from the sheet of heavy construction paper on which she is standing. [Courtesy W. C. Dilger, Cornell University.]

clearly show effects produced by the genes of both parents. They cut strips and try time and again to tuck them, but without success. Sometimes they fail to let go of the strip; after a lengthy bout of tucking, when their heads come forward again, the strip is still held tightly in their bills. Sometimes they let go of the strip, only to see it fall from the rump to the floor. It is as though the genes of one parent made them try to tuck but the genes of the other parent prevented them from doing it correctly. Eventually the hybrids learn that they cannot tuck, and begin carrying nesting material in their bills, but even the oldest and most experienced still gives at least a perfunctory flick of its head over its shoulder before flying to the nest with the material in its bill.

Evidence from Behavioral Analysis. Through detailed analysis of the motor patterns involved in a particular behavior and of the precise context in which each component of the behavior occurs, and through comparison of the results with those from similar analyses of other behaviors, a biologist can often convincingly identify the actions from which the behavior in question is derived. Consider,

for example, the evolution of courtship or agonistic displays. Such displays usually occur in situations where the animal is in a state of conflict between two or more drives. A courting animal has simultaneously high attack, escape, and mating drives, and an animal in an agonistic encounter experiences conflict between his attack and escape drives. The conflict often thwarts the complete performance of the behavior most appropriate to either of the separate drives. As a consequence, the animal frequently performs acts that seem out of context in the given situation, or performs an appropriate act but directs it at the wrong object, or starts to do something but doesn't complete it. Because such apparently irrelevant or redirected or incomplete actions occur so often in conflict situations, they have commonly been the raw material from which natural selection has molded new displays that communicate the motivations of the animals and thus help resolve the conflict situation. Detailed analysis can help reveal what actions were the raw material for any particular display.

Let us look for a moment at the types of actions mentioned above as raw materials for displays. The first type, irrelevant action—often called *displacement activity*—is an action performed in what appears to be the wrong context. A male Wood Thrush responding to Dilger's loudspeaker may be in such a state of conflict between attack and escape that he suddenly starts to scratch his head or to preen his wings or to eat, or he may even go to sleep. He has to do something, it seems, and if he cannot do something appropriate he does something inappropriate. In a similar way, when you are nervous over making some decision, you may drum your fingers on the desk or crack your knuckles or doodle. Such actions performed by the male thrush or by you may indicate to a perceptive observer something about the performer's current motivational state. The effect of natural selection is to exaggerate and ritualize such actions, increasing their information content and thus giving them a true display function. In other words, actions that were irrelevant in their original context come to have great relevance, and become appropriate and integral parts of situations of this sort. Displacement activities are most often actions that ordinarily function in the daily maintenance of the individual, such as preening, scratching, yawning, stretching, and eating.

The second type of action that may serve as raw material for evolution of displays is one performed in the appropriate context but directed at the wrong objects; such an action is often called *redirected activity.* A bird thwarted in attacking an intruder on his territory may peck vigorously at the branch on which he stands instead. A dog prevented from attacking an antagonist may bite viciously at a nearby object. A man angry at his boss may come home and yell at his wife. Like displacement activities, redirected activities may indicate to a perceptive observer the motivational state of the performer, and natural selection can ritualize them and cause their incorporation into displays.

A third source of motor patterns for displays

includes actions called *intention movements,* which are the incomplete initial stages of other actions. A bird crouches slightly before it flies. A man clenches his fist before striking an opponent. Even if the bird does not actually fly or if the man does not actually strike his opponent, the crouch or the clenched fist may serve as a signal to another individual, and may therefore come to have a ritualized display function quite apart from its initial significance as simply a movement preparatory to further action.

We see, then, that careful study can reveal to us the evolutionary source of the various components of behavior patterns such as displays, just as similar study reveals the evolutionary history of anatomical characters. In short, the usual methods of biological research can rewardingly be applied to animal behavior.

ORIENTATION BEHAVIOR

An aspect of animal behavior that has long intrigued scientist and nonscientist alike is the rather widespread ability of animals to find their way from place to place by means that are clearly not random. Some types of orientation are now fairly well understood, while others remain unexplained and present a continuing challenge to biologists.

Orientation by Visual Landmarks or by Smell

Many animals orient by visual landmarks. An example, is the female digger wasp, *Philanthus triangulum,* that can locate her nest with amazing accuracy when she returns from hunting. Tinbergen and Kruyt, who studied this phenomenon, put a ring of pine cones around the nest of a wasp while she was inside digging it (Fig. 12.19A). When the wasp emerged, she flew around the nest for about six seconds, presumably making a study of the locality.

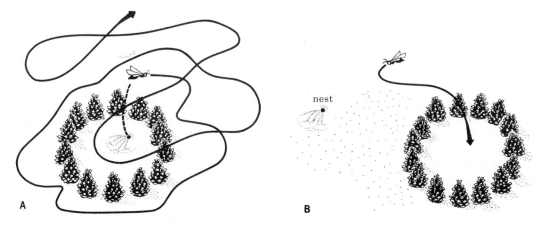

Fig. 12.19. Use of visual landmarks by female digger wasp in locating nest entrance.
(A) A ring of pine cones was placed around the nest entrance while the wasp was inside.
When she emerged, she made an orientation flight around the nest (black path) and then
flew off.   (B) While the wasp was gone, the ring of pine cones was moved a short distance.
The returning wasp went to the center of the ring of cones rather than to the true nest
entrance. [Redrawn from N. Tinbergen, *The Study of Instinct*, Oxford University Press,
1951.]

She then departed and was out of sight of the
nest for 90 minutes. While she was gone, the
experimenters moved the ring of pine cones
to a spot a foot away (Fig. 12.19B). When
the wasp returned with captured prey, she
went to the ring of pine cones, not to the actual
site of the nest. This experiment was repeated
many times, always with the same results. The
female wasp could never locate her nest until
the original situation was restored.

But what about wasps that nest in open flat
expanses of sand where there are no obvious
landmarks close to the nest? Experiments have
repeatedly shown that in these instances distant landmarks, such as a tree on the horizon,
play an important role; the wasp is remarkably
accurate at judging her position relative to
such distant landmarks.

Orientation by landmarks is also important
in the ability of mammals such as dogs, cats,
or horses to return home from several miles
away. Such animals often have a very good
map sense, and only a few familiar landmarks
or even rather subtle features such as the pitch
of the land can frequently give them enough
cues to orient themselves. There has, however,

been much exaggeration of this ability. Most
reports of pets returning home from distant
places completely unknown to them are either
not true as reported or must be attributed to
random wandering.

Another sort of cue often used by mammals,
particularly dogs, is, of course, scent. The
ability of some dogs to trail a man, a rabbit, or
a deer, and to backtrail when they find themselves in unfamiliar territory, is well known.
We with our poor olfactory sense find it hard
to imagine the sensory world most mammals
experience—a world in which olfactory information is received from hundreds of sources
every minute, a world in which nearly every
object is most clearly distinguished by its own
distinctive smell. Hence we often fail to appreciate the sensory basis for much of the behavior of such animals. We should be very
wary of the common tendency to ascribe to
them special senses that we do not possess;
usually (and perhaps always) the sensory differences are quantitative rather than qualitative.

We have already mentioned some examples
of orientation by olfactory cues: the locating

of a female by the male silkworm moth, the following of scent trails by ants. Perhaps one of the most dramatic examples of olfactory (or perhaps we should simply say chemical) orientation and navigation is that of the spawning runs of salmons. A young salmon hatches in a fresh-water stream and shortly thereafter swims downstream to the ocean, where it ranges widely for several years while growing and sexually maturing. But no matter how far it has ranged, when the time for it to spawn approaches, it returns unerringly to the same fresh-water stream in which it was hatched. The validity of this statement was demonstrated by a huge study in which several Canadian investigators marked 469,326 young sockeye salmon in a tributary of the Fraser River. Nearly 11,000 of these were recovered in the same stream several years later when the fish had reached spawning age. But not a single marked fish was ever found to have entered any other stream.

Arthur D. Hasler and his associates of the University of Wisconsin have shown that salmon have extremely acute chemoreceptors. They can be conditioned to differentiate between even very dilute rinses prepared from different water plants, or between water from different streams. These workers have shown, moreover, that salmon whose olfactory tissues have been destroyed or whose noses have been plugged with cotton cannot distinguish between odors and also cannot locate the right spawning stream. It seems, therefore, that salmon use their sense of smell in navigating back to their parental stream, and that the adult salmon must remember the odor of the stream in which they hatched and respond positively to it when their reproductive drive becomes high.

Orientation by Celestial Cues

We have already seen that honeybees can orient and navigate by the sun, and that they can communicate directions in terms of the sun's position. Many workers have suggested that orientation by celestial cues—the position of the sun during the day or of the stars or moon at night—may also be the basis for the most remarkable of all navigational feats, the migration and homing of birds.

Migration and Homing in Birds. For centuries men have marveled at the way many birds can travel thousands of miles from the place of their birth in the north to the wintering grounds of their species in the south, and back again the following spring. These migrations are not the result of random wandering; the members of each species usually follow a precise route characteristic of that species, often flying hundreds of miles each day or each night, and a few species make their entire migratory journey of several thousand miles nonstop. For example, the Pacific Golden Plover, a bird that cannot land on water, flies each fall from Alaska to its winter home in the Hawaiian Islands (Fig. 12.20). Migration clearly does not depend exclusively on orientation by landmarks; the Golden Plover just mentioned flies over the open ocean where there are no landmarks, and many other species also migrate over open ocean. Furthermore, the young birds have never before made the journey and could not be familiar with any landmarks. They do not learn the route from the experienced birds; in many species they do not leave the northern breeding grounds until several weeks after the older birds have departed, yet they set out unerringly along the same route that all the members of their species have followed for centuries. Not only must they be able to determine directions, but they must also have been born with a specific route across territory they have never seen engraved somehow in their nervous systems.

The navigational abilities of birds are not, of course, restricted to the migratory seasons. Homing pigeons are renowned for their ability to return to their home loft when released at distant points; they are frequently raced over

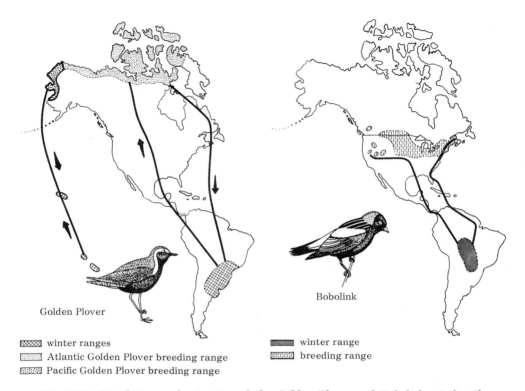

Golden Plover

Bobolink

▨▨▨ winter ranges
▦▦▦ Atlantic Golden Plover breeding range
▧▧▧ Pacific Golden Plover breeding range

▬▬▬ winter range
▥▥▥ breeding range

Fig. 12.20. Distribution and migration of the Golden Plover and Bobolink. Left: The Pacific Golden Plover flies over open ocean from its breeding grounds in Alaska to its winter range in Hawaii, the Marquesas Islands, and the Low Archipelago. The Atlantic Golden Plover follows one route south in autumn to its winter range in South America and another route north in spring. Right: Several separate colonies of Bobolinks have become established west of the main breeding ranges in the northern United States, but the birds from these colonies do not fly directly to the winter range in South America. Instead, they first migrate east to the ancestral flyway and then turn south. [Modified from *Migration of Birds*, U.S. Fish and Wildlife Service, 1950.]

distances from 100 to 600 miles, often averaging speeds of 50 or 60 miles an hour and sometimes making a 600-mile flight from an unfamiliar release point to their home loft in a single day. Other birds can perform similar feats; e.g. a Manx Shearwater was captured on the west coast of England and flown by plane to Boston, where it was released. It was back in its nest in England 12 days later, having flown over 3,000 miles across open ocean.

The Sun and Stars as Compasses. All manner of explanations for the orientational ability of birds have been offered, ranging from extraordinarily keen eyesight to hypothetical unique senses. Most promising has been work on the possibility of celestial orientation.

In 1952 Gustav Kramer, of Wilhelmshaven, Germany, found that caged Starlings and several other species could orient by the sun. At migration time, they became unusually active, and if they could see the sun they began to fly at the side of the cage that lay in the direction of their normal migratory route. If the apparent position of the sun was altered with mirrors, the direction of the birds' attempted flights was altered accordingly. If the sun was obscured by heavy clouds, the birds became disoriented.

Other workers have shown that some birds that migrate at night can tell directions from star patterns. If the young of European warblers, for example, are raised in completely closed soundproof chambers, where the light and temperature conditions are those of summer all year around, they begin to flutter restlessly about their cages during the night at precisely those times of year when their wild brethren would be migrating. In other words, despite the absence of any external cues to season, and despite their total lack of experience with seasons, something motivates the birds to begin flying at the correct migration times in fall and spring. As long as they are in their closed cages indoors, the flutterings are disoriented. But when they are put in an outdoor cage with a glass top, which allows them to see the night sky but nothing else, their activity is oriented in the direction in which their species would normally migrate. It seems that the night sky provides the warblers with enough cues for orientation.

Experiments with Indigo Buntings in a planetarium at the time of their fall migration have shown that they will orient in a direction that is south according to the stars represented, whether it is true south or not—a conclusive demonstration that the birds can orient by the stars.

The discovery that birds and many other animals can tell compass directions by observing the sun or the stars is a major step forward in our attempt to understand orientation behavior. But unfortunately it still does not explain homing behavior of the sort seen in pigeons or the Manx Shearwater mentioned above. Telling compass directions, such as south in fall and north in spring, is not the same thing as telling the homeward direction after being carried away from home. If you were to blindfold a person, take him 500 miles from home, remove the blindfold, give him a compass, and tell him to start walking straight

home, he could not do it unless he had more information than the compass alone provides.

What sort of environmental cues might a bird use to tell homeward direction? One hypothesis is that it might detect gradients in the earth's magnetic field and/or gradients in forces resulting from the earth's rotation. But all attempts to demonstrate that birds can detect these gradients have failed.

Another hypothesis, proposed by G. V. T. Matthews of Cambridge University, is that birds can tell homeward direction as well as compass directions by the sun. According to him, the height of the sun above the horizon at noon indicates to birds how far north or south they are (i.e. what their latitude is). In his view, the birds don't actually have to wait until noon to obtain this information, but can determine the height of the sun at noon by watching it move through a short section of its curving path and then projecting this path to the noon position. According to this sun-arc hypothesis, birds determine how far east or west of home they are by comparing the local sun time with the sun time back home. This means that birds must have their own internal physiological clock. This clock tells them very precisely what the time is back home, and the sun tells them the local time; a comparison of the two makes it possible to compute the longitude.

Unfortunately the weight of present evidence seems to be against Matthews' hypothesis. Experiments indicate that birds pay little attention to the sun's altitude, and there is no evidence that they can measure seconds of arc, as the hypothesis would require. In short, the most that can be said at present is that birds (and a great variety of other animals) certainly can determine compass directions from the sun and from the stars, but it has not been proved that they can determine their displacement from a given location by celestial cues. Much research is needed in this fascinating field. You will doubtless hear more about it in the future.

BIOLOGICAL CLOCKS

The Evidence for Biological Clocks

If birds, bees, and a great variety of other animals can determine compass directions by observing the sun, it follows that they must be able to compensate for its changing positions. The sun does not stay put; its position changes both during the course of a day and during the course of a year. Repeated experiments have shown that a bird in a circular cage with food chambers arranged around its periphery can be trained to go to a chamber lying in a particular direction of the compass. The cage can be moved to different localities or the bird can be put in the cage at different times of day without in any way interfering with its ability to locate the proper chamber. If it has been trained to eat at the north chamber, it will go to the north chamber in each experiment. In other words, it makes no difference whether the bird sees a sun low in the east in the morning, a higher sun nearer noon, or a sun in the west in the afternoon; each of these can tell it where north is. This would be possible only if the bird had some sort of internal clock enabling it to combine the time of day with the sun's position in order to calculate directions.

That such a clock does indeed exist has been demonstrated in a variety of ways. For example, honeybees dancing the wagging dance inside a dark hive compensate for the changing position of the sun, which they cannot see. If they continued to orient their dance in a manner indicating the location of a food source relative to the position of the sun as they last saw it, they would soon be giving the other bees erroneous information and these would depart in a wrong direction. This does not happen. The dancer slowly shifts the orientation of her dance relative to gravity, so that she is always indicating the direction of the food in terms of the position of the sun at that moment. This means that she has both a biological clock and "knowledge" of the rate at which the sun's position changes. Bees also quickly learn what time of day each species of nectar-yielding flower opens and visit it punctually every day; they are not telling time from external cues but are depending upon their own internal clock—they can do just as well when kept under conditions of constant light and temperature.

Numerous other examples could be mentioned. The leaves of many plants show regular movements in a cycle of approximately 24 hours, even if kept under constant conditions. Many flowers open and close in a similar 24-hour cycle. Adult insects of many species emerge from the pupa at a particular time of day, whatever the age of the pupa or the conditions it has experienced. Certain crabs become darker in the morning and lighter in the afternoon, even under constant conditions. Many animals show activity rhythms that vary with a period of approximately 24 hours, even if the animals are kept under constant conditions and have no external indication of the actual daily environmental cycle. Karl C. Hamner of the University of California at Los Angeles took hamsters, fruit flies, cockroaches, cockleburs, soybean plants, and bread molds to the South Pole and placed them on a turntable set to rotate at exactly the same speed as the earth but in the opposite direction. In other words, he exposed these organisms to conditions where no earthly indications of daily time exist. Yet the regular 24-hour cyclic activities of these organisms continued.

Manifestations of biological clocks are not restricted to the sorts of gross reactions of whole organisms so far mentioned. There is ample evidence that clock phenomena are characteristic of all living things, whether individual cells or whole multicellular plants or animals. Examples of cellular phenomena that vary in approximately 24-hour cycles include enzyme activity, osmotic pressure, respiration rate, growth rate, membrane permeability, biolumi-nescence, sensitivity to light and temperature, and reactions to various drugs. Physicians are becoming increasingly aware that the proper dosage of a drug may be very different at different times of day; in some cases, what constitutes a beneficial dose at one time may actually be lethal at another time.

We have dealt primarily with rhythms of about 24 hours, which are commonly called *circadian rhythms,* but other rhythms, including monthly and yearly ones, are also known to exist.

Effects of Environmental Conditions on the Clocks

Many manifestations of the internal clock have been studied in detail, but these should not be confused with the clock itself. At present, we know very little about the actual mechanism of the clock. We know that it cannot depend on the usual sort of enzyme-catalyzed reactions because it shows amazingly little temperature dependence; we have already discussed this point in connection with the role of the clock in the control of flowering (see p. 320). We know also that the basic period of the clock is innate. Erwin Bünning of the University of Tübingen, Germany, has shown that exposure of the fruit fly *Drosophila* to constant conditions for 15 consecutive generations fails to eliminate the essentially 24-hour rhythms of this insect. This does not mean that the clock is unresponsive to environmental conditions; it is, in fact, strongly influenced by them. Under normal conditions, the clock is constantly being reset by the environmental cycle. That of an organism kept under constant conditions for a long time will slowly get more and more out of phase with the environmental diurnal cycle. An illustration would be an insect whose activity rhythm has an innate period of 23 hours and 45 minutes (the innate period often deviates slightly from 24 hours); after 20 days

under constant conditions, the insect's activity cycle would be five hours out of phase with the actual diurnal cycle. To give another example of environmental influence on the clock: In plants and many lower animals, most cycles fail to operate if the organism has been exposed to constant light or constant darkness throughout its life; an environmental stimulus is necessary to trigger the beginning of such cycles, but a single stimulus is sufficient—it need not be repeated for the cycles to continue in most cases.

The fact that environmental conditions can reset the biological clock means that we can experimentally manipulate the clock. This has been done with Starlings. These birds can be trained to orient toward the north in an experimental cage, using the sun as their cue. If they are then put in a lightproof room for several weeks and exposed to an artificial day that begins and ends six hours later than the natural day, and if they are then again placed in the experimental cage and exposed to the sun, they will orient toward the east instead of toward the north. Their clock having been shifted six hours out of phase with the natural day, they interpret the sun's position erroneously.

It has been shown that when an organism is exposed to new conditions that shift the setting of its biological clocks, the clocks of its various cells or organs do not all necessarily shift together. Some may adjust to the new conditions in only two or three days, while others may take a week or more. Thus it is possible for the different organs of an individual to be thrown out of phase with each other. For example, an endocrine gland might be in the phase of its maximal secretion of hormone at the same time that the target organ was in a phase of relative unresponsiveness to the hormone. Or an enzyme system might be potentially most active at a time when its substrate was not available. Such uncoordinated phase shifts of the various biological clocks in an individual may well lead to serious physiological disturbances and perhaps to disease. It has even been suggested that the onset of cancer may be triggered by unbalanced phase shifts of this type.

Air and space travel, varying light regimes as a result of artificial lighting, less orderly activities, and other conditions characteristic of modern life may be altering the balance between the phases of our various clocks with profound effects of which we are as yet only dimly aware. Biological clocks will be an important field of research in the years ahead, as man increasingly subjects himself to conditions that can easily disrupt the balance between the cycles of his individual cells and organs.

REFERENCES

BEER, C. G., 1963–1964. "Ethology—The Zoologist's Approach to Behaviour," *Tuatara*, vol. 11, pp. 170–177, vol. 12, pp. 16–39.

CARTHY, J. D., 1958. *An Introduction to the Behavior of Invertebrates*. Macmillan, New York.

Cold Spring Harbor Symposium on Quantitative Biology: Biological Clocks, 1960. Biological Laboratory, Cold Spring Harbor, N.Y.

DILGER, W. C., 1956. "Hostile Behavior and Reproductive Isolating Mechanisms in the Avian Genera *Catharus* and *Hylocichla*," *Auk*, vol. 73, pp. 313–353.

———, 1960. "The Comparative Ethology of the African Parrot Genus *Agapornis*," *Zeitschrift für Tierpsychologie*, vol. 17, pp. 649–685.

DORST, J., 1961. *The Migration of Birds*. Houghton Mifflin, Boston.

ETKIN, W., ed., 1964. *Social Behavior and Organization Among Vertebrates*. University of Chicago Press, Chicago.

GRIFFIN, D. R., 1958. *Listening in the Dark*. Yale University Press, New Haven, Conn.

GUHL, A. M., 1961. "Gonadal Hormones and Social Behavior in Infrahuman Vertebrates," in *Sex and Internal Secretions*, 3rd edition ed. by W. C. Young, vol. 2. Williams & Wilkins, Baltimore.

IERSEL, J. J. A. VAN, 1953. "An Analysis of the Parental Behaviour of the Male Three-Spined Stickleback," *Behaviour*, sup. 3, pp. 1–153.

LANYON, W. E., and W. N. TAVOLGA, eds., 1960. *Animal Sounds and Communication*. American Institute of Biological Sciences, Washington.

LEHRMAN, D. S., 1961. "Gonadal Hormones and Parental Behavior in Birds and Infrahuman Mammals," in *Sex and Internal Secretions*, 3rd edition ed. by W. C. Young, vol. 2. Williams & Wilkins, Baltimore.

LINDAUR, M., 1961. *Communication Among Social Bees*. Harvard University Press, Cambridge, Mass.

MORRIS, D., 1956. "The Function and Causation of Courtship Ceremonies," *L'Instinct dans le comportement des animaux et de l'homme*. Fondation Singer-Polignac, Paris.

MOYNIHAN, M., 1955. "Remarks on the Original Sources of Displays," *Auk*, vol. 72, pp. 240–246.

ROE, A., and G. G. SIMPSON, eds., 1958. *Behavior and Evolution*. Yale University Press, New Haven, Conn.

SCHMIDT-KOENIG, K., 1965. "Current Problems in Bird Orientation," *Advances in the Study of Behavior*, vol. 1. Academic Press, New York.

SCOTT, J. P., 1958. *Animal Behavior*. University of Chicago Press, Chicago.

THORPE, W. H., 1961. *Bird-Song: The Biology of Vocal Communication and Expression in Birds*. Cambridge University Press, New York.

———, 1963. *Learning and Instinct in Animals*, 2nd ed. Methuen, London.

———, 1965. "The Ontogeny of Behavior," in *Ideas in Modern Biology*, ed. by J. A. Moore. Natural History Press, Garden City, N.Y.

———, and O. L. ZANGWILL, eds., 1961. *Current Problems in Animal Behaviour*. Cambridge University Press, New York.

TINBERGEN, N., 1951. *The Study of Instinct*. Oxford University Press, New York.

———, 1953. *The Herring Gull's World*. Collins, London.

———, 1953. *Social Behaviour in Animals*. Wiley, New York.

TINBERGEN, N., 1965. "Behavior and Natural Selection," in *Ideas in Modern Biology*, ed. by J. A. Moore. Natural History Press, Garden City, N.Y.

WATERS, R. H., D. A. RETHLINGSHAFER, and W. E. CALDWELL, 1960. *Principles of Comparative Psychology*. McGraw-Hill, New York.

WILSON, E. O., 1963. "The Social Biology of Ants," *Annual Review of Entomology*, vol. 8, pp. 345–368.

YOUNG, W. C., 1961. "The Hormones and Mating Behavior," in *Sex and Internal Secretions*, 3rd edition ed. by W. C. Young, vol. 2. Williams & Wilkins, Baltimore.

SUGGESTED READING

BEST, J. B., 1963. "Protopsychology," *Scientific American*, February. (Offprint 149.)

BLOUGH, D. S., 1961. "Experiments in Animal Psychophysics," *Scientific American*, July. (Offprint 458.)

CARR, A., 1965. "The Navigation of the Green Turtle," *Scientific American*, May. (Offprint 1010.)

CARTHY, J. D., 1956. *Animal Navigation*. Allen & Unwin, London.

DETHIER, V. G., and E. STELLAR, 1964. *Animal Behavior*, 2nd ed. Prentice-Hall, Englewood Cliffs, N.J.

DILGER, W. C., 1962. "The Behavior of Lovebirds," *Scientific American*, January.

EIBL-EIBESFELDT, I., 1961. "The Fighting Behavior of Animals," *Scientific American*, December. (Offprint 470.)

FRISCH, K. VON, 1950. *Bees: Their Vision, Chemical Senses, and Language*. Cornell University Press, Ithaca, N.Y.

———, 1962. "Dialects in the Language of the Bees," *Scientific American*, August. (Offprint 130.)

GLEITMAN, H., 1963. "Place-Learning," *Scientific American*, October. (Offprint 479.)

GRIFFIN, D. R., 1959. *Echoes of Bats and Men*. Doubleday Anchor Books, New York.

———, 1964. *Bird Migration*. Natural History Press, Garden City, N.Y.

GUHL, A. M., 1956. "The Social Order of Chickens," *Scientific American*, February. (Offprint 471.)

GUTTMAN, N., and H. I. KALISH, 1958. "Experiments in Discrimination," *Scientific American*, January. (Offprint 403.)

HASLER, A. D., and J. A. LARSEN, 1955. "The Homing Salmon," *Scientific American*, August. (Offprint 411.)

HESS, E. H., 1958. "Imprinting in Animals," *Scientific American*, March. (Offprint 416.)

———, 1964. "Imprinting in Birds," *Science*, vol. 146, pp. 1128–1139.

HOCKETT, C. F., 1960. "The Origin of Speech," *Scientific American*, September. (Offprint 603.)

HOLST, E. VON, and U. VON SAINT PAUL, 1962. "Electrically Controlled Behavior," *Scientific American*, March. (Offprint 464.)

JACOBSON, M., and M. BEROZA, 1964. "Insect Attractants," *Scientific American*, August. (Offprint 189.)

KORTLANDT, A., 1962. "Chimpanzees in the Wild," *Scientific American*, May. (Offprint 463.)

LEHRMAN, D. S., 1964. "The Reproductive Behavior of Ring Doves," *Scientific American*, November. (Offprint 488.)

LEVINE, S., 1960. "Stimulation in Infancy," *Scientific American*, May. (Offprint 436.)

LORENZ, K. Z., 1952. *King Solomon's Ring*. Crowell, New York.

———, 1958. "The Evolution of Behavior," *Scientific American*, December. (Offprint 412.)

ROEDER, K. D., 1965. "Moths and Ultrasound," *Scientific American*, April. (Offprint 1009.)

SHAW, E., 1962. "The Schooling of Fishes," *Scientific American*, June. (Offprint 124.)

THORPE, W. H., 1956. "The Language of Birds," *Scientific American*, October. (Offprint 145.)

TINBERGEN, N., 1952. "The Curious Behavior of the Stickleback," *Scientific American*, December. (Offprint 414.)

———, 1960. "The Evolution of Behavior in Gulls," *Scientific American*, December. (Offprint 456.)

WENNER, A. M., 1964. "Sound Communication in Honeybees," *Scientific American*, April. (Offprint 181.)

WILSON, E. O., 1963. "Pheromones," *Scientific American*, May. (Offprint 157.)

PART III

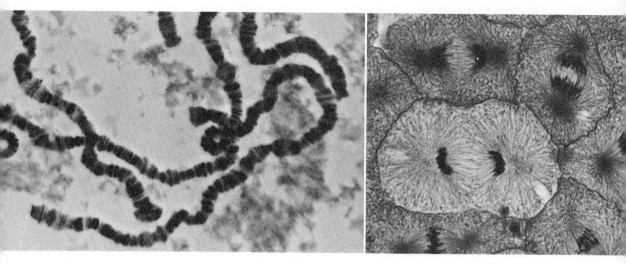

THE PERPETUATION OF LIFE

CELLULAR REPRODUCTION

I**N AN EARLIER CHAPTER, WE SAID THAT ONE** important part of the cell theory is that all cells arise from other cells—*omnis cellula e cellula*. It is now time for us to examine in some detail the process whereby old cells give rise to new ones, a process commonly called cell division. As one would assume in view of the complexity of even the simplest cells, this process is not merely a splitting in two of the parent cell. An intricate series of events must take place in orderly fashion before one cell can become two. It is these events that constitute the subject of this chapter.

THE CENTRAL IMPORTANCE OF THE NUCLEUS

We have repeatedly said that the nucleus is the control center of the cell. It contains the chromosomes, which bear the genes—the units of information that, passed down from generation to generation, determine the characteristics of each new organism and direct its myriad activities. Let us briefly review some of

Fig. 13.1. Photograph of *Acetabularia.* [Courtesy General Biological Supply House, Inc., Chicago.]

the experiments demonstrating the essential role of the nucleus in the life of the cell.

It is possible to remove the nucleus from an amoeba by surgical procedures or by using a micropipette. If this operation is performed carefully, the cytoplasm is not significantly damaged, and the cell can continue functioning for days or even weeks. Apparently the enzymes and organelles already formed can maintain the cell for that length of time. Eventually, however, the cell begins to "run down"; pseudopod formation diminishes and movement becomes sluggish, there is little if any feeding, the cell may become spherical, and finally death results. If a new nucleus is inserted into the cell within the first two or three days after the initial operation, the amoeba may resume activity, but if the new nucleus is inserted after six days, there is no response. Similar results have been obtained when nuclei have been removed from a variety of other types of cells, both plant and animal. Clearly, then, the nucleus is essential for the continued life of the

cell; normal function in some way depends upon it.

The importance of the nucleus in the transmission of hereditary information has been demonstrated in a variety of ways. Joachim Hämmerling of the Max Planck Institute for Marine Biology in Berlin carried out his demonstrations with the unicellular green alga *Acetabularia.* Individuals of this curious plant, though they are composed of only one cell, consist of a branching rootlike base, a stalk, and a cap (Fig. 13.1). The nucleus is in the base. Hämmerling worked with two closely related species, *Acetabularia mediterranea* and *Acetabularia crenulata.* The first species, often called med for short, has a disc-shaped cap, while *A. crenulata,* or cren for short, has an irregularly branched cap. Hämmerling showed that if he amputated the stalk and cap of a med individual and grafted a cren stalk without a cap onto the med base, a new cap was eventually regenerated, intermediate in appearance between med and cren. If this cap was amputated, the second cap regenerated was a typical med one (Fig. 13.2). In other words, this second cap did not take its characteristics from the cren stalk, on which it grew, but from the med base, which contained the nucleus. The reciprocal experiment yielded similar results; a cell consisting of a cren base and med stalk regenerated a cren cap. The nucleus had obviously been the controlling factor. The intermediate appearance of the first cap regenerated must be explained by the retention in the stalk of some influence from the original nucleus; by the time the second cap was formed, this influence had given way to that of the nucleus currently in the cell.

Theodor Boveri of the Munich Zoological Institute, working with eggs of sea urchins, had obtained similar results. He produced some eggs without nuclei by shaking the eggs at a critical time in their development. He then exposed both normally nucleated eggs and enucleated eggs to sperms from a different species of sea urchin. The normally nucleated eggs fertilized by these sperms hatched into hybrid larvae showing characteristics of both species. The enucleated eggs thus fertilized hatched into smaller than normal larvae that showed only the characteristics of the species from which the sperms had been obtained. Inasmuch as the cytoplasm of the two groups of eggs was identical, Boveri was confident that the differences between the larvae the eggs produced were due to their different nuclei.

If the nucleus carries the information or blueprint for the development of the new individual, it follows that when the cell divides the nuclear information must be transmitted in orderly fashion to both of the new cells. The division cannot be a simple splitting of the information into two halves because this would give neither of the new cells a satisfactory blueprint. Just as you cannot have two buildings erected by cutting one blueprint in two and giving half to each contractor, so two new cells cannot develop if each receives only half of the necessary information from the parental cell. If you wanted two contractors to erect identical buildings simultaneously, you would logically duplicate the necessary blueprint and give a complete copy to each contractor. The same applies to the cell. If a parental cell is to divide and produce two viable new cells, it must first make a complete copy of the genetic information in its nucleus and then, as it divides, give one complete copy to each daughter cell. In other words, division of the nucleus is not simply a process of halving; it is a process of duplicating genetic information and distributing the duplicates.

In the procaryotic cells of bacteria and blue-green algae, cell division appears to be a much less complex process than in the eucaryotic cells of true plants and animals. A ring of new wall material begins to form on the inner surface of the wall of the parent cell, usually at a point about midway of its length (Fig. 13.3). This ring slowly grows inward, cutting through both the cytoplasm and the nuclear area. This process is known as simple transverse fission or *binary fission.* Even with the electron microscope, no particular nuclear events associated with cell division have been observed, as they have been in the division of eucaryotic cells; no changes in the shape of the nuclear area can be detected. Genetic studies have shown, however, that each new cell possesses a single complete complement of genetic information, which means that the genetic material has been replicated and one set included in each daughter cell; before long, techniques may be devised that will enable us to detect and study the mechanism involved. This is a field in

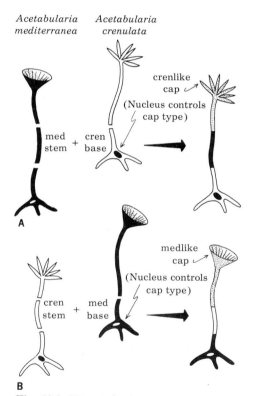

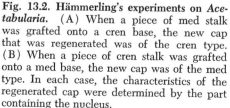

Fig. 13.2. Hämmerling's experiments on *Acetabularia.* (A) When a piece of med stalk was grafted onto a cren base, the new cap that was regenerated was of the cren type. (B) When a piece of cren stalk was grafted onto a med base, the new cap was of the med type. In each case, the characteristics of the regenerated cap were determined by the part containing the nucleus.

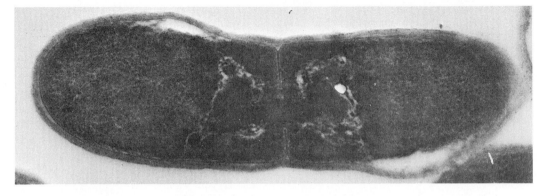

Fig. 13.3. Electron micrograph of a dividing bacterial cell. A ring of new wall has begun to form at the outside of the cell and is growing inward, cutting the cell in two. Notice that the nuclear area divides.   × 37,000.   [Courtesy G. B. Chapman, *J. Biophys. Biochem. Cytol.*, vol. 6, 1959.]

which exciting discoveries will almost surely be made in the next few years.

In eucaryotic cells, cell division involves an elaborate series of nuclear changes that can be seen and studied with the ordinary light microscope. They were, in fact, observed by many workers during the 1800's and described in detail by Walther Flemming of the German University of Prague in the 1880's. The remainder of this chapter is largely an account of our present understanding of these critically important nuclear events.

MITOTIC CELL DIVISION

Cell division involves two fairly distinct processes that often but not always occur together: division of the nucleus and division of the cytoplasm. The process whereby the nucleus divides to produce two new nuclei, each with the same number of chromosomes as the parental nucleus, is called *mitosis* (or karyokinesis). The process of division of the cytoplasm is called *cytokinesis.* We shall discuss mitosis and cytokinesis separately below.

Mitosis

As already mentioned, nuclear division entails,

first, precise duplication of the genetic material and, second, distribution of a complete set of the material to each daughter cell. All available evidence indicates that the duplication step occurs in the nucleus of the nondividing cell prior to the start of division proper. Mitosis, therefore, is largely concerned with distribution of the genetic material in an orderly fashion.

Evidence of many different sorts shows conclusively that the units of genetic information, which we call the genes, are located on the chromosomes. The number of chromosomes is usually constant for normal body cells of all individuals of the same species. For example, the nuclei of human body cells contain 46 chromosomes (Fig. 13.4), those of the fruit fly *Drosophila melanogaster* contain 8, and those of onion contain 16. Thus, if mitosis is to distribute a complete set of genetic instructions to each daughter nucleus, it must ensure that each receives a full set of chromosomes exactly like the set initially present in the parental nucleus; only in this way can a basic constancy of chromosome number and gene content in the somatic, or body, cells be maintained.

The duration of mitosis varies from about 30 minutes to several hours in different types of cells and under different environmental conditions. For convenience, it is customary to divide the mitotic process into a series of stages,

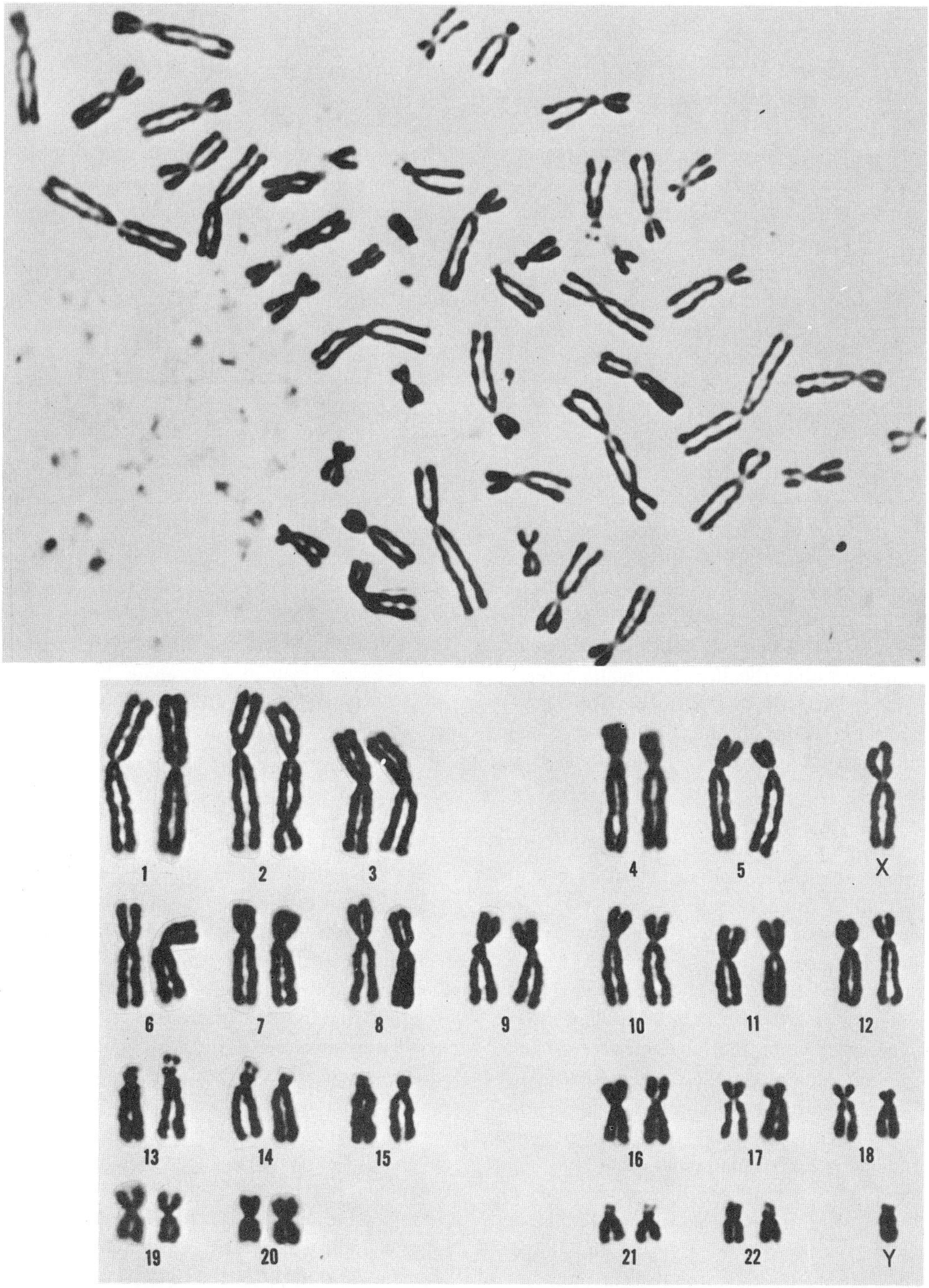

Fig. 13.4. Photograph of chromosomes of a human male. At bottom, the chromosomes have been arranged in pairs and numbered according to the accepted convention. [Courtesy Margery W. Shaw, University of Michigan.]

each designated by a special name. Although each stage will be discussed separately here, keep in mind that the entire process is a continuum, not a series of discrete occurrences.

Interphase. The nondividing cell is said to be in the interphase state. In past years, such a cell was commonly called a resting cell, but this terminology has been abandoned as grossly inappropriate. The interphase cell is definitely not resting; it is carrying out all the innumerable activities of a living, functioning cell—respiration, protein synthesis, growth, differentiation, etc. Furthermore, as already noted, we now know that it is during interphase that the genetic material is replicated in preparation for the next division sequence. Not all cells continue dividing, however; differentiated muscle and nerve cells are examples of cells that do not divide. Apparently, cells that are destined to divide again replicate their genetic material within the first few hours after the last division. Cells that do not carry out genetic replication within this period become so highly differentiated that, under normal circumstances, they never divide again. When we have achieved a better understanding of the factors that control this critical "decision"—whether genetic replication leading to further cell division will or will not occur—we shall surely have made a major advance in explaining developmental processes in general. And we shall surely have taken an important step toward understanding and possibly controlling the runaway cell division that characterizes cancer.

During interphase, the nucleus is clearly visible as a distinct membrane-bounded organelle, and one or more nucleoli are usually prominent. But chromosomes, as ordinarily pictured, are not visible in the nucleus (see Fig. 3.20, p. 73); there are no distinct rodlike bodies such as are seen so easily in a dividing cell. The only manifestation of the chromosomes is an irregular granular-appearing mass of chromatin material. Formerly, some workers insisted, in fact, that the chromosomes exist as distinct structures only during cell division and break up during interphase. More recent chemical and genetic evidence indicates that they continue to exist during interphase, but that they become very long, thin, and intertwined and hence cannot be recognized by present techniques.

In interphase animal cells, but not in most plant cells, there is a special region of cytoplasm just outside the nucleus that contains two small cylindrical bodies about 0.3–0.5 micron long and about 0.15 micron in diameter, oriented at right angles to each other. These are the *centrioles* (see Fig. 3.31, p. 86), which will move apart and organize the mitotic apparatus of the dividing cell. In many animal cells, this separation of the centrioles occurs just before the onset of mitosis, but in some cells it occurs during interphase long before mitosis begins. No centrioles have yet been detected in the cells of most seed plants, but they do occur in some algae, fungi, bryophytes (mosses, liverworts, etc.), and ferns in association with the production of motile sperms.

Prophase. The first stage of mitosis is called the prophase. It is, in a sense, a preparatory stage that readies the nucleus for the crucial event of mitosis—the separation of two complete sets of chromosomes into two daughter nuclei. As the two centrioles of an animal cell move toward opposite sides of the nucleus, the initially indistinct chromosomes begin to condense into visible threads, which become progressively shorter and thicker and more easily stainable with dyes. When the chromosomes first become visible during early prophase, they appear as long, thin, intertwined filaments, but by late prophase the individual chromosomes can be clearly discerned as much shorter rodlike structures. As the chromosomes become more distinct, the nucleoli become less distinct, often disappearing altogether by the end of prophase (Fig. 13.5). It seems probable that the condensing of the chromosomes is

1. INTERPHASE

nucleolus   centrioles

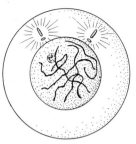

Chromosomes not seen as distinct
   structures.
Nucleolus visible.

2. EARLY PROPHASE

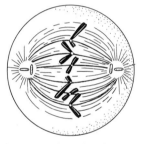

Centrioles moving apart.
Chromosomes appear as long
   thin threads.
Nucleolus becoming less distinct.

3. MIDDLE PROPHASE

aster

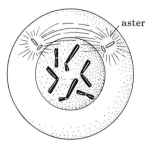

Centrioles farther apart, begin to
   organize spindle.
Each chromosome composed of
   2 chromatids attached by a
   common centromere.

4. LATE PROPHASE

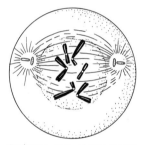

Centrioles nearly at opposite sides
   of nucleus.
Spindle nearly complete.
Nuclear membrane disappearing.
Chromosomes move toward equator.
Nucleolus no longer visible.

5. METAPHASE

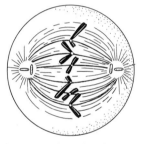

Nuclear membrane has disappeared.
Centromere of each double-stranded
   chromosome attached to a spindle
   fibril at spindle equator.

6. EARLY ANAPHASE

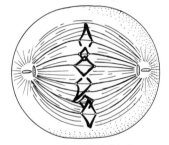

Centromeres have divided and
   begun moving toward
   opposite poles of spindle.

7. LATE ANAPHASE

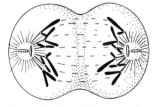

The 2 sets of new single-stranded
   chromosomes nearing respective
   poles.
Cytokinesis beginning.

8. TELOPHASE

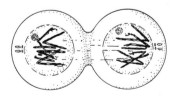

New nuclear membranes forming.
Chromosomes become longer, thinner,
   and less distinct.
Nucleolus reappearing.
Centrioles replicated.
Cytokinesis nearly complete.

9. INTERPHASE

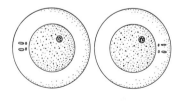

Nuclear membranes complete.
Chromosomes no longer visible.
Cytokinesis complete.

Fig. 13.5. Mitosis and cytokinesis of an animal cell.

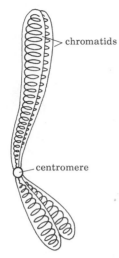

chromatids

centromere

Fig. 13.6. A late-prophase chromosome. It consists of two identical chromatids united at some point along their length by a single centromere. The chromatin of each chromatid is coiled and embedded in a matrix of other material.

largely a matter of their becoming coiled into a tight helix, which is then coiled again (Fig. 13.6); nucleolar material probably becomes coated on the outer surface of this coiled coil. One advantage of the shortening of the chromosomes during cell division is readily apparent; in their shorter form, they can be moved about freely without becoming hopelessly tangled. You may well ask, then, why the chromosomes do not simply remain in their shorter coiled form even during interphase. One probable reason is that the genetic material functions as a surface on which other molecules are synthesized, and only in the long, thin, uncoiled form is the surface sufficiently exposed to function in this way.

If an individual chromosome from a late-prophase nucleus is examined under very high magnification, it can be seen to consist of two separate strands called *chromatids* (Fig. 13.6). The two chromatids are united by a small body called a *centromere*, which is located near the end of some chromosomes and near the center of others. The replication process that occurred during interphase produced one of the chro-

matids by using the other as a model, in a manner to be discussed at length in a later chapter. Thus the two chromatids of a prophase chromosome are identical. Note that, contrary to what is frequently said, the interphase process that produced the second chromatid was not a splitting; it was a duplicating.

As the two centrioles of an animal cell move apart, they send out a system of thin fibrils that radiate in all directions (Fig. 13.5: 2). Some fibrils from one of the centrioles apparently link up with fibrils from the other centriole, so that by the end of prophase the fibrils are divided into two groups, the *spindle fibrils,* which form continuous links between the two centrioles, and the blindly ending astral fibrils, collectively called an *aster,* which radiate in other directions from each centriole (Fig. 13.7). Even though most higher-plant cells lack centrioles, they develop a spindle much like that in animal cells, but no asters are formed.

During late prophase, the double-stranded chromosomes, which at first were distributed essentially at random within the nucleus, begin to move toward the middle, or equator, of the biconical spindle formed by the spindle fibrils. Prophase ends when the nuclear membrane disappears and each chromosome moves to the midpoint of one of the spindle fibrils.

Metaphase. During the brief stage termed metaphase, the chromosomes are arranged on the equatorial plate of the spindle, and in side view appear to form a line across the middle of the spindle (Fig. 13.5: 5). Each double-stranded chromosome becomes attached by its centromere to a fibril of the spindle, and it is actually the centromeres that are lined up precisely along the equatorial plate, while the arms of the chromosomes may extend in any direction. Metaphase ends when each chromosomal centromere divides and each of the former chromatids thus becomes a separate single-stranded chromosome—in other words, when the total number of independent chromosomes in the nucleus is doubled. (Note that, in determining the number of chromosomes present in a nucleus, we count the number of separate centromeres, not the number of strands.)

Anaphase. Now begins the separation of two complete sets of chromosomes, the critical event for which the previous stages were the preparation. At the beginning of anaphase, the two new single-stranded chromosomes derived from each original double-stranded chromosome begin to move away from each other, one going toward one pole (centriole) of the spindle and the other going toward the opposite pole. A chromosome cannot move during anaphase unless its centromere is attached to a spindle fibril; it can be demonstrated that both the centromere and the fibril are necessary for the movement. A cell in early anaphase can be recognized by the fact that the chromosomes are in two equal groups a short distance apart. A cell in late anaphase contains two groups of chromosomes that are more widely separated, the two clusters having almost reached their respective poles of the spindle (Fig. 13.5: 7). Cytokinesis often begins during late anaphase.

Telophase. Telophase is essentially a reverse of prophase. The two sets of chromosomes, having reached their respective poles, become enclosed in new nuclear membranes as the spindle disappears. These new nuclear membranes are apparently assembled from membranous fragments already present in the cell. Then the chromosomes begin to uncoil and to resume their interphase form, while the nucleoli slowly reappear (Fig. 13.5: 8). The centriole of each nucleus usually replicates itself during late telophase. Cytokinesis is often completed during telophase. Telophase ends when the new nuclei have fully assumed the characteristics of interphase, thus bringing to a close the complete mitotic cycle.

Note that when the individual chromosomes fade from view at the end of telophase they are single-stranded, but when they reappear

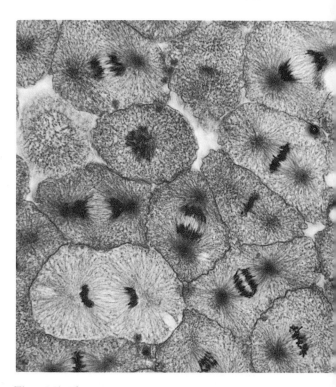

Fig. 13.7. Photograph of mitotically dividing cells of whitefish blastula. The asters around each centriole are prominent. Most of the cells shown here are in either metaphase or anaphase. [Courtesy General Biological Supply House, Inc., Chicago.]

during prophase in the next division sequence they are double-stranded, the replication, which unfortunately cannot be observed, having occurred during interphase. In summary, then, if prophase begins with a nucleus containing, say, six double-stranded chromosomes, telophase ends with two new nuclei each containing six single-stranded chromosomes. Mitosis separates the strands of the initially double-stranded chromosomes. Thus each new daughter cell has the same number and kinds of chromosomes as the parental cell, and hence each has the complete set of genetic information necessary to determine its characteristics and to guide its activities.

A word of caution is in order here. The description of mitosis given above holds for most eucaryotic cells, both plant and animal (with the differences noted concerning presence or absence of centrioles and asters). But it does not hold in all details for all eucaryotic cells. For example, in many protozoans the spindle forms inside the nucleus and the nuclear membrane never disappears; when the chromosomes have been separated into two clusters at telophase, the nucleus simply pinches in two.

The Movement of the Chromosomes. We have so far blithely described the sequential events of mitosis without trying to explain how the chromosomes move apart during anaphase, despite the fact that this movement is basic to the entire process. We now turn our attention briefly to this problem, but we must admit at the outset that no fully satisfactory explanation has yet been found. Much more research is needed on this question.

One theory holds that the chromosomes are pulled toward the poles of the spindle by the fibrils to which they are attached. It has been pointed out that the centromere, by which the chromosome is attached to the fibril, usually moves steadily, with the arms of the chromosome often dragging along behind; the moving chromosome thus appears V-shaped or J-shaped, depending upon the location of its centromere. Such an appearance would be expected if the limp chromosome were being pulled through relatively dense protoplasm by the portion of the fibril between the chromosome and the pole. But the same appearance would be predicted if the limp chromosome were being pushed through the protoplasm by the middle portion of the fibril, and such a pushing mechanism has been proposed as an alternative theory. Still a third theory is that the motive force comes, at least in part, from the centromere of the chromosome itself. Which if any of these theories or combination of them is correct remains to be determined. At present, the first theory—pulling action by the fibril—seems to have the most adherents, but the possible supplementary action of the centromere is also widely admitted.

One approach to investigation of the activity of the mitotic apparatus has been to remove it intact from the rest of the cell and study its properties in isolation. This was first accomplished in 1952 by Daniel Mazia of the University of California at Berkeley and Katsuma Dan of the Tokyo Metropolitan University. They used mild detergents that dispersed everything in dividing sea-urchin eggs except the mitotic apparatus, which was left intact. They were then able to show that the spindle fibrils are composed largely of protein molecules loosely bonded to each other. Mazia and co-workers found, in fact, that the mitotic apparatus contains at least 10 percent of all the protein in the dividing sea-urchin egg. It also contains some nucleic acid of the RNA type and a considerable amount of lipid. Dan and his co-workers showed that certain sulfur-containing groups are very common on the proteins of the spindle during prophase and metaphase but that these disappear as the chromosomes move toward the poles during anaphase. Presumably this change in some way reflects the activity of the spindle during anaphase, but this tantalizing hint has not yet led to further understanding.

If some variant of the pulling theory of chromosome movement is correct, it would seem logical to suppose that the sections of the fibrils between the chromosomes and the poles contract in a manner analogous to the contraction of muscle. Mazia and his co-workers have shown, in fact, that the mitotic apparatus itself contains an enzyme that splits ATP, just as the myosin in muscle does. And it has definitely been established that the chromosome-to-pole fibrils shorten to a tiny fraction of their original length. But as these fibrils shorten, they become neither thicker nor less straight; the electron microscope reveals that they retain the same diameter regardless of changes in their length. This seems inconsistent with a theory of musclelike contraction. As a result, an alternative theory has been proposed that the shortening is due to actual removal of some of the molecules from the chain of which the fibril is composed. Only further research can clarify the matter.

It is interesting to note that the centrioles, which play such an important role in making possible the movement of chromosomes in animal cells, are structurally identical with the basal bodies of cilia and flagella; when viewed in cross section with an electron microscope, they are seen to have the same arrangement of nine groups of peripheral fibrils. The basal bodies in some cells—notably the basal bodies of the flagella of sperm cells in many lower plants and in animals—are actually derived from the centriole. There is also evidence of structural relationship between centrioles and the centromeres of the chromosomes. Centrioles can sometimes organize the action of cilia and flagella; in some species, centromeres detached from their chromosomes have the same capacity. It seems, then, that in the course of evolution the same type of organelle has come to have three different functions and has been given three different names by biologists— centriole, centromere, and basal body. The underlying functional unity of the three forms of this organelle is obvious; all three are concerned with organized movement.

Cytokinesis

We said earlier that division of the cytoplasm frequently accompanies division of the nucleus, often beginning in late anaphase and reaching completion during telophase. But this is not always the case. Mitosis without cytokinesis is common in some algae and fungi, producing coenocytic plant bodies (bodies with many nuclei but with no, or few, cellular partitions). It regularly occurs during certain phases of reproduction in seed plants and certain other vascular plants. It is also common in a few lower invertebrate animals with coenocytic bodies. And it produces the multinucleate cells of vertebrate skeletal and cardiac muscle. Furthermore, examples are known in which mitosis without cytokinesis produces numerous nuclei in a limited amount of cytoplasm; later, cytokinesis cuts up this cytoplasm to produce many new cells in a very short time.

Cytokinesis in Animal Cells. Division of an animal cell normally begins with the formation of a *cleavage furrow* running around the cell. When cytokinesis occurs during mitosis, the location of the furrow is ordinarily determined by the orientation of the spindle, in whose equatorial region the furrow forms (Fig. 13.5: 7). The furrow becomes progressively deeper, until it cuts completely through the cell (and its spindle), producing two new cells.

Very little is known about the mechanism of formation of the cleavage furrow. According to one hypothesis, a contractile ring of cortical cytoplasm around the outside of the cell pinches the cell in two. Another hypothesis is that new membrane is formed and the furrow grows inward. Still another hypothesis suggests that some of the astral fibrils of the mitotic apparatus are attached to the cell surface and pull the surface inward to form the cleavage furrow. This last hypothesis, however, offers no explanation for the known cases where cytokinesis occurs long after mitosis is complete and the spindle has disappeared; furthermore, it has been shown that removal of the entire mitotic apparatus from a sea-urchin egg by micromanipulation does not inhibit furrow formation.

Cytokinesis in Plant Cells. Plant cells possess relatively rigid cell walls, which cannot develop cleavage furrows. Hence it is not surprising that cytokinesis in most plant cells is very different from cytokinesis in animal cells. A special membrane, called the *cell plate,* forms halfway between the two nuclei (at the equator of the spindle if cytokinesis accompanies mitosis; Fig. 13.8). The cell plate begins to form in the center of the cytoplasm and slowly becomes larger until its edges reach the outer surface of the cell and the cell's con-

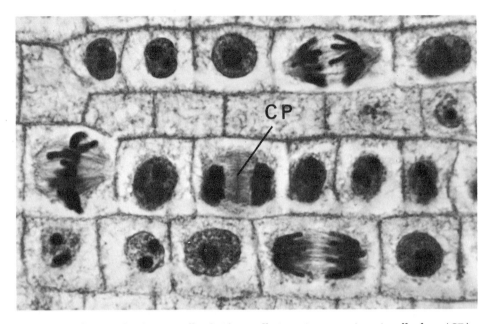

Fig. 13.8. Photograph of mitotically dividing cells in onion root tip. A cell plate (CP) can be seen as a faint dark line in the equatorial plane between two telophase nuclei. [Courtesy General Biological Supply House, Inc., Chicago.]

tents are cut in two. We see, then, that cytokinesis of a plant cell progresses from the middle to the periphery, whereas cytokinesis in animal cells progresses from the periphery to the middle.

The cell plate forms from membranous vesicles that first line up and then unite (Fig. 13.9). The endoplasmic reticulum apparently makes major contributions to the developing cell plate. Even though the cell plate develops from membranes, it probably does not form the outer cell membranes of the new cells. Instead, it seems to become impregnated with pectin and to form the middle lamella upon which the cellulose walls of the two new cells are deposited by the cell membranes that soon form.

MEIOTIC CELL DIVISION

Notice that the nuclei of the cells shown in Fig. 13.5, belonging to a hypothetical organism,

contain six chromosomes. But notice also that those six chromosomes are of only three different types, there being two of each type. Cells of this sort, with two of each type of chromosome, are said to be *diploid.* The somatic cells of the human body, as well as those of most higher plants and animals, are diploid. We have said that each somatic cell of a human being has 46 chromosomes and that each somatic cell of a fruit fly has eight; since these cells are diploid, it follows that the chromosomes in a human somatic cell are of 23 types and those in a fruit-fly somatic cell are of four types. Mitosis, as we have seen, produces new cells with exactly the same chromosomal endowment as the parental cell. Hence, whenever a human somatic cell divides mitotically, the new cells thus produced have 46 chromosomes of 23 different types, there being two of each type. But we also know that, in sexual reproduction, two cells (the egg and the sperm) unite to form the first cell (zygote) of the new individual. If those two cells (gametes) were produced by normal mitosis in human beings or fruit flies or our hypothetical organism, the zygote produced by their union would have double the normal number of chromosomes, and at each successive generation the number would again double, until the total chromosome number per cell would approach infinity. This does not happen; the chromosome number normally remains constant within a species. It follows, therefore, that at some point a different kind of cell division must take place, a division that reduces the number of chromosomes by half so that when the egg and sperm unite in fertilization the normal diploid number is restored. This special process of reduction division is called *meiosis*.

In all multicellular animals, meiosis occurs at the time of gamete production. Consequently each gamete possesses only half the species-typical number of chromosomes. It is important to note that in the reduction division of meiosis the chromosomes of the parental cell are not simply separated into two random halves; the diploid nucleus contains two of each type of chromosome, and meiosis partitions these chromosome pairs so that each

Fig. 13.9. Electron micrograph of a late-telophase cell in corn root, showing formation of cell plate. Mitosis has been completed, and the two new nuclei (N) are being formed; the chromosomes (dark areas in the nuclei) are no longer visible as distinct structures, but the nuclear membranes are not yet complete. A cell plate (CP) is being assembled from numerous small vesicular structures. At the lower end of the nucleus on the right, a length of endoplasmic reticulum can be seen that appears to run from the nuclear membrane to the cell wall, through the wall, and into the adjacent cell. × 14,000. [Courtesy W. G. Whaley *et al., Am. J. Botany,* vol. 47, 1960.]

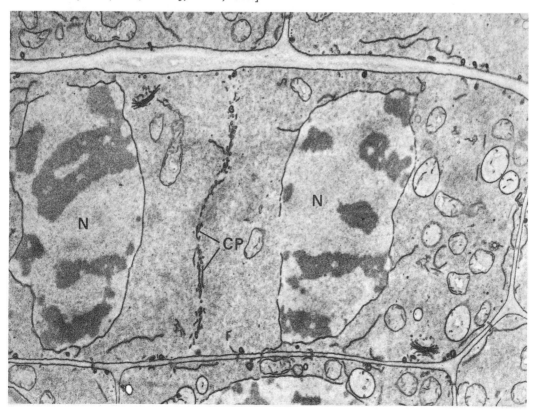

gamete contains one of each type of chromosome. Such a cell, with only one of each type of chromosome, is said to be *haploid.* When two haploid gametes unite in fertilization, the resulting zygote is diploid, having received one of each chromosome type from the sperm of the male parent and one of each type from the egg of the female parent.

The Process of Meiosis

Complete meiosis involves two successive division sequences, which result in four new cells, each of which is haploid. It is the first division sequence that accomplishes the reduction in the number of chromosomes; the second division sequence is essentially a mitotic one. Let us examine the nuclear events characteristic of meiosis, recognizing four stages, as in mitosis —namely, prophase, metaphase, anaphase, and telophase.

First Prophase.   Many of the events in the first prophase of meiosis resemble those in the prophase of mitosis. The individual chromosomes come slowly into view as they coil and become shorter, thicker, and more easily stainable. The nucleoli slowly fade from view, and, finally, the nuclear membrane disappears and the spindle is organized. Radioactive-tracer studies show that the replication of the genetic material occurs during the interphase that precedes prophase I, as in mitosis (but during early prophase of meiosis the chromosomes are not recognizably double-stranded).

The chief difference between prophase of meiosis and mitosis is that in meiosis the members of each pair of chromosomes (homologous chromosomes) move together and come to lie side by side in an intimate association (Fig. 13.10). They do not fuse together, but they do often intertwine. This pairing process is known as *synapsis.* Each chromosome being visibly double-stranded by this time, a synaptic pair can be seen to consist of two identical double-stranded chromosomes lying next to each other. Toward the end of prophase, the synaptic pair moves as a unit to the equator of the spindle.

First Metaphase.   In mitosis, the two chromosomes of each different type are completely independent of each other in their movements. They do not synapse, and each individual chromosome moves on its own to a separate fibril of the spindle. Hence, at metaphase of mitosis in our hypothetical organism of Fig. 13.5, each of the six chromosomes occupies a different fibril; similarly, each of the 46 chromosomes in a mitotically dividing human cell occupies a different fibril. But in meiosis, the two chromosomes of each type synapse, as we have seen, and move onto the spindle as a single unit. Hence, at metaphase I of meiosis in our hypothetical organism (Fig. 13.10: 4), only three of the spindle fibrils are occupied, not six. An entire synaptic pair, consisting of two chromosomes and four chromatids, is attached to each of these three fibrils. Now, at the start of metaphase in mitosis, there is only one chromosome on each fibril and thus only one centromere attached to it (before division of the centromere occurs). But at the start of metaphase I in meiosis, there are two chromosomes on each occupied fibril and thus two separate centromeres attached to it.

First Anaphase.   In mitosis, metaphase ends and anaphase begins when the single centromere of each double-stranded chromosome divides and the two separate single-stranded chromosomes thus formed move away from each other toward opposite poles of the spindle. But in the first division sequence of meiosis, two chromosomes with separate centromeres are attached to each occupied fibril from the beginning of metaphase. Hence there is no division of centromeres. The two double-stranded chromosomes of each synaptic pair

Fig. 13.10. Meiosis in an animal cell.

1. EARLY PROPHASE I

Chromosomes become visible as long, well-separated filaments; they do not appear double-stranded although other evidence indicates that replication has already occurred.

2. MIDDLE PROPHASE I

Homologous chromosomes synapse and become shorter and thicker.

3. LATE PROPHASE I

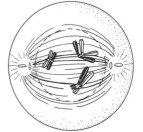

Chromosomes become clearly double-stranded. Nuclear membrane begins to disappear.

4. METAPHASE I

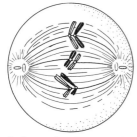

Each synaptic pair moves onto spindle as a unit and attaches to a single fibril at equator.

5. ANAPHASE I

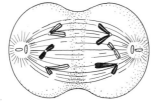

Centromeres do not divide. Double-stranded chromosomes move apart to opposite poles.

6. TELOPHASE I

New haploid nuclei form. Chromosomes are double-stranded when they fade from view.

7. INTERKINESIS

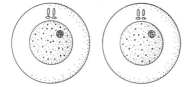

No replication of genetic material occurs

8. PROPHASE II

9. METAPHASE II

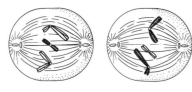

10. ANAPHASE II

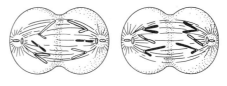

11. TELOPHASE II

12. INTERPHASE

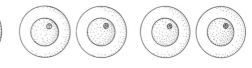

move away from each other toward opposite poles during anaphase. This means that, in our hypothetical organism, only three chromosomes move to each pole (Fig. 13.10: 5), in contrast to the six that move to each pole in mitosis. Notice, however, that because the synaptic pairing was not random but involved the two homologous chromosomes of each type, the two daughter nuclei get not just any three chromosomes but, instead, one of each of the three types.

First Telophase. Telophase of mitosis and meiosis are essentially the same, except that each of the two new nuclei formed in mitosis has the same number of chromosomes as the parental nucleus, whereas each of the new nuclei formed in meiosis has half the chromosomes that were present in the parental nucleus (Fig. 13.10: 6). At the end of telophase of mitosis, the chromosomes are single-stranded when they fade from view; at the end of telophase I of meiosis, the chromosomes are double-stranded when they fade from view.

Interkinesis. Following telophase I of meiosis, there is a short period called interkinesis, which is similar to an interphase between two mitotic division sequences except that no replication of the genetic material occurs and hence no new chromatids are formed (replication is unnecessary, since the chromosomes are already double-stranded when interkinesis begins).

Table 13.1 summarizes the differences between mitosis and the first division sequence of meiosis.

Second Division Sequence of Meiosis. The second division sequence of meiosis, which follows interkinesis, is essentially a mitotic one (Fig. 13.10: 8–11). The chromosomes do not synapse; they cannot, since the nucleus is haploid and there are no homologous chromosomes. Each double-stranded chromosome moves onto the spindle independently, and its centromere attaches to a fibril. At the end of metaphase II, the centromeres divide, and the new single-stranded chromosomes thus formed move away from each other toward opposite

TABLE 13.1

Comparison of Mitosis and First Division Sequence of Meiosis

Phase	Mitosis	Meiosis
Prophase	No synapsis; chromosomes move to spindle individually	Synapsis; chromosomes move to spindle in pairs
Metaphase	Each chromosome attached to separate fibril; centromeres divide	The two chromosomes of each pair attached to the same fibril; centromeres do not divide
Anaphase	Separation of new single-stranded chromosomes derived from one original double-stranded chromosome	Separation of old double-stranded chromosomes of each synaptic pair
Telophase	Formation of two new nuclei, each with same number of chromosomes as parental nucleus; chromosomes are single-stranded when they fade from view	Formation of two new nuclei, each with half the chromosomes present in parental nucleus; chromosomes are double-stranded when they fade from view
Interphase, Interkinesis	Replication of genetic material, with formation of new chromatids	No replication of genetic material and hence no new chromatids

poles of the spindle during anaphase II. The new nuclei formed during telophase II are haploid like the nuclei formed during telophase I, but their chromosomes are single-stranded instead of double-stranded.

In summary, then, the first meiotic division produces two haploid cells containing double-stranded chromosomes. Each of these cells divides in the second meiotic division; thus a total of four new haploid cells containing single-stranded chromosomes are produced.

The Timing of Meiosis in the Life Cycle

Meiosis in the Life Cycle of Animals. Higher animals exist as diploid multicellular organisms through most of their life cycle. At the time of reproduction, meiosis produces haploid gametes, which, when their nuclei unite in fertilization, give rise to the diploid zygote. The zygote then divides mitotically to produce the new diploid multicellular individual. The gametes—sperms and eggs—are thus the only haploid stage in the animal life cycle (see Fig. 13.14C).

In male animals, sperm cells (spermatozoa) are produced by the germinal epithelium lining the seminiferous tubules of the testes (Fig. 13.11). When one of the epithelial cells undergoes meiosis, the four haploid cells that result are all quite small but approximately equal in size (Fig. 13.12). All four soon differentiate into sperm cells with long flagella, but with very little cytoplasm in the head, which consists primarily of the nucleus. This process of sperm production is called *spermatogenesis.*

In female animals, the egg cells are produced within the follicles of the ovaries by a process called *oögenesis.* When a cell in the ovary undergoes meiosis, the haploid cells that result are very unequal in size. The first meiotic division produces one relatively large cell and a tiny one called a first *polar body* (Fig. 13.13). The second meiotic division of the larger of these two cells (secondary oöcyte)

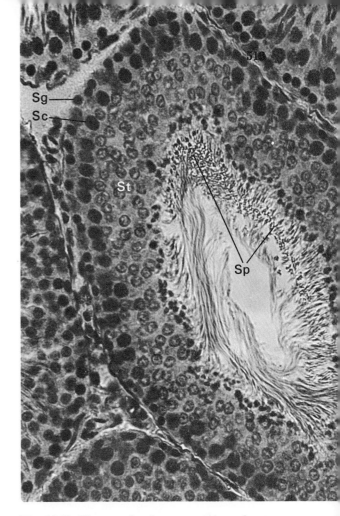

Fig. 13.11. Photograph of cross section of rat seminiferous tubule, showing spermatogenesis. The dark-stained outermost cells in the wall of the tubule are spermatogonia (Sg), which divide mitotically, producing new cells that move inward. These cells enlarge and differentiate into primary spermatocytes (Sc), which divide meiotically to produce secondary spermatocytes and then spermatids (St). The spermatids differentiate into mature sperm cells, or spermatozoa (Sp), whose long flagella can be seen in the lumen of the tubule in this photograph. [Courtesy Thomas Eisner, Cornell University.]

produces a tiny second polar body and a large cell, which soon differentiates into the egg cell (or ovum). The first polar body may or may not go through the second meiotic division. Thus, when a diploid cell in the ovary undergoes complete meiosis, only one mature ovum is produced (Fig. 13.12); the polar bodies are essentially nonfunctional. By contrast, a diploid

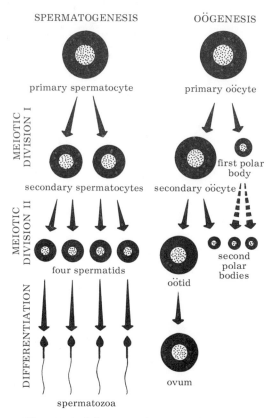

SPERMATOGENESIS   OÖGENESIS

primary spermatocyte   primary oöcyte

MEIOTIC DIVISION I

secondary spermatocytes   first polar body

secondary oöcyte

MEIOTIC DIVISION II

four spermatids   oötid   second polar bodies

DIFFERENTIATION

spermatozoa   ovum

Fig. 13.12. Schematic diagram of spermatogenesis and oögenesis in an animal. The first polar body does not divide in all animals.

cell undergoing complete meiosis in the testis gives rise to four functional sperm cells.

The advantage of the unequal cytokinesis of oögenesis is obvious. By this mechanism, an unusually large supply of cytoplasm and stored food is allotted to the nonmotile ovum for use by the embryo that will develop from it. In fact, the ovum provides almost all the cytoplasm and initial food supply for the embryo. The tiny, highly motile sperm cell contributes, essentially, only its genetic material.

Meiosis in the Life Cycles of Plants. That meiosis produces gametes in animals does not mean that it must do so in all organisms. There is no inherent reason why the cells resulting from meiosis must be specialized for sexual

reproduction. And, indeed, they are not specialized in this way in most plants. Meiosis in plants usually produces haploid reproductive cells called *spores*, and these spores often divide mitotically to develop into haploid multicellular plant bodies. Let us briefly examine the life cycle of a hypothetical plant in which meiosis produces spores rather than gametes (Fig. 13.14B). While this plant is in the diploid portion of its life cycle, certain cells in its reproductive organs divide by meiosis to produce haploid spores (stage 1). These spores divide mitotically and develop into haploid multicellular plants (stage 2). The haploid multicellular plant eventually produces cells specialized as gametes (stage 3). Notice, however, that the gametes of the plant are produced by mitosis, not meiosis, because the cells that divide to produce the gametes are already haploid. Two of these gametes unite to form the diploid zygote (stage 4), which divides mitotically and develops into a diploid multicellular plant (stage 5). In time, this plant produces spores, and the cycle starts over again.

The various groups of plants vary greatly as to the relative importance of the diploid and haploid phases of the life cycle. In some, for

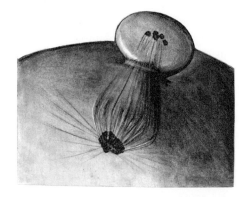

Fig. 13.13. Formation of a tiny first polar body on the surface of the much larger oöcyte of a whitefish. Before meiosis began, the nucleus of the primary oöcyte migrated to the periphery of the cell. The meiotic spindle is oriented at right angles to the surface of the oöcyte.

A PRIMITIVE PLANT

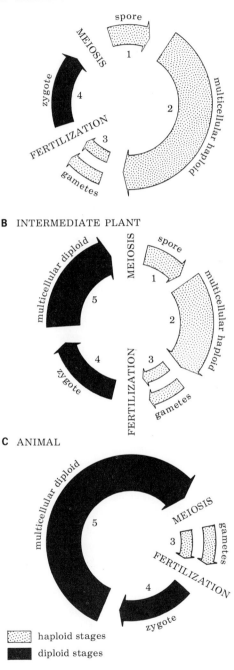

B INTERMEDIATE PLANT

C ANIMAL

haploid stages

diploid stages

Fig. 13.14. Three types of life cycles. (A) In some very primitive plants, the diploid phase is represented only by the zygote, which quickly divides by meiosis to produce haploid spores, which may divide mitotically to produce a multicellular haploid plant. (B) In most multicellular plants, there are two multicellular stages, one haploid and one diploid (stages 2 and 5); the relative importance of these two stages varies greatly from one plant group to another (the cycle shown here is an intermediate one in which stages 2 and 5 are nearly equal). In flowering plants, the multicellular diploid stage (stage 5) is the major one, and the multicellular haploid stage (stage 2) is much reduced, being represented by a tiny organism with very few cells. (C) Animals and a very few plants have a life cycle in which meiosis produces gametes directly, the spore stage (stage 1) and the multicellular haploid stage (stage 2) being absent.

example, the two phases, particularly stages 2 and 5 of Fig. 13.14B, are approximately equal, as shown in this figure. A very few plants have cycles almost like the animal life cycle shown in Fig. 13.14C; i.e. stages 1 and 2 are absent, and the haploid phase of the cycle is represented only by the gametes. In the flowering plants, stages 1 and 2 have not been abandoned altogether, but 2 has been reduced to a tiny three-to-eight–cell stage that is not free-living, and the plant spends most of its life cycle as a multicellular diploid organism (stage 5). At the opposite extreme are some primitive plants whose life cycles are almost completely the reverse of those of animals (Fig. 13.14A). There is no stage 5. The diploid zygote (stage 4) formed by union of gametes promptly undergoes meiosis to produce four haploid spore cells (stage 1), each of which divides mitotically and develops into a haploid multicellular stage (stage 2) in which the organism passes most of its life cycle. This multicellular plant eventually produces by mitosis cells specialized as gametes (stage 3), which unite to form the diploid zygote and start the cycle over again. In such an organism, then, the haploid phase of the cycle (particularly stage 2) is dominant and the only diploid stage—the zygote—is very transitory. The reproductive cycles of the various plant groups will be discussed in more detail in a later chapter.

Examination and comparison of the three life cycles illustrated in Fig. 13.14 allow us to make several important generalizations: (1) Meiosis produces either gametes, specialized for sexual reproduction, or spores, specialized for asexual reproduction; (2) only diploid cells can divide by meiosis, but both haploid and diploid cells can divide by mitosis; (3) if mitosis produces a multicellular organism after fertilization but before meiosis, that organism is diploid; (4) if mitosis produces a multicellular organism after meiosis but before fertilization, that organism is haploid; (5) the haploid phase of the life cycle of multicellular animals is represented only by the gametes (stages 1 and 2 being absent); (6) most multicellular plants include all five stages in their life cycles, but the relative importance of these varies greatly; (7) with some major exceptions, the haploid stages are dominant in the more primitive plants and the diploid stages are dominant in the more advanced plants.

The Adaptive Significance of Sexual Reproduction

Sexual reproduction is so widespread, being characteristic of the vast majority of both plants and animals, that we tend to regard it as a necessary characteristic of life. But it is not. Many plants and animals reproduce asexually, i.e. give rise to new individuals by mitotic cell division. Such reproduction is undeniably simpler than sexual reproduction, where the complicated processes of meiosis and fertilization must alternate with each other. We can legitimately ask, therefore, why asexual reproduction is not adequate for most organisms, why natural selection has so often favored sexual reproduction, with all the complex problems it entails.

We have seen that mitosis produces new cells with a genetic endowment identical to that of the parental cell; each new cell gets a set of chromosomes copied from the parental set. Hence the characteristics of offspring produced by mitosis will be essentially the same as those of the parent. In other words, asexual reproduction does not give rise to genetic variation. Suppose that our hypothetical species of Fig. 13.5 were to reproduce asexually (i.e. by mitosis). Suppose, further, that a certain individual of this species has gray fur and a long tail, and that the gene determining the gray coat color is located on its V-shaped chromosomes while the gene determining the long tail is located on its J-shaped chromosomes. When this individual reproduces asexually, all its offspring will get identical chromosomes; consequently they, too, will have gray fur and long tails. Now, suppose that another individual of this same species has a different form of the gene for coat color on its V-shaped chromosomes and a different form of the gene for tail length on its J-shaped chromosomes, with the result that this individual has black fur and a short tail. If this individual reproduces asexually, all of its offspring will have black fur and short tails like their parent. Each new generation, then, will include some individuals with gray fur and long tails and some with black fur and short tails. But asexual reproduction provides no way to produce new individuals with the gray form of the gene for coat color on their V chromosomes and the short form of the gene for tail length on their J chromosomes, or with the black form of the gene for coat color and the long form of the gene for tail length. Hence none of the new individuals will have the combination of gray fur and short tails or the combination of black fur and long tails. In short, none of the offspring can have genetic combinations different from those of the parent; mitosis provides no way in which the genes of one individual can be recombined with the genes of another individual.

But now let us look at the chromosomes of a diploid individual produced by sexual reproduction. The first cell (zygote) of this individual was formed by the union of two gametes, an egg from one parent and a sperm cell from a second parent. Each of these gametes contributed one chromosome of each type characteristic of the species. Thus, if our hypothetical organism of Fig. 13.5 was produced by sexual reproduction, it received one V chromosome, one J chromosome, and one I chromosome from its father and one V chromosome, one J chromosome, and one I chromosome from its mother. Hence, if one parent had gray fur and a long tail and the other had black fur and a short tail, some of the offspring may well have gray fur and short tails or black fur and long tails. Some of the genes of one parent have been recombined with genes from the other parent to produce progeny with characteristics different from those of either parent. Unlike mitotic asexual reproduction, sexual reproduction with its meiosis and fertilization augments variation in the population by recombining chromosomes and the genes they bear.

If our hypothetical diploid organism received one of each type of chromosome from its mother and one of each type from its father, you may ask whether, when cells of its reproductive tissue undergo meiosis, the chromosomes originally received from the mother are separated as a set from those originally received from the father. In other words, when cells containing all six chromosomes ($V_mV_pJ_mJ_pI_mI_p$, where the subscript m designates maternal chromosomes and the subscript p designates paternal chromosomes) divide by meiosis, do half of the haploid cells thus produced receive a set of maternal chromosomes only ($V_mJ_mI_m$) and the other half a set of paternal chromosomes only ($V_pJ_pI_p$), or are other combinations possible? The answer is that other combinations are not only possible but highly probable. The maternal and paternal chromosomes do not segregate as sets at meiosis. The segregation is random. When the two V chromosomes synapse and move as a pair onto the spindle, pure chance determines which of the two chromosomes comes to lie on which side of the equa-

tor. For example, if the spindle were oriented in the plane of this page, with one pole toward the left of the page and the other pole toward the right, it is a matter of chance whether the pair of V chromosomes would come to lie on the spindle with the maternal one on the left ($>$m $>$p) or with the paternal one on the left ($>$p $>$m). Similarly, it is purely a matter of chance whether the maternal or paternal J chromosome would come to lie on the left side of the equator when the synapsed J chromosomes move onto the spindle. The same is true of the I chromosomes. Since during anaphase I of meiosis the chromosomes lying on the left side of the equator will move to the left pole and the chromosomes lying on the right side of the equator will move to the right pole, it follows logically that it is purely a matter of chance which V, which J, and which I will move together to the left pole and be incorporated in one new haploid nucleus and which will move together to the right pole and be incorporated in the other new haploid nucleus. Thus all of the following combinations are equally probable:

$$V_pJ_pI_p \qquad V_pJ_mI_m$$
$$V_pJ_pI_m \qquad V_mJ_pI_m$$
$$V_pJ_mI_p \qquad V_mJ_mI_p$$
$$V_mJ_pI_p \qquad V_mJ_mI_m$$

That is, cells with any of the eight chromosomal combinations listed above can be produced by meiosis from a parental cell with the chromosomal makeup $V_mV_pJ_mJ_pI_mI_p$. A parental cell that contained four different kinds of chromosomes instead of three could produce even more combinations. And the number of possible chromosomal combinations obtainable by meiosis from a human cell with 23 different kinds of chromosomes is huge. The number of such possible chromosomal combinations for any given organism is equal to 2^n, where n is the number of types of chromosomes involved, i.e. the haploid number (3 in our hypothetical organism and 23 in a human). The number of possible chromosomal combination in the diploid zygote formed by union of gametes from two different parents is equal to $(2^n)^2$, where n is the haploid number. Thus a mating between two of our hypothetical organisms could potentially produce diploid offspring with 64 possible chromosomal combinations. (We leave it to you to calculate this number for human beings.)

We began by asking why natural selection has favored the more complicated process of sexual reproduction over the simpler one of asexual reproduction in such a wide variety of organisms. We then proceeded to show that sexual reproduction, by contrast with asexual reproduction, makes possible genetic recombination and thus increases the variation among individuals in the population. The question now becomes: Is such variation advantageous to the species? And the answer is clearly yes. Without genetic variation, there could be no evolution. Genetic variation is the evolutionary raw material upon which natural selection acts. If a species had no genetic variation, and thus could not evolve, it would soon be doomed to extinction. The environmental forces impinging upon any species are constantly changing, and the survival of the species depends, ultimately, on its ability to respond to those forces with evolutionary changes that maintain or increase its fitness. Sexual reproduction is one important factor in providing the raw material for such changes.

REFERENCES

Austin, C. R., 1965. *Fertilization*. Prentice-Hall, Englewood Cliffs, N.J.

DeRobertis, E. D. P., W. W. Nowinski, and F. A. Saez, 1965. *Cell Biology*, 4th ed. (title of earlier editions was *General Cytology*). Saunders, Philadelphia. (See esp. Chapter 14.)

SUGGESTED READING

Mazia, D., 1953. "Cell Division," *Scientific American*, August. (Offprint 27.)

———, 1961. "How Cells Divide," *Scientific American*, September. (Offprint 93.)

Swanson, C. P., 1964. *The Cell*, 2nd ed. Prentice-Hall, Englewood Cliffs, N.J. (See esp. Chapters 5–6.)

CHAPTER
14

PATTERNS OF INHERITANCE

So far we have offered no evidence for our oft-repeated assertion that there are units called genes located on the chromosomes in the nucleus, and that these units are passed on from generation to generation and exert control over the characteristics of the organisms. The experiments we cited demonstrating the importance of the nucleus in heredity and in normal cell function could be explained adequately without reference to such structures as chromosomes or genes. It is time, then, for us to examine the basis for the modern concepts of chromosomal inheritance.

MONOHYBRID INHERITANCE

Experiments by Mendel

We shall begin our examination of the chromosomal theory of inheritance by considering a series of experiments performed on ordinary garden peas during the years 1856 to 1868 by a modest Austrian monk named Gregor Mendel. Mendel gave an oral report on the results of these experiments in 1865 and published the same material in 1866.

Mendel's Results. Of the numerous characteristics of garden peas that Mendel studied, seven were particularly interesting to him. He noticed that each of these seven characteristics occurred in two contrasting forms (Table 14.1). Thus the seeds were either round or wrinkled, the flowers were either red or white, the pods were either green or yellow, etc. When Mendel cross-pollinated plants with contrasting forms of one of these characteristics, all the offspring were alike and resembled one of the two parents. When these offspring were crossed among themselves, however, some of their offspring showed one of the original contrasting traits and some showed the other. In other words, a trait that had been present in the grandparental generation but not in the parental generation reappeared.

Let us examine more closely some of Mendel's crosses. When plants having red flowers were crossed with plants having white flowers, all the offspring—the F_1 generation[1]—had red flowers (Fig. 14.1). Similarly, when plants having round seeds were crossed with plants having wrinkled seeds, all the offspring had round seeds. Apparently, one form of each characteristic had taken precedence over the other; i.e. red color had taken precedence over white in the case of flowers, and round form had taken precedence over wrinkled in the case of seeds. Mendel termed the traits that appear in the F_1 offspring of such crosses (in these examples, red flowers or round seeds) *dominant characters,* and the traits that become latent in such crosses (in these examples, white flowers or wrinkled seeds) *recessive characters.*

[1] The parental generation in such a cross is customarily designated as the P generation. The offspring are designated as the F_1 generation (meaning first filial generation), and the offspring of the F_1 generation are designated as the F_2 generation (meaning second filial generation). Mendel did not use these designations, but we shall use them throughout our discussion of his experiments.

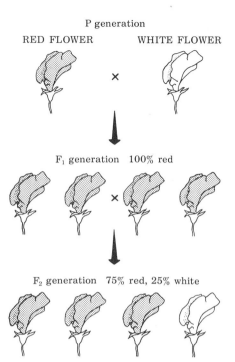

P generation

RED FLOWER   WHITE FLOWER

F_1 generation   100% red

F_2 generation   75% red, 25% white

Fig. 14.1. Results of Mendel's cross of red-flowered and white-flowered peas.

When Mendel allowed the F_1 peas from the cross involving flower color, all of which were red, to breed freely among themselves, their offspring (the F_2 generation) were of two types; there were 705 plants with red flowers and 224 plants with white flowers. The recessive character had reappeared in approximately one fourth of the F_2 plants. Similarly, when F_1 peas from the cross involving seed form, all of which had round seeds, were allowed to breed freely among themselves, their F_2 offspring were of two types; 5,474 had round seeds and 1,850 had wrinkled seeds. Again, the recessive character had reappeared in approximately one fourth of the F_2 plants. The same thing was true of crosses involving the other five characters that Mendel studied (Table 14.1); in each case, the recessive character disappeared in the F_1 generation but reappeared in approximately one fourth of the plants in the F_2 generation. We can summarize

TABLE 14.1

TABLE 14.1

Mendel's Results from Crosses Involving Single Character Differences

P characters	F_1	F_2	F_2 ratio
1. Round × wrinkled seeds	All round	5,474 round : 1,850 wrinkled	2.96 : 1
2. Yellow × green seeds	All yellow	6,022 yellow : 2,001 green	3.01 : 1
3. Red × white flowers	All red	705 red : 224 white	3.15 : 1
4. Inflated × constricted pods	All inflated	882 inflated : 299 constricted	2.95 : 1
5. Green × yellow pods	All green	428 green : 152 yellow	2.82 : 1
6. Axial × terminal flowers	All axial	651 axial : 207 terminal	3.14 : 1
7. Long × short stems	All long	787 long : 277 short	2.84 : 1

the results of the experiment involving flower color as follows:

$$P \qquad \text{red} \times \text{white}$$
$$\downarrow$$
$$F_1 \qquad \text{all red}$$
$$\downarrow$$
$$F_2 \qquad \text{¾ red} \quad \text{¼ white}$$

Mendel's Conclusions. From experiments of this type, Mendel drew the important conclusion that each pea plant possesses two hereditary factors for each character, and that when gametes are formed the two factors separate or segregate and pass into separate gametes, so that each gamete possesses only one factor for each character. Each new plant thus receives one factor for each character from its male parent and one for each character from its female parent. The fact that two contrasting parental traits, such as red and white flowers, can both appear in normal form in the F_2 offspring indicates that the hereditary factors must exist as separate particulate entities in the cell; they do not blend or fuse with each other. Thus the cells of an F_1 pea plant from the cross involving flower color contain, according to Mendel, one factor for red color and

one factor for white color, the factor for red being dominant and the factor for white being recessive. But their existence together in the same nucleus does not change the factors; the red and white factors do not alter each other. They remain distinct, and segregate unchanged when germ cells are formed.

You will have noticed that Mendel's conclusions are consistent with what we know about the chromosomes and their behavior in meiosis. The diploid nucleus contains two of each type of chromosome. Presumably each of the two chromosomes of any given pair bears genes for the same characters; hence the diploid cell contains two doses, which may or may not be identical, of each type of gene; these are the two hereditary factors for each character that Mendel described.[2] Since the members of each pair of chromosomes segregate during meiosis, gametes contain only one chromosome of each type and hence only one dose of each gene, just as Mendel deduced. In short,

[2] It will be necessary to consider other definitions of gene in the next chapter. For the moment, however, we can define a gene (Mendel's "factor") as a hereditary unit, located at a specific place or locus on a chromosome, that determines a particular character of the organism.

Mendel's theories seem rather obvious to us in view of our knowledge of the events of cell division. But we should remember that Mendel did his work before the details of cell division had been learned, before, in fact, the significance of chromosomes for heredity had been discovered. He arrived at his conclusions purely by reasoning from the patterns of inheritance he saw in his experiments, without any reference to the structural components of the cell or its nucleus. The chromosomal theory of inheritance, therefore, rests today on two independent lines of evidence, that from breeding experiments and that from microscopic examination of the nucleus. That these two lines of evidence should agree amazingly well is testimony to the strength of the theory.

The particulate theory of heredity is very different from the view, prevalent in Mendel's day, that each character of the offspring is a blend of the characters of the parents, a view that many people still hold today and express when, for example, they speak of the mixing of blood. We now know, of course, that the blood is not the hereditary material and that expressions like "related by blood" have little biological meaning. The blood of an individual is not simply a half-and-half mixture of his parents' blood or a mixture of four equal parts from his grandparents or of eight equal parts from his great-grandparents. His blood is distinctively his own, and its characteristics are determined by the particular hereditary factors for blood that he happens to have received from his ancestors—which ancestors is a question of chance.

We should not give you the impression that the publication of Mendel's classic paper in 1866 immediately changed the prevalent ideas about inheritance and gave birth to a flourishing new branch of biology. It did not. Apparently the scientific community of his day was unprepared for so radical a view of heredity, and it paid little heed to Mendel's results or theories. His paper was soon forgotten. It was not until 1900, after the details of cell

division had been worked out and the scientific community was in a more receptive mood, that Mendel's paper was rediscovered almost simultaneously by three different men, each of whom had independently performed experiments that led to the same conclusions as Mendel had reached 34 years before. These men were Hugo De Vries in Holland, Carl Correns in Germany, and Erich von Tschermak-Seysenegg in Austria.

A Modern Interpretation of Mendel's Experiments. Let us now re-examine Mendel's cross of garden peas of different colors, interpreting his results in modern terminology. Mendel was working with two different forms of the gene for flower color, one form that produced red flowers and another that produced white flowers. When a gene exists in more than one form, in this way, the different forms are called *alleles.* In the gene for flower color in peas, the allele for red is dominant while the allele for white is recessive. It is customary to designate genes by letters, using capital letters for dominant alleles and small letters for recessive alleles. We may thus designate the allele for red flowers in peas as C and the allele for white flowers as c. Now, a diploid cell contains two doses of each gene, one on each of two homologous chromosomes. Such a cell may thus have two doses of the same allele or one dose of one allele and one dose of another allele. Thus cells of a pea plant may contain two doses of the allele for red flowers (CC), or two doses of the allele for white flowers (cc), or one dose of the allele for red and one dose of the allele for white (Cc). Cells with two doses of the same allele $(CC$ or $cc)$ are said to be *homozygous.* Those with one each of two different alleles (Cc) are said to be *heterozygous.*

Note that one cannot tell by visual inspection whether a given pea plant is homozygous dominant (CC) or heterozygous (Cc), because the two types of plants will look alike; both will have red flowers. In other words, where one allele is dominant over another, the dominant allele takes full precedence over the recessive allele, and a heterozygous organism exhibits the trait determined by that dominant allele; one dose of the dominant allele is as effective as two doses in determining the character trait. This means that there is often no one-to-one correspondence between the different possible genic combinations (*genotypes*) and the possible appearances (*phenotypes*) of the organisms. Thus, in the example of flower color in peas discussed here, there are three possible genotypes, *CC, Cc,* and *cc,* but only two possible phenotypes, red and white.

We can now apply this understanding of genes to Mendel's pea cross and rewrite the summary of p. 521 as follows:

$$
\begin{array}{ccc}
\text{P} & CC & \times & cc \\
 & \text{red} & & \text{white} \\
 & & \downarrow & \\
\text{F}_1 & Cc & \times & Cc \\
 & \text{red} & & \text{red} \\
 & & \downarrow & \\
\text{F}_2 & CC \quad Cc \quad cC \quad cc \\
 & \text{red} \quad \text{red} \quad \text{red} \quad \text{white}
\end{array}
$$

Here we have shown both the genotypes and the phenotypes of the plants in the three generations. Mendel began with a cross in the parental generation between a plant with a homozygous dominant genotype (red phenotype) and a plant with a homozygous recessive genotype (white phenotype). All of the F_1 progeny had red phenotypes, because all of them were heterozygous, having received a dominant allele for red (C) from the homozygous dominant parent and a recessive allele for white (c) from the homozygous recessive parent. But when the F_1 individuals were allowed to cross freely among themselves, the F_2 progeny they produced were of three genotypes and two phenotypes; one fourth were homozygous dominant and showed red phenotypes, two fourths were heterozygous and showed red phenotypes, and one fourth were homozygous recessive and showed white pheno-

types. Thus the ratio of genotypes in the F_2 was $1:2:1$, and the ratio of the phenotypes was $3:1$.

How do we figure out the possible genotypic combinations in the F_2? This is an easy matter in a monohybrid cross (a cross involving only one character) such as this. All individuals in the F_1 generation are heterozygous (Cc); i.e. they have one of each of the two types of alleles. Each of these two alleles is located on a different one of the two chromosomes of a homologous pair. In meiosis, these two chromosomes synapse, move onto the spindle as a unit, and then separate, moving to opposite poles, so that the chromosome bearing the C allele is incorporated into one new haploid nucleus and the chromosome bearing the c allele is incorporated into the other new haploid nucleus. This means that half the gametes produced by such a heterozygous individual will contain the C allele and half will contain the c allele. When two such individuals are crossed (Fig. 14.2), there are four possible combinations of their gametes:

C from male parent, C from female parent
C from male parent, c from female parent
c from male parent, C from female parent
c from male parent, c from female parent

The first of these four possible combinations produces homozygous dominant offspring (red). The second and third possible combinations produce heterozygous offspring (also red). And the fourth possible combination produces homozygous recessive offspring (white). Since each of these four combinations is equally probable, we would expect, if a large number of F_2 progeny are produced, a genotypic ratio close to $1:2:1$ and a phenotypic ratio close to $3:1$, just as Mendel found.

An easy way to figure out the possible genotypes produced in the F_2 is to construct a so-called Punnett square. To do this, write along a horizontal line all the possible kinds of gametes the male parent can produce; in a vertical column to the left, write all the pos-

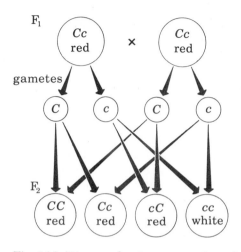

Fig. 14.2. Diagram showing gametes formed by F₁ individuals in Mendel's cross for flower color, and their possible combinations in the F₂.

A glance at this completed Punnett square shows that it yields the expected 1 : 2 : 1 genotypic ratio and, since dominance is present, the expected 3 : 1 phenotypic ratio. (See Fig. 14.3.)

Extensive investigation of a vast array of plant and animal species by thousands of scientists has demonstrated conclusively that the results Mendel obtained from his monohybrid crosses, and the interpretations he placed upon them, are not limited to garden peas but are of general validity. Whenever a monohybrid cross is made between two contrasting homozygous individuals, regardless of the character involved, the expected genotypic ratio in the F₂ is 1 : 2 : 1. And whenever dominance is involved, the expected phenotypic ratio is 3 : 1. If these ratios are not obtained in large samples, it can be assumed that some complicating condition is present, which must be discovered.

The Test Cross

We have seen that in a monohybrid cross involving dominance the homozygous dominant progeny and the heterozygous progeny have the same phenotype and cannot be distinguished by inspection. But it is often of prac-

sible kinds of gametes the female parent can produce; then construct squares for each possible combination of these, as follows:

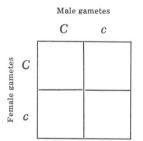

Next, write in each box first the symbol for the female gamete and then the symbol for the male gamete. Each box will then contain the symbols for the genotype of one possible zygote combination from the cross in question, as follows:

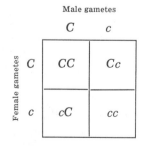

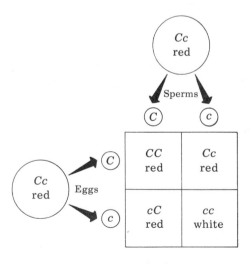

Fig. 14.3. Punnett-square representation of the same information as shown in Fig. 14.2.

tical importance to distinguish between individuals with these two different genotypes—in breeding, for example. Homozygous individuals breed true; i.e. matings between two such individuals produce offspring all of a single genotype and phenotype like their parents. But heterozygous individuals do not breed true; as we have seen, a cross between two such individuals may produce offspring of three different genotypes and two different phenotypes. Consequently the identification of homozygous individuals is of the utmost importance to an animal or plant breeder who is trying to establish true-breeding strains of animals or plants. This is no problem when the breeder is interested in a recessive character, because homozygous recessive organisms can readily be recognized by their phenotype. But if the breeder is interested in establishing a strain that is true-breeding for a dominant character, he needs a test that will enable him to tell whether a given individual is homozygous dominant or heterozygous.

The test used for this purpose is a cross between the individual of unknown genotype and a homozygous recessive individual, which can be recognized by its phenotype. Suppose, for example, we want to know whether a particular red-flowered pea plant has a genotype of CC or Cc. The most we can say from simple inspection is that it is red and hence must have at least one C allele; we write what we know about its genotype as $C-$; in other words, half of its genotype for this character is known and half is unknown and is designated by a dash. We now cross this plant with a white-flowering plant, which can only have the genotype cc. The results should give us the information we seek. If the plant in question has CC as its genotype, Cc, then the cross will turn out as follows:

$$CC \quad \times \quad cc$$
$$\text{red} \qquad \text{white}$$
$$\downarrow$$
$$Cc \quad Cc \quad Cc \quad Cc$$
$$\text{red} \quad \text{red} \quad \text{red} \quad \text{red}$$

If, however, the plant has the other possible genotype, Cc, then the cross will turn out as follows:

$$Cc \quad \times \quad cc$$
$$\text{red} \qquad \text{white}$$
$$\downarrow$$
$$Cc \quad Cc \quad cc \quad cc$$
$$\text{red} \quad \text{red} \quad \text{white} \quad \text{white}$$

In other words, the unknown half of the test plant's genotype may be either a C allele or a c allele. If it is a C allele, then the full genotype of the plant is CC and such a plant, when test-crossed with a homozygous recessive (cc) plant, will produce progeny all of which are heterozygous (Cc) and show a red phenotype (Fig. 14.4, top). If, on the other hand, the unknown is a c allele, then the full genotype of the plant is Cc and such a plant, when test-crossed with a homozygous recessive plant, will produce progeny half of which are heterozygous and show a red phenotype and half of which are homozygous recessive and show a white phenotype (Fig. 14.4, bottom). In practice, we make the cross $C- \times cc$ and observe the results. If we obtain a large number of progeny from this cross and all of them show the dominant phenotype (in this case, red flowers), the chances are great that the test plant's genotype is CC. If, however, we obtain progeny some of which show the dominant phenotype (red) and some of which show the recessive phenotype (white), we know that the test plant's genotype is Cc. We expect a 1 : 1 ratio in this case, but if our results happened to depart considerably from this expected ratio, we should still feel certain that the test plant's genotype is Cc. The reasons are obvious: If any of the progeny show the recessive phenotype, their genotype must be cc, which means that they received a c allele from each parent; hence the test plant must have a c allele in its genotype. Since we already know that it has at least one C allele, we combine these two pieces of information to write its genotype as Cc.

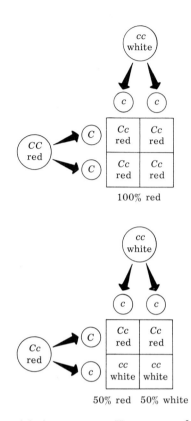

Fig. 14.4. A test cross. Homozygous dominant (CC) and heterozygous (Cc) red-flowered individuals are to be distinguished by crossing them with a homozygous recessive (cc) white-flowered individual. Top: If the red-flowered plant is homozygous, all the progeny of the test cross will be heterozygous (Cc) and will have red flowers. Bottom: If the red-flowered plant is heterozygous, 50 percent of the progeny will be heterozygous (Cc) and will have red flowers, and 50 percent will be homozygous recessive (cc) and will have white flowers.

Intermediate Inheritance

The seven characters of peas that Mendel used in the experiments reported in his paper were all of the kind in which one allele shows complete dominance over the other. Many characteristics in a variety of organisms show this mode of inheritance. But many others do not. In fact, there is evidence that Mendel himself studied some characters that do not exhibit

dominance, even though he did not take them into account in establishing his theory. Inheritance in which heterozygous individuals clearly show effects of both alleles is termed intermediate inheritance.

In some cases of intermediate inheritance, heterozygous individuals have a phenotype that is actually intermediate between the phenotype of individuals homozygous for one allele and the phenotype of individuals homozygous for the other allele. For example, crosses between homozygous red snapdragons and homozygous white snapdragons yield pink snapdragons. When these pink plants are crossed among themselves (Fig. 14.5), they yield red, pink, and white offspring in a ratio of $1 : 2 : 1$, as follows:

P		RR	$\times$	$R'R'$	
		red		white	
			$\downarrow$		
F_1		RR'	$\times$	RR'	
		pink		pink	
			$\downarrow$		
F_2	RR	RR'		$R'R$	$R'R'$
	red	pink		pink	white

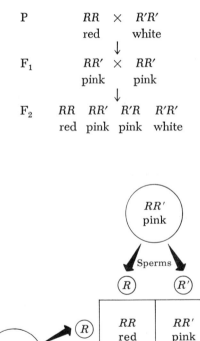

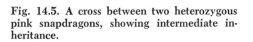

Fig. 14.5. A cross between two heterozygous pink snapdragons, showing intermediate inheritance.

Notice that when dominance is lacking both alleles are designated by a capital letter, the one being distinguished from the other by a prime, as here, or by a superscript; thus C^r might designate an allele for red color and C^w an allele for white.

In other cases of intermediate inheritance, the heterozygous phenotype is not so obviously intermediate between the two homozygous phenotypes, but is distinctively different from both of them. For example, in a certain strain of chickens, a mating between a black chicken and a splashed white chicken produces offspring all of which have a distinctive appearance called blue Andalusian. A cross between two blue Andalusians produces black, blue Andalusian, and splashed white offspring in a ratio of $1:2:1$, as follows:

P	black $\times$ white
	$\downarrow$
F_1	blue $\times$ blue
	$\downarrow$
F_2	black blue blue white

This is obviously a situation in which the two alleles, one for black and one for white, are interacting to produce a phenotype somewhat different from the gray that might be expected as the intermediate between black and white.

To summarize, the inheritance pattern of a system involving incomplete dominance differs in the following ways from that of a system involving complete dominance: (1) The F_1 offspring of a monohybrid cross between parents each of which is homogygous for a different allele have a phenotype different from both parents, and (2) the F_2 phenotypic ratio is $1:2:1$ (just like the genotypic ratio) rather than $3:1$.

DIHYBRID AND TRIHYBRID INHERITANCE

We have limited our discussion so far to crosses involving a single phenotypic character. Or, rather, we have so far chosen to ignore all but one character. The latter is a more accurate statement because all crosses involve many more than one character. Organisms contain thousands of genes, and it would be impossible to set up a cross in which only one character was allowed to vary. Let us now turn to crosses involving two (dihybrid), three (trihybrid), or more characters.

The Basic Dihybrid Ratio

Mendel did not limit his experiments on garden peas to ones in which single characters were involved. He performed a series of experiments involving two or more of the characters listed in Table 14.1. For example, he crossed plants having round yellow seeds with plants having wrinkled green seeds. The F_1 plants all had round yellow seeds. When these plants were crossed among themselves, the resulting F_2 progeny showed four different phenotypes:

315 had round yellow seeds
101 had wrinkled yellow seeds
108 had round green seeds
32 had wrinkled green seeds

In other words, the four different phenotypes occurred in a ratio of approximately $9:3:3:1$.

This experiment demonstrated that a dihybrid cross can produce some new plants that are phenotypically unlike either of the original parental plants; in this particular case, the new phenotypes were wrinkled yellow and round green. In other words, the genes for seed color and the genes for seed form do not necessarily stay together in the combinations in which they occurred in the parental generation. This means that the genes for seed color are on the chromosomes of one homologous pair and the genes for seed form are on the chromosomes of a different pair and, consequently, that the genes for the two characters segregate independently during meiosis.

The $9:3:3:1$ phenotypic ratio is characteristic of the F_2 generation of a dihybrid cross (with dominance) in which the genes for the two characters are *independent* (i.e. are located on nonhomologous chromosomes). Each independent gene behaves in a dihybrid cross in exactly the same way as in a monohybrid cross. If we examine Mendel's F_2 results given above, and think of the experiment as a monohybrid cross for seed color (ignoring seed form), we find that there were 416 yellow seeds (315 + 101) and 140 green seeds (108 + 32), which closely approximates the 3 : 1 F_2 ratio expected in a monohybrid cross. Similarly, if we treat the experiment as a monohybrid cross for seed form and ignore seed color, the F_2 results also show approximately a 3 : 1 phenotypic ratio. The dihybrid F_2 ratio of 9 : 3 : 3 : 1 is thus simply the product of two separate and independent 3 : 1 ratios.

Let us examine briefly the details of a cross of this type, using the symbols R for the allele for round seed and r for the allele for wrinkled seed, and the symbols G for the allele for yellow seed and g for the allele for green seed. In the summary of Mendel's cross below, the dash means that it does not matter phenotypically whether the dominant or the recessive allele occurs in the spot indicated.

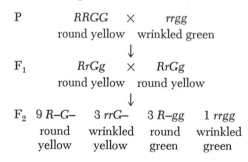

The round yellow parent could produce gametes of only one genotype, RG. The wrinkled green parent could produce only rg gametes. When RG gametes from the one parent united with rg gametes from the other parent in the process of fertilization, all the resulting F_1 offspring were heterozygous for both characters ($RrGg$) and showed the phenotype of the dominant parent (round yellow). Each of these

F_1 individuals could produce four different types of gametes, RG, Rg, rG, and rg (Fig. 14.6). When two such individuals were crossed, there were 16 possible combinations of gametes (4 × 4), as shown in the figure. These 16 combinations included nine different genotypes ($RRGG$, $RRGg$, $RRgg$, $RrGG$, $RrGg$, $Rrgg$, $rrGG$, $rrGg$, $rrgg$), which determined four different phenotypes in the ratio of 9 : 3 : 3 : 1. What would the phenotypic ratio have been if both characters had exhibited intermediate inheritance rather than dominance-recessiveness? What would have been the ratio if one character had exhibited dominance-recessiveness and the other character had exhibited intermediate inheritance?

One way to calculate the genotypic and phenotypic ratios in a dihybrid cross is to construct a Punnett square and then determine the number of boxes representing each genotype and phenotype. This method, a satisfactory one in a monohybrid cross, is not too tedious in a dihybrid cross, but it is prohibitively so in a trihybrid cross or a cross involving even more than three characters. There is an alternative procedure that is much easier. It is based on the principle that *the chance that a number of independent events will occur together is equal to the product of the chances that each event will occur separately.* Suppose we had wanted to know how many of the 16 combinations in Mendel's cross would produce the wrinkled yellow phenotype. We know that wrinkled is recessive; hence it would be expected in $\frac{1}{4}$ of the F_2 individuals in a monohybrid cross. We know that yellow is dominant; hence it would be expected in $\frac{3}{4}$ of the F_2 individuals. Multiplying these two separate values ($\frac{1}{4} \times \frac{3}{4}$) gives us $\frac{3}{16}$; three of the 16 possible combinations will produce a wrinkled yellow phenotype. Similarly, if we had wanted to know how many of the combinations would produce a round yellow phenotype, we could have multiplied the separate expectancies for two dominant characters ($\frac{3}{4} \times \frac{3}{4}$) to get $\frac{9}{16}$. Or, to use a more complex example, suppose we had

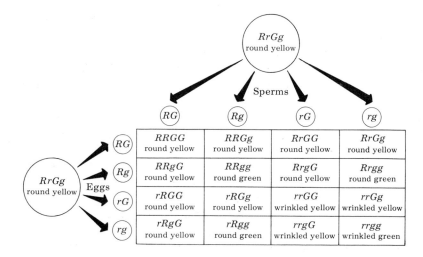

Fig. 14.6. Punnett-square representation of a mating of two F_1 individuals in one of Mendel's dihybrid crosses in peas.

performed a trihybrid cross involving the two seed characters and flower color, and we wanted to know what fraction of the F_2 individuals (produced by allowing $CcRrGg$ individuals to cross among themselves) would exhibit a phenotype combining red flowers, wrinkled seeds, and yellow seeds. The separate probability for red flowers in a monohybrid cross is ¾, that for wrinkled seeds is ¼, and that for yellow seeds is ¾. Multiplying these three values (¾ × ¼ × ¾) gives us ⁹⁄₆₄. This tells us that of the 64 possible combinations in a trihybrid cross, nine would produce the phenotype here specified. How many would produce a phenotype combining white flowers, round seeds, and green seeds?

Gene Interactions

Some dihybrid crosses involve two genes that are inherited independently but that exert their phenotypic effect on the same character. When two or more different genes interact with each other in determining a single character, the ratios obtained from crosses in which they are involved are sometimes different from the basic ratio. Let us look at examples of a few types of gene interaction.

Complementary Genes. Complementary genes are genes that are mutually dependent; neither can exert its phenotypic effect unless the other does also. For example, purple color in the flowers of sweet peas occurs only when both the dominant allele for a gene C and the dominant allele for another gene P are present together. In the absence of either dominant allele, the flowers are white. A dihybrid cross involving these characters can be summarized as follows:

P		$CCPP$ × $ccpp$	
		purple white	
		↓	
F_1		$CcPp$ × $CcPp$	
		purple purple	
		↓	
F_2	9 C–P–	3 C–pp 3 ccP–	1 $ccpp$
	purple	white white	white

Note that the four groups of genotypes shown in the F_2 are the ones that in a normal dihybrid cross would produce four different phenotypes in a ratio of $9:3:3:1$. But here they have produced only two phenotypes in a ratio of $9:7$, which is quite different from any ratio we have previously encountered. The last three phenotypic classes of the normal $9:3:3:1$ ratio have been combined.

In sweet peas, this curious gene interaction, where neither dominant allele can exert its effect unless the other dominant is also present, has been experimentally explained. C regulates the production of a necessary raw material for the anthocyanin pigment, and P regulates the conversion of this raw material into anthocyanin. It is not enough for the plant to have a C allele and make the raw material if it has no P and hence cannot convert the raw material into purple pigment. Conversely, it is not enough for the plant to have a P allele if it has no C and hence produces no raw material. In either case, the flower is white because no anthocyanin can be synthesized.

Epistasis. When one gene has the effect of masking the phenotypic expression of another gene, the first gene is said to be epistatic to the second. For example, in guinea pigs the gene for production of melanin is epistatic to that for deposition of melanin. The first gene has two alleles: C, which causes the pigment to be produced, and c, which causes no pigment to be produced; hence a homozygous recessive individual, cc, is an albino. The second gene has an allele B that causes deposition of much melanin, giving the guinea pig a black coat, and an allele b that causes deposition of only a moderate amount of melanin, giving the guinea pig a brown coat. Neither B nor b can cause deposition of melanin if C is not present to make the melanin. We can summarize a cross involving these two genes as follows:

Instead of an F_2 phenotypic ratio of $9:3:3:1$, this cross has yielded a ratio of $9:3:4$. The last two phenotypic classes of the normal $9:3:3:1$ ratio have been combined.

It is important to distinguish epistasis from dominance, which it superficially resembles. Dominance is the phenotypic expression of one member of a pair of alleles at the expense of the other. Epistasis is the masking by one gene of the phenotypic effect of another entirely different gene. Dominance refers to interaction between alleles, epistasis to interaction between nonallelic genes.

Collaboration. Sometimes two different genes influencing the same character interact to produce single-character phenotypes that neither gene alone could produce. One example of such collaborative interaction is the control of the form of the comb in chickens (Fig. 14.7). One gene, R, produces rose comb, while its recessive allele, r, produces single comb. Another gene, P, produces pea comb, while its recessive allele, p, also produces single comb.

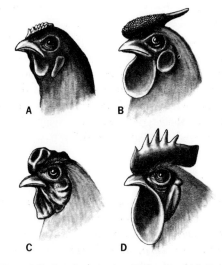

Fig. 14.7. Comb types in chickens. (A) Pea comb. (B) Rose comb. (C) Walnut comb. (D) Single comb. For a discussion of the genetics of this character, see text. [Redrawn from E. J. Gardner, *Principles of Genetics*, Wiley, 1960.]

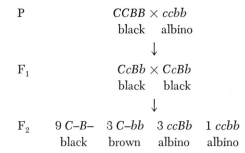

P	$CCBB \times ccbb$
	black albino
	↓
F_1	$CcBb \times CcBb$
	black black
	↓
F_2	9 C–B– 3 C–bb 3 $ccBb$ 1 $ccbb$
	black brown albino albino

When *R* and *P* occur together, they collaborate to produce walnut comb, a type of comb that neither could produce alone. Rose comb is characteristic of Wyandotte chickens, and pea comb is characteristic of Brahma chickens. A cross between a Wyandotte and a Brahma could be summarized as follows:

P   *RRpp* × *rrPP*
                  rose   pea
                        ↓

F_1 *RrPp* × *RrPp*
             walnut   walnut
                        ↓

F_2 9 *R–P–*   3 *R–pp*   3 *rrP–*   1 *rrpp*
       walnut   rose   pea   single

Modifier Genes. Probably no inherited characteristic is controlled exclusively by one gene pair. Even when only one principal gene is involved, its expression is influenced to some extent by countless other genes with individual effects that are often so slight that they are very difficult to locate and analyze. An example is eye color in human beings. Human eye color is generally regarded as controlled by one gene with two alleles, *B* for brown eyes and *b* for blue eyes. Since *B* is dominant over *b*, the genotypes *BB* and *Bb* both produce brown eyes and the genotype *bb* produces blue eyes. Blue-eyed people lack melanin pigment in the front layer of their irises; the blue is an effect of the black pigment on the back of the iris as it is faintly seen through the semi-opaque front layer of the iris. Brown-eyed people have branching pigment cells containing melanin in the front layer of their irises; these give the iris a brown color.

A description of the inheritance of eye color on the basis of a single-gene system assumes only two phenotypes, brown and blue. And it is, in fact, possible to assign most people to one or the other of these two phenotypic classes. But it is common knowledge that eyes occur in many shades of brown and many shades of blue. Indeed they exhibit a huge number of variations in hue, some of which are recognized in everyday terminology; we describe eyes as gray (genetically a form of blue) or black (genetically a form of brown). It is obvious, then, that an explanation of eye color in terms of a single-gene system is an oversimplification. Many modifier genes are also involved. Some affect the amount of pigment in the iris. Some affect the tone of the pigment (which may be light yellow, dark brown, etc.). Some affect the distribution of the pigment (even throughout the iris, or in scattered spots, or in a ring around the outer edge of the iris, etc.). Our understanding of the genetics of eye color is still very limited, and more research is needed.

Another good example of the action of modifier genes is seen in the size of the spots of Beagle dogs (Fig. 14.8). A very large number

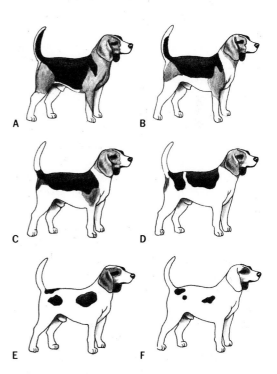

Fig. 14.8. Variation in spotting of Beagle dogs as a result of the action of many modifier genes.

of different modifier genes are involved. No one of these produces very marked effects, but in combination they can radically alter the dogs' appearance.

Multiple Gene Inheritance. The phenotypic characteristics we have discussed so far vary in a discontinuous fashion; i.e. a limited number of relatively distinct phenotypes can be recognized. Pea flowers are either red or white, pea seeds either yellow or green, chicken combs either walnut or rose or pea or single. True, modifiers may blur the boundaries of the classes, as in human eye color or spotting in dogs, but a fairly limited number of phenotypes—blue versus brown or spotted versus unspotted—can still be meaningfully discussed. Many characters, however, vary in a more continuous fashion; human height, human skin pigmentation, corn ear length, are just three of many possible examples. What can be said about the genetic basis of characteristics such as these?

One explanation commonly given is that in such cases two or more separate genes affect the same character in the same way in an additive fashion. Suppose that we are studying the height of a hypothetical plant species. We might assume that height is controlled by three separate genes, each of which occurs in two allelic forms, and that one allele of each gene contributes one inch in height while the other has no effect on height. We might designate the alleles that contribute to height as A^1, B^1, and C^1, and we might designate the alleles that do not contribute as A^0, B^0, and C^0. Suppose that the minimum height against which these genes work is 10 inches. Then a plant with the genotype $A^0A^0B^0B^0C^0C^0$ would be 10 inches tall, because it has no genes for increased height. At the other extreme would be a plant with the genotype $A^1A^1B^1B^1C^1C^1$, which would be 16 inches tall, because it has six superscript-one genes each of which contributes an additional inch to the 10-inch base. Between these two extremes would be plants having from one

to five superscript-one genes, with heights from 11 to 15 inches.

If we calculate the probable frequency of each of the F_2 height classes in a cross between an $A^0A^0B^0B^0C^0C^0$ individual and an $A^1A^1B^1B^1C^1C^1$ individual, we will find that these frequencies, when graphed (Fig. 14.9), approximate a normal curve; the extremes of 10 inches and 16 inches are very rare, and the intermediate heights are much more common. This distribution is very similar to the distribution of phenotypic frequencies actually found in examples of continuously varying characteristics. The more genes are added to such a model, the smoother the curve of phenotypic frequencies becomes. If we remember that modifier genes and environmental influences will also affect the phenotype, we can easily imagine that plants with the genotype $A^1A^0B^1B^1C^1C^0$ will not all be precisely 14 inches tall. Some will be slightly less than 14 inches, and some will be slightly more. The

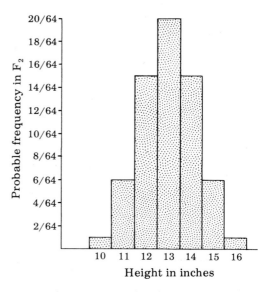

Fig. 14.9. Bar graph showing probable frequency of phenotypes in F_2 generation of a hypothetical cross involving multiple gene inheritance. The phenotypes have the so-called normal distribution. For discussion of this cross, see text.

other height classes will likewise show internal variation. Hence we can imagine that in our hypothetical plant there will be individuals showing almost every conceivable height between the two extremes of 10 and 16 inches; they will not occur in seven clearly distinct classes differing from each other in precise multiples of one inch.

This type of explanation, assuming two or more genes interacting in an additive fashion, has been proposed for many continuously varying characters, including those mentioned at the beginning of this section (human height and skin color and corn ear length). In many ways, it is not a completely satisfactory explanation. For example, it is difficult to establish how many genes are involved in any given case; the assumption that all the genes contribute equally is an obvious oversimplification, and the often profound effects of environment complicate the analysis of the data. Nevertheless, the multiple gene hypothesis is frequently a useful one, and until some better model is proposed geneticists will doubtless continue employing it. Much more research is needed on this subject.

PENETRANCE AND EXPRESSIVITY

In the first few sections of this chapter, we assumed that whenever an individual has a dominant gene he will show the phenotypic effect of that gene, and that whenever he is homozygous for a recessive gene he will show the phenotype associated with that recessive gene. We assumed, in short, that genes have 100 percent penetrance—that they will always produce their characteristic phenotype when they are present in the proper condition. But now we have seen that two or more genes may interact in a variety of ways, that complementarity and epistasis, for example, make the expression of one gene dependent on some other gene. It is therefore possible for an in-

dividual to carry a dominant gene that is not expressed phenotypically. It is also possible for a large number of modifier genes to suppress the expression of a dominant gene. And when a gene is expressed, there are many possible degrees of intensity of expression. We can speak, therefore, of the penetrance and expressivity of a gene. *Penetrance* is the percentage of individuals that, when carrying a given gene in proper combination for its expression, actually express that gene's phenotype. *Expressivity* denotes the manner in which the phenotype is expressed.

The concepts of incomplete penetrance and variable expressivity are illustrated by a gene in human beings that causes a condition known as blue sclera, in which the whites of the eyes appear bluish. This gene usually behaves as a simple dominant, and anyone who possesses the gene, whether in heterozygous or homozygous form, should show the blue-sclera phenotype. But it has been found that only about nine out of ten people who possess the gene actually show the phenotype. We can say, therefore, that the penetrance of this gene is about 90 percent (or 0.9). Among those showing the phenotype, the expressivity is variable, the intensity of the bluish coloration ranging from very pale whitish blue to very dark blackish blue.

Figure 14.10 shows a portion of the pedigree of the Hancock family of Virginia, a family that has for many generations had many members with syndactyly of the ring and little fingers (the two fingers are joined by a web of muscle and skin; Fig. 14.11). This character, like blue sclera, exhibits incomplete penetrance and variable expressivity. Of the more than 50 persons in this family known to have had syndactyly, all but one had a parent who also had syndactyly. Of the more than 75 family members who had parents with normal fingers, only one had syndactyly. This pattern of inheritance is very close to the one expected for a dominant character; as a rule, only individuals with a parent showing the character will show the

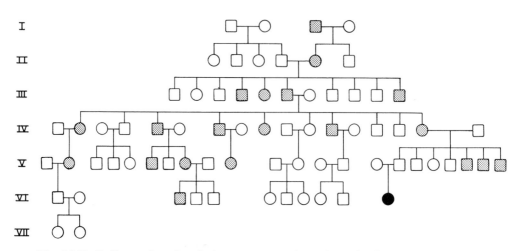

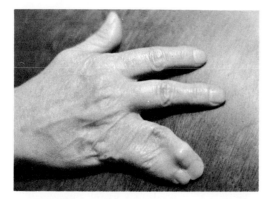

Fig. 14.10. Pedigree of syndactyly in seven generations of one family. Squares represent males and circles represent females. Stippling indicates syndactyly and white indicates normal condition. The character appears to be inherited as a simple autosomal dominant; i.e. there is no correlation with sex, and individuals with syndactyly have a parent who also shows this trait. There is one exception: an individual (see black circle) who has syndactyly even though neither of her parents show the trait. Presumably the gene was present in her father without expression.

Fig. 14.11. Photograph showing syndactyly. [Courtesy S. B. Moore.]

character themselves, because anyone carrying the dominant gene ordinarily shows its phenotype. (By contrast, a recessive character often appears in persons neither of whose parents showed the character, because they were heterozygous.) We can say, then, that the pedigree in Fig. 14.10 makes it appear that syndactyly in this family is inherited as a simple dominant, and that the abnormality in the one girl both

of whose parents had normal fingers probably indicates that the gene for syndactyly has incomplete penetrance; the girl's father must have been carrying the gene, even though he did not exhibit its phenotype. The gene shows variable expressivity in that some individuals have the two fingers incompletely webbed, most have the two fingers fully webbed, and a few have three fingers webbed.

Both of the examples cited above make it clear that penetrance and expressivity are aspects of the same phenomenon. Lack of penetrance of the gene for blue sclera produces white color, which is simply one extreme of the expressivity gradient from white through very pale blue to dark blue. Lack of penetrance of the gene for syndactyly is simply one extreme of the expressivity gradient from incomplete webbing of two fingers to full webbing of three fingers.

As we have indicated, incomplete penetrance and variable expressivity may be due to peculiarities of the genetic background against which the gene in question must act. This explanation points up a general truth: *The action of no gene can be fully understood apart from the overall genetic makeup of the individual organism in which it occurs.*

Penetrance and expressivity may also be affected by environmental influences. For example, *Drosophila* homozygous for the gene for vestigial wings have wings that are only tiny stumps if they are reared at normal room temperatures (about 72°F). But if they are reared at temperatures as high as 88°F, their wings grow almost as long as normal. Himalayan rabbits are normally white with black ears, nose, feet, and tail (Fig. 14.12), but if the fur on a patch on the back is plucked and an ice pack is kept on the patch, the new fur that grows there will be black; the gene for black color can express itself only if the temperature is low, which it normally is only at the body extremities. A human being with genes for great height will not grow tall if raised on a starvation diet. Numerous other examples could be cited.

We see, then, that the expression of a gene depends both on the other genes present (the genetic environment) and on the physical environment (temperature, sunlight, humidity, diet, etc.). We don't inherit characters. We inherit only genes, only potentialities; other factors govern whether or not the potentialities are realized. All organisms are products of both their inheritance and their environment. No either-or question is appropriate here.

THE EVALUATION OF EXPERIMENTAL RESULTS

The Meaning of Predicted Ratios. We have mentioned ratios such as as $1 : 2 : 1$, $3 : 1$, $1 : 1$, and $9 : 3 : 3 : 1$, expected in the results of various types of crosses. We should now examine more closely what a prediction of this kind means. Does it mean that in a cross such as $Cc \times cc$ the expected ratio is exactly $1 : 1$, that exactly equal numbers of red-flowering and white-flowering pea plants are expected to be produced? No, it does not. It simply means that the chances that any given plant produced by this cross will have red flowers as opposed to white flowers are fifty-fifty, and that if large numbers of offspring are produced by this cross we expect the ratio of red-flowering to white-flowering plants to approximate $1 : 1$. The situation is the same with regard to the sex of human children. The chances that any particular new baby will be a boy instead of a girl are roughly fifty-fifty, and we expect that in any large number of young children, such as all those born in a fair-sized city this year, the ratio of boys to girls will closely approximate $1 : 1$. But we are not particularly surprised if any given family has four sons and one daughter or six daughters and one son. In short, in any small sample, large departures from the predicted results are not unusual or surprising.

Fig. 14.12. Effect of temperature on expression of a gene for coat color in the Himalayan rabbit. (A) Normally only the feet, tail, ears, and nose are black. (B) Fur is plucked from a patch on the back, and an ice pack is applied to the area. (C) The new fur grown under the artificially low temperatures is black. Himalayan rabbits are normally homozygous for the gene that controls synthesis of the black pigment, but the gene is active only at low temperatures (below about 92°F). [Modified from A. M. Winchester, *Genetics*, Houghton Mifflin, 1951.]

Let us examine, for a moment, the basis for the prediction of a 1 : 1 ratio in the progeny of the $Cc \times cc$ cross. All gametes produced by the homozygous recessive parent in this cross will be alike with respect to the gene for flower color; all will bear the c allele. It is therefore the heterozygous parent in this cross that determines which of the two possible genotypes (Cc or cc) the offspring will have. The diploid cells of this parent have one C allele and one c allele in their nuclei. When these cells undergo meiosis, half of the new haploid cells receive the chromosome bearing the C allele and half receive its homologous chromosome bearing the c allele. Therefore half the gametes produced by this plant carry the C allele and half carry the c allele. Which of these two types of gametes will be involved in any given fertilization is, apparently, purely a matter of chance. Consequently the probability that any given gamete from the homozygous recessive parent in this cross will be fertilized by a gamete carrying the C allele and produce a red-flowering offspring is 0.5 (or you may express it as 50 percent or as a fraction, ½, if you prefer). Likewise, the probability for fertilization by a gamete carrying the c allele, which would result in a white-flowering offspring, is 0.5. If 100 fertilizations occur, you would expect approximately 50 red-flowering offspring (0.5×100) and approximately 50 white-flowering offspring. This is the basis for the predicted 1 : 1 ratio. The whole matter hinges on the segregation in meiosis of the C and c alleles of the heterozygous parent and the incorporation of these alleles into gametes that have an equal probability of fertilizing the gametes of the other parent. But since the type of gamete involved in each individual fertilization is purely a matter of chance, it would actually be surprising to get an exact fifty-fifty split in a sample of 100, even though that is the prediction.

The Need for Statistical Analysis. Now suppose we actually made a cross in which we predicted that the phenotypic results would show a 1 : 1 ratio. Suppose, further, that our actual results are 45 of one phenotype and 55 of the other. A ratio of 45 : 55 is fairly close to 1 : 1, and we might well conclude that our actual results are close enough to the predicted results to justify assuming that the deviation is due to chance alone. But suppose in another similar cross we get actual results of 5 and 15. This is a bit further from the predicted 1 : 1 ratio. Should we conclude that here, too, the deviation can reasonably be attributed to chance, or should we conclude that there is some genetic explanation for the deviation, that our original prediction should have been slightly different? Scientists in all fields of research constantly encounter the same fundamental question—whether the deviations they observe in their experimental results are significant or not. They cannot rely simply on a guess. They cannot just say, "That looks pretty close to what I predicted," or "that looks rather far off, perhaps I overlooked something." Instead, they have established generally agreed upon standards based on the mathematical probability that the observed deviations in their sample could occur by chance alone. This type of mathematical treatment of data is known as statistical analysis.

One point is immediately apparent: In determining statistical significance, the size of the sample is of critical importance. A large deviation from the predicted results is not unusual in small samples, but the same percentage of deviation in a large sample may be very surprising. We said earlier that a family with four sons and one daughter would not be considered unusual, even though the predicted sex ratio is 1 : 1. But, if out of 500 children born in a city in a particular year, 400 were boys and only 100 were girls, we would strongly suspect that something was amiss. When the predicted ratio is 1 : 1, an observed ratio of 4 : 1 is not alarming in a sample of only 5, but in a sample of 500 it is cause for re-examination of the whole situation. Or, to take another example, if we toss a coin 10 times, we predict that the result will be 5 heads and 5 tails, but we are not greatly surprised if in fact we get 7 heads and 3 tails (a ratio of 7 : 3 instead of 1 : 1). But if we toss the coin 100 times and get 70 heads and only 30 tails (again a 7 : 3 ratio), we question the situation, suspecting that something might be wrong with the coin or with the way it is being tossed. In other words, a ratio of 7 : 3 seems reasonable enough when the sample is small but unreasonable when the sample is large. Clearly, then, tests of significance must take into account both the amount of deviation and the sample size.

Statisticians have devised many mathematical tests whereby experimental or observational data may be evaluated. Though these tests differ in their form and in the sorts of data to which they can validly be applied, all are simply ways of calculating the probability that the deviations of the observed values are due to chance alone. According to the convention usually followed, deviations for which the probability that they are due to chance is as high as 0.05 (one in 20) or higher are regarded as not statistically significant; they are presumed to be chance deviations that can be disregarded, and the observed results are held to fit the predictions reasonably well. If the probability that the deviations are due only to chance is less than one in 20, then the deviations are considered statistically significant; i.e. it is concluded that the results do not fit the predictions and that some modification of the predictions may be necessary. (A statistical test often used in genetics—the chi-square test—is described in the appendix to this chapter.)

MULTIPLE ALLELES

From our discussion so far, you may have gotten the impression that genes can have only two allelic forms, which may exhibit either a dominant-recessive or an intermediate relation-ship to each other. This is not so. Genes may exist in any number of different allelic forms. Of course, under normal circumstances, the maximum number of different alleles for each gene that any individual can possess is two, because he has only two doses of each gene. But many other alleles may be present in the population to which he belongs.

Eye Color in Drosophila. The first example of multiple alleles was discovered in the little fruit fly, *Drosophila melanogaster*, which, from the genetic point of view, is one of the most extensively studied species in existence. These flies normally have red eyes. But individuals with white, eosin, wine-colored, apricot, ivory, or cherry eyes also occur. It has been shown that each of these different eye colors is controlled by a different allele of the eye-color gene. At least 14 different alleles for eye color have been discovered, and others may well exist. The allele for the wild-type eye (red) is dominant over all the rest, but when any two of the others occur together in a heterozygous fly they produce an intermediate phenotype.

Human A-B-O Blood Types. A well-known example of multiple alleles in man, and one that is relatively simple since only a few alleles are involved, is that of the A-B-O blood groups. The erythrocytes of human beings may contain antigen of a type known as agglutinogen. Blood plasma may contain antibodies called agglutinins, which react with the cellular antigens. When cells containing a particular antigen are mixed with plasma containing the corresponding antibody, the cells tend to clump together, or agglutinate. Obviously, then, a person's blood plasma cannot contain antibodies corresponding to the antigens present in his own erythrocytes; such antibodies would make his blood clump and he would die. The normal person's plasma does contain antibodies for whatever antigens of this series are *not* present in his own cells. This is one of the few cases where a person's body normally synthesizes antibody against an antigen to which it has not actually been exposed.

The cellular antigens in this series are of two types, designated A and B. The corresponding antibodies in the plasma are designated anti-A and anti-B. The blood types produced by various normally occurring combinations of antigens are designated by the antigens involved. Thus the erythrocytes of type-A blood contain antigen A, those of type-B blood contain antigen B, those of type-AB blood contain both antigen A and antigen B, and those of type-O blood contain neither antigen. Table 14.2 summarizes the antigen and antibody content of blood of each of the four major blood types in the A-B-O series.

The presence of these antigens and antibodies in the blood has important implications for blood transfusions. Because the antibodies present in the plasma of blood of one type will tend to react with the antigens in the erythrocytes of other blood types and cause clumping, it is always best, when transfusions are to be given, to obtain a donor who has the same blood type as the patient. It has been found, however, that when such a donor is not available blood of another type may be used, provided that the *plasma of the patient* and the *erythrocytes of the donor* are compatible; in other words, one can usually ignore the erythrocytes of the patient and the plasma of the donor. The reason is that, unless the transfusion is to be a massive one or is to be made very rapidly, the donor's plasma is sufficiently diluted during transfusion so that little or no agglutination occurs. This means that type-O blood can be given to anyone because its erythrocytes have no antigens and thus are obviously compatible with the plasma of any patient; type-O blood is sometimes called the universal donor. But type-O patients can receive transfusions only from type-O donors because their plasma contains both anti-A and anti-B and thus is obviously not compatible with the erythrocytes of any other class of donor. Conversely, people with type-AB blood, whose plasma contains no antibodies, are universal recipients but cannot act as donors for any except type-AB patients. Table 14.3 summarizes these transfusion relationships.

At first glance, you might suppose that two independent genes are involved in the A-B-O system, one determining whether the A antigen is present and another determining whether the B antigen is present. But this is not the case. It has been shown that the in-

TABLE 14.2

Antigen and Antibody Content of the Blood
Types of the A-B-O Series

| Blood type | Blood contains | |
	Cellular antigens	Plasma antibodies
O	None	anti-A and anti-B
A	A	anti-B
B	B	anti-A
AB	A and B	None

TABLE 14.3

Transfusion Relationships of the
A-B-O Blood Groups

Blood group	Can act as donor to	Can receive blood from
O	O, A, B, AB	O
A	A, AB	O, A
B	B, AB	O, B
AB	AB	O, A, B, AB

heritance of the A-B-O groups is best described by a theory of three alleles,[3] which are here designated I^A, I^B, and i (they are sometimes also designated L^A, L^B and L^O). Both I^A and I^B are dominant over i, but neither I^A nor I^B is dominant over the other. Accordingly, the four blood-type phenotypes correspond to the genotypes indicated in Table 14.4.

Blood typing is often used as a source of evidence in paternity cases in court. For example, a man with type-O blood could not possibly be the father of a child with type-A blood whose mother is type-B. The child's true father must be either type-A or type-AB, because the child must have received his I^A allele from his father; an O man has no such allele. Similarly, a man with type-AB blood could not possibly be the father of a type-O child, because the child must have received an i allele from his father, but an AB man has no such allele. Note that this test of possible paternity is strictly a negative one. It is sometimes possible to say definitely that a particular man is not the father of a particular child, but it is never possible on this basis to say that a man is the father of a child. If a man with type-A blood is accused of being the father of a type-A child whose mother is type-B, blood typing does not help settle the question. The child's father is either type-A or type-AB, but since there are millions of type-A and type-AB men in the world the man's type-A blood does not constitute evidence that he is the father.

The frequencies of the various A-B-O blood types vary in populations of different ancestral extraction. Thus, in the United States, the approximate frequencies in the white population are: 45 percent O, 41 percent A, 10 percent B, and 4 percent AB; in the Negro population, the frequencies are: 47 percent O, 28 percent A, 20 percent B, and 5 percent AB. Even greater differences are found in some other populations, as indicated in Table 14.5. As might be expected, anthropologists have found data on the frequencies of blood types useful in tracing the prehistoric movements and derivations of the various subgroups of the human species.

Notice that in many human populations the most frequent phenotype is type O, which corresponds to the homozygous recessive genotype, and that in these populations, accord-

TABLE 14.4

Genotypes of the A-B-O- Blood Types

Blood type	Genotype
O	ii
A	$I^A I^A$ or $I^A i$
B	$I^B I^B$ or $I^B i$
AB	$I^A I^B$

[3] Actually, four alleles are now known. What we here designate as the I^A allele is really two different but very similar alleles, I^{A_1} and I^{A_2}. This means that there are actually six blood types (O, A, A_1, A_2, B, A_1B, A_2B), instead of four. For our purposes, however, we can ignore this complication.

TABLE 14.5

Frequencies of A-B-O Blood Groups in Selected Populations

Population	O	A	B	AB
United States Whites	45%	41%	10%	4%
United States Negroes	47	28	20	5
African Pygmies	31	30	29	10
African Bushmen	56	34	8	2
Australian Aborigines	34	66	0	0
Pure Peruvian Indians	100	0	0	0
Tuamotuans of Polynesia	48	52	0	0

ingly, the *i* allele is more common than the I^A or I^B alleles. Here we have a good illustration of an important fact: Whether an allele is dominant or recessive does not determine whether it will be common or rare in the population. Many beginning students have the mistaken impression that dominant alleles are the common ones and recessive alleles are the rarer ones. "Dominant" and "recessive" describe the way the alleles interact when they occur together in a heterozygous individual; these terms do not indicate which allele determines the more advantageous phenotype. Natural selection tends to increase the frequency of the allele that determines the more adaptive phenotype, whether that allele is dominant or recessive, and it tends to decrease the frequency of the allele that determines the less adaptive phenotype; it is this that determines which allele is the more common.

Human Rh Blood Factors. Another series of blood antigens is designated as Rh (which stands for rhesus monkey, the animal in which the antigens were first discovered). The Rh series includes at least nine different antigens, and some authorities believe that the inheritance of these antigens is best explained by a theory of multiple alleles; if this theory is correct, the Rh alleles would constitute one of the largest series of multiple alleles known in man (larger series are known in some other species). Other authorities prefer to explain Rh inheritance in terms of three or more separate genes that lie close together on the same chromosome and have very similar functions. Which if either of these two theories is correct has some importance in terms of our understanding of the nature of the gene, but from the medical point of view the matter is much simpler.

The clinician ordinarily divides the subjects he tests into two phenotypic classes designated Rh-positive and Rh-negative. Rh-positive individuals have the Rh antigen in their erythro-cytes, while Rh-negative individuals do not (more precisely, their antigen is such a weak one that it can be disregarded). About 85 percent of the white population in the United States is Rh-positive, and 15 percent is Rh-negative. Rh-negative is much rarer in people of Mongoloid or Negroid extraction.

For convenience, let us assume that Rh-positive is the phenotype produced by a dominant gene *Rh*, and that Rh-negative is the phenotype produced by its recessive allele *rh*.[4] This assumption allows us to treat the genetics of Rh blood types like a simple monohybrid cross, even though we actually know that the Rh-positive phenotype can be produced by any one of a number of slightly different alleles that produce slightly different antigens. On this assumption, the possible genotypes and their phenotypes would be as follows:

Phenotypes	*Genotypes*
Rh $^+$	*RhRh* or *Rhrh*
Rh $^-$	*rhrh*

Whereas a person's blood plasma may contain anti-A or anti-B antibody without stimulation by the corresponding antigen, it will not contain any antibody against the Rh antigen unless the body is sensitized to the antigen by exposure to it. Thus the blood of a normal unsensitized Rh-negative person contains neither Rh antigen in its cells nor Rh antibody in its plasma. But if an Rh-negative person is mistakenly given a transfusion of Rh-positive blood, this exposure to the antigen will sensitize him and stimulate his plasma cells to begin synthesizing antibodies. If the same patient is later given a second transfusion of Rh-positive blood, the antibodies now present in his plasma will react with the antigens in the donated blood to cause clumping, which may kill the patient. It is important, therefore, that patients

---

[4] Notice that we are here using a two-letter symbol for a single gene. Thus *Rh* is the symbol for a single dominant allele, and *rh* is the symbol for a single recessive allele. Do not make the mistake of thinking that the *r* and the *h* stand for different things.

and donors be carefully typed for both the A-B-O blood group and the Rh factor.

The Rh factor also has medical importance in certain cases of pregnancy. If an Rh-negative woman (genotype *rhrh*) marries an Rh-positive man (genotype *RhRh* or *Rhrh*), some of their children may be heterozygous and have the Rh-positive phenotype. Often this causes no trouble; there is no direct connection between the circulatory systems of the mother and the fetus in the normal placenta, and hence there can be no mixing of blood. But in the late stages of some pregnancies, a small defect in the placenta may allow some seepage of blood between the two circulatory systems. If this happens to an Rh-negative mother bearing an Rh-positive fetus, seepage of fetal blood into the mother's circulatory system has the same effect as though she had been given a transfusion of Rh-positive blood. Her plasma cells are stimulated to begin synthesizing Rh antibody. Ordinarily there is no immediate harm, because the baby is born before the mother's blood contains appreciable quantities of antibody. But if this sensitized mother later bears a second or third Rh-positive fetus, and if seepage across the placenta again develops, antibodies from the maternal blood may enter the fetal circulation and react with the fetal cells, causing a disease known as erythroblastosis fetalis (or simply Rh disease), which, unless treated promptly, is often fatal to the baby.

It must be emphasized that erythroblastosis fetalis does not occur in all second or later pregnancies of Rh-negative women married to Rh-positive men. First, the husband may be heterozygous, in which case the chances are fifty-fifty that any given child will have Rh-negative blood like the mother and cause no trouble. Second, if seepage across the placenta does not develop, there will be no trouble; there are cases on record of Rh-negative women that have borne more than ten healthy Rh-positive children. Third, our treatment here is an oversimplification in that it lumps together

as Rh-positive all individuals whose erythrocytes contain Rh antigens, even though there are many forms of the antigen, corresponding to a whole series of different Rh-positive alleles; actually only one of these forms of the Rh antigen (determined by an allele designated as *Rh⁰*) is usually involved in erythroblastosis fetalis, and other forms will cause no trouble. And even if a fetus does develop the disease, physicians have learned that if the newborn infant is promptly given a massive transfusion that replaces all its blood (contaminated with antibodies from the mother) with blood free of antibodies, the chances are good that it will live and develop normally.

MUTATIONS AND DELETERIOUS GENES

A variety of influences can cause slight changes in the chemical structure of a gene. Such changes are called mutations. The rate at which any particular gene undergoes mutation is ordinarily extremely low. But every individual organism has a very large number of different genes, and the total number of genes in all the individuals of a species is vast indeed. Hence mutations are constantly occurring within a species, pure chance determining in which individual any given mutation will occur. Now, every living organism is the product of billions of years of evolution and is a finely tuned, smoothly running, astoundingly intricate mechanism, in which the function of every part in some way influences the function of every other part. By comparison, the best Swiss watch is simple indeed. If you were to take such a watch, remove its back, and make some random change in its parts, the chances are very great that you would make it run worse instead of better. A random change in any delicate and intricate mechanism is far more likely to damage it than to improve it. Mutational changes in genes being random, it is easy to understand why in the vast majority of cases new mutations are deleterious. Only very rarely is a new mutation beneficial.

Heterozygous Versus Homozygous Effects. When a new deleterious allele arises by mutation, natural selection can act against it only if it causes some change in the organism's characteristics. Selection acts directly on phenotypes and only indirectly on genotypes. Deleterious mutations that are dominant will be expressed phenotypically and can thus be eliminated from the population rapidly by natural selection. But many new mutations are recessive to the normal alleles. And since the probability that the same mutation will occur twice in the same individual is vanishingly slight, most new alleles occur in combination with the normal allele in diploid cells; i.e. the diploid cell is heterozygous, containing one normal allele and one new allele produced by mutation. If a new allele is recessive, and if it occurs in heterozygous condition, it can have little immediate phenotypic effect on the organisms that possess it—its deleterious effects cannot be fully expressed—and therefore natural selection cannot eliminate it from the population very rapidly. Deleterious alleles that are not dominant may be retained in the population in heterozygous condition for a long time.

When two individuals both carrying the same deleterious recessive allele in heterozygous condition mate, about one fourth of their progeny will be homozygous for the deleterious allele, and these homozygous offspring will have the harmful phenotype. In some cases, the phenotype may even kill the organism. An allele whose phenotype, when expressed, results in the death of the organism is called a *lethal.* The occurrence of lethals can modify the phenotypic ratios obtained in the progeny of some crosses, as the following example shows.

In chickens, one allele of a certain gene, when it occurs in heterozygous condition with the normal allele, causes the chicken to be a "creeper," with short crooked legs (Fig. 14.13). When two creeper chickens are crossed, their offspring are of two phenotypes, normal and creeper, in a ratio of approximately 1 : 2. Now, this is a different ratio from any we have previously encountered. The explanation for it is that about one fourth of the incubated eggs fail to hatch, the embryos dying early in their development. If these dead embryos are regarded as a third phenotypic class, then the cross can be said to have produced a phenotypic ratio of 1 : 2 : 1, the typical one for the F_2 generation of a monohybrid cross where dominance is lacking. The ratio of 1 : 2 seen in the live chicks is the result of the lethality of the creeper allele when it occurs in homozygous condition.

There are numerous instances in which alleles that are harmful or even lethal when homozygous are actually beneficial when heterozygous. For example, in England there is a breed of cattle called Dexter, a good beef producer, for which it is impossible to establish a purebreeding herd because some of its most desirable characteristics are caused by the heterozygous expression of a gene that is lethal when homozygous.

An example in human beings is the gene for sickle-cell anemia in Africa. When homo-

Fig. 14.13. A creeper hen. Her legs are very short and she cannot walk normally. Such a hen is heterozygous for a gene that is lethal when homozygous. [From a photograph by C. D. Mueller in A. M. Winchester, *Genetics,* Houghton Mifflin, 1951.]

zygous, this gene results in a serious abnormality of the red blood cells in which the cells are curved like a sickle and bear long filamentous processes (Fig. 14.14). These abnormal cells tend to form clumps and to clog the smaller blood vessels. The resulting impairment of the circulation leads to severe pains in the abdomen, back, head, and extremities, and to enlargement of the heart and atrophy of brain cells. In addition, the tendency of the deformed red blood cells to rupture easily brings about severe anemia. As might be expected, victims of sickle-cell anemia usually suffer an early death. Individuals who are heterozygous for the sickle-cell gene sometimes show mild symptoms of the disease, but the condition is not serious. It might be supposed that natural selection would operate against the propagation of any gene so obviously harmful and that such a gene would be held at very low frequency in the population. This seems to be true among Negroes in the United States. But the gene is surprisingly common in many parts of Africa, being carried by as much as 20 percent of the Negro population. What is the explanation? A. C. Allison of Oxford, England, has found that individuals who are heterozygous for this gene have a much higher than normal resistance to malaria. Since malaria is very common in many parts of Africa, the gene must be regarded as beneficial when heterozygous. Thus, in Africa, there is selection for the gene because of its heterozygous effect on malarial resistance and selection against it because of its homozygous production of sickle-cell anemia. The balance between these two opposing selection pressures determines the frequency of the gene in the population.

The gene for sickle-cell anemia is a dramatic example of a gene that has more than one effect. Such a gene is said to be *pleiotropic.* Pleiotropy is, in fact, the rule rather than the exception. All genes probably have many effects on the organism. Even when a gene produces only one visible phenotypic effect, it

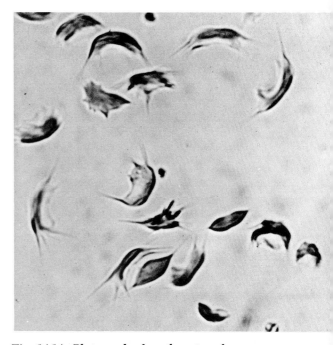

Fig. 14.14. **Photograph of erythrocytes of a person with sickle-cell anemia.** The cells are curved and bear long filamentous processes. [Courtesy J. W. Harris, Cleveland Metropolitan General Hospital.]

doubtless has numerous physiological effects more difficult for us to detect.

The Effect of Inbreeding. The conditions under which genes cause deleterious phenotypes explain the danger in marriages between closely related human beings. Everyone probably carries in heterozygous combination many genes that would cause harmful effects if present in homozygous combination, including some lethals. But because most of these deleterious genes originated as rare mutations, and are limited to a tiny percentage of the population, the chances are slight that two unrelated persons who marry will be carrying the same deleterious recessive genes and produce homozygous offspring that show the harmful phenotype. The chances are much greater that two closely related persons will be carrying the same harmful recessives, having received them from common ancestors, and that, if they marry, they will have children homozygous for the deleterious traits. In short, close inbreeding increases the percentage of homozygosity, as Fig. 14.15 shows. This figure is based on some classic work with guinea pigs by Sewall Wright of the University of Chicago. You can see from it that brother-sister matings and matings between double first cousins cause rapid increases in homozygosity, that matings between first cousins cause only moderate increases, and that, contrary to popular notion, matings between second cousins cause negligible increases.

Diploidy Versus Haploidy. Before leaving this discussion of mutation, harmful genes, and the implications of homozygosity versus heterozygosity, we might speculate for a moment on the adaptive significance of the fact that the diploid stages of the life cycle have such a marked dominance over the haploid stages in most of the higher plants and animals. Why would natural selection have favored diploidy rather than haploidy? One possible reason is that new harmful mutations immediately exert

their effect in a haploid organism; they cannot be masked by a dominant allele. But in diploid species, an organism can survive such a mutation if the new allele is recessive, and the mutant gene can be carried for generations in the population, perhaps exerting a beneficial effect when heterozygous. Such a gene may also serve as a latent source of variation; the day may come when the environmental conditions or the genetic makeup of the organism has changed so much that the gene is no longer deleterious even when homozygous.

SEX AND INHERITANCE

Sex Determination

The Sex Chromosomes. We have said repeatedly that a diploid individual has two of each type of chromosome, identical in size and shape, and hence two doses of each gene. But we must now qualify that statement somewhat. In most higher organisms (both plants and animals) where the sexes are separate (i.e. where males and females are separate individuals), the chromosomal endowments of males and females are different, and one or the other of the two sexes has one chromosomal pair consisting of two chromosomes that differ markedly from each other in size and shape. These are the *sex chromosomes*, which play a fundamental role in determining the sex of the individual. All other chromosomes are called *autosomes.*

Let us first look at the chromosomes in *Drosophila* and in human beings. In each case, the sex chromosomes are of two sorts: one bearing many genes, conventionally designated the *X chromosome*, and one of a different shape and bearing only a few genes, designated the *Y chromosome*. Females characteristically have two X chromosomes and males have one X and one Y. The diploid number in *Drosophila* is eight (four pairs); so a female has three pairs of autosomes and one pair of

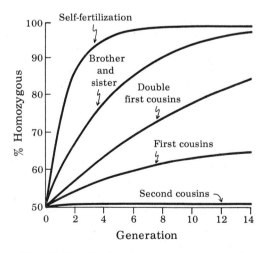

Fig. 14.15. Graph showing percentage of homozygotes in successive generations under different inbreeding systems. [Modified from Sewall Wright, *Genetics,* vol. 6, 1921.]

X chromosomes, and a male has three pairs of autosomes and a pair of sex chromosomes consisting of one X and one Y (Fig. 14.16). The diploid number in human beings is 46 (23 pairs); so a female has 22 pairs of autosomes and one pair of X chromosomes, and a male has 22 pairs of autosomes and a pair of sex chromosomes consisting of one X and one Y. This means that when a female produces eggs by meiosis, all the eggs receive one of each type of autosome plus one X chromosome. When a male produces sperm cells by meiosis, half the sperm cells receive one of each type of autosome plus one X chromosome and half receive one of each autosome plus one Y chromosome. In short, all the egg cells are alike in chromosomal content, but the sperm cells are of two different types occurring in equal

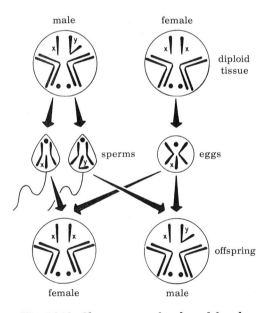

Fig. 14.16. **Chromosomes of male and female** *Drosophila melanogaster.* There are three pairs of autosomes and one pair of sex chromosomes. Males have one X chromosome and one Y chromosome; these separate at meiosis, so half the sperms carry an X and half carry a Y. Females have two X chromosomes, so all eggs have one X. The sex of the offspring depends upon which type of sperm fertilizes the egg. [Modified from A. M. Winchester, *Genetics*, Houghton Mifflin, 1951.]

numbers (Fig. 14.16). When fertilization takes place, the chances are approximately equal that the egg will be fertilized by a sperm carrying an X chromosome or by a sperm carrying a Y chromosome. If fertilization is by an X-bearing sperm, the resulting zygote will be XX and will develop into a female. If fertilization is by a Y-bearing sperm, the resulting zygote will be XY and will develop into a male.[5] We see, therefore, that the sex of an individual is normally determined at the moment of fertilization and depends upon which of the two types of sperm fertilizes the egg.

Since meiosis in the male must produce exactly equal numbers of X sperms and Y sperms we would predict that in a large population exactly equal numbers of boys and girls would be conceived. But many studies have shown that in the United States about 114 boys are conceived for every 100 girls.[6] Why this departure from the predicted results? Many factors are doubtless involved, since the ratio may vary from country to country and even from family to family. The genetic background and the age and health of the parents have been shown to be of influence. These factors must produce differentials between the two types of sperm in such characteristics as their ability to survive the conditions in the female genital tract, or their rate of movement from the vagina to the point of conception in the oviduct, or their ability to penetrate the outer surface

[5] The XY system, where XX is female and XY is male, is characteristic of many animals, including all mammals. It is also found in many plants with separate sexes. Birds, butterflies and moths, and a few other animals have just the opposite system, where XX is male and XY is female (to distinguish this system from the usual XY system, the symbols Z and W are often substituted—ZZ being male and ZW being female). A completely different mechanism of sex determination exists in the Hymenoptera (bees, wasps, ants, etc.), where the males hatch from unfertilized eggs and are haploid while the females hatch from fertilized eggs and are diploid.

[6] Since more males than females die during embryonic development, the ratio at birth is about 106 : 100, and a higher rate of mortality of males after birth brings the numbers of the two sexes into balance by about the age of ten; thereafter there are more females than males in any age group.

of the egg. It is apparent, then, that X sperms and Y sperms differ in their physical attributes (e.g. Y sperms may be slightly lighter than X sperms, since the Y chromosome is smaller than the X chromosome, and this may affect the speed at which the sperms can swim). Recently, techniques have been devised that may enable animal breeders to make a partial separation of the two types of sperm in bull semen. The day will almost certainly come when the two types of sperm in human semen can be separated in the laboratory, thus making it possible, through use of artificial insemination, to select the sex of a child.

Bridges' Ratio Theory of Sex in *Drosophila*. In anaphase of normal meiosis, the members of each homologous pair of chromosomes separate and move to opposite poles, so that the resulting gametes have one of each type of chromosome. Occasionally, however, the chromosomes of one pair fail to separate properly (this is called nondisjunction) and both move to the same pole, with the result that one of the daughter cells receives one too many chromosomes and the other daughter cell receives one too few. For example, two chromosomes of autosomal type number 21 sometimes occur in a human gamete, which thus has a total of 24 chromosomes instead of the normal 23; if such a gamete is involved in fertilization, the resulting zygote has 47 chromosomes (the normal two of most types plus three of type number 21) instead of the normal 46.[7] Sometimes it is the sex chromosomes that fail to separate in meiosis, and XXX or XXY individuals result. When this happens in *Drosophila*, the XXY flies are essentially normal females and the XXX flies

are abnormal females (sometimes called superfemales, although they are actually not as well developed as normal females). Rather rarely, flies are produced that have three of each type of autosome and two sex chromosomes; these flies show abnormal sexual development. From observations on these abnormalities in *Drosophila*, C. B. Bridges of Columbia University formulated a ratio theory of sex determination (Table 14.6). He suggested that if the ratio of the number of X chromosomes to the number of autosomes of each type is 1.0, the individual is a female and if the ratio is 0.5 the individual is a male (a normal female has two X chromosomes and two of each type of autosome, which gives the 2/2 or 1.0 ratio, while a normal male has only one X chromosome and two of each type of autosome, which gives the 1/2 or 0.5 ratio). According to Bridges' theory, an XXX fly is a superfemale because its X/A ratio is 3/2 or 1.5, which is higher than that of a normal female, and an XXY is a female because its X/A ratio is 1.0, the same as that for a normal female (Bridges thought the Y chromosome played no role and could be disregarded). Similarly, an individual

---

TABLE 14.6

Ratio Theory of Sex Determination in *Drosophila*

Number of X chromosomes	Number of each type of autosome (A)	X/A ratio	Phenotype
3	2	1.5	Superfemale
2	2	1.0	Normal female
2	3	0.67	Intersex
1	2	0.5	Normal male
1	3	0.33	Supermale

with three of each type of autosome and two X chromosomes would be an intersex because its X/A ratio would be 2/3 or 0.67, which is intermediate between that for normal females and that for normal males.

Bridges' ratio theory of sex determination, which assigns no significant role to the Y chromosome, was strengthened by the discovery that some animals, such as grasshoppers, lack the Y chromosome entirely; the females have two X chromosomes and the males a single unpaired X, the female thus having one more chromosome than the male (in some species of grasshoppers the total numbers are 22 and 21 respectively). Such a system of sex determination is known as the XO system, where O designates the absence of a chromosome.

The Role of the Y in Human Sex Determination. For many years, it was thought that Bridges' ratio theory applied to man, but more recently it has been shown that this theory, based on *Drosophila,* does not hold for man. Apparently the human Y chromosome bears genes with strong male-determining properties, and it is the presence of the Y that determines maleness and its absence that determines femaleness. Thus, whereas an XXY *Drosophila* is a female, an XXY human is a male.

Sex-Linked Characters

There are many genes that occur on the X chromosome and not on the Y chromosome. Such genes are said to be sex-linked. The inheritance patterns for the characteristics controlled by such genes are quite different from those of characteristics controlled by autosomal genes, for obvious reasons. The females have two doses of each sex-linked gene, one from each parent, but the males have only one dose of each sex-linked gene, and that one dose always comes from the mother since the father contributes a Y chromosome instead of an X.

Hence, in the male, all sex-linked characteristics are inherited from the mother only. And since the male has only one dose of each sex-linked gene, recessive genes cannot be masked; consequently, recessive sex-linked phenotypes occur much more frequently in males than in females.

Sex linkage was discovered in 1910 by the great American geneticist Thomas Hunt Morgan of Columbia University. It was Morgan who first began the systematic utilization of *Drosophila* in genetic studies. Use of this little fruit fly made it possible to perform in a few months experiments that it would have taken Mendel years to perform on peas. *Drosophila* can be easily and economically cultured in large numbers in the laboratory, and they can produce a new generation every ten or twelve days. In addition, they are subject to a remarkable number of easily detectable genetic variations. We owe much of our modern knowledge of genetics to work on this tiny insect.

Let us examine the first sex-linked trait discovered by Morgan—that of white eye color in *Drosophila.* This trait is controlled by a recessive allele *r.* The normal red eye color is controlled by a dominant allele *R.* If a homozygous red-eyed female is crossed with a white-eyed male, all the F_1 offspring, regardless of their sex, have red eyes, since they receive from their mother an X chromosome bearing an allele for red. In addition, the F_1 females receive from their father an X chromosome bearing an allele for white eyes, but the allele for red, being dominant, masks its presence. The F_1 males, like the females, receive from their mother an X chromosome bearing an allele for red eyes. But unlike the females, they receive no gene for eye color from their father, who contributes a Y chromosome instead of an X (in writing the genotype of a male for a sex-linked character, the Y is customarily shown in order to indicate clearly that no second X chromosome is present and hence that there is no second dose of the sex-linked gene). We can summarize this cross as follows (♀ denotes females, ♂ males):

P   RR   ×   rY
        red-eyed ♀   white-eyed ♂
             ↓

F_1 Rr   ×   RY
       red-eyed ♀   red-eyed ♂
             ↓

F_2 RR   rR   RY   rY
    red-   red-   red-   white-
   eyed ♀   eyed ♀   eyed ♂   eyed ♂

Notice that when the F_1 flies of this cross are allowed to mate among themselves, the F_2 flies thus produced show the customary 3 : 1 phenotypic ratio of a monohybrid cross where dominance is present. But notice also that this 3 : 1 ratio is rather different from the 3 : 1 ratio obtained in a cross involving autosomal genes. In an autosomal cross, there is no correlation of phenotype with sex, but in this cross all F_2 individuals showing the recessive phenotype are males. In other words, an autosomal cross gives a 3 : 1 F_2 ratio for both females and males, but this cross yielded females of only one phenotype and males with a 1 : 1 phenotypic ratio.

Now let us examine the reciprocal cross, where the parental generation consists of homozygous white-eyed females and red-eyed males. We can summarize this cross as follows:

P   rr   ×   RY
     white-eyed ♀   red-eyed ♂
             ↓

F_1 rR   ×   rY
     red-eyed ♀   white-eyed ♂
             ↓

F_2 rr   Rr   rY   RY
  white-   red-   white-   red-
  eyed ♀   eyed ♀   eyed ♂   eyed ♂

Notice that the phenotypic makeup of both the F_1 and the F_2 generations differs both from a normal autosomal cross and from the reciprocal cross for this same sex-linked trait. In the F_1, the dominant phenotype appears only in females, rather than in all individuals regardless of sex; while all females show the dominant phenotype, all males show the recessive phenotype. In the F_2, instead of a 3 : 1 ratio, there is a 1 : 1 ratio in each sex. Comparison of the two reciprocal crosses shown above makes it clear that when a sex-linked trait is involved in a cross, it is very important which parent shows the trait (or carries the gene for the trait); the results of reciprocal crosses are not the same. By contrast, in crosses involving autosomal genes, it makes no difference which parent possesses the gene in question; the results of reciprocal crosses are identical.

Two well-known examples of recessive sex-linked traits in man are red-green color blindness and hemophilia ("bleeder's disease"). Color blindness occurs in about 8 percent of the white men in the United States and in about 4 percent of the Negro men. It occurs in only about one percent of the white women and about 0.8 percent of the Negro women. It is expected, of course, that more men than women will show such a trait, because a man needs only one dose of the gene to show the phenotype, and he can inherit this one dose from a heterozygous mother who is not herself color-blind. But for a woman to be color-blind, she must have two doses of the gene (i.e. be homozygous), which means not only that her father must be color-blind but also that her mother must either be color-blind or be a heterozygous carrier of the gene. Since the gene is not very common in the population, it is not likely that two such people will marry; hence the low number of color-blind women.

In our discussion of sex-linkage, we have referred only to genes on the X chromosome and have ignored the Y. There are apparently very few genes on the Y; we have mentioned the maleness determiners, which, believed absent in *Drosophila*, are thought to be on the Y in human beings. Genes that are on the Y and not on the X are termed holandric. The phenotypic traits they control appear, of course, only in males. There are a few genes in man that occur on both the X and the Y; their inheritance patterns are the same as for autosomal genes.

Sex-Influenced Characters

The fact that some genes are sex-linked should not lead you to assume that all genes for characters commonly associated with sex are sex-linked. They are not. As we saw above, sex-linked genes may control characters not customarily regarded as "sexual." And many genes that do control "sexual" characters are located on the autosomes. For example, many genes that control growth and development of the sexual organs, such as the penis, the vagina, the uterus, or the oviducts, or that control distribution of body hair, size of breasts, pitch of voice, or other secondary sexual characteristics, are autosomal and are present in individuals of both sexes. That their phenotypic expression is different in the two sexes indicates that they are sex-limited, not that they are sex-linked. Apparently, the sex hormones actually enter the nuclei of cells and influence the activity of the genes, either inhibiting or stimulating them. There is increasing evidence, in fact, that most (and perhaps all) hormones produce their effects by acting directly on certain genes. The hormones may be among the most important types of environmental influence impinging on the genes.

LINKAGE

The patterns of inheritance we have discussed so far amply support Mendel's so-called first law, or Law of Segregation—that in each individual the genes occur in pairs,[8] and that in the formation of gametes the members of each pair separate and pass into different gametes,

[8] To be more precise, we should say that in each *diploid* individual the genes occur in pairs, since the haploid individuals of lower plants obviously have only one dose of each gene.

so that each gamete has only one of each type of gene. But numerous experiments have shown that there are important exceptions to Mendel's so-called second law, or Law of Independent Segregation, which states that when two or more pairs of genes are involved in a cross, the members of one pair segregate independently of the members of all other pairs. All dihybrid and trihybrid crosses so far discussed in this chapter agree with this law. But there are many crosses that do not.

The Chromosomal Basis of Linkage. Mendel knew nothing about chromosomes; he derived his principles exclusively from data from crosses, and either he was lucky enough to have worked only with crosses that yielded $9 : 3 : 3 : 1$ phenotypic ratios in the F_2 generation or he chose to ignore crosses that did not fit this ratio (or obvious modifications of it). But shortly after the rediscovery of Mendel's paper in 1900, W. S. Sutton of Columbia University pointed out that Mendel's conclusion that hereditary factors (genes) occur in pairs in somatic cells and separate in gametogenesis was in striking accord with the recent cytological evidence that somatic cells contain two of each kind of chromosome and that these chromosomes segregate in meiosis. Sutton suggested that the chromosomes are the bearers of the genes and that this explained the correspondence between Mendel's results and the cytologists' discoveries. Our discussion in most of this chapter has followed Sutton's theory.

But a moment's thought will convince you that Sutton's theory that the genes are located on the chromosomes is incompatible with the unmodified form of Mendel's second law. *Drosophila* have only four pairs of chromosomes, garden peas have only seven pairs, human beings have only 23 pairs, and other species have similarly limited numbers of pairs. Since each species has thousands of different genes, it follows that there must be many different genes on each chromosome. And since it is whole chromosomes that segregate independently in meiosis, it follows that only genes that are located on different chromosomes can segregate independently of each other; genes located on the same chromosome cannot separate and hence must move together during meiosis. Such genes are said to be **linked.** We must, therefore, modify Mendel's second law, restricting its application to pairs of genes located on different chromosomes, i.e. to genes that are not linked.[9]

One of the first examples of linkage was reported in 1906 by William Bateson and R. C. Punnett of Cambridge University. They crossed sweet peas that had purple flowers and long pollen with ones that had red flowers and round pollen. All the F_1 plants had purple flowers and long pollen, as expected (it was already known that purple was dominant over red and that long was dominant over round). The F_2 plants from this cross did not show the expected $9:3:3:1$ ratio, however, but a highly anomalous one. Next, Bateson and Punnett tried a test cross, crossing the F_1 plants back to homozygous recessive plants (with red flowers and round pollen). According to the Law of Independent Segregation, such a test cross should have yielded a ratio of $1:1:1:1$. But it did not; it yielded a ratio of approximately $7:1:1:7$. Using the symbols B for purple, b for red, L for long, and l for round, we can summarize this test cross as follows:

BbLl	×	*bbll*
purple-long		red-round

↓

7 *BbLl*	1 *Bbll*	1 *bbLl*	7 *bbll*
purple-long	purple-round	red-long	red-round

[9] Mendel reported on crosses involving seven different characters (see Table 14.1), the genes for each of which segregated independently of all the others. If Mendel had studied any eighth character he would have found (since garden peas have only seven pairs of chromosomes) that its genes segregated *with* those of one of the other seven characters and hence did not bear out his conclusions. It is hard to believe that Mendel had the incredible luck of choosing precisely seven characters all of which were independent. One suspects that he must have studied other characters but that he ignored them when he wrote his paper.

You will recall that, in a test cross, the phenotypic ratio of the offspring depends on the genotype of the parent showing the dominant phenotype, since the recessive parent produces only one kind of gamete. In this example, the homozygous recessive red-round parent can produce only bl gametes. Hence it is the gametes of the heterozygous purple-long parent that determine the phenotype of the offspring. According to the Law of Independent Segregation, this parent should produce four kinds of gametes (BL, Bl, bL, and bl) in equal numbers. When united with the bl gametes from the homozygous recessive parents, BL gametes should give rise to purple-long offspring, Bl gametes to purple-round, bL to red-long, and bl to red-round, and these four phenotypes should occur in equal numbers; hence the expected $1:1:1:1$ ratio. But the results Bateson and Punnett actually obtained make it appear that the heterozygous parent produced far more BL and bl gametes than Bl and bL gametes. They proposed an elaborate theory to explain these results, but it was not until 1910 that T. H. Morgan, who had obtained similar results from *Drosophila* crosses, provided the explanation accepted today. He postulated that the anomalous ratios were caused by linkage.

Crossing-Over. If in Bateson and Punnett's cross the genes for purple and long and the genes for red and round were linked, we would expect the *BbLl* parent in the test cross to have produced only two kinds of gametes, BL and bl. This means that the test cross should have yielded offspring of only two phenotypes, purple-long and red-round, in equal numbers. Yet the cross also yielded some purple-round and red-long offspring. How could the *BbLl* parent have produced Bl and bL gametes? Morgan suggested that some mechanism occasionally breaks the original linkages between purple and long and between red and round and establishes in a few individuals new linkages between purple and round and between red and long. The mechanism whereby this recombination is presumed to occur is called crossing-over.

Crossing-over apparently takes place while the homologous chromosomes are synapsed during the first division sequence of meiosis. It is believed that chromatids in each of the two homologous chromosomes break at corresponding points and then exchange parts (Fig. 14.17). Suppose one of the chromosomes in a synaptic pair bears a gene A near one end and a gene B near the other end, and that the other chromosome bears genes a and b at corresponding points. If one chromatid of the first chromosome and one chromatid of the second chromosome break at corresponding points between the two genes, and if the two chromatids ex-

change parts before repair of the break occ[...] then this breakage-fusion mechanism will gi[...] rise to one chromatid bearing genes A and b[...] and to another chromatid bearing genes a and B. If this crossing-over had not occurred, two of the four gametes produced by meiosis would have carried genes A and B and two would have carried genes a and b; there would have been no Ab or aB gametes. But after crossing-over, each of the four gametes carries different genes (AB, Ab, aB, ab). Crossing-over thus increases the number of different genetic combinations that any given cross can produce, and it therefore contributes to variability in the population.

Chromosomal Mapping. If we assume, as Morgan did, that breakage is about equally probable at any point along the length of a chromosome, it follows that the farther apart two linked genes are on the chromosome, the more frequent will breakage occur between them, because there are more points between them at which a break may occur. Or, to be more precise, the frequency of crossing-over between any two linked genes will be proportional to the distance between them. Consequently we can use the percentage of crossing-over as a tool for mapping the locations of genes on chromosomes.

The percentage of crossing-over gives us no information about the absolute distances between genes—we cannot state these distances in microns or millimicrons—but it does give us relative distances. By convention, one unit of map distance on a chromosome is the distance within which crossing-over occurs one percent of the time. In the test cross of Bateson and Punnett, 2 out of 16 of the offspring were recombinant products of crossing-over. Two is 12.5 percent of 16; hence the genes controlling flower color and pollen shape in the sweet peas of this cross are located 12.5 map units apart.

Suppose we know that linked genes B and L are 12.5 map units apart. And suppose we find another gene, A, linked with these, that crosses over with gene L 5 percent of the time.

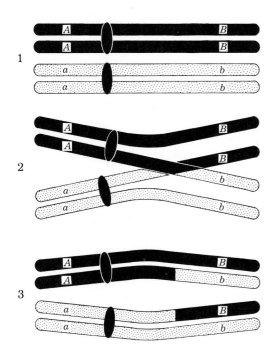

Fig. 14.17. Schematic diagram of crossing-over. (1) The two homologous double-stranded chromosomes, one bearing alleles A and B and the other alleles a and b, lie side by side in synapsis. (2) Corresponding breaks occur in one chromatid of each chromosome, and the fragments are exchanged. (3) After crossing-over, one chromatid of the first chromosome bears alleles A and b and one chromatid of the second chromosome bears alleles a and B.

…e the order of the genes?

…s B–A–L:

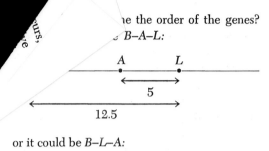

or it could be B–L–A:

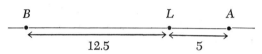

Obviously, the way to decide between these two alternatives is to determine the frequency of crossing-over between A and B. If this frequency is 7.5 percent (12.5 − 5.0), then we know that the first alternative is correct; if it is 17.5 percent (12.5 + 5.0), then we know that the second alternative is correct. In this way, by determining the frequency of crossing-over between each gene and at least two other known genes, it is possible to build up a map showing the arrangement of many different genes on a chromosome (Fig. 14.18).

One important implication of the frequencies of crossing-over and the mapping they make possible should be noted. All known frequencies agree with a model of the chromosome in which the genes are sequentially arranged along the chromosome. Therefore, one possible definition of the gene is that it is a point (or locus) on a chromosome that controls one or more characteristics of the organism. If two characters are always linked, and recombination never occurs between them, then we assume that they are controlled by the same point on the chromosome, i.e. by the same gene. If, on the other hand, crossing-over does occur between them, even if ex-

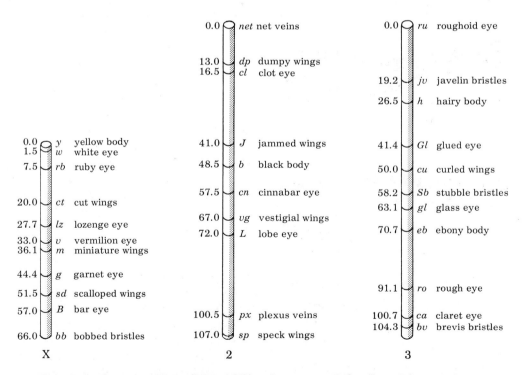

Fig. 14.18. Chromosome map of Drosophila melanogaster. Only a few of the many known genes are shown. The figures indicate their position in cross-over map units from the zero end of the chromosome. Neither the Y chromosome nor the tiny fourth chromosome is shown.

tremely seldom, then we can say that they must be controlled by different points on the chromosome, i.e. by different genes. Crossing-over is thus the test whether two characters are controlled by one chromosomal locus (gene) or by two separate chromosomal loci (genes). According to this view, the gene is the smallest unit of recombination. We shall later examine other possible definitions of the gene.

Giant Chromosomes. Morgan's theory of the gene, which proposed that the genes are bound together in sequence in a limited number of paired linkage groups, that genes belonging to homologous linkage groups can undergo orderly recombination by crossing-over, and that the frequency of crossing-over reveals both the linear order and the relative distances apart of the genes in each linkage group, was derived from breeding experiments and did not depend upon knowledge of the chromosomes. Morgan and most other geneticists of his day were convinced of the validity of Sutton's theory that the genes are located on the chromosomes, but they recognized that the evidence for Sutton's theory was entirely circumstantial. They knew that genes occur in pairs, and that chromosomes do too. They knew that the members of each pair of genes separate at meiosis, as do the chromosomes. And they knew that the number of linkage groups in each species examined corresponds to the number of pairs of chromosomes (there are four linkage groups and four pairs of chromosomes in *Drosophila,* and there are ten linkage groups and ten pairs of chromosomes in corn). But no one had ever actually demonstrated the presence of a gene on a chromosome. And, strictly speaking, no one has done so yet; no one can point out an individual gene under a microscope. But there is now stronger evidence for the chromosomal theory of genes than when Morgan was formulating his concept of the gene.

Some of this evidence has come from the study of the giant chromosomes that occur in the salivary glands of the larvae of many flies,

including *Drosophila.* These chromosomes are more than 200 times larger than normal chromosomes, and they can easily be studied in detail through an ordinary microscope. It has been suggested that the giant chromosomes are the result of repeated replication of the chromosomal material during interphase without accompanying separation of the strands by mitosis, and that each chromosome is therefore composed of a very large number of identical strands lying side by side. These chromosomes were first described in 1881, but it was not until 1930 that geneticists first paid serious attention to them and began to realize their potentialities as material for study of the arrangement of genes.

When stained appropriately, these giant chromosomes have a banded appearance (Fig. 14.19). The bands, which differ in width and the spacings between them, enable the worker who is thoroughly familiar with them to recognize with great precision the various regions of the chromosome. It has been possible by detailed comparative studies of chromosome abnormalities to determine the location of individual genes in relation to the bands. For a while, geneticists hoped that each band represented one gene, but this did not prove to be true; each band usually contains a number of different genes. Cytological studies of this sort have provided a second way of mapping the arrangement of the genes on the chromosomes. Such mapping has fully corroborated that based on crossing-over frequencies with regard to the sequence of the genes, but not with regard to the spacing between them (Fig. 14.20). Apparently the assumption that breaks can occur with equal facility at all points along the chromosomes—an assumption basic to mapping by crossing-over frequencies—is incorrect. However, even though maps based on cytological examination give a more accurate picture of the actual placement of the genes, maps based on crossing-over frequencies are still constructed because they are more useful in predicting the results of crosses involving linking genes.

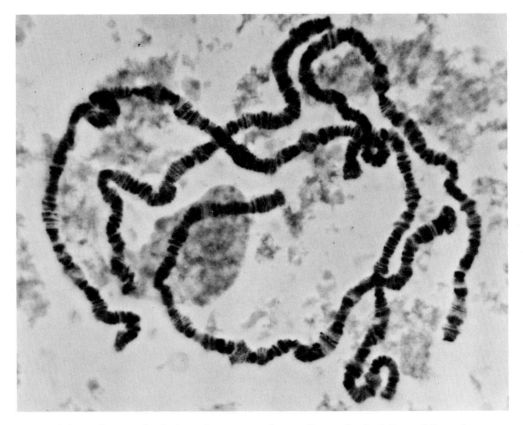

**Fig. 14.19. Photograph of giant chromosomes from salivary gland of *Drosophila melano-
gaster*.** Note the pattern of banding by which different parts of the chromosomes can be
identified.   [Courtesy General Biological Supply House, Inc., Chicago.]

CYTOLOGICAL
MAP   GENETIC MAP

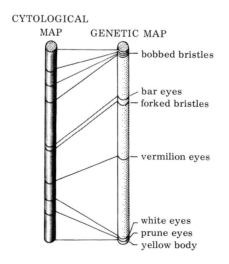

— bobbed bristles

— bar eyes
— forked bristles

— vermilion eyes

— white eyes
— prune eyes
— yellow body

**Fig. 14.20. Comparison of cytological and
genetic (cross-over) maps of portion of the
X chromosome in *Drosophila melanogaster*.**
The two methods of mapping yield the same
sequence for the genes, but the spacing is very
different. [Modified from *Biological Science*,
Houghton Mifflin, 1963. Used by permission
of the Biological Sciences Curriculum Study.]

GENETICS PROBLEMS

The best way to gain an understanding of genetics is to work with it. The fundamental principles discussed above will become clearer to you, and you will grasp them more surely, if you carefully think through the following problems, which illustrate the various patterns of inheritance treated in this chapter. Additional problems will be found in the genetics textbooks listed among the references at the end of the chapter.

1. Assume that white color is dominant over yellow color in squash. If pollen from the anthers of a heterozygous white-fruited plant is placed on the pistil of a yellow-fruited plant, show, using ratios, the genotypes and phenotypes you would expect the seeds from this cross to produce.

2. In human beings, brown eyes are usually dominant over blue eyes. Suppose a blue-eyed man marries a brown-eyed woman whose father was blue-eyed. What proportion of their children would you predict will have blue eyes?

3. If a brown-eyed man marries a blue-eyed woman and they have ten children, all brown-eyed, can you be certain that the man is homozygous? If the eleventh child has brown eyes, will that prove what the father's genotype is?

4. A brown-eyed man whose father was brown-eyed and whose mother was blue-eyed married a blue-eyed woman whose father and mother were both brown-eyed. The couple has a blue-eyed son. For which of the individuals mentioned can you be sure of the genotypes? What are their genotypes? What genotypes are possible for the others?

5. If the litter resulting from the mating of two short-tailed cats contains three kittens without tails, two with long tails, and six with short tails, what would be the simplest way of explaining the inheritance of tail length in these cats? Show genotypes.

6. In the fruit fly *Drosophila melanogaster*, vestigial wings and hairy body are produced by two recessive genes located on different chromosomes. The normal alleles, long wings and hairless body, are dominant. Suppose a vestigial-winged hairy male is crossed with a homozygous normal female. What types of progeny would be expected? If the F_1 from this cross are permitted to mate randomly among themselves, what progeny would be expected in the F_2? Show complete genotypes, phenotypes, and ratios for each generation.

7. Suppose a hairy female heterozygous for vestigial wing is crossed with a vestigial-winged male heterozygous for the hairy character. What will be the characteristics of the F_1?

8. In some breeds of dogs, a dominant gene controls the characteristic of barking while trailing. In these dogs, another independent gene produces erect ears; it is dominant over its allele for drooping ears. Suppose a dog breeder wants to produce a pure-breeding strain of droop-eared barkers, but he knows that the genes for silent trailing and erect ears are present in his kennels. How should he proceed?

9. In hogs, a gene that produces a white belt around the animal's body is dominant over its allele for a uniformly colored body. Another gene produces a fusion of the two hoofs on each foot, a condition known as syndactyly; this gene is dominant over its allele, which produces normal hoofs. Suppose a uniformly colored hog homozygous for syndactyly is mated with a normal-footed hog homozygous for the belted character. What would be the phenotype of the F_1? If the F_1 individuals are allowed to breed freely among themselves, what genotype and phenotype ratios would you predict for the F_2?

10. In watermelons, the genes for green color and for short shape are dominant over their alleles for striped color and for long shape. Suppose a plant with long striped fruit

is crossed with a plant that is heterozygous for both of these characters. What phenotypes would this cross produce and in what ratios?

11. In peas, a gene for tall plants (*T*) is dominant over its allele for short plants (*t*). The gene for smooth peas (*S*) is dominant over its allele for wrinkled peas (*s*). Calculate both phenotypic ratios and genotypic ratios for the results of each of the following crosses:

$$TtSs \times TtSs$$
$$Ttss \times ttss$$
$$ttSs \times Ttss$$
$$TTss \times ttSS$$

12. A dominant gene, *A*, causes yellow color in rats. The dominant allele of another independent gene, *R*, produces black coat color. When the two dominants occur together (*A–R–*), they interact to produce gray. Rats of the genotype *aarr* are cream-colored. If a gray male and a yellow female, when mated, produce offspring approximately ⅜ of which are yellow, ⅜ gray, ⅛ cream, and ⅛ black, what are the genotypes of the two parents?

13. What are the genotypes of a yellow male rat and a black female that, when mated, produce 46 gray and 53 yellow offspring?

14. In Leghorn chickens, colored feathers are due to a dominant gene, *C*; white feathers are due to its recessive allele, *c*. Another dominant gene, *I*, inhibits expression of color in birds with genotypes *CC* or *Cc*. Consequently both *C–I–* and *cc––* are white. A colored cock is mated with a white hen and produces many offspring, all colored. Give the genotypes of both parents and offspring.

15. If the dominant gene *K* is necessary for hearing, and the dominant gene *M* results in deafness no matter what other genes are present, what percentage of the offspring produced by the cross *kkMm* × *Kkmm* will be deaf? (Assume that there is no linkage.)

16. What fraction of the offspring of parents, each with the genotype *KkLlMm*, will be *kkllmm*?

17. Suppose two *DdEeFfGgHh* individuals are mated. What would be the predicted fre-

quency of *ddEEFfggHh* offspring from such a mating?

18. If a man with blood type B, one of whose parents had blood type O, marries a woman with blood type AB, what will be the theoretical percentage of their children with blood type B?

19. Both Mrs. Smith and Mrs. Jones had babies the same day in the same hospital. Mrs. Smith took home a baby girl, whom she named Shirley. Mrs. Jones took home a baby girl, whom she named Jane. Mrs. Jones began to suspect, however, that her child had been accidentally switched with the Smith baby in the nursery. Blood tests were made; Mr. Smith was type A, Mrs. Smith was type B, Mr. Jones was type A, Mrs. Jones was type A, Shirley was type O, and Jane was type B. Had a mixup occurred?

20. When Mexican Hairless dogs are crossed with normally-haired dogs, about half the pups are hairless and half have hair. When, however, two Mexican Hairless dogs are mated, about a third of the pups produced have hair, about two thirds are hairless, and some deformed puppies are born dead. Explain these results.

21. Suppose a pigeon breeder finds that about one fourth of the eggs produced by one of his prize pairs do not hatch. Of the young birds produced by this pair, two thirds are males. Give a possible explanation for these results. (Remember the mechanism of sex determination in birds; see footnote 5, p. 545.)

22. Red-green color blindness is inherited as a sex-linked recessive. If a color-blind woman marries a man who has normal vision, what would be the expected phenotypes of their children with reference to this character?

23. Suppose that gene *b* is sex-linked, recessive, and lethal. A man marries a woman who is heterozygous for this gene. If this couple had many normal children, what would be the predicted sex ratio of these children?

24. A man and his wife both have normal color vision, but a daughter has red-green color

blindness, a sex-linked recessive trait. The man sues his wife for divorce on grounds of infidelity. Can genetics provide evidence supporting the man's case?

25. It is exceedingly difficult to determine the sex of very young chickens, but it is easy to tell, by visual observation, whether or not they are barred. The barred pattern is inherited as a sex-linked dominant. Set up a cross so that the sex of all chicks can be determined when they hatch. (Remember that chickens are birds.)

26. In cats, short hair is dominant over long hair; the gene involved is autosomal. Another gene, B^1, which is sex-linked, produces yellow coat color; its allele B^2 produces black coat color; and the heterozygous combination B^1B^2 produces tortoise-shell coat color. If a long-haired black male is mated with a tortoise-shell female homozygous for short hair, what kind of kittens will be produced in the F_1? If the F_1 cats are allowed to interbreed freely among themselves, what are the chances of obtaining a long-haired yellow male?

27. The diagram at right shows three generations of the pedigree of deafness in a family. Black circles indicate deaf persons. An arrow on a circle indicates a male; a cross below a circle indicates a female.
Is the condition of deafness in this pedigree inherited as (1) a dominant autosomal characteristic? (2) a recessive autosomal characteristic? (3) a sex-linked dominant charac-

teristic? (4) a sex-linked recessive characteristic? (5) a holandric characteristic?

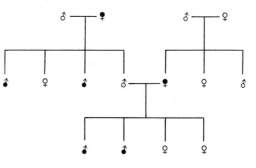

28. In *Drosophila melanogaster*, there is a dominant gene for gray body color and another dominant gene for normal wings. The recessive alleles of these two genes result in black body color and vestigial wings respectively. Flies homozygous for gray body and normal wings were crossed with flies having black bodies and vestigial wings. The F_1 progeny were then test-crossed, with the following results:

Gray body, normal wings	236
Black body, vestigial wings	253
Gray body, vestigial wings	50
Black body, normal wings	61

Would you say that these two genes are linked? If so, how many units apart are they on the chromosome?

29. The cross-over frequency between linked genes A and B is 40%; between B and C, 20%; between C and D, 10%; between C and A, 20%; between D and B, 10%. What is the sequence of the genes on the chromosome?

APPENDIX: THE CHI-SQUARE TEST

One test of statistical significance particularly applicable to many genetic experiments is the so-called chi-square (χ^2) test. The formula for chi-square is as follows:

$$\chi^2 = \Sigma(d^2/e)$$

where d is the deviation from the expected value, e is the expected value, and Σ means "the sum of."

Let us return to the two hypothetical crosses discussed on p. 536, in each of which we expected that the phenotypic results would show a 1 : 1 ratio. In one cross we actually got values of 45 and 55 instead of 50 and 50, and in the other we got values of 5 and 15 instead of 10 and 10. We want to know in each case whether the deviation of the observed from the expected values can reasonably be attributed to chance or whether we must look for some other explanation. Let us first determine the chi-square value for the $45:55$ experiment:

	First phenotype	Second phenotype
Observed values	45	55
Expected values (e)	50	50
Deviation (d)	-5	$+5$
Deviation squared (d^2)	25	25
d^2/e	$25/50 = 0.5$	$25/50 = 0.5$
$\chi^2 = \Sigma(d^2/e)$	$= 0.5 + 0.5 = \mathbf{1.0}$	

Next let us determine the chi-square value for the $5:15$ experiment, following the same procedure:

	First phenotype	Second phenotype
Observed values	5	15
Expected values (e)	10	10
Deviation (d)	-5	$+5$
Deviation squared (d^2)	25	25
d^2/e	$25/10 = 2.5$	$25/10 = 2.5$
$\chi^2 = \Sigma(d^2/e)$	$= 2.5 + 2.5 = \mathbf{5.0}$	

Notice that in each of these experiments the absolute deviations of the observed values from the expected values are the same—a deviation of 5 in each phenotype. But notice also that the chi-squares obtained in the two experiments are very different, that for the experiment based on a sample of 20 being five times as large as that for the experiment based on a sample of 100. This illustrates well how sensitive chi-square is to sample size. It is the difference in sample size alone that has made the great difference in the two chi-square values.

Each of our experiments involved only two classes, in this case two different phenotypes. Hence our chi-square values were calculated on the basis of only two squared deviations. But suppose we had been analyzing an experiment involving three different phenotypes. Then the chi-square would have been calculated on the basis of three squared deviations, and it is only reasonable to expect that the chi-square value obtained would have been higher than one based on only two. It is clear, then, that in evaluating chi-square values one must take into account the number of classes on which they are based. By convention, the number of independent classes in a chi-square test

is termed the degrees of freedom. The number of independent classes is usually one less than the total number of classes in the experiment. Thus, in our experiments involving two phenotypes, there is only one independent class and one degree of freedom, while in an experiment involving three phenotypes there would be two independent classes and two degrees of freedom. A moment's thought will tell you why this is so. In our experiment based on a sample of 100, once we know that 45 offspring show the first phenotype, we automatically know that 55 must show the other phenotype. Since we know the total, the number in one class automatically tells us the number in the other class. In other words, the number in the second class is dependent upon the number in the first class. Therefore, only the first class is an independent class. Similarly, if we perform an experiment involving three different phenotypes, and if the total number of observations in our sample is 100, once we know the number showing the first and second phenotypes we automatically know the number showing the third phenotype, because the number in the third class is dependent upon the number in the first two classes. To repeat: In evaluating chi-square values, one must remember that the number of degrees of freedom is usually one less than the total number of classes.

We now know the chi-square values (1.0 and 5.0) and the degrees of freedom (one for each experiment) for our two hypothetical experiments. The next step is to consult a table of chi-square values such as Table 14.7. This table shows five different chi-square values for each of a series of different degrees of freedom, and gives the probability that an amount of deviation as great as or greater than that represented by each chi-square value would occur strictly by chance. For example, if we look in the table opposite one degree of freedom, we see that a deviation as great as or greater than that represented by a chi-square value of 3.84 can be expected to occur as a result of chance one time in 20; i.e. its chance probability (p) is 0.05. Similarly, at one degree of freedom, a chi-square value as high as or higher than 6.64 has a chance probability of 0.01 (one in 100). Or at two degrees of freedom, a value as high

TABLE 14.7

Probabilities for Certain Values of Chi-Square*

Degrees of freedom	$p = 0.20$ (1 in 5)	$p = 0.10$ (1 in 10)	$p = 0.05$ (1 in 20)	$p = 0.01$ (1 in 100)	$p = 0.001$ (1 in 1,000)
1	1.64	2.71	3.84	6.64	10.83
2	3.22	4.60	5.99	9.21	13.82
3	4.64	6.25	7.82	11.34	16.27
4	5.99	7.78	9.49	13.28	18.46
5	7.29	9.24	11.07	15.09	20.52
6	8.56	10.64	12.59	16.81	22.46
7	9.80	12.02	14.07	18.48	24.32
8	11.03	13.36	15.51	20.09	26.12
9	12.24	14.68	16.92	21.67	27.88
10	13.44	15.99	18.31	23.21	29.59
15	19.31	22.31	25.00	30.58	37.70
20	25.04	28.41	31.41	37.57	45.32
30	36.25	40.26	43.77	50.89	59.70

* Based on a larger table in R. A. Fisher, *Statistical Methods for Research Workers*, 10th ed., Oliver & Boyd, 1946.

as or higher than 5.99 has a chance probability of 0.05.

Now let us evaluate the results obtained in the first of our hypothetical experiments. Here the deviation of our results from the expected was such as to yield a chi-square value of 1.0. The experiment had one degree of freedom. According to the table, a value as high as or higher than 1.64 has a chance probability of 0.20; i.e. a chance deviation from the expected as great as or greater than that represented by 1.64 will occur about once in five trials. Our chi-square is less than 1.64; hence the amount of deviation in our experiment can be expected even more often than once in five trials. Statisticians have arbitrarily decided that deviations having a chance probability as great as or

greater than 0.05 (one in 20) will not be considered statistically significant. The deviation in our experiment has a chance probability much greater than 0.05. Hence this deviation is not regarded as statistically significant. It is presumed to be a chance deviation, which can be disregarded. Our analysis having shown that the experimental results agree well with the predicted results, we need not modify the assumptions on which we based the predictions.

In our second experiment, the chi-square value representing the deviation from the expected results turned out to be 5.0. Again there was one degree of freedom. We look in the table opposite one degree of freedom and find that our value of 5.0 is greater than 3.84, which has a probability of 0.05 (one in 20), but less than 6.64, which has a probability of 0.01 (one in 100). This means that the probability that the deviation in this experiment resulted purely from chance is less than 0.05 but greater than 0.01. We have said that statisticians regard deviations that have a chance probability as great as or greater than 0.05 as not statistically significant. They regard deviations having a chance probability between 0.05 (one in 20) and 0.01 (one in 100) as statistically significant. And they regard deviations having a chance probability of less than 0.01 as highly significant. According to this convention, then, the results of our second experiment are significant, but not highly significant; i.e. they differ significantly but not highly significantly from the expected results. We suspect that some factor other than chance was involved in producing the disagreement between our results and our predictions, but we wouldn't stake our lives on it. We do, however, start looking for a reasonable explanation; perhaps our observations were at fault, or perhaps an error was made in carrying out the experiment, or perhaps we must modify our assumptions concerning the genetics involved in this cross, so that we can make better predictions. In other words, we don't immediately abandon our theory, just because our results and predictions in this one experiment did not agree, but we do become suspicious of our theory and perform other experiments designed to test it further. In this particular case, one of the first things we should do is perform a similar experiment using a larger sample to minimize chance error.

REFERENCES

GARDNER, E. J., 1960. *Principles of Genetics.* Wiley, New York.

PETERS, J. A., ed., 1959. *Classic Papers in Genetics.* Prentice-Hall, Englewood Cliffs, N.J. (A collection of 28 important papers.)

SINNOT, E. W., L. C. DUNN, and T. DOBZHANSKY, 1958. *Principles of Genetics,* 5th ed. McGraw-Hill, New York.

SNYDER, L. H., and P. R. DAVID, 1957. *The Principles of Heredity,* 5th ed. Heath, Boston.

SRB, A. M., R. D. OWEN, and R. S. EDGAR, 1965. *General Genetics,* 2nd ed. Freeman, San Francisco.

STERN, C., 1960. *Principles of Human Genetics,* 2nd ed. Freeman, San Francisco.

SUGGESTED READING

BEARN, A. G., and J. L. GERMAN, III, 1961. "Chromosomes and Disease," *Scientific American,* November. (Offprint 150.)

BONNER, D. M., and S. E. MILLS, 1964. *Heredity,* 2nd ed. Prentice-Hall, Englewood Cliffs, N.J.

LEVINE, R. P., 1962. *Genetics.* Holt, Rinehart & Winston, New York.

MENDEL, G., 1948. *Experiments in Plant Hybridisation.* Harvard University Press, Cambridge, Mass. (This is a translation of Gregor Mendel's original paper, which was first published in 1866.)

MITTWOCH, U., 1963. "Sex Differences in Cells," *Scientific American,* July. (Offprint 161.)

MOORE, J. A., 1963. *Heredity and Development.* Oxford University Press, New York.

CHAPTER
15

THE NATURE OF THE GENE AND ITS ACTION

IN THE LAST CHAPTER, WE POSTULATED THE existence of physical units of inheritance, the genes, which interact with environmental influences to determine the phenotypic characteristics of the organism; and we cited evidence for their arrangement in linear sequence along the chromosomes. Presenting, as we did, a model of the gene based almost entirely on deductions from inheritance patterns, we obviously left some fundamental genetic problems untouched. We said nothing about the chemical nature of the genes; we did not say how the genetic material is replicated, how genes influence the characteristics of the organism, or how they regulate the myriad activities of a living cell. In effect, we treated the genes as though they were a string of beads of unknown composition somehow exerting almost magical control over the visible attributes of living things. Not many years ago this was all any textbook could do. Nothing was known of the chemical makeup of genes; nor was it known how they are replicated or how they influence the phenotype. But that is all changed. The enormous advances of the last twenty years—indeed of the last five years—in our understanding of the control mechanisms of living cells constitute nothing short of a revolution, a revolution with such far-reaching implications that many scientists have claimed it will eventually prove more important to the future of the human species than the birth of the atomic age in physics. It is to these revolutionary discoveries that this chapter will be devoted.

THE CHEMICAL NATURE OF THE GENETIC MATERIAL

The Discovery of DNA and Its Function

The Composition of Chromosomes. If the genes are located on the chromosomes, an obvious first step in ascertaining the chemical nature of genes is to determine the types of compounds present in the chromosomes. Once this has been done, experiments could be devised to discover which of the chromosomal compounds is the bearer of genetic information. What, then, is the chemical composition of chromosomes?

In 1869 Friedrich Miescher, a Swiss biochemist who was studying the proteins of pus cells, showed that when such cells are treated with pepsin to render the proteins soluble, the nuclei shrink but remain essentially intact. He showed, further, that the same nuclear material that can withstand peptic digestion also behaves totally unlike protein when treated with a variety of other reagents, and that it contains phosphorus in addition to the carbon, oxygen, hydrogen, and nitrogen that would be expected if it were a protein. Miescher called this nonproteinaceous material "nuclein"; since it is acidic, later workers have called it "nucleic acid." Further research has shown that cells contain several different sorts of nucleic acids, some not restricted to the nucleus; the type studied by Miescher was *deoxyribonucleic acid,* or **DNA** for short.

In 1914 Robert Feulgen, a German chemist, devised a method of selectively staining DNA a brilliant crimson. Feulgen developed his technique in test-tube experiments and did not apply it to whole cells until ten years later. When at last he did, he found that the nuclear DNA is located in the chromosomes. Feulgen staining has since been applied to a great variety of cells by numerous workers. Using this technique, two teams, André Boivin and Roger and Colette Vendrely of the University of Strasbourg, France, and Alfred E. Mirsky and Hans Ris of the Rockefeller Institute, independently measured the DNA content of nuclei from many types of cells and showed conclusively that all the body cells of a given organism ordinarily contain the same amount of DNA, despite the fact that cells from such different tissues as liver, kidney, heart, nerve, and muscle differ drastically in the amounts of other substances they contain. These workers showed, further, that egg and sperm cells contain only half as much DNA as the somatic cells. Since it was already assumed that mitosis distributes a complete set of genes to every somatic cell, regardless of its eventual role, and that meiosis distributes to every gamete cell exactly half the amount of genetic material found in the somatic cells, the discovery that the amount of DNA is usually constant in all somatic cells within a species but is halved in the gametes suggested that DNA might be the essential material of the genes.

But many workers refused to take this possibility seriously. It was known that the chromosomes of most organisms contain protein in addition to nucleic acid, and most biologists assumed that the protein must be the genetic material because, in their view, only protein had the chemical complexity necessary to encode so much information. Discovery that the amount of structural protein in the chromosomes, unlike the amount of DNA, is not constant but varies with the overall activity of the cell did not, by and large, cause this long-held conviction to be relinquished.

Most chromosomes consist principally of a complex of nucleic acid and protein. This would seem to indicate that genes are composed of nucleic acid or of protein or of the complex of the two (nucleoprotein). In the early 1940's, each of these three possibilities had its advocates, with the majority favoring protein. Today, almost all biologists are convinced that DNA is the genetic material. To understand how this shift has come about, we must leave our old friends *Drosophila* and peas, and turn to microorganisms such as bacteria, viruses, and molds.

DNA Versus Protein. In 1928 Fred Griffith, an English medical bacteriologist, published a paper describing some of his experiments on pneumococci, the bacteria that cause pneumonia. Griffith studied two different strains of pneumococci, a virulent one (strain S) with a thick surface capsule of polysaccharide and a nonvirulent one (strain R) without a capsule. He showed that if he injected mice with live strain-R bacteria, the mice survived. Mice injected with live strain-S bacteria soon died, but mice injected with heat-killed strain-S bacteria survived. These results (Table 15.1) were readily understandable. But the results of another of his experiments were thoroughly perplexing; he injected mice with a mixture of live strain R and heat-killed strain

TABLE 15.1

Griffith's Results

Bacteria injected	Reaction of mice
Live strain R	Survived
Live strain S	Died
Dead strain S	Survived
Live strain R plus dead strain S	Died

S and found that the mice died. How could a mixture of nonvirulent and dead bacteria have killed the mice? He examined the bodies of the dead mice and found that they were full of live strain-S bacteria! Where had they come from? After many careful experiments, Griffith became convinced that somehow the live unencapsulated strain-R bacteria had been transformed into live capsulated strain-S bacteria by material from the dead strain-S cells. The transformed bacteria, when cultured, reproduced new strain-S bacteria. Presumably, hereditary material from the dead bacteria had entered the live strain-R cells and changed them into strain-S cells.

Other workers repeated Griffith's experiments and obtained similar results. Methods were developed for bringing about the transformation in the test tube. James L. Alloway of the Rockefeller Institute even showed that live strain-R cells in a test tube could be transformed into strain-S bacteria by fluid in which dead strain-S cells had been dissolved; whole strain-S cells were not necessary. Apparently the hereditary characteristics of the virulent strain were transmitted to the cells of the nonvirulent strain by some substance that could withstand both the killing and the dissolving of the cells in which it had originally been contained.

The work of Griffith, Alloway, and others in the late 1920's and early 1930's was interesting to other biologists, but its significance was not appreciated at that time. It was not until 1944 that O. T. Avery, Maclyn McCarty, and Colin MacLeod of the Rockefeller Institute demonstrated that the transforming principle was DNA. Nothing else was necessary. From our present perspective, this seems like strong evidence that DNA rather than protein or a nucleoprotein complex is the essential genetic material, but at that time many scientists remained unconvinced.

During the next ten years, however, the evidence for DNA steadily became stronger. At least 30 different examples of bacterial *transformation* by purified DNA were described. And strong evidence came from another source —the studies of bacterial viruses by Alfred D. Hershey and Martha Chase of the Carnegie Laboratory of Genetics at Cold Spring Harbor, New York. These scientists worked with a special type of virus that attacks the bacterium *Escherichia coli,* which is abundant in the human digestive tract. This type of bacteria-destroying virus is called *bacteriophage,* or simply phage for short.

Evidence from a variety of sources shows that viruses are composed of two chief components, a protein coat or shell and a nucleic acid core. The electron microscope has revealed that phage viruses are structurally more complex than many other types (Fig. 15.1). Their protein coat is divided into a head region and an elongate tail region made up of a hollow core, a surrounding sheath, and six distal fibers. All of the DNA is in the head. Electron micrographs show that when a phage attacks a bacterial cell it becomes attached by the tip of its tail to the wall of the bacterial cell (Fig. 15.2); apparently the tip of the tail contains a protein that reacts specifically with receptor sites of the bacterial wall. There is no

evidence that the protein coat of the phage ever actually enters the bacterial cell; yet within a few minutes after the phage becomes attached to the wall, new phage particles appear within the bacterium and the bacterial cell soon ruptures, releasing hundreds of new bacteriophage particles into the surrounding medium. It can be shown that these new phage are genetically identical with those that initiated the infection. Hereditary material must have been injected into the bacterial cell by the phage particles attached to its wall, and this hereditary material from the phage must have usurped the metabolic machinery of the bacterium and put it to work manufacturing new phage.

Hershey and Chase designed an experiment to determine whether the infecting phage injects into the bacterium only DNA or only protein or some of both. They made use of the fact that DNA contains phosphorus while protein does not and of the fact that protein contains sulfur while DNA does not. They cultured phage on bacteria grown on a medium containing a radioactive isotope of phosphorus (P^{32}) and a radioactive isotope of sulfur (S^{35}). The phage particles incorporated the P^{32} into their protein, and they incorporated the S^{35} into their DNA. Hershey and Chase then infected nonradioactive bacteria with the radioactive phage. They allowed sufficient time for the phage to become attached to the walls of the bacteria and inject hereditary material. Then they agitated the bacteria in a blendor in order to detach what remained of the phage from their surfaces. Analysis of these remains showed that they contained S^{35} but no P^{32}, an indication that only the empty protein coat had been left outside the bacterial cell. Analysis of the bacteria showed that they contained P^{32} but no S^{35}, an indication that only DNA had been injected into them by the phage. DNA alone was sufficient to transmit to the bacteria all the genetic information necessary to cause them to produce new phage. This experiment, reported in 1952, supported the

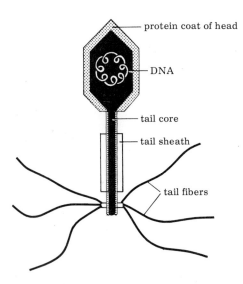

Fig. 15.1. Diagram of a bacteriophage.

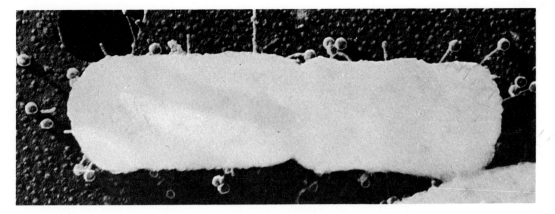

Fig. 15.2. Electron micrograph of a bacterial cell with numerous phage particles attached to its surface. × 50,000. [Courtesy T. F. Anderson, *Ann. Inst. Pasteur (Paris)*, vol. 93, 1957.]

earlier conclusions based on transformation experiments that nucleic acids, not proteins, constitute the genetic material.

The Molecular Structure of DNA

The Chemical Components of DNA. Miescher found that his nuclein (DNA) contained nitrogen, phosphorus, carbon, oxygen, and hydrogen. But a single molecule of DNA is very large, containing many thousands of atoms. How could the arrangement of such a huge number of atoms be worked out in detail to give a picture of the molecular structure of DNA? Many chemists attacked this problem, and by the time of the Second World War much had been learned about DNA.

Fortunately for our understanding, DNA, like the other large organic molecules that we have examined (polysaccharides, fats, and proteins), proved to be composed of a few relatively simple building-block compounds bonded together in sequence. These building-block compounds are called *nucleotides*. Each nucleotide, in turn, is composed of three still smaller constituent parts: a phosphate group, a five-carbon sugar called deoxyribose, and an organic nitrogen-containing base. Both the

phosphate group and the base are bonded to the sugar (Fig. 15.3). Four different kinds of nucleotides occur in DNA; they are alike in containing the phosphate and deoxyribose, but they differ in their nitrogenous bases. One nucleotide contains a base called *adenine*, another contains *guanine*, another *thymine*, and another *cytosine*. The structurally similar adenine and guanine are known as purines; thymine and cytosine are known as pyrimidines. As Fig. 15.4 shows, purines have a double-ring structure while pyrimidines have a single ring.

The nucleotides within a DNA molecule are bonded together in such a way that the sugar of one nucleotide is always attached to the phosphate group of the next nucleotide in the

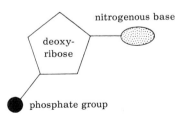

Fig. 15.3. **Diagram of a nucleotide from DNA.** A phosphate group and a nitrogenous base are attached to deoxyribose, a five-carbon sugar.

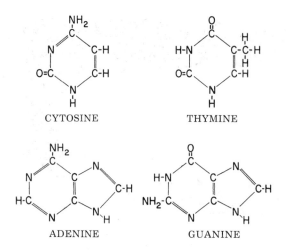

CYTOSINE   THYMINE

ADENINE   GUANINE

Fig. 15.4. The four nitrogenous bases in DNA. The two single-ring bases, cytosine and thymine, are pyrimidines; the two double-ring bases, adenine and guanine, are purines.

sequence (Fig. 15.5). Thus a long chain of alternating sugar and phosphate groups is established, with the nitrogenous bases oriented as side groups off this chain. The order in which the four different nucleotides occur differs for different DNA molecules, and it is apparently this order that determines the specificity of the DNA.

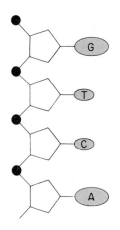

Fig. 15.5. Portion of a single chain of DNA. Nucleotides are hooked together by bonds between their sugar and phosphate groups (G, guanine; T, thymine; C, cytosine; A, adenine).

For a time, it was thought that the four nucleotides occur in equal amounts in DNA, but it was later shown that they do not. However, E. Chargaff and his colleagues at Columbia University did show in 1950 that, regardless of other differences in the composition of different samples of DNA, they were invariably alike in one important respect: The number of adenine nucleotides in any given DNA molecule was always the same as the number of thymine nucleotides, and the number of guanine nucleotides was always the same as the number of cytosine nucleotides. No reason why the amount of adenine should equal the amount of thymine, or why the amount of guanine should equal the amount of cytosine, was known.

The Spatial Configuration of the DNA Molecule. By 1950 much was known about the chemical composition of DNA. But almost nothing was known about the spatial arrangement of the atoms within the DNA molecule; nor was it known how this molecule, if it really was the stuff of which genes were made, could contain within it the necessary information for replicating itself and for controlling cellular function. About this time, several workers, among whom Maurice H. F. Wilkins and his co-workers at King's College, London, were outstanding, began applying the techniques of X-ray diffraction analysis to DNA. These techniques, which are applicable only to crystalline or partly crystalline material, are difficult to apply to solutions of DNA, which are viscous and almost gluelike in consistency. By 1953, however, Wilkins had learned to prepare crystalline fibers of DNA by slowly withdrawing a needle point from a DNA solution. He was therefore able to obtain much sharper X-ray diffraction patterns than had previously been possible. These diffraction patterns revealed three major periodicities in the crystalline DNA: one of 3.4 angstroms, one of 20 angstroms, and one of 34 angstroms.

Now began a collaboration that was to yield

a short publication which would rank as one of the major milestones in the history of biology. James D. Watson and Francis H. C. Crick, working in the Cavendish Laboratory at Cambridge University, decided to try to develop a model of the structure of the DNA molecule by combining what was known about the chemical content of DNA (particularly Chargaff's rule of adenine-thymine equality and guanine-cytosine equality) with the information gained from Wilkins' X-ray diffraction studies and with the available information concerning the exact distances between bonded atoms in molecules, the angles between bonds, and the sizes of atoms. Watson and Crick built scale models of the component parts of DNA and then attempted to fit them together in a way that would agree with what had been learned from all these separate sources.

They were certain that the 3.4-angstrom periodicity discovered by Wilkins corresponded to the distance between successive nucleotides in the DNA chain and that the 20-angstrom periodicity corresponded to the width of the chain. But what about the 34-angstrom periodicity? To explain this third periodicity, they postulated that the chain of nucleotides was coiled in a helix. (To visualize a helix, think of the chain as though it had been wound around a long cylinder; a helix is not the same thing as a spiral, which is wound around a cone, not a cylinder.) The 34-angstrom periodicity would thus correspond to the distance between successive turns of the helix, and it would indicate how tightly the chain was wound. Since 34 is exactly ten times the 3.4-angstrom distance between successive nucleotides, it would follow that each turn of the helix must be ten nucleotides long.

Having made these essential assumptions about the meaning of the X-ray diffraction data, Watson and Crick then tried to correlate them with the information from other sources. They immediately ran into a discrepancy. They calculated that a single chain of nucleotides coiled in a helix that was 20 angstroms wide and had turns that were 34 angstroms long would have a density only half as great as the known density of DNA. An obvious inference was that the DNA molecule is composed of two nucleotide chains rather than one. Now they had to determine the relationship between the two chains within the double helix. They tried several arrangements of their scale model and found that the one that best fitted all the data was one in which the two nucleotide chains were wound in opposite directions around a hypothetical cylinder of appropriate diameter, with the purine and pyrimidine bases oriented toward the interior of the cylinder (Fig. 15.6). With the bases oriented in this manner, hydrogen bonds between the bases of opposite chains could supply the force to hold the two chains together and to maintain the helical configuration. In other words, the DNA molecule, when unwound, would have a ladderlike structure, with the uprights of the ladder formed by the two long chains of alternating sugar and phosphate groups, and with each of the cross rungs of the ladder formed by two nitrogenous bases loosely bonded to each other by hydrogen bonds (Fig. 15.7).

It soon became clear to Watson and Crick that each cross rung must be composed of one purine base and one pyrimidine base. Their scale model showed that the available space between the sugar–phosphate uprights was just sufficient to accommodate three ring structures. Hence two purines opposite each other occupied too much space, because each had two rings for a total of four, and two pyrimidines opposite each other did not come close enough to bond properly, because each had only one ring. Therefore adenine–guanine, thymine–cytosine, adenine–adenine, guanine–guanine, thymine–thymine, and cytosine–cytosine cross rungs could not occur in the molecule. This left four possible pairings: adenine–thymine, adenine–cytosine, guanine–thymine, and guanine–cytosine. But further examination revealed that, although adenine and cytosine were of the proper size to fit together

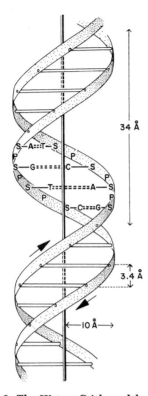

Fig. 15.6. The Watson-Crick model of DNA. The molecule is composed of two polynucleotide chains held together by hydrogen bonds between their adjacent bases (S, sugar; P, phosphate; A, T, G, C, nitrogenous bases). The double-chained structure is coiled in a helix (shown here wound around a hypothetical rod). The width of the molecule is 10 angstroms; the distance between adjacent nucleotides is 3.4 angstroms; and the length of one complete coil is 34 angstroms.

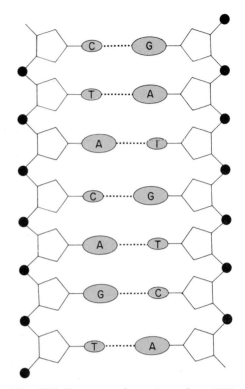

Fig. 15.7. Diagram of portion of a DNA molecule uncoiled. The molecule has a ladderlike structure, with the two uprights composed of alternating sugar and phosphate groups and the cross rungs composed of paired nitrogenous bases. Note that each cross rung has one purine base (large oval) and one pyrimidine base (small oval). When the purine is guanine (G), then the pyrimidine with which it is paired is always cytosine (C); when the purine is adenine (A), then the pyrimidine is thymine (T).

into the available space, they could not be arranged in a way that would permit hydrogen bonding between them; the same was true of guanine and thymine. Therefore neither adenine–cytosine nor guanine–thymine cross rungs could occur in the DNA molecule. This left only adenine–thymine and guanine–cytosine. Both of these base pairs seemed to fulfill all requirements. It did not seem to matter in which order the bases occurred; thymine–adenine was as satisfactory as adenine–thymine, and cytosine–guanine was as satisfactory as guanine–cytosine. The essential requirement

seemed to be that adenine and thymine always be paired with each other and that guanine and cytosine always be paired. This pairing would, of course, explain Chargaff's rule; the amounts of adenine and thymine in any DNA molecule are always equal because these two bases are always paired, and, similarly, the amounts of guanine and cytosine are always equal because these are always paired.

In summary, then, the Watson-Crick model of the DNA molecule shows a double helix with the two main chains composed of alternating sugar and phosphate groups, these chains being loosely bonded together by hydrogen bonds between adenine and thymine from opposite chains and between guanine and cytosine from opposite chains. This model, in essentially the same form in which it was first proposed by Watson and Crick in April, 1953, has been consistently supported by later research, and it has received general acceptance. Watson, Crick, and Wilkins have been awarded Nobel Prizes for this critically important work.

The Replication of DNA

The Theory of Watson and Crick. DNA, if it is the genetic substance, must have built into it the information necessary to replicate itself and to control the cell's attributes and functions. One of the most satisfying things about the Watson-Crick model of DNA is that it immediately suggests a way in which the first of these two requirements may be met.

Since the DNA of all organisms is alike in being a polymer composed of only four different nucleotides, the characteristics that distinguish the DNA of one gene from the DNA of another gene must be the total number of nucleotides, the ratio of adenine and thymine to guanine and cytosine, and the sequence in which the four possible types of cross rungs (adenine–thymine, thymine–adenine, guanine–cytosine, and cytosine–guanine) occur. The basic question of genetic replication is, then: Assuming that an adequate supply of the four nucleotides is already synthesized in the cells, what tells the cell's biochemical machinery how to put these nucleotide building blocks together in exactly the quantities and sequences characteristic of the DNA already present in the cell?

Watson and Crick pointed out that if the two chains of a DNA molecule are separated by rupturing the hydrogen bonds between the base pairs, each chain provides all the information necessary for synthesizing a new partner. Since an adenine nucleotide must always

pair with a thymine nucleotide, and since a guanine nucleotide must always pair with a cytosine nucleotide, the sequence of nucleotides in one chain determines precisely what the sequence of nucleotides in its complementary chain must be. In other words, if the cell separated the two chains in its DNA molecules, it could then line up separate nucleotides next to each of the single chains, putting each type of nucleotide next to its proper partner. Once the nucleotides had been arranged in the proper sequence, they could be bonded together to form a complete new chain. Thus, separating the two chains of a DNA molecule and then using each chain as a template or mold against which to synthesize a new partner for it would result in two complete double-chained molecules identical to the original molecule (Fig. 15.8).

Experimental Support of the Theory. Satisfying as it was, this explanation of DNA replication was pure speculation, unsupported

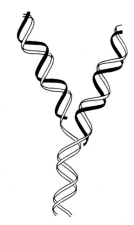

Fig. 15.8. Replication of DNA. As the two polynucleotide chains of the old DNA (white) uncoil, new polynucleotide chains (black) are synthesized on their surfaces. The process produces two complete double-chained molecules each of which is identical in base sequence to the original double-chained molecule. [Modified from F. W. Stahl, *The Mechanics of Inheritance*, © 1964, by permission of Prentice-Hall, Inc., Englewood Cliffs, N.J.]

by any experimental evidence, when it was first put forward by Watson and Crick in 1953. Since then, convincing evidence has come from the work of a number of investigators. We have space to mention only two supporting experiments here.

In 1957 Arthur Kornberg and his associates at Washington University in St. Louis reported that they had established a system in which DNA synthesis would take place in a test tube. They extracted the enzymes necessary for DNA synthesis from cells of *Escherichia coli* and combined these enzymes with a plentiful supply of the four nucleotides as raw material; these nucleotides contained a radioactive isotope of carbon (C^{14}). ATP was added as a source of energy. When they then added some primer DNA to this mixture of enzymes, nucleotides, and ATP, and incubated the preparation for a suitable period, they found, on analysis, that some new DNA containing C^{14} was present. The labeled nucleotides had been built into DNA chains. This synthesis would not occur unless the primer DNA was present. Kornberg was able to show that the ratio of adenine and thymine to guanine and cytosine in the new DNA was precisely the same as that in the primer DNA. In other words, all the evidence indicated that the newly synthesized DNA was identical with the primer DNA. Kornberg received a Nobel Prize for this work.

Kornberg's experiment seemed to demonstrate that DNA synthesis cannot take place in the absence of primer DNA, which presumably provides the information necessary to guide the synthesis. It also strongly suggested that new DNA is always a copy of the primer DNA. But it did not actually provide any evidence that the copy mechanism works in the way proposed by Watson and Crick. More direct support for their model came from an experiment reported in 1958 by Matthew S. Meselson and Frank W. Stahl of the California Institute of Technology.

These workers grew *Escherichia coli* for many generations on a medium in which the nitrogen source contained only the heavy isotope N^{15}. Eventually all the DNA in these bacteria contained the heavy isotope instead of the normal isotope N^{14}. Then the nitrogen source was abruptly changed from N^{15} to N^{14}. Cell samples were removed at regular intervals thereafter, and the DNA was extracted from them and subjected to a complicated procedure designed to separate DNA of different densities. The experiment showed that when cells containing only heavy DNA (i.e. DNA in which both chains had only N^{15} in their purine and pyrimidine bases) were allowed to undergo one division on the N^{14} medium, the DNA of the new cells was intermediate in density between heavy DNA and light DNA. In other words, the nitrogen in the DNA of the new cells was half N^{15} and half N^{14}. This is precisely what would be expected if the two chains of the heavy parental DNA separated and acted as templates for the synthesis of new partners from nucleotides containing only N^{14} (Fig. 15.9). Each new DNA molecule should be composed of one heavy chain from the parent and one light chain newly synthesized, the molecule thus having intermediate density. To prove that all the N^{15} really was in one chain of the intermediate-density DNA and all the N^{14} in the other chain, Meselson and Stahl subjected the DNA to a treatment that breaks the hydrogen bonds between the bases and separates the chains. Sure enough, this procedure produced heavy chains and light chains; the two isotopes had not been distributed randomly throughout the DNA molecule, but had been localized each in one of the chains, just as would be predicted from the Watson-Crick theory.

THE MECHANISM OF GENE ACTION

We have seen that the Watson-Crick model of DNA provides an easily understood explana-

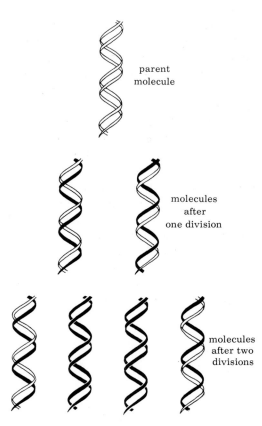

parent
molecule

molecules
after
one division

molecules
after two
divisions

Fig. 15.9. Diagram of results of the Mesel-son-Stahl experiment. The parent DNA molecule (white chains) contained only heavy nitrogen. After one division, the DNA had an intermediate density, an indication that half the nitrogen in each molecule was heavy and half was light. The two heavy parental chains had separated, and each had acted as the template for synthesis of a complementary light chain (black). Even after several additional duplications, the two original heavy parental chains remained intact. [Redrawn from M. S. Meselson and F. W. Stahl, *Proc. Nat. Acad. Sci.*, vol. 44, 1958.]

tion for genetic replication, and that there is convincing experimental evidence in support of that explanation. Now we must ask what our newly gained knowledge of the chemistry of heredity can tell us about the way in which genes control cellular function. How can the DNA gene be related to phenotypically expressed inherited traits? How can nucleic acid in the nucleus control what goes on in the cytoplasm—control it so precisely that rabbit zygotes develop into rabbits and human zygotes develop into human beings?

The One-Gene–One-Enzyme Hypothesis

The Hypothesis. Alkaptonuria, a hereditary disease in human beings in which the urine is very dark-colored, has been known to physicians for over three hundred years. More than a hundred years ago, it was shown that the darkening of the urine is caused by the presence in it of a chemical called alkapton. Normal individuals possess an enzyme that catalyzes the oxidation of alkapton to carbon dioxide and water, but those who have alkaptonuria lack this enzyme and must thus excrete alkapton in its undegraded form. In 1909 Archibald Garrod, an English physician, showed that alkaptonuria is inherited as a simple Mendelian recessive. Apparently the normal gene is necessary for production of the enzyme that oxidizes alkapton; persons homozygous for the mutant form of the gene do not produce the enzyme.

Phenylketonuria is another rare disease related to alkaptonuria. Persons with the disease excrete phenylpyruvic acid in the urine, and they are invariably severely feeble-minded. Normal individuals oxidize phenylpyruvic acid to a closely related compound, but phenylketonurics lack the enzyme that catalyzes this reaction. Like alkaptonuria, this disease is inherited as a simple Mendelian recessive. Again it is clear that the normal gene is necessary for production of an enzyme that persons homozygous for the mutant allele cannot produce.

Alkaptonuria, phenylketonuria, and other similar examples that could be cited should have suggested to geneticists that there is a close relationship between genes and enzymes. But for many years most geneticists ignored the implication of work like Garrod's. Then in the 1930's several workers studied the genetics of eye-pigment formation in a series of *Dro-*

sophila eye-color mutants. They were able to show that synthesis of normal eye pigment involves a series of reactions that produce identifiable intermediate compounds and that each of these reactions is under genetic control. Gene mutations result in alterations of these chemical reactions and thus change the pigment produced by them. A relationship between genes and specific enzymes seemed to be indicated, and a new field of genetics, often called biochemical genetics, began to emerge from such studies.

But concepts of gene action remained rather nebulous until the early 1940's, when George W. Beadle and Edward L. Tatum, then at Stanford University, proposed their "one-gene–one-enzyme" hypothesis. According to this hypothesis, the production or specificity of each enzyme in the cell is controlled, in its principal aspects, by one and only one gene. In other words, genes exert their control over cellular function by controlling the enzymes that control the chemical reactions of the cell; these reactions, in turn, determine the phenotypic characteristics.

Evidence from *Neurospora*. Beadle and Tatum formulated their one-gene–one-enzyme hypothesis on the basis of the results they obtained from their pioneering experiments on red bread mold, *Neurospora crassa*. In the years since their work in the early 1940's, *Neurospora* has taken its place alongside such organisms as *Drosophila* and corn as one of the genetically most extensively studied living things. It has many advantages as an experimental organism: (1) It is easily cultured in the laboratory. (2) It has a life cycle of only ten days. (3) It sometimes reproduces sexually, but it also readily multiplies asexually; hence new strains can be propagated without the genetic change that would result from sexual recombination. (4) It is normally haploid, which means that recessive genes cannot be hidden by dominant alleles. And (5) when it produces spores by meiosis, the products of

each meiosis are packaged together in a spore sac in a definite order (Fig. 15.10), which makes it possible to analyze directly the genotypic frequencies produced by a cross, without the necessity of relying solely on statistical analysis.

Wild type *Neurospora* can be grown on a minimal nutrient medium of known composition. Beadle and Tatum used X rays to induce mutations affecting the nutrient requirements of the mold. Their procedure was as follows (Fig. 15.11): Asexual spores were irradiated to induce mutations, and then the spores were germinated on a complete medium (one composed of the normal minimal medium plus all the known vitamins and amino acids and several alternative carbon sources). This procedure ensured that most nutritional mu-

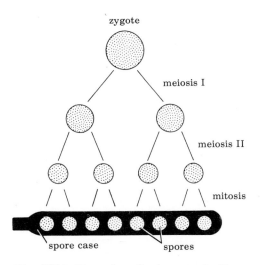

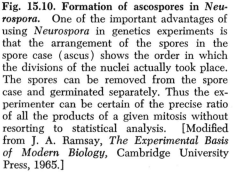

Fig. 15.10. Formation of ascospores in *Neurospora*. One of the important advantages of using *Neurospora* in genetics experiments is that the arrangement of the spores in the spore case (ascus) shows the order in which the divisions of the nuclei actually took place. The spores can be removed from the spore case and germinated separately. Thus the experimenter can be certain of the precise ratio of all the products of a given mitosis without resorting to statistical analysis. [Modified from J. A. Ramsay, *The Experimental Basis of Modern Biology,* Cambridge University Press, 1965.]

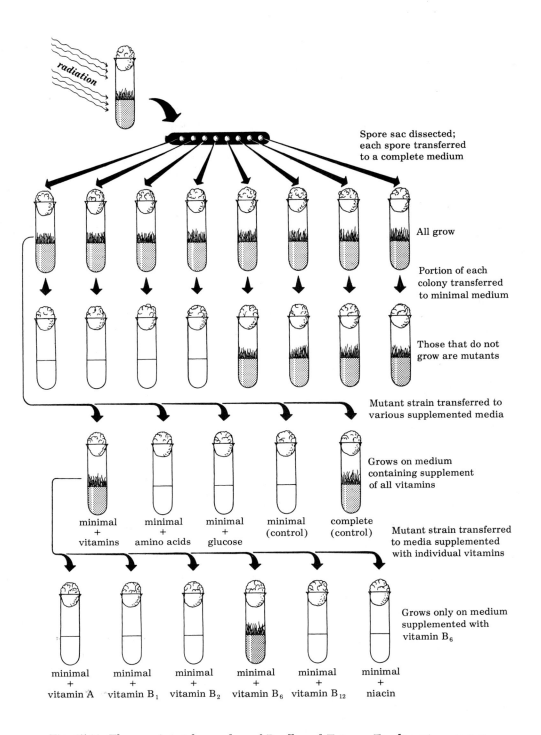

Fig. 15.11. The experimental procedure of Beadle and Tatum. For discussion, see text.

tants would survive and grow, because compounds they might no longer be able to synthesize for themselves were readily available in the medium. Once sufficiently large colonies had been established on the complete medium, a small portion of each colony was transferred onto minimal medium. This step revealed that some of the colonies were unable to grow on the minimal medium, hence that they must be mutant strains requiring some nutrient not supplied by this medium. The mutant strains having thus been located, the next step was to try to determine which of the supplements present in the complete medium but not in the minimal medium was needed by each strain. First, small portions of each mutant colony were transferred from the complete medium to each of three new media: minimal plus all known vitamins, minimal plus all amino acids, and minimal plus alternative carbon sources (usually glucose substituted for sucrose). By observing on which of these three media the mutant would grow, it was possible to learn whether the unknown nutrient needed by the mutant was a vitamin, an amino acid, or a simpler carbon source. Suppose, for example, that a particular mutant failed to grow on minimal plus amino acids or minimal plus alternative carbon but did grow on minimal plus vitamins. This would indicate that the nutrient needed was a vitamin. Now samples of this mutant strain could be transferred from complete medium to a series of media each of which consisted of minimal medium plus one vitamin. If the mold grew only on a medium containing vitamin B_6, this would indicate that the nutrient it needed was vitamin B_6. The mutation must have destroyed the mold's capacity to synthesize this compound for itself, probably by failing to provide an enzyme necessary for the synthesis.

Beadle and Tatum isolated a large number of different mutant strains by this method. In every case where the mutant had lost the ability to synthesize a particular nutrient, they found that the character was inherited in a pattern that indicated the action of only one gene. It was this finding that led them to formulate the one-gene–one-enzyme hypothesis. Since enzymes are proteins, as was demonstrated in the late 1920's by James B. Sumner of Cornell University and John H. Northrop of the Rockefeller Institute, this was, in effect, a one-gene–one-protein hypothesis, a proposal that, somehow, each gene controls the synthesis of a protein. Beadle and Tatum were awarded Nobel Prizes for their important work on the genetics of *Neurospora*.

Apparent Exceptions. In the years after the enunciation of the one-gene–one-enzyme hypothesis, numerous examples were found that did not seem to fit this neat formulation. In some cases, it was shown that mutations of either of two or more genes could produce the same nutrient requirement. In other cases, mutation of a single gene might result in two new nutritional requirements. Further study showed, however, that in many such cases the one-to-one relationship between genes and enzymes still held. Mutation of two different genes might cause the same new nutrient requirement if, for example, the product of the reaction catalyzed by the enzyme associated with the first gene was the necessary substrate for the reaction catalyzed by the enzyme associated with the second gene, as follows:

$$A \xrightarrow{\text{enzyme-1}} B \xrightarrow{\text{enzyme-2}} C$$

Absence of either enzyme would result in an inability to synthesize compound C, which might then have to be supplied preformed in the nutrient medium. This, then, would not really be an exception to the one-gene–one-enzyme relationship. Similarly, mutation of a single gene might result in two new nutritional requirements if the reaction catalyzed by the enzyme associated with that gene produced two different essential products, as follows:

$$D \xrightarrow{\text{enzyme}} E + F$$

In this case, both E and F might have to be supplied preformed in the nutrient medium if the enzyme was absent. Again, this would not really be an exception to the hypothesized relationship.

Another type of apparent exception emerged from studies of the genetics of hereditary blood defects such as sickle-cell anemia. It had been shown that sickle-cell anemia results from mutation of a single gene. Vernon M. Ingram of Cambridge University demonstrated in 1956 that the abnormal behavior of the erythrocytes in this disease is due to the replacement of glutamic acid by another amino acid, valine, at one point in the hemoglobin molecule. The entire hemoglobin molecule consists of about 600 amino acids arranged in four polypeptide chains of two different types. Thus each of the two identical half molecules consists of two different polypeptide chains composed of about 300 amino acids. Sickle-cell hemoglobin differs from normal hemoglobin in only one of these 300 amino acids. Yet this slight difference is sufficient to produce a serious, often fatal, disease. This point in itself is remarkable, but also remarkable is the fact that mutation of a gene in the nucleus could cause such a precise change in a protein of the cytoplasm. Ingram's discovery served to strengthen the idea that genes encode the information that directs the synthesis of proteins, and it thus seemed to support a one-gene–one-protein concept. But soon thereafter it was found that another hereditary blood disease, which also involves alteration of the hemoglobin molecule, segregates independently from sickle-cell anemia and must, therefore, be controlled by a different gene. Apparently, then, two different genes are responsible for the same protein. Does this disprove the one-gene–one-enzyme hypothesis? Most biologists have agreed that this and similar examples make it necessary to alter the hypothesis slightly. Each gene, it is proposed, instead of being responsible for a single protein, is responsible for a single polypeptide chain. The two hemoglobin diseases involve alterations of different polypeptide chains; hence different genes are involved.

In its one-gene–one-polypeptide form, the hypothesis of Beadle and Tatum still seems compatible with the facts known to us, but you should be aware that true exceptions may yet be discovered. We shall have to make one qualification later when we see that some genes may control the activity of other genes without themselves controlling the synthesis of any protein.

The Synthesis of Proteins

If it is assumed that genes control the cell's activities by controlling the synthesis of protein enzymes, the next question becomes: By what mechanism is this gene-controlled synthesis of proteins accomplished? Here we enter one of the areas of greatest ferment in all modern biology. A few years ago, almost nothing was known about protein synthesis. Today, it is the subject of hundreds of papers and of highly elaborate models. New experimental data are flooding in from laboratories all over the world. Ideas current one month are abandoned the next. In such an active and turbulent field as this, it is hard to decide which concepts should be included in an elementary textbook; the risk is giving an air of dogma to ideas that may soon prove to be flawed. Yet it would be wrong to exclude from a general treatment of the science of biology one of its most important and exciting aspects. And despite the fluidity of ideas in this field, there has emerged a series of core concepts that have withstood the onslaught of extensive experimental investigation and have won wide acceptance, at least provisionally. It is around those core concepts that we shall attempt to build our discussion, but we must warn the reader that he should be prepared to read tomorrow that something he read today is completely out of date.

The Problem of Sequence. We saw in an earlier chapter that polysaccharides such as starch and cellulose are long polymers. But those polymers are built up by serial repetition of identical units—molecules of glucose—and the order in which the building blocks are linked presents no problem. Proteins, too, are long polymers. But they are composed of some 20 different units—the amino acids—and the sequence in which those units are linked is of critical importance. It is the necessity for specifying this sequence that makes protein synthesis so much more complex than polysaccharide synthesis.

If genes really specify amino acid sequences for proteins, and if DNA really is the stuff of which genes are made, we would expect that the sequence of bases in the DNA somehow indicates the sequence in which amino acids must be linked in protein synthesis. The problem then becomes one of translating nucleotide base sequence into amino acid sequence. One of the first points to establish is whether the translation is normally direct or indirect, i.e. whether protein is somehow synthesized on the DNA template itself or whether some intermediate agent is involved. There has long been evidence that, although a limited amount of protein may be synthesized in the nucleus, most protein synthesis takes place in the cytoplasm. Since, with a few notable exceptions, DNA is largely restricted to the nucleus, it follows that the protein is probably not synthesized along a DNA template as new DNA is. The information, presumably coded in nucleotide sequences in the DNA, must be transmitted from the nucleus to the sites of protein synthesis in the cytoplasm. How?

RNA and the Ribosomes. Several workers showed in the early 1940's that cells in tissues where protein synthesis is particularly active, such as the silk gland of silkworms and the vertebrate pancreas, contain large amounts of a nucleic acid named *ribonucleic acid,* usually designated *RNA.* This nucleic acid is present in only limited quantities in cells that do not produce protein secretions, such as those in

muscle and kidney. There seemed to be a definite correlation between protein synthesis and RNA. Furthermore, it had long been known that RNA, unlike DNA, occurs in the cytoplasm as well as in the nucleus. Later studies showed that cell-free systems (i.e. test-tube systems that contain no living cells) could be made to carry out protein synthesis if they contained RNA, but if their RNA was destroyed all protein synthesis ceased. And radioactive-tracer experiments revealed that RNA is synthesized in the nucleus and moves from the nucleus into the cytoplasm. All these lines of evidence pointed to the possibility that RNA might be the chemical messenger between the DNA of the nucleus and the metabolic machinery of the cytoplasm.

Though RNA and DNA are very similar compounds, they differ in three important ways: (1) The sugar in RNA is ribose, while that in DNA is deoxyribose (it is the sugars that give the two nucleic acids their different initials). (2) RNA contains **uracil** in place of the thymine in DNA; thus the pyrimidine bases in RNA are cytosine and uracil, while those in DNA are cytosine and thymine. And (3) RNA is ordinarily single-stranded, while DNA is usually double-stranded.

Despite these differences, it is obvious that DNA could easily act as a template for the synthesis of RNA. The synthesis would proceed in essentially the same way as that of new DNA. The two strands of a DNA molecule would uncoil. Then ribonucleotides (i.e. nucleotides containing ribose instead of deoxyribose) would be lined up along one of the DNA strands: a uracil ribonucleotide opposite each adenine on the DNA; an adenine ribonucleotide opposite each thymine; a cytosine ribonucleotide opposite each guanine; and a guanine ribonucleotide opposite each cytosine (Fig. 15.12). In other words, the sequence of deoxyribonucleotides in the single DNA strand would determine the sequence of ribonucleotides for the synthesis of an RNA strand. Once the ribonucleotides were arranged in the proper

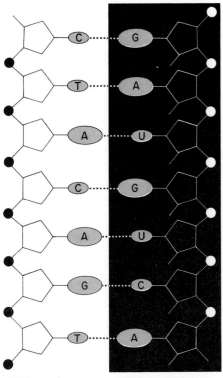

DNA template   RNA transcription

Fig. 15.12. Synthesis of RNA on a DNA template. The sugar in RNA is slightly different from that in DNA, and uracil (U) takes the place of the thymine in DNA.

order, they could be bonded together, and then the new RNA molecule could separate from the DNA and travel from its place of synthesis on the chromosome of the nucleus to its functional location in the cytoplasm. According to this model, then, DNA acts as a template or mold not only for the synthesis of new DNA just before a cell undergoes division, but also for the synthesis of RNA when the cell is metabolically active but is not dividing. In corroboration of this model, it has been shown that RNA can be synthesized in a test tube if single-stranded DNA (prepared by heating double-stranded DNA and then cooling it so rapidly that the separated strands cannot reassociate) is added as a primer. The RNA thus synthesized has a base content apparently com-

plementary to that of the DNA primer, as the model predicts.

Electron microscopy has revealed that a high percentage of the cytoplasmic RNA is located in the *ribosomes,* and these organelles seem to be the sites of protein synthesis. There is convincing evidence, however, that the RNA that constitutes the structural basis (together with protein) of the ribosomes is not the RNA that acts as the template for protein synthesis. A single bacterial cell may be able to synthesize a thousand or more different proteins, and it sometimes switches its synthetic activity very rapidly from one to another, so that in the course of a relatively short time it may synthesize a large number of different proteins. There is not enough ribosomal RNA to account for such a large number of different proteins unless the RNA undergoes rapid turnover. But radioactive-tracer studies indicate that the structural RNA of the ribosomes does not turn over rapidly; the same ribosome may act as the site of synthesis for many different proteins without any change in its structural RNA. Considerations such as these led François Jacob and J. Monod of the Pasteur Institute in Paris to suggest in 1961 that the RNA that acts as the template for protein synthesis is a messenger form of RNA that is copied from the genes active at the moment in the nucleus, after which it moves from the nucleus to the ribosome, where it acts as the template for synthesis of only a few protein molecules before it is broken down. The ribosome itself, and the structural RNA of which it is partly composed, would simply be an unspecific device capable of synthesizing any protein according to the information supplied to it by *messenger RNA.* The ribosome would thus be analogous to a modern manufacturing machine that receives its instructions from a tape fed into it.

The existence of a form of RNA that behaves in the manner predicted for messenger RNA by Jacob and Monod was soon demonstrated, and their idea has gained general acceptance. It has been shown, however, by

Jonathan Warner, Alexander Rich, and their colleagues at the Massachusetts Institute of Technology that each molecule of messenger RNA ordinarily becomes associated with more than one ribosome. Four, five, or more ribosomes usually become attached to a single long messenger molecule and move along it in sequence. Apparently, as each ribosome moves along the messenger RNA strand, it "reads" the information coded in the RNA and builds a polypeptide chain according to that information (Fig. 15.13). In other words, as each ribosome moves along the nucleotide chain of the RNA, it manufactures a polypeptide chain by translating the nucleotide sequence into an amino acid sequence. The complex of ribosomes associated with a single strand of messenger RNA has been called a *polyribosome* (or sometimes simply a polysome) (Fig. 15.14).

Transfer RNA and Its Role. We have seen, then, that messenger RNA, synthesized on DNA in the nucleus, moves to the ribosomes and functions as a template for protein synthesis, the sequence of its nucleotide bases providing the information that determines the sequence of amino acids in the protein. We must now ask whether the amino acids interact directly with the messenger RNA or whether some intermediate agent or adapter molecule is involved. There is strong evidence in support of the second alternative. Mahlon B. Hoagland and his associates at Harvard University demonstrated in 1957 that amino acids become attached to RNA *before* they arrive at the ribosomes. This RNA is neither messenger RNA nor structural ribosomal RNA, but a third type consisting of relatively small molecules located in the more soluble portion of the cytoplasm. It has been shown that each molecule of this soluble RNA binds a single molecule of amino acid and transports it to the ribosome; hence the name *transfer RNA*. There is at least one form of transfer RNA specific for each of the 20 amino acids; i.e. the amino acid arginine will combine only with transfer RNA specialized to transport arginine, and the amino acid leucine will combine only with transfer RNA specialized to transport leucine, etc. Just what makes the structure of each of the more than 20 different transfer RNA's specific for a single amino acid is not yet known.

According to the model now generally ac-

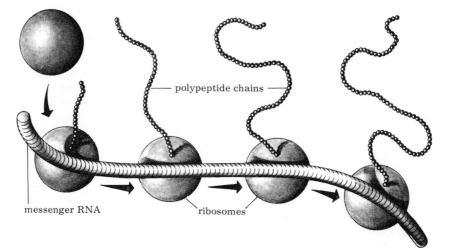

Fig. 15.13. **Synthesis of polypeptide chains by the ribosomes.** As the ribosomes move along the messenger RNA, they "read" the coded information and synthesize a polypeptide chain according to that information.

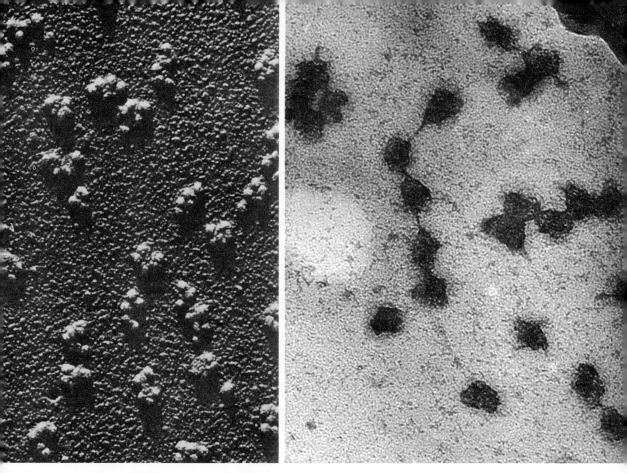

Fig. 15.14. Polyribosomes. Left: Each polyribosome consists of a cluster of four, five, or more ribosomes. × 100,000. Right: When very highly magnified (× 400,000), the ribosomes of each polyribosome are seen to be connected by a thread, which is presumed to be messenger RNA. [Courtesy Alexander Rich, Massachusetts Institute of Technology.]

cepted, a molecule of amino acid is first activated by ATP and is then picked up by the appropriate transfer RNA (Fig. 15.15). The transfer RNA carries the amino acid to a polyribosome. There the transfer RNA becomes attached to the messenger RNA by base pairing of the Watson-Crick type. If the code for each amino acid is a certain short sequence of bases on the single-stranded messenger RNA, and if each of the transfer RNA's has in an exposed position an unpaired base sequence complementary to the messenger sequence for its particular amino acid, then the transfer RNA molecules must line up along the messenger RNA in a sequence determined by the coded information in the messenger RNA. This lining up of the transfer RNA along the messenger

RNA automatically lines up the amino acids in the proper sequence. Once the amino acids have been ordered in this manner, peptide bonds are formed between them and the polypeptide chain thus formed is set free. The synthesis having been completed, the transfer RNA's become detached from the messenger RNA and move away to pick up another load of amino acids and repeat the process.

Let us suppose that each amino acid is coded by a particular sequence of three bases on the messenger RNA. Let us suppose, further, that the triplet of bases CCG (i.e. cytosine, cytosine, guanine) codes for the amino acid proline, that GUA (guanine, uracil, adenine) codes for valine, that UGG codes for tryptophane, and that UUU codes for phenyl-

One strand of **DNA** acts as template for synthesis of messenger RNA

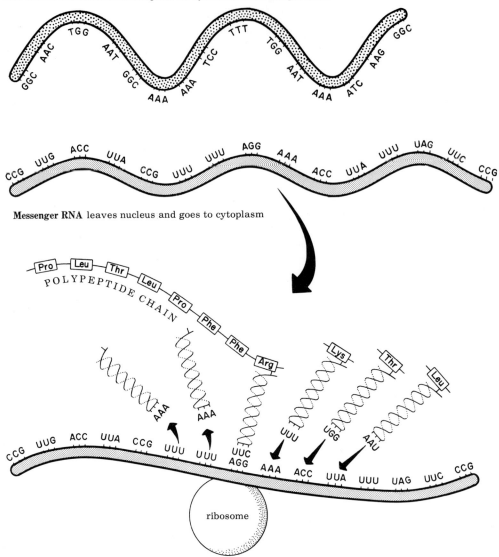

Messenger RNA leaves nucleus and goes to cytoplasm

Polypeptide chain is synthesized as ribosome moves along messenger RNA
Amino acids are brought into proper position by specific transfer RNA's that couple
   briefly with complementary triplets on messenger RNA

Fig. 15.15. Model for control of protein synthesis by the genes. Messenger RNA is synthesized on one of the polynucleotide chains of the DNA of the gene. This messenger RNA then goes into the cytoplasm and becomes associated with ribosomes. The various types of transfer RNA in the cytoplasm pick up the amino acids for which they are specific and bring them to the ribosome as it moves along the messenger RNA. Each transfer RNA bonds to the messenger RNA at a point where a triplet of bases complementary to an exposed triplet on the transfer RNA occurs. This ordering of the transfer RNA molecules automatically orders the amino acids, which are then linked by peptide bonds. Synthesis of the polypeptide chain thus proceeds one amino acid at a time in an orderly sequence as the ribosome moves along the messenger RNA. As each transfer RNA donates its amino acid to the growing polypeptide chain, it uncouples from the messenger RNA and moves away into the cytoplasm, where it can be used again.

alanine. We would predict, according to our model, that the transfer RNA for proline would have in an exposed position the sequence GGC, which is complementary to CCG, the messenger code sequence for proline. Similarly, we would predict that transfer RNA for valine would have in an exposed position the sequence CAU (which is complementary to GUA), that transfer RNA for tryptophane would have an exposed ACC (complementary to UGG), and that transfer RNA for phenylalanine would have an exposed AAA (complementary to UUU). Whenever a molecule of proline-transfer RNA with an attached molecule of proline approaches a strand of messenger RNA, its exposed GGC triplet can bond to the messenger strand at only those points where the messenger strand has a CCG triplet. Similarly, the exposed CAU triplet of valine-transfer RNA can bond to the messenger RNA only at points where a GUA triplet occurs, etc. Thus the three-base code sequences on the messenger RNA determine precisely the order in which the different transfer RNA's with their attached amino acids will bond to the messenger molecule, and this order determines the one in which the amino acids will be linked in the polypeptide chain being synthesized.

If the code units on the messenger RNA are really three nucleotides long, then transfer RNA's only three nucleotides long would suffice for the base pairing necessary to line up amino acids. But detailed studies of transfer RNA's have revealed that they are actually 70–80 nucleotides long; the function of most of the additional bases is still unknown. Like other forms of RNA, transfer RNA's are single-stranded, but there is evidence that the single chain folds back on itself and that base pairing between portions of the same chain occurs in some places (Fig. 15.16). Amino acids are picked up by one of the free ends of the chain. Though the location of the unpaired coding sequence (anticodon) on the RNA molecule is unknown, some models suggest that it is

at the end opposite the site of amino acid binding (as shown in Fig. 15.16). In 1965 Robert W. Holley and his co-workers at Cornell University published a description of the complete nucleotide sequence in alanine-transfer RNA from yeast—the first nucleic acid of any type for which the chemical structure became known. Work of this sort should soon lead to much fuller knowledge of the three-dimensional configuration and biological activity of transfer RNA's, as well as to better understanding of the structure of nucleic acids in general.

A Summary of the Model. At the risk of being repetitious, let us now summarize the model of protein synthesis outlined here. When the double-stranded DNA that constitutes a particular gene is activated, its two nucleotide chains uncoil and separate, and one of the chains acts as the template for synthesis of a

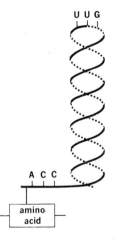

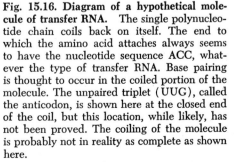

Fig. 15.16. Diagram of a hypothetical molecule of transfer RNA. The single polynucleotide chain coils back on itself. The end to which the amino acid attaches always seems to have the nucleotide sequence ACC, whatever the type of transfer RNA. Base pairing is thought to occur in the coiled portion of the molecule. The unpaired triplet (UUG), called the anticodon, is shown here at the closed end of the coil, but this location, while likely, has not been proved. The coiling of the molecule is probably not in reality as complete as shown here.

molecule of single-stranded messenger RNA. This messenger RNA leaves the nucleus and moves into the cytoplasm, where it becomes associated with a cluster of ribosomes. The messenger RNA acts as the template for synthesis of polypeptide chains as the ribosomes move along it. Amino acids to be incorporated into the polypeptide chains are first activated by ATP and then picked up by molecules of transfer RNA, of which one or more type is specific for each of the 20 different amino acids. Each of these transfer RNA's has an exposed sequence of bases complementary to the sequence of bases on the messenger RNA that codes for its particular amino acid. Each molecule of transfer RNA, having picked up an amino acid from the cytoplasmic pool, moves to a ribosome and attaches to the messenger RNA at a point where the appropriate base sequence occurs. This ordering of the transfer RNA's along the messenger RNA molecule also orders the amino acids attached to them. Once the amino acids have been moved into the proper sequence in this way, peptide linkages are formed between them, and the resulting polypeptide falls away. The transfer RNA's uncouple from the messenger RNA and move away to pick up another load of amino acids.

According to this model, then, the flow of information is as follows: The DNA of the gene determines the messenger RNA, which determines protein enzymes, which control chemical reactions, which produce the characteristics of the organism.

The Genetic Code

The Codon. In discussing the model of protein synthesis, we assumed that the nucleic acid code unit, or codon, for each amino acid is three nucleotides long. We should now examine the basis for this assumption. We are dealing with a code that has only four elements—the four different nucleotides in messenger RNA (which reflect a corresponding

four nucleotides in DNA)—and a system that must be capable of coding for at least 20 different amino acids. It follows that the codon cannot be only one nucleotide long, because such a system could code for only four amino acids. It also follows that the codon cannot be two nucleotides long, because only 16 combinations would be possible. If the codon is three nucleotides long, there are 64 possible combinations, which is more than enough to code for 20 amino acids. Therefore the codon must be at least three nucleotides long. Since nucleic acids must code an immense amount of information within a small space, natural selection might be expected to have favored the shortest codon system that would do the job— namely, one no more than three nucleotides long. To be sure, what is expected and what actually is are not always the same. In this instance, however, convincing evidence supports the concept of a triplet codon; we shall describe some of this evidence below.

Overlapping Versus Nonoverlapping Codes. For the moment, let us assume that the genetic code is based on triplet codons. The first question we shall try to answer is whether the code is overlapping or nonoverlapping. Suppose that a particular piece of messenger RNA has the following sequence of nucleotides (where A stands for adenine, G for guanine, U for uracil, and C for cytosine):

CAUCAGGUA

If the code were a completely overlapping one, this piece of messenger RNA would code for seven amino acids; CAU would indicate the first amino acid, AUC would indicate the second, UCA the third, CAG the fourth, etc., as follows:

CAU
AUC
UCA
CAG
AGG
GGU
GUA

If the code were a nonoverlapping one, this piece of RNA would code for only three amino acids; CAU would indicate the first, CAG the second, and GUA the third, as follows:

CAUCAGGUA

What sort of evidence would allow us to choose between these alternatives? Notice that in a completely overlapping code each nucleotide (except the first two and the last two) would be included in the codons for three amino acids. Thus the first U in our hypothetical piece of messenger RNA would be in the following three codons: CAU, AUC, UCA. By contrast, each nucleotide in a nonoverlapping code would be included in only one codon; e.g. the first U would appear only in the CAU codon. It is clear that if the code is completely overlapping, a mutation substituting one nucleotide for another in a nucleic acid strand should result in a change of three adjacent amino acids in the protein determined by this nucleic acid; but if the code is nonoverlapping, such a substitution should change only one amino acid in the protein. Now, Ingram's discovery that the hemoglobin of sickle-cell anemia differs from normal hemoglobin in only one amino acid would seem to indicate that a single mutation can result in an alteration of a single amino acid; it is apparently not necessary for three adjacent amino acids to be changed together. This conclusion has been supported by numerous experiments on tobacco mosaic virus, in which a number of mutations that change only one amino acid have been found.

A further consideration is that an overlapping code would limit the order in which amino acids could be arranged in a protein. Thus the amino acid determined by CAU could be followed only by an amino acid whose codon begins with AU. There would be a maximum of only four such amino acids (determined by AUA, AUG, AUU, and AUC); the amino acid coded by CAU could never be followed by one coded by CCG or by one coded by UAA, etc. But all attempts to demonstrate that such limitations on amino acid sequence actually occur in proteins have failed. Most scientists are now agreed that the genetic code is nonoverlapping.

Reading the Code. The assumption that the code is nonoverlapping raises another problem. If the codons in our hypothetical piece of messenger RNA are CAU, CAG, and GUA, how does the cell's synthetic machinery "know" that it should read these particular triplets and not such triplets as AUC and AGG? To put it another way, how does the metabolic machinery recognize the proper triplet "words" if all these are strung together in one long RNA molecule? One possibility would be some sort of punctuation between the codons, as follows:

CAU,CAG,GUA

But no chemical basis for such punctuation has been found.

Another hypothesis, widely favored a few years ago, was that only the proper triplets were meaningful, i.e. coded for an amino acid; all other triplets would be nonsense triplets and code for nothing. To use our hypothetical example, CAU, CAG, and GUA would each be a meaningful triplet coding for some amino acid, but all other possible triplets in this sequence (AUC, UCA, AGG, GGU) would be nonsense triplets, corresponding to no amino acid. This hypothesis seemed reasonable in view of the fact that a triplet code utilizing four symbols makes 64 different triplets possible though only 20 are needed to code for amino acids; the other 44 possible triplets, presumably being superfluous, might be nonsense. But this hypothesis has now been abandoned. Most of the 44 triplets that it predicted would be nonsense have been found to be meaningful; consequently most overlapping triplets are meaningful. There may be a few nonsense triplets among the 64 possibilities, but there are not many. It is now known that two or more different triplets often code for the same amino acid; e.g. both UUG and UUA probably code for leucine (see Fig. 15.15). A code such as this, where two or more words or codons may mean the same thing, is said to be degenerate.

A third way of explaining how the cell reads the correct triplets has been proposed by Crick. It is really a very simple explanation. Crick suggests that the sequence of triplets is "read" from a fixed point, i.e. that the metabolic machinery begins at one end of the chain of nucleotides and "reads" along the chain, taking each successive nonoverlapping triplet in turn. Thus, if CAU in our hypothetical example is at the front end of the chain, the cell must read it first and must read CAG next and GUA next:

CUA CAG GUA

Crick and his associates at Cambridge University performed a series of experiments (reported in 1961) that strongly supported both his suggestion and the idea that the codon is three nucleotides long. They treated bacteriophage T4 with compounds called acridines, which tend to delete or insert nucleotides in DNA. Let us suppose that a particular gene[1] begins with the following sequence of bases:

ATTGCATTGACTACCGACGCA

This sequence should be read as follows:

ATT GCA TTG ACT ACC GAC GCA

If Crick's hypothesis of reading from one end is correct, we would expect that deleting a single nucleotide near the front end would cause the nucleic acid completely to lose its function, because the cell would read incorrect triplets from that point on to the other end. For example, if a mutation deleted the fourth nucleotide from the left (G) in our hypothetical sequence, then the cell—proceeding, let us assume, from left to right—would read the sequence as follows:

ATT CA TTG ACT ACC GAC GCA

[1] We are here using a modified Beadle and Tatum definition of a gene as the length of DNA that codes for a single polypeptide chain.

In other words, a completely different chain of amino acids would be synthesized, if, indeed, any synthesis occurred at all; only the first amino acid would be the correct one. Similarly, if a mutation added a nucleotide near the beginning of the chain, we would expect the nucleic acid to lose its function. For example, if an additional T were added in our hypothetical chain immediately after the first triplet, the cell would read the sequence as follows:

ATT T GCA TTG ACT ACC GAC GCA

Again, the altered series of nucleotides would code for a polypeptide chain completely different from that coded by the original one. Crick found that when his acridine treatment produced single deletion or addition mutations near the front end of the nucleic acid of a particular gene, that gene's normal function was destroyed just as predicted.

Crick also predicted that if a deletion or addition mutation occurred near the terminal end of the nucleotide chain (near the right end in our example), the gene's function would frequently be only slightly altered, because the cell would read correct triplets along most of the length of the gene. For example, if the normal nucleotide sequence is

ATT GCA TTG ACT ACC GAC GCA

and if the fourth nucleotide from the right were deleted, the cell would read the sequence as follows:

ATT GCA TTG ACT ACC GA GCA

The first five triplet codons would be normal and would code for the normal amino acids; the sixth codon would have been changed from GAC to GAG and would code for an incorrect amino acid; and the last codon, normally GCA, would not be read at all because only two nucleotides (C and A) would remain. Thus the chain of seven amino acids coded by the normal gene would have been altered to a chain of six amino acids, of which the sixth is incorrect. If the active site of this polypeptide were near the altered end, such a mutation would probably cause loss of all function. But if the active site were nearer the other end or the middle of the polypeptide chain, such a mutation might alter but not entirely destroy the enzyme's activity. Crick's experiments showed that this is what actually happens; when he altered the bacteriophage gene by a single deletion or addition near the terminal end, some activity remained.

We have seen that a single deletion mutation near the front end of the nucleotide chain of a gene destroys function. Crick reasoned that if this result is caused by the cell's reading incorrect codons beyond that point, and if the codons really are triplets, three deletion mutations close together should partly restore activity, because the cell would read correct codons beyond the point of the third deletion. For example, if the normal nucleotide sequence is

$$\downarrow\ \downarrow\ \downarrow$$
ATT GCA TTG ACT ACC GAC GCA

and if the three nucleotides indicated by arrows were deleted, then the cell would read the sequence as follows:

ATT CX XTG ACT ACC GAC GCA

The first triplet and the last four would be the same in the altered version and in the normal one, and would code for the correct amino acids. The second two triplets in the normal sequence (GCA and TTG) would have been replaced by a single CTG triplet. Thus the mutation would have resulted in a nucleic acid that codes for a polypeptide chain or enzyme similar to the normal one (the alteration may look large in our example, where the polypeptide chain is only six or seven amino acids long, but an actual protein would usually be more than 100 amino acids long). We would expect such an altered enzyme to show at least a little of the activity characteristic of the normal enzyme. Crick found that this is indeed the case. One or two deletions near the front

end of the nucleotide chain destroyed activity, but a third deletion mutation in the same vicinity partly restored it. Similarly, three addition mutations located close together resulted in partial activity. And the combination of one deletion and one addition, if these were close together, gave partial activity. Thus Crick's experiments not only gave strong support to his theory that the codons are read from a given point, but they also strengthened the widely accepted theory that the codon is three nucleotides long.

Spacing. Let us now turn to another important question about the genetic code: What designates the ending of one gene[2] and the beginning of another? It might be easier to answer this question with reference to higher organisms if we knew how the DNA and the protein of the chromosomes are arranged. If, for example, the DNA for each gene were a separate molecule attached to a chromosomal backbone of protein, there would be no problem; the end of a gene would be the end of its DNA molecule, and the hundreds of DNA molecules corresponding to the hundreds of genes on each chromosome would somehow be attached in sequence to the protein backbone of the chromosome. But it seems doubtful that the DNA of each gene is a separate molecule. The chromosomes of viruses and bacteria are apparently composed almost exclusively of nucleic acid; they clearly have no protein backbone. The entire chromosome in these microorganisms gives every indication of being one long DNA molecule, and there is no hint where on this molecule one gene ends and another begins. In the absence of evidence to the contrary, it seems reasonable for the present to assume that each DNA molecule of higher organisms also represents more than one gene.

The end of the nucleotide sequence coding for a single polypeptide chain might possibly

[2] Here also we are assuming that a gene is the length of DNA that codes for a single polypeptide chain.

be indicated by a nonsense triplet, which could cause a break either in transcribing the DNA into messenger RNA or in the ribosomal reading of the messenger RNA. In other words, if TAA is a nonsense triplet (and there is some evidence that it may be), then the nucleotide sequence

CTT TTG TTT ATA TAA CAC GCC ACG

might represent parts of two genes, with the TAA triplet acting as a spacer between them, as follows:

last codon of one gene	spacer	first codon of another gene
↓	↓	↓

CTT TTG TTT ATA｜TAA｜CAC GCC ACG

This possibility is favored by many scientists at the present time, but there is as yet little experimental evidence either for or against it (perhaps there will be by the time you read this book).

Deciphering the Code. We have discussed the evidence that the sequence of nucleotides in nucleic acid constitutes a code that determines the sequence of amino acids in polypeptide chains, and we have examined reasons for thinking that the code consists of codons three nucleotides long, that it is nonoverlapping, that it is degenerate, that it is read in an orderly manner from one end, and that the spacers may be nonsense codons. With all these conclusions about the mechanics of the code in mind, let us now trace the paths followed in deciphering the code—in assigning triplets to amino acids. How has it been possible to construct a dictionary permitting the translation of a nucleotide sequence into an amino acid sequence?

As you would expect, there is an enzyme that catalyzes the synthesis of messenger RNA along a DNA template. In 1955 Marianne Grunberg-Manago and Severo Ochoa of New York University showed that another enzyme catalyzes the synthesis of RNA without a DNA pattern; it simply links nucleotides together in

random order. Marshall W. Nirenberg, J. Heinrich Matthaei, and their co-workers at the National Institutes of Health, and Ochoa and his collaborators working independently, used this enzyme to synthesize ribonucleotide chains of known composition. If the only nucleotide made available to the enzyme was uracil, then a long polyuracil· chain was synthesized:

UUUUUUUUUUUU

Similarly, if only adenine was made available, a polyadenine chain was formed. When poly-U is used in place of normal messenger RNA in a cell-free system for protein synthesis, a polypeptide chain composed of only phenylalanine results—a clear indication that UUU codes for phenylalanine. Similarly, AAA has been shown to code for lysine, and CCC has been shown to code for proline. GGG may code for glycine.

Understandably enough, it has been more difficult to assign triplets composed of two or three different nucleotides. If, for example, both uracil and guanine are available to the enzyme, RNA molecules containing eight different triplets—UUU, GUU, UGU, UUG, GGU, GUG, UGG, and GGG—will be formed. This synthetic RNA could potentially act as the template for synthesis of a polypeptide chain containing as many as eight different amino acids (assuming that none of the eight triplets are nonsense ones and that each of them codes for a different amino acid—which may not be the case). Since the sequence in which the eight triplets occur in the RNA is random, and thus different for each molecule, and since the sequence is unknown, it is very difficult to determine which of the eight triplets codes for which amino acid. Nevertheless, it is possible to obtain much information from such procedures if the initial concentrations of U and G in the system are precisely controlled. Suppose, for example, that the system is supplied with a mixture of U and G in the proportions of 3 : 1, and that, as a result, the RNA synthesized contains three times as much U as G. Since the enzyme is believed to bond nucleotides together in random order, it is possible to calculate the relative frequencies with which each of the eight possible triplets would be expected to occur. Three fourths of the nucleotides in the initial mixture were uracil, and one fourth were guanine; therefore the expected frequency of UUU triplets is $\frac{3}{4} \times \frac{3}{4} \times \frac{3}{4} = \frac{27}{64}$, and the expected frequency of GGG triplets is $\frac{1}{4} \times \frac{1}{4} \times \frac{1}{4} = \frac{1}{64}$. Similarly, the expected frequency of UUG triplets is $\frac{3}{4} \times \frac{3}{4} \times \frac{1}{4} = \frac{9}{64}$ (or one third that of UUU), and this same frequency is expected for the other triplets containing two uracils and one guanine (UGU, GUU). The expected frequency for each of the triplets containing one uracil and two guanines (UGG, GUG, GGU) is $\frac{3}{64}$ (or one ninth that of UUU). The theoretical distribution of frequencies is tabulated below:

Triplet	Expected frequency
UUU	27/64
GUU	9/64
UGU	9/64
UUG	9/64
GGU	3/64
GUG	3/64
UGG	3/64
GGG	1/64

Now suppose this synthetic RNA is used as a template for synthesis of polypeptide chains in a cell-free system. And suppose that each of the amino acids cysteine, valine, and leucine is found to occur in the polypeptide chains approximately one third as often as phenylalanine. The obvious deduction would be that these three amino acids are coded by the three triplets with expected frequencies one third as great as the expected frequency for UUU (we already know that UUU codes for phenylalanine). These three triplets are GUU, UGU, and UUG. But which of these three triplets codes for which of the amino acids? The procedure described here cannot tell us this. The most it can tell us is that each of the amino acids cysteine, valine, and leucine is probably coded by a triplet composed of two uracils and one guanine, but we cannot determine the

sequence of these bases for any one of the amino acids by this technique.

Many experiments like the one outlined above were performed, and the dictionaries that were prepared represented an encouraging start. But little further progress toward deciphering the genetic code was possible until the sequence of bases within each triplet could be analyzed. Then, in 1964, Philip Leder and Marshall W. Nirenberg of the National Institutes of Health developed a technique for forming a complex between ribosomes and RNA trinucleotides (three nucleotides bonded together in sequence) of known composition. They showed that these trinucleotides would then act as though they were short pieces of messenger RNA, and that transfer RNA's would couple with them. For example, if they used a trinucleotide with the composition UUU, phenylalanine-transfer RNA would couple with it. This technique proved to be the key to unlocking the details of the code. Since it is relatively easy to synthesize trinucleotides with a particular base sequence, each of the 64 possible triplets could be synthesized, complexed with ribosomes, and exposed to a mixture of transfer RNA's. By establishing which transfer RNA coupled with which trinucleotide, it became possible to determine the codons for each amino acid. Nirenberg and his associates performed a series of such experiments during 1965; their results make possible the construction of genetic dictionaries like the one shown in Table 15.2.

MUTATIONS

Mutations—changes in the genetic material— are caused by many different environmental agents, including X rays, cosmic rays, ultraviolet radiation and other types of high-energy radiation, as well as numerous chemicals. As you know, much research is currently in progress to determine the probable long-term effects of the steady increase of mutagenic agents

TABLE 15.2

The Genetic Code*

First base in the codon	Second base in the codon				Third base in the codon
	U	C	A	G	
U	Phenylalanine	Serine	Tyrosine	Cysteine	U
	Phenylalanine	Serine	Tyrosine	Cysteine	C
	Leucine	Serine	*Nonsense*	?	A
	Leucine	Serine	*Nonsense*	Tryptophane	G
C	Leucine	Proline	Histidine	Arginine	U
	Leucine	Proline	Histidine	Arginine	C
	Leucine (?)	Proline	Glutamine	Arginine	A
	Leucine	Proline	Glutamine	Arginine	G
A	Isoleucine	Threonine	Asparagine	Serine	U
	Isoleucine	Threonine	Asparagine	Serine	C
	?	Threonine	Lysine	Arginine	A
	Methionine	Threonine	Lysine	Arginine	G
G	Valine	Alanine	Aspartic acid	Glycine	U
	Valine	Alanine	Aspartic acid	Glycine	C
	Valine	Alanine	Glutamic acid	Glycine	A
	Valine	Alanine	Glutamic acid	Glycine	G

* Some of the codon assignments shown here are still tentative.

that our civilization is producing in our environment.

Let us now examine the various types of mutations and attempt to correlate them with the present understanding of the chemical nature of genes and chromosomes. For our purposes, we can divide mutations into two groups: chromosomal mutations and genic mutations. We shall discuss these separately.

Chromosomal Mutations

Chromosomal Rearrangements. We have already discussed crossing-over, which is a type of chromosomal rearrangement in which exactly corresponding segments are exchanged between homologous chromosomes. There are other kinds of chromosomal rearrangements; some involve exchange of segments between nonhomologous chromosomes, others involve alterations within a single chromosome.

In one common form of alteration, called **translocation,** a portion of one chromosome breaks off and then fuses onto a nonhomologous chromosome, thereby changing the linkage groups. Suppose, for example, that the bar chromosomes in a certain species bear the genes *ABCDEFG* and that the J-shaped chromosomes bear the genes *LMNOPQRST*. If the end of one of the bar chromosomes that bears the genes *EFG* were to break off and fuse onto the end of one of the J chromosomes, the result would be a shorter bar chromosome bearing only the genes *ABCD* and a longer J chromosome bearing the genes *LMNOPQRSTEFG*. Figure 15.17 shows a translocation actually studied in *Drosophila*. By changing the linkage relationships of genes, translocations can have important effects on phenotypes.

Fig. 15.17. A translocation in *Drosophila*. A piece of one of the third chromosomes is transferred to the end of one of the second chromosomes. [Redrawn from A. M. Winchester, *Genetics*, Houghton Mifflin, 1951.]

Note that in the example just cited, the one chromosome could receive additional genes by translocation only because another chromosome had lost part of its length. That other chromosome had thus undergone a ***deletion***, which is another type of chromosomal alteration. In this particular example, the deleted part was not lost to the cell, because it fused onto another chromosome. But sometimes deleted portions do not fuse onto any chromosome and are lost entirely. Any chromosomal fragment that does not have a centromere will fail to move along the spindle during cell division and hence will not be incorporated into either daughter nucleus. One of the harmful effects of intense radiation on somatic cells is the large amount of chromosomal breakage that it produces, with the consequent loss of important genes on deleted fragments.

Sometimes a piece breaks off one chromosome and fuses onto the end of the homologous chromosome. Such an alteration, called a ***duplication***, is like a translocation except that homologous rather than nonhomologous chromosomes are involved. An example would be loss of the *ABC* portion from a chromosome bearing the genes *ABCDEFG* and fusion of this portion onto the homologous chromosome. The chromosome from which the deletion occurred would thus bear only the genes *DEFGH*, while

the chromosome undergoing the duplication would bear the genes *ABCABCDEFGH*.

Another common form of chromosomal alteration, involving only one chromosome, is called an ***inversion***. A portion of a chromosome breaks out, turns around, and fuses back in its original position but with its ends reversed. Suppose a chromosome bears the genes *RSTUVWXYZ*, in that order. If the *UVWX* segment were to break out and become reattached in reverse order, the result would be a chromosome with the gene sequence *RSTXWVUYZ* (Fig. 15.18). Some such inversions have little phenotypic effect, since the same genes are still all present on the same chromosome. But sometimes there is a phenotypic change, apparently the result of what is known as the ***position effect***. The expression of a given gene may be influenced by the genes close to it on the chromosome. In the original sequence, gene *U* was located be-

before synapsis

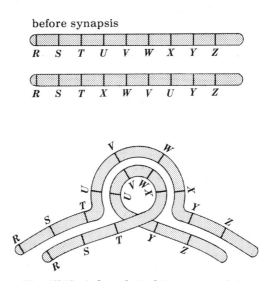

Fig. 15.18. A hypothetical inversion and its effect on synapsis. Top: The upper chromosome has the normal gene sequence; the lower chromosome has undergone an inversion—the *UVWX* part has broken out, turned around, and fused back in. Bottom: When the normal chromosome and the chromosome with the inversion synapse during meiosis, they form complicated loops that bring corresponding genes into adjacent positions.

tween genes *T* and *V* and was at a distance from gene *Y*; but in the inverted sequence, *U* is between *V* and *Y* and is at a distance from *T*. Any effect *T* may have had on the expression of *U* may be reduced as a result of the inversion, while an effect of *Y* on *U* may be increased. Another effect of this inversion would be to increase the frequency of crossing-over between *U* and *T* and to decrease it between *U* and *Y*. There is evidence that natural selection tends to favor inversions that reduce crossing-over between genes that act together to produce a beneficial phenotype, and to operate against inversions that disrupt such advantageous groupings. Inversions may thus play an important evolutionary role in conserving favorable gene groupings.

Changes in Chromosome Number. As we saw in the last chapter, the separation of chromosomes in cell division does not always proceed normally, and chromosomes that should have moved away from each other to opposite poles of the spindle move instead to the same pole and become incorporated into the same daughter nucleus. The result may be a new cell or an organism with one or two extra chromosomes; in persons suffering from Mongolism, for example, the nuclei of the cells contain three chromosomes of type number 21 instead of the normal two. Occasionally cell division may be so aberrant that all the chromosomes move to the same pole, giving rise to a daughter cell with twice the normal number of chromosomes. If this happens during meiosis, the gamete produced is diploid instead of haploid. If such a gamete unites at fertilization with a normal haploid gamete, a triploid zygote results; if it unites with another diploid gamete, also produced by aberrant meiosis, a tetraploid zygote results. Cells or organisms that have more than two complete sets of chromosomes (i.e. that are triploid, tetraploid, hexaploid, etc.) are said to be *polyploid.* Polyploidy has apparently occurred rather frequently in plants, and has sometimes given rise

to new species that are adaptively superior to the original diploid species under certain environmental conditions. Polyploidy can be stimulated in the laboratory by treating plants with certain chemicals that cause nondisjunction during cell division. This procedure has been used in the production of many of the new strains of cultivated plants developed in the last few decades. Polyploidy is apparently very rare in animals, and it has not been an important factor in the origin of new animal species.

Genic Mutations

Alterations in the DNA that change the information content of the molecules and thus produce new alleles are called genic mutations. If we define a gene as a nucleotide sequence coding for one polypeptide chain, a number of types of genic mutations are possible. We have already mentioned two such types while discussing Crick's experiments on how the genetic code is read—deletion of nucleotides from the sequence and addition of extra nucleotides to the sequence. A third type of mutation is *base substitution*—the exchange of one nucleotide for a different one. A codon that normally has the base composition CGG might be changed to CAG. This new triplet would code for a different amino acid. Base substitutions that produce nonsense triplets often seriously reduce or destroy the activity of the enzyme coded by the gene. Base substitutions that result in replacement of one amino acid by another usually have less severe effects on the activity of the enzyme; its activity may be somewhat reduced or its sensitivity to environmental conditions may be altered, but rarely is there complete inactivation.

Deletion, addition, and base substitution are all types of mutations that could be predicted on the basis of the known DNA structure. But another type of genic mutation not so easily predicted has been found also. This is *intragenic recombination*—the recombination of parts of genes. For example, suppose the nucleus of a diploid cell contains a chromosome bearing allele *M*. This gene is a nucleotide chain, perhaps 1,000 nucleotides long. Suppose that the codon sequence of part of this chain is as follows:

TAC CTG AAA CGG AAA ATT GCA TTT

Suppose, further, that the homologous chromosome bears a slightly different allele, *m*, and that the part of its base sequence corresponding to that shown above for *M* is as follows:

TAC CCG AAA CCC AAA ATT GGA TTA

Note that the two alleles differ in the second, fourth, seventh, and eighth triplets. If recombination of the first four bases in *M* with the last four bases in *m* were to occur, the new allele thus produced would have the following base sequence:

TAC CTG AAA CGG AAA ATT GGA TTA

We have seen that whole genes can be exchanged between homologous chromosomes by the mechanism of crossing-over, which is believed to involve breakage and fusion of the chromosomes. Might intragenic recombination like that above involve breakage-fusion at points within a gene (in our hypothetical case, at the point between the fourth and fifth triplets)? For a variety of reasons, many scientists at first ruled out breakage-fusion as the mechanism of intragenic recombination. It seemed to them most unlikely that breaks could occur almost simultaneously at exactly corresponding points within two DNA molecules. They assumed that the breakage-fusion of intergenic crossing-over in higher organisms must occur at points on the chromosomes between DNA molecules, not within the molecules. What other possible mechanisms for intragenic recombination were there? One suggested alternative was called copy-choice. According to this model, the intragenic recombination occurs in the course of DNA replication during interphase. Suppose that replication has begun and

the two nucleotide chains of each DNA molecule have begun to separate. And suppose that by chance the complement of the *M* chain from one DNA molecule and the complement of the *m* chain from its homologous molecule lie very close together in the nucleus. Then it might be possible for a nucleotide chain to be assembled partly along the *M* template and partly along the *m* template. In other words, the synthesis of the new chain might begin on the *M* template and then be switched onto the *m* template. We might visualize this so-called copy-choice error as shown in Fig. 15.19. Instead of making a complete copy of *M*, the copying mechanism might accidentally shift from *M* to *m* when halfway through, with the result that one end of the new chain would be copied from *M* and the other end from *m*. This copy-choice error would accomplish recombination between parts of *M* and *m* without any breakage-fusion. The new allele thus formed would code for another form of the enzyme that would have some of the character-

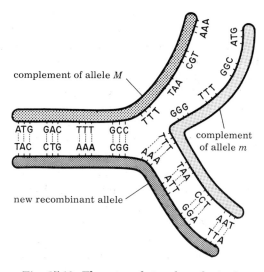

Fig. 15.19. The copy-choice hypothesis for intragenic recombination. Copying begins on the complement of allele *M*, but then switches onto the complement of allele *m*. The new DNA molecule thus produced is like *M* at one end and like *m* at the other end.

istics of the *M* form of the enzyme and some of the characteristics of the *m* form.

Having outlined for you the copy-choice model of intragenic recombination, we must now admit that all recent evidence is against it and that it has few supporters today. Attention has shifted back to breakage-fusion, especially since experiments with radioactively labeled DNA strands have definitely shown that breakage-fusion can produce crossing-over in bacteriophage, where the entire chromosome is believed to be one long DNA molecule. Contrary to expectation, then, reciprocal breaks can occur within DNA molecules. But if breakage-fusion proves to be the mechanism of intragenic recombination after all, we can offer no good explanation why two separate DNA strands should break almost simultaneously between exactly the same two nucleotides. The need for extensive additional research is obvious.

NOW WHAT IS A GENE?

We have used the word "gene" in a variety of ways in this and the last chapter. Mendel did not use this term but spoke of characters and their corresponding "factors" or "elements" in the germ cells. From 1902 onward, it was generally agreed that the factors of inheritance are associated with the chromosomes. These factors were first called "genes" by Wilhelm Johannsen, a Danish botanist, in 1911. T. H. Morgan's work with *Drosophila* led to a conception of the gene as the smallest unit of recombination; as we indicated in the last chapter, two characters were regarded as determined by different genes if they could be recombined, and as determined by the same gene if they could not be recombined. Physically, the genes were thought of as tiny particles arranged in linear sequence on the chromosomes. Recombination between linked genes was explained by a crossing-over mechanism when the chromosomes broke at points between the particles.

Though defined essentially as the unit of recombination, the gene in classical genetics was also regarded as the unit of mutation and as the unit of function, i.e. as the smallest unit whose alteration by mutation would change the phenotype and as the smallest unit of control over the phenotype. This was a satisfyingly unified concept of the gene. But our modern knowledge of the structure of the genetic material and its function has destroyed this unified concept and given rise to a variety of different candidates for the designation "gene." It is now clear that the units of recombination, mutation, and function are not identical. Seymour Benzer of Purdue University has given these units the following names:

recon: unit of recombination

muton: unit of mutation

cistron: unit of function

A fourth unit—the codon, unit of coding—can be added to the list. Although no conclusive proof is at hand, all available evidence indicates that recombination can take place between any two nucleotides—which would make the recon only one nucleotide long. As we saw above, some mutations apparently change only one nucleotide in a nucleotide chain; hence the muton would also be only one nucleotide long and would be the same as the recon. The codon is larger than the recon and muton, being probably three nucleotides long. And longest of all is the cistron, the unit of function, which is usually the nucleotide chain determining one polypeptide chain (some cistrons do not determine polypeptide chains but function instead as templates for transfer RNA or structural ribosomal RNA or as units exerting control over the activity of other cistrons). Since an average polypeptide chain contains about 300–500 amino acids, it follows that the average cistron must be 900–1,500 nucleotides long, and that some cistrons must be even longer.

According to a strict application of Morgan's

definition of the gene, it would be synonymous with the recon. Since the recon and the muton are probably the same thing, the gene would then be the unit of both recombination and mutation. But such a gene would be a very small entity, difficult to analyze and lacking in the functional attributes traditionally assigned to the gene. A second alternative would be to regard the gene and the codon as synonymous. The gene would then be a slightly larger entity, but it would lack almost all the attributes of the traditional gene. At the other extreme, the definition of the gene implicit in the one-gene–one-enzyme hypothesis of Beadle and Tatum would make the gene synonymous with the cistron; it would then be the unit of function but not the unit of recombination or of mutation. But equating the gene with the cistron has the advantage of emphasizing physiological activity and of postulating a less complex relationship between genes and phenotypic characteristics. Probably the majority of biochemical geneticists today follow the one-gene–one-polypeptide principle and regard the gene as equivalent to the cistron. It is this definition of the gene that we used in the present chapter in our discussions of the mechanism of gene action and of genic mutations. According to this definition, the genes are fairly large and complex entities; they can no longer be regarded as "irreducible units of inheritance," as Beadle called them as recently as 1948. They are essentially irreducible if one is concerned with the determination of a functional protein, but they are not irreducible if one is concerned with recombination or with mutation or with coding for individual amino acids.

It must be emphasized that the biochemical or physiological definition of the gene, while recognized in theory by most geneticists, is seldom used in practice in work on higher plants or animals. When we speak of the genes for vestigial wings or forked bristles in *Drosophila,* or of the genes for attached ear lobes or curly hair in human beings, or of the genes for tall plants or wrinkled seeds in garden peas, we have no proof that we are talking about entities that would agree with the biochemical definition of the gene; we have no proof that these are cistrons. For only a very small number of "genes" is anything known about the DNA of which they are composed or about the enzymes associated with their phenotypic expression. For practical purposes, most genes are—and will continue to be for many years—Morgan-type genes based on analysis of recombination of phenotypic traits. It may seem strange that geneticists continue to employ several different definitions of the gene for different purposes. But a term like "gene" is not important in itself; it is important only as a device that aids understanding and helps formulate the aims of new investigations. As our understanding and our research change, so must our language. We must not let a rigid terminology hamper our work. If at the present stage in our knowledge, one definition is more useful in one context and another definition is more useful in another context, then so be it.

EXTRACHROMOSOMAL INHERITANCE

The Genetic Role of Normal Cytoplasmic Structures

Our attention in this and the preceding chapter has been focused on the chromosomal genes as the hereditary units that determine the characteristics of organisms. But are the chromosomal genes the only hereditary constituents of cells? Or might there be others? It was recognized as early as 1909 that a few inherited traits do not obey Mendelian laws—e.g. certain traits that seem to be inherited exclusively from the mother, traits in which the sperm cell apparently plays no role whatever. Since almost all the cytoplasm of a zygote is contributed by the egg cell, it was suggested that such traits might be controlled by cytoplasmic rather than nuclear factors. It was not until more recent times, however, that much interest centered on the possibility of cytoplasmic inheritance.

There is now strong evidence that such cytoplasmic structures as plastids, mitochondria, centrioles, and the basal bodies of cilia and flagella are self-replicating, and that their characteristics are at least partly determined by hereditary control factors located within themselves. For example, if all plastids (and proplastids) are removed from a single-celled organism like *Euglena* (which can survive heterotrophically), neither the altered cell nor its asexually produced descendants can regain chloroplasts. Nuclear genes cannot restore these important structures to the cell. But such a cell can be surgically reinfected with chloroplasts, and the new chloroplasts will divide and perpetuate themselves. If a strain of *Euglena* with normal chloroplasts has all its plastids destroyed (by treatment with such chemical agents as streptomycin or antihistamine) and is then reinfected with certain types of abnormal plastids, the abnormal plastids will multiply and will be passed on to the cell's descendants indefinitely. Since the nuclear genes are not altered by this experiment, the hereditary perpetuation of the plastid abnormality must be due to factors inherent in the plastids themselves. Numerous experiments with a great variety of species of flowering plants have shown that many characteristics of the chloroplasts are inherited exclusively from the maternal plant, as would be expected if their controlling factors are cytoplasmic. It must be emphasized, however, that some characteristics of chloroplasts are inherited in a Mendelian manner and are apparently dependent upon chromosomal genes. In other words, evidence for a cytoplasmic role in the inheritance of structures like plastids, mitochondria, centrioles, and basal bodies does not mean that nuclear genes cannot also influence the phenotype of these structures. The total phenotype probably results from the combined effects of nuclear and cytoplasmic determiners.

The idea that hereditary control is not restricted entirely to the nucleus has given rise to a concept of *plasmagenes,* units of inheritance analogous to nuclear genes but located in plastids, mitochondria, or other cytoplasmic bodies. Recently, evidence has been obtained that some of these cytoplasmic bodies contain small amounts of DNA. Thus plasmagenes may well have the same chemical basis as nuclear genes. If, however, all plasmagenes are composed of DNA, the number of plasmagenes in a cell must be small compared to the number of nuclear genes, because the great bulk of the cell's DNA is in the nucleus. Another possibility is that some plasmagenes might be composed of RNA, which is relatively abundant in the cytoplasm. It is known that the genetic material in viruses that attack higher plants usually consists of RNA rather than DNA, and there is no obvious reason why some limited amounts of RNA could not function as hereditary material in higher plants and animals as well. Much more research is needed to clear up our present exceedingly hazy understanding of cytoplasmic inheritance.

Episomes

The Sex Factor in *Escherichia coli*. As we saw earlier, it was demonstrated in 1944, by Avery, MacLeod, and McCarty, that when live bacteria are transformed by materials extracted from dead bacteria of another strain, the transforming principle is DNA; genetic material from the dead bacteria somehow becomes incorporated into the control apparatus of the live bacteria. This discovery of genetic exchange, even though the exchange might be regarded as accidental, reopened an old question—whether bacteria have any sort of normal genetic exchange and recombination analogous to that due to sexuality in higher organisms. For years it had been assumed that bacteria lacked any form of sexuality, but now that assumption needed to be re-examined.

In 1946 Joshua Lederberg and Edward L.

Tatum, then at Yale University, published the results of an elegant experiment they had performed to determine whether genetic recombination occurs naturally in *Escherichia coli*. These scientists used techniques similar to those developed earlier by Beadle and Tatum when working on *Neurospora*. They isolated two mutant strains of *E. coli*, each of which lacked the ability to synthesize a particular pair of amino acids; i.e. the first mutant was unable to synthesize amino acids A and B, and the second mutant was unable to synthesize amino acids C and D. The mutants could be grown only on a nutrient medium that contained the respective amino acids. But when the two mutant strains were mixed on a minimal medium (one lacking all four of the critical amino acids), some healthy colonies were formed and these could subsist indefinitely on the minimal medium. Apparently the individuals in these colonies could synthesize all four of the amino acids. It seemed that they had somehow inherited both the first strain's ability to synthesize C and D and the second strain's ability to synthesize A and B. In short, they appeared to be the result of recombination of traits from the two original mutant strains. Lederberg and Tatum demonstrated that direct contact between the cells of the two strains was necessary for this recombination to occur. Such contact is not necessary for transformation. Hence they concluded that this recombination was not the result of transformation.

A few years later, it was shown by several researchers that the recombination demonstrated by Lederberg and Tatum is brought about through a process called *conjugation,* which is analogous to sexual mating in higher organisms. Two bacterial cells come to lie very close to each other, and a cytoplasmic bridge or tube forms between them. This bridge is visible under the electron microscope (Fig. 15.20). Genetic material can pass through the bridge from one cell to the other.

It has been found that conjugation can occur only between cells of different mating types.

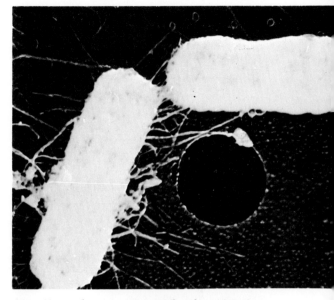

Fig. 15.20. Electron micrograph of conjugating bacteria. [Courtesy T. F. Anderson, *Ann. Inst. Pasteur (Paris)*, vol. 93, 1957.]

A type F^- cell cannot conjugate with another F^- cell. Similarly, F^+ cannot conjugate with F^+. But F^- and F^+ can conjugate with each other. Furthermore, the transfer of DNA is always from F^+ into F^-; i.e. F^+ acts as a donor and F^- acts as a recipient. F^+ is thus analogous to a male, and F^- to a female. Apparently F^+ cells differ from F^- cells in containing in their cytoplasm a so-called *sex factor.* This factor can easily be transferred from one cell to another by contact. Hence when F^- and F^+ cells are mixed, the F^+ cells have a pronounced tendency to convert the F^- cells into F^+. The products of $F^- \times F^+$ crosses are always F^+. If this were the only type of cross possible, one would expect that all cells would eventually be F^+ and that no further conjugation could take place. But conjugation in other types of crosses does not always convert the recipient cell from female into male, as we shall see.

Within F^+ strains, there are usually a very few cells that are hundreds of times more potent than ordinary F^+ cells. These cells, called

Hfr cells (for high-frequency recombination),
mate avidly when they come into contact with
F^- cells. Pure strains of *Hfr* bacteria have been
isolated, and it is these that are usually used
in experiments on conjugation. Crosses of the
$F^- \times Hfr$ type do not usually convert the F^-
cells into F^+ or *Hfr;* the female remains a
female. Extensive study of conjugation in
E. coli by several workers, especially E. L.
Wollman and François Jacob of the Pasteur
Institute in Paris and Lederberg, working primarily at the University of Wisconsin, have
shown that F^+ cells can donate only the sex
factor with perhaps one or a few other genes
attached to it, while *Hfr* cells can donate many
genes but usually not the sex factor.

Bacterial "nuclei" apparently contain only
one chromosome (remember that bacterial
"chromosomes" differ from the chromosomes of
higher organisms, particularly in being composed almost exclusively of DNA). When an
F^- cell and an *Hfr* cell conjugate, the *Hfr*
chromosome moves slowly through the cytoplasmic tube connecting the two cells (Fig.
15.21). Only rarely does the F^- cell receive
the entire *Hfr* chromosome, however. Usually
the cells break apart before the transfer has
been completed. When they break apart, the
chromosome also breaks, and the F^- cell retains whatever portion has already entered it,
the *Hfr* cell being left with the remainder. The
genes always enter the F^- cell in a regular
sequence that is characteristic of the particular
Hfr strain being studied. Some genes are always transferred, even in conjugations that are

**Fig. 15.21. Conjugation between *Hfr* and *F⁻*
bacteria.** The chromosome of the *Hfr* cell
moves into the F^- cell; the end opposite the
one to which the sex factor (S-shaped body)
is attached always leads. Conjugation usually
ends before the entire chromosome has moved
across; so the end with the sex factor ordinarily remains in the *Hfr* cell. Since the chromosome moves at a fairly steady rate, disrupting conjugation at measured times after its
inception permits mapping of the genes on
the bacterial chromosome.

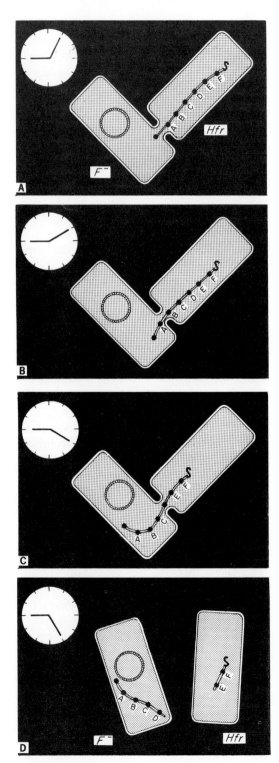

very brief, while others are transferred only when conjugation lasts longer. This indicates that the same end of the chromosome always enters the F^- cell first. Thus, if the genes on an *Hfr* chromosome were arranged in the sequence

ABCDEFGHIJKLMN

and if the *A* end were the leading end, then a short conjugation might transfer only genes *ABC*, a moderately long conjugation might transfer genes *ABCDEFGH*, and a longer conjugation might transfer genes *ABCDEFGHIJKL*. Wollman and Jacob developed a technique for separating conjugating bacteria by agitating them in a blendor. They showed that the number of genes transferred is proportional to the length of time the conjugating pair is left undisturbed, which means that the chromosome moves at a constant speed. Hence the sequence and distance apart of the genes on a bacterial chromosome can be mapped by disrupting conjugation at carefully measured intervals after the mixing of F^- and *Hfr* strains and then determining which genes have entered the F^- cells (Fig. 15.21).

Comparison of the maps obtained for different strains of *Hfr* has revealed that the genes are always arranged in the same order, but that each different *Hfr* strain has a different gene at the anterior end of its chromosome. It is as though the chromosome was originally a circle instead of a rod, and the circle had been broken to form a rod, with the break occurring at a different point on the circle in each strain (Fig. 15.22). The electron microscope has shown that the chromosome is indeed in the form of a circle in F^- and F^+ strains, but that it is a rod in *Hfr* strains. These observations have led to the following theory.

The sex factor, which is known to be absent in F^- cells, is free in the cytoplasm of F^+ cells, where, presumably, several copies of it are usually present in each cell (Fig. 15.23). In this free cytoplasmic form, the sex factor can easily be spread from cell to cell when the

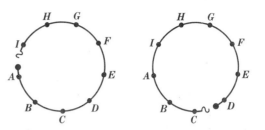

Fig. 15.22. Model of integration of sex factor with the bacterial chromosome. When the sex factor (S-shaped body) attaches to the circular chromosome, it breaks the circle at that point. The point of attachment and break varies from strain to strain, so that, although the order of the genes is the same from strain to strain, the gene at the anterior end of the chromosome is different. Thus the chromosome at left will move during conjugation with the gene sequence *ABCDEFGHI-Sex*, while the one at right will move with the sequence *DEFGHIABC-Sex*.

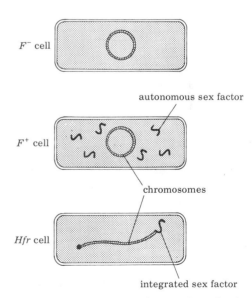

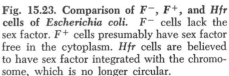

Fig. 15.23. Comparison of F^-, F^+, and *Hfr* cells of *Escherichia coli*. F^- cells lack the sex factor. F^+ cells presumably have sex factor free in the cytoplasm. *Hfr* cells are believed to have sex factor integrated with the chromosome, which is no longer circular.

cells come into contact; for this reason, mixing of F^- and F^+ cells usually results in conversion of many of the F^- cells into F^+ cells. But, according to the theory, the sex factor at times attaches itself onto the chromosome, breaking the circle at the point where it attaches and converting the circular chromosome into a rod with the sex factor on one end. In this rod-shaped form, the chromosome can be transferred from cell to cell during conjugation far more easily than it could in its circular form. Hence, when the sex factor breaks the circular chromosome of an F^+ cell, it converts that cell into a far more potent *Hfr* cell. It is further hypothesized that the integrated sex factor suppresses all autonomous sex factors. Since the rod-shaped chromosome always moves during conjugation with the sex factor at the rear end, and since transfer of the chromosome is seldom complete, this suppression of the autonomous sex factors would explain why an $F^- \times Hfr$ cross does not usually convert the F^- cell into an F^+ or *Hfr* cell; the recipient cell in such a cross does not ordinarily receive the sex factor.

From this brief summary of sexuality in bacteria, you can see that the sex factor differs in its behavior from every other component of the cell so far discussed. At times it is apparently free in the cytoplasm and is, in effect, a plasmagene. At other times it is attached to the chromosome and behaves like all other chromosomal genes. Jacob and Wollman have given the name *episomes* to genetic elements that exhibit this dual behavior. All episomes may exist in the cell in either of two states: the autonomous or detached state, in which their replication is independent of chromosomal replication, and the integrated state, in which they are attached to the chromosome and replicate synchronously with it. Episomes are non-essential to the individual cell, as is illustrated by F^- strains of *E. coli*, which lack the sex factor; but when present, their effects may be very important. Episomes may prove to be the bridge that unites nuclear and cytoplasmic genetics.

Proviruses. Earlier in this chapter, we mentioned the experiments of Hershey and Chase, which showed that bacteriophage viruses inject their DNA contents into the bacterial cells they attack, but leave their protein coats outside. When virulent phage (i.e. phage that kill the bacteria they invade) do this, the viral DNA promptly takes control of the bacterial cell's metabolic machinery and puts it to work manufacturing new viral DNA and new viral protein. These two components are then put together to produce new infective virus particles. About 20–25 minutes after the initial injection of the viral DNA, the bacterial cell lyses, or bursts, releasing as many as one hundred or more new viruses, which may then attack other bacterial cells and start the **lytic cycle** over again (Fig. 15.24).

In the early 1920's, it was discovered that when certain strains of bacteria are mixed with certain other strains, the latter undergo lysis (i.e. they burst). The strains that cause other strains to lyse are called lysogenic strains. The explanation for lysogeny remained a mystery for many years. Then in 1953 André Lwoff and his colleagues at the Pasteur Institute in Paris found that if they exposed lysogenic bacteria to ultraviolet light or X rays or various chemicals, the bacteria would lyse within an hour, releasing large numbers of infectious virus particles. Apparently the lysogenic bacteria had been carrying viruses within their cells, but these viruses had not become active and had not usurped the cell's metabolic machinery until exposed to the inducing action of the ultraviolet light, X rays, or chemicals. Presumably, however, the viruses within an occasional lysogenic bacterial cell would become active normally, and the cell would lyse. This release of infective viruses by a tiny fraction of the lysogenic cells would explain why mixing the lysogenic strain with a susceptible strain would cause lysis of the cells of the susceptible strain.

This discovery by Lwoff that viruses can sometimes be present in an inactive state inside their host cells showed that some viruses must

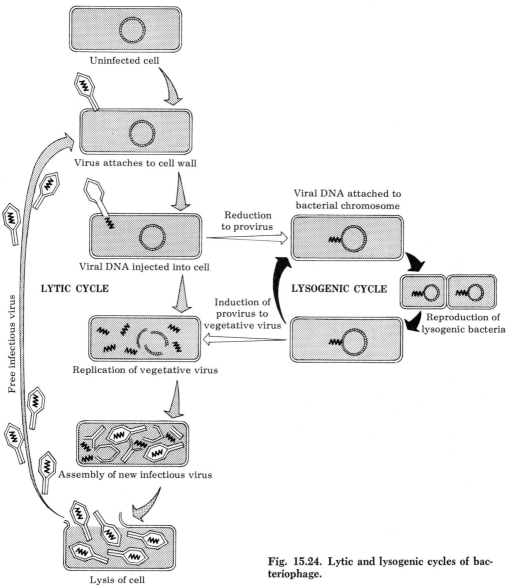

Fig. 15.24. Lytic and lysogenic cycles of bacteriophage.

be temperate rather than virulent. Virulent phages invariably kill their hosts. Temperate phages may or may not kill their hosts, depending upon a variety of conditions. When they do not kill their hosts, their injected DNA becomes associated with the bacterial chromosome, usually by becoming attached to it at a definite position. While attached to the bacterial chromosome, the viral DNA behaves as an addi-

tional part of that chromosome: It is replicated with the rest of the chromosome; it can be transferred from one cell to another during conjugation; its genes can undergo genetic recombination with bacterial genes; and its genes can even produce phenotypic effects on the host bacterium, such as modifications of colony morphology, changes in the properties of the cell wall, and changes in the production of antigens and enzymes. It has been shown, for example, that diphtheria bacteria can produce the toxin that causes the disease only if they are carrying a specific type of viral gene. And viral genes confer on the bacterium in which they reside immunity from further infection by the same type of virus. We see, then, that the DNA of temperate viruses has the properties of an episome for the bacterium. It can exist in an autonomous or vegetative state, replicating independently and eventually destroying the cell, or it can exist in the integrated state (in which it is usually called *provirus*), functioning and replicating as a portion of the bacterial chromosome (Fig. 15.24).

Not only do viral genes sometimes act as bacterial genes, but the reverse is also true. When temperate viruses are in the vegetative state and have put the bacterial cell to work making more viruses, small fragments of the bacterial chromosome may become enclosed in the new viral coats (either as DNA fragments separate from the viral DNA or as additional portions of the viral chromosome). If a temperate virus carrying bacterial DNA in this manner infects a new host, it will inject both viral and bacterial DNA into this new host. Sometimes the injected bacterial genes undergo recombination with the new host's genes. The virus has thus acted as a vehicle for transferring genes from one bacterial cell to another (Fig. 15.25). This process is called *transduction.* It was first described in 1952 by Norton D. Zinder and Joshua Lederberg at the University of Wisconsin.

As you will have realized from this discussion, it is not easy to make a distinction between bacterial genetics and viral genetics. A piece of DNA functioning as a bacterial gene at one time may function as a viral gene a little later. Thus it is not always meaningful to distinguish between bacterial and viral genes. To mention an extreme example, it is theoretically

Fig. 15.25. Model of transduction by bacteriophage.

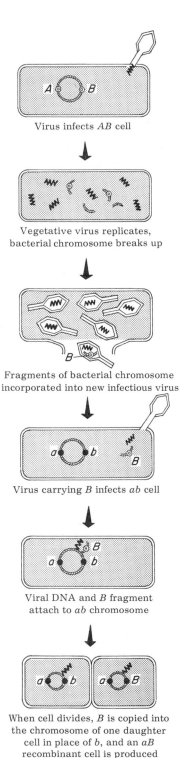

Virus infects *AB* cell

Vegetative virus replicates, bacterial chromosome breaks up

Fragments of bacterial chromosome incorporated into new infectious virus

Virus carrying *B* infects *ab* cell

Viral DNA and *B* fragment attach to *ab* chromosome

When cell divides, *B* is copied into the chromosome of one daughter cell in place of *b*, and an *aB* recombinant cell is produced possible for all the genes in a bacterial cell to be proviral; and, conversely, it is possible that all viral genes came originally from host cells. If viral DNA can act as episomes in the cells of higher organisms (as it almost certainly can and does) and if viruses can transduce genes in higher organisms (as they probably can), then the genetics of viruses and the genetics of higher organisms also become intertwined. Some of the genes that produce important phenotypic effects in the human body may be proviral. And the genes of some viruses may have been derived originally from human chromosomes. And viruses may transduce genes from the cells of one person to the cells of another, which might lead to important genetic alterations of somatic cells (somatic genetics is a subject on which very little research has been done so far). If all these possibilities make genetics far more complex and confusing than it seemed a few years ago when our knowledge did not go much beyond Mendelian genetics, they also make this subject one of the most exciting and promising of modern biology.

REFERENCES

CARLSON, E. A., 1966. *The Gene: A Critical History.* Saunders, Philadelphia.

HARTMAN, P. E., and S. R. SUSKIND, 1964. *Gene Action.* Prentice-Hall, Englewood Cliffs, N.J.

HOLLEY, R. W., *et al.*, 1965. "Structure of a Ribonucleic Acid," *Science,* vol. 147, pp. 1462–1465.

INGRAM, V. M., 1965. *The Biosynthesis of Macromolecules.* Benjamin, New York.

JINKS, J. L., 1964. *Extrachromosomal Inheritance.* Prentice-Hall, Englewood Cliffs, N.J.

MARKERT, C. L., 1964. *Developmental Genetics.* Prentice-Hall, Englewood Cliffs, N.J.

SAGER, R., and F. J. RYAN, 1961. *Cell Heredity.* Wiley, New York.

SRB, A. M., R. D. OWEN, and R. S. EDGAR, 1965. *General Genetics,* 2nd ed. Freeman, San Francisco.

STAHL, F. W., 1964. *The Mechanics of Inheritance.* Prentice-Hall, Englewood Cliffs, N.J.

UHL, C. H., 1965. "Chromosome Structure and Crossing Over," *Genetics,* vol. 51, pp. 191–207.

SUGGESTED READING

ALLFREY, V. G., and A. E. MIRSKY, 1961. "How Cells Make Molecules," *Scientific American,* September. (Offprint 92.)

BEADLE, G. W., 1948. "The Genes of Men and Molds," *Scientific American,* September. (Offprint 1.)

BENZER, S., 1962. "The Fine Structure of the Gene," *Scientific American,* January. (Offprint 120.)

BONNER, D. M., and S. E. MILLS, 1964. *Heredity,* 2nd ed. Prentice-Hall, Englewood Cliffs, N.J.

CRICK, F. H. C., 1954. "The Structure of the Hereditary Material," *Scientific American,* October. (Offprint 5.)

———, 1957. "Nucleic Acids," *Scientific American,* September. (Offprint 54.)

———, 1962. "The Genetic Code," *Scientific American,* October. (Offprint 123.)

DAVIDSON, E. H., 1965. "Hormones and Genes," *Scientific American,* June. (Offprint 1013.)

DEERING, R. A., 1962. "Ultraviolet Radiation and Nucleic Acid," *Scientific American,* December. (Offprint 143.)

EDGAR, R. S., and R. H. EPSTEIN, 1965. "The Genetics of a Bacterial Virus," *Scientific American,* February. (Offprint 1004.)

FRAENKEL-CONRAT, H., 1964. "The Genetic Code of a Virus," *Scientific American,* October. (Offprint 193.)

GIBOR, A., and S. GRANICK, 1964. "Plastids and Mitochondria," *Science,* vol. 145, pp. 890–897.

HOAGLAND, M. B., 1959. "Nucleic Acids and Proteins," *Scientific American,* December. (Offprint 68.)

HOLLAENDER, A., and G. E. STAPLETON, 1959. "Ionizing Radiation and the Cell," *Scientific American,* September. (Offprint 57.)

HOLLEY, R. W., 1966. "The Nucleotide Sequence of a Nucleic Acid," *Scientific American,* February.

HOTCHKISS, R. D., and E. WEISS, 1956, "Transformed Bacteria," *Scientific American,* November. (Offprint 18.)

HURWITZ, J., and J. J. FURTH, 1962. "Messenger RNA," *Scientific American,* February. (Offprint 119.)

INGRAM, V. M., 1958. "How Do Genes Act?" *Scientific American,* January. (Offprint 104.)

JACOB, F., and E. L. WOLLMAN, 1961. "Viruses and Genes," *Scientific American,* June. (Offprint 89.)

LEVINE, R. P., 1962. *Genetics.* Holt, Rinehart & Winston, New York.

MIRSKY, A. E., 1953. "The Chemistry of Heredity," *Scientific American,* February. (Offprint 28.)

MULLER, H. J., 1955. "Radiation and Human Mutation," *Scientific American,* November. (Offprint 29.)

NIRENBERG, M. W., 1963. "The Genetic Code: II," *Scientific American,* March. (Offprint 153.)

RAMSAY, J. A., 1965. *The Experimental Basis of Modern Biology.* Cambridge University Press, New York. (See esp. Part III.)

RICH, A., 1963. "Polyribosomes," *Scientific American,* December. (Offprint 171.)

SAGER, R., 1965. "Genes Outside the Chromosomes," *Scientific American,* January. (Offprint 1002.)

SINSHEIMER, R. L., 1962. "Single-Stranded DNA," *Scientific American,* July. (Offprint 128.)

SPIEGELMAN, S., 1964. "Hybrid Nucleic Acids," *Scientific American,* May. (Offprint 183.)

STENT, G. S., 1953. "The Multiplication of Bacterial Viruses," *Scientific American,* May. (Offprint 40.)

STERN, H., and D. L. NANNEY, 1965. *The Biology of Cells.* Wiley, New York. (See esp. Chapters 12–14.)

WATSON, J. D., 1965. *Molecular Biology of the Gene.* Benjamin, New York.

WOLLMAN, E. L., and F. JACOB, 1956. "Sexuality in Bacteria," *Scientific American,* July. (Offprint 50.)

CHAPTER

16

DEVELOPMENT

Pʀᴏʙᴀʙʟʏ ɴᴏ ᴏᴛʜᴇʀ ᴀsᴘᴇᴄᴛ ᴏғ ʙɪᴏʟᴏɢʏ ɪs so amazing to biologists and nonbiologists alike as the development of a complete new organism from one cell, a development that proceeds in such a precisely controlled manner that all the intricate organization of cells, tissues, organs, and organ systems characterizing the functioning adult comes into being with rarely a flaw. In the last few chapters, we have examined the genetic information that controls development and ensures that a mouse zygote develops into a mouse, an oak zygote into an oak, and an earthworm zygote into an earthworm. It is now time for us to examine briefly a few representative patterns in the development of plants and animals and then try to relate them to possible control mechanisms.

DEVELOPMENT OF AN ANGIOSPERM PLANT

As our first representative pattern of development, let us take the principal events in the development of an angiosperm. We shall make no attempt to discuss this development in great detail or even to mention all the important events; our purpose is simply to give you some familiarity with the kinds of events that any model of developmental control must seek to explain.

The Seed and Its Germination

The egg cell of an angiosperm plant is retained within the ovary of the maternal plant and is fertilized there by a sperm nucleus from a pollen grain. After fertilization, the zygote undergoes a series of mitotic divisions and develops into a tiny *embryo.* This embryo, together with a food-storage tissue called the *endosperm,* becomes enclosed in a tough protective *seed coat.* The resulting composite structure, made up of embryo, endosperm, and seed coat, is called a *seed.* The embryo in some seeds, such as peas and beans, absorbs all the endosperm before the seed is released from the parent plant. In other species, such as corn, the embryo does not absorb significant quantities of the endosperm until the seed begins to germinate. The early division stages of the embryo usually do not last long, and by the time the ripe seed is released from the parent plant it is quite dry and its embryo has usually become dormant. The seed may last for months or years in this dormant state.

Germination of a seed begins with the imbibition of much water, which greatly increases the volume of the seed (sometimes as much as 200 percent). The resulting hydration of the protoplasm increases enzymatic activity, and the metabolic rate of the embryo shows a marked rise. This higher metabolic rate makes possible resumption of active cell division, synthesis of new protoplasm, and increase in cell size by uptake of water. The growing embryo soon bursts out of the seed coat and rapidly assumes a characteristic plant form, with distinguishable shoot and root.

The embryo consists of an elongate axis, to which are attached one or two *cotyledons*

(commonly called seed leaves) (Fig. 16.1). In most plants, the principal function of the cotyledons is the absorption of food from the endosperm; the cotyledons thus become the immediate source of stored food upon which the early growth of the embryo depends. The portion of the embryonic axis above the point at which the cotyledons are attached is called the *epicotyl;* it consists primarily of a pair of miniature leaves and a tiny bud. The epicotyl is the primordium, or rudiment, from which most of the shoot develops. The portion of the embryonic axis below the point of attachment of the cotyledons is called the *hypocotyl;* its lower end, often called the radicle, will form the primary root of the plant.

The first part of the embryo to emerge from the seed is the hypocotyl, which promptly turns downward (no matter what the orientation of the seed may be) and develops root hairs; it also soon gives rise to secondary roots. By the time the epicotyl begins its rapid development, the hypocotyl has already formed a young root system capable of anchoring the plant to the substrate and of absorbing water and minerals. In some dicots (which have, as the term "dicot" indicates, two cotyledons), the upper portion of the hypocotyl elongates and forms an arch, which pushes upward through the soil and emerges into the air (Fig. 16.2). Once the hypocotyl arch is exposed to light, a phototropic response causes it to

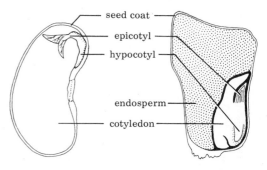

Fig. 16.1. Diagram of dicot and monocot seeds. Left: A dicot seed (bean). Right: A monocot seed (corn).

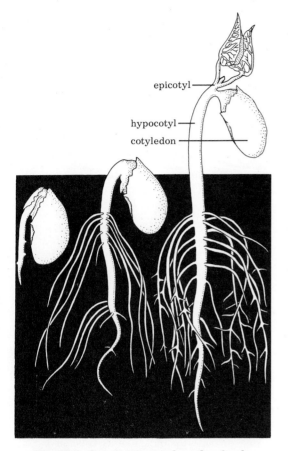

epicotyl

hypocotyl

cotyledon

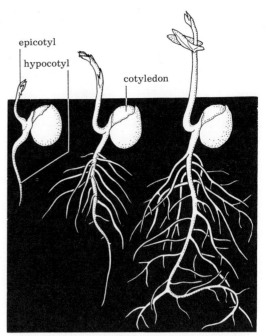

epicotyl

hypocotyl

cotyledon

Fig. 16.3. Germination and early development of a pea. The development of a pea differs from that of a bean in that no hypocotyl arch is formed and the cotyledons remain beneath the soil.

Fig. 16.2. Germination and early development of a bean. The hypocotyl emerges from the seed first and forms a young root system (left). As the upper portion of the hypocotyl elongates, it forms an arch that pushes out of the soil into the air (middle). It then straightens, pulling the cotyledons out of the ground as the epicotyl begins its development (right).

straighten, pulling the cotyledons and the epicotyl out of the soil. The epicotyl then begins to elongate. In such plants, of which the garden bean is an example, the shoot of the mature plant is mostly of epicotyl origin, but a short region (usually less than an inch) at the base of the stem is derived from the hypocotyl. Other dicots, of which the garden pea is an example, show a slightly different pattern of germination (Fig. 16.3). In these plants, no hypocotyl arch forms and the cotyledons are

never raised above ground. Instead, the epicotyl begins to elongate soon after the young root system has begun to form. Unlike the end of the hypocotyl, that of the epicotyl always grows upward and soon emerges from the soil. In such plants, the entire shoot is of epicotyl origin. A similar pattern is seen in monocots like corn (which have only one cotyledon but a large endosperm) (Fig. 16.4).

Growth and Differentiation of the Plant Body

Growth in Length. The seedling plant grows in length rather slowly at first, then enters a longer period of much more rapid growth, and finally slows down again or even stops as it approaches maturity. If the height (or weight) of the plant is plotted against age, the resulting growth curve is roughly S-shaped (Fig. 16.5). This same general shape also characterizes the growth curves of animals and even the growth curves of populations of plants or animals (in which the number of individuals is plotted against the age of the population). There are, however, important differences from species to species. For example, the growth curves for perennial plants and many invertebrate animals differ from those of mammals because such organisms continue to grow to some extent throughout their lives, while mammals usually cease growing after they reach maturity. Some annual plants cease growing after they reach the flowering stage,

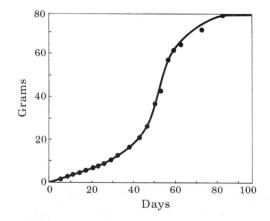

Fig. 16.5. A typical S-shaped growth curve. This particular graph shows increase in weight of a young corn plant. [Redrawn from D'A. W. Thompson, *On Growth and Form*, Cambridge University Press, 1942 (from G. Backman, after Stefanowska).]

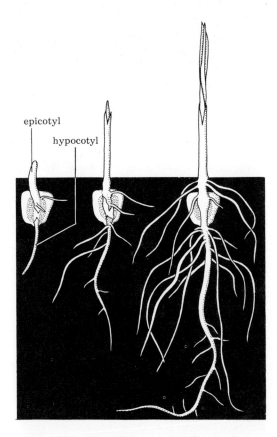

Fig. 16.4. Germination and early development of corn, a monocot.

and their growth curves resemble those of mammals.

Growth in length of the shoot and root of a young plant involves two principal processes, cell multiplication and cell elongation. Both processes are ordinarily restricted to a relatively limited region near the apex of the shoot or root. Let us look first at the root.

The extreme tip of a root is covered by a conical *root cap* consisting of a mass of nondividing parenchyma cells (Fig. 16.6). These cells secrete a gelatinous substance that lubricates the surface of the root cap and facilitates the pushing of the root tip through the soil as the root elongates. As the tip moves through the soil, some of the cells on the surface of the root cap are abraded. They are replaced by new cells added to the cap by the *apical meristem,* a zone of cell multiplication located just behind the cap. This zone, which is composed of relatively small, actively dividing cells, is usually restricted to an area a millimeter long or less. Most of the new cells produced by the meristem are laid down on the side away from the root cap. These cells are left behind as the meristem lays down additional new cells in front of them and the tip

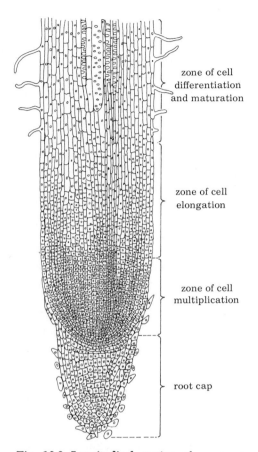

zone of cell
differentiation
and maturation

zone of cell
elongation

zone of cell
multiplication

root cap

Fig. 16.6. Longitudinal section of a young barley root. [Modified from H. J. Fuller and O. Tippo, *College Botany,* Holt, 1949.]

continues to move through the soil. It is these new cells, derived from the apical meristem, that will form the primary tissues of the root.

As the new cells become further removed from the meristem by the deposition of additional intervening cells, the mitotic activity of most of them slows down and eventually terminates. Once the cells have ceased dividing, they begin to absorb water rapidly and to enlarge; most of this enlargement is elongation rather than increase in width. As we saw in another chapter, this cell elongation is under the control of hormones, particularly auxins (and gibberellins in stems). Apparently, one of the

first steps in the elongation process is an increase in area of the cell wall, which produces a corresponding increase in the volume of the cell. This increase in volume reduces the wall pressure and therefore increases the suction pressure, with the result that inward diffusion of water increases. Most of this water enters the rapidly expanding vacuole. In the fully elongated cell, the vacuole occupies most of the volume, the cytoplasm being restricted to a very thin layer next to the walls. Note that this cell growth in plants differs greatly from cell growth in animals, where most increase in size is attributable to formation of more cytoplasm rather than to vacuolation.

The zone of cell elongation in the root is just behind the zone of cell multiplication, or meristem. It usually extends only a few millimeters along the root (Fig. 16.6). For example, in a corn seedling the fastest elongation occurs about 4 mm. from the root tip, and cells more than 10 mm. behind the tip have completed their elongation. The situation is similar in bean seedlings (Fig. 16.7). The elongation in this zone has the effect, of course, of pushing the root tip through the soil faster than if it were driven only by the production of new cells in the zone of multiplication.

Growth of the stem is basically similar to growth of the root. New cells are produced by an apical meristem (which is not, however, covered by any structure analogous to the root cap), and these cells then elongate, pushing the apex upward. The most obvious difference between growth of the stem and growth of the root is the lateral production of leaves by the growing tip of the stem. At regular intervals, an increase in the rate of cell division under a localized region of the sloping surface of the apical meristem of a stem gives rise to a series of swellings that function as leaf primordia (Fig. 16.8). The point at which each leaf primordium arises from the stem is called a *node,* and the length of stem between two successive nodes is called an *internode* (see Fig. 3.39, p. 95). Most increase in length

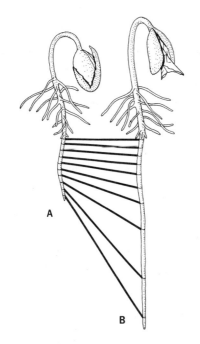

Fig. 16.7. Growth of a bean root. Note that the parts of the root immediately behind the tip in (A) are those that have undergone the most elongation by stage (B). [Modified from V. A. Greulach and J. E. Adams, *Plants: An Introduction to Modern Botany,* Wiley, 1962.]

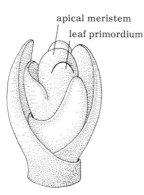

apical meristem
leaf primordium

Fig. 16.8. A bud. [Used by permission from J. D. Dodd, *Form and Function in Plants,* © 1962 by The Iowa State University Press.]

of the stem results from elongation of the cells in the young internodes.

At the tip of the stem is a series of internodes that have not yet undergone much elon-

gation. The tiny leaf primordia that separate these internodes curve up and over the meristem, with the older, larger ones enveloping the younger, smaller ones (Fig. 16.9). The resulting compound structure, consisting of the apical meristem and a series of unelongated internodes enclosed within the leaf primordia, is called a **bud.** Commonly, the bud is protected on its outer surface by overlapping scales, which are modified leaves that grow from the base of the bud. When a dormant bud "opens" in the spring, the scales curve away from the bud and then fall off, and the internodes that were contained within the bud begin to elongate rapidly. As the nodes become further and further separated, mitotic activity (mostly in one plane) in the leaf primordia gives rise to young leaves with the characteristics of the species; the pattern of the cell divisions determines whether the leaves will be entire or lobed, simple or compound. Once the leaves are fully formed, the leaf primordia lose their meristematic activity. But before this happens, a small mound of meristematic tissue usually arises in the angle between the base of each leaf and the internode above it. Each of these new meristematic regions gives rise to a lateral or **axillary bud** with the same essential features as the terminal buds already described (Fig. 16.10). Elongation of the internodes of the lateral buds produces branch stems (you will recall that, since roots have no buds, branch roots originate in an entirely different way—from the pericycle deep within the primary root).

Differentiation of Tissues. Cell division and cell elongation cannot alone produce all the essential features of the fully developed plant, of course. All the new cells produced by the apical meristems are fundamentally alike. Yet some of these cells will become collenchyma, some will become xylem vessels, some will become sieve cells, etc. The process whereby a cell changes from its immature form to some one mature form is called *differentiation.* In the growing root or stem, cells have begun

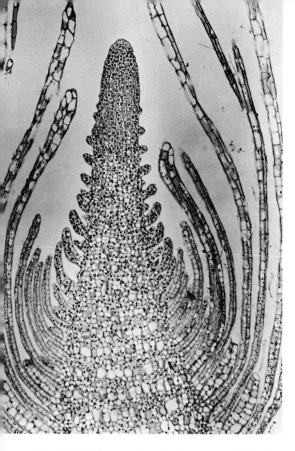

Fig. 16.9. Photograph of stem tip of *Elodea*. [Courtesy Thomas Eisner, Cornell University.]

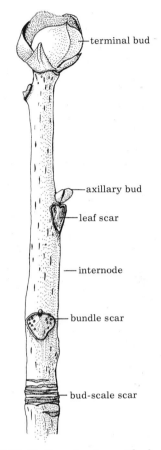

Fig. 16.10. Portion of a stem. The bud-scale scar shows where the dormant terminal bud of the previous winter was; the length of stem between the bud-scale scar and the terminal bud is one year's growth. Leaf scars show where petioles were attached to the stem. The bundle scars within each leaf scar show where the vascular bundles passed into the petiole. The axillary bud will give rise to a branch stem during the next growing season.

to differentiate by the time they have finished elongating. Thus, immediately behind the zone of cell elongation in a root is a zone of cell differentiation and maturation in which the definitive tissues of the adult root take shape (Fig. 16.6).

Three concentric areas can be distinguished even in the zone of elongation of a root when it is viewed in cross section (Fig. 16.11A). These are (1) an outer layer called the *proto-derm;* (2) a wide area of parenchymatous *ground tissue* located beneath the protoderm; and (3) an inner core of *provascular tissue* composed of particularly elongate cells. The protoderm rapidly matures into the epidermis, and most of the newly differentiated epidermal cells just behind the zone of elongation bear root hairs. The ground tissue of the middle layer matures into the cortex and endodermis. And the provascular core differentiates into the primary tissues of the stele: primary xylem,

primary phloem, pericycle, and vascular cambium (Fig. 16.11B–C). Differentiation in the growing stem follows a similar pattern except that there are usually two areas of ground tissue: one between the protoderm and the provascular cylinder, which gives rise to the cortex and endodermis, and a second inside the provascular cylinder, which becomes the pith.

As we saw in an earlier chapter, increase in

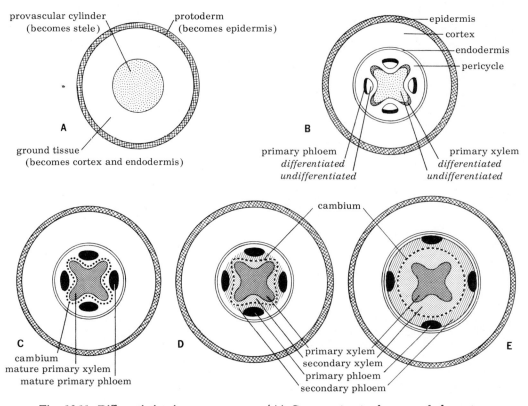

Fig. 16.11. Differentiation in a young root. (A) Cross section in the zone of elongation. Three distinct concentric areas can already be detected. (B) At a slightly later stage of development, the protoderm has differentiated into epidermis; the ground tissue has differentiated into cortex and endodermis; and the provascular cylinder has begun to differentiate into primary xylem and primary phloem. (C) Differentiation in the provascular cylinder is complete, and the cambium is about to become active. (D) Divisions in the cambium have given rise to secondary xylem and secondary phloem, which are located between the primary xylem and primary phloem. (E) The areas of secondary tissue continue to thicken as more and more new cells are produced by the cambium.

circumference of the root or stem depends upon the formation of secondary tissues composed of cells derived from lateral meristems, particularly the vascular cambium. As cells of the vascular cambium undergo mitosis, many new cells are produced on the inner face of the cambium and these differentiate into secondary xylem, while other new cells are produced on the outer face of the cambium and differentiate into secondary phloem (Fig. 16.11D–E). As more and more secondary vascular tissue is formed and the circumference increases steadily, the old epidermis and cortex are broken

and sloughed off. These are replaced by a secondary protective tissue, the cork, composed of cells derived from a new lateral meristem, the *cork cambium,* which forms from a layer of the old cortex or from the pericycle or even from the older phloem.

DEVELOPMENT OF A MULTICELLULAR ANIMAL

As a second example of developmental pattern, let us examine some of the major events in the development of a multicellular animal, especially a vertebrate. Again, our purpose is not to describe these events fully or even to mention all the important ones; it is simply to give you some familiarity with the kinds of events that occur.

Embryonic Development

Early Cleavage Stages. We saw in an earlier chapter that certain cells are early set aside as egg primordia in the ovary of a female animal. These cells grow to an unusually large size, and when they then undergo meiosis, the divisions are unequal and almost all the cytoplasm is retained in the ripe ovum, the other haploid cells being the tiny polar bodies that soon deteriorate. The sperm, on the other hand, is an unusually small cell with very little cytoplasm. The ovum thus furnishes most of the initial cytoplasm for the embryo (hence the much greater importance of the mother than of the father in the transmission of cytoplasmically inherited traits).

The penetration of the sperm into the ovum stimulates the ovum to begin development into an embryo. Note we said that the *penetration* is the trigger, not the fusion of the sperm nucleus with the egg nucleus, even though this fusion is the actual event of fertilization. Apparently, true fertilization is not necessary to induce embryonic development in many animals, even ones that do not normally reproduce parthenogenetically (i.e. without fertilization of the egg). It is easy, for example, to induce unfertilized frog eggs to begin development in the laboratory by pricking them with a fine needle dipped in blood, or by giving them a mild electric shock, or by changing the salt concentration in the surrounding fluid, or even by just shaking them. A few such eggs will develop into viable normal-appearing tadpoles. Adult rabbits have been produced from unfertilized eggs by similar procedures. (What would be the sex of all such parthenogenetically produced rabbits?)

In normal development, the zygote begins a rapid series of mitotic divisions immediately after fertilization has taken place. Since the pattern of these cleavages is greatly influenced by the amount of yolk (stored food) in the egg, let us first examine the pattern in amphioxus, a tiny marine chordate whose egg has very little yolk, and then compare the initial development of amphioxus with that of other animals whose eggs have more yolk.

The early cleavages of the zygote are not accompanied by protoplasmic growth. They produce a grapelike cluster of cells called a *morula,* which is little if any larger than the single egg cell from which it is derived (Fig. 16.12). The cytoplasm of the one large cell is simply partitioned almost equally into many new cells that are much smaller. As cleavage continues, the cells become arranged in a hollow sphere called a *blastula* (Fig. 16.12E). The cavity inside the sphere is called the *blastocoel.*

Gastrulation in Amphioxus. Next begins a series of complex movements that are important in establishing the definitive shape and pattern of the developing embryo. The establishment of shape and pattern in all organisms is called *morphogenesis* (meaning the genesis of form). Morphogenetic movements of large masses of cells always occur during the early developmental stages of animals; they are much less common in plants, although other movements produced by differential growth rates play an important role, as we saw in our examination of phototropic and geotropic responses.

In the development of amphioxus, the movements that occur after formation of the blastula (when it is composed of about 500 cells) convert it into a two-layered structure called a *gastrula.* The process of gastrulation begins when a small depression, or invagination, starts to form at a point on the surface of the blastula where the cells are somewhat larger than those on the opposite side (Fig. 16.12F). The differ-

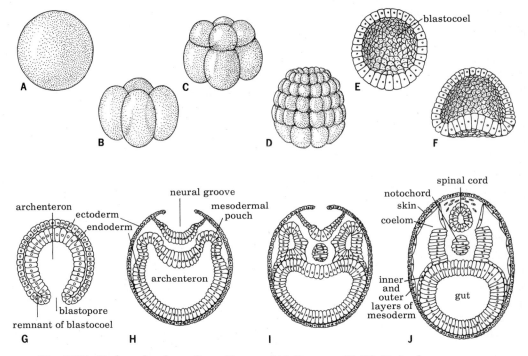

Fig. 16.12. Early embryology of amphioxus. (A) Zygote. (B–D) Early cleavage stages forming a morula (C) and then a blastula (D). (E) Longitudinal section through a blastula, showing the blastocoel. (F–G) Longitudinal sections through an early and a late gastrula. Notice that the invagination is at the vegetal pole of the embryo, where the cells are largest. (H–I) Cross sections through an early and a late neurula. Invagination of the dorsal ectoderm is giving rise to the spinal cord, and pouches off the endoderm are giving rise to the mesoderm. (J) A later embryo in which both the spinal cord and the mesoderm are taking their definitive form. Notice that there is a cavity (the coelom) in the mesoderm.

ences in cell size are not very great in amphioxus embryos; they are more pronounced in many other animals. The smaller cells make up the *animal hemisphere* of the embryo. The larger cells make up the *vegetal hemisphere.* It is at the pole of the vegetal hemisphere that the invagination of gastrulation typically occurs. As gastrulation proceeds, and more and more cells move to the point of invagination and then fold inward, the invagination becomes larger and larger. Eventually the invaginated cell layer comes to lie almost against the outer layer, thus nearly obliterating the old blastocoel (Fig. 16.12G). The resulting gastrula is a two-layered cup, with a new cavity that opens to the outside via the *blastopore,* which is at the point where invagination first

began. The new cavity, called the *archenteron,* will become the cavity of the digestive tract, and the blastopore will become the anus.

Gastrulation, as it occurs in amphioxus, first produces an embryo with two primary cell layers, an outer *ectoderm* and an inner *endoderm.* A third primary layer, the *mesoderm,* soon begins to form between the ectoderm and the endoderm. In amphioxus, the mesoderm originates as pouches pinched off the endoderm (Fig. 16.12H–J). In many other animals, it arises from inwandering cells derived primarily from the area around the blastopore where the ectoderm and endoderm meet.

Gastrulation in Eggs with More Yolk. In the amphioxus egg, which has little yolk and in which the distinction between animal and vegetal hemispheres is only slight, the early cleavages are nearly equal (i.e. the new cells are of nearly the same size) and gastrulation can occur in a direct and uncomplicated manner. Many eggs have far more yolk in their vegetal hemisphere, and this deposit of stored food imposes complications and limitations on such processes as cleavage and gastrulation. Generally, the more yolk an egg contains, the more cleavage tends to be restricted to the animal hemisphere and the more gastrulation departs from the pattern in amphioxus.

Frog eggs, which contain far more yolk than those of amphioxus but much less than those of most birds, may serve as examples of eggs with an intermediate yolk mass (Fig. 16.13). The first two cleavages, which are perpendicular to each other, cut through both the animal and vegetal poles, producing cells of roughly the same size. But the next cleavage is horizontal and located decidedly nearer the animal pole; thus the four cells produced at the animal end of the egg are considerably smaller than the four at the vegetal end. From this stage onward, many more cleavages occur in the animal hemisphere of the embryo than in the vegetal hemisphere.

Early in its second day of development, the frog embryo begins gastrulation. Simple invagination at the vegetal pole is not mechanically feasible because of the large mass of inert yolk. Instead, portions of the cell layer of the animal hemisphere move down around the yolk mass and then fold in at the edge of the yolk. This involution begins at what will be the dorsal

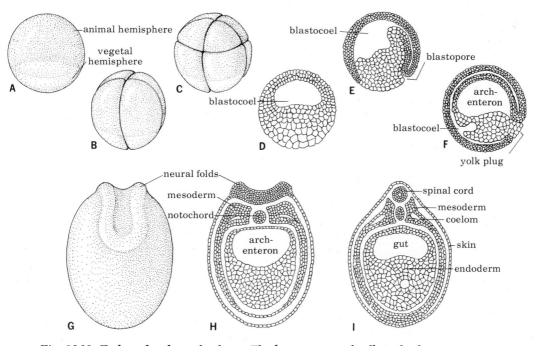

Fig. 16.13. **Early embryology of a frog.** The large amount of yolk in the frog egg causes its pattern of gastrulation to differ from that in amphioxus. (A) Zygote. (B–C) Early cleavage stages. Note that the first horizontal cleavage is nearer the animal pole, much larger cells thus being produced at the vegetal pole. (D) Longitudinal section of a blastula. (E–F) Longitudinal sections of two gastrula stages. (G) An early neurula, showing the neural folds and neural groove. (H) Cross section of a neurula after formation of mesoderm. (I) Cross section of a later embryo, showing definitive spinal cord.

side of the yolk mass, forming initially a crescent-shaped blastopore at the edge of the yolk. This infolding slowly spreads to all sides of the yolk, so that the crescent blastopore is converted into a circle. Movement of the other cells around the yolk eventually encloses this material almost completely within the cavity of the newly forming digestive tract.

Birds' eggs contain so much yolk that the small disc of cytoplasm on its surface is dwarfed by comparison (Fig. 16.14). No cleavage of the massive yolk is possible, and all cell division is restricted to the small cytoplasmic disc. (Note that the yolk and the small lighter-colored cytoplasmic disc on its surface constitute the true egg cell; the white of the egg is outside the cell.) The gastrulation process is of necessity greatly modified in such eggs. Neither invagination of the vegetal pole as in amphioxus nor involution around the edges of the vegetal pole as in a frog can occur. Instead, the endoderm splits away from the under side of the ectoderm, and then cells from the upper layer (primordial ectoderm and mesoderm) involute along the longitudinal midline of the embryo to form the mesoderm. This involution gives rise to a clearly visible line or streak on the surface of the cytoplasmic disc; the streak is, in effect, a very elongate blastopore.

The fates of cells in different parts of the three primary layers of vertebrates have been determined by staining them with dyes of different colors and then following their movements. As you might expect, the ectoderm eventually gives rise to the outermost layer of the body—the epidermal portion of the skin—and to structures derived from the epidermis, such as hair, nails, the eye lens, many glands, and the epithelium of the nasal cavity, mouth, and anal canal. As you might also expect, the endodermis gives rise to the innermost layer of the body—the epithelial lining of the digestive tract and of other structures derived from the digestive tract, such as the respiratory passages and the lungs, the liver, the pancreas, the

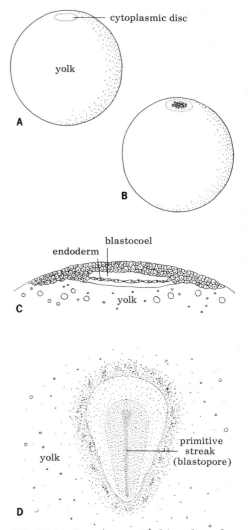

Fig. 16.14. Some stages in the early embryology of a chick. (A) The zygote. A small cytoplasmic disc lies on the surface of a massive yolk. (B) Early cleavage. There is no cleavage of the yolk. (C) Section through a blastula. (D) Surface view of a gastrula. Involution of cells along the midline of the embryo during gastrulation produces a clearly visible primitive streak, which is essentially a very elongate blastopore.

thyroid, and the bladder. The mesoderm gives rise to most of the tissues in between, such as muscle, blood, and connective tissue, including bone.

One major tissue located topographically

between the skin and the gut does not develop from the mesoderm. This is the nervous tissue, which, curiously enough, is derived from the ectoderm. Soon after gastrulation, the ectoderm becomes divided into two components, the epidermis and the neural tube. A sheet of ectodermal cells lying along the midline of the embryo above the newly formed digestive tract bends inward and forms a long groove extending most of the length of the embryo (Fig. 16.13H). The dorsal folds that border this groove then move toward each other and fuse together, converting the groove into a long tube lying beneath the surface of the back. This neural tube becomes detached from the epidermis above it, and in time differentiates into the spinal cord and brain (Fig. 16.13I; see also Fig. 16.12H–J).

We see, then, that the morphogenetic movements of gastrulation and neurulation give shape and form to the embryo, and bring masses of cells into the proper position for their later differentiation into the principal tissues of the adult body. In effect, the movements mold the embryonic mass into the structural configuration upon which differentiation will superimpose the finer detail of the finished organism.

Later Embryonic Development.   Much must happen to convert a gastrula into a fully developed young animal ready for birth. The individual tissues and organs must be formed; in a vertebrate, the four limbs must develop; the elaborate system of nervous control must be established; etc. The complexity and precision that must be involved in these developmental changes are staggering to contemplate. For example, approximately 43 muscles, 29 bones, and many hundreds of nervous pathways must form in each human arm. If the arm is to function properly, all these components must be arranged in a precisely correlated manner. Each muscle must have exactly the right origins and insertions; each bone must be jointed to the next bone beyond it in a certain

way; each nerve fiber must have all the proper synaptic connections with the central nervous system and must terminate on the right effector cells. Incredibly sensitive mechanisms of developmental control must operate if such an intricate structure can arise from a mass of initially undifferentiated cells. Yet the developmental processes that produce all these later embryonic changes are the same ones we have seen at work in the early embryo—cell division, cell growth, cell differentiation, and morphogenetic movements. Bursts of mitotic activity in some areas and cessation of cleavage in other areas alter the balance between the parts. Special patterns of cell growth produce important changes in size and shape. Through differentiation, cells may lose particular capacities, but may become highly efficient at performing other functions that previously they could perform only slightly. Foldings and pouchings establish the primordia of lungs and glands, of eyes and bladder. Even cell death plays an important role in the normal development of the living animal; e.g., fingers and toes become separated by the death of the cells between them, and initially solid cords of mesodermal tissue become hollow blood vessels by death of their innermost cells.

It is beyond the scope of this book to discuss in detail the many events that occur during later embryonic development. Yet it is these events that mold morphologically similar gastrulas into a fish in one instance, a rabbit in another, and a human being in still another, depending upon the genetic endowment of the gastrula in question. The developmental events are programed differently for each different species, and an understanding of how such different programs arise and how they are carried out is one of the important goals of developmental biologists.

The Relationship Between Ontogeny and Phylogeny.   One interesting aspect of the differences in the developmental programs of different species should be mentioned here. It has long been recognized that the early embryos of most vertebrates closely resemble one another. For example, the early human embryo has a well-developed tail and also a series of gill pouches in the pharyngeal region (Fig. 16.15). Consequently it looks very much like an early fish embryo. And it looks even more like an early bird or rabbit embryo. Soon after Darwin put forth his theory of evolution in 1858, it was realized that such similarities in development reflect an ancestral relationship; human and fish embryos resemble each other because human beings and fish share a common remote ancestry. Careful study also revealed that, in the course of its development, the embryo of a species seems to pass through a succession of stages that resemble the stages through which the evolution of that species passed. This apparent parallelism led E. H. Haeckel to formulate his "principle of recapitulation": that ontogeny repeats phylogeny (ontogeny is the course of an individual's development, and phylogeny is its evolutionary history). According to Haeckel's principle, the sequence of developmental stages in an individual's development corresponds to the sequence of ancestors from which it has descended. Thus, if mammals evolved from reptiles, which evolved from amphibians, which evolved from fish, then a mammalian embryo should first develop into a fish, then into an amphibian, then into a reptile, and finally into a mammal. In short, each new evolutionary advance would be added onto the end of the already existing developmental sequence. Evolution from reptile to mammal would simply mean changing the developmental sequence from fish–amphibian–reptile to fish–amphibian–reptile–mammal.

The modern view is that Haeckel's idea was a gross oversimplification. Ontogeny does *not* repeat phylogeny in any strict or literal sense. An individual's developmental stages do not correspond to its successive adult ancestors. A mammalian embryo never develops into a fish or an amphibian, and it doesn't even come close to doing so. What does happen is that a mammalian embryo passes though some of the same stages as an early fish embryo, and it passes through stages similar to some an amphibian or reptile embryo passes through. Ontogeny does not repeat the adult stages of phylogeny, but it does repeat, in an altered form, some of the ontogeny of ancestral forms.

This similarity in early developmental stages simply means that ontogeny is not completely changed every time one species evolves from another. Instead, slight alterations that cause a shift in direction at some point in the developmental sequences are made. The new species (let's call it A) in effect uses a slightly altered version of the developmental program it inherited from the previous species (B). Since B, in turn, used a slightly altered version of the developmental program of its ancestor (C), and since C used a slightly altered program inherited from its ancestor (D), it follows that A uses an ontogeny derived from that of D. Therefore the ontogeny of a species will closely resemble the ontogenies of recent ancestors, and it will resemble less closely the ontogenies of more distant ancestors. The more remote the ancestor, the fewer the similarities. In general, when the relationship is remote, the similarities are restricted to the very early stages of development, because beyond those early stages evolutionary changes have grossly altered the direction of development. Thus the ontogenies of fish and mammals show a close resemblance to each other only in their very early stages, after which they take quite different directions. The ontogenies of amphibians and mammals resemble each other closely somewhat longer before they diverge strongly. And the ontogenies of reptiles and mammals closely resemble each other through many of their early stages before the divergences becomes very noticeable. In summary, evolution is not the simple tacking of extra stages to earlier ontogenies; nor is it the creation *de novo* of new ontogenies. It is something between the two: the modification of old ontogenies in new directions.

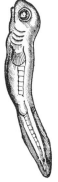

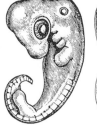

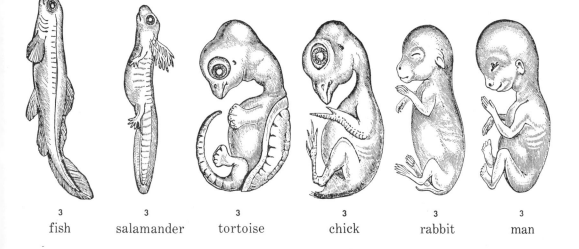

fish   salamander   tortoise   chick   rabbit   man

Fig. 16.15. A comparison of vertebrate embryos at three stages of development. [Reprinted from G. J. Romanes, *Darwin and After Darwin,* Open Court Publishing Co., 1901.]

Postembryonic Development

The extent to which an animal has developed by the time of birth varies greatly among different species. Some young animals are entirely self-sufficient from the time they are born and neither need nor receive parental care. Others can run about and feed themselves as soon as they are born, but still benefit from a limited amount of parental care; baby chicks and ducks are examples. Still other animals are born while still at an early stage of development, and are nearly helpless and totally dependent upon parental care; baby human beings and baby Robins are examples (just-hatched baby Robins are blind, almost devoid of feathers, and unable to stand). The extent of development at birth is often (though not always) a reflection of the length of the embryonic period, which is usually correlated in animals that lay eggs with the amount of yolk the eggs contain. Among birds particularly, species that have a short incubation period for the eggs characteristically have altricial (poorly developed) young, while species that have a longer incubation period characteristically have precocial (well-developed) young; e.g. Robins incubate their eggs only 13 days, while chickens have a 21-day incubation period. Regardless of their state of development at birth, however, all animals continue to undergo major developmental changes during their postembryonic life.

Growth. Although postembryonic development involves some cell multiplication and cell differentiation (though seldom any major morphogenetic movements), the preponderant factor by far in such development in many animals is growth in size. As indicated earlier in this chapter, growth usually begins slowly, then goes through a more rapid period, and then slows down again or stops. This pattern yields the characteristic S-shaped growth curve shown in Fig. 16.5. It must be emphasized that, although the general shape of this curve

holds for most organisms, its details vary in important ways from species to species. The slope of the curve is different for different species, depending upon whether they grow very rapidly for a shorter time or more slowly for a longer time (compare, for example, the rate of increase in weight of a calf and a child). The shape of the curve is seldom as smooth as it appears in a generalized growth curve, because so many factors can affect the rate of growth. In most mammals, growth slows down for a while immediately after weaning, and it often varies greatly during puberty; such irregularities are reflected in bumps and dips in the curve (Fig. 16.16). An especially marked departure from the smooth generalized curve is seen in the growth of arthropods. These animals can undergo only limited growth between molts because the hard exoskeleton that encases their bodies can be stretched only slightly. However, at each molt there is a sharp burst of growth during the short period after the old exoskeleton has been shed and before the new one has hardened. The resulting growth curve shows a steplike pattern (Fig. 16.17).

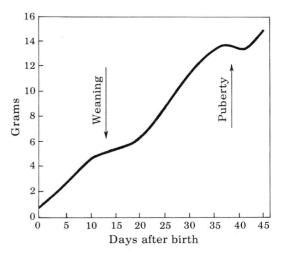

Fig. 16.16. Growth in weight of a mouse. The rate of growth is slower at weaning and at puberty. [Modified from D'A. W. Thompson, *On Growth and Form*, Cambridge University Press, 1942 (after W. Ostwald).]

We have so far discussed growth as though it occurred at the same rate and at the same time in all parts of the body. But it does not. It is obvious to anyone that the differences between a baby chick and an adult hen or rooster, or the differences between a newborn baby and an adult human being, are not attributable merely to an overall size difference. Just as striking are the differences in body proportions. The head of a young child is far larger in relation to the rest of his body than is that of the adult. And the child's legs are much shorter in relation to his trunk than are those of the adult. If the child's body were simply to grow as large as an adult's while maintaining the same proportions, the result would be a most unadultlike individual (Fig. 16.18). Distinctive body proportions normally develop in the adult because the various parts of the body grow at quite different rates or stop growing at different times (Fig. 16.19).

Two closely related species that differ in size are frequently also quite different in body proportions not because of any basic difference

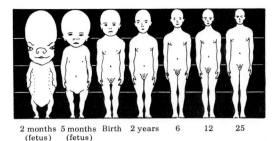

2 months 5 months Birth 2 years 6 12 25
(fetus) (fetus)

Fig. 16.18. Changes in body proportions during human fetal and postnatal growth. The head grows proportionately much more slowly than the limbs. [Modified from *Morris' Human Anatomy*, ed. by C. M. Jackson, Blakiston, 1925.]

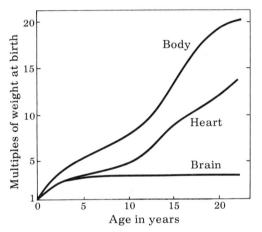

Fig. 16.19. Graph showing differences in relative growth of body, heart, and brain of a man. [Modified from D'A. W. Thompson, *On Growth and Form*, Cambridge University Press, 1942 (from Quetelet's data).]

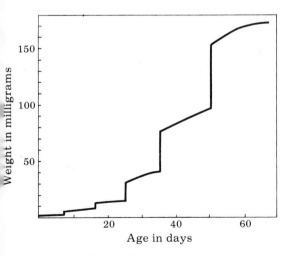

Fig. 16.17. Growth in weight of an insect. The growth spurts of this water boatman (*Notonecta*) occur at the time of molt, when the old exoskeleton has been shed and the new one has not yet fully hardened. [Modified from V. B. Wigglesworth, *The Principles of Insect Physiology*, Methuen, 1947.]

in the growth patterns of the two species but simply because a slight increase in overall body size automatically results in disproportionate increases in some parts of the body. In elk, for example, the size of the antlers increases much faster than the overall body size. Thus a slight increase in body size is always accompanied by a disproportionately large increase in the size of the antlers. Consequently, if species A grows slightly larger than species B, then A will have antlers that are much larger in relation to its body size. A slight difference in body size between two species can thus produce many striking differences in proportions between them.

Larval Development and Metamorphosis. We have said that growth in size rather than cell division or cell differentiation is commonly the principal mechanism of postembryonic development. But this is not always true. Many aquatic animals, particularly those leading sessile lives as adults, go through a *larval* stage that bears little resemblance to the adult (Fig. 16.20). The series of developmental changes (not just increase in size) that convert an immature animal into the adult form is called *metamorphosis.* The rather drastic metamorphosis of a larva into an adult frequently involves extensive cell division and differentiation, and sometimes even morphogenetic movement; growth alone could not accomplish so complete a change in form.

In many aquatic animals, dispersal of the species depends upon the larval stage; the tiny larvae either swim or are passively carried by currents to new locations, where they settle down and undergo metamorphosis into sedentary adults. In other species, such as frogs, where the adult is not sedentary, the adaptive significance of the larval stage (the tadpole in the case of frogs) seems less a matter of dispersal than one of exploiting alternative food sources during the developmental stages (tadpoles feed primarily on microscopic plant material, while adult frogs are carnivorous and take some fairly large prey).

Although a larval stage occurs in the life history of many aquatic animals, probably the most familiar larvae are those of certain groups of terrestrial insects, including flies, beetles, wasps, butterflies, and moths. The young fly, wasp, or beetle is a grub that bears no resemblance to the adult. The young butterfly or moth is a caterpillar. In the course of their larval lives, these insects molt several times and grow much larger, but this growth does not bring them any closer to an adult appearance; they simply become larger larvae (Fig. 16.21). Finally, after they have completed their larval development, they enter an inactive stage called the *pupa,* during which they are usually enclosed in a case or cocoon. During the pupal stage, most of the old larval tissues are destroyed, and new tissues and organs develop from small discs of cells that were present in the larva but never underwent much development. The adult that emerges from the pupa is thus radically different from the larva; it is almost a new organism built from the raw materials of the larval body.

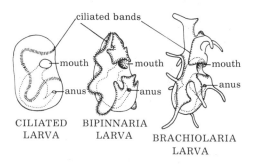

CILIATED LARVA   BIPINNARIA LARVA   BRACHIOLARIA LARVA

Fig. 16.20. Three different larval stages of the starfish, *Asterias vulgaris.* The gastrula develops into the ciliated larva, which changes into the bipinnaria larva, which changes into the brachiolaria larva, which metamorphoses into the characteristic starfish body form.

Fig. 16.21. Life stages of an insect with complete metamorphosis. The stages shown here are (from left to right): egg, young larva, full-grown larva, pupa, adult. Several intermediate larval stages are omitted. Note that as the larva grows it does not become more like the adult. The shift from larval to adult characteristics occurs during the pupal stage. The insect shown here is a *Phyllophaga* beetle. [Redrawn from H. H. Ross, *A Textbook of Entomology,* Wiley, 1956.]

Insects that have a pupal stage and undergo the type of development described above are said to have *complete metamorphosis.* The sharp distinction between the larval and adult stages in such insects has provided the opportunity for evolution in two quite different directions. The larvae and adults have often evolved adaptations for living in different habitats and utilizing different foods. In general, the larva is more specialized for feeding and growth, while the adult is more specialized for active dispersal and reproduction.

Complete metamorphosis is not a characteristic of all insects. Many, such as grasshoppers, cockroaches, bugs, and lice, have *gradual metamorphosis* (Fig. 16.22). The young of such insects resemble the adults except that their body proportions are different (the wings and reproductive organs, especially, are poorly developed). They go through a series of molts during which their form gradually changes and becomes more and more like that of the adult, largely as a result of differential growth of the various body parts. They have no pupal stage and no wholesale destruction of the immature tissues.

Aging and Death. Discussions of development often stop with the completely matured adult. But development in its full biological sense does not cease then. The adult organism is not a static entity; it continues to change, and hence to develop, until death brings the developmental process to an end.

The term "aging" is applied to the complex of developmental changes that lead, with the passage of time, to the deterioration of the mature organism (Table 16.1) and ultimately to its death. For many years, little research was devoted to aging, but now it has become a major field of investigation. Modern scientific progress and improved medical techniques have greatly increased man's ability to protect himself against disease, starvation, and the destructive forces of the physical environment. More and more people are living to an ad-

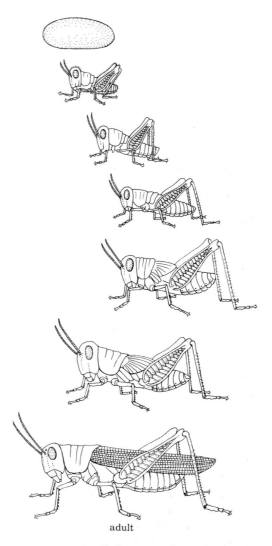

adult

Fig. 16.22. Gradual metamorphosis of a grasshopper. At each succeeding nymphal stage, the insect becomes more like an adult.

vanced age. And as the life expectancy increases and the proportion of the population in the upper age brackets rises, the changes associated with aging become more obvious and more important to all of us. We may expect massive scientific assaults on the problems of aging—a field in which our knowledge at present is rather meager.

We know so little about the factors involved in aging that it is difficult to separate fact from

TABLE 16.1

Average Decline in a Human Male
from Ages 30 to 75

Characteristic	Percent decline
Weight of brain	44
Number of axons in spinal nerve	37
Velocity of nerve impulse	10
Number of taste buds	64
Blood supply to brain	20
Output of heart at rest	30
Speed of return to normal pH of blood after displacement	83
Number of glomeruli in kidney	44
Glomerular filtration rate	31
Vital capacity of lungs	44
Maximum O_2 uptake during exercise	60

fiction. A few facts, however, seem well established. Aging seems to be correlated with specialization of cells for one or a few highly specific functions. Cells that remain relatively unspecialized in this sense, i.e. that remain more versatile, and that continue to divide do not age as rapidly (if at all) as cells that have lost the capacity to divide. Thus bacteria and some other unicellular organisms cannot be said to age. They may, in fact, be potentially immortal, for any cell that is not destroyed eventually divides to produce two young cells; division is thus a process of rejuvenation. Within the body of a multicellular animal, tissues like muscle and nerve that have lost the capacity for cell division slowly deteriorate, while others like the liver and pancreas, where active cell division can still occur, age much more slowly. Furthermore, animals that continue to grow as long as they live seem to show

fewer symptoms of aging than, for example, mammals and birds, which cease growing soon after they reach maturity.

The same pattern is seen in plants. Many annual plants practically cease growing soon after the flowering period, when their fruit begins to form, and they age and die soon afterward. But some woody perennials, of which the giant sequoia and the redwoods are extreme examples, may live for hundreds or thousands of years, always continuing to grow. In effect, they circumvent the problem of aging by forming vast numbers of new cells each year while equally vast numbers of their older cells die. The individual specialized cells age and die, but the continued youthful activity of the meristems keeps the living part of the plant young and vigorous. A sequoia, as an organism, may be over 4,000 years old, but it contains no living cells that are more than a few years old.

We see, then, that the aging and death of individual cells and the aging and death of the multicellular organism as a whole are two rather different things. Paradoxical as it may at first seem, the sequoia retains youthful attributes in part because many of its cells age and die. The death of these cells is functionally necessary for the continued life of the plant; e.g., it is only after the cells of the xylem die that they can function in internal transport. Similarly, the death of individual cells, as we have seen, plays an essential role in the development of an animal embryo and in the complete metamorphosis of some insects. And early death of individual red blood cells and epidermal cells is perfectly normal even in a young healthy mammal. Aging of the whole organism is, therefore, not simply a matter of the death of its cells, but one of the deterioration and death of those cells and tissues that cannot be replaced.

What makes irreplaceable tissues age? We don't know. However, we do know some of the factors that contribute to aging. For example, we know that some cells die as a result of disease or injury, and that when this happens in a tissue like muscle, no new muscle cells can be formed to replace the ones lost. Wound healing in such cases involves growth of connective (scar) tissue, which serves as a "patching" material but cannot, of course, function like the original muscle cells. As more and more irreplaceable cells die, the increased burden placed on the remaining cells of that type may contribute to their aging. We know also that changing hormonal balance, such as that caused by a drop in the level of sex hormones, may disturb the function of a variety of tissues and perhaps cause them to function less well. And we know that as cells become older they tend to accumulate some metabolic wastes that they apparently cannot expel, and these wastes may contribute to the eventual deterioration of the cells. And we know that the number of collagen fibers (and their thickness) increases in the intercellular ground substance of connective tissue, and that elastic fibers become thicker and less elastic, perhaps as a result of increased binding of calcium ions. Such changes, which are fundamentally a continuation of the course of development that began with the initial formation of connective tissue in the embryo, contribute to loss of elasticity in the skin, hardening of the arteries, and stiffening of the joints. Once set in motion, it seems, the development of connective tissue cannot be halted when it has reached an optimal level, but must continue inexorably, contributing to the destruction of the organism it helped build. But all these factors—replacement of diseased or injured tissue by connective tissue, increased functional burden on the remaining cells, altered hormonal balance, deposition of waste materials in older cells, changes in the intercellular ground substance, etc.—though they are doubtless involved in aging, are really not explanations but symptoms. The real question is why these changes occur, and to this question scientists cannot as yet give satisfying answers.

Various theories of aging have been proposed. Some investigators have suggested that somatic cells slowly cease to function and eventually die as a result of damage done to them by radiation (particularly X-rays and cosmic rays). However, all laboratory experiments indicate that radiation damage is greatest to actively dividing cells—the cells that age most slowly. Furthermore, the amount of radiation damage would be proportional to the chronological age of the cells, but we know that aging is a function of physiological age, not of chronological age; e.g. a five-year-old rat is physiologically very old indeed, and its tissues show pronounced symptoms of aging, whereas five-year-old tissues in a human being are not yet even mature. Other workers have suggested that the ceaseless stresses of life wear down the body's ability to maintain its steady state, eventually upsetting its physiological balance to such a degree that death results. But this theory remains rather nebulous and difficult to translate into concrete terms. Still other investigators put major emphasis on intrinsic rather than extrinsic factors. They suggest that the changes characteristic of aging are programed in the genes just like the earlier developmental changes, and that, although extrinsic environmental factors certainly influence aging, they do so only by speeding up or slowing down processes that would occur anyway. These processes may involve a decline in the production of important enzymes or an altered chemical balance or physical structure with a resulting loss of ability to perform certain functions; or they may involve development of auto-immune reactions (allergies against parts of the organism's own body) that result in destruction of essential tissues by antibodies; or they may involve rupture of lysosomes and release of destructive hydrolytic enzymes within the cells.

Whatever the processes of aging may be, it seems clear that we cannot expect to understand them fully until we know much more about how developmental processes in general are regulated by the interaction of inherited and environmental influences. The basic problems in understanding aging, then, are essentially the same as those of embryonic development or maturation. Aging is simply another aspect of the general phenomenon of development.

THE PROBLEM
OF DIFFERENTIATION

As was stressed in an earlier chapter, mitosis gives each new daughter cell a complete set of chromosomes exactly like that in the parental cell. Since the genes (except plasmagenes, which are usually distributed equally to the daughter cells) are located in precise sequences on the chromosomes, it follows that all the somatic cells in a multicellular organism are genotypically identical. There is no evidence that any genes are normally lost or gained in the course of a cell's development;[1] there is, indeed, every reason to think that the genetic endowment of a nerve or muscle cell is exactly the same as that of a liver or bone cell in the same individual. If, then, all the cells in the embryo of a multicellular plant or animal have precisely the same genetic potentials, the factors that determine for any given cell which of those potentials will be realized and which will not are presumably separate

---

[1] There are two apparent exceptions to the finding that differentiation does not normally involve gain or loss of genes. The first is that in some species the somatic cells become polyploid while the germ cells that will give rise to gametes remain diploid. In these species, polyploidy probably does influence cellular differentiation when it occurs, but it is a gain only of duplicate genes, not of qualitatively different genes. The second seeming exception is that in a very few species, of which gall midges are an example, the somatic cells have fewer chromosomes than the germ cells. The zygote of a gall midge has about 40 chromosomes. At the time of the fifth cleavage in the embryo, only 8 of the chromosomes move properly on the mitotic spindles in most cells; the other 32 chromosomes dissolve, and their material becomes dispersed throughout the cytoplasm and is lost. Thus somatic cells of the gall midge have only 8 chromosomes, and only the few cells early set aside to form the germ cells retain the full 40. However, this reduction of the number of chromosomes occurs in all somatic cells and hence is not correlated with their ultimate differentiation into nerve, muscle, connective tissue, epithelium, etc.

from the genes. One of the principal tasks of developmental biology is to identify those factors and relate them to the genes.

A satisfactory model of development must explain how the two types of control factors—genetic and nongenetic—interact to produce differentiated cells, tissues, and organs. It must give us some basis for understanding how the epicotyl of a germinating seed becomes negatively geotropic while the genetically identical hypocotyl becomes positively geotropic. It must give us some framework for explaining why cells produced to the outside by vascular cambium develop into phloem while genetically identical cells produced to the inside develop into xylem. It must help us understand why some epidermal cells in an animal embryo fold inward and form nervous tissue while other genetically identical epidermal cells remain on the surface and form skin. And it must give us insight into how genetically identical cells can form a grub at one time and an adult beetle at another. This is an immense challenge to developmental biologists, and they have a very long way to go before they can fit all the pieces of the puzzle together for a clear and complete picture of development. But much has already been learned; many of the pieces have been discovered, and some have been tentatively fitted together. Let us look at a few of the results.

The Effects of Qualitatively Unequal Cleavages

If embryonic cells cannot be distinguished on the basis of genetic content, it is logical to look for differences in their cytoplasm. We have already seen that the cytoplasm of the unfertilized egg is often not homogeneous. Most animal eggs contain stored food material, or yolk, which, being usually concentrated in one part of the cell, establishes a distinction between animal and vegetal hemispheres. Another distinction between them is that the animal hemisphere often has much more pigment in the cytoplasm than the vegetal hemisphere does. It is reasonable to think that other materials may be similarly restricted to certain regions of the cytoplasm. Therefore the daughter cells produced by cleavage of the egg cell may very well not share equally in all the cytoplasmic materials. We know, for example, that the cells formed from the vegetal hemisphere of a frog egg contain more yolk and less pigment than the cells formed from the animal hemisphere. This difference in cytoplasmic content influences the future development of the cells.

Suppose that in a hypothetical zygote all the molecules of an important compound are distributed in a band in one part of the cell (Fig. 16.23). The orientation of the band relative to the direction of the first cleavage is obviously very important in such a cell. If the cleavage cuts across the band, each of the daughter cells will receive approximately equal amounts of the important compound. If, however, the first cleavage runs parallel to the band, one daughter cell will receive all of the compound and the other will receive none. If cells containing the compound tend to develop in one way and cells lacking the compound tend to develop in

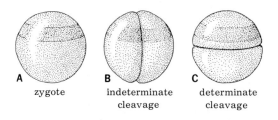

A zygote   B indeterminate cleavage   C determinate cleavage

Fig. 16.23. Indeterminate and determinate cleavage. (A) In this hypothetical zygote, a particularly important material is distributed in a band near one end of the cell. (B) A cleavage that cuts across this band, giving equal amounts of the important material to each daughter cell, might well be indeterminate; i.e. each cell might retain full developmental potential. (C) A cleavage running parallel to the band, giving all the material to one daughter cell, might well be determinate; the nuclei of the two daughter cells would have different cytoplasmic environments and thus different developmental potentials.

another way, a cleavage that gives all of the compound to one daughter cell determines, in part, the future course of development of the daughter cells.

There is good experimental evidence that the first cleavage is determinate in some animals and indeterminate in others. In annelid worms and molluscs, for example, if the two cells produced by the first cleavage are separated, each will develop into only half an embryo. The first cleavage has obviously separated important cytoplasmic regions and thus restricted the developmental potential of the cells. The different regions of some eggs can easily be recognized by their characteristic colors or textures. If, before cleavage begins, the material in one of these regions is pushed into a different part of the egg (by centrifugation, for example), the embryo develops abnormally, because the displaced material proceeds to form whatever organ it would have formed in its correct position.

On the other hand, the first cleavage is not determinate in most vertebrates and echinoderms (starfish, sea urchins, sand dollars, sea cucumbers, etc.). As early as 1891, Hans Driesch, working in Naples, Italy, showed that if he separated the cells of a two-celled embryo of a sea urchin by shaking the embryo in a vial of sea water, each cell developed normally into a whole sea-urchin larva. When he did the same thing to a four-celled embryo, each of the four isolated cells again developed normally. But if he separated the cells of an eight-celled embryo, the cells developed abnormally. The first two cleavages were indeterminate, but the third was partly determinate. There is good evidence that in the sea urchin the first cleavages are indeterminate because of their direction, not because of an absence of cytoplasmic inhomogeneity in the egg cell. If we experimentally cut the egg in two instead of allowing it to divide normally, the two halves will develop into normal larvae if the cut is made meridionally (the same direction as the normal first cleavage), but they will not develop normally if the cut is made along the equator between the animal and vegetal hemispheres.

Similar experiments can be performed on frog eggs. If, after the first cleavage, the two cells are disjoined, each will develop into a normal tadpole. Yet the indeterminacy of the early cleavages does not mean that regional cytoplasmic differences do not exist in the egg. Shortly after fertilization and before the first cleavage, a crescent-shaped region near the boundary between the animal and vegetal hemispheres becomes distinctly grayish. The normal first cleavage cuts across this gray crescent, as it is called, giving part of the crescent to each daughter cell, and these cells retain the potential of forming a complete embryo if separated. But it is possible experimentally to divide the embryo in such a manner that all of the gray crescent is in one half. When this is done, and the halves are separated, the half with the gray crescent develops normally but the other half forms only an unorganized mass of cells.

It is much more difficult, of course, to experiment with mammalian eggs and early embryos than with those of sea urchins or frogs, and for that reason we know less about them. If an investigator wants to perform a microsurgical experiment on mammalian eggs, he must obtain the eggs by operating on a female at precisely that moment in her reproductive cycle when ripe eggs are present. After the microsurgery has been completed, he must culture the eggs in a complex sterile medium until they reach the blastula stage, and then transplant them into the uterus of another female who is in just the right physiological condition to receive them. Difficult as this procedure is, it has made possible some important experiments, which have indicated that the early cleavages are indeterminate, as in other vertebrates. This was, of course, expected, because only if cleavage is indeterminate can an animal give birth to identical twins.[2]

In animals in which the first few cleavages are not determinate, a determinate cleavage eventually occurs. It is a valid generalization, therefore, to say that one of the factors that first affect the developmental direction of embryonic cells is their cytoplasmic content, as determined by the extent of regional cytoplasmic differences in the zygote and the pattern of the early cleavages.

The Effects of Environmental Influences

The cytoplasm is the immediate environment of the nucleus, and we have seen that differences in the cytoplasm can exert a profound influence on differentiation. It seems reasonable to suppose that a comparable influence is exerted by the environment external to the cytoplasm. We would expect that different cells, depending upon their location in the embryo, would be exposed to a somewhat different combination of environmental factors, and that these factors might help determine the developmental direction followed by the cells. Countless experiments have shown this expectation to be correct.

Effects of the Physical Environment. A number of physical factors may affect the activity of a developing cell. Among these are temperature, light, humidity, gravity, and pressure. In an earlier chapter, we mentioned the role of temperature in influencing the development of pigmentation in Himalayan rabbits (see p. 535). And we mentioned the influence of temperature on the vestigial-wing character in *Drosophila*. Numerous other examples could be cited. If a seedling plant is grown exclusively in the dark, no mature chloroplasts form, the entire shoot remains colorless, and the plant eventually dies; light is an

---

[2] Identical twins develop from isolated cells derived from the same zygote. Nonidentical (fraternal) twins develop from separate zygotes when two egg cells are released from the ovaries at the same time and are fertilized by different sperms. Consequently, identical twins are genetically identical, whereas fraternal twins are no more alike genetically than any two siblings. Fraternal twins are much more common than identical twins.

essential factor in inducing the development of chloroplasts and the synthesis of chlorophyll. And we saw in our discussion of plant hormones that light, through its effect on auxin and phytochrome, plays a critical indirect role in such developmental phenomena as increase in shoot length and initiation of flowering.

The influence of physical factors on development has been demonstrated with particular clarity in the early development of the brown alga *Fucus* (commonly called rockweed), which grows on intertidal rocks along northern coasts. The fertilized egg cell (zygote) of *Fucus* is spherical at first and has no visible suface features that would indicate separate cytoplasmic regions. However, shortly after fertilization, the zygote becomes asymmetrical, as a small protuberance forms on one side (Fig. 16.24). This protuberance permanently determines the polarization of the embryo that will develop from the zygote. The first cleavage is always oriented in such a way that the side of the zygote bearing the protuberance becomes one daughter cell and the side without the protuberance becomes the other daughter cell. The cell with the protuberance always proceeds to form the holdfast, a rootlike structure that anchors the plant to the rocks. The other cell always forms the more erect part of the plant. D. M. Whitaker of Stanford University studied the factors that determine where on the zygote the protuberance will form. He found that a number of asymmetric environmental conditions play a role, the most important being illumination. The protuberance

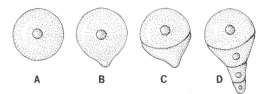

Fig. 16.24. Early development of *Fucus* egg. (A) The zygote. (B) Formation of a protuberance on one side of the zygote. (C–D) The orientation of the first few cleavages is determined by the location of the protuberance.

forms on the side away from the light. When lighting is equal on all sides but a temperature gradient is maintained across the zygote, the protuberance forms on the warmer side. Similarly, in a pH gradient, the protuberance forms on the side with the lower pH. If illumination, temperature, and pH are all equal on all sides but other zygotes are present in the culture, the protuberance forms on the side nearest the other zygotes. Finally, if the zygote is spun in a centrifuge, the protuberance forms on the side farthest from the center of the centrifuge. The adaptive significance of some of these reactions is understandable; a holdfast growing away from light and toward the pull of gravity would normally be going in the right direction to encounter the rocks at the bottom of the water. But how these physical environmental factors exert their effect on the cell—what cytoplasmic or nuclear changes they cause—is still unknown.

Effects of Chemicals from Neighboring Cells. It has been known for many years that the development of each cell is influenced by the cells around it. Most of this influence is presumably exerted by means of chemicals, some of which can probably move from cell to cell only when there is direct contact between the cells, while others can diffuse or be carried across considerable distances between the cells; an example of a diffusible chemical would be auxin from a terminal bud, which affects the development of lateral buds and the vascular cambium.

The importance of auxin in inducing differentiation can be demonstrated particularly well through tissue cultures. Cultured cells from a stem or root often revert to a relatively undifferentiated condition and form a homogeneous mass. If an intact bud is grafted onto the mass, auxin from the bud induces some of the cells to differentiate into xylem and others into phloem. Often these newly differentiated vascular tissues are arranged in a circle resembling the normal vascular cylinder. It can be shown that the inductive action of auxin varies as a result of differences in other factors influencing the cells. If pith cells are cultured on a medium containing two parts per million of auxin, the cells do not divide but grow to an unusually large size. If, however, the pith tissue is molded into a cylinder and the same concentration of auxin is inserted into the apical end of the cylinder, the cells undergo many divisions and some of them differentiate into xylem. The difference in response to the same inducing stimulus must be attributed to the different locations—superficial or internal—of the cells. In these examples, the chemical involved is produced so regularly as to be well known as a hormone. But probably all cells, not merely those specialized as sources of hormone, produce chemicals that influence the development of other cells. In most instances, the chemicals have not been identified and may be secreted in only minute quantities. Nevertheless, they play a central role in the development of an embryo.

Some of the first definitive studies on embryonic induction in an animal were performed in 1905 by Warren H. Lewis of Johns Hopkins University. Lewis worked on the development of the eye lens in frogs. In normal development, the eyes form as lateral outpockets from the brain. When one of these outpockets, or optic vesicles as they are called, comes into contact with the epidermis on the side of the head, the contacted epidermal cells promptly undergo a series of changes and form a thick plate of cells that sinks inward, becomes detached from the epidermis, and eventually differentiates into the eye lens (Fig. 16.25). Lewis cut the connection between one of the optic vesicles and the brain before the vesicle came into contact with the epidermis. He then moved the vesicle posteriorly into the trunk region of the embryo. Despite its lack of connections to the brain, the vesicle continued to develop, and when it came into contact with the epidermis of the trunk, that epidermis differentiated into a lens. The epidermis on the head that would normally have formed a lens

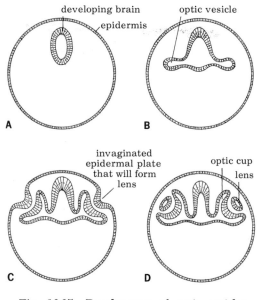

Fig. 16.25. Development of optic vesicles and their induction of lenses in a frog. See text for discussion.

failed to do so. Clearly, the differentiation of epidermal tissue into lens tissue depends upon some inductive stimulus from the underlying optic vesicle. Later experiments have shown that if a barrier is inserted between the vesicle and the epidermis no lens develops. Other experiments have shown that the regulation is not all one-way; the lens, once it begins to form, also influences the further development of the vesicle. If epidermis from a species with normally small eyes is transplanted to the sides of the head of a species with large eyes, the eyes that are formed do not have a large cup (formed from the vesicle) and a small lens, as might be expected. Instead, both the cup and the lens are intermediate in size and correctly proportioned to each other. Obviously, each influenced the other as they both developed together. Feedback is just as important in the control of embryonic development as it is in nervous or hormonal control of the fully-formed organism.

Further strong support for the concept of embryonic induction came from experiments performed in 1924 by Hans Spemann and Hilde Mangold of the University of Freiburg, Germany. Spemann had earlier demonstrated the importance of the gray crescent in the early cleavages of salamanders. Now he and Mangold turned their attention to the early-gastrula stage and particularly to the *dorsal lip of the blastopore,* a region made up of cells derived from the former gray-crescent portion of the zygote. In the normal embryo, the cells of the dorsal lip of the blastopore fold inward and develop into mesodermal structures. But they also seem to exert an important effect on the ectodermal cells lying over them; those ectodermal cells differentiate into the brain and spinal cord. Spemann and Mangold tried transplanting the dorsal lip of the blastopore from its normal position on a light-colored embryo to the belly region of another darker-colored embryo. After the operation, gastrulation occurred in two places on the recipient embryo— at the site of its own blastoporal lip and at the site of the implanted lip. Eventually two nervous systems were formed, and sometimes even two complete embryos developed, joined together ventrally (Fig. 16.26). Most of the tissue in both embryos was dark-colored, an indication that the transplanted blastoporal lip had altered the course of development of cells derived from the host. Similar transplants of tissues from other regions of the embryos failed to produce comparable results. The dorsal lip of the blastopore must play a crucial role in

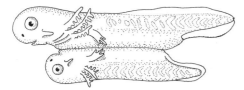

Fig. 16.26. Induction by dorsal-lip tissue. A piece of tissue from the dorsal lip of the blastopore of one salamander larva, when implanted in the ventral region of another larva, induced formation of a twin. [Redrawn from J. Holtfreter and V. Hamburger, in *Analysis of Development,* Saunders, 1955.]

determining the form of the early embryo, probably by inducing the formation of the neural groove, which in turn is important in establishing the longitudinal axis of the embryo and in inducing other structures (such as the eye lenses already mentioned).

Spemann and Mangold called the dorsal lip of the blastopore the *"organizer."* They envisioned the entire developmental process as one in which a succession of principal organizer regions, each taking over where the previous one has left off, control the differentiation of the major tissues and organs. We now know that, although the dorsal lip of the blastopore has a particularly important inductive function, induction is a general phenomenon not limited to a small number of organizer regions. Inductive tissue interactions are the rule rather than the exception in embryonic development.

Chemical Induction in Regeneration. Chemical induction has also been shown to play a fundamental role in regeneration of lost body parts. Almost all embryonic animals have extensive regenerative capacities. Some animals retain these capacities after they reach maturity, while others lose them. An adult starfish or hydra can be chopped into many pieces and each piece can regenerate all necessary parts to become a whole individual. An earthworm can regenerate a new head or tail. Half a planarian can regenerate the other half. Salamanders and lizards can regenerate new tails. But adult birds and mammals cannot regenerate whole new organs; regeneration in these animals is mostly limited to the healing of wounds.

It has been shown in many cases that regeneration normally depends upon the nerve supply in the regenerative region. For example, if a leg of a salamander is amputated, one of the first things that happen during the healing of the wound is penetration of the wound tissue by nerve fibers growing outward from the spinal cord. Meanwhile the scar tissue that first formed begins to disappear, and a mound of rapidly dividing undifferentiated cells develops. Gradually this mound comes to look more and more like the normal limb bud of an embryonic salamander (Fig. 16.27). It slowly elongates, and after several weeks a distinct elbow and digits appear. This rudimentary limb continues to grow, and its cells continue to differentiate into muscle, tendon, bone, connective tissue, etc., until finally it has become a fully functional new leg. But if the nerves leading to the stump of an amputated leg are removed, no regeneration occurs, and the stump itself shrivels and disappears. Regeneration of the leg will take place only if an abundant supply of nerve fibers is present. Apparently it makes no difference whether the fibers are motor or sensory, or whether they are somatic or autonomic; it is only the total number per unit volume of tissue that is important. The evidence is very strong that the nerve fibers release some chemical necessary for regenerative development and that there must be enough fibers to provide an adequate supply of this chemical inducer. The inducer is also necessary for normal maintenance; if the nerve supply to a normal limb is partly destroyed (as often happens to human beings who have suffered spinal injuries), the muscles of that limb usually begin to atrophy.

Discoveries such as these naturally raised the question whether normal loss of regenerative capacities is a result of an inadequate nerve supply (it could also be a result of de-

creased responsiveness to the regeneration-inducing chemical released by the nerves). To test this possibility, Marcus Singer, then at Cornell University, performed a revealing experiment on frogs. Young tadpoles have considerable regenerative capabilities, but adult frogs do not; a young tadpole whose leg is amputated quickly grows a new one, but an older tadpole can only partly regenerate a lost leg, and an adult frog cannot regenerate a leg at all. It has been shown that the number of nerve fibers in a tadpole's leg does not increase as rapidly as the volume of other tissues in the leg, and that this relative decline in the number of nerve fibers exactly parallels the gradual loss of regenerative capacity. Singer amputated a front leg of a frog. Then he dissected the large sciatic nerve from the corresponding hind leg without cutting its connections to the spinal cord. Next, he pulled this nerve forward under the skin of the thigh, flank, and abdomen to the stump of the amputated front leg and implanted the ends of the nerve in the stump. With this increased nerve supply, the stump proceeded to regenerate a new leg. Singer concluded that every part of the body probably has the latent power to regenerate and needs only sufficient inductive stimulation to do so.

Morphogenetic Fields. Not all the chemicals influencing the developmental directions of cells are stimulatory. Many, in fact, are inhibitory, or else they are stimulatory to some cells and inhibitory to others. Auxin is an example; in normal development, it stimulates differentiation of xylem but it inhibits development of lateral buds. There is abundant evidence, in both plants and animals, that as a particular tissue or organ develops it releases substances that inhibit formation of the same kind of tissue or organ in the immediate area. For example, frog embryos cultured with pieces of tissue from an adult frog heart do not develop a normal heart, and embryos cultured with pieces of adult brain do not develop a normal brain. Similar inhibitions seem to op-

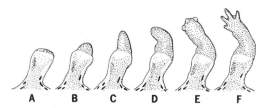

Fig. 16.27. Regeneration of a salamander arm. [Adapted from M. Singer, "The Regeneration of Body Parts," *Sci. Am.*, October, 1958. Copyright © 1958 by Scientific American, Inc. All rights reserved.]

erate in determining the position of a new leaf on a growing stem. Each new leaf emerges at a point separated by some critical distance from the nearest older leaves and from the shoot apex. If one of the nearby older leaves is removed, the new leaf develops at a point closer to the position of the removed leaf than it would normally occupy. It seems that each leaf is surrounded by a morphogenetic field that somehow prevents the formation of a new leaf within it. This concept of morphogenetic fields, first proposed by C. M. Child of the University of Chicago, has been found applicable to both plants and animals. It seems to be a general phenomenon. Thus, in an animal embryo, we can speak of head fields, tail fields, heart fields, leg fields, etc.

The Gradualness of Differentiation

The Developmental-Landscape Model. How can we put together the facts and ideas we have just discussed and construct a meaningful picture of the course of cell differentiation? We begin with the assumption that all the cells of a single organism usually have the same genetic potential. Therefore other factors must determine which potentialities are expressed. The first restrictions on the potential of an embryonic cell are frequently the result of qualitative (and sometimes also quantitative) differences in the early cleavages, which give the nuclei of the different cells different cytoplasmic environments and thus presumably bring about the activation of different genes. As development proceeds, the extracellular environment of the cells becomes less uniform. For example, some cells are located more internally and hence are exposed to less illumination, more pressure, more chemicals from neighboring cells, and probably a different pH. Such differences in the environmental conditions of the various cells further intensify the differences in their developmental directions. As the cells and tissues become more and more differentiated, they exert an increasingly

strong influence on all other cells in their vicinity via chemicals that they secrete. Some of these chemicals block certain of the pathways that the neighboring cells might otherwise have followed; other chemicals tend to induce the neighboring cells to follow alternative pathways. As those cells respond developmentally to the host of influences impinging upon them, they in their turn alter the environment of the cells in their vicinity. And so the snowballing effect proceeds. Each step in the differentiation of one cell alters the influence that cell will have on all other cells. The environment of each cell is constantly changing as development continues, and the changes in the environment profoundly affect the activity of the genes.

C. H. Waddington of the University of Edinburgh has suggested that differentiating cells can be compared with balls rolling down a slope cut by many valleys (Fig. 16.28). Each ball rolls into one of the valleys. This valley soon branches into two or more separate valleys, and each of these eventually branches in its turn. At each point of branching, the ball enters one of the alternative valleys. As it passes each intersection, the number of alter-

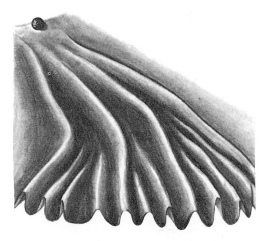

Fig. 16.28. Developmental-landscape model. As the ball rolls down the hill past each branch in the valleys, its potential becomes progressively more restricted.

native pathways still open to it diminishes. Since the ball cannot roll uphill, it cannot normally retrace its course and take a different route. Finally it reaches the bottom of the slope at a point determined by the particular alternative pathways it took at each point of branching. Similarly, an early embryonic cell may follow any of a large number of different developmental pathways. Once it has differentiated as ectoderm, however, it cannot ordinarily go back and form a mesodermal or endodermal structure. It has passed the first branching point in the developmental landscape. Now it can form any ectodermal structure, which still leaves it many alternatives. But soon it passes a second important branching point; it either sinks inward as the neural groove forms and differentiates into nervous tissue, or it remains on the surface and differentiates as epidermis. Suppose it follows the former course. Many alternatives are still open to it. It may form part of the brain or part of the spinal cord; it may become part of the somatic or part of the autonomic nervous system; it may differentiate as a multipolar neuron or a bipolar neuron or a unipolar neuron; etc. But as each branching point is passed, the total number of alternatives still ahead diminishes, until finally the cell has become some one kind of fully differentiated cell. Differentiation is thus a matter of progressive determination, a gradual restricting of development to one of the many initially possible pathways.

Evidence from Tissue Transplants and from Reaggregation of Cells. The gradualness of differentiation, as depicted by Waddington's model, can be demonstrated by transplantation experiments. If in a very early amphibian gastrula a piece of tissue from the part of the presumptive ectoderm that will later participate in the formation of the spinal cord is exchanged with a piece of tissue from the part of the ectoderm that will form epidermis, each transplanted tissue develops into whatever is appropriate for its new location; the tissue that

would have formed nerve now forms epidermis, and vice versa. Location is the important factor at this stage. If the same kind of exchange is made a short time later, however, the results are entirely different. The piece that would have formed nerve in its original location also forms nerve in its new location, and the piece that would have formed epidermis forms epidermis in its new location. Something has happened in the late gastrula that has caused the cells from the two different parts of the ectoderm to set out on different developmental pathways. In the late gastrula, the part of the ectoderm that will form the nerve cord and brain is underlain by mesoderm derived from the dorsal lip of the blastopore, while this is not yet true of the part of the ectoderm that will form epidermis. It can be shown that it is induction from the underlying mesoderm that starts the differentiation into nervous tissue.

Now suppose that instead of being moved to an epidermal location, presumptive spinal cord is moved to the location where the optic vesicles will form. We know from the previous experiment that the tissue has been determined as nerve, but will it form only spinal cord or can it still form other parts of the nervous system? If this experiment is performed very soon after neurulation has begun, the transplanted tissue will form optic vesicle; its location in the developing nervous system is the important factor. But if the experiment is performed after the nervous system has begun to assume its definitive form, the transplanted tissue will form spinal cord, regardless of its new location. It has already passed another critical point in its differentiation, and altering its location does not reverse its development. We see, then, that the tissue first differentiates as nervous tissue and later as a particular type of nerve. Differentiation is gradual; it does not occur all at once.

The gradualness of differentiation can also be demonstrated by the reaggregation of separated cells. In 1907 H. V. Wilson of the University of North Carolina discovered that if he dissociated the cells of the body of a sponge by pressing it through a fine sieve, the dispersed cells migrated over the surface of the culture dish until they encountered one another and clumped together to form multicellular aggregates. These aggregates, if suitably cultured, grew into complete new sponges with the architecture characteristic of the sponge before disruption by the sieve. Later workers showed that if the cells of two sponges of different species (colored differently) were dispersed and then mixed together, they would sort themselves and aggregate by species. These results led other workers to wonder if the capacity of cells for recognizing and aggregating with their own kind was a general phenomenon not limited to sponges. This it proved to be.[3] When the cells of the mesodermal and ectodermal layers of a gastrula were dispersed (by mild digestion with trypsin) and then mixed with one another, they moved together to form a clump with the ectodermal cells on the outside and the mesodermal cells on the inside. Clearly, ectodermal cells could recognize other ectodermal cells and mesodermal cells could recognize other mesodermal cells; and mesoderm and ectoderm could recognize each other and establish the proper inside-outside relationship. Evidently the two types of cells, mesodermal and ectodermal, were already partly differentiated. If the same experiment was performed with cells from a later embryo, mesodermal cells aggregated not just with any other mesodermal cells, but with mesodermal cells from the same part of the embryo as they. Thus presumptive liver cells clumped together and formed liver lobules; presumptive heart cells clumped together and formed lumps of beating heart muscle; presumptive kidney cells clumped together and constituted characteristic kidney capsules and tubules; etc. In other

words, in this later embryo, the cells had differentiated further and were no longer simply mesodermal as against ectodermal; they were now determined as future liver or heart or kidney cells. They had moved farther down the valleys of Waddington's developmental landscape.

THE REGULATION OF GENE ACTION

In our discussion so far, we have put much emphasis on the role of the extranuclear environment in regulating development. But we have also said repeatedly in this book that the genes control cellular activities and through them the developmental process. Let us now examine some possible mechanisms whereby the environment might interact with the genes to regulate development.

Regulation of Enzymes Versus Regulation of Genes. One conceivable way in which genes and the environment might both contribute to the regulation of development would be for every gene to keep synthesizing the messenger RNA for which it codes and for the environmental influences then to regulate either the synthesis of enzymes on the RNA or the activity of the enzymes once synthesized. The genes would thus determine the chemical reactions possible for the cell and the environment would determine which of these would actually occur by altering the chemical and physical characteristics of the cytoplasm.

There is no doubt that the environment does indeed greatly influence the synthesis and activity of enzymes in a living cell. Probably every chemical and physical parameter of the environment affects cellular metabolism to some extent. And anything that affects the activity of the enzymes in a cell must certainly affect the cell's development. The question thus becomes: Does the environment regulate de-

---

[3] It was found that the ability of cells to recognize other cells of similar tissue type is a general phenomenon, but that the recognition of species, demonstrated in sponges, is not so general. Thus retina cells from a chick and retina cells from a mouse will clump together to form a new composite retina.

velopment only through its effect on enzymes, or do environmental influences also affect the genes? In other words, does the extranuclear environment regulate only the products of the genes, or does it also regulate the activity of the genes themselves?

If the latter alternative is correct, and the environmental factors that influence development exert their effect, in part, by regulating the activity of genes, it would be reasonable to suppose that a necessary aspect of cellular differentiation is a change in the properties of the nucleus. Such changes have, in fact, been demonstrated by nuclear-transplant experiments, performed according to a method first perfected on frog embryos in 1953 by Robert W. Briggs and Thomas J. King of the Institute for Cancer Research in Philadelphia. According to this method, frog eggs are stimulated to begin development by pricking them with a glass needle. Then the nucleus is removed from the egg. Another nucleus obtained from a partly differentiated cell of a developing embryo is inserted into the egg to take the place of its original nucleus. When the transplanted nucleus is one obtained from a blastula, the egg develops normally—an indication that nuclei in the blastula have not undergone any stable change and still retain the capacity of directing all aspects of development. But if the transplanted nuclei are obtained from a gastrula, the eggs usually do not develop normally; except for a small percentage, the embryos produced are abnormal or their development is arrested at some stage. Apparently the nuclei of the gastrula have undergone some change, though the extent of this change varies, as indicated by the great variability in the results of the experiments. When nuclei from cells of swimming tadpoles are transplanted into egg cells, the results are more uniform; most of the embryos show arrested development at a very early stage (though a very few may develop normally). Such experiments seem to indicate that the more differentiated a cell becomes the more likely are some rela-

tively stable changes in its nucleus that limit its potentialities.

Such results obviously lead to the question whether the nuclear changes are irreversible. The evidence so far is inconclusive, but most biologists working in this field consider it unlikely. They can point, for example, to the small percentage of nuclei from swimming tadpoles that do direct normal development when transplanted into an egg cell. And they can point to the resumption of embryonic characteristics by cells in regions where regeneration of lost parts is taking place. And even more convincing, they can point to studies where single differentiated cells from the body of an adult plant have been observed to revert to the embryonic condition and then give rise to a complete new plant when cultured under carefully controlled conditions. Thus F. C. Steward and his colleagues at Cornell University have grown whole carrot plants from single phloem cells cut out of the root (see p. 311). Making a comparably differentiated cell from the body of a higher animal resume its total initial potency and give rise to a complete animal has not proved possible so far, but that is no reason to assume it can't be done. Not many years ago most biologists would probably have said it couldn't be done with a carrot.

Experiments such as those outlined above indicate that something alters the properties of the nucleus during development, that the nuclear genes don't simply churn out all their possible products in a continuous and unalterable way, but that they themselves, as well as their products, are subject to regulatory influences. Many other lines of evidence support the notion that environmental factors can directly affect the activity of the genes. One of these deserves special mention. Many years ago, it was noticed that the giant chromosomes in the cells of the salivary glands and a few other tissues of the larvae of flies (Diptera) sometimes have curiously puffed-out regions located at certain points along their length (Fig. 16.29). However, the possible significance of these

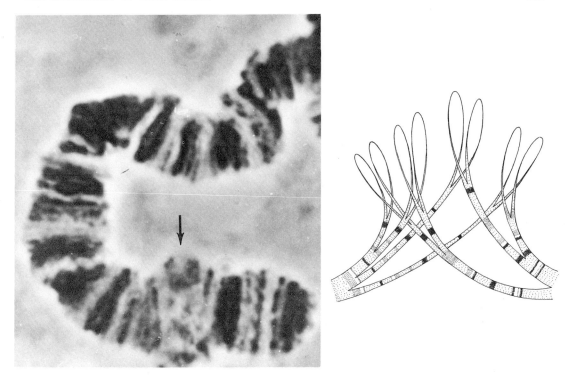

Fig. 16.29. Chromosome puffing. Left: Photograph of a giant chromosome of *Drosophila*, showing a puff (arrow). Right: Drawing showing how the chromosomal fibrils in the puff are spread, exposing maximum surface for synthesis. [Micrograph: Courtesy Edwin G. Vann, Northwestern University.]

chromosome puffs was overlooked. Then in 1952 Wolfgang Beermann, working at the Max Planck Institute for Marine Biology in Wilhelmshaven, Germany, and, working independently, Clodowaldo Pavan and Martha E. Breuer at the University of São Paulo, Brazil, suggested that the puffs indicate regions on the chromosomes where genes are especially active. They were able to show that the locations of puffs are different on chromosomes in different tissues and that they are different in the same tissue at different stages of development, although at any given time all the cells of any one type in any given tissue show the same pattern of puffing.

If the correlation of puffing pattern with developmental stages really does mean that the puffs indicate the location of active genes, we would expect to find that they are sites of active synthesis of messenger RNA. It can easily be demonstrated that unpuffed bands of the chromosome contain essentially only DNA and protein and that puffs contain, in addition, much RNA. That this RNA is being synthesized at the puff and has not simply accumulated there after synthesis elsewhere can be shown by injecting radioactive uridine into the larvae. Uridine is used by the cells as a precursor of uracil, a nitrogenous base that is incorporated into RNA but not into DNA. When this experiment is performed, radioactivity soon appears in the puffs (and in the nucleoli, which contain large deposits of ribosomal RNA), but it does not appear in other parts of the cell until much later—an indication that RNA is indeed being synthesized at the site of the puffs. Furthermore, it can be shown that the RNA made in one puff differs chemically from the RNA made in a puff at a different position on the chromosome, as would be expected if each gene codes for a different messenger RNA.

Puffs thus provide a way of determining visually whether or not changes in the extranuclear environment can alter the pattern of gene activity. As expected, they can. For example, if ecdysone, the hormone that causes molting in insects, is injected into a fly larva, the chromosomes rapidly undergo a shift in their puffing pattern, taking on that characteristically found at the time of molting in normal untreated individuals. If treatment is stopped, the puffs characteristic of molting disappear. If treatment is begun again, they reappear. Or if chromosomes are transplanted into a different type of cell or into the same type of cell at a different developmental stage, they quickly lose the puffs characteristic of the donor cells and develop ones characteristic of the type and stage of the recipient cells. Puffing can be prevented entirely by treatment with actinomycin, which is known to be an inhibitor of nucleic acid synthesis.

Qualitative Versus Quantitative Regulation. Regulatory factors can evidently act directly on the genes, but by what process? As we have indicated, there is no evidence that the environmental factors influencing development normally add or delete genes. Steward's demonstration that a fully differentiated cell can revert to the embryonic condition and give rise to all the structures of a new plant reinforces that conclusion. If the number of genes remains the same, it seems reasonable to suppose that development involves changes in the activity of the various genes—that gene activity, unlike gene structure, is readily susceptible to regulation. The question then arises whether the regulatory changes are qualitative or quantitative or both. In short, do environmental influences regulate what a gene makes or only how much it makes?

A classic experiment performed in 1932 by Hans Spemann and Oscar E. Schotté at the University of Freiburg suggested that inducers act quantitatively, not qualitatively. In salamanders, the ectodermal tissue of the mouth is induced to form teeth by the endodermal tissue with which it is in contact. In frogs, the corresponding ectoderm forms horny jaws instead of true teeth. Spemann and Schotté transplanted a piece of ectoderm from the flank of a frog embryo to the mouth region of a salamander. The transplanted tissue developed into horny jaws. It had been induced by the salamander endoderm, but instead of forming salamander teeth it formed the corresponding structures of a frog, namely horny jaws. Apparently all the salamander inducers could do was to turn on the appropriate genes; they could not alter what those genes would make. Numerous other experiments have yielded similar results, and it is now generally accepted that environmental influences act by turning on or off the synthetic activity of the various genes; there is no evidence that they in any way determine what those genes will make. According to the current view, each gene can make one and only one kind of messenger RNA, as coded by the sequence of its nucleotides. Regulators of the genes determine if and when each gene will synthesize its particular messenger RNA.

As would be expected if this is true, the amounts of certain important enzymes vary from cell to cell, and these variations are correlated with the developmental conditions of the cells. The amount of variation is vastly different for different enzymes, however. The quantities of some enzymes vary only slightly, while those of other enzymes show very great variation. This has led to the convention of dividing enzymes into two categories: constitutive enzymes, which are synthesized under almost all conditions, and inducible enzymes, which are synthesized only under certain rather limited conditions. In general, the synthesis of the messenger RNA for an inducible enzyme is stimulated by the substrate on which the enzyme acts and is inhibited (negative feedback) by the products of the reaction the enzyme catalyzes.

A particularly good illustration of this interaction between the nuclear genes and compounds in the cytoplasm has been provided by the work of Sol Spiegelman and his colleagues at the University of Illinois. They found that when viral DNA enters the cell of a bacterial host and takes control of its metabolic machinery, the enzymes and other proteins necessary for production of new virus particles are synthesized sequentially rather than simultaneously. As might be expected, the sequential synthesis of protein reflects a sequential synthesis of messenger RNA's in the nucleus. Spiegelman infected bacterial cells with virus and then, after a measured interval, added a compound that inhibits protein synthesis but does not interfere with RNA synthesis. Then, at given intervals, he analyzed by chromatography the messenger RNA that the cells contained. He found that when the cell could no longer manufacture protein, it kept on synthesizing the same messenger RNA that it was synthesizing just before the inhibitor was added, instead of proceeding to make the next messenger RNA's in the sequence, as an uninhibited cell would do. In other words, the one gene could not be turned off and the next gene turned on until the nucleus received feedback information from the cytoplasm telling it that the messenger RNA from the first gene had accomplished its mission and synthesized the appropriate protein. Experiments such as this are giving us new insight into possible mechanisms whereby the correct temporal sequence of developmental events may be achieved in a living organism.

The Jacob-Monod Model of the Regulation of Gene Action. François Jacob and Jacques Monod have proposed a stimulating model of gene regulation based on their studies of enzyme synthesis in *Escherichia coli.* They were particularly interested in an enzyme involved in the utilization of lactose. This enzyme is inducible in normal wild-type bacteria, but Jacob and Monod found a mutant strain in which the enzyme is constitutive, i.e. produced continuously. They were able to show by recombination experiments that the mutant gene, which is recessive, is not the gene that specifies the structure of the enzyme; in fact, the two genes are located at some distance from each other on the chromosome. Apparently the gene that had undergone mutation is one that regulates the activity of the structure-specifying gene. Since the mutant allele is recessive, Jacob and Monod suggested that the normal allele of the *regulator gene* must manufacture a substance that somehow represses the activity of the *structural gene* (the one that specifies the enzyme), while the mutant allele must lack the ability to synthesize this *repressor substance.* Jacob and Monod also found another mutant strain in which the same enzyme is constitutive, but in this instance the mutant was dominant, not recessive. The gene involved proved to be different both from the regulator gene already known and from the structural gene, although it is located against one end of the structural gene. When the mutant allele of this gene is present, the structural gene is active whether or not the regulator gene is making repressor substance; the mutant is insensitive to repressor substance. Jacob and Monod called this third gene the *operator gene.*

Comparable regulator and operator genes were discovered in other systems—an indication that regulator-operator-structural gene complexes are the rule rather than the exception in bacteria. Jacob and Monod attempted to formulate a model that would relate the three types of genes to what was already known about the effects of the cytoplasmic environment (particularly the chemical environment) on gene activity (Fig. 16.30). According to their model, each operator gene acts as a switch that turns on or off the synthetic activity of the structural gene (or genes) next to it. When turned on, the structural genes synthesize messenger RNA, which goes to the

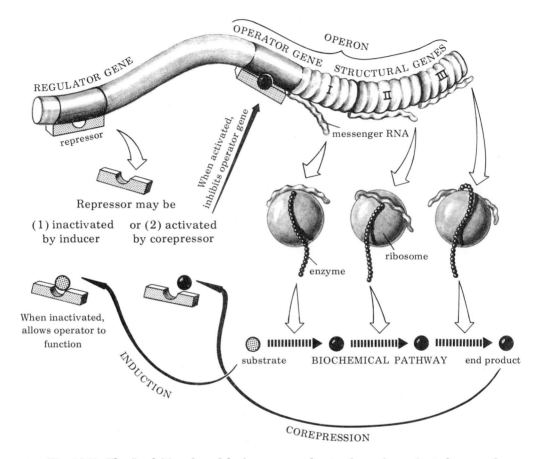

Fig. 16.30. The Jacob-Monod model of gene control. As shown here, the inducers and corepressors are sometimes the substrate and end product, respectively, of the biochemical pathway, but this is not always the case. For discussion, see text.

ribosomes in the cytoplasm and acts as the template for protein (enzyme) synthesis. In many cases, a single operator gene probably controls the activity of a whole series of structural genes arranged in linear sequence next to it on the chromosome; the operator gene and its cluster of structural genes are collectively called an *operon.* It has been found that the structural genes in any given operon specify enzymes with related functions, usually the enzymes of a single metabolic pathway, and that the sequence of the genes within the operon corresponds to the sequence of the biochemical steps catalyzed by the enzymes they specify (this is a truly elegant example of the interrelationship of structure and function).

Thus a single operator gene can turn on or off a whole biochemical pathway at once, not just one reaction in that pathway; the adaptive advantage of such coordinated activity is obvious.

If an operator gene acts as an on-off switch for a group of structural genes, what controls the switch? According to the Jacob-Monod model, each operator gene is itself controlled by the combined action of a regulator gene and substances from the cytoplasmic environment. Each regulator gene manufactures a repressor substance that, when activated, combines with certain operator genes and prevents them from initiating synthesis of messenger RNA along the structural genes they control. In the absence of activated repressor substance, the operator genes are active and the structural genes under their control are active. The role of the cytoplasmic environment consists in determining whether the repressor substance produced by the regulator gene will be activated or not. According to some variants of the model, there are two types of repressor substances: those that are active when synthesized and those that are inactive when synthesized. Repressor substances of the first type can immediately repress the activity of operator genes unless prevented from doing so by an *inducer substance* from the cytoplasm.[4] The inducer, which is usually a small molecule of some sort (sometimes the substrate for the enzyme specified by the first structural gene in the operon in question), probably combines with the repressor substance and inactivates it, thus leaving the operator genes are free to function unless the messenger RNA along their associated structural genes. In the case of repressor substances of the second type (inactive when synthesized by the regulator genes), the corresponding operator genes are free to function unless the repressor substance is activated by combining with an appropriate *corepressor substance* from the cytoplasm (sometimes the product of the reaction catalyzed by the enzyme specified by the last gene in the operon in question). According to other variants of the model (including that shown in Fig. 16.30), some repressor substances can combine with either an inducer or a corepressor from the cytoplasm. When combined with an inducer, the repressor substance is inactivated and the operator gene is free to function; when combined with a corepressor, the repressor substance is activated and combines with the operator gene, thereby blocking its function.

You should be aware that the Jacob-Monod model of gene regulation is highly speculative and will almost certainly undergo many changes

as more experimental evidence is obtained. Remember, too, that the model is based largely on data from experiments on bacteria and that it is not yet clear how well it applies to higher organisms (this is also true of much of the molecular genetics discussed earlier in this book). Furthermore, the model is based chiefly on the normal regulatory activities of already differentiated cells, and it is possible, though unlikely, that different control mechanisms operate during embryonic development. Despite all these reservations, the Jacob-Monod model is a very useful one. It gives us a way of relating all that is now known concerning developmental mechanisms at the genetic level, and it helps us see what kinds of experiments are likely to be most productive in the future. This is all we can ask of any model.

If there really are such things as regulator and operator genes, we shall probably have to modify our definition of genes once more. Toward the end of the last chapter, we redefined a gene as a length of DNA that specifies the amino acid sequence in one polypeptide chain. But it is entirely possible that regulator and operator genes do not code for polypeptide chains. Hence we may have to recognize two separate classes of genes—structural and controlling. Only structural genes would meet our previous definition. A controlling gene (whether regulator or operator) would be a length of DNA that controls the activity of other lengths of DNA. One wonders how many more changes, as yet undreamed of, will be made in the definition of the gene as biological science reveals more and more about the fundamental basis of life.

DEVELOPMENT OF IMMUNOLOGIC CAPABILITIES IN VERTEBRATES

We mentioned in an earlier chapter that an important defense against disease in vertebrate animals is their ability to manufacture antibodies that can inactivate or destroy invading

---

[4] It is important to remember that cytoplasmic substances are called inducers or corepressors according to whether their effect is to induce or repress gene activity, not according to whether they activate or inactivate repressor substance.

antigens. Recent work on the development of this immunologic capability in young animals is throwing new light on developmental problems in general. And new approaches for studying the interplay between differentiating cells and their chemical environment are being opened up by research on the ways in which both antigens and chemicals produced by the animal's own body, such as hormones, contribute to the control of the differentiation and activity of the plasma cells that synthesize specific antibodies. Let us examine briefly some of the discoveries that have been made about this fascinating aspect of developmental biology.

The Nature of Immunologic Reactions. Only in the last few years have we begun to develop an idea how immunologic reactions work, and we are still far from having a clear picture of the process, although the reactions themselves have been the subject of much study since the English physician Edward Jenner discovered in 1796 that people develop immunity to smallpox if they are artificially injected with material that induces a very mild form of the disease (actually cowpox). Further dramatic demonstrations of the immune reaction were made by Louis Pasteur in France during the latter half of the nineteenth century.

Among the many investigations Pasteur conducted, one was devoted to a disease of cattle and sheep called anthrax, which was ravaging the herds of Europe at that time. Having become convinced that a certain type of bacterium caused the disease, he exposed bacteria of this type to temperatures that were high enough to weaken them but not to kill them. When he injected these weakened bacteria into healthy sheep, the sheep became slightly ill, but thereafter they exhibited immunity to further infection by this disease. To convince the skeptics of his day, who, of course, had little understanding of the action of microbes as causal agents of disease or of immunologic reactions, Pasteur arranged a demonstration

attended by his most influential contemporaries. With these as witnesses, he injected weakened bacteria into 25 sheep, leaving 25 others uninjected as controls. Several weeks later, with the witnesses again assembled, he gave all 50 sheep a massive injection of fully active bacteria, more than enough to kill any normal healthy sheep. A few days later, all 25 control sheep were dead, while all 25 of the treated sheep were alive and healthy.

In modern terminology, we would say that Pasteur's sheep reacted to the weakened anthrax bacteria by producing antibodies against them. But what does this mean? What are antibodies anyway? Many experiments have shown that they are proteins and that they belong to the group of globulin proteins of the blood plasma, particularly the gamma globulins. It has been further shown that these proteins are synthesized by specialized cells called *plasma cells*, which apparently descend from certain white blood cells called lymphocytes (see p. 269). Plasma cells usually occur in the lymphoid tissues of the lymph nodes, spleen, liver, thymus, bone marrow, etc., and in more limited lymphoid areas associated with the lungs and the intestinal tract. The plasma cells of the spleen seem to be among the most active in production of antibodies, as can be demonstrated by surgical removal of one or more of the main lymphoid areas and determination of the concentration of gamma globulin in the blood several months later.

In most cases, the initiation of synthesis of a particular type of antibody depends upon stimulation of the lymphoid tissue by an antigen, which is frequently but not always a protein. The antigen is usually a substance foreign to the organism's own body, such as a part of a bacterium or virus or foreign-tissue cell. The antigen stimulates the plasma cells to synthesize and release antibodies highly specific for that particular antigen. The antibodies have a great affinity for the antigen and react with it, thereby destroying or inactivating it. In some cases, the antibody apparently combines with the antigen in such a way as to cover or mask the active sites of the antigen, much as a sheath may cover the cutting edge of a knife (Fig. 16.31); poisons released by invading bacteria are often neutralized in this manner. Other antibodies dissolve parts of the cell walls of bacteria, causing them to disintegrate. Still others cause bacteria to clump together, thereby making them less active and more susceptible to being captured by the filtering action of the lymph nodes. And others seem to make the antigens more susceptible to phagocytosis by the leukocytes.

Antibody Specificity. One of the most intriguing and least understood aspects of antigen-antibody reactions is the amazing specificity of most antibodies. How is detailed information about the antigen's structure conveyed to the plasma cells so that they can synthesize the appropriate antibody? According to one current hypothesis, the antigen is used by the plasma cells as a kind of mold or template against which the antibodies are made. In this way, the molecules of antibody could be given a shape enabling them to "fit" against the antigen molecules and to react easily with them. A prominent alternative hypothesis suggests that the organism is born with an enormous variety of different plasma cell types, each with the inherited ability to recognize one or perhaps several specific kinds of antigens and to synthesize the appropriate antibodies.[5] According to this hypothesis, an invading antigen simply stimulates the particular plasma cells sensitive to it. Which, if either, of these two hypotheses is close to the truth can be determined only after much more extensive research.

At the moment, the available evidence seems to favor the second hypothesis (commonly called the selective hypothesis). If, as the first hypothesis suggests, the antigen were used as a

[5] If one version of this selective hypothesis is correct, the different plasma cells differ genetically, and we would have to modify our earlier statement that the various cells of an organism are genetically identical and that differentiation is simply the realization of one of several potentialities.

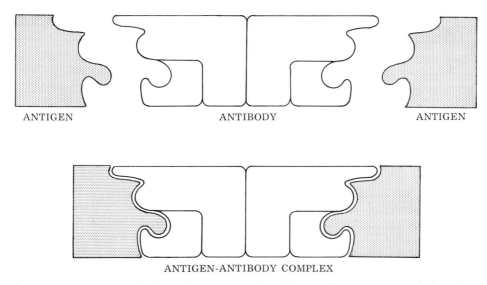

ANTIGEN   ANTIBODY   ANTIGEN

ANTIGEN-ANTIBODY COMPLEX

Fig. 16.31. Antigen-antibody reaction. Top: The evidence indicates that an antibody molecule has two identical halves, each composed of one large component and one small component. Bottom: The two active surfaces of the antibody molecule probably fit against the active surfaces of two antigen molecules, thus inactivating them.

template, it would seem essential for the antigen to enter the plasma cell. If, on the other hand, the antigen just stimulates the plasma cell, it could do this at the surface of the plasma cell without actually entering it. Experiments with radioactive antigen have shown that very little antigen enters the plasma cells —a finding that supports the selective hypothesis. To many scientists, however, this hypothesis, though it seems to fit the present data well, is unattractive because of the vast number of different types of plasma cells it postulates. There is every indication that the body can manufacture specific antibody against almost any protein or even protein fragment, as well as against certain other types of chemical compounds. When one considers the many billions of proteins that must exist, the idea that we have a different type of plasma cell specialized to make antibody against each possible antigen becomes less appealing.

Recognition of "Self." Research in immunology has implications of far more importance than simply the development of new and better vaccines for protection against disease—important as that is. The whole question of how the body recognizes some substances as "self" and others as "not self," which has a vital bearing on the problem of transplanting tissues and organs from one individual to another, is involved here. It has been known for years that under normal circumstances, if a piece of skin, for example, is transplanted from one person to another, the recipient's body may soon reject the graft; the foreign tissue is destroyed by an immune reaction. The same is true of transplants of kidneys, hearts, etc. This rejection by the body of foreign tissue has been the chief barrier to surgical replacement of severely damaged organs, a procedure that would open a whole new approach to the treatment of many now hopelessly ill patients. Here the immune reaction, which is a major defense against harmful foreign substances that might cause disease, is itself the major barrier against

effective treatment of many wounds and diseases. The defense system cannot distinguish between harmful and helpful foreign substances, and destroys both.

Since the distinction seems to be between "self" and "not self," the body apparently being able to tell which substances are part of itself and which are not, an obvious possibility for successful transplants would be to use identical twins. Such individuals develop from the same fertilized egg cell and thus have identical genes. Presumably, those genes would control the synthesis of identical substances in the two individuals. The body of one twin could therefore not distinguish between its own parts and parts taken from the other twin; both would be identified as "self." Numerous transplants between identical twins have been tried, and the results have borne out the predictions. The transplants have been accepted by the recipient's body. Most widely publicized have been cases in which a kidney from a healthy twin was transplanted to his twin dying of kidney failure (if the kidneys are normal and healthy, one is sufficient; hence the donor can give one away without impairing his own health).

But few people have identical twins who can come to their aid when they need a transplant. Clearly, the real hope for the future is transplantation from healthy unrelated donors or, for such organs as the heart, from the bodies of persons who have recently died or from other animals such as apes, monkeys, and baboons. A number of such transplants have, in fact, been tried, with X-ray or chemical suppression of the tissues involved in the immune reactions. Many such attempts have failed, and the others have been only partly successful. It is very difficult, with the techniques now available, to suppress the immune reaction sufficiently to prevent rejection of the transplant without at the same time severely damaging the patient in other ways. Of course, in any such attempt, the patient must be given constant massive doses of antibiotic drugs, because his own defenses against infection have been suppressed.

Basic to a real understanding of immune reactions is more knowledge of the way immunologic capabilities develop and of the way the body distinguishes between "self" and "not self." Many advances have been made in this currently very active field in the last five years or so, but our information is still scanty.

In 1945 R. D. Owen of the California Institute of Technology discovered that in some cases nonidentical twin calves each had the antigens normal to their own erythrocytes and also the antigens characteristic of their twin's erythrocytes. The calves were healthy, but they were not destroying, or in any way rejecting, the antigens from their nonidentical twin. Their bodies should have identified their twin's antigens as "not self" and made antibodies against them. Why were they not doing so? Owen showed that the circulatory systems of the calves had been interconnected early in their embryonic development and that they must have exchanged blood-forming elements during this time. Apparently, at this early embryonic stage the calves exhibited immunologic tolerance to an exchange that, after birth, would have resulted in antibody formation. Such observations led to the hypothesis that the early embryo lacks immunologic mechanisms, that these develop later, and that when they develop, all substances present in the body at that time are identified as "self." In other words, if foreign substances could be gotten into the embryo soon enough, they would be considered "self" when the immunologic mechanisms developed.

Numerous experiments have demonstrated that this hypothesis is correct. Mice injected as early embryos with cells from another mouse will accept grafts from that mouse after they are born. Such experiments have shown, further, that immunologic capabilities do not develop all at once, but develop gradually during and after embryonic development. Immunologic capabilities against some antigens may arise early in embryonic life, while tolerance to other antigens may remain until several weeks after birth. This suggests a system involving different elements each responsible for immunologic capabilities against different antigens. Presumably each such element matures normally if its antigen is absent from the system. If, however, its antigen is present in quantity at the time it starts to mature, the element fails to mature, perhaps because it is destroyed by the antigen. According to this hypothesis, then, substances can be identified as "self" or "not self" by the mature organism because the "self" substances were present at the critical time during development and destroyed or inactivated the immunologic elements that started to develop against them, while "not self" substances were not present at the critical developmental moment and, consequently, immunologic elements against them were free to mature.

The Role of the Thymus. We said earlier that the plasma cells, which are the ones that produce antibodies, develop from lymphocytes. We would expect, then, that immunologic capabilities could develop only after the appearance of lymphocytes in the embryo. Morphologic studies have shown that lymphocytes develop in the embryonic thymus well before they appear in the circulation or in other lymphoid tissues such as the spleen and lymph nodes. It would seem reasonable to suppose, therefore, that the thymus plays an important role in the development of immunologic capabilities. Numerous recent studies have shown that this is indeed the case.

You should be aware, however, that this logical and rather obvious linking of the thymus with the development of immunologic capabilities does not, in fact, reflect the way our knowledge developed. The path to understanding is apt to appear as straightforward after its discovery as it appeared nebulous and equivocal before. So it is with the thymus. In man, this organ is a two-lobed, glandular-appearing structure located in the upper part of the chest just behind the sternum (breast-bone) (Fig. 16.32); its size and shape are frequently different in other vertebrates, but its cellular structure and location are much the same. In an embryo, or in a child below the age of 10 or 12, the thymus is large and prominent, while in adults it is usually atrophied and difficult to locate. For decades it was an embarrassment to biologists that they could assign no function to the thymus. True, it was known to produce lymphocytes, but the function of these cells was also unclear. And besides, the production of lymphocytes is not peculiar to the thymus; these are also produced by many other tissues. It was suggested that the thymus functions as an endocrine gland, producing hormones, but the standard experiments to demonstrate such activity all failed; surgical removal of the organ seldom produced significant effects on the animal.

Finally, Jacques F. A. P. Miller, working in England in 1961, performed the critical experiment. In an extremely delicate and difficult operation, he removed the thymuses from a group of newborn mice. During the three or four months most of them survived, many in-

teresting changes were demonstrated in them. For example, many lost the capacity to produce antibodies. And most of them would accept and retain skin grafts from other mice and even from rats. None of these effects were produced when the thymus was removed from mice three or four weeks old. Apparently the thymus is essential to the development and maturation of immunologic capabilities, but is no longer necessary once those capabilities are mature, unless they have been destroyed by radiation or chemicals and must be re-established by the thymus. It is because all earlier experiments had been performed on older animals that the functional significance of the thymus had so long been in question. In the few years since Miller's experiment, many other investigators have corroborated his findings, and the thymus has become the subject of much new interest and research.

Two principal functions have been attributed to the thymus. First, it is thought that early in the development of the lymphoid system some of the lymphocytes produced in the thymus migrate to such areas of the body as the lymph nodes, spleen, etc., settle down there, and give rise to the lymphoid elements that later make those areas capable of producing antibodies. In other words, according to this hypothesis, the thymus provides the initial supply of lymphocytes for the other lymphoid areas, and these initial cells give rise to descendent lines of lymphocytes and plasma cells, making further stocking from the thymus unnecessary. Though there is experimental evidence to support this hypothesis, there is also evidence against it, and it must be considered unproved at the time of this writing (the matter may have been settled by the time you read this book).

The second function attributed to the thymus is release of hormones that stimulate differentiation of incipient plasma cells in the lymphoid tissue; these incipient plasma cells then develop into functional plasma cells producing antibodies when stimulated by the ap-

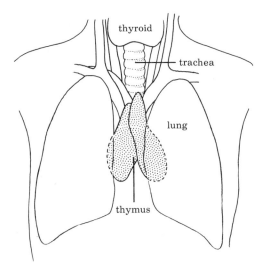

Fig. 16.32. Location of the thymus in the human.

propriate antigens. In other words, full development of plasma cells, according to this hypothesis, requires two different types of inducing stimuli: (1) a general stimulus by thymal hormones, which initiates differentiation of all types of incipient plasma cells, followed by (2) a specific stimulus by an antigen, which stimulates functional maturation of only those cells with a potential for making antibodies against that particular antigen. Evidence for the first half of this hypothesis comes from experiments in which the thymus was removed from newborn mice, put into a container impermeable to whole cells, and then (while still in the container) implanted in the mice. Such mice developed essentially normal immunologic capabilities, an indication that some stimulus from the implanted thymus had enabled their lymphoid tissues to develop normally. Since the stimulus from the thymus could not involve transfer of whole cells, because of the container, it is assumed that some diffusible chemical (a hormone) is involved. Support for the second half of the hypothesis comes from work with animals raised in germ-free chambers. The lymphoid tissues of these animals, lacking stimulus from bacteria, viruses, etc., are much retarded in their development. On the other hand, the lymphoid tissues of animals injected with antigens while they are still in their mother's uterus develop much sooner than normal.

Immunologic Disease. Though we normally think of the immunologic mechanisms of the body as a defense against disease, there is increasing evidence that these very mechanisms may at times be responsible for disease symptoms. In some cases, the invading microbes or other foreign materials do not themselves cause much, if any, damage to the host. It is the immunologic response of the host that actually does the damage. Allergies are examples of this type of disease. Several viral diseases are known in which the virus itself does no harm, but the body's immunologic reaction produces such severe symptoms that death sometimes results.

Still another recent discovery is that occasionally the immunologic mechanisms get out of control and become sensitized to some part of the animal's own body, producing antibodies against it and causing interference with or even destruction of that part. In such cases, the ability to distinguish between "self" and "not self" is impaired, and the body begins to destroy itself. Clearly, immunology is a field in which much work remains to be done.

REFERENCES

AREY, L. B., 1965. *Developmental Anatomy,* 7th ed. Saunders, Philadelphia.

BALINSKY, B. I., 1960. *An Introduction to Embryology.* Saunders, Philadelphia.

BARTH, L. G., 1964. *Development: Selected Topics.* Addison-Wesley, Reading, Mass.

BERRILL, N. J., 1961. *Growth, Development and Pattern.* Freeman, San Francisco.

BONNER, J. T., 1952. *Morphogenesis.* Princeton University Press, Princeton, N.J. (Also available in paperback, Atheneum, New York, 1963.)

BRACHET, J., 1960. *The Biochemistry of Development.* Pergamon, Oxford.

FLICKINGER, R. A., ed., 1966. *Developmental Biology.* Wm. C. Brown, Dubuque, Iowa. (A collection of 16 papers.)

GOOD, R. A., and A. E. GABRIELSEN, 1964. *The Thymus in Immunobiology.* Harper & Row, Hoeber Medical Division, New York.

LEOPOLD, A. C., 1964. *Plant Growth and Development.* McGraw-Hill, New York.

MARKERT, C. L., 1964. *Developmental Genetics.* Prentice-Hall, Englewood Cliffs, N.J.

MAYER, A. M., and A. POLJAKOFF-MAYBER, 1963. *The Germination of Seeds.* Macmillan, New York.

NEEDHAM, A. E., 1964. *The Growth Process in Animals.* Van Nostrand, Princeton, N.J.

RUDNICK, D., ed., 1960. *Developing Cell Systems and Their Control.* Ronald, New York.

———, 1962. *Regeneration.* Ronald, New York.

SPEMANN, H., 1938. *Embryonic Development and Induction.* Yale University Press, New Haven, Conn. (Reprinted by Hafner, New York, 1962.)

STEWARD, F. C., *et al.,* 1964. "Growth and Development of Cultured Plant Cells," *Science,* vol. 143, pp. 20–27.

THOMPSON, D'A. W., 1942. *On Growth and Form,* rev. ed. Macmillan, New York.

TORREY, T. W., 1962. *Morphogenesis of the Vertebrates.* Wiley, New York.

WADDINGTON, C. H., 1962. *New Patterns in Genetics and Development.* Columbia University Press, New York.

WARDLAW, C. W., 1952. *Morphogenesis in Plants.* Methuen, London.

WILLIER, B. H., and J. M. OPPENHEIMER, eds., 1964. *Foundations of Experimental Embryology.* Prentice-Hall, Englewood Cliffs, N.J. (A collection of 11 important papers.)

WILSON, E. B., 1925. *The Cell in Development and Heredity,* 3rd ed. Macmillan, New York.

SUGGESTED READING

BEERMANN, W., and U. CLEVER, 1964. "Chromosome Puffs," *Scientific American,* April. (Offprint 180.)

BIALE, J. B., 1954. "The Ripening of Fruit," *Scientific American,* May. (Offprint 118.)

BILLINGHAM, R. E., and W. K. SILVERS, 1963. "Skin Transplants and the Hamster," *Scientific American,* January. (Offprint 148.)

BONNER, J. T., 1963. "How Slime Molds Communicate," *Scientific American,* August. (Offprint 164.)

BURNET, M., 1961. "The Mechanism of Immunity," *Scientific American,* January. (Offprint 78.)

———, 1962. "The Thymus Gland," *Scientific American,* November. (Offprint 138.)

DODD, J. D., 1962. *Form and Function in Plants.* Iowa State University Press, Ames. (See esp. Chapter 6.)

EBERT, J. D., 1959. "The First Heartbeats," *Scientific American,* March. (Offprint 56.)

———, 1965. *Interacting Systems in Development.* Holt, Rinehart & Winston, New York.

FISCHBERG, M., and A. W. BLACKLER, 1961. "How Cells Specialize," *Scientific American,* September. (Offprint 94.)

FRIEDEN, E., 1963. "The Chemistry of Amphibian Metamorphosis," *Scientific American,* November. (Offprint 170.)

GRAY, G. W., 1957. "The Organizer," *Scientific American,* November. (Offprint 103.)

GREULACH, V. A., and J. E. ADAMS, 1962. *Plants: An Introduction to Modern Botany.* Wiley, New York.

GROBSTEIN, C., 1964. "Cytodifferentiation and Its Controls," *Science,* vol. 143, pp. 643–650.

KONIGSBERG, I. R., 1964. "The Embryological Origin of Muscle," *Scientific American,* August. (Offprint 191.)

LEVEY, R. H., 1964. "The Thymus Hormone," *Scientific American,* July. (Offprint 188.)

MILLER, J. F. A. P., 1964. "The Thymus and the Development of Immunologic Responsiveness," *Science,* vol. 144, pp. 1544–1551.

MOORE, J. A., 1963. *Heredity and Development.* Oxford University Press, New York.

MOSCONA, A. A., 1961. "How Cells Associate," *Scientific American,* September. (Offprint 95.)

NOSSAL, G. J. V., 1964. "How Cells Make Antibodies," *Scientific American,* December. (Offprint 199.)

PUCK, T. T., 1957. "Single Human Cells in Vitro," *Scientific American,* August. (Offprint 33.)

SILVERSTEIN, A. M., 1964. "Ontogeny of the Immune Response," *Science,* vol. 144, pp. 1423–1428.

SINGER, M., 1958. "The Regeneration of Body Parts," *Scientific American,* October. (Offprint 105.)

SPERRY, R. W., 1959. "The Growth of Nerve Circuits," *Scientific American,* November. (Offprint 72.)

SPIERS, R. S., 1964. "How Cells Attack Antigens," *Scientific American,* February. (Offprint 176.)

STERN, H., and D. L. NANNEY, 1965. *The Biology of Cells.* Wiley, New York. (See esp. Section C.)

STEWARD, F. C., 1963. "The Control of Growth in Plant Cells," *Scientific American,* October. (Offprint 167.)

SUSSMAN, M., 1964. *Growth and Development,* 2nd ed. Prentice-Hall, Englewood Cliffs, N.J.

SWANSON, C. P., 1964. *The Cell,* 2nd ed. Prentice-Hall, Englewood Cliffs, N.J.

TELFER, W., and D. KENNEDY, 1965. *The Biology of Organisms.* Wiley, New York. (See esp. Chapter 5.)

VERZÁR, F., 1963. "The Aging of Collagen," *Scientific American,* April. (Offprint 155.)

WADDINGTON, C. H., 1953. "How Do Cells Differentiate?" *Scientific American,* September. (Offprint 45.)

————, 1962. *How Animals Develop.* Harper Torchbooks, New York.

WIGGLESWORTH, V. B., 1959. "Metamorphosis and Differentiation," *Scientific American,* February. (Offprint 63.)

WILLIAMS, C. M., 1950. "The Metamorphosis of Insects," *Scientific American,* April. (Offprint 49.)

PART IV

THE BIOLOGY OF
POPULATIONS AND COMMUNITIES

CHAPTER
17

EVOLUTION

THE SUBJECT OF EVOLUTION WAS BRIEFLY introduced in Chapter 1 as a unifying principle for the study of all the topics that were to follow. That introduction was necessarily far from complete. But the succeeding chapters have provided a background that now enables us to take a closer look at the mechanisms of evolution.

EVOLUTION AS CHANGE IN THE GENETIC MAKEUP OF POPULATIONS

In our earlier discussion, we indicated that the modern theory of evolution includes two basic concepts—first, that the characteristics of living things change with time and, second, that the change is directed by natural selection. You will recall that the change we are here discussing is not change in an individual during its lifetime, although such change is a universal and important attribute of life; rather, we are concerned with changes in the characteristics of populations over the course of many generations. An individual cannot evolve, but a population can. The genetic makeup of an individual is set from the moment of conception; most of the changes during its lifetime are simply changes in the expression of the developmental potential inherent in its genes. But in populations, both the genetic makeup and the expression of the developmental potential can change; the former—change in the genetic makeup of a population in successive generations—is evolution.

Genetic Variation as the Raw Material for Evolution

A population is composed of many individuals. With rare exceptions, no two of these are exactly alike. In human beings, we are well aware of the uniqueness of the individual, for we are accustomed to recognizing different individuals at sight, and we know from experience that each person has distinctive anatomical and physiological characteristics, as well as distinctive abilities and behavior traits. We are also fairly well aware of this uniqueness in such common domesticated animals as dogs, cats, and horses. But sometimes we overlook the similar individual variation in less familiar species such as robins, squirrels, earthworms, starfish, dandelions, and corn plants. Yet even though this variation may be less obvious to our unpracticed eye, it exists in all such species, from the smallest unicellular organisms to the largest whales. A population, then, is made up of a large number of individuals that share some important features but differ from one another in numerous ways, some rather obvious, some very subtle. It follows that if there is selection against certain variants within a population and selection for other variants within it, the overall makeup of that population may change with time, since its characteristics at any given time are determined by the individuals in it.

Exclusively Phenotypic Variation and Variation Produced by Somatic Mutations. Any phenotypic variation within a population may give rise to reproductive differentials between individuals, whether or not the variation reflects corresponding genetic differences. Thus variations produced by exposure to different environmental conditions during development, or produced by disease or accidents, are subject to natural selection. But even though the action of natural selection on all types of variations alters the immediate makeup of a population, it is only its action on variations reflecting genetic differences that has any long-term effect on the population. Variation that is exclusively phenotypic is not raw material for evolutionary change.

Our discussion of genetics will have made it clear that developing one's athletic prowess by extensive practice, or developing one's intellect by education, or maintaining one's health by correct diet and prompt medical treatment of all illnesses cannot alter the genes in the germ cells. The gametes will carry the same genetic information that they would have carried if one had not practiced athletics or trained one's mind or guarded one's health. This does not mean that the genes cannot affect the next generation's potential athletic or mental ability or potential health; they almost certainly do so. It only means that practice, education, diet, and medical treatment do not alter the genetic message. Hence selection that acts on variations produced exclusively by practice, education, diet, or medical treatment cannot result in biological evolution (though it might result in cultural evolution).

There is also some genetic variation that is not raw material for evolutionary change. This is variation produced by somatic mutations. It would be possible, for example, for an important mutation to occur in an ectodermal cell of an early animal embryo. All the cells descended from the mutant cell would be mutants also. The result might be a major change in the animal's nervous system, but the change could not be passed on to the animal's offspring. The ectodermal cells are not the ones that give rise to gametes. Mutations in somatic cells cannot alter the genes in the germ cells, but it is the germ cells that will produce the gametes. Hence selection that acts on variations produced by somatic mutations cannot result in evolutionary change in sexually reproducing organisms.

Lacking genetic data, many prominent biologists of the last century and of the early part of this century rejected the idea that exclusively phenotypic variation or variation resulting from somatic mutation cannot serve as evolutionary raw material, and even today this idea is far from obvious to many nonbiologists. We have concentrated on the theory of evolution by natural selection proposed by Darwin and Wallace and modified by the discoveries of many later workers. But this theory had an influential rival in another scientific hypothesis of evolution proposed during the last century —that of evolution by the inheritance of acquired characteristics, an old and widely held idea often identified with Jean Baptiste de Lamarck (1744–1829), who was one of its more prominent supporters in the early 1800's.

According to the Lamarckian hypothesis, somatic characteristics acquired by an individual during its lifetime can be transmitted to its offspring. Thus the characteristics of each generation would be determined, in part at least, by all that happened to the members of the preceding generations—by all the modifications that occurred in them, including those caused by experience, use and disuse of body parts, and accidents. Evolutionary change would be the gradual accumulation of such acquired modifications over many generations. The classic example (though now rather hackneyed) is the evolution of the long necks of giraffes. A Lamarckian view would be that ancestral giraffes with short necks tended to stretch their necks as much as they could to reach the tree foliage that served as a major part of their food. This frequent neck stretching caused their offspring to have slightly longer necks. Since these also stretched their necks, the next generation had still longer necks. And so, as a result of neck stretching to reach higher and higher foliage, each generation had slightly longer necks than the preceding generation. The modern theory of natural selection explains the long necks of giraffes in a fundamentally different way. According to this theory, ancestral giraffes probably had short necks, but the precise length of the neck varied from individual to individual because of their slightly different genotypes. If the supply of food was somewhat limited, then individuals with longer necks had a better chance of surviving and leaving progeny than those with shorter necks. This does not mean that all the individuals with shorter necks perished or that all with longer necks survived to reproduce; it simply means that a slightly higher proportion of those with longer necks survived and left offspring. As a result, the proportion of individuals with genes for longer necks increased slightly with each succeeding generation.

Although the hypothesis of evolution by inheritance of acquired characteristics is held in low esteem by most modern biologists, it was a logical and reasonable one when first proposed. It has simply not stood the test of further scientific research. In Lamarck's day (as in Darwin's), nothing was known about the mechanism of inheritance. Mendel had not yet performed his experiments on garden peas. It was not illogical, therefore, to assume that a change in any part of the body could be inherited. As long ago as the days of ancient Greece it had been suggested that particles, or pangenes, from all parts of the body come together to form the eggs and semen. This Greek idea of *pangenesis* would provide a hypothetical genetic basis for the Lamarckian hypothesis. If a long-distance runner built up his leg muscles, and if the pangenes in them were thereby altered, then when the runner formed semen the pangenes for leg muscles in his semen would be the altered type and would confer larger leg muscles on his children. One of the most telling points against Lamarckianism is the refutation of the idea of pangenesis upon which it depends. We now know that somatic cells do not affect the genotype of the germ cells; immense alterations of the somatic cells can be brought about without in any way influencing the hereditary information in the gametes. And despite extensive testing, inheritance of acquired characteristics has never been demonstrated. We must conclude that this hypothesis is no longer tenable.

Genetic Variation. We have already discussed the various sources of genetic variation in a population. Ultimately, of course, all new alleles arise by mutation. But once a variety of alleles is in existence, recombination becomes a mechanism that provides almost endless genotypic variation in the population. The variation resulting from meiosis and recombination at fertilization in biparental organisms has already been cited as of immense importance. Crossing-over, translocation, and other chromosomal aberrations are further mechanisms of recombination. And in microorganisms, and perhaps in higher organisms, the newly discovered processes of transformation and transduction constitute still other mechanisms of recombination. It is becoming increasingly doubtful that any major group of organisms, from viruses to the most complex plants and animals, is completely devoid of some mechanism of recombination. Together, mutation and recombination provide the genetic variability upon which natural selection can act to produce evolutionary change.

We must emphasize again, however, that natural selection can act on genetic variation only when it is expressed as phenotypic variation. A completely recessive allele never occurring in the homozygous condition would be totally masked from the action of natural selection. However, few if any alleles are in fact completely recessive against all genetic backgrounds; most alleles that we ordinarily call recessive probably have some very slight phe-

notypic effect (if we include as part of the phenotype all metabolic, physiological, anatomical, and behavioral attributes of the organism). Such recessive alleles may thus be exposed to some degree to the action of natural selection, although the action may be so slight as to be nearly insignificant.

The Gene Pool and Factors That Affect Its Equilibrium

The Gene Pool. We have said that evolution is change in the genetic makeup of populations in successive generations. To understand evolution, therefore, it is necessary to know something about population genetics. Our study of the genetics of individuals in an earlier chapter was based on the concept of the genotype, which is the genetic constitution of an individual. Our study of the genetics of populations will be based in a similar manner on the concept of the gene pool, which is the genetic constitution of a population. The gene pool is the sum total of all the genes (including plasmagenes) possessed by all the individuals in the population.

You will recall that the genotype of a diploid individual can contain a maximum of only two alleles of any given gene. But there is no such restriction on the gene pool of a population. It can contain any number of different allelic forms of a gene. We characterize the gene pool with regard to any given gene by the frequencies, or ratios, of the alleles of that gene in the population. Suppose, to use a simple example, that gene A occurs in only two allelic forms, A and a, in a particular sexually reproducing population. And suppose that allele A constitutes 90 percent of the total of both alleles while allele a constitutes 10 percent of the total. We would say, then, that the frequencies of A and a in the gene pool of this population are 0.9 and 0.1. If those frequencies were to change with time, the change would be evolution. When we say that evolution is change in the genetic makeup of populations, what we mean is that it is change in the gene frequencies within gene pools. Therefore we can determine what factors cause evolution by determining what factors can produce a shift in gene frequencies.

The Hardy-Weinberg Law. Let us examine more carefully our hypothetical population in which allele A has a frequency of 0.9 and allele a has a frequency of 0.1. How can we calculate the genotype ratios that will be present in this population? If we assume that all possible genotypes have an equal chance of surviving, this calculation is not hard to make. If the ratio of A to a in the entire population is 9 : 1, then the ratio of sperms carrying allele A to sperms carrying allele a is 9 : 1. And the ratio of eggs with allele A to eggs with allele a is also 9 : 1. Using this information, we can set up a Punnett square much like those we used for crosses between two individuals, as follows:

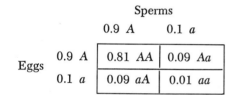

Notice that the only difference between this and a Punnett square for a cross between individuals is that here the sperms and eggs are not those produced by a single male and a single female but those produced by all the males and females in the population, with the frequency of each type of sperm and egg shown on the horizontal and vertical axes respectively. Filling in the square (by combining the indicated alleles and multiplying their frequencies) tells us that the frequency of the homozygous dominant genotype (AA) in the population will be 0.81, the frequency of the heterozygous

genotype (Aa) will be 0.18, and the frequency of the homozygous recessive genotype (aa) will be 0.01.[1]

We have thus fully characterized the gene pool of the present generation of our hypothetical population with regard to alleles A and a and the genotypes they form. Now we want to know whether the frequencies we have found will change in successive generations—in short, whether the population will evolve. It is common for beginners to assume that the more frequent allele (in this case A) will automatically increase in frequency while the less frequent allele (a) will automatically decrease in frequency and eventually be lost from the population. This assumption is incorrect. The rarity of a particular allele in a population does not doom it to automatic disappearance, as we can verify by using the known frequencies for one generation to compute the frequencies for the next generation. We have said that the gene frequencies in the gene pool of the present generation of our hypothetical population are 0.9 and 0.1 and that the genotype ratios are 0.81, 0.18, and 0.01. If we use these figures to set up a Punnett square (or binomial expression) and compute the corresponding values for the next generation, we find that they are the same ones we started with. The gene frequencies of the next generation are also 0.9 and 0.1, and the genotype ratios are 0.81, 0.18, and 0.01. We could perform the

---

[1] The same results could have been gotten without setting up a Punnett square by expanding the binomial expression $(p + q)^2$, where p is the frequency of one allele and q is the frequency of the other allele. This binomial is expanded as follows:

$$(p + q)^2 = p^2 + 2pq + q^2$$

If, using our example, we let p and q be the frequencies of alleles A and a respectively, then

$$
\begin{aligned}
& p^2 &+&\quad 2pq &+&\quad q^2 \\
=\ & (0.9)(0.9) &+& 2(0.9)(0.1) &+& (0.1)(0.1) \\
=\ & 0.81 &+& 0.18 &+& 0.01
\end{aligned}
$$

Thus the three terms of the expanded binomial indicate the frequencies of the three genotypes:

$$
\begin{aligned}
p^2 &= 0.81 = \text{frequency of } AA \\
2pq &= 0.18 = \text{frequency of } Aa \\
q^2 &= 0.01 = \text{frequency of } aa
\end{aligned}
$$

same calculation for generation after generation, always with the same results; neither the gene frequencies nor the genotype ratios would change. We must conclude, therefore, that evolutionary change is not usually automatic, that it occurs only when something disturbs the genetic equilibrium. This was first recognized in 1908 by G. H. Hardy of Cambridge University and W. Weinberg, a German physician, working independently. In summary, according to the Hardy-Weinberg Law, *under certain conditions of stability both gene frequencies and genotype ratios remain constant from generation to generation in sexually reproducing populations.*

Necessary Conditions for Genetic Equilibrium. We must now examine the "certain conditions" that the Hardy-Weinberg Law says are necessary for the gene pool of a population to be in genetic equilibrium. These conditions are as follows:

1. The population must be large enough to make it highly unlikely that chance alone could significantly alter gene frequencies.
2. Mutations must not occur, or else there must be mutational equilibrium.
3. There must be no immigration or emigration.
4. Reproduction must be totally random.

In theory, a population would have to be infinitely large for chance to be completely ruled out as a causal factor in the changing of gene frequencies. In reality, of course, no population is infinitely large, but many natural populations are large enough so that chance alone would not be likely to cause any appreciable alteration in the gene frequencies in their gene pools. Any breeding population with more than 10,000 members of breeding age is probably not significantly affected by random change. But gene frequencies in small isolated populations of, say, less than 100 breeding-age members are highly susceptible to random fluctuations, which can easily lead to loss of an allele from the gene pool even when that allele is an adaptively superior one. In such populations, in fact, there are relatively few alleles with intermediate frequencies; apparently the tendency is for most alleles either to be soon lost or to become fixed as the only allele present. In other words, small populations tend to have a high degree of homozygosity, while large populations tend to be more variable. Thus chance may cause evolutionary change in small populations, but since this change, often called **genetic drift,** is not much influenced by the relative adaptiveness of the different genes, it is essentially an indeterminate evolution, as likely to take one direction as another.

The second condition for genetic equilibrium —either no mutation or mutational equilibrium —is probably never met in any population. Mutations are always occurring. There is no known way of stopping them. Most genes probably undergo mutation once every 50,000 to 1,000,00 duplications; the rate of mutation for different genes varies. As for mutational equilibrium, very rarely, if ever, are the mutations of alleles for the same character in exact equilibrium; i.e. the number of forward mutations per unit time is rarely exactly the same as the number of back mutations.[2] For example, suppose mutations of allele A into allele a are forward mutations and mutations of a into A are back mutations:

$$A \; \underset{\text{back mutation}}{\overset{\text{forward mutation}}{\rightleftharpoons}} \; a$$

These two mutations will rarely occur at precisely the same rate; either the forward or the back mutation will be more frequent. This *mutation pressure* will tend to cause a slow shift in the gene frequencies in the population. The more stable allele will tend to increase in frequency, and the more mutable allele will

---

[2] By convention, the mutation from the more common allele to the less common one is called the forward mutation, and the reverse is called the back mutation.

tend to decrease in frequency, unless some other factor offsets the mutation pressure. But even though mutation pressure is almost always present, it is probably seldom a major factor in producing changes in gene frequencies in a population. Mutation is so slow that, acting alone, it would take an enormous amount of time to produce much change (except in the origin of polyploidy, which we shall not discuss here). And, furthermore, mutation is random; its trend is frequently in a direction different from that in which other factors are causing the organism actually to evolve. Mutations increase variability and are thus the ultimate raw material of evolution, but they seldom determine the direction or nature of evolutionary change.

If a gene pool is to remain in genetic equilibrium, it obviously cannot accept immigrants from other populations that would introduce new genes. And it cannot suffer loss of genes from the gene pool by emigration. A high percentage of natural populations, however, probably experience at least a small amount of gene migration, and this factor, which enhances variation, tends to upset Hardy-Weinberg equilibria. But there are doubtless populations that experience no gene migration, and in many instances where migration does occur it is probably sufficiently slight to be essentially negligible as a factor causing shifts in gene frequencies. We can conclude, therefore, that this third condition for genetic equilibrium is sometimes met in nature.

The fourth condition for genetic equilibrium in a population is that reproduction be totally random. Here it is necessary to clarify what biologists mean by reproduction in this context. They do not mean simply the mating process *per se*. Rather, they mean the vast number of factors that contribute to the reproductive continuity of the population: selection of a mate, physical efficiency and frequency of the mating process, fertility (percentage of zygote formation), total number of zygotes produced at each mating, percentage of zygotes that lead

to successful embryonic development and birth, survival of the young until they are of reproductive age, fertility of the young, and even, in some cases, survival of postreproductive adults when their survival affects either the chances of survival of the young or their reproductive efficiency. If reproduction is to be totally random, all these factors must be random; i.e. they must be independent of genotype. This condition is probably never met in any population. The factors mentioned here are probably always correlated in part with genotype; i.e. an organism's genotype influences its selection of a mate, the physical efficiency and frequency of its mating, its fertility when mated with organisms of other genotypes, the total number of zygotes it produces at each mating, the percentage of successful births of its embryos, the survival and fertility of its young, and its postreproductive survival, In short, there is probably no aspect of reproduction that is totally devoid of correlation with genotype. Nonrandom reproduction is the universal rule. And nonrandom reproduction, in the broad sense in which the term has been defined here, is synonymous with natural selection. Natural selection, then, is always operative in all populations.

In summary, of the four conditions necessary for the genetic equilibrium described by the Hardy-Weinberg Law, the first (large population size) is met reasonably often, the second (no mutation) is never met, the third (no migration) is met sometimes, and the fourth (random reproduction) is never met. It follows that complete equilibrium in a gene pool is not expected, that evolutionary change is a fundamental characteristic of the life of populations.

The Role of Natural Selection

Changes in Individual Gene Frequencies Caused by Natural Selection. Let us now return for a moment to our hypothetical population in which the initial frequencies of the alleles *A* and *a* are 0.9 and 0.1 and the genotype frequencies are 0.81, 0.18, and 0.01. We saw earlier that these frequencies will not change automatically with the passage of time, that they change only when something disturbs the genetic equilibrium. Now we have seen that mutation pressure (to a slight extent) and *selection pressure* (to a greater extent) are always disturbing the genetic equilibrium of a population. Suppose that natural selection acts against the dominant phenotype in our example, and that this negative selection pressure is strong enough to reduce the frequency of *A* in the present generation from 0.9 to 0.8 before reproduction occurs. (Of course there will be a corresponding increase in the frequency of *a* from 0.1 to 0.2, since the two frequencies must total 1.0.) Now let us set up a Punnett square (or binomial expression) and calculate the genotype ratios that will be present in the zygotes of the second generation:

Sperms

		0.8 *A*	0.2 *a*
Eggs	0.8 *A*	0.64 *AA*	0.16 *Aa*
	0.2 *a*	0.16 *aA*	0.04 *aa*

We find that the genotype ratios of the zygotes in the second generation are different from those in the parental generation; instead of 0.81, 0.18, and 0.01, the ratios are 0.64, 0.32, and 0.04 (Fig. 17.1). If selection now acts against the dominant phenotype in this generation, and thereby again reduces the frequency of *A*, the genotype ratios in the third generation will be different from those of both preceding generations; the frequency of *AA* will be lower and that of *aa* will be higher. If this same selection pressure were to continue for many generations, the frequency of *AA* would fall very low and the frequency of *aa* would rise very high. Thus natural selection would have caused a change from a population in which 99 percent of the individuals showed the dominant phenotype and only one percent showed the recessive phenotype to a population in which very few showed the dominant phenotype and most showed the recessive phenotype. This evolutionary change of the phenotype most characteristic of the population would have occurred without the necessity of any new mutation, simply as a result of natural selection.

Rather than deal only with a hypothetical example, let us cite an actual situation in which selection has produced a radical shift in gene frequencies. Soon after the discovery of the antibiotic activity of penicillin, it was found that certain bacteria, *Staphylococcus aureus,* which cause numerous infections, including boils and abscesses, quickly developed resistance to the drug. Higher and higher doses of penicillin were necessary to kill the bacteria, and the resistant bacteria became a serious problem in hospitals. Clearly, under the influence of the strong selection exerted by the penicillin, the bacterial population had evolved. This phenomenon has been studied extensively under experimental conditions in the laboratory. In such experiments, a culture containing hundreds of millions of bacteria is exposed to a moderate dose of penicillin. Most of the cells are killed, but a few survive. When the descendants of these survivors are later exposed to the same moderate dose of penicillin, most survive. Two possible explanations for these results come to mind. The gene for resistance may already be present in the population before the experiment begins, and the drug may simply kill all the bacteria that lack this gene, leaving only those that have the resistant gene to reproduce the culture; in other words, the penicillin may simply cause very strong selection pressure against the nonresistant gene, thereby producing a major shift in gene frequencies. Or the drug may both induce the mutation that gives rise to the gene for resistance and kill those cells in which the mutation fails to occur. Many studies have shown that the first alternative is the correct one. The drug

NO SELECTION

FIRST GENERATION

Genotype	AA	Aa	aa
Frequency	0.81	0.18	0.01

Gametes **without** selection

$A = 0.9$ $a = 0.1$

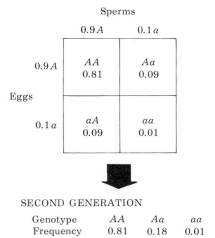

SELECTION

FIRST GENERATION

Genotype	AA	Aa	aa
Frequency	0.81	0.18	0.01

Gametes **after** selection

$A = 0.8$ $a = 0.2$

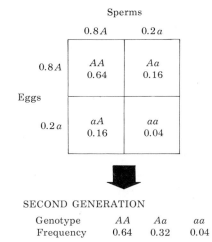

SECOND GENERATION

Genotype	AA	Aa	aa
Frequency	0.81	0.18	0.01

SECOND GENERATION

Genotype	AA	Aa	aa
Frequency	0.64	0.32	0.04

Fig. 17.1. Comparison of genotype frequencies under selection and no selection. Left: When there is no selection, the genotype frequencies in a Hardy-Weinberg population are the same in the second and all later generations as in the first generation. Right: When there is selection, the genotype frequencies change from one generation to the next. In this hypothetical case, discussed in more detail in the text, the frequencies of A and a in the gene pool of the first generation were initially 0.9 and 0.1, but natural selection altered these to 0.8 and 0.2 before reproduction occurred. Consequently the initial genotype frequencies in the second generation are different from the initial ones in the first generation.

does not induce mutations for resistance; it simply selects against nonresistant bacteria. Some genes determining metabolic pathways that confer resistance to penicillin are already present in low frequency in most populations, having arisen earlier as a result of random mutations. If such genes were not already present in a population exposed to penicillin, no cells would survive and the population would be wiped out. This does not mean that new mutations cannot improve the resistance; in fact, continued selection with penicillin usually leads to gradually increased resistance, which is almost certainly due in part to new mutations that enhance resistance and to selective increase in

the frequencies of these new mutant genes. But the mutations are not produced by the same conditions that select for the mutant genes once they arise. That mutations beneficial in an environment containing penicillin should arise when this drug is administered is purely a matter of chance; the same mutations would probably arise in the absence of penicillin.

Evolution of drug resistance in bacteria is not entirely comparable to evolution in biparental organisms, because intense selection can change gene frequencies much more rapidly in haploid asexual organisms than in biparental ones. The recombination that occurs at every generation in a biparental species often re-establishes genotypes eliminated in the previous generation; this does not happen in asexual organisms. Nevertheless, even very small selection pressures can produce major shifts in gene frequencies in biparental populations when the time scale is one in which 50,000 years is a rather brief period. J. B. S. Haldane has shown that if a given dominant allele increases the fitness of the individuals that carry it by one part in 1,000 (e.g. if 1,000 AA or Aa individuals survive to reproduce for every 999 aa individuals that survive to reproduce), then the frequency of the dominant allele could increase from 0.00001 to 0.99 in only 23,400 generations. In other words, a selection pressure of only 0.001 could cause a very rare allele to become very common in only 23,400 generations. "Only" in conjunction with 23,400 generations may sound incongruous, but remember that many plants and animals have at least one generation a year, and that in very few species is the generation time more than 10 years (man being one of the few exceptions). Hence 23,400 generations often means less than 23,400 years and rarely more than 234,000 years. Both of these are relatively short spans of time when measured on the geologic time scale. Even a selection pressure as low as 0.0001 (one part in 10,000) would be a major factor in a breeding population of 5,000 or more individuals on such a time scale.

Changes in Polygenic Characters Caused by Natural Selection. So far, we have discussed situations in which we have posited only two clearly distinct phenotypes determined by two alleles of a single gene. But in reality the vast majority of characters on which natural selection acts are influenced by many different genes, most of which have multiple alleles in the population; the expression of many characters, moreover, is influenced considerably by environmental conditions. Consequently such characters usually show variation with a whole range of values, which often tend to have a frequency distribution that, when graphed, approximates the so-called normal or bell-shaped curve (Fig. 17.2); variation with a skewed distribution also occurs, however. Theoretically, either genetic variation alone or variation in environmental conditions alone could cause phenotypic variation approximating these two types of curves, but in most actual cases both factors are involved.

If the environmental conditions should change, with a consequent shift in the selection pressure, we would expect that as a result of changing gene frequencies the curve of phenotypic variation would shift also. A hypothetical case is illustrated in Fig. 17.3. Graph 17.3A shows the annual rainfall at which the plants in a particular population would grow best (let us assume that the conditions under which a plant will grow best are genetically determined). The actual annual rainfall in the area where this population occurs averages 20 inches, as indicated by arrow 1. The population contains a very few plants (S) that would

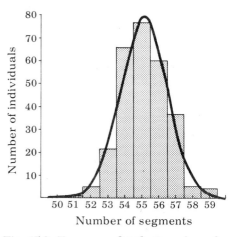

Fig. 17.2. **Frequency distribution of number of segments in a sample of millipeds of the species *Narceus annularis.*** The pattern of variation in segment counts (shown by the vertical bars) approximates, but does not exactly fit, the bell-shaped normal curve of probability.

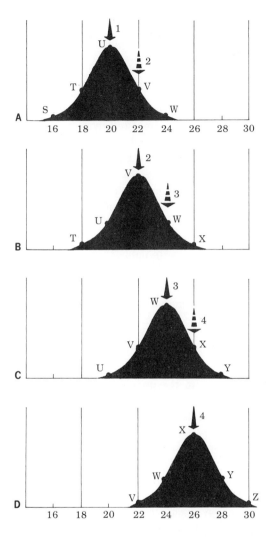

Fig. 17.3. Evolutionary change of a hypothetical plant population in response to changing rainfall. The horizontal axis indicates the annual amount of rainfall at which plants characterized by various genetically determined phenotypes (symbolized by S, T, U, etc.) grow best. The vertical axis indicates frequencies of the phenotypes in the population. The curves show the frequencies of the various phenotypes in the population at different times, under conditions of average annual rainfall indicated by the solid black arrows. (A) shows the frequency distribution of phenotypes during a long period with an annual rainfall averaging about 20 inches. When the annual rainfall slowly increases to 22 inches (broken arrow 2), the frequency distribution of phenotypes slowly shifts to that shown in (B), where it tends to remain as long as the average annual rainfall continues at 22 inches (solid arrow 2). But if rainfall again slowly increases, this time to 24 inches (broken arrow 3), the frequency distribution shifts to position (C). Another increase in rainfall to 26 inches (arrow 4) results in still another shift in the population to condition (D). See text for more complete discussion.

the V-plants (which grow best when the annual rainfall is about 22 inches) will do better, and a higher percentage of them would be expected to survive and reproduce than under the former conditions. Therefore the frequency of V-plants should increase. Similarly, the W-plants (which grow best when the annual rainfall is about 24 inches) will now grow better than formerly, and they too should increase in frequency. Conversely, the T-plants and the U-plants will not grow as well as formerly, and they should decrease in frequency. And the S-plants, only a few of which managed to survive when the annual rainfall was 20 inches, would now be so poorly adapted to the prevalent conditions that none could survive. These changing frequencies, produced by the shift in the selection operating on the population, would give rise to the new curve shown in Fig. 17.3B. If the average annual rainfall continues to increase over a period of years until it reaches 24 inches (arrow 3), the W-plants and X-plants should increase in frequency, the U-plants and V-plants should de-

grow best if the annual rainfall were about 16 inches and a very few (W) that would grow best if the annual rainfall were about 24 inches. Plants that would grow best if the annual rainfall were about 18 inches (T) or 22 inches (V) are fairly common in the population. But by far the most numerous are plants (U) that grow best when the annual rainfall is about 20 inches. Now let us suppose that the average annual rainfall in the area in question slowly increases over a period of years until it is 22 inches (arrow 2) instead of 20 inches. Under these new environmental conditions, crease in frequency, and the T-plants should disappear; these shifts would give rise to the curve shown in Fig. 17.3C. If the average annual rainfall then slowly increases to 26 inches (arrow 4), it should cause further shifts in frequencies, producing the curve shown in Fig. 17.3D. Thus the changing environmental conditions have given rise to selection pressures that have caused the population to evolve. If the population had not been sufficiently variable genetically to have the potential to change when the environment changed, it would have been much reduced or it might even have become extinct.

The Creative Role of Natural Selection. Notice that in our hypothetical plant population the changing selection did not just skew the curve to the right, as might happen when the variation in the gene pool is small. Instead, it caused the extremes as well as the mean (average) of the population to shift to the right. The shift eventually was so great, in fact, that a class of plants (X) not even present in the original population became the largest class. But, you might ask, if X-plants, Y-plants, and Z-plants were not present initially, how did they arise in the descendent populations? One possibility is that, purely by chance, new mutant genes arose that made their possessors grow better in wetter habitats; such mutant genes would have been strongly selected for and would rapidly have spread through the population. But if moisture preference is influenced by many different genes, as is highly likely, new classes such as X, Y, and Z could arise without the necessity of any new mutations, simply through the separate increase in frequency of many different genes, which would then be more likely to occur together and produce a new phenotype. Haldane has calculated how long it would take for a new phenotype to be created in this way. He has shown that if each of 15 independent genes is present in one percent of the individuals of a population, then all 15 genes will occur together in only one of 10^{30} individuals. But there has never been a population of higher organisms containing anywhere near 10^{30} individuals (in fact, individual higher plants have never totaled 10^{30} at any time during the history of life on earth). Hence the chances that all 15 genes would occur together in even one individual in a real population are exceedingly small, and the chances that all 15 would occur together in any appreciable number of individuals are infinitely small. In other words, we can be certain that the phenotype produced by the combined action of all 15 genes does not exist in the population. But, according to Haldane, if there is moderate natural selection for each of the 15 genes, it would take only about 10,000 years for each gene to increase from a frequency of one percent to a frequency of 99 percent. Once each gene is present in 99 percent of the population, 86 percent of the individuals in it will have all 15 genes and hence will show the phenotype that was peviously nonexistent in the population. Thus selection, even in the absence of new mutation, can produce new phenotypes by combining genes in new ways.

An actual illustration of the sort of change outlined in the hypothetical example above is provided by a long-term selection experiment performed on corn by agronomists at the University of Illinois. These agronomists selected for high oil content of the corn kernels; the selection was continued for 50 generations. There was a steady increase in oil content throughout most of this period (Fig. 17.4). The kernels of the original stock of corn plants averaged about 5 percent oil; those of the plants in the fiftieth generation after selection averaged about 15 percent (higher than any individuals in the first generation), and there was no indication that a maximum had been reached. That this steady change over the course of 50 generations must have been due to the formation of new gene combinations as a result of selection rather than to the occurrence of a series of new mutations can be seen

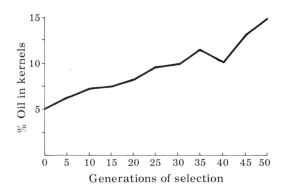

Fig. 17.4. Results of 50 generations of selection for high oil content in corn kernels. [Modified from *Biological Science*, Harcourt, Brace & World, 1963. Used by permission of the Biological Sciences Curriculum Study.]

from a few simple calculations. The agronomists raised between 200 and 300 corn plants in each generation. Multiplying by 50, we find that the total number of plants raised in the experiment was between 10,000 and 15,-000. But the usual rate of mutation per gene in corn is as low as one in 50,000 plants or lower. Hence it is unlikely that even one mutation contributing to an increase in oil content occurred during the experiment, and it is certain that there was no series of such mutations. Therefore the gradual increase in oil content during the 50 generations of selection must have been due to the formation of new gene combinations, not to mutations.

The new gene combinations produced by selection often have the result of changing formerly recessive alleles into dominant ones. It is important to remember that an allele is not automatically either dominant or recessive; it is the genetic background against which it must function (i.e. the other genes present in the same individual) that determines its activity. When that background changes through shifting gene frequencies, the enzyme-making activity of the individual allele may also change, because every gene influences the activity of every other gene to some extent. We saw earlier that most new mutant alleles are

recessive, and that they may be carried in low frequency in the population indefinitely without being expressed phenotypically. When, generations later, selection alters the genetic background in such a manner that the allele becomes dominant (i.e. becomes more active), the phenotype it produces (which is new to the population, even though the gene is not) provides new variation as raw material upon which selection may act. Thus the evolution of dominance as a result of selection is in a very real sense a creative process.

To summarize: In biparental populations, selection (whether natural or artificial) determines the direction of change largely by altering the frequencies of genes that arose through random mutation many generations before, thus establishing new gene combinations and gene activities that produce new phenotypes. Mutation is not usually a major directing force in evolution; the principal evolutionary role of new mutations (and new gene combinations) consists in replenishing the store of variability in the gene pool and thereby providing the potential upon which future selection can act.

The Conservative Role of Natural Selection. So far, we have emphasized the creative role of natural selection in leading to new gene combinations and in giving direction to evolution. But natural selection plays an extremely important conservative role also. Each species of organism, in the course of its evolution, comes to have a constellation of genes that interact in very precise ways in governing the developmental, physiological, and biochemical processes upon which the continued existence of the species depends. Anything that disrupts the harmonious interaction of its genes is usually deleterious to the species. But in a sexually reproducing population, favorable groupings of genes tend to be dispersed and new groupings formed by the recombination that occurs when each generation reproduces. Most of these new groupings will be less adaptive than the original grouping (although a few may be more adaptive). And the vast majority of new mutations tend to disrupt rather than enhance the established harmonious relationships among the genes. If unchecked, recombination and random mutation would therefore tend to destroy the favorable gene groupings upon which the fitness of the species rests. Selection, by constantly acting to eliminate all but the most favorable gene combinations, counteracts the disrupting, disintegrating tendency of recombination and mutation and is thus the chief factor maintaining stability where otherwise there would be chaos.

Effective Selection Pressure as the Algebraic Sum of Numerous Separate Selection Pressures.   Until now, we have treated the selection pressure acting on a gene as though it were a simple, unitary factor. But, in fact, most genes are subject to many separate selection pressures, some of them conflicting. Most and perhaps all genes have many different effects (pleiotropy), and it is most unlikely that all effects of any given gene will be advantageous. Whether a gene increases or decreases in frequency is determined by whether the sum of the various positive selection pressures produced by its advantageous effects is greater or smaller than the sum of the negative selection pressures produced by its harmful effects. If the algebraic sum (an addition taking into account plus and minus signs) of all the separate selection pressures is positive, the gene will increase in frequency, but if the algebraic sum is negative, the gene will decrease in frequency.

Many cases are known in which the effects of a given gene are more advantageous in the heterozygous than in the homozygous condition. We mentioned in an earlier chapter that in African Negroes the gene for sickle-cell anemia occurs much more frequently than we might expect in view of its highly deleterious effect when homozygous. This is because the gene, when heterozygous, confers on the possessor a partial resistance to malaria. The equi-

librium frequency of the sickle-cell gene is thus determined by at least three separate selection pressures: the strongly negative selection pressure on the homozygotes, the weaker negative selection pressure on the heterozygotes as a result of their mild anemia, and the fairly strong positive selection pressure on the heterozygotes as a result of their resistance to malaria. This explanation is doubtless a gross oversimplification, because the gene almost certainly has other effects, each of which must produce some differential in reproduction.

Situations in which heterozygotes are favored over homozygotes are frequent in natural populations. In many cases, such heterozygote superiority (often called heterosis or overdominance) causes balanced polymorphic variation. *Polymorphism* is the occurrence in a population of two or more fairly sharply distinct forms of a genetically determined character (Fig. 17.5). For example, human populations are polymorphic with regard to blood groups; the same population usually includes type-A, type-B, type-AB, and type-O individuals. Several species of snails occur in banded

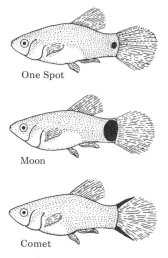

Fig. 17.5. Polymorphism in the fish *Xiphophorus maculatus*. Notice the differences in the black spots at the base of the tail. [Redrawn from M. Gordon, *Advances in Genet.*, vol. 1, 1947.]

and unbanded forms. The red fox occurs in both red and silver color forms. The adults of some species of herons occur in both pigmented and white forms. Several species of butterflies occur in two or more quite distinct patterns. In general, though by no means always, polymorphic characters are determined by only a few genes, whereas characters that show more continuous variation are determined by a large number of genes. Heterozygote superiority favors polymorphism because it results in the retention in the population of both alleles at frequencies higher than one would predict on the basis of the selection acting on the homozygous phenotypes. Thus, if Aa individuals are adaptively superior to both AA and aa individuals, both allele A and allele a will be retained in fairly high frequency in the population; neither allele will be eliminated, as would tend to happen if one of the homozygotes were superior. Therefore all three possible genotypes—AA, Aa, and aa— will occur frequently in each generation, and if each of these produces a noticeably different phenotype the population will be polymorphic.

Polymorphism itself is advantageous in many cases. For example, if a polymorphic species lives in an environment that is subdivided into many local areas where slightly different conditions prevail, one of the forms may do better in one area and another may do better in another area; the polymorphism thus enables the species to exploit more completely the subdivisions of its variable environment. Sometimes one form of a polymorphic species is adaptively superior at one time of year, and another form is adaptively superior at another time of year (Fig. 17.6); its polymorphism gives the species better overall survival throughout the year than it would have if all of its individuals were of one form.

Effective selection pressure is determined by many separate selection pressures, whether the character is a simple one controlled by only one or a few genes or whether it is a complex one controlled by many different genes. As an

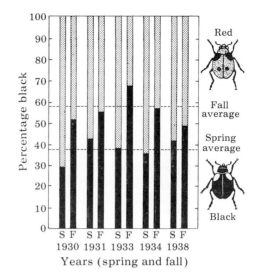

Fig. 17.6. Polymorphism in the ladybird beetle *Adalia bipunctata.* The frequency of the black morphs (black bars) averages much higher in the fall than in the spring; conversely, the red morphs (stippled bars) are much more frequent in the spring than in the fall. Apparently the black morphs are better adapted for life in the summer, and the red morphs are better adapted for life in the winter. [Modified from B. Wallace and A. M. Srb, *Adaptation,* Prentice-Hall, 1964, after Timoféeff-Ressovsky.]

example of the determination of a complex character, let us consider the selection pressures on plumage in dabbling ducks. Many closely related species of dabbling ducks (Mallard, Pintail, Gadwall, etc.) occur together in most of North America. Hybridization takes place among them because the females sometimes err in their selection of mates.[3] Since the hybrids are apparently less viable than the parents, there has been strong selection for showy male plumage, distinctive for each species, that helps reduce the number of mating errors. No such selection pressure has operated on the females. These brownish nondescript

---

[3] In most species of birds, including the ducks, it is the female that chooses the mate. The male displays until some female chooses him. Hence it is more important that the female be able to recognize the males of her own species than that the male be able to recognize the females.

birds closely resemble one another and are probably much less easily seen by predators than the males, whose bright plumage doubtless makes them more subject to predation—a liability that must cause strong selection against such plumage. But the positive selection resulting from reduced mating errors is apparently greater than the negative selection resulting from predation, and the showy plumage of the males has been maintained and even enriched. The situation is different, however, on some isolated islands where only one species of dabbling duck exists and where, therefore, no mating errors can occur. Here the negative selection predominates, and the males have lost their showy plumage and resemble the more protectively colored females.

ADAPTATION

Every organism, in a sense, is a complex bundle of immense numbers of adaptations. We have already examined a host of adaptations in the earlier chapters of this book, adaptations concerned with nutrient procurement, gas exchange, internal transport, regulation of body fluids, hormonal and nervous control, effector activity, reproduction, development, etc. We should pause here to say more explicitly what we mean by adaptation and to evaluate the idea behind the word.

An adaptation is any genetically controlled characteristic that aids an individual organism, or the species to which it belongs, to survive and reproduce in the environment it inhabits. Adaptations may be structural, physiological, or behavioral. They may be genetically simple, controlled by only one or a few genes, or they may be genetically complex, controlled by large numbers of genes. They may involve individual cells or subcellular components, or they may involve whole organs or organ systems. They may be highly specific, of benefit only under very limited circumstances, or they may be general, of benefit under many and varied circumstances.

Let us look now at a few particularly striking examples of adaptation, which will help clarify the processes by which adaptations come into being.

Growth Habit in Pasture Plants. A good example of the rapidity with which a population may become adapted to changed environmental conditions is provided by a study published in 1937 by W. B. Kemp of the Maryland Agricultural Experiment Station. The owner of a pasture in southern Maryland had seeded the pasture with a mixture of grasses and legumes. Then he divided the pasture into two parts; one was heavily grazed by cattle, while the other was protected from the livestock and left to produce hay. Three years after this division, Kemp obtained specimens of blue grass, orchard grass, and white clover from each part of the pasture and planted them in an experimental garden where all the plants were exposed to the same environmental conditions. He found that the specimens of all three species from the heavily grazed half of the pasture exhibited dwarf, rambling growth, while specimens of the same three species from the ungrazed half exhibited vigorous, upright growth. In only three years' time, the two populations of each species, known to have been identical initially because one batch of seed was used for the entire pasture, had become markedly different in their genetically determined growth pattern. Apparently the grazing cattle in the one half of the pasture had devoured most of the upright plants, and only plants low enough to be missed had survived and set seed. There had been, in short, intense selection against upright growth in this half of the pasture and correspondingly intense selection for the adaptively superior dwarf, rambling growth. By contrast, in the other half of the pasture, where there was no grazing, upright growth was adaptively superior, and dwarf plants would have been unable to compete effectively.

Adaptations of Flowers for Pollination. The flowering plants depend upon external agents to carry pollen from the male parts in the flowers of one plant to the female parts in the flowers of another plant. The flowers of each species are adapted in shape, structure, color, and odor to the particular pollinating agents upon which they depend, and they provide a particularly clear illustration of the adaptiveness of evolution. In the following examples, note the close correlation between the pollinators and the species they pollinate.

Bees are attracted by bright colors and by sweet, aromatic, or minty odors; they are active only during the day, and they usually alight on a petal before moving into the part of the flower containing the nectar and pollen. Bee flowers have showy, brightly colored petals that are usually blue or yellow but seldom red (bees can see blue or yellow light well, but they cannot see red at all); they usually have a sweet, aromatic, or minty fragrance; they are generally open only during the day; and they often have a special protruding lip upon which the bees can land. Hummingbirds, on the other hand, can see red well but blue only poorly; they have a very poor sense of smell; and they ordinarily do not land on flowers but hover in front of them while sucking the nectar. Flowers pollinated primarily by hummingbirds are usually red or yellow, are nearly odorless, and lack any protruding landing platform. In contrast to both bees and hummingbirds, moths are most active at dusk and during the night, and the flowers they pollinate are mostly white and are open only during the late afternoon and night. These flowers often have a very heavy fragrance that helps guide the moths to them. The bases of the petals of flowers pollinated by bees, birds, or moths are often fused to form a tube whose length corresponds closely to the length of the tongue or bill of the particular species most important as the pollinator of that plant (Fig. 17.7).

Unlike bees, hummingbirds, and moths, the short-tongued flies (which feed primarily on carrion, dung, humus, sap, and blood) are attracted by rank odors rather than by sweet ones, and they rely very little on vision in lo-

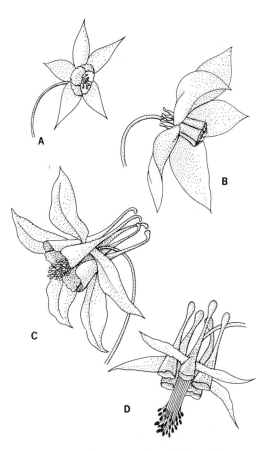

Fig. 17.7. Characters of columbine flowers correlated with their pollinators. (A) *Aquilegia ecalcarata*, pollinated by bees. (B) *A. nivalis*, pollinated by long-tongued bees. (C) *A. vulgaris*, pollinated by long-tongued bumblebees. (D) *A. formosa*, pollinated by hummingbirds. The length and curvature of the nectar tubes of the flowers are correlated with the length and curvature of the bees' tongues and the hummingbirds' bills. [Adapted from V. Grant, "The Fertilization of Flowers," *Sci. Am.*, June, 1951. Copyright © 1951 by Scientific American, Inc. All rights reserved.]

cating food. The flowers of plants that depend on these flies for pollination are usually dull-colored and very ill-smelling. These flowers are sometimes shaped in such a way that they temporarily entrap the flies that enter them; thus they ensure that the flies become covered with pollen before they escape and fly to another flower. Trapping mechanisms are also common in flowers pollinated by beetles.

A particularly dramatic example of adaptation for pollination is seen in some species of orchids, where the flowers resemble in both shape and color the females of certain species of wasps or bees. The male wasp or bee is stimulated to attempt to copulate with the flower and becomes covered with pollen in the process. When he later attempts to copulate with another flower, some of the pollen from the first flower is deposited on the second flower. So complete is the deception that sperms have actually been found inside the orchid flowers after a visit by the male insect.

Flowers that are pollinated by wind rather than by animals characteristically lack bright colors, special odors, and nectar. In fact, most of them have no petals, and their sexual parts are freely exposed to the air currents. The pollen grains produced by these flowers are particularly small and light, and it is not unusual for them to be blown hundreds of miles.

We see, then, that the characteristics of flowers are not simply pleasant curiosities of nature that serve no practical function. They are important adaptations evolved in response to fundamental selection pressures. Our aesthetic enjoyment should not blind us to the essential role they play in the survival of the plant species.

Defensive Secretions of Arthropods. Many arthropods possess glands whose secretions act as repellents against predators. In some species, the secretions are merely released as a liquid ooze when the animal is disturbed, while in others the secretion is forcibly expelled as a spray that may be aimed very precisely toward the source of the disturbance. The secretions are usually odorous and irritating, particularly if they hit a sensitive part of the predator, such as the mouth, nose, or eyes. For example, the carabid beetle *Calosoma prominens* sprays a compound called salicylaldehyde from the tip of its abdomen, and it can aim the jet of spray

precisely enough to hit a single ant attacking one of its legs. Ants hit by the spray are instantly repelled. The spray is also effective against vertebrate predators such as Blue Jays and grasshopper mice, but relatively ineffective against toads.

A particularly instructive example is the secretion of a mixture of acetic acid (vinegar) and caprylic acid by the whipscorpion *Mastigoproctus giganteus*, which has been studied in detail by Thomas Eisner and his co-workers at Cornell University. The secretion is sprayed from two slitlike openings located on a knob at the end of the abdomen (Fig. 17.8). The animal can aim the spray very accurately in almost all directions. If a whipscorpion is tethered and one of its front legs is pinched with a pair of forceps, the postabdominal knob is rotated in such a way that a jet of spray is directed at the pinched leg (Fig. 17.9). If a rear leg is pinched next, a second jet of spray is discharged in that direction. Eisner has tested the effectiveness of the whipscorpion's secretion in repelling a variety of predators. When an ant grasps an appendage of a whipscorpion, it is instantly sprayed and promptly flees, stopping at intervals to drag its body and mouthparts against the substrate in what appears to be a cleansing activity. Other arthropod predators are similarly repelled. These predators do not, however, seem to learn to avoid whipscorpions and will attack again after having recovered from a previous spraying, only to be again repelled. Many vertebrate predators, by contrast, learn to avoid whipscorpions after one or two encounters. Eisner and his collaborators describe the experience of two jays with a whipscorpion as follows:

When the bird finally attacked, it did so by approaching the whipscorpion slowly, with the head lowered, gently grasping one of its legs with the bill. The response was immediate and spectacular. Obviously hit by a directed spray, the bird jumped back and hopped around aimlessly, shaking its head intermittently and with such vigour that it occasionally lost its footing

Fig. 17.8. A whipscorpion. Defensive secretions are sprayed from two slitlike openings in the knob at the end of the abdomen. The long "whip" arises from this knob. The stout pincerlike appendages are called pedipalps. [Courtesy Thomas Eisner, Cornell University.]

Fig. 17.9. Aiming of defensive spray by a whipscorpion. A whipscorpion is tethered on the end of a metal rod. Top: The left front leg is pinched with forceps. The animal bends the abdominal knob forward and accurately directs spray toward the point of attack. The droplets of spray produce a change of color in the special indicator paper on which the animal is standing, so that one can see where they hit. Middle: Next, the right rear leg is pinched, and spray is accurately aimed at the new point of attack. Bottom: The animal's "pincers" (pedipalps) are pinched, and again a jet of spray is accurately aimed. [Courtesy Thomas Eisner, Cornell University.]

and fell awkwardly to the side. After a few seconds it returned to the perch, but continued to show occasional head-shaking and very pronounced intermittent ruffling of plumage. The nictitating membrane was seen to be drawn back and forth over the surface of each eye in a very rapid and at first almost continuous wiping motion that lasted for several minutes. During the next hour the whipscorpions were left in the cages, but neither of the two birds made additional attacks, nor did they come down from their perch when their customary insect food was offered. . . . Only after the whipscorpions were removed could they be enticed to eat.[4]

It must be emphasized that spraying arthropods are sometimes injured or even killed by a predator before the predator is repelled. For example, when Eisner put two whipscorpions into a cage with full-grown lizards, the lizards quickly seized them; though the spray soon induced the lizards to drop the whipscorpions, this did not happen soon enough to prevent one whipscorpion from receiving a cut in the side and the other from being fatally crushed. Such events, however, do not indicate that the defensive secretion is an adaptive failure, since vertebrates such as lizards may learn from one or two unpleasant experiences of this sort and subsequently avoid this type of prey on sight alone. It must be remembered that it is populations that evolve, and if a few individuals in a population are killed while predators are learning that its members are unpleasant, the character that makes them unpleasant may still be very strongly adaptive; it ensures that far fewer members of the population will fall victim to predators than would otherwise be the case. A defensive mechanism need not be one hundred percent effective to confer a significant advantage on the species.

[4] From T. Eisner *et al.,* "Defense Mechanisms of Arthropods: I. The Composition and Function of the Spray of the Whipscorpion, *Mastigoproctus giganteus* (Lucas) (Arachnida, Pedipalpida)," *Journal of Insect Physiology,* vol. 6, 1961, pp. 272–298.

Cryptic Coloration in Animals. The fact that many animals blend into their surroundings so well as to be nearly undetectable has been recognized for many years, and recent careful studies have confirmed that, as had been assumed, cryptic coloration (Fig. 17.10) is an adaptive characteristic that helps animals escape predation. One such study was conducted by F. B. Sumner of the Scripps Institution of Oceanography in California. Sumner investigated predation by Galápagos penguins upon mosquito fish (*Gambusia partuelis*), which can contract or expand their pigment cells to become lighter or darker, depending upon their background. He established that the penguins caught 70 percent of the fish that contrasted with their background but only 34 percent of the fish that resembled their background. Sumner also exposed mosquito fish to large sunfish and found that the sunfish captured 53 percent of the contrastingly colored prey but only 25 percent of the cryptically colored prey. In a similar experiment, F. B. Isely of Trinity University in San Antonio, Texas, studied predation by chickens, turkeys, and native birds on grasshoppers of various colors on differently colored backgrounds. He found that 88 percent of the nonprotected grasshoppers were eaten whereas only 40 percent of the cryptically colored ones were eaten.

One of the most extensively studied cases of cryptic coloration is the so-called industrial melanism of moths. Since the mid-1800's, many species of moths have become decidedly darker in industrial regions. This is actually a case of polymorphism where the less frequent of two forms has become the more frequent, and vice versa; the originally predominant light form in certain species of moths has given way, in industrial areas, to the dark (melanic) form. For example, the first black specimens of the species *Biston betularia* were caught around Manchester, England, in 1848; by 1895 melanics constituted about 98 percent of the total population in the area. It has been calculated that for such a remarkable shift in frequency to

Fig. 17.10. Cryptic coloration of pocket mice inhabiting adjoining areas in New Mexico. Top: *Perognathus intermedius ater* on black lava. Bottom: *Perognathus apachi gypsi* on white gypsum sand. [From paintings by Allan Brooks, from S. B. Benson, 1933, courtesy Museum of Vertebrate Zoology, University of California, Berkeley.]

have occurred in so short a time the melanic form must have had at least a 30 percent advantage over the light form, which is a selection pressure much higher than any we have assumed in our theoretical discussion thus far.

In 1937 E. B. Ford of Oxford University proposed the following explanation for this striking evolutionary change. The species of moths exhibiting the rapid shift to melanism, though unrelated to one another, all habitually rest during the day in an exposed position on tree trunks or rocks, being protected from predation only by their close resemblance to their background. In former years, the tree trunks and rocks were rather light-colored and often covered with light-colored lichens. Against this background, the light forms of the moths were astonishingly difficult to see, whereas the melanic forms were quite conspicuous (Fig. 17.11). It would be expected, therefore, that predators such as birds would have captured melanics far more easily than the cryptically colored light moths. The light forms would thus have been strongly favored, and they would have occurred in much higher frequency than melanics. But with the advent of extensive industrialization, tree trunks and rocks were blackened by soot, and the lichens, which are particularly sensitive to such pollution, disappeared. In this altered environment, the melanic moths would have resembled the background more closely than the light moths. Thus selection would have been reversed and would now have favored the melanics, which would consequently have increased in frequency.

You will note that Ford's hypothesis stresses the role of differential predation by birds on the two color forms of the moths. But this idea ran into opposition from both entomologists (students of insects) and ornithologists (students of birds). Both groups agreed that birds capture very few resting moths and exhibit no selectivity as to the color of the few they do capture. Hence they argued that Ford's hypothesis could not be correct. But despite their unanimity, Ford's critics could present no re-

liable data to support their views; they were arguing on the basis of casual uncontrolled observations, though admittedly these had been made by many people over a period of many years. Finally, in the mid-1950's, H. B. Kettlewell of Oxford decided to perform a series of carefully planned field experiments designed to settle the matter one way or the other. He released approximately equal numbers of the light and melanic forms of *Biston betularia* onto trees in a rural area in the county of Dorset, England, where the tree trunks were light-colored, lichens were abundant, leaf washings revealed very little pollution, and the wild population of the moth was about 94.6 percent light-colored. A direct watch on the resting moths was maintained, with the help of binoculars, from blinds where the observer could not be seen by potential bird predators. It was found that several species of insectivorous birds do prey by sight on the moths and that, of 190 moths observed to be captured by birds, 164 were melanics and only 26 were light forms. Furthermore, of approximately 500 marked individuals of each color form released in another experiment, roughly twice as many light moths as melanic moths were recaptured in traps set up in the Dorset woods, an indication that more of the light moths had survived. It was plain that predation was an important selective factor among the moths, and that melanics were more subject to predation under the conditions prevailing in the Dorset woods than were light-colored moths.

Taken alone, however, these experiments did not prove conclusively that the factor favoring the light moths over the melanics was their resemblance to their background. The results could be explained by assuming, for example, that the melanics were preferred by the birds because of some difference in flavor. Therefore Kettlewell duplicated the experiments under the reverse environmental conditions—in woods near Birmingham, England, where the tree trunks were blackened with soot, lichens were absent, leaf washings revealed heavy pollu-

Fig. 17.11. Cryptic coloration of peppered moths. Left: Light and dark morphs of *Biston betularia* at rest on a lichen-covered tree trunk in unpolluted countryside. The light moth is very difficult to see (it is slightly below and to the right of the dark moth). Right: Light and dark morphs on a soot-covered tree trunk near Birmingham, England. Here the light form is the easier to see. [From the experiments of Dr. H. B. D. Kettlewell, Oxford University.]

tion, and the wild population of the moth was about 85 percent melanic. The results of these experiments were the reverse of those in the Dorset experiments; birds were observed to capture nearly three times as many light moths as melanics, and roughly twice as many melanics were recaptured in traps. Here also predation was an important selective factor, but here it was the melanics that had the adaptive advantage. These experiments by Kettlewell prove that birds do hunt by sight, and that those moths that most closely resemble the background on which they rest have much the best chance of escaping predation.

Warning Coloration and Mimicry in Animals. Whereas some animals have evolved cryptic coloration, others (particularly insects)

have evolved colors and patterns that contrast boldly with their background and thus render them clearly visible to potential predators. Many of these animals are in some way disagreeable to predators; they may taste bad, or they may smell bad, or they may sting or secrete poisonous substances. In other words, they are animals that a predator will usually reject after one or two unpleasant encounters with them. Such animals benefit by being gaudily colored and conspicuous because predators that have experienced their unpleasant features learn to recognize and avoid them more easily in the future. Their flashy appearance is protective because it warns potential predators that they should stay away. In fact, the warning is sometimes so effective that, after unpleasant experiences with one or two warn-

ingly colored insects, some vertebrate predators simply avoid all flashily colored insects,
whether or not they resemble the ones they encountered earlier. G. D. H. Carpenter demonstrated this by offering over 200 different species of insects to an insectivorous monkey. The
monkey accepted 83 percent of the cryptically colored insects but only 16 percent of
the warningly colored ones, even though many
of the insects belonged to species the monkey
had probably not previously encountered.

Species not naturally protected by some unpleasant character of their own often closely
resemble (mimic) in appearance and behavior
some warningly colored unpalatable species.
Such a resemblance is adaptive; the mimic
species suffers little predation because predators cannot distinguish it from its unpleasant
models. This phenomenon is called *Batesian
mimicry.* Convincing evidence for the effectiveness of this type of mimicry in protecting the
mimic species comes from the elegant experiments of Jane van Z. Brower now of Amherst
College. In one experiment, she fed specimens
of a butterfly species called the Viceroy
(*Limenitis archippus*) to a group of caged jays,
which accepted the Viceroys readily. Then she
offered the jays specimens of a distasteful
butterfly called the Monarch (*Danaus plex-
ippus*), which the Viceroy mimics (Fig. 17.12).
After a few trials, the jays refused to eat the
Monarchs. When they were again offered
Viceroys, the jays now also refused to eat these,
even though they had earlier eaten them readily. A few unpleasant encounters with the
Monarchs had caused the jays to reject their
mimics, the Viceroys.

In another series of experiments, Brower
produced an artificial model-mimic system as
follows: She used starlings as the predators and
mealworms, which starlings ordinarily eat vor-
aciously, as prey. She put a band of green paint
on some of the mealworms and a band of
orange paint on the others. Some of the green-
banded worms were dipped into a solution of
a chemical that is very distasteful to starlings;

Fig. 17.12. An example of Batesian mimicry.
Top: The Monarch butterfly, a distasteful
species. Bottom: The Viceroy, a species that
mimics the Monarch. Species in the group to
which the Viceroy belongs ordinarily have a
quite different appearance.

these worms were used as the "models." The
rest of the green-banded worms were dipped
only into distilled water and therefore remained palatable; these worms were the
"mimics." None of the orange-banded worms
were made distasteful. Green was chosen as
the "warning color" for the distasteful worms
because in nature this color is usually associated with cryptically colored rather than with
warningly colored species and the birds would
therefore have been unlikely to have associated an unpleasant experience with it previously. It was demonstrated that the paint itself
was not distasteful to the birds. Each starling
was given 10 trials per day for about 16 days,
each trial consisting of two mealworms—one
orange-banded and one green-banded. Of the
green-banded worms, different groups of birds
received a different proportion of "mimics"
(palatable) to "models" (unpalatable because

of having been dipped into the distasteful chemical)—variously 10, 30, 60, and 90 percent—for the 16 days of the experiment. After a few unpleasant encounters with the "models," the birds learned to recognize and avoid them, with the result that the green-banded "mimics" also escaped predation, particularly when the percentage of "mimics" presented to the starlings was 60 percent or less. Even when the percentage of "mimics" was as high as 90 percent and the percentage of "models" only 10 percent, 17 percent of the "mimics" escaped predation. With one exception, all the starlings readily ate the orange-banded worms throughout the experiments, a demonstration that the birds had not simply learned to avoid all mealworms and that their avoidance of the palatable green-banded ones ("mimics") was due to the resemblance of these worms to the unpalatable green-banded ones (the "models").

Brower's original experimental proof of the adaptiveness of mimicry, published in 1960, has provided a vigorous new quantitative approach to this intriguing subject. And her experiments have made it necessary to revise some long-held ideas about mimicry. For example, it was generally believed that for Batesian mimicry to be effective the model species must be more common than the mimic species, i.e. that in any given trial a predator must be more likely to get an unpalatable than a palatable mouthful. Otherwise, it was thought, the predator would not readily learn to associate the appearance of the prey with an unpleasant rather than a pleasant experience. But Brower's experiments showed that, if the model is distasteful enough, mimicry is still very effective when the ratio of mimics to models is as high as 60 to 40 and that mimics benefit to some degree even when the ratio is 90 to 10. In other words, the proportion of mimics to models does not have a set maximum value beyond which the effectiveness of the mimicry starts breaking down; this value differs for different cases of mimicry and depends upon how distasteful the model is, how tasty the mimic is,

and how many alternative sources of food are available to the predators. That just a few unpleasant specimens among many outwardly similar pleasant ones should be able to discredit the whole lot is understandable enough; if in a particular bag of candy, all pieces of which looked alike, one out of ten pieces had an extremely unpleasant taste, we should probably quickly learn to avoid taking any candy from that bag on the principle that the risk of so disagreeable an experience is not worth taking.

We have so far discussed only Batesian mimicry—mimicry of a distasteful species by one not distasteful, i.e. mimicry based on deception. A second kind of mimicry, called **Müllerian mimicry,** involves the evolution of a similar appearance by two or more distasteful species. In this type of mimicry, each species is both model and mimic. Each species has some defensive mechanism, but if each had its own characteristic appearance, the predators would have to learn to avoid each species separately; the learning process would thus be a more demanding one, and some individuals of each species would have to be sacrificed to the learning process. If, however, several protected species evolve more and more toward one appearance type, they come to constitute a single prey group from the standpoint of the predators and avoidance is more easily learned.

The Possibility of Nonadaptive Characters. Some critics have claimed that many characters present in high frequencies in populations are nonadaptive. In some cases, these claims have been based on failure to consider all relevant factors. For example, one critic of the idea that cryptic coloration is protective counted the cryptically colored and noncryptically colored insects in the crops and stomachs of insectivorous birds. He found that large numbers of both types of insects had been eaten and concluded, on the basis of this evidence, that the coloration of cryptically colored insects does not protect them and must be nonadaptive, i.e. that it is not favored by natural selection. This worker, however, had failed to obtain data on the relative abundance of the two types of insects before they were caught. Only by comparison with such data could the stomach counts be reliably evaluated. For example, if it were found that there were five cryptically colored insects for every two noncryptically colored ones in the area of the study, and if the birds' stomachs contained three cryptically colored ones for every two noncryptically colored ones, then we would conclude that the cryptically colored insects had, in fact, been protected, because in proportion to their original numbers fewer of them had been caught. As we have repeatedly emphasized, an adaptation need not be, and in reality never is, one hundred percent effective.

Other critics have insisted that, even though a well-developed character such as precise mimicry or functional wings or warm-bloodedness or the mammalian middle-ear structure may be adaptive, incomplete stages leading to them cannot be adaptive. In other words, according to these critics, either such characters must arise all at once as major evolutionary jumps or, if they evolve gradually by the accumulation of many small changes, then the process of accumulation must be directed by some force other than natural selection. The fossil record, laboratory experiments, and careful field studies all reveal that major evolutionary changes seldom arise all at once, that the usual pattern is one of gradual accumulation of many small changes as gene frequencies and combinations shift over the generations. Mutations with large phenotypic effects, which would be necessary to produce major changes in one big jump, are practically always lethal or at least detrimental to survival, because they constitute such a great disturbance to the delicately balanced genetic systems in which they arise. The question therefore becomes: Are the numerous tiny changes that produce the early stages of a major new character adaptive, or is

their increase in frequency in the population caused by some directing force other than natural selection? The answer seems to be that even the incipient stages are adaptive. For example, even a very slight resemblance to a distasteful species may improve the chances for survival of an unprotected species enough for that slight resemblance, and any further changes that enhance it, to increase in frequency. Or even the faintest resemblance of an orchid flower to a female wasp may increase the chances of pollination enough for that resemblance to increase in frequency. The point to remember is that an adaptive value so slight as to be undetectable by us may yet be great enough to result in evolutionary change, given the time scale on which evolution occurs.

You will recall our earlier discussion of Haldane's calculations that a positive selection pressure of only 0.001 could increase the frequency of a dominant allele from 0.00001 to 0.99 in only 23,400 generations, and that even a selection pressure as low as 0.0001 could be a major factor toward producing evolutionary change in a reasonably large population. But if a character that increased fitness by one part in 1,000 affected viability, we would need an experimental population of at least 16 million to detect it, even using our best statiscal tests. For all practical purposes, such a large experimental population, particularly of higher organisms, is an impossible requirement. Therefore we must conclude that the mere fact that we cannot see the adaptive significance of a character does not entitle us to state categorically that it has none. Statements that a particular minor character of some organism is "obviously nonadaptive" still appear much too frequently in the biological literature. No character is "obviously" nonadaptive. This does not mean that there is no such thing as a nonadaptive character; it simply means that we can never be sure of the nonadaptiveness of any specific character.

But if we admit the theoretical possibility of

nonadaptive characters (i.e. characters that are selectively nearly neutral), we must ask how they could increase in frequency and become characteristic of a population.[5] (We may exclude from this discussion once-adaptive vestigial organs that have simply not yet been completely eliminated by negative selection.) One possibility is, of course, that nonadaptive characters may increase in frequency purely by chance (genetic drift); we saw earlier, however, that major evolutionary changes would be unlikely to occur by chance alone in any except very small populations. A second possibility, and a far more likely one, is that the nonadaptive character is determined by the same gene (or group of genes) that determines some other character that is definitely adaptive. In other words, the nonadaptive character is an incidental effect of a pleiotropic gene. If the gene increases in frequency because one of its phenotypic effects is strongly favored by natural selection, then the other phenotypic characters determined by it will, of necessity, also increase in frequency, and some of these other characters may be nonadaptive. In fact, it is even possible for decidedly deleterious characters to increase in frequency as a result of pleiotropy, as we saw earlier in our discussion of effective selection pressure (sickle-cell anemia, for example, has increased because the same gene in the heterozygote determines an advantageous resistance to malaria). However, as pleiotropic genes[6] increase in frequency, there is often an accompanying change in the genetic background, caused by natural selection, that tends to make the beneficial effects of the gene dominant and its deleterious effects recessive.

[5] Actually, it is highly improbable that any character can be entirely neutral against all the genetic backgrounds in a population and under all the varied environmental conditions to which any population is exposed. Hence all we mean by nonadaptive is "very slightly advantageous" or "very slightly disadvantageous."

[6] Actually, all genes are probably pleiotropic.

SPECIES AND SPECIATION

We have so far discussed only one major aspect of evolution, the gradual change of a given population through time. Now we must turn to another of its major aspects, the processes whereby a single population may split, giving rise to two or more different descendent populations. But before we can discuss this topic meaningfully, we must pause to examine more carefully the populations we have so casually mentioned heretofore. For our purposes, we may define a population of sexually reproducing organisms as a group of individuals that share a common gene pool (i.e. that interbreed to a larger or smaller extent).

Units of Population

Demes. A deme is a small local population, such as all the deer mice or all the red oaks in a certain woodland or all the perch in a given pond. Although no two individuals in a deme are exactly alike, the members of a deme do usually resemble one another more closely than they resemble the members of other demes, for two reasons: (1) they are more closely related genetically, because pairings occur more frequently between members of the same deme than between members of different demes; and (2) they are exposed to more similar environmental influences and hence to more nearly the same selection pressures.

It must be emphasized that demes are not clear-cut permanent units of population. Although the deer mice in one woodlot are more likely to mate among themselves than with deer mice in the next woodlot down the road, there will almost certainly be occasional matings between mice from different woodlots. Similarly, although the female parts of a particular red oak tree are more likely to receive pollen from another red oak tree in the same woodlot, there is an appreciable chance that they will sometimes receive pollen from a tree in another nearby woodlot. And the woodlots themselves are not permanent ecological features. They have only a transient existence as separate and distinct ecological units; neighboring woodlots may fuse after a few years, or a single large woodlot may become divided into two or more separate smaller ones. Such changes in ecological features will produce corresponding changes in the demes of deer mice and red oak trees. Demes, then, are usually temporary units of population that intergrade with other similar units.

Species. Notice that intergradation is between "similar" demes. We expect some interbreeding between deer mice from adjacent demes, but we do not expect interbreeding between deer mice and house mice or between deer mice and black rats or between deer mice and gray squirrls. Nor do we expect to find crosses between red oaks and sugar maples or even between red oaks and pin oaks, even if they occur together in the same woodlot. In short, we recognize the existence of units of population larger than demes and both more distinct from each other and longer-lasting than demes. One such unit of population is that containing all the demes of deer mice. Another is that containing all the demes of red oaks. We call these larger units species.

For centuries, it has been recognized that the variation between living organisms does not form a continuum—that there are, instead, many discontinuities in the variation, that plants and animals seem to be divided naturally into many separate and distinct "kinds," or species. This does not mean that all the individuals of any one species are precisely alike; far from it: any two individuals are probably distinguishable from each other in a variety of ways. But it does mean that all the members of a single species share certain biologically important attributes and that, as a group, they are genetically separated from other such groups. That such groups exist in nature has

been recognized even by primitive peoples. Ernst Mayr of Harvard University cites a tribe in New Guinea that had 136 different names for what biologists later showed to be 137 species of local birds; the natives had confused only two species.

But although the existence of discrete clusters of living things that can be called species has long been recognized, the concept of what a species really is has changed many times in the course of history. One such concept is that each species is a static, immutable entity typified by some ideal form to which all the real individuals belonging to that species are rough approximations. According to this concept, individual variation results from the imperfection with which the individuals reflect the ideal characteristics. This static, typological concept, widely held by nonbiologists and once popular among biologists as well, contradicts all that we have learned about evolution. The modern concept of species rejects the notion that there is some immutable ideal type for every species. A species, in the modern view, is a genetically distinctive group of natural populations (demes) that share a common gene pool and that are reproductively isolated from all other such groups. Or, to word it another way, a species is the largest unit of population within which effective **gene flow** (exchange of genetic material) occurs or can occur.

Notice that the modern concept of the species says nothing about how different from each other two populations must be to qualify as separate species. Admittedly, most species can be separated by fairly obvious anatomical, physiological, or behavioral characters, and biologists frequently rely on these in determining species. But the final criterion is always reproduction—whether or not there is actual or potential gene flow. If there is complete intrinsic reproductive isolation between two outwardly almost identical populations (i.e. if there can be no gene flow between them), then those populations belong to different species despite their great similarity. On the other hand, if two populations are strikingly unlike each other but there is effective gene flow between them, then those populations belong to the same species. Anatomical, physiological, or behavioral characters simply serve as clues toward the identification of reproductively isolated populations; they are not in themselves regarded as determining whether a population constitutes a species.

Intraspecific Variation. We have already discussed the sorts of variation that may occur between individuals of a single deme as a result of mutation and recombination, particularly the latter. And we have seen that this variation is very important biologically, whether it involves almost imperceptible and intergrading differences or striking polymorphic discontinuities. But there is another sort of intraspecific variation that we have not yet discussed. This is variation between the demes of a single species, i.e. variation that is correlated with geographical distribution.

There is usually so much gene flow between adjacent demes of the same species that differences between them are slight. For example, the ratio of alleles A and a may be 0.90 to 0.10 in one deme and 0.89 to 0.11 in the adjacent deme. But the farther apart geographically two demes are, the smaller is the chance of direct gene flow between them, and hence the greater is the probability that the differences between them will be more marked. If, for example, we collect a sample of 500 deer mice from Plymouth County, Massachusetts, 500 from Crawford County, Pennsylvania, and 500 from Roanoke County, Virginia, we shall find numerous differences that will enable us to distinguish between the three populations quite readily—much more readily than we could distinguish between the populations in three adjacent counties in Massachusetts or in three adjacent counties in Pennsylvania. Some of this geographic variation may reflect chance events such as genetic drift or the occurrence

in Massachusetts of a mutation that would be favorable in all populations of deer mice but that has not yet spread to Pennsylvania or Virginia. But much of the geographic variation probably reflects differences in the selection pressures impinging on the populations as a result of the differences between the environmental conditions in their respective ranges. In other words, much geographic variation is adaptive. Each local population or deme tends to evolve adaptations to the specific environmental conditions in its own small portion of the species range. Such geographic variation is found in the vast majority of animal and plant species.

When geographic variation in important environmental conditions is very irregular, there is frequently a correspondingly irregular variation between the demes of the species living in the areas in question, particularly if the demes are rather isolated from each other so that there is relatively little interbreeding between them. Often, however, environmental conditions vary geographically in a more regular manner; there are shifts in temperature with latitude or with altitude on mountain slopes, or shifts in rainfall with longitude, as in many parts of the western United States, or shifts in topography with longitude, e.g. as one moves from the Atlantic coast to the Central States. Such environmental gradients are usually accompanied by genetic-variation gradients within the species of animals and plants that inhabit the areas involved. Most species show north–south gradients in many characters, and east–west gradients are not uncommon (Fig. 17.13). Altitudinal gradients in various characters are also often found (Fig. 17.14). When a character of a species shows a gradual variation correlated with geography, we speak of that variation as forming a *cline.* For example, many mammals and birds exhibit north–south clines in average body size, being larger in the colder climates farther north and smaller in the warmer climates farther south. Similarly, many mammalian species show north–south clines in the

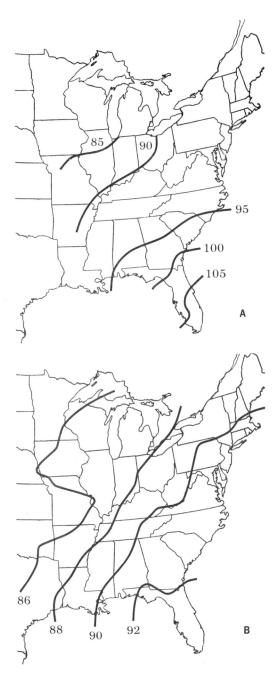

Fig. 17.13. Clinal variation. (A) Map showing by means of isophene lines (lines connecting equal values) the geographic variation in the mean number of subcaudal scales of the snake *Coluber constrictor* (the racer). (B) Isophene map showing geographic variation in the apical taper of leaves of the milkweed *Asclepias tuberosa*. The numbers represent degree of apical taper. [A: Modified from W. Auffenberg, *Tulane Stud. Zool.*, vol. 2, 1955. B: Modified from R. E. Woodson, *Ann. Missouri Botan. Garden*, vol. 34, 1947.]

many characters that vary clinally, but the various clines frequently do not coincide in direction, location, or intensity; one character may show clinal variation from north to south, another from east to west, and still another from northwest to southeast.

Sometimes geographically correlated genetic variation is not as gradual as in the clines discussed above. There may be a rather abrupt shift in some character in a particular part of the species range. Suppose, for example, that the average height of a certain species of plant decreases very gradually as one moves northward from Florida through Georgia, South Carolina, and North Carolina, then decreases very rapidly in the counties of southern Virginia, and then decreases only slightly as one continues to move northward through northern Virginia, Pennsylvania, and New York. Such variation forms a stepped cline; i.e. the abrupt shift in height in southern Virginia breaks the otherwise gradual geographic variation and constitutes a step in the north–south cline (Fig. 17.15). When such an abrupt shift in a genetically determined character occurs in a geographically variable species, some biologists designate the populations on the two sides of the step as *subspecies* or *races*. These terms are also sometimes applied to more isolated populations, such as those on different islands or in separate mountain ranges or, as in fish, in

size of such extremities as the tails and ears, these parts being smaller in the demes farther north.[7] A single widespread species often has

[7] Increase in average body size with increasing cold is so common in homeothermic animals that this ten-

dency has been generalized as "Bergmann's rule"; the tendency toward decrease in the size of the extremities with increasing cold has been generalized as "Allen's rule." What is the adaptive significance of these clines?

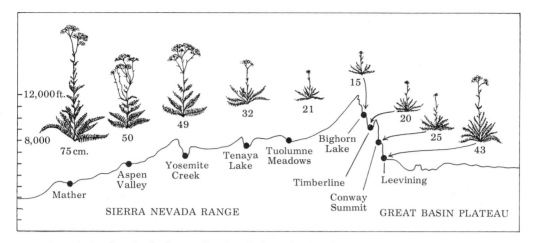

Fig. 17.14. Altitudinal cline in height of the milfoil *Achillea lanulosa*. The higher the altitude, the shorter the plants. This variation was shown to be genetic (i.e. not merely a phenotypic reaction) by moving plants from the locations indicated to a test garden at Stanford where all were exposed to the same environmental conditions; the differences in height were still evident. [Modified from J. Clausen, D. D. Keck, and W. M. Hiesey, *Carnegie Inst. Wash. Publ.*, no. 581, 1948.]

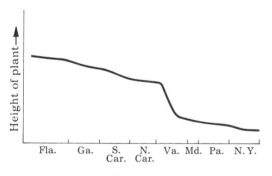

Fig. 17.15. Graph showing stepped clinal variation in a hypothetical plant. See text for discussion.

separate rivers, when the populations are recognizably different genetically but are believed potentially capable of interbreeding freely. Subspecies or races (the two terms, as used here, are equivalent) may be defined, then, as groups of natural populations within a species that differ genetically and that are partly isolated from each other reproductively because they have different ranges.

Note that two subspecies of the same species

cannot, by definition, long occur together geographically, because it is only the limitation on interbreeding imposed by distance that keeps them genetically distinctive. If they occurred together, they would interbreed freely and any distinction between them would quickly disappear. Some biologists have argued against the formal recognition of subspecies, in the first place because the distinctions between them are often made arbitrarily on the basis of only one character—the fact that other characters may form entirely different patterns of variation being ignored (Fig. 17.16)—and, second, because most units so recognized probably have only a transitory existence as separate entities and do not, as was once thought, go on to become fully separate species.

As a result of intraspecific geographic variation (whether irregular, clinal, or racial), two populations belonging to the same species but occurring in two widely separated localities often look no more like each other than they look like populations belonging to other species. Such intraspecific dissimilarity serves to emphasize the point made earlier that it is not · the degree of morphological resemblance that

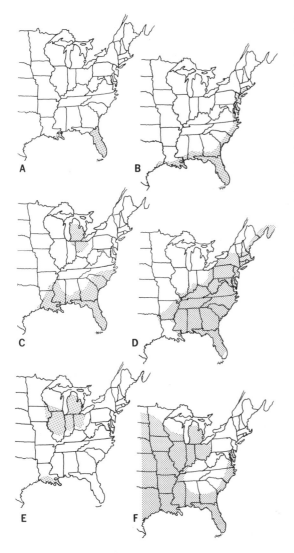

Fig. 17.16. Discordant geographic variation in six characters of the snake *Coluber constrictor* in the eastern United States. No two of the characters vary together. (A) Areas where red eyes are found in juveniles. (B) Areas where red ventral spots are found on juveniles. (C) Areas where the loreal scale is in contact with the first supralabial scale in at least 10 percent of the specimens. (D) Areas where black adults are found. (E) Areas where dark postocular stripes are found. (F) Areas where full-grown adults have white chins. [Redrawn from W. Auffenberg, *Tulane Stud. Zool.*, vol. 2, 1955.]

determines whether or not two populations belong to the same species; it is whether they are reproductively isolated from each other. There are even cases where two widely separated populations are regarded as belonging to the same species even though the respective individuals, when brought together, are incapable of producing viable offspring. The reason they are considered members of the same species is that they are connected by an unbroken chain of intermediate populations that permit gene flow between them. One of the best-known cases of this kind is that of the leopard frog, *Rana pipiens*, in the eastern United States, studied by John A. Moore of Columbia University. Moore has shown that if frogs from New England are crossed with frogs from southern Florida, many of the embryos die early in their development, apparently because the rate of development of the northern frogs is very different from that of the southern frogs, and the hybrids, which receive genes for both types of development, exhibit an abnormal developmental pattern. If only the New England and Florida populations existed, it could reasonably be concluded that these represent two different species. But there are many populations of leopard frogs in the areas between New England and Florida, which, when they are compared, reveal north–south clines in several characters, including rate of development. It can be shown that crosses between frogs from New England and New Jersey produce normal offspring and that crosses between frogs from New Jersey and Virginia or from Virginia and the Carolinas or from the Carolinas and Georgia or from Georgia and Florida produce normal offspring. In other words, each population can interbreed with the populations immediately to the north and to the south. Thus, although there can be no direct gene exchange between the populations in New England and Florida, there can be (and is) gene exchange between them via the intermediate populations. Because of the uninterrupted gene flow between the populations at the ends of the cline, these must be regarded as members of a single species.

Speciation

Having examined the meaning of the term "species," let us now direct our attention to the origin of species, a process often called speciation. In particular, we shall concentrate on the process of divergent speciation whereby one ancestral species gives rise to two or more descendent species, which, as they evolve, diverge more and more (i.e. become less and less like each other).

The Role of Geographic Isolation. Species being defined in terms of reproductive isolation rather than morphological distinctiveness, the fundamental question of divergent speciation becomes: How can two sets of populations that initially share a common gene pool come to have completely separate gene pools? That is, how does the possibility of effective gene flow between the two sets of populations disappear? How do barriers to the exchange of genes arise?

Most biologists are agreed that in the vast majority of cases (excluding speciation by polyploidy) the initiating factor in speciation is geographic separation. As long as all the populations of a species are in direct or indirect contact, gene flow will continue throughout the system and no splitting can occur, although various populations within the system may diverge in numerous characters and thus give rise to much intraspecific variation of the sorts discussed above. But if the initially continuous system of populations is divided by some geographic feature that constitutes a barrier to the dispersal of the species, then the separated population systems will no longer be able to exchange genes and their further evolution will therefore be independent. Given sufficient time, the two separate population systems will become less and less like each other as each evolves in its own way. At first, the only reproductive isolation between them will be geo-

graphic—isolation by physical separation—and they will potentially still be capable of interbreeding; according to the modern concept of species, they will still belong to the same species. Eventually, however, they may become genetically so different that there would be no effective gene flow between them even if they should again come into contact. When this point in their gradual divergence has been reached, the two population systems constitute two separate species.

There are at least three compelling reasons why geographically separated population systems will diverge in time. First, chances are that the two systems will have somewhat different initial gene frequencies; because most species exhibit geographic variation, it is most unlikely that a geographic barrier would divide a variable species into portions that are exactly alike genetically. It would be much more likely to separate populations that are already genetically different, such as the terminal portions of a cline. Separation can occur in other ways than through the splitting of a once-continuous distribution by a new geographic barrier. When, as often happens, a small number of individuals manage to cross an already existing barrier and found a new geographically isolated colony, these founders will, of course, carry with them in their own genotypes only a small percentage of the total genetic variation present in the gene pool of the parental population, and the new colony will thus have gene frequencies very different from those of the parental population. Obviously, if two populations have different genetic potentials from the moment of their separation, their future evolution is likely to follow different paths.

A second reason why separated population systems will diverge in the course of their evolution is that they will probably experience different mutations. Mutations are random (though some are more probable than others), and the chances are good that some mutations will occur in one of the populations and not in the other, and vice versa. Since there is no gene flow between the populations, a new mutant gene arising in one of them cannot spread to the other.

The third reason for evolutionary divergence of isolated populations is that they will almost certainly be exposed to different environmental selection pressures, since they occupy different ranges. The chances that two separate ranges will be identical in every significant environmental factor are essentially nil.

In addition to these three reasons for divergence, a fourth—genetic drift—would be important in small populations, as when a few founder individuals start a new colony.

The barriers that can cause the initial spatial separation leading to speciation are of many different types. A barrier is any physical or ecological feature that prevents the movement across it of the species in question. What is a barrier for one species may not be a barrier for another. Thus a prairie is a barrier for forest species but not, obviously, for prairie species. A mountain range is a barrier to species that can live only in lowlands, a desert is a barrier to species that require a moist environment, and a valley is a barrier to montane species. On a grander scale, oceans and glaciers have played a role in the speciation of many plants and animals. Let us look at a few actual examples of geographic isolation leading to speciation.

One of the most frequently cited examples is that of the Kaibab squirrel, which occurs on the north side of the Grand Canyon, and of the Abert squirrel, which occurs on the south side. The two kinds of squirrels are clearly very closely related and doubtless evolved from the same ancestor, but they almost never interbreed at present because they do not cross the Grand Canyon. Biologists are not agreed whether these two squirrels have reached the level of full species or whether they should be considered well-marked geographic variants of a single species, but the fact remains that the Grand Canyon has acted as a barrier separating the two sets of populations, and that those

populations have, as a result, evolved divergently until they have at least approached the level of fully distinct species. The Grand Canyon also separates the range of the gray-tailed antelope squirrel from that of the closely related white-tailed antelope squirrel, and it separates the range of the rock pocket mouse from that of the long-tailed pocket mouse.

On islands of the Pacific, in many instances, two closely related species of snails, clearly descended from the same ancestral population, live in valley woodlands separated by treeless ridges that the snails apparently cannot cross. Blind cave beetles (genus *Pseudanophthalmus*) living in different caves in the eastern United States have often diverged to the level of full species. Two river systems only a few miles apart but with no interconnections often have their own species of minnows. A different species of tree creeper is found in each of five major savanna-woodland areas in Australia (Fig. 17.17).

Intrinsic Reproductive Isolation. According to the model of divergent speciation outlined above, the initial factor preventing gene

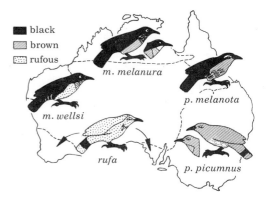

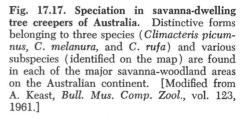

Fig. 17.17. Speciation in savanna-dwelling tree creepers of Australia. Distinctive forms belonging to three species (*Climacteris picumnus*, *C. melanura*, and *C. rufa*) and various subspecies (identified on the map) are found in each of the major savanna-woodland areas on the Australian continent. [Modified from A. Keast, *Bull. Mus. Comp. Zool.*, vol. 123, 1961.]

flow between two closely related population systems is ordinarily an extrinsic one—geography. Then, the model says, as the two populations diverge, they accumulate differences that will lead, given enough time, to the development of intrinsic isolating mechanisms, which are biological characteristics that prevent the two populations from occurring together or from interbreeding effectively when (or if) they again occur together. In other words, speciation is initiated when external barriers make the two population systems completely *allopatric* (having different ranges), but is not completed until the populations have evolved intrinsic mechanisms that will keep them allopatric or that will keep their gene pools separate even when they are *sympatric* (having the same range) (Fig. 17.18). Let us now examine the various kinds of intrinsic isolating mechanisms that may arise. One possible classification of intrinsic isolating mechanisms is shown in Table 17.1. Each of the mechanisms shown in the table is discussed below.

1. *Ecogeographic isolation.* Two population systems, initially separated by some extrinsic barrier, may in time become so specialized for different environmental conditions that even if the original extrinsic barrier is removed they may never become sympatric, because neither can survive under the conditions where the other occurs. In other words, they may evolve genetic differences that will maintain their geographic separation. An example is seen in two well-known tree species of the genus *Platanus*. *Platanus occidentalis* (the sycamore or buttonwood tree) occurs in the eastern United States, while *P. orientalis* (the oriental plane tree) occurs in the eastern part of the Mediterranean region. They can be artificially crossed and the hybrids are vigorous and fertile. But the two kinds of trees are regarded as fully distinct species because such hybridization would not occur naturally. Each species is adapted to the climate in its own native range, and the climates in the two ranges are so different that neither species will long sur-

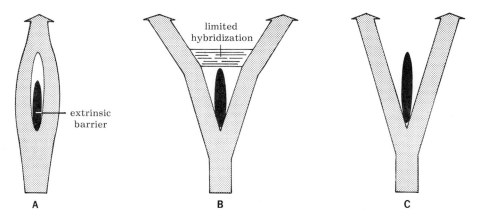

Fig. 17.18. Model of geographic speciation. (A) An extrinsic barrier (geographic) divides a population, but the barrier breaks down before the two subpopulations have been isolated long enough to have evolved intrinsic reproductive isolating mechanisms; hence the populations fuse back together. (B) Two populations are isolated by an extrinsic barrier long enough to have evolved incomplete intrinsic reproductive isolating mechanisms. When the extrinsic barrier breaks down, some hybridization occurs. But the hybrids are not as well adapted as the parental forms; hence there is a strong selection pressure favoring forms of intrinsic isolation that prevent mating, and the two populations diverge more rapidly until mating between them is no longer possible. This rapid divergence is called character displacement. (C) Two populations are isolated by a geographic barrier so long that by the time the barrier breaks down they are too different to interbreed.

TABLE 17.1

Intrinsic Isolating Mechanisms

Mechanisms that prevent mating	1. Ecogeographic isolation 2. Habitat isolation 3. Seasonal isolation 4. Behavioral isolation 5. Mechanical isolation	Mechanisms operative in the parents, preventing fertilization
Mechanisms that prevent production of hybrid young after mating	6. Gametic isolation 7. Developmental isolation	
Mechanisms that prevent perpetuation of hybrids	8. Hybrid inviability 9. Hybrid sterility 10. Selective hybrid elimination	Mechanisms operative in the hybrids, preventing their success

vive under natural conditions in the range of the other. Thus there are genetic differences that under natural conditions would prevent gene flow between the two species. Their separation is not merely geographic; it is both geographic and genetic.

2. *Habitat isolation.* When two sympatric populations occupy different habitats within their common range, the individuals of each population will be more likely to encounter and mate with members of their own population than with members of the other population. Their genetically determined preference for different habitats thus helps keep the two gene pools separate. There are numerous examples of such habitat isolation. *Bufo fowleri* and *B. americanus* are two closely related toads that can cross and produce viable offspring. But in those areas where the ranges of the two toads overlap, *B. fowleri* normally breeds in the quieter water of streams, while *B. americanus* breeds in shallow rainpools. *Progomphus obscurus* is a dragonfly that lives in northern Florida, while its close relative *P. alachuensis* lives in southern Florida. The ranges of the two species overlap in north-central Florida, but there the two species occupy different habitats, *P. obscurus* being restricted to rivers and streams and *P. alachuensis* being restricted to lakes. In California, the ranges of *Ceanothus*

thyrsiflorus and *C. dentatus,* two species of wild lilacs, overlap broadly, but *C. thyrsiflorus* grows on moist hillsides with good soil, while *C. dentatus* grows on drier, more exposed sites with poor or shallow soil.

3. *Seasonal isolation.* If two closely related species are sympatric but breed during different seasons of the year, interbreeding between them will be effectively prevented. For example, *Pinus radiata* and *P. muricata,* two species of pine, are sympatric in some parts of California. They are capable of crossing, but do so rather seldom under natural conditions because *P. radiata* sheds its pollen early in February while *P. muricata* does not shed its pollen until April. *Salvia munzii* and *S. clevelandii,* two related species of sage, are sympatric in California, but exhibit complete seasonal isolation because the former is past its flowering season before the latter begins to flower. *Reticulitermes hageni* and *R. virginicus,* two closely related species of termites, are sympatric in southern Florida, but the mating flights of the former occur from March through May while those of the latter occur in the fall and winter months. Five different species of frogs belonging to the genus *Rana* are sympatric in much of eastern North America, but the period of most active mating is different for each species (Fig. 17.19).

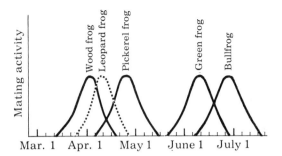

Fig. 17.19. **Mating seasons at Ithaca, New York, for five species of frogs of the genus Rana.** The period of most active mating is different for each species. Where the mating seasons for two or more species overlap, different breeding sites are used. [Modified from B. Wallace and A. M. Srb, *Adaptation,* © 1964. By permission of Prentice-Hall, Inc., Englewood Cliffs, N.J.]

4. *Behavioral isolation.* In the chapter on behavior, we discussed the immense importance of behavior in courtship and mating. And we emphasized the fundamental role behavior patterns play in species recognition among animals. We saw, for example, that many of the dabbling ducks sympatric in the eastern United States have elaborate courtship displays, usually combined with striking color patterns in the males, and that these function in minimizing the chances that the females will select as a mate a male of the wrong species. We also noted the complex interplay of behavioral patterns during the courtship of stickleback fish. Each species of stickleback has its own courtship pattern, and where two species are sympatric, crosses rarely occur because a courtship between members of different species involves so many wrong responses that the courtship is unlikely to proceed all the way to the spawning stage. A particularly interesting example of visual displays functioning in species recognition has been reported by Joselyn Crane of the Beebe Tropical Research Station, Trinidad. She found twelve different species of crabs of the genus *Uca* actively courting on the same small beach (only about 600 feet square) in Panama. Each species had its own characteristic display, consisting of waving the large

claw (cheliped), elevating the body, moving around the burrow, etc. (Fig. 17.20). Miss Crane found that the displays were so distinctive that she could recognize each species from a considerable distance merely by the form of its display.

Auditory stimuli are important in species recognition among many animals, particularly birds and insects, and help prevent mating between related species. In several instances, specialists have noticed that two or three very different songs were sung by what had been considered members of a single species of cricket. Upon investigation, it was found that each song was, in fact, sung by a different species, but the species were so similar morphologically that no one had previously distinguished between them. Despite the morphological similarity of these closely related crickets, they do not hybridize in nature even when they are sympatric, because females do not respond to the stridulation of a male of a different species.

Fig. 17.20. **Male Uca crab giving mating display.** The large cheliped is waved in the air as the crab elevates its body and moves around the burrow. Details of the display differ from species to species.

5. *Mechanical isolation.* If structural differences between two closely related species make it physically impossible for matings between males of one species and females of the other to occur, the two populations will obviously not exchange genes. If, for example, one species of animal is much larger than the other, matings between them may be very difficult, if not impossible. Or if the genital organs of the males of one species and the females of the other do not fit, mating will be prevented. The fact that the copulatory organs vary greatly from species to species in many animal groups led long ago to the so-called "lock-and-key" hypothesis, which holds that the male and female genitalia are so precisely fitted to each other that even slight changes in the structure of either would make copulation impossible. This hypothesis has proved to be incorrect in many groups. For example, the male copulatory organs (gonopods) of millipeds are usually very different in different species (Fig. 17.21) and have consequently been used as the basis for much of the classification of these animals, but the female genitalia of related species are often almost indistinguishable, which must indicate that the major isolating mechanism between the species is not a lock-and-key lack of fit. But despite the evidence against the lock-and-key theory in many animal groups, it probably does hold in a few, among them several subfamilies of snails in which interspecific matings are physically very difficult.

Mechanical isolation is probably much more important in plants than in animals, particularly in plants that depend upon insect pollinators. Consider milkweeds, for example. In these plants, the pollen is contained in small sacs that stick to the legs of insects. The female part of each flower (stigma) has slits in it into which the sac must be inserted if pollination is to take place. This insertion is not easy, and few of the sacs carried from one flower to another on the legs of an insect ever actually get inserted into a stigma. Insertion of a pollen sac from one species of milkweed into the

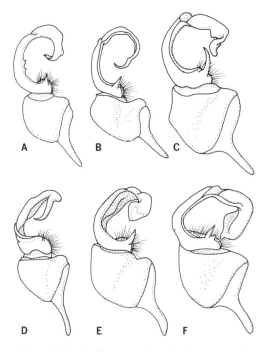

Fig. 17.21. **Male gonopods of six species of millipeds of the genus *Brachoria*.** The shape of the distal portion of the male gonopods is distinctive for each species; yet the genitalia of the females of these species are nearly indistinguishable from one another. The animals being eyeless, the male gonopods do not function in visual species recognition; no functional or evolutionary explanation for the differences in these structures has yet been found.

stigma of a different species is essentially impossible because both the sacs and the slits in the stigma vary in shape from species to species. Thus even though several closely related species of milkweeds are sympatric in many parts of the world, hybridization between them is almost nonexistent. Another example is provided by *Salvia apiana* and *S. mellifera*, two closely related species of sages that are sympatric in California. They are reproductively isolated by habitat and seasonal mechanisms and by the behavior of their pollinators. In addition, as has recently been demonstrated, mechanical features play a role. Whereas *S. mellifera* is pollinated by relatively small bees, the flowers of *S. apiana* can be entered only by very large bees whose weight is sufficient to cause the landing platform (lower lip of corolla) to unfold and permit free entrance into the flower. We have already mentioned the orchids in which the flowers resemble female bees and elicit pseudocopulation by the male bees. The flowers of each species of orchid resemble the females of a different species of bee; as a result, each orchid species is pollinated by only one species of bee, and no hybridization occurs.

6. *Gametic isolation.* Even if individuals of two different animal species mate or the pollen from one plant species gets onto the stigma of another, actual fertilization may not take place. For example, if cross-insemination occurs between *Drosophila virilis* and *D. americana,* the sperms are rapidly immobilized by the unsuitable environment in the reproductive tract of the female and they never reach the egg cells. In other species of *Drosophila,* interspecific matings cause an antigenic reaction in the genital tract of the female; the walls of the vagina swell enormously and kill the sperms before they reach the eggs. In tobacco, 68 different interspecific combinations are known in which no cross-fertilization will take place, even when the pollen is placed on the stigma, because the sperm nucleus from the pollen is unable to reach the egg nucleus in the ovule.

7. *Developmental isolation.* Even when cross-fertilization occurs, the development of the embryo is often irregular and may cease before birth. We have already mentioned this phenomenon in crosses between leopard frogs from New England and from southern Florida. The eggs of fish can often be fertilized by sperms from a great variety of other species, but development is usually arrested in the early stages. Crosses between sheep and goats produce embryos that die long before birth.

8. *Hybrid inviability.* Hybrids are often weak and malformed and frequently die before they reproduce; hence there is no actual gene flow through them from the gene pool of the one parental species to the gene pool of the other parental species. An example of hybrid inviability is seen in certain tobacco hybrids, which form tumors in their vegetative parts and die before they flower.

9. *Hybrid sterility.* Some interspecific crosses produce vigorous but sterile hybrids. The best-known example is, of course, the cross between the horse and the donkey, which produces the mule. Mules have many characteristics superior to those of both parental species, but they are sterile. No matter how many mules are produced, the gene pools of horses and donkeys remain distinct, because there is no gene flow between them.

10. *Selective hybrid elimination.* The members of two closely related populations may be able to cross and produce fertile offspring. If those offspring and their progeny are as vigorous and well adapted as the parental forms, then the two original populations will not remain distinct for long if they are sympatric, and it will no longer be possible to regard them as full species. But if the fertile offspring and their progeny are less well adapted than the parental forms, then they will soon be eliminated. There will be some gene flow between the two parental gene pools via the hybrids, but not much. The parental populations are consequently regarded as separate species. Usually, if they are sympatric, they will rapidly evolve more effective isolating mechanisms. The reason is clear. Since the hybrids are inferior and tend to die out within a generation or two, those individuals of the parent species that tend to mate with members of their own species will, in the long run, have more descendants than those individuals that tend to mate with members of the wrong species. In other words, there will be selection for correct mating and selection against wrong mating. Gene combinations that lead to correct mate selection will increase in frequency, and com-

binations that lead to incorrect selection will decrease, until eventually all hybridization ceases.

Situations in which only one of the ten isolating mechanisms discussed above is operative are extremely rare. Ordinarily two, three, four, or more all contribute to keeping two species apart. For example, closely related sympatric plant species often exhibit habitat and seasonal isolation in addition to some form of hybrid incapacity. In general, sympatric species, whether plant or animal, tend rapidly to evolve one or more of the forms of isolation that prevent mating (habitat, seasonal, behavioral, mechanical) rather than depend only on those forms that prevent the birth or perpetuation of hybrids. The reasons are similar to those discussed in the preceding paragraph; those individuals that tend to mate with members of the wrong species will leave fewer descendants than those that mate with members of their own species. Wrong matings produce gamete wastage, whether fertilization takes place or not, or whether the hybrids are viable or not.

Speciation by Polyploidy. The model of speciation discussed above involves the gradual divergence of geographically separated populations. There is another way in which new species may arise—an almost instantaneous process that makes it entirely possible for a parent to belong to one species and its offspring to belong to a different species. This process is speciation by polyploidy. It has apparently been common in plants but very rare in animals.

One type of polyploid speciation, called autopolyploidy, involves a sudden multiplication of the number of chromosomes in an otherwise normal organism, usually as a result of the nondisjunction of chromosomes during meiosis. An example of this type of polyploidy was discovered by Hugo De Vries, one of the early geneticists, while he was making extensive studies of the evening primrose, *Oenothera lamarckiana*. This diploid species has 14 chro-

mosomes. During De Vries' studies, a new form suddenly arose. This new form, to which he gave the species name of *Oenothera gigas*, had 28 chromosomes (i.e. it was tetraploid). It was reproductively isolated from the parental species because hybrids between O. *lamarckiana* and O. *gigas* were triploid (they received one of each type of chromosome from their O. *lamarckiana* parent and two of each type from their O. *gigas* parent), and triploid individuals, because of the highly irregular distribution of their chromosomes at meiosis, are sterile. It is characteristic of autopolyploidy that the polyploids are fertile and can breed with each other, but cannot cross with the diploid species from which they arose. Hence polyploid populations fulfill all the requirements of the modern definitions of species—they are genetically distinctive and they are reproductively isolated—although botanists do not always choose to give each such polyploid form a formal species name.

A second type of polyploid speciation, called allopolyploidy, involves a multiplication (usually a doubling) of the number of chromosomes in a hybrid between two species. This type of polyploidy has probably been far more important in speciation than autopolyploidy. Suppose one species has a chromosome type A; if we assume that the species is diploid, its genotype relative to this chromosome will be AA. Suppose another related species has no A chromosome but has in its place a type B; its diploid chromosomal genotype will thus be BB. Hybrids between these two species will have the genotype AB. But if the A and B chromosomes are sufficiently different, they will not synapse in meiosis. Hence the hybrids will not be able to produce normal gametes and will be sterile. But if the number of chromosomes in the hybrids is doubled in some way, then their genotype will be AABB. In this case, the two A chromosomes will synapse in meiosis and the two B chromosomes will synapse. Hence the AABB individuals will be able to produce normal gametes and will be fertile. They will, in effect, be diploid, since they will have only two of each type of chromosome. But they will have a complete diploid set from each of the parental species. The AABB individuals will be able to breed freely among themselves, but they will be unable to cross with either of the parental species. Consequently the allopolyploid population must be regarded as a distinct species.

Allopolyploid plants are frequently larger and more vigorous than the parental diploid plants. They are often more aggressive invaders of new habitats. When conditions become unfavorable and the environment is rapidly changing, the diploids are usually the first to become extinct. Hence allopolyploid speciation has probably played an important role in the perpetuation of some plant groups during periods of widespread environmental change.

Allopolyploidy has also proved of great importance in the production of valuable new crop plants. As soon as it was realized that many of our most useful plants, such as oats, wheat, cotton, tobacco, potato, banana, coffee, and sugar cane, are polyploids, plant breeders began trying to stimulate polyploidy, and many new varieties resulted. It was found that a chemical called colchicine would readily induce polyploidy. One of the first artificially produced allopolyploids came from a cross made in 1924 between the radish and the cabbage. Unfortunately, it had the root of the cabbage and the shoot of the radish. Other crosses have yielded more desirable results.

Adaptive Radiation. One of the most striking aspects of life is its extreme diversity. A bewildering array of different species now occupy this globe. And the fossil record shows us that of the species that have existed at one time or another those now living represent only a tiny fraction. Clearly, then, divergent evolution—the evolutionary splitting of species into many separate descendent species—has been an exceedingly frequent occurrence.

Is it possible to account for such a degree of evolutionary radiation by the models outlined above? In particular, could opportunities for geographic isolation have been sufficient to lead to all the speciation not caused by polyploidy? After all, a complex of four, five, or more closely related species occurs very often within a quite limited area. For example, 28 different species of the milliped genus *Brachoria,* many of them sympatric, are confined to a small portion of the deciduous forests of the eastern United States (Fig. 17.22). How could so much speciation have occurred in so small an area if geographic isolation was a necessary factor? In an attempt to answer such questions, let us turn to a particularly instructive and historically important example—the finches on the Galápagos Islands, which played a major role in leading Charles Darwin to

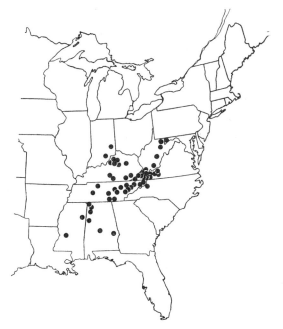

Fig. 17.22. Distribution of 28 species of millipeds of the genus *Brachoria.* The black dots indicate all known localities for these millipeds, many of which are sympatric. All of the speciation in this genus must have occurred within this very limited area in the eastern United States.

formulate his theory of evolution by natural selection.

The Galápagos Islands lie astride the equator in the Pacific Ocean roughly 600 miles west of the coast of Ecuador, to which country they now belong (Fig. 17.23). These islands have never been connected to South America or to any other land mass; nor have they been connected to each other. They apparently arose from the ocean floor as volcanoes somewhat more than a million years ago. At first, of course, they were completely devoid of life, and were thus an environment open to exploitation by whatever species from the South American mainland might chance to reach them. Relatively few species ever did so. The only land vertebrates present on the islands before man got there were six species of reptiles (one snake, a huge tortoise, and four lizards, including two very large iguanas), two species of mammals (a rice rat and a bat), and a limited number of birds (including two species of owls, one hawk, one dove, one cuckoo, one warbler, two flycatchers, one swallow, four mockingbirds, and the famous Darwin's finches).

The 14 species of Darwin's finches (Fig. 17.24) constitute a separate subfamily found nowhere else in the world. They are believed to have evolved on the Galápagos Islands from some unknown finch ancestor that colonized the islands from the South American mainland. We can readily understand how the descendants of the geographically isolated colonizers would have undergone so much evolutionary change as to become, in time, very unlike their mainland ancestors. More perplexing at first glance is the manner in which the descendants of the original immigrants would have split into the separate populations that gave rise to today's 14 different species. The point to remember is that we are dealing not with a single island but with a cluster of more than 15 separate islands. The finches will not readily fly across wide stretches of water, and they show a strong tendency to remain near

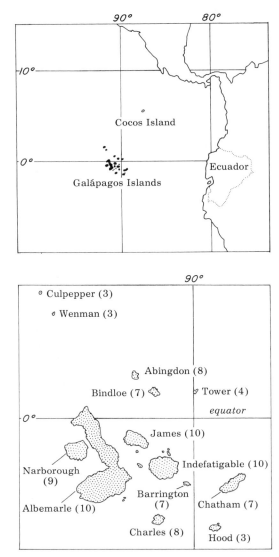

Fig. 17.23. The Galápagos Islands. Top: The islands are located about 600 miles off the coast of Ecuador. Cocos Island is about 600 miles northeast of the Galápagos. Bottom: The islands shown in greater detail. The number in parentheses after each name indicates the number of species of Darwin's finches that occur on the island. The island names shown here are the English ones, which Darwin used. The Ecuadorian government has renamed the majority of the islands, but most of the biological literature continues to use the older English names. [Modified from D. Lack, *Darwin's Finches,* Cambridge University Press, 1947.]

their home area. Hence a population on any one of the islands is effectively isolated from the populations on the other islands. We can suppose that the initial colony was established on some one of the islands where the colonizers, perhaps blown by high winds, chanced to land. Later, stragglers from this colony wandered or were blown to other islands and started new colonies. In time, the colonies on the different islands diverged for the reasons already outlined in our model of geographic speciation (different initial gene frequencies, different mutations, different selection pressures, and, in such small populations as some of these must have been, genetic drift). What we might expect, therefore, is a different species, or at least a different race, on each of the islands. But this is not what has actually been found; most of the islands have more than one species of finch, and the larger islands have ten (Fig. 17.23, bottom). How can we account for this?

Let us suppose that form A evolved originally on Indefatigable Island and that the closely related form B evolved on Charles Island. If, later, form A had spread to Charles Island before the two forms had been isolated long enough to evolve any but minor differences, the two forms might have interbred freely and merged with each other. But if A and B had been separated long enough to have evolved major differences before A invaded Charles Island, then A and B might have been intrinsically isolated from each other (i.e. been full species), and they might have been able to coexist on the same island without interbreeding (Fig. 17.25). If they formed occasional hybrids, those hybrids might well have been less viable than the parental forms. Accordingly, natural selection would have favored individuals that mated only with their own kind, and this selection pressure would have led rapidly to more effective intrinsic isolating mechanisms preventing the gamete wastage involved in cross-matings. It has been shown, in fact, that Darwin's finches recognize mem-

bers of their own species by the size and shape of their beaks (Fig. 17.26), and that they show little interest in members of a different species.

We have now arrived at a point in our hypothetical example where Indefatigable is occupied by species A and Charles is occupied by both A and B. It would be highly unlikely that A and B could coexist indefinitely if they utilized exactly the same food supply or the same nesting sites; the ensuing competition would be very severe, and the less well adapted species would tend to be eliminated by the other unless it evolved differences that minimized the competition. In other words, wherever two or more species occur together, natural selection would favor the evolution of different feeding and nesting habits. This is precisely what we find in Darwin's finches. The 14 species form four groups (genera). One group includes six species that live primarily on the ground; of these, some feed primarily on seeds and others feed mostly on cactus flowers. Of the species that feed on seeds, some feed on large seeds, some on medium-sized seeds, and some on small seeds. The second group contains six species that live primarily in trees. Of these, one is a vegetarian and the others eat insects, but the insect eaters differ from one another in the size of their prey and in the way they catch them (Fig. 17.27). A third group contains only one species, which has become very un-finch-like and strongly resembles the warblers of the mainland. The fourth group contains only one species, restricted to Cocos Island, which is about 600 miles northeast of the Galápagos Islands and about 300 miles from Panama.

Now, if on Charles Island selection favored the rapid evolutionary divergence of species A and B in characters that would reduce the chances of their interbreeding and that would minimize competition between them, it follows that the population of species A on Charles Island would become less and less like the population of species A on Indefatigable Island. Eventually these differences might be-

come so great that the two populations would be intrinsically isolated from each other and would thus be separate species. We might now designate as species C the Charles population derived from species A. The geographic separation of the two islands would thus have led to the evolution of three different species (A, B, and C) from a single original species. The process of island hopping followed by divergence could continue indefinitely and produce many additional species. It was doubtless such a process, involving initial divergence on separate islands followed by intensification of differences when sympatry later developed, that led to the formation of the 14 species of Darwin's finches.

Now let us apply the principles learned from Darwin's finches to the case of the 28 species of *Brachoria* millipeds confined to a small area in the eastern United States (see Fig. 17.22). These animals live in the humus layer on the floor of deciduous forests. They are rather sluggish and seldom move very far. It would have been easy for populations to become isolated in local forested areas separated by less hospitable regions. Such allopatric populations could have become sufficiently different so that, when conditions changed and they became sympatric, they would behave as full species. The same sorts of processes as seen on islands could account for radiation in a continental area. And on a somewhat larger geographic scale, the same processes could account for the observed adaptive radiation in insects, fish, reptiles, birds, mammals, and many plant groups. In

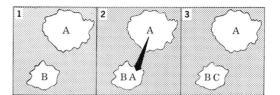

Fig. 17.25. Model of speciation on the Galápagos Islands. (1) An ancestral form colonized two islands, and the two populations, being isolated from each other, eventually evolved into separate species A and B. (2) Some individuals of A colonize B's island. The two species coexist, but intense competition between them leads to rapid divergent evolution. (3) This rapid evolution of the population of A on B's island causes it to become more and more different from the original species A, until eventually it is sufficiently distinct to be considered a full species, C, in its own right.

short, adaptive radiation on islands, like that of Darwin's finches, is dramatic and lends itself particularly well to analysis, but it does not differ in principle from adaptive radiation under other circumstances. Thus it helps show that our model of speciation can account for the great amount of divergence necessary to produce the immense diversity that characterizes life. No other mechanism, except polyploidy in some plant groups, seems to be needed.

The Species Problem

It would be wrong to leave you with the impression that the modern definition of species

Fig. 17.24. Darwin's finches. The finches numbered 1–6 are the ground finches (*Geospiza*). Those numbered 7–12 are the tree finches (*Camarhynchus*). Number 13 is the Warbler Finch (*Certhidea olivacea*). The Cocos Finch (*Pinaroloxias inornata*) is not shown. 1. Large Cactus Ground Finch (*G. conirostris*). 2. Large Ground Finch (*G. magnirostris*). 3. Medium Ground Finch (*G. fortis*). 4. Cactus Ground Finch (*G. scandens*). 5. Sharp-beaked Ground Finch (*G. difficilis*). 6. Small Ground Finch (*G. fuliginosa*). 7. Woodpecker Finch (*Camarhynchus pallidus*). 8. Vegetarian Tree Finch (*C. crassirostris*). 9. Large Insectivorous Tree Finch of Charles Island (*C. pauper*). 10. Large Insectivorous Tree Finch (*C. psittacula*). 11. Small Insectivorous Tree Finch (*C. parvulus*). 12. Mangrove Finch (*C. heliobates*). [*Biological Science: Molecules to Man*, Houghton Mifflin, 1963. Reprinted by permission of the Biological Sciences Curriculum Study.]

Fig. 17.26. Beak differences in Darwin's finches on the central islands. The differences may appear slight at first glance, but they have important functional implications for the birds' diets and for species recognition in mating. Top row (diagonally downward from left to right): *Geospiza magnirostris, G. fortis, G. fuliginosa.* Second row: *G. difficilis debilirostris, G. scandens, Camarhynchus crassirostris.* Third row: *C. psittacula, C. parvulus, C. pallidus.* Fourth row: *C. heliobates, Certhidea olivacea, Pinaroloxias inornata.* [Modified from D. Lack, *Darwin's Finches,* Cambridge University Press, 1947, after Swarth.]

can be applied without difficulty in all cases, or, indeed, that it is even valid in all cases. The details of the definition itself are controversial and can provoke heated arguments between biologists. Although most of them accept the major ideas on which the definition rests, and although most of them, if they were to study the same set of natural populations, would probably agree in the great majority of instances which populations represent full species and which do not, there would be a small percentage of populations on which they could not agree. These are the cases where the modern definition of species is hard to apply or invalid. Let us examine a few such cases.

Asexual Species. One obvious case where the definition is invalid is that of asexual organisms. The definition we have used assumes interbreeding and therefore holds only for sexually reproducing organisms. What can we say about asexual organisms? Do they form species? If so, are those species comparable to sexual ones? These questions are not easily answered. Asexual organisms do seem to form recognizable groups or kinds even though the members of a group cannot exchange genes. Gaps, or discontinuities in the variation, occur between the various kinds just as they do between sexual species. One possible explanation for the groupings is that not all variants would be equally well adapted and hence only those

individuals whose genotypes produce well-adapted phenotypes would survive in significant numbers. Since there would be a limited number of superiorly adapted "types," all those individuals falling within the bounds of one

Fig. 17.27. The Woodpecker Finch. One of the insectivorous tree finches of the Galápagos has evolved most unusual feeding habits somewhat like those of mainland woodpeckers. It chisels into wood after insects, but it lacks the long tongue that a true woodpecker uses to probe the insect out of the crack. Instead, it pokes into the crack with a cactus spine or twig that it holds in its beak. This is one of the few known cases of use of a tool by a bird.

such type would constitute a natural group that could be called a species and all those falling within the bounds of another adaptive type would constitute a second species. The asexual species thus determined would resemble sexual species in that the latter, too, represent adaptive peaks. The two types of species would, therefore, play comparable ecological roles, but they would nonetheless differ fundamentally from a genetic and evolutionary point of view. Asexual organisms thus pose a perplexing and vexing problem for students of speciation, one that does not, however, invalidate the species concept for sexual organisms. There are relatively few groups, primarily among the microorganisms, in which gene exchange is totally absent. Among higher organisms, the few instances of completely asexual reproduction usually represent evolutionary blind alleys of little importance in the overall history of life.

Fossil Species. A second case where the modern definition of species cannot be applied literally is that of fossil forms descended from one another. It is obviously impossible to apply the criterion of interbreeding when one is comparing a form with its ancestors of a million years earlier. The modern definition of species can be applied strictly only when one is comparing contemporaneous forms, i.e. forms occurring in only one time transect. All that paleontologists can do when comparing forms from different time transects is use morphological criteria and classify two forms as separate species when they differ from each other to about the same degree as related forms known to be species on reproductive grounds. For practical purposes, paleontologists usually regard gaps in the fossil record as breaks between species, even though they are fully aware that no gaps actually occurred in the lineages of the organisms.

Populations at an Intermediate Stage of Divergence. Our model of allopatric speciation assumes that geographically isolated populations will slowly diverge by essentially imperceptible stages until they have reached the level of full species. The intrinsic reproductive isolation that makes them full species itself evolves gradually. Hence there is no precise point at which the diverging populations suddenly reach the level of full species. It would never be possible to say objectively that two populations in one generation have not quite reached the level of fully separate species, but that the two populations of the very next generation have done so. There will be time transects in the history of any two diverging lineages when the populations are in a hazy intermediate state between the condition where they would obviously belong to the same species and the condition where they would obviously be two separate species. But our definition of species makes no provision for such intermediate stages. It assumes that two populations either exhibit intrinsic reproductive isolation or that they do not, i.e. that they either belong to different species or that they belong to the same species. It does not explicitly recognize the conditions "nearly species" or "almost species" or "barely species." Consequently such intermediate stages, when they are encountered, must always pose a problem to biologists intent on rigid categorization of what in nature is a fluid system. But the existence of intermediate stages does not invalidate the concept of speciation, because that very concept, in its modern form, predicts them.

Allopatric Species. One of the most obvious and frequently encountered problems in applying the modern definition of species arises when two populations are closely related and completely allopatric. Since they are allopatric, they are obviously not exchanging genes. But the definition is not based on extrinsic isolation; it is based on intrinsic isolation. There must be neither actual nor potential effective gene flow if the two populations are to be regarded as separate species. How can potential gene flow be determined? One way that immediately comes to mind is to release a large sample of individuals from one population in the range of the other and then see if free interbreeding takes place, and if so, whether the hybrids are as viable as the parents. But there are obvious reasons why wholesale introduction of foreign plants and animals is seldom desirable; in fact, in many cases it is illegal. An alternative would be to bring individuals from the two allopatric populations together in the laboratory and see if they will interbreed. Sometimes this procedure is useful. If one finds that the individuals will breed freely with other members of their own population but will not breed freely with members of the other population, then it is reasonable to conclude that the two populations are intrinsically isolated and should be considered separate species.

But what if interbreeding occurs freely between members of different populations in the laboratory? Does this mean that the two popu-

lations must be regarded as belonging to the same species? No, the inbreeding simply demonstrates that certain types of intrinsic isolation do not exist between the populations. It does not demonstrate that other types of intrinsic isolation do not exist. For example, under natural conditions ecogeographic or habitat isolation may exist, but these might very well be inoperative under laboratory conditions. Or behavioral isolation may be operative in nature but not in the laboratory; it is known that many species of animals that will have nothing to do with each other in the wild, because of important differences in their behavior patterns, will mate in the laboratory, where their normal behavior patterns break down. Therefore, when members of two different allopatric populations cross in the laboratory and produce viable offspring, the question whether they belong to the same or to different species remains unanswered. The question also remains unanswered, of course, for the many species that will not breed at all under laboratory conditions.

In many cases, then, there is no good test to determine whether two allopatric populations belong to the same or to different species. The usual practice in such cases is to determine the extent to which the two populations differ and then to compare this degree of difference with that seen in related sympatric species. If the differences between the allopatric populations are of the same order of magnitude as (or greater than) those that distinguish sympatric species, the allopatric populations are considered fully separate species; if the differences are less than those that usually distinguish sympatric species, the two allopatric populations are regarded as belonging to the same species.

Use of the degree of difference as an index to the probable presence or absence of intrinsic reproductive isolating mechanisms between allopatric populations may be the best that can be done in many cases, but it is nevertheless an unsatisfactory procedure. It rests on the assumption that allopatric populations are intrinsically isolated only if they differ from each other at least as much as related sympatric species differ from each other. But this assumption is frequently not valid. We have already seen that when closely related species become sympatric they often rapidly evolve greater differences in characters that will reduce the chances of hybridization and minimize the competition between them. This phenomenon of rapid divergence between sympatric species has been called *character displacement* by William L. Brown of Cornell University and Edward O. Wilson of Harvard University (see Fig. 17.18B). They have pointed out that character displacement is very common in sympatric species and that, as a result, one should generally expect to find greater differences between sympatric than between allopatric species. Therefore, taking the differences between sympatric species as a yardstick against which

to measure differences between allopatric populations probably often results in classifying allopatric populations as members of the same species when in reality they are intrinsically isolated and should be regarded as separate species.

THE CONCEPT OF PHYLOGENY

Recognizing that unlike species have often evolved from a common ancestor and that all forms of life probably stem from the same remote beginning, biologists naturally want to understand the relationships between the species alive today and to know from what sorts of ancestors they have descended. In other words, they want to know the evolutionary history of the various forms of life. Such evolutionary history is called phylogeny (Fig. 17.28).

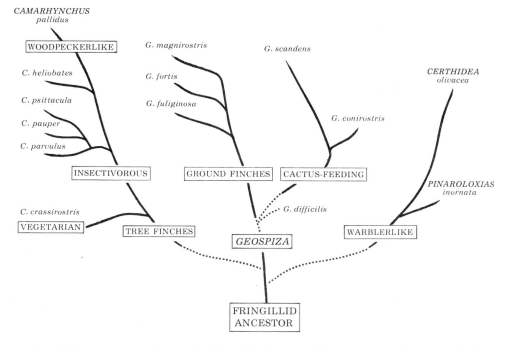

Fig. 17.28. A phylogenetic tree for Darwin's finches. This is an example of a method biologists frequently use in attempting to show the hypothetical connections between related organisms. No phylogenetic tree should be taken too seriously, however, because the evidence is usually sufficient only to indicate the broad outlines of the tree (if that), and much guesswork (preferably educated guesswork) goes into the adding of details. [Redrawn from D. Lack, *Darwin's Finches*, Cambridge University Press, 1947.]

Determining Phylogenetic Relationships

Sources of Data. When a biologist sets out to reconstruct the phylogeny of a group of species that he thinks are related, he faces a herculean task. Usually he has before him only the species living today. He cannot observe their phylogenetic history. In most cases, he can never know with certainty exactly what that history was. To reconstruct it as closely as possible, he must make educated inferences based on observational and experimental data that appear relevant, if only remotely so. Those data can usually be interpreted in several different ways, and only experience and good judgment can help the biologist choose among them.

The usual procedure in attempting to reconstuct phylogenies is to examine as many different characteristics of the species in question as possible and to determine in which characters they differ and in which they are alike. The assumption is that the differences and resemblances will reflect, at least in part, their true phylogenetic relationships. Ordinarily, as many different types of characters as possible are used in the hope that misleading data from any single character will be detected by a lack of agreement with the data from other characters.

The most easily studied and widely utilized characters pertain to morphology, including external morphology, internal anatomy and histology, and the morphology of the chromosomes in cell nuclei. It is particularly helpful,

of course, when morphological characters of living species can be compared with those of fossil forms. The fossil record is the most direct source of evidence about the stages through which past forms of life passed, but unfortunately that record is usually very incomplete and is subject to the same sorts of errors of interpretation as are characters of living species. Many groups of organisms have no fossil record suitable for working out the relationships between species; at best, the fossils may suggest the broad outlines of the evolution of major groups. Even in those groups where fossils are abundant, only characters of the hard parts of the organisms' bodies have usually been preserved. Nevertheless, in some groups, of which the horses are an outstanding example, the fossil record has provided much phylogenetic information that could have been obtained from no other source (Fig. 17.29).

Another source of information frequently used in studying phylogenies is embryology. Morphological characters are often easier to interpret if the manner in which they develop is known. For example, if it can be shown that a particular structure in organism A and a structure of quite different appearance in organism B both develop from the same embryonic primordium, then the resemblances and differences between those structures in A and B take on a phylogenetic significance that they would not have if they developed from entirely different embryonic primordia. Embryological evidence often allows us to trace the probable evolutionary changes that have occurred in

Fig. 17.29. Evolution of horses. The fairly complete fossil record of horses has enabled paleontologists to work out a reasonable picture of the evolutionary history of the group. *Hyracotherium* lived in the Eocene epoch about 55 million years ago. It was a small animal, only about the size of a fox terrier. It had four toes on each front foot and three on each rear foot. It was a browser, feeding on trees and bushes. *Mesohippus,* which lived during the Oligocene epoch about 35 million years ago, was a bit larger, and its front feet, like the rear feet, had only three toes. *Merychippus,* which was a grazer, lived during the Miocene about 25 million years ago. It had three toes on each foot, the middle one much larger than the other two, which were short and thin and did not reach the ground. *Equus,* the modern horse, is much larger than the ancestors shown here. It has only one toe on each foot. [Modified from G. G. Simpson, *Horses,* Oxford University Press, 1951.]

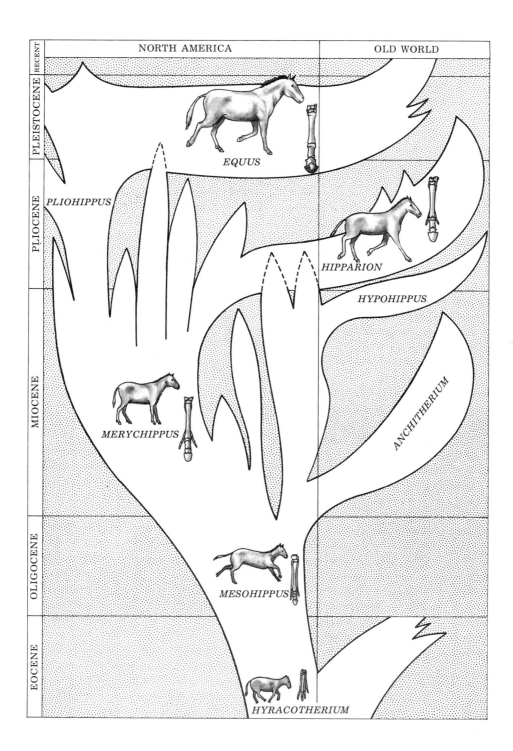

important structures and helps us reconstruct the probable chain of evolutionary events that led to the modern forms of life. For example, the fact that pharyngeal gill pouches appear briefly during the early embryology of mammals, including man, is thought to indicate that the distant ancestors of land vertebrates were aquatic.

Life histories have also played an important role in phylogenetic studies. The stages through which plants pass during their life cycles are particularly important sources of information, as we shall see when we examine the algae and the fungi, for example.

The morphology of the adult and embryo, combined when possible with information from the fossil record and from life histories, has traditionally been the basic source of data upon which phylogenetic theories have been based. In addition, comparative physiology, comparative behavior, and comparative ecology have supplied valuable information and will doubtless increase in importance as the effort to interrelate form and function grows. More recently, techniques have been developed for comparing the proteins of different species (e.g. those in the blood) by means of chromatography or electrical separation (electrophoresis), and the use of such techniques will probably become more widespread in the future. A technique has even been developed for determining the degree of similarity between the DNA of different species.

Whenever new techniques for studying organisms are devised, the data they produce provide another source of information for the systematists.[8] In modern biology, it has become the task of the systematist to gather together and correlate all that is known about the organisms he studies, and to try to reconstruct, in the light of modern evolutionary theory, some sort

of intelligible picture of the organisms and their relationships with one another. The systematist is thus just what the term implies; he is the one who tries to fit together into an orderly system all of the information gathered about the organisms by the anatomists, the paleontologists, the cytologists, the physiologists, the geneticists, the embryologists, the ethologists, the ecologists, the biochemists, and others.

The Problem of Convergence. Whether an investigator is using traditional morphological data or is making comparisons between DNA, whether he is obtaining information from physiology or from behavior or from life histories, he is still faced with the problem of interpreting the similarities and differences that he finds. He must always ask himself, for example, whether close similarities in a particular character really indicate close phylogenetic relationship or whether they simply reflect similar adaptation to the same environmental situation. The latter phenomenon is common in nature and is a frequent source of confusion in phylogenetic studies. When organisms that are not closely related become more similar in one or more characters because of independent adaptation to similar environmental situations, they are said to have undergone convergent evolution, and the phenomenon is called convergence (Fig. 17.30). Whales, which are mammals descended from terrestrial ancestors, have evolved flippers from the legs of their ancestors; those flippers superficially resemble the fins of fish, but the resemblances are due to convergence and they do not indicate a close relationship between whales and fish. Both arthropods and terrestrial vertebrates have evolved jointed legs and hinged jaws, but these similarities do not indicate that arthropods and vertebrates have evolved from a common ancestor that also had jointed legs and hinged jaws; there is good reason to think that these two groups of animals evolved their legs and jaws independently and that their legless ancestors were not closely related. The "moles" of Australia are not true moles but marsupials

---

[8] Systematists are also often called taxonomists. The branch of biology in which they specialize is called systematics or taxonomy. As the above description of the work of systematics indicates, "systematics is the scientific study of the kinds and diversity of organisms and of any and all relationships among them" (definition by George Gaylord Simpson).

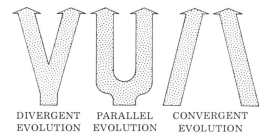

DIVERGENT PARALLEL CONVERGENT
EVOLUTION EVOLUTION EVOLUTION

Fig. 17.30. Patterns of evolution. In divergent evolution, one stock splits into two, which become less and less like each other as time passes. In parallel evolution, two related species evolve in much the same way for a long period of time, probably in response to similar environmental selection pressures. Convergent evolution occurs when two groups that are not closely related come to resemble each other more and more as time passes; this is usually the result of occupation of similar habitats and adoption of similar environmental roles.

(mammals whose young are born at a very early stage of embryonic development and complete their development in a pouch on the mother's abdomen); they occupy the same habitat in Australia as the true moles occupy in other parts of the world and have, as a result, convergently evolved many startling similarities to the true moles (Fig. 17.31).

The preceding discussion makes it evident that when similarities between two species are being studied by systematists, an attempt is made to determine whether the similarities are probably *homologous* (inherited from a common ancestor) or merely *analogous* (similar in function and often in superficial structure but of different evolutionary origins). Thus the wings of robins and those of bluebirds are considered homologous; i.e. the evidence indicates that both were inherited from a common avian ancestor with wings. But the wings of robins and the wings of butterflies are only analogous because, though they are functionally similar structures, they were not inherited from a common ancestor but were evolved independently and from different ancestral structures.

It is always important to indicate in what sense two structures are considered homologous or analogous. Thus the wings of birds and the

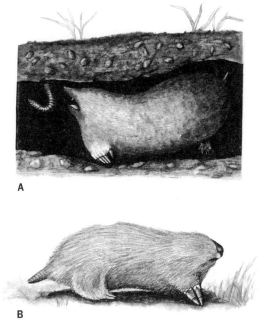

A

B

Fig. 17.31. Convergence between placental (A) and marsupial (B) moles. These two animals are not related, but they have similar habits and have convergently evolved many startling similarities.

wings of bats are not homologous as wings, for they were evolved independently, but they contain homologous bones, both types of wings having evolved from the forelimbs of ancient vertebrates that were ancestors to both birds and mammals. Similarly, the flippers of whales and seals evolved independently of each other, but both evolved from the front legs of land-mammal ancestors. Thus the flippers are homologous in the sense that both are forelimbs, with the same basic bone structure as other vertebrate forelimbs, but the modifications that make them flippers are analogous, not homologous.

Primitive Versus Advanced. Once all the data concerning a group of organisms have been brought together and analyzed as to similarities and differences, and once similarities have been evaluated as to probable homology and analogy, reasonable speculations can be made regarding the degree of relationship between the various organisms. But in any attempt to reconstruct the evolutionary history of the organisms, it is necessary to consider development in time; it is necessary to determine the direction in which the evolution of the characteristics of the organisms has proceeded. Suppose, for example, that the species in one group of beetles have three segments in their tarsi (feet), while the species in another group have four, and the species in still another group have five. Before speculations concerning the phylogeny of these beetles can be made, it must be determined whether the common ancestors of all three groups had three, four, five, or some other number of segments in their tarsi. Has there been an evolutionary gain of segments or an evolutionary loss of segments or both? In the language of the systematists: What is the primitive condition? The meaning of "primitive" is older, more like the ancestral condition. The contrasting term is "advanced," which means newer, less like the ancestral condition. Note that the terms "primitive" and "advanced" do not imply any value judgment that one is better than the other; nor do they imply that one is more complex than the other; they refer only to relative sequence in time.[9]

Two other terms, "specialized" and "generalized," are sometimes confused with "primitive" and "advanced." These terms refer to the relationships of organisms, or particular characteristics of organisms, to their environment. "Specialized" means adapted to a special, usually rather narrow, way of life. "Generalized" means broadly adapted to a greater variety of different types of environments and ways of life. Generalized characteristics are likely to be more primitive, and specialized ones more advanced, but this is far from being an absolute rule.

---

[9] For the beetles, all available evidence indicates that the larger number of tarsal segments is primitive and that the smaller number is advanced; i.e. there has been an evolutionary reduction in the number of segments.

In general, within any particular group of organisms, the more primitive characters will be the ones that have evolved more slowly. Hence systematists have made a great effort to learn which characters tend to evolve slowly (i.e. to be conservative) and which tend to evolve rapidly (i.e. to be labile). The most reliable way of learning this is, of course, to examine the fossil record. However, many groups have fossil records so poor that the results of such an examination are unsatisfactory. In such cases, it is necessary to deduce which characters are conservative and which are labile by study of contemporary organisms. One may assume, for example, that if a particular structure occurs in basically the same form in a great variety of only distantly related organisms, the characters of that structure are conservative and therefore provide more information about the primitive condition than would characters of some structure that varies greatly from species to species. Unfortunately, it is seldom possible to generalize from one group of organisms to another as to which sorts of characters are conservative and which are labile. Labile and conservative characters differ from group to group and must be determined separately for each.

Phylogeny and Classification

Over a million different species of animals and over 350,000 different species of plants are known. To deal with this vast array of organic diversity, biologists obviously need some sort of orderly system by which species can be classified in a logical and meaningful manner. Many different kinds of classifications are possible. We could, for example, classify flowering plants according to their color; all white-flowered species could be put in one group, all red-flowered species could be put in a second group, all yellow-flowered species could be put in a third group, etc. Or we could classify these same plants according to their average height; all species less than an inch tall could be put in one group, all species more than an inch but less than a foot tall could be put in a second group, all species more than a foot but less than three feet tall could be put in a third group, etc. Or we could classify the same plants according to the environment in which they grow; all species that grow primarily in fields could be put in one group, all species that grow primarily in forests could be put in a second group, all species that grow primarily in lakes could be put in a third group, etc. Each of these three systems of classification, and many others that could be devised, would impose a measure of order, but how meaningful, how informative, would they be? Obviously the information they would convey— about flower color, about average height, about habitat—is of an incidental kind that would fail to set apart fundamentally different organisms.

The classification system used in biology today, by contrast, conveys morphological information to the morphologist, physiological information to the physiologist, ecological information to the ecologist, and so forth. It is a system based on phylogenetic relationships that automatically encodes information about every aspect of the organisms it classifies.

The Classification Hierarchy. Suppose you had to classify all the people on earth on the basis of where they live. You would probably begin by dividing the entire world population into groups based on country. This subdivision separates inhabitants of the United States from the inhabitants of France or the inhabitants of Argentina, but it still leaves very large groups that must be further subdivided. Next, you would probably subdivide the population of the United States by states, then by counties, then by city or village or township, then by street, and finally by house number. You could then do the same thing for Mexico, England, Australia, and all the other countries (using whatever political subdivisions in those countries correspond to states, counties, etc. in the United States). This procedure would enable you to place every individual in an orderly

system based on categories that form a hierarchical system, as follows:

> Country
> State
> County
> City
> Street
> Number

Note that each level in this hierarchy is contained within and is partly determined by all levels above it. Thus, once the country has been determined as the United States, a Mexican state or a Canadian province is excluded. Similarly, once the state has been determined as Pennsylvania, a county in New York or one in California is excluded.

The same ideas apply to the classification of living things on the basis of phylogenetic relationships. Again a hierarchy of categories is used, as follows:

> Kingdom
> Phylum or Division
> Class
> Order
> Family
> Genus
> Species

Each category in this hierarchy is a collective unit containing one or more groups from the next-lower level in the hierarchy. Thus a genus is a group of closely related species (Fig. 17.32); a family is a group of related genera; an order is a group of related families; a class is a group of related orders; etc. The species in any one genus are believed to be more closely related to each other than to species in any other genus; the genera in any one family are believed to be more closely related to each other than to genera in any other family; and the families in any one order are believed to be more closely related to each other than to families in any other order; etc. Using this system, we can classify man, wolf, Herring Gull, and red oak as shown in Table 17.2.

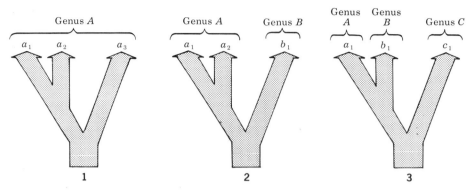

Fig. 17.32. **Alternative generic grouping for three related species.** Biologists try to group species in a way that will indicate their phylogenetic relationships. Thus a genus is a group of related species. But how closely related? There is no absolute answer to this question. Some biologists (the "lumpers") like large genera containing many subdivisions (subgenera or "species groups"); others (the "splitters") prefer small compact genera, containing only species that are very closely related. In the drawing, three alternative ways of grouping three related species are shown. The first recognizes only one genus, the second recognizes two, and the third recognizes three.

Notice that this table shows us immediately that the four species are not closely related, but that man and wolf are more closely related to each other, both being Mammalia, than either is to a bird such as the Herring Gull. And it shows us that the mammals and the bird are more closely related to each other than to the red oak, which is in a different kingdom. These relationships enable us to make many predictions about the similarities and differences we will find in the morphology, physiology, and ecology of the four species. The particular four species used in this table are all well known, and the relationships between them are probably intuitively clear to you, but many species are not so well known and the relationships between them not so clear. Much research may be necessary before they can be fitted into the classification system with any degree of certainty, and their assignment to genus or family (or even order) may have to be changed as more is learned about them.

Hierarchical classification systems similar to the one in current use have been employed by naturalists for many centuries. The current system dates from the work of a great Swedish naturalist Carolus Linnaeus (1707–1778), who wrote extensively on the classification of both plants and animals during the first half of the eighteenth century.[10] His system used kingdoms, classes, orders, genera, and species. The phylum and family categories were added to the system later. Now, it should be obvious to you that the rationale upon which Linnaeus based his system was very different from the phylogenetic one employed today. He worked a century before Darwin, and he had no conception of evolution. He doubtless thought of each species as an immutable entity, the product of a divine creation. He was simply grouping organisms according to similarities, primarily morphological. That his results were so similar to those obtained today is a reflection of the fact that morphological characters, being products of evolution, tell us much about evolutionary relationships. The Linnaean system would, however, produce results quite different from those of the modern phylogenetic system whenever it had to deal with cases of convergence or cases where gross morphological simi-

[10] His real name was Carl von Linné, but he usually wrote it in its Latinized form, and this practice is usually followed today.

TABLE 17.2

Classification of Four Species

Category	Man	Wolf	Herring Gull	Red oak
Kingdom	Animalia	Animalia	Animalia	Plantae
Phylum or Division	Chordata	Chordata	Chordata	Tracheophyta
Class	Mammalia	Mammalia	Aves	Angiospermae
Order	Primates	Carnivora	Charadriiformes	Fagales
Family	Hominidae	Canidae	Laridae	Fagaceae
Genus	*Homo*	*Canis*	*Larus*	*Quercus*
Species	*sapiens*	*lupus*	*argentatus*	*rubra*

larities are a poor indicator of phylogenetic relationships.

An outline of a modern classification of living things is given on pp. 917–922.

Nomenclature. The modern system of naming species also dates from Linnaeus. Before him, there had been little uniformity in the designation of species. Some species had a one-word name, others had two-word names, and still others had names consisting of long descriptive phrases. For example, the pre-Linnaean name for the common carnation was *dianthus floribus solitariis, squamis calycinis subovatis brevissimis, corollis crenatis,* and the name for the honeybee was *Apis pubescens, thorace subgriseo, abdomine fusco, pedibus posticis glabris utrinque margine ciliatis.* Linnaeus simplified things by giving each species a name consisting of two words: first, the name of the genus to which that species belongs and, second, a designation for that particular species. Thus the above-mentioned species of carnation became *Dianthus caryophyllus,* and the honeybee became *Apis mellifera.* Other species in the genus *Dianthus* have the same first word in their name, but each has its own specific designation (e.g. *Dianthus prolifer, Dianthus barbatus, Dianthus deltoides*). No two species can have the same name.[11] Notice that the names are always Latin (or Latinized) and that the genus name is capitalized while the specific name is not.[12] Both names are customarily written in italics (underlined if handwritten or typed). The correct name for any species, according to the present rules laid down in the International Rules of Botanical Nomenclature and the International Rules of Zoological Nomenclature, is usually the oldest validly proposed name.[13]

The same Latin scientific names are used

[11] More precisely, no two species of plants can have the same name, and no two species of animals can have the same name. Since the International Rules of Botanical Nomenclature and the International Rules of Zoological Nomenclature are completely separate, it is possible for a plant and an animal to have the same name. There is also a separate International Bacteriological Code of Nomenclature.

[12] This rule always holds for zoological names, but specific botanical names are sometimes capitalized when they are based on the name of a person or on other proper nouns.

[13] For purposes of priority, botanical naming dates from the publication of Linnaeus' *Species Plantarum* in 1753, and zoological naming dates from the publication of the 10th edition of his *Systema naturae* in 1758.

throughout the world. This uniformity of usage ensures that each scientist will know exactly which species another scientist is discussing. There would be no such assurance if common names were used; not only would any given species have a different name in each language, but often it would have two or three names in a single language. For example, the plant named *Bidens frondosa* is known by all of the following English names: beggar-ticks, stick-tight, bur marigold, devil's bootjack, pitchfork weed, and rayless marigold. Furthermore, a single common name is frequently applied to several different species. For example, "gopher" is the name of a turtle in Florida and the name of a rodent in Kansas, and "raspberry" is the common name for more than a hundred different species of plants.

REFERENCES

ALLEE, W. C., A. E. EMERSON, O. PARK, T. PARK, and K. P. SCHMIDT, 1949. *Principles of Animal Ecology*. Saunders, Philadelphia. (See esp. Section V, "Ecology and Evolution.")

DARWIN, C., 1859. *The Origin of Species by Means of Natural Selection*. John Murray, London. (Many modern editions are available, e.g. Modern Library, 1948, or, in paperback, New American Library, 1958.)

DOBZHANSKY, T., 1951. *Genetics and the Origin of Species*, 3rd ed. Columbia University Press, New York.

EHRLICH, P. R., and R. W. HOLM, 1963. *The Process of Evolution*. McGraw-Hill, New York.

FORD, E. B., 1964. *Ecological Genetics*. Wiley, New York.

GRANT, V., 1963. *The Origin of Adaptations*. Columbia University Press, New York.

MAYR, E., 1942. *Systematics and the Origin of Species*. Columbia University Press, New York.

———, ed., 1957. *The Species Problem*. American Association for the Advancement of Science, Washington.

———, 1963. *Animal Species and Evolution*. Harvard University Press, Cambridge, Mass.

———, E. G. LINSLEY, and R. L. USINGER, 1953. *Methods and Principles of Systematic Zoology*. McGraw-Hill, New York.

MOODY, P. A., 1962. *Introduction to Evolution*. 2nd ed. Harper, New York.

SIMPSON, G. G., 1949. *The Meaning of Evolution*. Yale University Press, New Haven, Conn. (Paperback edition, 1960.)

———, 1953. *The Major Features of Evolution*. Columbia University Press, New York.

STEBBINS, G. L., 1950. *Variation and Evolution in Plants*. Columbia University Press, New York.

SUGGESTED READING

BURNETT, A. L., and T. EISNER, 1964. *Animal Adaptation*. Holt, Rinehart & Winston, New York.

DOBZHANSKY, T., 1950. "The Genetic Basis of Evolution," *Scientific American,* January. (Offprint 6.)

EISELEY, L. C., 1956. "Charles Darwin," *Scientific American,* February. (Offprint 108.)

GRANT, V., 1951. "The Fertilization of Flowers," *Scientific American,* June. (Offprint 12.)

KETTLEWELL, H. B. D., 1959. "Darwin's Missing Evidence," *Scientific American,* March. (Offprint 842.)

LACK, D., 1947. *Darwin's Finches*. Cambridge University Press, New York. (Paperback edition, Harper Torchbooks, 1961.)

———, 1953. "Darwin's Finches," *Scientific American,* April. (Offprint 22.)

STEBBINS, G. L., 1966. *Processes of Organic Evolution*. Prentice-Hall, Englewood Cliffs, N.J.

WALLACE, B., 1966. *Chromosomes, Giant Molecules, and Evolution*. Norton, New York.

———, and A. M. SRB, 1964. *Adaptation*, 2nd ed. Prentice-Hall, Englewood Cliffs, N.J.

CHAPTER
18

ECOLOGY

Ecology is usually defined as the study of the relationships between organisms and their environment. As used here, the word "environment" has a very broad meaning; it embraces all those things extrinsic to the organism that in any way impinge upon it. It includes not only light, temperature, rainfall, humidity, and topography, but also parasites, predators, mates, and competitors. Anything not an integral part of a particular organism is part of that organism's environment. We have already discussed several topics that can be regarded as aspects of ecology—among others, osmotic interactions between organisms and their environmental media, the problems that plants and animals face in obtaining nutrients and exchanging gases, the behavioral responses of organisms to environmental stimuli, and the role of the environment in evolution. It is plain that ecology is an enormously broad and complex subject. We cannot hope to do more in this chapter than touch lightly on a few of the basic ecological concepts.

By convention, an organism's environment is usually divided into two principal components —the *physical environment* and the *biotic en-*

vironment. The physical environment includes all nonliving extrinsic things, conditions, or influences, and the biotic environment includes all living things that, directly or indirectly, influence the life of the organism. Although these two components of the environment are not really as easily separated as our definitions might seem to imply, it is often convenient to discuss them separately, and we shall do so here.

THE PHYSICAL ENVIRONMENT

The Medium and the Substratum

All organisms, whether plant or animal, are surrounded by either fluids or air. Even organisms such as those in soil, which, superficially, appear to be in another medium, are really in water or air—in the case of soil organisms, the water or air in the spaces between the soil particles. We have indicated in earlier chapters that of these two basic media water is the ancestral one, and that the individual cells even of air organisms can remain active only if they are kept moist.

Sea water is the most stable medium in which organisms can live. It undergoes remarkably little fluctuation in salt content, oxygen and carbon dioxide content, pH, or temperature. Only near the surface of the ocean or near the shore are fluctuations likely to be appreciable, and even there they are usually quite slow. Fresh water undergoes much greater fluctuations, particularly in very small ponds. In the course of a year, its temperature may vary many degrees. And since temperature has a marked effect on the solubility of oxygen in water, the oxygen content may also vary greatly. The amount and type of soil and debris carried into streams and lakes by rainwater running off the neighboring land may profoundly alter the mineral content and the pH of the streams and lakes, and it may radically change the depth to which light can

penetrate. Air, by contrast, seldom undergoes significant changes in chemical makeup, but it is subject to often extreme and rapid fluctuations in temperature and humidity. The amount of oxygen is much greater in air than in water.

A few organisms spend much of their lives suspended in air, and many spend their entire lives suspended in water. But most land organisms and many aquatic ones spend much of their time attached to or moving upon a solid surface or substratum. The characteristics of that substratum are important components of the organism's physical environment. Plants, for example, are often very sensitive to small differences in soils. These tend to vary in many characteristics, such as soil depth, physical properties, chemical content, and origin. A vertical section of soil (Fig. 18.1) usually shows a thin layer of partly decomposed plant litter on the surface; a layer of topsoil, usually well aerated and containing much organic material; a layer of subsoil, which is less favorable for root growth; and layers of parent material, usually rock in various stages of weathering, from which the soil particles are derived. The thickness of the topsoil is of great importance in determining what plant growth can occur.

The composition of the topsoil is also of great importance. Most soils are a complex of mineral particles, organic material, water, soluble chemical compounds, and air. In this complex, the dominant components by far are the mineral particles, which are composed largely of compounds of silicon and aluminum. They vary in size from tiny clay particles to coarse sand grains. One classification, according to the diameter of the particles, is as follows:

Sand	0.05–2.00 mm.
Silt	0.002–0.05 mm.
Clay	Less than 0.002 mm.

The proportions of clay, silt, and sand particles in any given soil determine many of its other characteristics. For example, very sandy soils, which contain less than 20 percent of silt and clay particles, have many air-filled spaces,

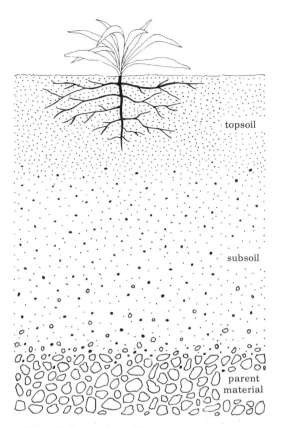

Fig. 18.1. A soil profile.

but they are so porous and their particles have so little affinity for water that water rapidly drains through them and they are unsuitable for growth of many kinds of plants. As the percentage of clay particles increases, the water retention of the soil also increases until, in excessively clayey soils, the drainage is so poor and the water is held so tightly to the particles that the air spaces become filled with water; few plants can grow in such waterlogged soil. Although different species of plants are adapted to different soil types, most do best in soils of the type known as *loams,* which contain fairly high percentages of each size particle (e.g. 24 percent clay, 29 percent silt, 30 percent fine sand, and 17 percent coarse sand). In such a soil, there is good but not excessive drainage and there is good aeration; the soil

particles are surrounded by (or contain) a shell of water, but there are numerous air-filled spaces between them.

Loams usually also contain considerable amounts of organic material (roughly 3–10 percent), mostly of plant origin. As this material decomposes, inorganic substances required for good plant growth are released into the soil. The organic material thus contributes to soil fertility. But it also plays another very important role; since it usually has a rather porous spongy texture, it helps loosen clayey soils and increase the proportion of pore spaces, thus promoting drainage and aeration. This is particularly true when the organic material is in the form of *humus,* which is composed mostly of decomposition products from cellulose and lignin. It is interesting that humus has the opposite effect on sandy soils, where it tends to reduce pore size by binding the sand grains together, thereby increasing the amount of water held in the soil. Thus we see that not only are organisms influenced by their physical environment but they, in turn, modify that environment.

The proportion of clay particles is not only important in determining the physical structure of soils and its aeration and water-holding capacity; it is also important in determining the amounts and the availability to plants of certain soil nutrients—in part because of the influence of the clay particles on water movement. If, for example, water percolates downward through the soil very rapidly and in large quantities, it will tend to leach many important ions from the soil, carrying them deep into the underlying rock layers, where roots cannot reach them. Nitrate ions are especially susceptible to leaching, and sulfate, calcium, and potassium ions may also be rapidly removed from the soil.

Excessive removal of calcium is particularly serious because it tends to make the soil become more acid. Although many plants grow best in slightly acid soils, most do not do well in strongly acid ones (however, some species, such as rhododendrons and cranberries, prefer very acid conditions). The acidity of the soil influences the availability of iron, manganese, phosphate, and some other ions, as well as the activity of soil organisms, many of which are inhibited by high acidity.

We have repeatedly spoken of the "availability" of ions to plants. Chemical analyses that give the total amount of the various ions present in soils can be somewhat misleading; because a certain proportion of these ions is not free, their availability to plants may be very different from what their total amount might seem to imply. A complex equilibrium generally exists between ions free in the soil water and ions adsorbed on the surface of colloidal clay and organic particles. Many factors, of which acidity is a prime example, can shift this equilibrium, either increasing the proportion of ions bound to the particles, and thus reducing availability, or increasing the proportion of free ions available in the soil solution.

The various characteristics of soils briefly mentioned here play a part not only in determining how many and what kinds of plants are likely to grow in any given region, but also in influencing the occurrence of soil animals. Earthworms, nematode worms, and millipeds, for example, are all sensitive to the structure, drainage, acidity, and chemical composition of soils. And animals that do not live in the soil are, of course, indirectly influenced in their distributions by soil types, because of their dependence upon plants as the source of high-energy organic nutrients.

Solar Radiation

All life on earth depends, ultimately, on radiation from the sun. This may be a truism, but it is such a vital truism that it bears repeating. With the exception of the relatively unimportant chemosynthetic organisms, all forms of life obtain their high-energy organic nutrients, either directly or indirectly, from photosynthesis. Thus the amount of incident sunlight is

a major factor in determining the abundance of organisms on different parts of the earth. Where sunlight is absent or in short supply, green plants will be absent or in short supply. And the only heterotrophic organisms living in such places will be those that can utilize nutrients brought into their dark environment from others where there is sunlight. For example, organisms living in the depths of the ocean, where light cannot penetrate, are either scavengers feeding on dead bodies or on waste products that sink from the upper layers of water where light is plentiful and life abundant, or they are predators or parasites feeding on the scavengers.

Light is, of course, also essential to many organisms as a vehicle for bringing them information about their surroundings. The vast majority of animals have photoreceptors of some sort, and we have seen that many plants also depend upon light as a regulating stimulus for numerous of their life processes.

Still another fundamental role of solar radiation is the maintenance of environmental temperatures. Indeed, far more of the solar energy reaching the earth is converted into the heat energy of air and water and soil than is converted into chemical-bond energy by photosynthesis. Since most organisms are very sensitive to the temperature of their surroundings, it follows that temperature is one of the determinants of plant and animal distributions.

When we think of temperature limitations on distributions, we often concentrate on the variation of temperature with latitude or with altitude. We are all aware that as one moves north or south, or as one moves up or down mountain slopes, both the average temperatures and the high and low temperature extremes to which one may be subjected change. We therefore expect latitudinal and altitudinal limitations on plant and animal distributions that are imposed, at least in part, by temperature. But while gross changes with latitude or altitude are certainly of great importance, local temperature variation is often critical in determining exactly where within the overall species range individuals of a particular species will be found.

Temperature variations can be very local indeed. Someone living only a few miles from the weather station serving his community may hear over the radio that the temperature is 20°F. Checking his own outdoor thermometer, he may find that it registers 12°F—8° less than the temperature at the station. The difference could easily be even greater. Within a single lot, variations of several degrees may occur between sheltered and exposed places, between points near the ground and points at various elevations above the ground. The same sorts of highly local variations may be found in humidity, wind velocity, barometric pressure, amount of sunlight, soil type, etc. It follows, then, that one should not expect to find exactly the same kinds of organisms living at all points within even a very small area. Plants and animals don't live under the generalized climatic conditions announced for the region by the Weather Bureau; they live under microclimatic conditions that may vary radically over the area covered by the regional announcement.

It is the microclimatic conditions that ecologists must analyze if they want to understand fully the conditions under which the organisms they study really live. When they say that the climate and soil of eastern Pennsylvania are appropriate for a given species, they do not mean that every part of eastern Pennsylvania is appropriate; they only mean that the species occurs in many local areas within eastern Pennsylvania. And when they say that plant species A ranges from South Carolina in the south to central New York in the north, and from the Atlantic coast to central Ohio in the west, they do not mean that one should expect to find individuals of species A everywhere within that large area; they only mean that there are places within that overall range where the species occurs and that there are no places outside that range where it occurs.

Heat from solar radiation plays a fundamental role also in the cycling of water within the environment. When rainwater falls on the land, some of it quickly evaporates again into the atmosphere. Of the water that does not immediately evaporate, some is absorbed by plants or is drunk by animals, some runs off the surface of the land into streams and lakes, and some percolates down through the soil into the water table below. The water in the streams and lakes and that in the subsurface water table eventually finds its way to the ocean. There is constant evaporation from streams, lakes, and oceans, and also from the bodies of plants and animals. The energy for most of this evaporation comes either directly or indirectly from solar radiation. The endless cycling of water to earth as rain, back to atmosphere through evaporation, and back again to earth as rain maintains the various freshwater environments and also provides the vast quantities of water necessary for life on land; in addition, it is a major factor in modifying temperatures. The tremendous importance of rainfall for terrestrial and fresh-water life requires no elucidation here; one need only think of the contrast between a desert and a lush tropical forest.

THE FLOW OF ENERGY AND MATERIALS

Limiting a discussion of environment to its physical aspects, as we tried to do in the preceding section, is a rather artificial procedure. Soils, for example, can be fully understood only if the effects on them of the plants and animals living in and on them are considered. Plant roots break up the soil in which they grow, and they remove substances from the soil and add other substances to it. The plant shoots shield the soil beneath them, thereby altering the patterns of rainfall, humidity, light, and wind to which the soil is subject. And when the plants die, their substance adds organic material to the soil, changing both its physical and chemical makeup. Microorganisms in the soil alter its composition profoundly. Soil animals, such as earthworms and millipeds, constantly work the soil, breaking down its organic components and moving materials between different soil layers. On a larger scale, the numbers and kinds of organisms living in any given region can influence the rainfall, humidity, temperature, and wind patterns of that region, just as those same physical parameters, in turn, influence the organisms. In short, there is constant interaction between the physical and biotic elements of the environment. Neither can be fully understood alone. Together, the physical features of the environment of any given area and all the organisms living in that area constitute an ecological system, usually called an *ecosystem* for short. One can think of a given lake or field or forest or desert as an ecosystem.

The life within an ecosystem is characterized by several levels of organization. An ecologist might disregard the levels below that of the individual (molecular, cellular, tissue, organ, and organ system) and concern himself with individual organisms, or with *populations,* which are groups of individuals belonging to the same species, or with *communities,* which are units composed of all the populations living in a given area. Most of the first half of this book dealt with the way individuals (and lower levels of organization) function. In this chapter, we shall deal primarily with the life of populations and communities.

As we have seen in many connections, life represents a high level of organization, a state therefore inherently unstable and ever tending toward disruption. Life continues because there is continual input of energy into the system, energy that makes possible the ordering of the materials of which living things are composed. There is a constant interplay, therefore, between forces that tear down life and forces that build it up. This interplay occurs at all the levels of organization that characterize life, from the molecular and cellular to the community. We have already examined cellular and organismic metabolism; we shall here consider community metabolism, the flow of energy and materials through the community or through the ecosystem of which it is a part.

Food Chains and Energy Pyramids

We have already seen that the outside source of energy for the community is sunlight trapped by green plants (or photosynthetic bacteria) in the process of photosynthesis. And we have seen that heterotrophic organisms—animals and some plants—obtain the energy they need by eating green plants or by eating other heterotrophic organisms that ate green plants. There is, in short, a movement of energy and materials from one organism to another within any self-contained community. It is customary to designate each sequence of organisms through which such movement may occur as a *food chain.* In most real communities, there are so many different possible food chains, and these are so complexly intertwined, that together they form a community *food web* (Fig. 18.2). No matter how long a food chain or how complex a food web may be, however, certain basic characteristics are always present. Every food chain or web always begins with autotrophic organisms, green plants in the vast majority of cases; such autotrophs are the *producers* for the community. And every food chain or web always ends with *decomposers,* the organisms of decay, which are usually bacteria and fungi that release simple substances re-usable by the producers. The links between the producers and the decomposers are more variable. The producers may die and be acted upon directly by the decomposers, in which event there are no intermediate links. Or the producers may be eaten by *primary consumers,* the herbivores. These, in turn, may be either acted upon directly by decomposers or fed upon by *secondary consumers* such as

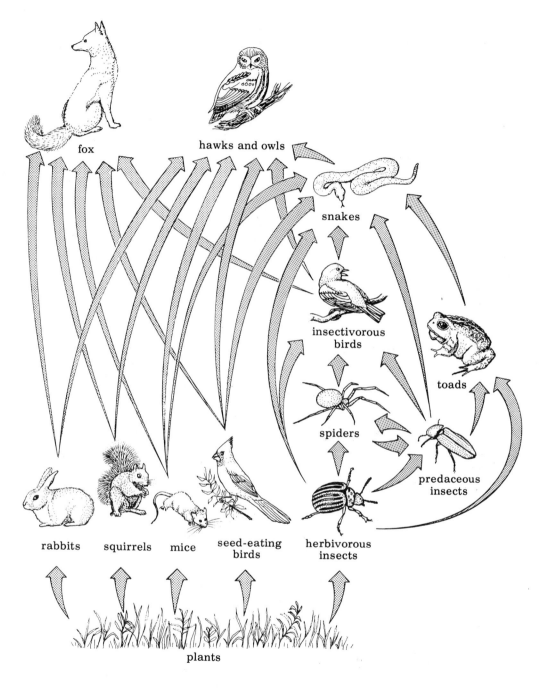

Fig. 18.2. Diagram of a hypothetical food web. No real food web would be as simple as this one.

carnivores or parasites or scavengers (Fig. 18.3).

Ecologists speak of the successive levels of nourishment in the food chains of a community as *trophic levels.* Thus all the producers together constitute the first trophic level; the primary consumers (herbivores) constitute the second trophic level; the herbivore-eating carnivores constitute the third trophic level, and so on. The species that comprise each trophic level differ from one ecosystem to another, but in general the pattern is the same. At each successive trophic level there is loss of energy from the system,[1] a loss predictable from the Second Law of Thermodynamics, which states that every energy transformation involves loss of some usable energy (see p. 112). Because of this unavoidable loss of energy, the total amount of energy at each trophic level is less

[1] This loss is often estimated by measuring the respiration at each trophic level.

than at the preceding level, usually much less. There is less energy in the herbivores of a community than in the plants of that community, and there is less energy in the carnivores than in the herbivores, etc. Thus the distribution of energy within a community can be represented by a pyramid, with the first trophic level (producers) at the base and the last consumer trophic level at the apex (Fig. 18.4).

The *pyramid of energy* just described is a necessary consequence of physical law and is thus characteristic of all ecosystems. Several other attributes of ecosystems sometimes fit a pyramidal model because they are related to the flow of energy through the system, but they are not themselves consequences of physical law and therefore often deviate from the model. One example is the *pyramid of biomass* (Fig. 18.5A). In general, the decrease of energy at each successive trophic level means that less biomass can be supported at each level. Thus the total mass of carnivores in a given community is almost always less than the total mass of herbivores. The size, growth rate, and longevity of the species at the various trophic levels of a community are important in determining whether or not the pyramidal model will hold for the biomass of that community. Thus, in some aquatic communities where the

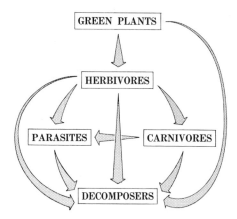

Fig. 18.3. Diagram of the relationships between the principal trophic levels in an ecosystem. The green plants are the producers, which are eaten by the herbivores, the primary consumers. The primary consumers may in turn be eaten by parasites or carnivores, the secondary consumers. Producers or consumers may die and become food for decomposer organisms.

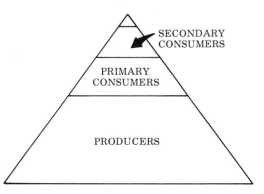

Fig. 18.4. The pyramid of energy. There is much more energy at the producer level in an ecosystem than at the consumer levels, and there is more at the primary consumer level than at the secondary consumer level.

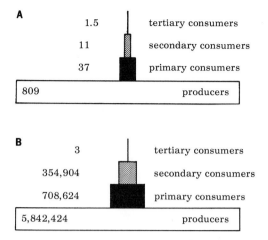

Fig. 18.5. Examples of the pyramids of biomass and numbers. (A) Pyramid of biomass in the aquatic ecosystem of Silver Springs, Florida. Figures represent grams of dry biomass per square meter. (B) Pyramid of numbers in a bluegrass field. [Modified from E. P. Odum, *Fundamentals of Ecology*, Saunders, 1959.]

producers are small algae with high metabolic and reproductive rates, there may be a greater biomass of consumers than of producers at any given moment, but the total mass of all the algae that live during the course of a year is greater than the total mass of consumers that live during that year.

The interrelationships between the organisms at different trophic levels exert some influence on the size of the organisms. Thus carnivores are frequently larger and stronger than their herbivorous prey. And secondary carnivores are frequently larger than the primary carnivores on which they feed. Now, since total biomass tends to decline at successive trophic levels, if the size increases at successive levels, it follows that the number of individuals must decline at each level (except at the decomposer level). Consequently, in some communities there is a *pyramid of numbers,* there being fewer individual herbivores than plants, and fewer individual carnivores than herbivores (Fig. 18.5B). However, there are many communities in which no pyramid of numbers oc-

curs. For example, plant-eating insects are often far smaller than their food plants, and there may be many more individual insect consumers than plants even though their biomass is less. And food chains involving parasites tend to have reversed size relationships, because the parasite is smaller and usually more numerous than the host.

Cycles of Materials

We have seen that energy is steadily drained from the ecosystem as it is passed along the links of a food chain. The system cannot continue functioning without a constant input of energy from the outside. In other words, there is no such thing as an energy cycle. But this is not the case with materials. The same materials can be used over and over again, and hence can be passed round and round through the ecosystem indefinitely. We can, therefore, speak of cycles of materials. Let us examine two examples—the carbon cycle and the nitrogen cycle.

The Carbon Cycle. The carbon dioxide present in the atmosphere and dissolved in water constitutes the reservoir of inorganic carbon from which almost all organic carbon is derived. It is photosynthesis, largely by green plants, that extracts the carbon from this inorganic reservoir and incorporates it into the complex organic molecules characteristic of life (Fig. 18.6). Some of these organic molecules are soon broken down again, and their carbon is released as CO_2 by the plants in the process of respiration. But much of it remains in the plant bodies until they die or are eaten by animals. The carbon obtained from plants by animals may be released as CO_2 during respiration, or it may be eliminated in more complex compounds in the body wastes, or it may remain in the animals until they die. Usually the wastes from animals and the dead bodies of both plants and animals are broken down (respired) by the decomposers, and the

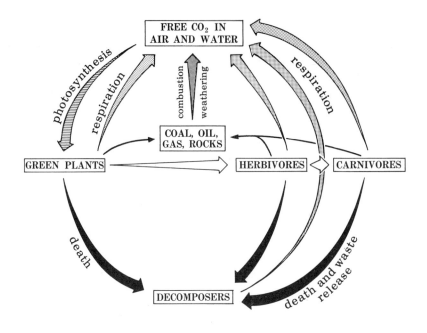

Fig. 18.6. The carbon cycle.

carbon is released as CO_2. Notice that whether the carbon follows a short pathway involving only one or two trophic levels or a longer pathway involving three, four, or more trophic levels, most of it eventually returns as CO_2 to the air or water whence it began. This is, then, a true cycle (or, more precisely, a complex of interlocking cycles); carbon is constantly moving from the inorganic reservoir to the living system and back again.

The pathways just outlined are all ones through which carbon moves rather rapidly. Complete passage through the system may take only minutes or hours or at most a few years. There are alternative pathways, however, that take much longer. The dead bodies of organisms occasionally fail to be decomposed promptly and are converted instead into coal, oil, gas, rock (particularly limestone), or diamond. Carbon in these forms may be removed from circulation for very long periods, perhaps

permanently; but some of it may eventually return to the inorganic reservoir if the coal, oil, and gas are burned or if the rocks are sufficiently weathered. Man has of course greatly accelerated the return of such carbon to the active cycle.

The Nitrogen Cycle. Another critical element in community metabolism is nitrogen. It is, as we have already seen, a constituent of the amino acids of which proteins are composed and of the nucleotides of which nucleic acids are composed. The reservoir of inorganic nitrogen is the gaseous N_2, which comprises roughly 78 percent of the atmosphere. But N_2 has very little biological activity. It enters the bodies of all organisms, but comes back out of most of them without having played any significant role in their life processes. Some microorganisms, however—a few bacteria, the blue-green algae, and a few fungi—can use N_2 in the synthesis of substances that can be utilized by other organisms. This process is known as *nitrogen fixation.* Although some nitrogen fixation may also occur as a result of electrical discharges, such as lightning, the amount is minimal, and it is biological nitrogen fixation by microorganisms that provides most of the usable nitrogen for the earth's ecosystems (Fig. 18.7).[2]

Some of the nitrogen-fixing bacteria live in a close symbiotic relationship with the roots of higher plants, where they occur in prominent

[2] Some nitrogen is also provided by industrial processes.

nodules (Fig. 18.8).[3] The legumes (plants belonging to the pea family) are particularly well known for their numerous root nodules, but plants of some other families have them also.[4] Other nitrogen-fixing microorganisms live free in soil or water. All of these nitrogen-fixing

[3] The nitrogen-fixing bacteria in the nodules of legumes belong to the genus *Rhizobium.* Two of the best-known genera of free-living nitrogen-fixing bacteria are *Azotobacter* and *Clostridium.* Apparently most, and possibly all, blue-green algae can carry out nitrogen fixation. Several species of soil yeasts (fungi) can do so also.

[4] Among the nonleguminous plants with symbiotic nitrogen-fixing microorganisms in nodules are species of alder (*Alnus*), oleaster (*Elaeagnus, Hippophae,* and *Shepherdia*), wax myrtle (*Myrica*), and New Jersey tea (*Ceanothus*).

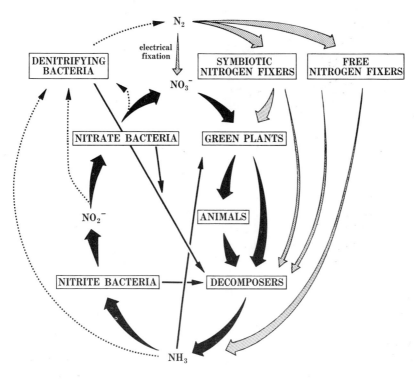

Fig. 18.7. The nitrogen cycle. Stippled arrows indicate paths of nitrogen fixation, by which nitrogen from the atmosphere is added to the main soil–organism part of the cycle. Dotted arrows indicate the paths of denitrification, by which nitrogen is removed from the main soil–organism cycle and returned to the atmosphere.

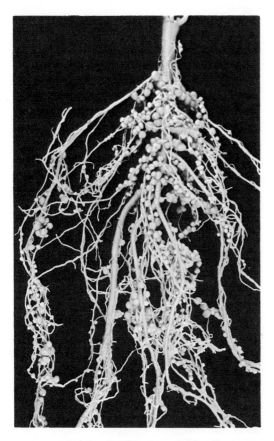

Fig. 18.8. Photograph of roots of a legume (bird's-foot trefoil), showing nodules. [Courtesy Nitragin Co., Milwaukee, Wis.]

microorganisms can reduce N_2 to ammonia (NH_3), which is often in the form of ammonium ions (NH_4^+). They then either use the ammonium in the synthesis of organic nitrogen-containing compounds or excrete it into the soil or water in which they live.

The symbiotic bacteria in root nodules promptly release much of the fixed nitrogen they produce into the host plant's cytoplasm, primarily in the form of amino acids. It has been estimated that as much as 90 percent of the fixed nitrogen can be liberated into the host's cytoplasm in this way, there being little or no storage of fixed nitrogen within the bacteria or the nodules. Consequently legumes can grow well in soils that are very poor in avail-

able nitrogen. The bacteria in their nodules not only supply the plants with all the fixed nitrogen they need, but actually produce a surplus, some of which is excreted from the roots of the legumes into the soil. Thus legumes (and the other plants that have similar nodules) tend to increase the fertility of the soil in which they grow. Farmers often build up the nitrogen content of their fields by periodically planting them to legumes.

The nitrogen-fixing microorganisms that live free in the soil or water release large quantities of ammonia into the surrounding medium. When they die, the fixed nitrogen in their cells is broken down to ammonia by decomposer organisms. The decomposers act in the same way upon the organic nitrogen compounds in the bodies of green plants or animals or other microorganisms when they die, and upon the nitrogen compounds in the urine and feces of animals. Some of this free ammonia is picked up as ammonium ions by the roots of higher plants, particularly certain grasses and forest trees, and incorporated into more complex compounds. But most flowering plants utilize nitrate in preference to ammonia, and the evidence indicates that nitrate is the main source of nitrogen for higher plants. This nitrate is produced from ammonia in the soil by nitrifying bacteria.

The process of **nitrification** is usually accomplished by two different groups of bacteria, working in sequence. The first group converts ammonium ions into nitrite (NO_2^-), and the second group converts this nitrite into nitrate (NO_3^-).[5] The nitrate released into the soil by the latter bacteria can be picked up by the roots of plants. Most of the nitrate in the roots is quickly incorporated into organic nitrogen compounds and then either stored, primarily in cell vacuoles, or transported to other parts of the plant body through the vascular tissue. The

[5] Among the most important genera of nitrite bacteria are *Nitrosomonas*, *Nitrosocystis*, and *Nitrosospira*. Among the most important genera of nitrate bacteria are *Nitrobacter*, *Nitrocystis*, and *Bactoderma*.

nitrogen compounds in the plant body may eventually again be broken down to ammonia by decomposers when the plant dies or when an animal that ate the plant dies or excretes it. Notice, then, that nitrogen can cycle repeatedly from plants to decomposers to nitrifying bacteria to plants without having to return to the gaseous N_2 state in the atmosphere. In this respect, the nitrogen cycle differs from the carbon cycle, where every turn of the cycle includes a return of CO_2 to the atmosphere.

Although nitrogen need not return to the atmosphere at every turn of the cycle, there is a steady drain of some of it away from the soil or water and back to the atmosphere. This is because some bacteria carry out a process of *denitrification;* i.e. they convert ammonia or nitrite or nitrate into N_2 and release it. In short, the denitrifying bacteria remove nitrogen from the soil–organism part of the nitrogen cycle and return it to the atmosphere, while the nitrogen-fixing microorganisms do the reverse—they take nitrogen from the atmosphere and add it to the soil–organism part of the cycle.

This brief summary of the carbon and nitrogen cycles, which suggests the complexity of the movement of materials through an ecosystem, may help you appreciate the interdependence of the different species within a stable ecosystem and, in particular, the fundamental and essential role played by microorganisms. Because they are not observed as easily as the larger plants and animals, we have a tendency to forget about them. Too often, we think only of the harmful microorganisms, particularly those that cause diseases, and fail to recognize that our continued existence depends upon other microorganisms.

INTERSPECIFIC INTERACTIONS

We have already seen that the various species of organisms that live in the same area and are thus part of the same community and ecosystem affect one another in a variety of ways. The herbivores depend upon the green plants for their high-energy carbon compounds and organic nitrogen compounds. Carnivores depend upon herbivores for these same materials. The green plants depend upon microorganisms for nitrogen fixation and for nitrification of ammonia. All organisms, plant and animal, depend upon the decomposers to rid the environment of the dead bodies and excreta that would otherwise soon prohibit life. Earthworms and millipeds and other soil animals work the soil and change its characteristics, thereby influencing the number and kinds of plants that can grow in it. Tall plants shade the ground below them and also change the wind patterns and humidity to which the organisms living beneath them are exposed. Plants provide shelter and nesting sites for animals. And so on. We could continue this list of interactions almost indefinitely. The point is simply that a community is not just a collection of different species that happen to be able to live under the prevailing conditions in the area; it is an integrated system of species that are, to a greater or lesser extent, dependent upon each other.

It is much beyond the scope of this book, of course, to attempt to examine at length all the various kinds of interspecific interactions that exist in most communities. Here we shall discuss only a few of the main interactions not covered elsewhere.

Symbiosis

The term "symbiosis" is used in a variety of ways in the biological literature. Some authors apply it only to cases where two species live together to their mutual benefit. Others apply it not only to cases where both species benefit but also to those where one species benefits while the other is not harmed. We shall use the word in a broader sense. Etymologically, symbiosis simply means "living together," without any implied value judgments. This is the meaning it was given when it was first introduced into biology, and this is the meaning it will have in this book. We shall, however, recognize three categories of symbiosis. The first is *commensalism,* which means a relationship in which one species benefits while the other receives neither benefit nor harm. The second is *mutualism,* where both species benefit. The third is *parasitism,* where one species benefits and individuals of the other species are harmed. We can summarize the distinctions as follows (a plus sign means benefit, a minus sign means harm, and a zero means no significant effect):

Relationship	Species A	Species B
Commensalism	+	0
Mutualism	+	+
Parasitism	+	−

Commensalism. The advantage derived by the commensal species from its association with the host frequently involves shelter, support, transport, or food, or several of these. For example, in tropical forests numerous small plants, called epiphytes, usually grow on the branches of the larger trees or in forks of their trunks. These commensals, among which species of orchids and bromeliads are prominent, are not parasites. They use the host trees only as a base of attachment and do not obtain nourishment from them. They apparently do no harm to the host except when so many of them are on one tree that they stunt its growth or cause limbs to break. A similar type of commensalism is use of trees as nesting places by birds.

Sometimes it is difficult to tell what benefit is involved in a commensal relationship. For example, certain species of barnacles occur nowhere except attached to the backs of whales, and other species of barnacles occur nowhere except attached to the barnacles that are attached to whales. Just what advantages either of these groups of barnacles enjoys is not clear. They do, of course, get a relatively unoccupied base for attachment, and they get transport that increases the dispersal of their species. But it is hard to see how these benefits alone would

have sufficed for the evolution of such specificity.

In some cases of commensalism, however, the benefit is dramatically obvious. For example, certain species of fish regularly live in association with sea anemones, deriving protection and shelter from them and sometimes stealing some of their food. These fish swim freely among the tentacles of the anemones, even though those tentacles quickly paralyze other fishes that touch them. The anemones regularly feed on fish; yet the particular species that live as commensals with them sometimes actually enter the gastrovascular cavity of their host, emerging later with no apparent ill effects. The physiological and behavioral adaptations that make such a commensal relationship possible must be quite extensive. Another striking example is a small tropical fish (*Fierasfer*) that lives in the rectum of a particular species of sea cucumber. The fish periodically emerges to feed and then returns to its curious abode by first poking its host's rectal opening with its snout and then quickly turning so that it is drawn tail first into the rectal chamber. Still another example is a tiny crab that lives in the mantle cavity of oysters. The crab enters the cavity as a larva and eventually grows too big to escape through the narrow opening between the two valves of the oyster's shell. It is thus a prisoner of its host, but a well-sheltered prisoner. It steals a few particles of food from the oyster but apparently does it no significant harm.

Mutualism. Examples where a symbiotic relationship benefits both species are common. We have already mentioned several in earlier chapters. For instance, the relationship between a flowering plant and its insect pollinators is clearly mutualistic. So is the relationship between a legume and the nitrogen-fixing bacteria in its root nodules. And so is the relationship between a termite or a cow and the cellulose-digesting microorganisms in its digestive tract, or between a human being and the bacteria in his intestine that synthesize vitamin B_{12}. The plants we call lichens are actually composites formed of an alga and a fungus united in such close mutualistic symbiosis that they give the appearance of being one plant. Apparently the fungus benefits from the photosynthetic activity of the alga, and the alga benefits from the water-retaining properties of the fungal walls.

As this discussion of commensalism and mutualism (particularly the former) implies, the division of symbiosis into three subcategories is in many ways an arbitrary one. Commensalism, mutualism, and parasitism are all parts of a continuous spectrum of possible interactions. We called the relationship between epiphytes and their hosts commensalism, but we said that sometimes the host is harmed. In such cases, should we call the relationship parasitism? We spoke of commensalistic interactions between certain fish and sea anemones, and pointed out that both the fish and the anemones had probably evolved special physiological and behavioral adaptations making their relationship possible. Would the anemones have evolved such adaptations unless the relationship was beneficial to them? And if so, is this a case of mutualism rather than commensalism? We saw that oyster crabs steal food from their host. Are we certain that this is not significantly detrimental to the host? By what measure do we decide how much harm is significant and how much is not? Should we call this relationship parasitism? We called the association of algae and fungi to form lichens mutualism. But are we sure that the algae derive significant benefit from the association? After all, we know that the algal species in lichens are perfectly capable of free living whereas the fungal species usually are not. Might we have been too ready to say that the algae are shielded from desiccation by the fungi? Should we classify lichens as commensalistic associations, or even as parasitic ones? It really isn't very important which category we apply to most of these cases. The cate-gories are only human creations designed to help us organize what we know about nature. What is important is that we keep in mind how commensalism, mutualism, and parasitism grade into each other and that we recognize that each real-life case of symbiosis is different from all others, and must be studied and analyzed on its own merits.

Parasitism. Just as there are no sharp boundaries between parasitism annd commensalism, or even between parasitism and mutualism, there is no strict delimitation between parasitism and predation. Mosquitoes and lice both suck the blood of mammals; yet we usually call only the latter parasites. Foxes and tapeworms may both attack rabbits, but foxes are called predators and tapeworms are called parasites. The usual distinction is that a predator eats its prey quickly and then goes on its way, while a parasite passes much of its life on or in the body of a living host, deriving food from the host in a manner that is harmful to the host. Obviously this is not always a clear distinction. How long must one organism live on the body of another to be classed as a parasite? But though there will always be intermediate cases, it is profitable to distinguish between predation and parasitism, because each of these is a mode of existence followed by many different kinds of organisms and each involves its own characteristic sorts of adaptations.

Parasites are customarily divided into two types: external parasites and internal parasites. The former live on the outer surface of their host, usually either feeding on the hair, feathers, scales, or skin of the host or sucking its blood. Internal parasites may live in the lumina of the various tubes and ducts of the host's body, e.g. the digestive tract or respiratory passages or urinary ducts; or they may bore into and live embedded in tissues such as muscle or liver; or, in the case of viruses and some bacteria and protozoans, they may actually live inside the individual cells of their host.

External parasitism has probably sometimes evolved from what was once a commensal relationship. And in some cases, internal parasitism has probably evolved from external parasitism. External parasites doubtless wander occasionally into one of the body openings of their host, such as the mouth, nasal openings, or anus. Most presumably cannot long survive in the quite different environment they encounter there. But it seems reasonable to suppose that in the course of thousands or millions of years some wanderers might have had genetic constitutions enabling them to survive in the new habitat they found inside the host's body. From such a beginning the specializations that ordinarily characterize the more advanced internal parasites could have evolved. Other internal parasites may have evolved from free-living forms that were frequently swallowed by accident or inhaled on dust particles. Again, most would have been killed, but over the ages an occasional few may have been genetically preadapted to survive under the new conditions, and they may have given rise to lineages that became increasingly specialized for the new way of life.

However it arose, internal parasitism is usually marked by much more extreme specializations than external parasitism. The habitats available inside the body of another living organism are completely unlike those outside, and the unusual problems they pose have resulted in evolutionary adaptations quite different from those seen in free-living forms. For example, internal parasites have frequently lost organs or whole organ systems that would be essential in a free-living species. Tapeworms, for instance, have no digestive system. They live in their host's intestine, where they are bathed by the products of the host's digestion, which they can absorb directly across their body wall without having to carry out any digestion themselves.

Because of their frequent evolutionary loss of structures, internal parasites are often said to be degenerate. "Degenerate," of course, implies no value judgment, but simply refers to the

lack, common in parasites, of many structures present in their free-living ancestors. From an evolutionary point of view, loss of structures useless in a new environment is an instance of positive adaptation. Such loss is just as much an evolutionary advance, a specialization, as the development of increased complexity in some other environment. Specialization does not necessarily mean increased structural complexity; it only means the evolution of characteristics particularly suited to some special situation or way of life. In internal parasites—or cave animals, which frequently lack eyes—the development and maintenance of structures that no longer serve a useful function would require energy that the organism might use to more advantage in some other way. And some useless structures, such as eyes in both internal parasites and cave animals, might well be a handicap in these special environments, because they would be a likely point of infection. It is readily understandable, therefore, that natural selection might favor those individuals in which such useless organs are either relatively small or lacking entirely. The concept of evolutionary loss of unused structures as a result of differential survival and reproduction (natural selection) of different genotypes should not be confused with the Lamarckian idea that use and disuse can directly influence the size of the structures in an organism's progeny.

Structural degeneracy is far from being the only sort of special adaptation commonly seen in internal parasites. They often have body walls that are highly resistant to the destructive enzymes and antibodies of the host. Tapeworms, for example, are constantly bathed by the potent digestive juices of their host; yet their enzyme-resistant cuticle protects them from being digested. And tapeworms have very specialized heads, with hooks and suckers, that enable them to anchor themselves and avoid being expelled by the often vigorous peristaltic contractions that move the other contents of the host's intestine.

Perhaps the most striking of all adaptations

of internal parasites are those concerned with their life histories and reproduction. Individual hosts don't live forever. If the parasitic species is to be perpetuated, therefore, a mechanism is needed for changing hosts. At some point in their life cycle, then, all internal parasites move from one host individual to another. But this is seldom simple. Rarely can a parasite move directly from one host to another of the same species. For example, consider the life cycle of a beef tapeworm. The eggs of such a tapeworm living in a man's intestine are shed in the host's feces. A cow eats plants contaminated with human feces, and the tapeworm eggs hatch in the cow's intestine. The young larvae bore through the wall of the cow's intestine, enter a blood vessel, and are carried by the blood to a muscle, where they encyst (become surrounded by a bladderlike case and lie inactive). If a man then eats the raw or insufficiently cooked beef, the tapeworm larva becomes activated in his intestine, its head attaches itself to the intestinal wall, and a mature worm develops. The beef tapeworm thus passes through two hosts during its life cycle: an intermediate host (cow), in which it undergoes some of its early development, and a final host (man), in which it matures.

As life cycles of internal parasites go, the one just described is rather simple. It is not unusual for a life cycle to include two or three intermediate hosts and/or a free-living larval stage. But such a complex development makes the chances that any one larval parasite will encounter the right hosts in the right sequence exceedingly poor. The vast majority die without completing their life cycle. It is therefore understandable that internal parasites should characteristically produce huge numbers of eggs. Although they may be structurally degenerate in other ways, they usually have extremely well-developed reproductive structures. In fact, some internal parasites seem to be little more than a sac of highly efficient reproductive organs. Furthermore, most internal parasites are capable of uniparental reproduction. The chances are poor enough that a larva

will find a suitable host itself; they are even poorer that it will find one in which a prospective mate also lives. Obligatory biparental reproduction would thus be an additional handicap in an already difficult situation.

In the course of their evolution, parasites usually develop special features of behavior and physiology that make them better adjusted to the particular characteristics of their host and more efficient at competing with other parasites. This means that they often tend to become more and more specific. Where an ancestral organism may have parasitized all species in a particular family, each of its various descendants may parasitize only species in a particular genus, or they may even be so specific that each can parasitize only one species of host at each stage in its development. This evolutionary trend toward specificity is manifest in another way too; parasites often tend to become more specific not only with regard to their host species but also with regard to the part of the host's body they can inhabit. Some external parasites may live only on the head of their host, others only on the back, and still others only on the legs. Internal parasites inhabiting the digestive tract of their host are often restricted to one small section of that tract. G. A. School of McGill University examined the distribution of eight species of nematode worms in the intestines of the European tortoise. He found that the different species of worms differed in their linear distribution within the intestine (some being most common near the anterior end and others in the middle third of the intestine), and that they also differed in their radial distribution (some being more abundant near the mucosa and others being distributed more generally throughout the lumen).

It must be remembered, of course, that the host species is also evolving, and that there is strong selection pressure for its evolution of more effective defenses against the ravages of its parasites. There is thus a constant interplay between host and parasite. As the one evolves better defenses, the other evolves ways of counteracting them—these counteractions leading to pressure on the host to evolve still better defenses, against which the parasite may then evolve new means of surviving, and so forth. Although this sort of mutual evolution will continue as long as the host-parasite relationship exists, a dynamic balance is usually reached eventually, the host surviving without being seriously damaged and the parasite prospering moderately well too. It is, in fact, decidedly disadvantageous to the parasite to kill its host. We have said that many parasites are host-specific. If they should cause the extinction of their host, then they themselves would also become extinct. Therefore the balance eventually reached is not due solely to the evolution of better defenses by the host. It is also due to the parasite's evolving in such a way that it becomes better adjusted to its host and causes less serious disturbance.

Probably most long-established host-parasite relationships are balanced ones. Relationships that result in serious disease in the host are usually relatively new ones, or ones in which a new and more virulent form of the parasite has recently arisen, or ones where the host showing the serious disease symptoms is not the principal host of the parasite. For example, the American Indians suffered severely when exposed to pathogens first brought to North America by European colonists, even though some of those same pathogens caused only mild symptoms in the Europeans who had been exposed to the pathogens for many centuries and in whom the host-parasite relationship had nearly reached a balance. Many examples are known where man is only an occasional host for a particular parasite and suffers severe disease symptoms, although the wild animal that is the major host shows few ill effects from its relationship with the same parasite.

Predation

We shall here regard a predator as an organism that is free-living and that feeds on other living organisms. This is an admittedly broad definition, which embraces both carnivores (predators that eat other animals) and herbivores (predators that eat plants). Most predators are animals, but a few are plants, as we saw in an earlier chapter. Many carnivorous predators and some herbivorous ones kill their prey, but a few carnivores (e.g. mosquitoes, biting flies) and many herbivores devour only a portion of their prey and the prey generally recovers. Predators are usually much less prey-specific than parasites.

The effect of a predatory species on its prey species varies. Sometimes the predator severely limits the numbers or distribution of its prey, often to a point far below what the environmental resources could support, and the prey may become extinct. In other cases, the predator plays only a minor role in the life of the prey, usually because it is much rarer than the prey or because it commonly utilizes some other food source. There is, of course, a continuous gradient of possibilities between these two extremes. Representing a fairly common middle ground are those cases where the predator helps hold down the prey population, but not so severely as to endanger the continued existence of the species. This degree of predation is, in fact, often decidedly beneficial to the prey species (though not, of course, to the individuals eaten); it helps regulate the population size of the prey and prevent it from outrunning its resources. The same thing can be said of parasitism. We shall return to this idea later.

As in parasitism, long-established predator-prey relationships in a stable ecosystem tend to evolve toward a dynamic balance in which the predation is an important regulatory influence in the life of the prey species but not a real threat to its survival. This sort of balance is, of course, beneficial to the predator as well as to the prey, because extinction or severe depression of the prey population would diminish the future resources of the predator and in some cases might even lead to its extinction as well. Factors involved in the predator-prey balance include the relative numbers and sizes of the two species, the vulnerability of the prey to the predator, the extent to which the predator can (or does) utilize other food sources, and the amount of energy obtained by the predator from consuming one prey individual.

We shall return to the subject of predation when we discuss population regulation later in this chapter.

Interspecific Competition

Ecologists use the word "competition" in many different ways. Some define it very broadly to cover any interaction that is harmful to one or both of the interacting individuals, including parasitism and predation. We shall use a more restricted definition, one that excludes parasitism and predation, and regard competition as an interaction where both parties are harmed. If we were to fit the concept into the list on p. 722, it would be symbolized by minus-minus. Ordinarily competition occurs when a number of organisms (of the same or of different species) utilize the same limited resource. Thus interspecific competition may involve food, water, sunlight, shelter, space, nesting sites, etc. The more similar the requirements of the species involved, the more intense the competition. Or, as biologists often put it, the more the niches of the species overlap, the more intense the interspecific competition.

The Concept of Niche. Niche is another important concept in ecology that is defined in a variety of ways. Here it will be used to denote the functional role and position of an organism in the ecosystem. Niche should not be confused with *habitat,* which is the physical place where the organism lives. The characteristics of the habitat help define the niche, but they alone are far from sufficient. Also involved is what the organism eats; how and where it finds and captures its food; what extremes of heat and cold, dry and wet, sun and shade, and other climatic factors it can withstand, and what values of these factors are optimal for it;

at what time of year and what time of day it is most active; what its parasites and predators are; where, how, and when it reproduces; etc. In short, every aspect of an organism's existence helps define that organism's niche. It must be emphasized that niche is an abstract concept and as such can never be fully measured. The most we can do is measure certain of the more important parameters of an organism's niche.

The following graphic method of representing the niche of a species has been proposed: Consider one environmental variable, X_1, such as temperature. Determine the high and low extremes the species in question can tolerate; plot these on a coordinate, and connect them by a line. Do the same for a second environmental variable, X_2, and draw its line at right angles to the first one. These two lines together determine a rectangular surface.

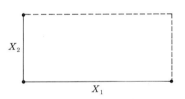

Now determine the values for a third environmental variable, X_3, and connect them by a line oriented at right angles to the other two. The three lines together now determine a volume within which every point corresponds to some combination of values for the three variables that would permit the species to survive.[6]

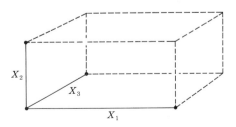

[6] There is an important complication that partly invalidates this procedure: The environmental variables are seldom completely independent. Thus, for example, the temperature extremes a species can tolerate may be different at different humidities.

If you were to continue this procedure, adding more and more variables each determining a different dimension, you would obtain a multidimensional hypervolume. If you included a dimension for every variable relevant to the species in question, the resulting multidimensional hypervolume would represent the niche of the species.

Since it is difficult to grasp a system involving more than three dimensions, and since it is also difficult to illustrate such a system on a two-dimensional surface such as a page of this book, it may be helpful to represent the niche by a shape rather than a volume. According to this method, the possible values for each variable (X_1, X_2, X_3, . . . , X_n) are indicated by a line having a unique orientation but having its origin at the same point as the origin of all the other lines. Then the ends of the lines are connected, and the resulting shape represents the niche.

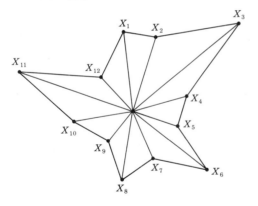

Consequences of Intense Competition. There is a principle to which most (though not all) ecologists subscribe to the effect that two different species cannot for long simultaneously occupy the same niche in the same place.[7] But it is implicit in our definition of niche that no two species could ever occupy

the same niche. To do so, they would have to be identical in every respect and hence they would be one species, not two. What, then, is the value of this principle? Its value is much like that of the Hardy-Weinberg Law, which also describes a situation that would never really occur. It helps us understand why the different species living together in a stable community ordinarily occupy quite distinct niches, and it helps us understand the sorts of interactions that will result when two species with very similar (though not identical) niches occur together.

The more similar the two niches are, the more likely it is that both species will utilize in common and in the same way at least one limited resource (food, shelter, nesting sites, etc.). They will therefore be competing for that limited resource. Such competition usually leads to one (or two) of three possible outcomes: (1) The competitive superiority of one of the rival species may be such that the other is driven to extinction. (2) One species may be competitively superior in some regions, and the other may be superior in other regions with different environmental conditions, with the result that one is eliminated in some places and the other is eliminated in other places; i.e. sympatry disappears, but both species survive in allopatric ranges. (3) The two species may rapidly evolve in divergent directions under the strong selection pressure resulting from their intense competition. Natural selection would favor those individuals with characteristics differing from those of the other species, because such characteristics would tend to minimize competition. In other words, the two species would rapidly evolve greater differences in their niches. This is the phenomenon we called character displacement in the preceding chapter. Whether extinction, range restriction, character displacement, or a combination of the last two, will be the outcome in any given case of intense interspecific competition is determined by a host of factors too complex to discuss here.

---

[7] This statement is sometimes called Gause's axiom or the competitive exclusion principle.

Let us look at a few well-studied examples of competition and its consequences. G. F. Gause of the University of Moscow worked with two closely related species of protozoans, *Paramecium caudatum* and *Paramecium aurelia,* in laboratory cultures. When cultured separately, the population curve for each species had a typical sigmoid shape (Fig. 18.9). But when the two species were cultured together, the population growth rate of *P. aurelia* was slower than normal and *P. caudatum* failed to survive. Similar results were obtained by Thomas Park and his colleagues at the University of Chicago. They worked with flour beetles of the genus *Tribolium.* When *T. confusum* and *T. castaneum* were kept together in the same container of flour, one or the other species always became extinct. The conditions of temperature and humidity under which the competition between the two species of beetles took place greatly influenced which species would win. Thus *T. castaneum* usually won under hot-wet conditions, while *T. confusum* usually won under cool-dry conditions. The competition between the flour beetles was not for food, which was plentifully available for both. Apparently it was more a matter of competition for space. Crowding and the resultant conditioning of the medium had slightly different effects on the natality, mortality, and rate of development of the two species, and thus determined which would survive and which would become extinct.

J. H. Connell's study of barnacles on the Scottish coast provides a good example of competition between two species whose niches overlap but are sufficiently distinct for both species to survive by occupying slightly different habitats. A species of the genus *Chthamalus* occupies the upper part of the intertidal zone, and a species of *Balanus* occupies the lower part of the intertidal zone (Fig. 18.10). The boundary between the two distributions is roughly the level of the mean high neap tide.[8] Casual

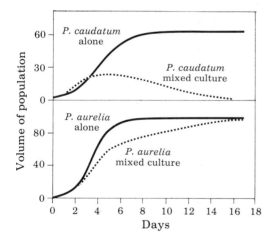

Fig. 18.9. Effect of competition between two species of *Paramecium.* The solid curves show the growth of population volume of each species alone in a controlled environment with a fixed food supply. The dotted curves show the change in population volume of the same species when in competition with each other under the same conditions. [Modified from G. F. Gause, *Science*, vol. 79, 1934.]

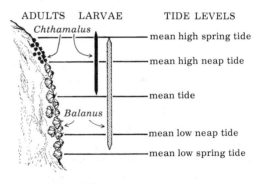

Fig. 18.10. Effect of competition between two species of barnacles. Although there is a broad area in which the larvae of both species settle, competition eliminates most of the overlap by the time the adult stage is reached, *Chthamalus* being largely restricted to the zone above the level of the mean high neap tide and *Balanus* to the zone below this level. See text for more complete description. [Modified from J. H. Connell, *Ecology*, vol. 142, 1961.]

[8] Neap tides are the lowest tides of a lunar month.

examination of the distribution of these two species of barnacles on the intertidal rocks would not reveal whether they were kept separate by competition or by different responses to physical factors such as the percentage of time out of water. Connell artificially kept one study area clear of *Balanus* and another clear of *Chthamalus*. He found that the larvae of *Chthamalus* would settle and grow in the upper portion of the zone normally occupied by *Balanus* as long as *Balanus* was not there. In the reciprocal experiment, *Balanus* larvae would settle in the *Chthamalus* zone but could not survive there even if no *Chthamalus* were present. Apparently each species could occupy a portion of the intertidal zone (roughly between the levels of the mean high spring tide and the mean high neap tide for *Chthamalus* and below the mean tide for *Balanus*) from which the other was barred by physical factors. But in the intermediate zone where physical factors permitted each species to survive (roughly between the levels of mean high neap tide and mean tide), it was competition that kept them separate, *Balanus* usually eliminating *Chthamalus*.

It is not always easy to detect the differences between the niches of two or more closely related sympatric species. At first glance, the species may appear to be occupying the same niche in a stable way and thus to discredit the exclusion principle. But closer study usually reveals differences of fundamental importance. Robert MacArthur, then at the University of Pennsylvania, studied a community where several closely related species of warblers (small insect-eating birds) occurred together and found that their feeding habits were significantly different. Myrtle Warblers fed predominantly among the lower branches of spruce trees; Black-throated Green Warblers fed in the middle portions of the trees; and Blackburnian Warblers fed toward the tops of the same trees and on the outer tips of the branches. We have noted similar differences in feeding habits between sympatric Galápagos finches.

POPULATIONS AS UNITS OF STRUCTURE AND FUNCTION

Whatever aspect of ecology is being considered —whether it is the flow of energy and materials in the ecosystem, or symbiosis, or competition, or community structure and change—the reference is generally to species, or local subdivisions of species, rather than to individuals. Hence the species and the local populations of which it is composed are levels of biological organization to which we must direct special attention.

Intraspecific Organization

We have seen that when two or more sympatric species have broadly overlapping niches, particularly as concerns resources in short supply, they are thrown into intense competition, often with quite disruptive results. But competition is obviously not restricted to the interspecific situation. Individuals belonging to the same species utilize the same resources, and, if those resources are limited, they must compete with one another. Thus intraspecific competition is also an important aspect of the dynamics of an ecosystem. But the matter is more complicated than that. Members of the same species may compete, but, to some extent at least, they must also cooperate. In some cases, the cooperation may be very extensive, as in colonial organisms or in animals that habitually live together in herds or flocks. The extreme of intraspecific cooperation is seen, of course, in animals (e.g. man and a few insects) that form societies. On the other hand, there are some species of animals and many plant species in which the individuals pass much of their lives without any cooperative activity, their intraspecific interactions being largely restricted to antagonistic ones. Yet even in these species cooperation must sometimes occur if the species is to be perpetuated; the individuals must mate with each other (unless the species is completely asexual).

We see, therefore, that within a species there are two opposing sets of forces that influence relationships between individuals—disruptive forces, particularly competition, which tend to drive the individuals apart (in both the spatial and the evolutionary sense), and cohesive ones, particularly reproduction but often also increased protection from predators and from destructive weather, which tend to hold the individuals together. It is not surprising, therefore, that organisms have evolved a variety of intraspecific organizational mechanisms that help balance the conflicting disruptive and cohesive forces. We have already discussed at some length the role of intraspecific communication, particularly pheromones and visual and vocal displays, in this regard. We shall here examine a few other aspects of intraspecific organization.

Spacing. Within any given area, the individuals of a population could be distributed uniformly, randomly, or in clumps (Fig. 18.11). Uniform distributions are relatively rare. They occur only where environmental conditions are fairly uniform throughout the area and where, in addition, there is intense competition or antagonism between individuals. For example, in some mature forests the large trees may have an almost uniform distribution (i.e. they may be spaced at regular intervals) because competition for sunlight is so intense. Creosote bushes are often spaced almost uniformly over a desert area because the roots of each bush give off toxic substances that prevent germination of seedlings in a circular zone around the base of the bush. Recently it has been shown that some aromatic shrubs give off volatile growth inhibitors that prevent root growth of seedlings in the vicinity, and this emanation sometimes produces quite regular spacing of the shrubs.

Random distributions are also relatively rare. They occur only where the environmental conditions are uniform, where there is no intense competition or antagonism between individuals, and where, moreover, there is no tendency for the individuals to aggregate. Since the chances that all three of these conditions will be met simultaneously are obviously poor, ecologists must usually work with nonrandom distributions, which complicates the sampling procedures and statistical tests they may use.

Clumping is by far the most common distribution pattern for both plants and animals in nature, for several reasons: (1) The environmental conditions are seldom uniform throughout even a relatively small area. Variations in soil, in topography, in the distributions of other species, and in such microclimatic factors as moisture, temperature, and light may produce important habitat differences within the area. The organisms will obviously tend to occur in those spots where such factors are most favorable. (2) Reproductive patterns frequently favor clumping. This is particularly true in plants that reproduce vegetatively and in animals where the young remain with their parent. (3) Animals often exhibit behavior patterns that lead to active congregation in loose groups or in more organized colonies, schools, flocks, or herds. And even sexual attraction produces a departure from the theoretical con-

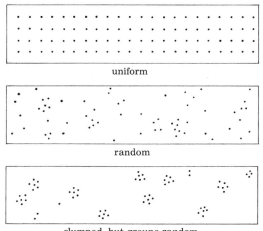

uniform

random

clumped, but groups random

Fig. 18.11. Uniform, random, and clumped distributions.

ditions necessary for a completely random distribution.

A clumped distribution may increase competition for nutrients, food, space, or light, but this deleterious effect is often offset by some beneficial ones. For example, trees growing together in a hedgerow on the great plains may compete more intensely for nutrients and light than if they were widely separated, but they may be better able to withstand strong winds. And the clump, which has less surface area in proportion to mass than an isolated tree, may be better able to conserve moisture and to modify its own microclimate and microhabitat in other ways. Aggregations of animals frequently reduce the rate of temperature change in their midst—an effect that is particularly important in cold weather. For example, during the winter coveys of quail huddle tightly together and in this way withstand low temperatures that would kill isolated birds. A group of animals may also have an advantage in locating food and in withstanding attacks by predators. Light-sensitive animals often survive exposure to illumination longer if they are in a group. Thus we see that the optimum density for population growth and survival is often an intermediate one; undercrowding may be as deleterious as overcrowding (Fig. 18.12).

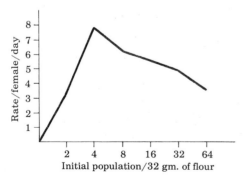

Fig. 18.12. Effect of initial population density upon rate of population growth in *Tribolium confusum.* The rate of growth per female per day is highest at intermediate densities. [Modified from W. C. Allee *et al., Principles of Animal Ecology*, Saunders, 1949.]

Territoriality and Home Range. Some of the simplest sorts of animal populations show little if any internal social organization. But many aggregations, particularly in the vertebrates and in the more complex invertebrates, exhibit considerable internal organization and integration. One frequent aspect of this organization is the phenomenon of *territoriality,* in which an individual or a pair defends a definite area from intrusion by other individuals (particularly males of the same species). We discussed the role of displays in territorial defense in an earlier chapter. Several types of territories have been recognized. One type is an area within which mating, nesting, and feeding during the breeding season all occur. Another is an area for mating and nesting, feeding occurring elsewhere. Still others are areas used for mating only, areas used for nesting only, areas used for roosting or feeding only, etc. Whatever the type, territoriality seems to function in spacing individuals in such a manner that the most severe aspects of competition and individual antagonism are minimized and social stability is improved.

Territoriality also plays a role in controlling the size of the breeding population. Although territories tend to be larger when population pressure is low and smaller when population pressure is high, there is usually a minimum requisite territory below which successful reproduction will not occur. The size of the minimum territory varies greatly from species to species, being rather large in animals that are only mildly social and sometimes quite small in highly social animals such as nesting gulls.

Even though most animals frequently travel beyond the borders of their defended territory, particularly in search of food, they tend to remain within a fairly limited area for long periods, sometimes for their entire lives. This area is called a *home range.* For example, the home range of whitetail deer is about 0.5–2 square miles, that of cottontail rabbits averages about 14 acres, and that of meadow mice averages about a fifteenth of an acre.

Social Hierarchies. Another aspect of organization frequently found in animal aggregations, particularly those of vertebrates, is a social hierarchy. For example, a newly established flock of hens will establish within a few days a series of dominance-subordination relationships that will effectively order the individuals within the flock. These relationships are based on the first few hostile encounters between each pair of birds. Bird A may be particularly large and aggressive, and may win her encounters with all other individuals of the flock. She thus becomes the dominant bird, and in future encounters the other hens will often move away from her without attempting to resist. Similarly, bird B may become established as dominant over all other birds in the flock except A. In other words, B can peck C or D without their pecking back, but B submits to pecking from A without pecking back. In this way, a flock of ten hens might come to have a *peck order* that could be diagrammed as follows:

$$A \rightarrow B \rightarrow C \rightarrow D \rightarrow E \rightarrow F \rightarrow G \rightarrow H$$

where A is dominant to all the other birds, and has the "right" to peck them without being pecked back, and H is dominant to none. Sometimes the peck orders are less simple. For example, D might have been particularly aggressive when she happened to have her initial encounters with A, and A may have been tired or ill at the time, with the result that, although D is subordinate to B and C, and B and C are subordinate to A, D may be dominant to A:

$$A \rightarrow B \rightarrow C \rightarrow D \rightarrow E \rightarrow F \rightarrow G \rightarrow H$$

Among the numerous factors that help determine an animal's position in a social hierarchy are age, size, strength, sex, health, hormonal condition, seniority in the group, and location of the first encounter. Once established, however, a "peck-right system" like that in chickens tends to become more or less fixed, and an old or ill individual may continue to dominate more vigorous associates long after it has lost the capacity to defeat them in physical combat. The reason is probably that, once the dominance-subordination relationship for each combination of individuals has been established, the subordinate individual makes no effort to retaliate when pecked by the dominant one and thus fails to discover that conditions have changed. A peck-right system thus tends to inhibit social mobility. In some other animals, the hierarchial system is a more fluid one. In pigeons, for example, a subordinate bird will often give at least token resistance to a dominant one. In such a "peck-dominance system," changes in the physical condition of individuals are more quickly discovered and exploited, and there is thus more social mobility than in a peck-right system.

A social hierarchy, once established, tends to give order and stability to the relationships within the group. There is less tension, and there is less fighting and disturbance. When, for example, one flock of chickens is allowed to establish a stable peck-order and another is kept disrupted by frequent additions of new members and removal of old ones, the birds in the unstable flock eat less, gain less weight, lay fewer eggs, fight more, and suffer more wounds.

Societies. There may be some division of labor within the social aggregations discussed above. For example, one individual may serve as a lookout for a prairie-dog town, or one crow may stay in a tall tree as a sentinel while the rest of the flock is feeding in a cornfield. Or an experienced old doe may serve as leader of a herd of red deer. But such division of labor is primitive in comparison with that characteristic of some animal societies. Societies are long-lasting animal aggregations with extensive division of labor and internal organization.

They have evolved independently in several groups of animals, notably the insects and mammals. Among the insects, all termites and ants and some bees and wasps live in societies. Insect and human societies have many superficial resemblances, but when examined more closely they are found to be fundamentally different. These two groups of animals are so different in so many of their other biological attributes that it is not surprising to discover that their convergent evolution of society living is based on radically different organizational and behavioral mechanisms.

All insect societies are large, highly specialized families. Typically, a single inseminated female, the queen (sometimes accompanied by workers, as in honeybees), founds a new social unit by laying eggs which hatch into larvae that develop into workers and (in ants and termites) soldiers. Thus the division of labor in insect societies is based on major biological differences between individuals—in short, on the presence of different castes. Just how the castes are determined is not fully understood, and the process is not the same in different insects. In Hymenoptera (ants, bees, and wasps), workers hatch from fertilized eggs and are sterile females. The size of the cell in which a given female larva develops and the amount and type of food it is given are evidently important elements in determining whether the larva will become a queen or a worker (or a soldier in ants); pheromones may also be involved. In most cases, hymenopteran males, whose sole function is insemination of a new queen, hatch from unfertilized eggs and are haploid. In termites, which are not closely related to Hymenoptera, workers and soldiers may be of either sex and may, in some species and under certain conditions, develop into reproductives. Apparently, primer pheromones secreted by soldiers and reproductives play a major part in determining the number of new soldiers and reproductives that will develop.

The organization and integration of insect societies are based not only on the caste system but also on behavior patterns that are primarily instinctive and hence subject to very little modification. During the course of their development, however, individuals may perform a variety of tasks. For example, worker honeybees usually serve as nurse bees for roughly the first two weeks after metamorphosis, first incubating the brood and preparing brood cells, and later feeding the larvae. Then they may become house bees for a week or two, acting as storekeepers, housecleaners, wax secreters, or guards. Finally, they may become field bees for four or five weeks, foraging for nectar and pollen. The individual has no choice of roles in this system; her role is determined by a combination of caste, stage of development, and the conditions of the hive. And she cannot long survive apart from the group to which she belongs.

By contrast, human societies are not simply specialized family groups. Family groups are important, of course, but they constitute only one component of a human society. A human society is typically an aggregation of many individuals and family groups, in which most adult members take part in reproduction; there is no setting aside of one or two individuals to serve as reproductive machines for the entire group while the other individuals remain sterile. Division of labor is not primarily based on biological differences or castes, and behavior patterns are greatly modified by learning. There is, in short, considerable choice of roles, and an individual can change groups and even survive for extended periods apart from any group.

Both types of societies are highly adapted functional groups. Both have been biologically successful. But one should keep their differences in mind and not make the mistake of generalizing too readily from one to the other.

Population Density and Its Regulation

The density of a population can be expressed in number of individuals per unit area or volume (e.g. 50 pine trees per acre) or in terms of biomass per unit area or volume (e.g. 4 tons of clover per acre). Number of individuals is a satisfactory measure when the size of the individuals in the population is nearly uniform, but when size is rather variable, as it frequently is with plants and some animals, biomass gives a more accurate idea of the population's importance in the flow of energy and materials through the ecosystem. Whatever measure is used, population density is usually found to be quite variable. There do seem to be definite upper limits, however. The theoretical upper limit of density is determined by the interaction of several factors, including the total energy flow in the ecosystem (i.e. its productivity), the trophic level to which the species in question belongs, and the size and metabolic rate of the individuals. In other words, energy would always be an ultimate limiting factor for any population. There is just so much energy available at a particular trophic level in any given ecosystem, and there can be no more biomass than that amount of energy can support. But actual densities often fluctuate at levels well below the theoretical maximum possible level. Study of the factors that regulate the densities of real populations in nature is thus a major aspect of modern ecology.

Births, Deaths, and Survival. The immediate determiners of population size are the numbers of births and deaths per unit time and the average survival time. If the number of births rises but the number of deaths falls, remains the same, or rises more slowly, then the population will increase. Conversely, if the number of deaths rises but the number of births falls, remains the same, or rises more slowly, then the population will decrease. So much is obvious. What we really want to know is how the birth and death rates and average survival time are governed. That they are governed in part by environmental influences is clear from the fact that the actually observed values for these three population parameters are quite

different from the values that are theoretically possible.

The standard customarily used in evaluating actually observed birth rates is the maximum potential birth rate, which is the theoretical maximum under ideal conditions. It can be estimated by determining the birth rate per reproductive-age female (or sometimes simply per 1,000 individuals without regard to sex or age) under the best conditions that can actually be found. The birth rates commonly encountered will usually fall well below the maximum, an indication that one way environmental factors can influence population size is by causing changes in the rate of production of new individuals.

The theoretical minimum mortality for a population is the number of deaths expected if all deaths were the result of "old age," i.e. if all individuals lived to the end of their potential life span. Of course, the average longevity in any real population will be far below the potential physiological longevity—an indication, once again, that environmental factors influence population dynamics. Since minimum mortality is not usually found in nature, it is often useful to determine the mortality rates for the various age groups in a population. Such data show us what stages in the life cycle are most susceptible to environmental control, and allow us to compute the percentage of individuals that will still be alive at the end of each age interval. The results may be graphed as a survivorship curve (Fig. 18.13).

The curves in Fig. 18.13 illustrate several different survivorship patterns. Curve A approaches the pattern that would be expected if all the individuals in the population realized the average physiologically possible longevity. There would be full survival through all of the early age intervals (as shown by the horizontal curve), and then all the individuals would die more or less at once and the curve would fall suddenly and precipitously. Curve D approaches the other extreme, where the mortality is exceedingly high among the very

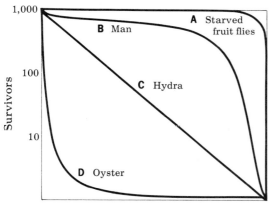

Fig. 18.13. Four different types of survivorship curves. The vertical coordinate has a logarithmic scale. For explanation, see text. [Modified from E. P. Odum, *Fundamentals of Ecology*, Saunders, 1959, after Deevey.]

young but where any individual surviving the earliest life stages has a good chance of surviving for a long time thereafter. Between these two extremes is the condition represented by curve C, where the mortality rate at all ages is constant. The survivorship curves for most wild-animal populations are probably intermediate between curves C and D, and the curves for most plant populations are probably near the extreme of D. In other words, high mortality among the young is the general rule in nature.

Changes in environmental conditions may radically alter the shape of the survivorship curve for any given population, and the altered mortality rates in turn may have profound effects on the dynamics of the population and on its future size. For example, one of the chief causes for the enormous increase in the population of human beings has been a great reduction in mortality during the early life stages as a result of improvements in sanitation, nutrition, and medical care. These improvements have caused a shift in the human survivorship curve from one intermediate between curves C and D in primitive societies to one approach-

ing A in the most advanced societies. There is no evidence that the shift is due to a rise in the human birth rate per reproductive-age female (in fact, the birth rate has almost certainly fallen) or, despite all the advances of modern medicine, to an increase in the potential life span.

Biotic Potential and Environmental Resistance. We have seen that the maximum possible birth rate for a population almost always far exceeds the actual ecological birth rate, and we have seen that the potential physiological longevity is usually far greater than the average ecological longevity. In other words, under natural conditions, the number of births is lower and the number of early deaths is higher than would be expected under ideal conditions. One way to understand the dynamics of real populations is to find out what to expect of a population under ideal conditions and then try to determine how actual conditions modify this expected pattern. Let us assume, then, that we can study a population that is stationary, has a stable age distribution, and exists in an unlimited environment (i.e. one where the amount of food, space, light, and other resources is not limiting, and where the actions of other organisms are not limiting—which means that there is no predation, parasitism, or competition). The maximum population growth rate under such ideal conditions is called the *biotic potential.* It has been defined as "the inherent property of an organism to reproduce, to survive, i.e., to increase in numbers."

Every species, whether plant or animal, unicellular or multicellular, has an enormous biotic potential. You are doubtless familiar with the dramatic calculations of what would happen if a pair of organisms produced a full complement of offspring and if all those offspring survived to produce a full complement of offspring in their turn, and so on for a number of generations. For example, one pair of houseflies starting breeding in April could have

191,010,000,000,000,000,000 descendants by August if all their eggs hatched and if all the resulting young survived to reproduce. One biologist[9] has made the following calculations concerning 100 starfish found living along a small sector of the Pacific coast just north of San Francisco:

Assuming that half of these were females, and that each produced one million eggs (a modest estimate), the population in the next year would be about 50,000,000. These would include about 25,000,000 females, all of which would again produce about a million eggs each. It is obvious that, if the ordinary rate of reproduction were to continue for even a few generations with 100 percent survival of all offspring, soon the starfish would fill the seas and be pushed out across the lands by the sheer pressure of reproduction. Indeed, at the rate of reproduction here described, it would take only fifteen generations for the number of starfish to exceed the estimated number of electrons in the visible universe (10^{79})!

We mentioned in Chapter 1 that such calculations as these played an important role in leading Charles Darwin to formulate his theory of natural selection. Darwin himself made the following statement concerning the reproductive potential of elephants:

The elephant is reckoned the slowest breeder of all known animals, and I have taken some pains to estimate its probable minimum rate of natural increase; it will be safest to assume that it begins breeding when thirty years old, and goes on breeding till ninety years old, bringing forth six young in the interval, and surviving till one hundred years old; if this be so, after a period of from 740 to 750 years there would be nearly nineteen million elephants alive descended from the first pair.[10]

Someone has extended Darwin's calculations to show that in 100,000 years one pair of elephants would have so many living descendants that they would fill the visible universe.

That such astounding population explosions as those outlined above do not in fact occur is evidence enough that there are always limiting factors on any actual population, which prevent it from realizing its full biotic potential. The difference between the biotic potential and the actual rate of increase may be considered a measure of the **environmental resistance,** which is simply the sum total of the environmental limiting factors acting on the population in question.

Density-Independent and Density-Dependent Limiting Factors. If a population were not subjected to any limiting factors and could thus realize its full biotic potential, its growth would accelerate in an exponential fashion (Fig. 18.14A); its growth curve, when graphed, would rapidly approach the vertical. Real growth curves do start out exponentially, but exponential growth cannot long continue, because environmental limiting factors soon come into play. Sometimes the limiting factors cause an abrupt stop in the exponential growth, pro-

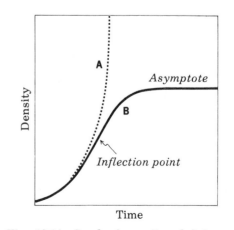

Fig. 18.14. Graph of an unimpeded (exponential) growth curve (A) and the more normal S-shaped (logistic) growth curve (B). See text for discussion.

ducing a growth curve similar to that shown in Fig. 18.15. In these cases, the limiting factors do not become particularly effective until late in the increase, and then they suddenly become very effective, usually causing a rapid decline in population density. Such a population growth pattern is characteristic of some small insects with short life cycles, where the population grows very rapidly during a period of favorable weather and then falls off when the weather changes. Notice that the limiting factor here is independent of the population density; the change in the weather is not caused by the increase in the population, and its limiting effect would be as severe, essentially, on a small population as on a large one.

Figure 18.14B illustrates a different sort of growth curve, where the increase is slow at first, then becomes very rapid, and finally slows down again as the population size approaches an equilibrium position. The curve is thus S-shaped (this type of curve is known as a sigmoid or a logistic curve). In mathematical terms, growth accelerates logarithmically at first, then departs more and more from a logarithmic base until it reaches an inflection point where the acceleration becomes negative, and then approaches an asymptote that repre-

sents the limiting size of the population. This limiting size is often called the **carrying capacity** of the environment (Fig. 18.16). It is the maximum population that the environment can support indefinitely. It must be emphasized that growth curves seldom trace as smooth a curve as that shown in Fig. 18.16. Fluctuations are the rule, in fact (Fig. 18.17). Some-

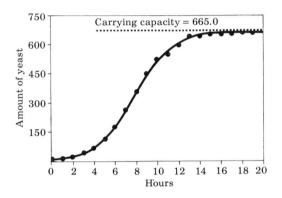

Fig. 18.16. Growth curve of a laboratory population of yeast cells. [Modified from W. C. Allee *et al.*, *Principles of Animal Ecology,* Saunders, 1949, after Pearl.]

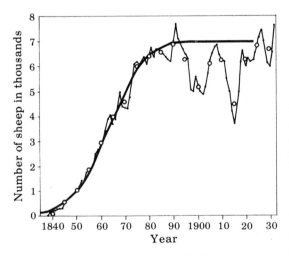

Fig. 18.17. Growth curve of the sheep population of South Australia. The smooth curve is the hypothetical logistic curve around which the real curve seems to fluctuate. [Modified from J. Davidson, *Trans. Roy. Soc. S. Australia,* vol. 62, 1938.]

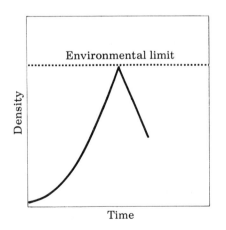

Fig. 18.15. A growth curve in which the environmental limiting factors did not become effective until late, and then produced a sudden sharp decline.

times these fluctuations result from corresponding fluctuations in the physical environment, which raise and lower the carrying capacity. But density fluctuations also occur in the laboratory, where environmental conditions are kept as constant as possible. Thus it is usually only in a rather crude way that real growth patterns approximate a sigmoid curve.

A sigmoid growth curve is produced when the limiting factors become increasingly effective as the density of the population rises, i.e. when the limiting factors are at least partly density-dependent. The distinction between density-dependent and density-independent limiting factors is not always clear-cut, but the concepts are nevertheless useful in elucidating the sorts of environmental influences that help regulate population densities. Strictly speaking, a density-independent factor would be one that exerts a constant influence regardless of population density, but it is customary to consider factors that exert an influence of constant percentage as also density-independent. For example, if a hunter killed five rabbits every year regardless of the density of the rabbit population, he would be a density-independent limiting factor in the strict sense, but if he killed 5 percent of the local rabbit population each year, he would also frequently be considered a density-independent factor. A density-dependent limiting factor, by contrast, would be a hunter who killed 5 percent of the rabbits when the density was low, 20 percent when the density was intermediate, and 50 percent when the density was high. In other words, a density-dependent limiting factor is one whose intensity is at least partly determined by the density of the very population it helps limit.

Gross climatic factors and astronomical events like the diurnal light cycle and the annual changes in photoperiod ordinarily act in a density-independent way, whereas biotic factors (e.g. parasitism, predation, competition, endocrinological and behavioral changes) usually act in a density-dependent way. There are exceptions in both cases, however, and there are also factors that are regularly either density-dependent or density-independent according to the particulars of the situation.

Parasitism and Predation as Density-Dependent Limiting Factors. Admitting, then, that there is no hard-and-fast rule by which to classify factors as density-independent or density-dependent in any actual situation, let us look briefly at some of the factors that are usually density-dependent. Parasitism and predation are in this category. As the population of the host or prey increases, a higher percentage is usually victimized, because the individuals—having perhaps been forced into less favorable situations or being weaker on account of the greater drain on available resources—become easier to find and attack. Furthermore, there is evidence that as the relative densities of prey shift, predators that take a variety of prey species tend to alter their hunting patterns and concentrate on the most common species.

As the density of a prey species increases, the density of the predators feeding on it often increases also. This increase in predators, together with their increased concentration on the particular prey species, may be one factor that causes the density of the prey to fall again. But as the density of the prey falls, there is usually a corresponding, but slightly later, fall in the density of the predator. The result is often a series of density fluctuations like those shown in Fig. 18.18, where the fluctuations of the predator (the lynx in this case) closely follow those of the prey (the hare), but with a characteristic time lag. Such linked fluctuations of predator and prey seem to indicate that the major limiting factor for the predator is the availability of its food and that predation is probably one important limiting factor for the prey. The length of the time lag between a change in one population and the response in the other is one factor in determining the extent of the density fluctuations; in general, the longer the time lag, the greater the period

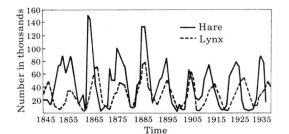

Fig. 18.18. Fluctuations in abundance of lynx and snowshoe hare over a period of ninety years. The oscillations of the lynx population seem to follow those of the hare population. The index of abundance used here (vertical coordinate) is the number of pelts received by the Hudson's Bay Company. [Redrawn from D. A. MacLulich, *Univ. Toronto Studies*, Biol. Ser., no. 43, 1937.]

and amplitude of expected oscillation in the system.

We mentioned earlier that in stable predator-prey systems predation is often decidedly beneficial to the prey population, even though it is destructive to individuals. This cardinal fact of ecology is frequently overlooked by well-meaning but misguided people who consider parasites and predators repugnant and evil (forgetting or ignoring the fact that man himself is the most destructive predator alive). Wishing to "protect" the prey from their enemies (sometimes so that there will be more for human hunters to shoot), they go out and kill the predators. The results are often very different from what they expected. A classic example is that of the deer on the Kaibab Plateau on the north side of the Grand Canyon in Arizona. Prior to 1907 there was a stable population of about 4,000 deer on the plateau; the population was kept at this level, which was well below the estimated carrying capacity of the vegetation, by healthy populations of pumas and wolves. Then between 1907 and 1923 a concerted effort was made to free the deer of their "enemies" by exterminating the pumas and wolves. As a result, the deer population increased to 100,000 by 1925. But this number was far beyond the carrying capacity

of the range, and it was not long before the area was stripped of most of the vegetation on which the deer feed—grass, tree seedlings, shrubs, etc. In the two following years, over half the deer starved to death and the population continued to fall for many years. Not only had extermination of the predators thoroughly disrupted the previously stable deer population, but the huge population explosion of the deer disrupted the previously stable vegetation of the range and seems actually to have lowered the carrying capacity of the range to a level below what it had been in 1904 when the whole misguided effort began.

Similar difficulties have sometimes arisen when predator-prey stability has inadvertently been destroyed by pesticides. For example, application of certain insecticides to strawberries in an attempt to destroy cyclamen mites that were damaging the berries killed both the cyclamen mites and the carnivorous mites that preyed on them. But the cyclamen mites quickly reinvaded the strawberry fields, while the predatory mites did not. The result was that the cyclamen mites, now free of their natural predators, rapidly increased in density and did more damage to the strawberries than if the insecticides had never been applied.

Competition as a Density-Dependent Limiting Factor. Competition is one of the chief density-dependent limiting factors. The continued healthy existence of most organisms depends upon utilization of some environmental resources that are in limited supply, such as food, water, space, or light. As the population density increases, the competition for these limited resources becomes more intense and the deleterious results of the competition become more and more effective in limiting the population; this is true of both intraspecific and interspecific competition. To take a familiar example, if flowers are planted too close together in a flower bed the plants will be weak and spindly and will produce few if any blooms. Only if they are thinned, either artificially or by the natural death of the weakest individuals, will they grow well. The same sort of competition for space, light, water, and nutrients operates in a forest and keeps down the density of the trees. The decline of the lynx population following each decline in the hare population, illustrated in Fig. 18.18, and the drastic decline of the Kaibab deer following the decline in the vegetation, are two examples where intense competition for food may be regarded as the immediate limiting factor.

There has been much difference of opinion between ecologists during the past twenty years concerning the relative importance of density-dependent and density-independent limiting factors in nature, some workers vigorously championing the first, others, with equal vigor, championing the second.[11] Much of the dissension has revolved around conflicting estimates of the frequency and intensity of competition under natural conditions. It is not the function of a book such as this to try to resolve the argument. Suffice it to say that the majority of present workers believe that competition, predation, and other density-dependent factors are of very great importance and are probably the principal limiting factors in nature, but that density-independent factors may play an important role in limiting some organisms, particularly those with very short life cycles characterized by a growth curve like that shown in Fig. 18.15, where a sudden strong density-independent limitation brings growth to an end before density-dependent factors can become operative and give the curve a sigmoid form. Some workers are very specific in their assignment of the principal density-dependent limiting factors to the various trophic levels. They suggest that populations of producers are limited by competition for resources, particularly light but sometimes also water or minerals; that populations of secondary consumers (parasites and predators) and populations of decomposers are limited by competition for food; and that populations of primary consumers (herbivores) are usually limited by predation. Whether they are right can be shown only by much more research.

Endocrinological and Behavioral Mechanisms as Density-Dependent Limiting Factors. In recent years, some ecologists have suggested that endocrine and behavioral phenomena may be important in limiting populations—that "within broad limits set by the environment, density-dependent mechanisms have evolved within the animals themselves to regulate population growth and curtail it short of the point of suicidal destruction of the environment."[12] For example, in numerous laboratory experiments with mice, increasing population density was accompanied by hypertrophy of the adrenal cortex and by degeneration of the thymus. Somatic growth was suppressed; sexual maturation was delayed (or even totally inhibited at very high densities); and reproduction by mature mice was diminished. The effects on reproduction included delayed spermatogenesis in males and, in females, prolonged estrous cycles, reduced rate of uterine implantation, and inadequate lactation. There was also evidence of increased intra-uterine mortality of the embryos. Furthermore, it was found that crowding of female mice before pregnancy could result in permanent behavioral disturbances in the young they later produced. There seems, then, to be an endocrine feedback mechanism that could help regulate and limit population size by altering the reproductive rate. Presumably, as the density rises and aggressive behavior increases, endocrine disturbance rises and the reproductive rate falls;

---

[11] One of the chief spokesmen for the champions of density-independent factors is H. G. Andrewartha of the University of Adelaide, Australia. A major spokesman for the other camp is A. J. Nicholson of the Commonwealth Scientific and Industrial Organization in Australia. References to publications by both these men are given at the end of the chapter.

[12] J. J. Christian and D. E. Davis, "Endocrines, Behavior, and Population," *Science*, vol. 146, 1964, p. 1550.

conversely, as the density and aggressive behavior decrease, the reproductive rate rises.

It has long been known that very dense populations often experience severe disease epidemics. There is now evidence that this proneness to epidemics is not due solely to the greater ease of spread of the pathogens; a density-induced change in host resistance is apparently also involved. Numerous experiments have shown that increased population density is accompanied by a marked depression of both inflammatory responses and antibody formation, with a resultant increase in susceptibility to infection or parasitism. There is also an increased susceptibility to the harmful effects of various toxic substances.

The theory that endocrine changes of the sorts mentioned above act as major density-dependent limiting factors in nature has been severely criticized by some workers on the grounds that it is largely based on laboratory work with densities much higher than those that would actually occur in nature. It is true that comparable endocrine changes have been observed in natural populations of a few species. And the intermittent crowding likely to occur in nature has been imitated in the laboratory; experiments have shown that mice exposed to a few short periods of crowding every day actually show greater hypertrophy of the adrenal cortex than mice exposed to continuous crowding. Nevertheless, endocrine changes have not been found in many wild animals undergoing population stress, and the importance of such changes in population regulation remains unclear.

In some cases, crowding induces physiological and behavioral changes that result in increased emigration from the crowded region. Such changes can be observed in many species of aphids (small insects that suck the juices of plants). During seasons of the year when conditions are favorable, they are represented largely by wingless females reproducing parthenogenetically. But when conditions deteriorate and competition becomes intense, sexually reproducing winged females develop and these may move out of the area in which they were born. Similarly, in the fungus fly, *Oligarces paradoxus,* individuals reproduce parthenogenetically without ever fully maturing to the winged adult stage as long as there is an abundant supply of fresh food. But when the food supply deteriorates, in either quantity or quality, and competition becomes intense, the insects go through a complete developmental sequence leading to winged adults, which fly to other more hospitable areas.

One of the best-known examples of physiological and behavioral changes induced by crowding is that of the solitary and migratory phases seen in several species of locusts, particularly *Locusta migratoria* in Eurasia. Individuals of the migratory phase have longer wings, a higher fat content, a lower water content, and a darker color than solitary-phase individuals, and they are much more gregarious and are more readily stimulated to marching and flying by the presence of other individuals. The solitary phase is characteristic of low-density populations, and the migratory phase is characteristic of high-density ones. As the density of a given population rises, the proportion of individuals developing into the migratory phase rises; the sight and smell of other locusts seem to play an important role in triggering this line of development. When the proportion of migratory-phase individuals has risen sufficiently high, enormous swarms emigrate from the crowded area, consuming nearly all the vegetation in their path and often completely devastating agricultural crops.

COMMUNITY CHANGE

A biotic community—which is the living part of an ecosystem, i.e. the assemblage of species living in a given area—is not a static entity; it is a changing, dynamic system. Almost everyone has had the experience of returning after a few years to a spot he remembers as an open field and finding it overrun with bushes or even covered by a young forest. Many schoolchildren have performed the experiment of inoculating a culture medium with pond water and watching the succession of protozoan populations that rise to dominance in the culture; first one species will be dominant, then it will decline and another will gain ascendancy, only to decline in its turn and be replaced by another, and so on. Clearly, any attempt to understand the biology of communities entails study of the sorts of change to which communities are prone.

Ecological Succession

The Characteristics of Succession. The more or less orderly process of community change is called succession. It involves replacement, in the course of time, of the dominant species within a given area by other species. A farmer's field is allowed to lie fallow. A crop of annual weeds grows in it during the first year. Many perennial herbs appear in the second year and become even more common in the third year. Soon, however, these are superseded as the dominant vegetation by woody shrubs, and they may in turn be replaced eventually by trees. Or a lake dries up, and its sandy bottom becomes covered with grass, which later gives way to trees.

But why the change? Why does succession occur? The cause cannot be climate, because succession will occur even if the climate remains the same. Climate may be a major factor in determining what sorts of species will follow one another, but the succession itself must result from other changes. The most important of these are the modifications of the physical environment produced by the community itself. Most communities tend to alter the area in which they occur in such a way as to make it less favorable for themselves and more favorable for other communities. In effect, each community in the succession sows the seeds of its own destruction. Consider the alterations initiated by pioneer communities on land. Usually these communities will produce a layer of litter on the surface of the soil. The accumulation of litter affects the runoff of rainwater, the soil temperature, and the formation of humus. The humus, in turn, contributes to soil development and thus alters the availability of nutrients, the water relations, the pH and aeration of the soil, and the sorts of soil organisms that will occur. But the organisms characteristic of the pioneer communities that produced these changes may not prosper under the new conditions, and they may be replaced by invading competitors that do better in an area with the new type of soil.

Though much of the modification of the habitat that produces succession is due to the action of living organisms, other forces may also contribute. Among these are physiographic changes. For example, greater depth in the channel of a stream may result in better drainage of a swamp; or an overflowing stream may deposit rich silt on nearby bottomland. Such changes will soon be followed by changes in vegetation.

Though successions in different places and at different times are not identical—the species involved are often completely different—some ecologists have nevertheless formulated generalizations that they have reason to think hold true in most cases where both autotrophs and heterotrophs are involved: (1) The species composition changes continuously during the succession, but the change is usually more rapid in the earlier stages than in the later ones. (2) The total number of species represented increases initially and then becomes more or less stabilized or even declines in the older stages. This is particularly true of the heterotrophs, whose variety is usually much greater in the later stages of the succession. (3) Both the total biomass in the ecosystem and the amount of nonliving organic matter increase during the succession until a more stable stage has been reached. (4) The food webs become more complex, and the relations between species in them become better defined or more specialized. (5) Although the amount of new organic matter synthesized by the producers remains approximately the same, except at the very beginning, the percentage utilized at the various trophic levels rises. In summary, if these ecologists are right, the trend of most successions is toward a more complex ecosystem in which less energy is wasted and hence a greater biomass can be supported without an increase in the supply of energy.

Some Examples of Succession. One of the first examples of succession studied in detail (by H. C. Cowles of the University of Chicago) was that on the sand dunes at the southern end of Lake Michigan. Lake Michigan once extended much farther south than it does today. As the lakeshore gradually receded northward, it left exposed a series of successively younger beaches and sand dunes. Thus someone who starts at the water's edge and walks

south for several miles will pass through a series of communities (Fig. 18.19) that represent various successional stages beginning with bare beach and culminating in an old well-established forest dominated by beech and sugar-maple trees. Let us examine these stages in more detail.

1. The lower beach near the water's edge has no land life, because it is frequently exposed to the destructive action of waves.
2. The middle beach is ordinarily dry in summer but is occasionally washed by the waves produced by severe winter storms. Conditions of life are very severe and exclude biennial and perennial plants, but a few succulent annuals similar to those that inhabit deserts grow there in summer.
3. Conditions on the upper beach are much less severe than on the lower and middle beaches and the flora is richer, but vegetation is still very sparse. Decay of driftwood has begun adding some organic matter to the substratum.

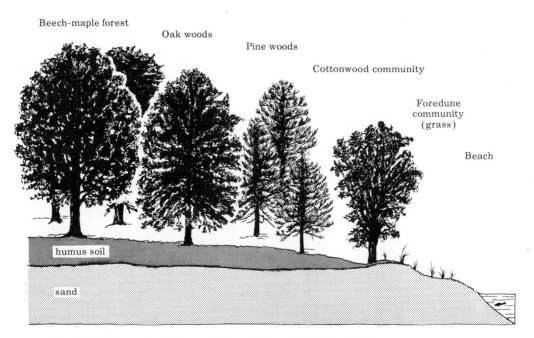

Fig. 18.19. Successional stages at the southern end of Lake Michigan.

4. Behind the upper beach is the foredune community, a pioneer community dominated by sand-binding beach grasses. Tiger beetles, grasshoppers, and burrowing spiders are characteristic animals of this community.

5. The first tree-bearing stage in this succession is a cottonwood community, a loosely organized pioneer community on sands that have usually been partly bound by the roots of grasses but are still subject to considerable shifting by the wind.

6. The cottonwood community grades into a community dominated by jack pine, juniper, and bearberry, where the soil has a considerable humus component.

7. The pine community grades, in turn, into a forest dominated by oaks.

8. The oak community grades into a forest dominated by sugar-maple and beech trees growing in a deep humus-rich moist soil.

During the walk from the lakeshore to the beech-maple forest, an observant person would notice many changes in the physical environment—a progressive decrease in total light intensity at ground level, a decrease in wind velocity and in the rate of evaporation, an increase in soil moisture and in relative humidity, and an increase in the amount of humus in the soil and the amount of leaf mold on its surface. Presumably, this series of communities and environmental changes, seen contemporaneously as one moves laterally away from the lake, duplicates approximately the series of successional stages through which the area now covered by the beech-maple forest must have passed since the time when it was a wave-washed beach.

Another much-studied type of succession is that occurring in ponds. Sediments washed from the surrounding land begin to fill the pond, and the dead bodies of planktonic organisms add organic material. Soon pioneer submerged vascular plants appear in the shallower water near the margins of the pond.

Their roots hold the silt, and the lake bottom is built up faster where they are growing. In addition, as these plants die, their bodies accumulate faster than decomposers can break them down. Soon the water is shallow enough for broad-leaved floating pondweeds, such as water lilies, to displace the submerged species, which now become established in a zone farther out in the pond, where conditions are more favorable for them. But as the bottom continues to build up, the floating pondweeds are in their turn displaced by emergent species (plants that have their roots in the mud of the bottom but their shoots extending into the air above the water), such as cattails, bulrushes, and reeds. These plants grow very close together and hold the sediment tightly, and their great bulk results in rapid accumulation of organic material. Soon conditions are dry enough for a few terrestrial plants to gain a foothold. Now an area that was formerly part of the pond is newly formed dry land. This entire sequence can sometimes be seen as a nearly continuous series of zones girdling a pond or lake. With the passage of the years, the pond becomes smaller and smaller as the zones move nearer and nearer its center. Eventually nothing of the pond remains.

Successions need not begin with land reclaimed from lakes or ponds as in the two preceding examples. Consider instead a bare rock surface. The first pioneer plants may be lichens, which grow during the brief periods when the rock surface is wet and lie dormant during periods when the surface is dry. The lichens release acids that corrode the rock. Dust particles and bits of dead lichen may collect in the tiny crevices thus formed, and pioneer mosses may gain anchorage there. The mosses grow in tufts or clumps that trap more dust and debris and gradually form a thickening mat. A few fern spores or seeds of grasses and annual herbs may land in the mat of soil and moss and germinate. These may be followed by perennial herbs. As more and more such plants survive and grow, they catch and hold still more mineral and organic material, and the new soil layer thus becomes thicker. Later, shrubs and even trees may start to grow in the soil that now covers what once was a bare rock surface.

Succession on abandoned croplands, plowed grasslands, or cutover forests often proceeds relatively quickly in its initial stages, because the effects of the previous communities have not been wholly erased and the physical conditions are not as bleak as on a beach or a bare rock surface. Suppose, for example, that a cornfield in Georgia is abandoned. The very first year it will be covered with annual weeds, such as ragweed, horseweed, and crabgrass. In the second year, ragweed, goldenrod, and asters will probably be common, and there will be much tall grass. The grass will usually be dominant for several years, and then more and more shrubs and tree seedlings will appear. The first tree seedlings to grow well in the unshaded field will be pines, and eventually a pine forest will replace the grass and shrubs. But pine seedlings do not grow well in the shade of older pines. Seedlings of oaks, hickories, and other deciduous trees are more shade-tolerant, and these trees gradually develop in the lower strata of the forest beneath the old pines, eventually replacing them. The deciduous forest thus formed is more stable and will ordinarily maintain itself for a very long time. As can be seen from Fig. 18.20, changes corresponding to the succession of dominant plants also take place in the animal portion of the community.

Climax and Biome

The Concept of Climax. If man or some other disruptive factor doesn't interfere, most successions eventually reach a stage that is much more stable than those that preceded it. The community of this stage is called the *climax community.* It has much less tendency than earlier successional communities to alter its environment in a manner injurious to itself.

In fact, its more complex organization, larger organic structure, and more balanced metabolism enable it to buffer its own physical environment to such an extent that it can be self-perpetuating. Consequently, it may persist for centuries, not being replaced by another stage so long as climate, physiography, and other major environmental factors remain essentially the same. It must be emphasized, however, that a climax community is not static; it does slowly change, and will change rapidly if there are major shifts in the environment, either physical or biotic. For example, fifty years ago chestnut trees were among the dominant plants in the climax forests of much of eastern North America, but they have been almost completely eliminated by a fungal blight, and the present-day climax forests of the region are dominated by other species. Thus there can be no absolute distinction between climax and the other stages of succession; the difference between them is relative.

Since the beginning of the century, some American ecologists have held that all succession in a given large climatic region will converge to the same climax type—that there is only one type of climax community for the region and that any sites dominated by other communities have not yet reached climax, no matter how stable and long-lasting they may seem. Thus a beech-maple forest has been considered the climax for most of the northeastern United States, and a white spruce–balsam fir forest has been considered the climax for much of Canada. The proponents of this so-called monoclimax hypothesis regard plant communities as objectively real and discrete entities with recognizable boundaries—as entities comparable to species, describable in analogous ways, and amenable to categorization and classification.

However, many ecologists object to this view. They argue that each species is distributed according to its own particular biological potentialities, and that the aggregation of species characterizing any given community is the for-

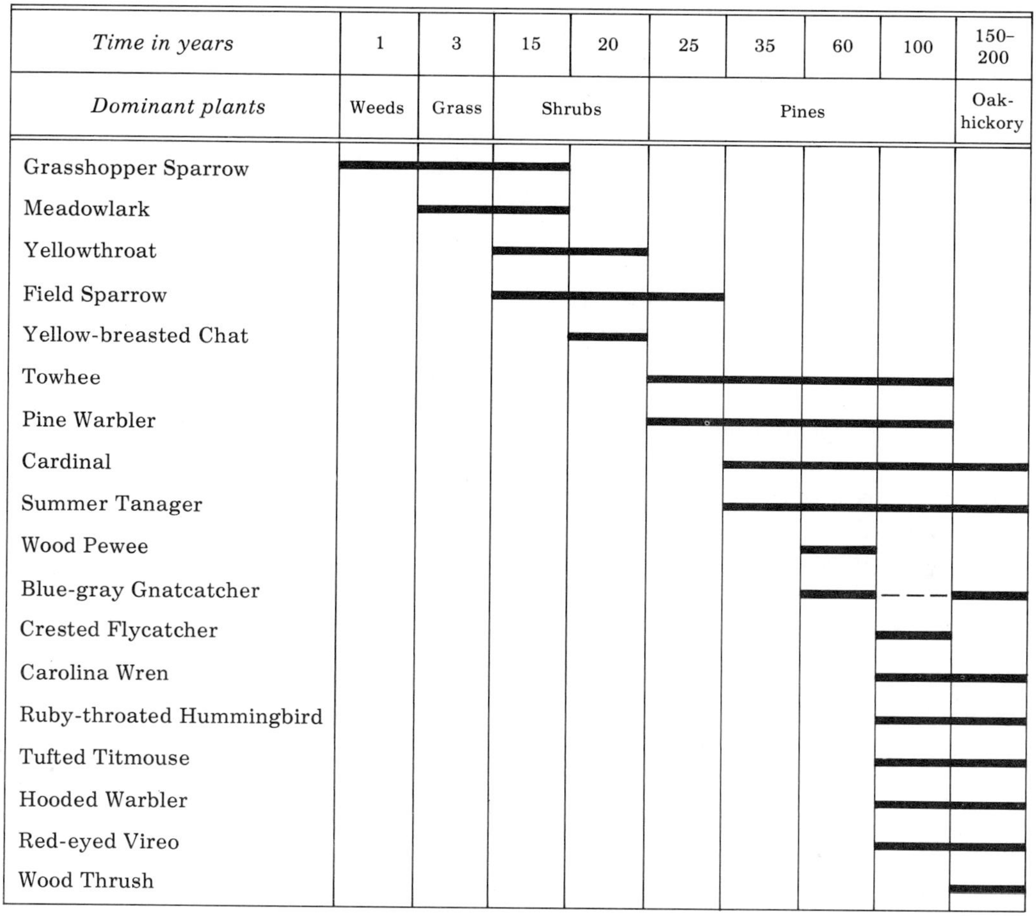

Time in years	1	3	15	20	25	35	60	100	150–200
Dominant plants	Weeds	Grass	Shrubs		Pines				Oak-hickory
Grasshopper Sparrow									
Meadowlark									
Yellowthroat									
Field Sparrow									
Yellow-breasted Chat									
Towhee									
Pine Warbler									
Cardinal									
Summer Tanager									
Wood Pewee									
Blue-gray Gnatcatcher									
Crested Flycatcher									
Carolina Wren									
Ruby-throated Hummingbird									
Tufted Titmouse									
Hooded Warbler									
Red-eyed Vireo									
Wood Thrush									

Fig. 18.20. Bird succession on an area of abandoned upland farmlands in Georgia. The bars indicate when each of the bird species was present in a density of at least one pair per 10 acres. In the early (weed and grass) stages, Grasshopper Sparrows and Meadowlarks were the dominant bird species. During the shrub stage, Yellowthroats and Field Sparrows became dominant. Pine Warblers and Towhees dominated the young pine forests, and Red-eyed Vireos, Wood Thrushes, and Cardinals dominated the oak-hickory forests. [Based on data in E. P. Odum, Fundamentals of Ecology, Saunders, 1959.]

tuitous product of local environmental conditions and whatever plant and animal species happen to be available in the area. Since environmental conditions such as microclimate, soil characteristics, topographic features, wind patterns, and so on, vary continuously in both space and time, vegetation, these ecologists point out, would also vary continuously in both space and time. Boundaries between communities would seldom be distinct, because the distributions of the various species comprising those communities would not be correlated with one another. If a traveler along the Mississippi River Basin carefully noted which tree species occur where, he would see that the different species drop out or make their appearance at different places, with little apparent correlation with each other. Thus there would be no place where he would notice any abrupt change in the community; yet the small changes from mile to mile would be cumulative, so that after traveling many miles he would find himself in a community with a species composition almost completely different from that of the community in which his journey began. This view of communities as parts of a gradually changing continuum, whose characteristics at any specific place are uniquely determined by a combination of local physical conditions, local biotic factors, local species distributions, and a considerable element of chance, leads to the conclusion that similarities between climax communities in different places are only approximate. Hence there would be no absolute climax for any region. Climax would have meaning only in relation to the individual site and its environmental conditions. One should determine the climax for a given spot not by referring to some theoretical regional climax but by actually observing what populations replace others and then maintain themselves in a stable condition.

Which of these opposing views of climax communities comes closer to the facts (or whether some combination of the two is more nearly correct) has not yet been resolved. Each view has its advocates at the present time. Most of the evidence from recent studies, however, seems to support the idea that each site has its own unique climax and that the attempt to fit all the climax communities of a large region into a single regional climax determined largely by the regional climate is not particularly fruitful. It is probably more productive in most cases to emphasize study of the gradients between the individual local climaxes in an attempt to learn how changes in the component parts of communities are correlated with changing environmental conditions.

Biomes. Even though the present trend is away from definition of regional climaxes in terms of aggregations of particular dominant and subdominant species, most biologists find it convenient to recognize a limited number of major climax formations called biomes. Thus,

instead of saying that nearly all local communities in the northeastern United states tend to converge toward a regional climax of beech-maple forest, they say simply that in a large portion of North America the majority of local climaxes are deciduous forests of some type, i.e. the dominant form of plant life ("plant formation") is usually deciduous trees. They do not insist that every site within the deciduous-forest biome is converging toward a deciduous forest; local conditions may sometimes determine a climax community in which grass is dominant or in which pine trees are dominant. And they do not insist that all those sites within the biome that do have a deciduous-forest climax must be dominated by beech and maple; they expect the importance of individual species to vary from one place to another. In short, they think of biomes as no more than generalizations about the most common climax of the region.

Let us briefly survey some of the world's major biomes (Fig. 18.21). In the far northern parts of North America, Europe, and Asia is the *tundra.* The tundra is the most continuous of the earth's biomes, forming a circumpolar band interrupted only narrowly by the North Atlantic and the Bering Sea. It corresponds roughly to the region where the subsoil is permanently frozen. The land has the appearance of a gently rolling plain, with many lakes, ponds, and bogs in the depressions (Fig. 18.22). "Tundra" is a Siberian word meaning north of the timberline. There are, in fact, a few trees on the tundra, but they are small, widely scattered, and clearly not the dominant vegetation except locally. Much of the ground is covered by mosses (particularly sphagnum), lichens (particularly so-called reindeer moss), and a few species of grasses. There are numerous small perennial herbs, which are able to withstand frequent freezing and which grow rapidly during the brief cool summers, often carpeting the tundra with brightly colored flowers. Reindeer, caribou, arctic wolves, arctic foxes, arctic hares, and lemmings are among the principal mammals; polar bears are common on parts of the tundra near the coast. Vast numbers of birds, particularly shorebirds (sandpipers, plovers, etc.) and waterfowl (ducks, geese, etc.), nest on the tundra in summer, but they are not permanent residents and migrate south for the winter. Insects, particularly flies (including mosquitoes), are incredibly abundant. In short, far from being a barren lifeless land as many people think, the tundra teems with life. It is true, however, that though the number of individual organisms on the tundra is often very large, the number of different species is quite limited.

South of the tundra, in both North America and Eurasia, is a wide zone dominated by coniferous forests. This is the *taiga* (Fig. 18.23). Like the tundra, it is dotted by countless lakes, ponds, and bogs. And like the tundra, it has very cold winters. But it has longer and somewhat warmer summers, during which the subsoil thaws and vegetation grows abundantly. The number of different species living in the taiga is larger than on the tundra, but it is considerably smaller than in biomes farther south. Though conifers (including spruce, fir, and tamarack) are the most characteristic of the larger plants in the taiga, some deciduous trees (e.g. paper birch) are also common. Moose, black bear, wolves, lynx, wolverines, martens, squirrels, and many smaller rodents are important mammals in the taiga communities. Birds are abundant in summer.

The biomes south of the taiga do not form such definite circumglobal belts as do the tundra and the taiga. There is more variation in the amount of rainfall at this latitude, and consequently more longitudinal variation in the types of climax communities that predominate. In those parts of the temperate zone where rainfall is abundant and the summers are relatively long and warm, as in most of the eastern United States, most of central Europe, and part of eastern Asia, the climax communities are frequently dominated by broad-leaved trees. Such areas constitute the *deciduous-forest biomes* (Fig. 18.24). They characteristically include many more species than the taiga to the north.

Tropical areas with abundant rainfall are (or, more correctly, were) usually covered by *tropical rain forests,* which include some of the most complex communities on earth (Fig. 18.25). The diversity of species is enormous; a temperate forest is composed of two or three, or at most ten, dominant tree species, but a tropical rain forest may be composed of a hundred or more. One may actually have difficulty finding any two trees of the same species within an area of many acres. The dominant trees are usually very tall, and their interlacing tops form dense canopies that intercept much of the sunlight, leaving the forest floor only dimly lit even at midday. The canopy likewise breaks direct fall of rain, but water drips from it to the forest floor much of the time, even when no rain is actually falling. It also shields the lower levels from wind and hence greatly reduces the rate of evaporation. The lower levels of the forest are consequently very humid. Temperatures near the forest floor are nearly constant. The pronounced differences in the microenvironmental conditions at different levels within such a forest result in a striking degree of vertical stratification; many species of animals and epiphytic plants (plants growing on the large trees) occur only in the canopy, others occur only in the middle strata, and still other species occur only on the forest floor. Some vertical stratification is found in any community, particularly any forest community, but nowhere is it so extensively developed as in a tropical rain forest.

Huge areas in both the temperate and tropic regions of the world are covered by *grassland* biomes (Fig. 18.26). These are areas where either the relatively low total annual rainfall (10–20 inches) or the uneven seasonal occurrence of rainfall makes conditions inhospitable for forests but suitable for often luxurious growth of grasses. Temperate and tropical grasslands are remarkably similar in appear-

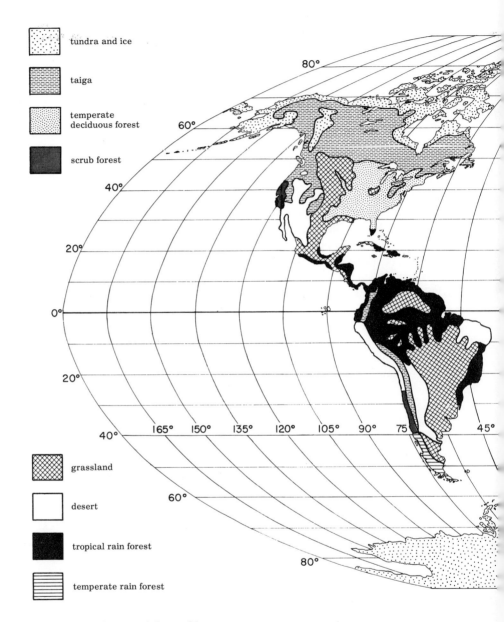

tundra and ice

taiga

temperate
deciduous forest

scrub forest

grassland

desert

tropical rain forest

temperate rain forest

Fig. 18.21. The major biomes of the world.

ance, although the particular species they contain may be very different. In both cases, there are usually vast numbers of large and conspicuous herbivores, often including ungulates (e.g. bison and pronghorn antelope in the United States). Burrowing rodents or rodent-

like animals are often common (e.g. prairie dogs in the western United States).

In places where rainfall is very low, often less than 10 inches per year, not even grasses can survive as the dominant vegetation, and *desert* biomes occur (Fig. 18.27). Deserts are

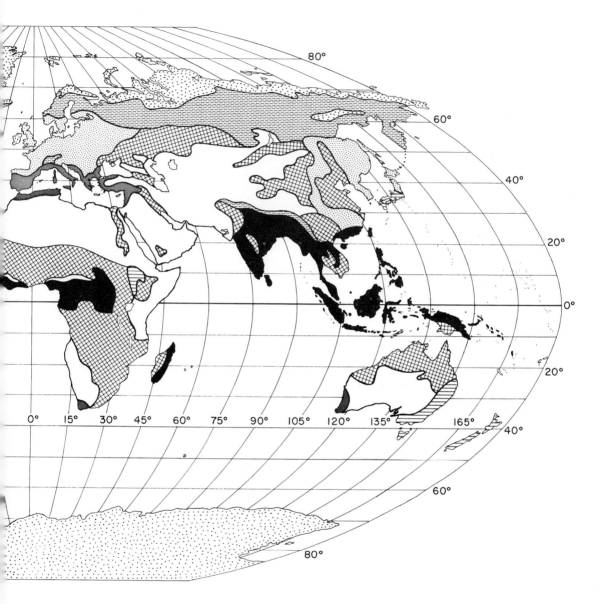

subject to the most extreme temperature fluctuations of any biome type; during the day
they are exposed to intense sunlight, and the
temperature of both air and soil may rise very
high (to 105°F or higher for air temperature
and to 160°F or higher for surface tempera-

ture), but in the absence of the moderating influence of abundant vegetation, heat is rapidly
lost at night, and a short while after sunset
searing heat has usually given way to bitter
cold. Some deserts, such as parts of the Sahara,
are nearly barren of vegetation, but more com-

Fig. 18.22. Tundra. [Courtesy Daniel Q. Thompson, Cornell University.]

Fig. 18.23. Northern coniferous forest. [Courtesy O. H. Hewitt, Cornell University.]

Fig. 18.24. Temperate deciduous forest. [Courtesy N. F. Snyder, Cornell University.]

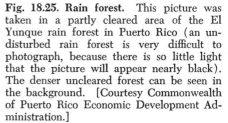

Fig. 18.25. Rain forest. This picture was taken in a partly cleared area of the El Yunque rain forest in Puerto Rico (an undisturbed rain forest is very difficult to photograph, because there is so little light that the picture will appear nearly black). The denser uncleared forest can be seen in the background. [Courtesy Commonwealth of Puerto Rico Economic Development Administration.]

Fig. 18.27. Desert. [Courtesy Elmer S. Phillips, Cornell University.]

Fig. 18.26. Grasslands in midwestern United States. [Courtesy Elmer S. Phillips, Cornell University.]

monly there are scattered drought-resistant shrubs (e.g. sagebrush, greasewood, creosote bush, and mesquite) and succulent plants that can store much water in their tissues (e.g. cactuses in New World deserts and euphorbias in Old World deserts). In addition, there are often many small rapid-growing annual herbs with seeds that will germinate only when there is a hard rain; once they germinate, the young plants shoot up, flower, set seed, and die, all within a few days. Most desert animals are active primarily at night or during the brief periods in early morning and late afternoon when the heat is not so intense. During the day, they remain in cool underground burrows or in cavities in plants or, in the case of some spiders and insects, in the shade of the plants. Among the animals often found in des-

erts are rodents (e.g. the kangaroo rat), snakes, lizards, a few birds, arachnids, and insects. Most usually show numerous remarkable physiological and behavioral adaptions for life in their hostile environment.

We have seen that moving laterally on the earth's surface, as from north to south, one may pass through a series of different biomes. The same thing is true if one moves vertically on the slopes of tall mountains. Climatic conditions change with altitude, and the biotic communities change accordingly (Fig. 18.28). Thus arms, or isolated pockets, of the taiga extend far south in the United States on the slopes of the Appalachian Mountains in the east and of the Rockies and Coast Ranges in the west. There are even tundralike spots on the highest peaks.

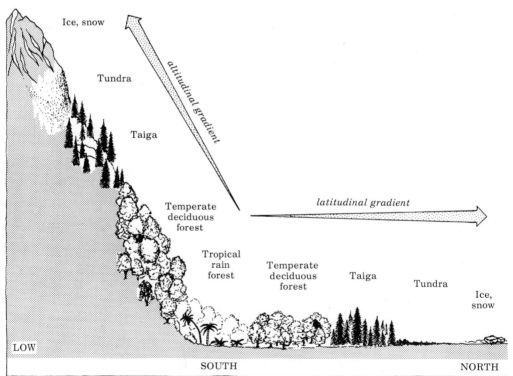

Fig. 18.28. The correspondence between latitudinal and altitudinal life zones in eastern North America.

BIOGEOGRAPHY

We indicated in our discussion of climax communities that the ranges of different species are never fully correlated. It follows that the complex of environmental factors determining range boundaries is unique for each species. There is, however, one generalization that can be made regarding population dispersal, whatever the factors tending to limit it: Since the reproductive capacity always exceeds the carrying capacity of the environment, there is always pressure within a population to expand its niche or to spread into new territories. There is a selective premium on genotypes that improve the capacity of individuals for occupying new habitats within the same community or for invading habitats in other communities. It is with the latter alternative—extension of the range into new areas, so that the species becomes a part of new communities—that we shall be concerned here.

Dispersal of Species

Conditions for Successful Colonization. Before a species can successfully spread into a new area, at least three major conditions must be met.

First, the species must possess the *physiological potential* to survive and reproduce in the new area. For example, it must be able to utilize some source of food in the new area, and it must be able to withstand the rigors of the new climate. Once the species has colonized the new area, it will be under intense selection pressure to evolve better adaptations for surviving and reproducing. But evolutionary improvement comes after the fact of colonization. The colonization itself is possible only if the species already is at least minimally *preadapted* for survival under the new environmental conditions. By "preadapted" we do not, of course, mean to imply any foresight, any intentional preparation for the move into

strange territory; we mean simply that characteristics evolved in the previous habitat are at least minimally suited to the new habitat as well.

Second, the species must have the *ecological opportunity* to become established in the new habitat. This often means that the colonizing species must not encounter much competition at first. There must be an essentially unoccupied niche that it can fill. The reason is simple: Even if the colonizer has the physiological potential for surviving in the new habitat, chances are that it will be less well adapted to the new conditions than species that have been in the area for a longer time. If one of the established species occupies a niche very similar to the one the colonizer could potentially fill, the established species may well have the competitive advantage and be able to prevent the colonizer from taking hold. This is not always the case, however; if conditions in the new range are very similar to those in the old, a colonizing species may sometimes be competitively superior to an established species and be able to eliminate it.

Third, the species must have *physical access* to the new range. It is useless for the species to have the physiological potential and ecological opportunity for surviving in a new range if it has no way of getting there. Doubtless many common North American mammals could survive and prosper in Australia, but unless they have some way of getting there this potential range extension will be unrealized.

Means of Dispersal. There are many different ways in which organisms may be dispersed from one place to another. Most obvious for many animals is active locomotion—walking, crawling, swimming, or flying. Even many sedentary marine animals have a free-swimming larval stage. Active locomotion may carry the members of a single generation only a short distance from their point of origin, but over many generations the cummulative effect may spread the species over hundreds or thousands of miles. This progressive dispersal in the course of a long series of generations may at first glance seem too slow to be of much significance, but it is not. Probably all organisms can disperse fast enough so that if favorable habitats were continuous they could spread over the entire earth in a relatively short time, as measured on the geological and evolutionary time scale.

Large and heavy animals as we are, we tend to think automatically of active locomotion as the principal means of dispersal of organisms. But for plants and for many very small animals, passive transport is the chief means of dispersal. For example, the seeds or spores of many plants may be blown very long distances, and insects, spiders, small molluscs, and other invertebrates have been known to be blown hundreds of miles by the strong winds of storms. Pilots sometimes encounter large numbers of insects being swept along by the fast-moving air currents at high altitudes. Aquatic organisms may similarly be swept along by strong water currents. Even some fairly large terrestrial plants and animals may be carried across many miles of water on floating logs or rafts of matted vegetation. Many such logs and rafts are swept out to sea by large rivers like the Amazon and the Congo, particularly during floods. A raft about 100 feet square, composed of soil and decaying organic matter laced together by roots, was sighted in the Atlantic Ocean off the coast of North America in 1892. Many shrubs and several trees 30 feet tall were growing on it. This raft, which looked for all the world like a floating island, is known to have drifted at least 1,000 miles.

Some plants and small animals are dispersed by birds and mammals. For example, the seeds of many plants pass through the digestive tracts of higher animals without being harmed, and may germinate and grow if the animal's feces are deposited in a favorable place. Birds sometimes transport seeds long distances in this way. There is also some evidence that plant seeds and the eggs and larvae of some small aquatic animals may be transported on the feathers or feet of swimming or wading birds. Of course man is by far the most important agent of dispersal at the present time; but he is a relatively new arrival on the biological scene, and older distribution patterns cannot be explained in terms of his activities.

The recent history of Krakatoa, a small island between Java and Sumatra in the East Indies, constitutes a natural experiment in colonization of new territory by both plants and animals, and well illustrates the types of dispersal enumerated here. On August 27, 1883, a violent volcanic explosion destroyed much of the island and left the rest completely covered by a layer of hot ashes and pumice 20 to 200 feet deep. There is no evidence that any life remained on the island. The island nearest to Krakatoa was 12 miles away, but most of the life on it was destroyed by toxic gases and a thick layer of ashes produced by the explosion. The next-closest island was about 25 miles away. In short, Krakatoa suddenly became an island devoid of life, separated by 25 miles of open ocean from the nearest significant source of potential colonizers.

Nine months after the eruption, a biologist visited the island and, though he searched diligently, the only living thing he could find was a lone spider busily spinning a web. The spider had almost certainly been blown to the island. However, three years later numerous plants were found growing along the beaches, and several species of ferns and grasses were growing farther inland. The beach plants were of the kind found on the beaches of almost all tropical Pacific islands—plants whose seeds are highly resistant to sea water and are regularly carried long distances by ocean currents. The ferns found growing so soon on Krakatoa reproduce by means of very light spores that can easily be carried by even gentle air currents.

By 1896, thirteen years after the explosion, the island was fairly well covered with vegetation, but plants still were more abundant near the shores than in the interior. Most of the plants were ones distributed by sea currents and wind, but about 9 percent must have arrived by other intermediaries, probably birds. By 1906, the island was densely covered with plants, and there were 263 species of animals living there; most were insects, but there were four species of land snails, two species of reptiles, and 16 species of birds. Many of the insects either flew or were blown to the island, but some of them (and perhaps the reptiles also) probably arrived on floating logs or rafts. The diversity of life on Krakatoa has continued to rise in the years since 1906. Organisms spread by wind and ocean current, and actively flying animals such as birds, bats, and insects, continue to dominate, but the percentage of organisms arriving by other means has steadily risen. If a person with no knowledge of the island's history were to visit Krakatoa today, he would hardly guess that less than one hundred years ago this was a lifeless mass of ash and steaming lava.

Biogeographic Regions of the World

Some species have readier physical access than others to a region that they might potentially colonize; thus it was easier for small animals that could be blown by wind or carried on rafts to get to Krakatoa than it was for large mammals to get there. In other words, the geological or ecological zones that intervene between any two regions will be much more effective as barriers to dispersal for some species than for others. A wide expanse of ocean may almost completely prohibit movement of horses or elephants, but coconut palms may cross it in fair numbers, because their large water-resistant seeds can float in sea water for many weeks without harm. A grassland separating two forested areas may be an almost insuperable barrier for some forest animals and prevent them from moving from one forest to the other. Other forest animals may have difficulty crossing the grasslands but may do so occasionally, and still others may cross

the grasslands freely. In short, what is a barrier to dispersal for one species may be a possible but difficult route of dispersal for another or an easily negotiated path for a third. We must therefore understand the sorts of routes and barriers that are effective for different species if we are to understand the distribution patterns of organisms on the earth's surface.

But even if we fully understood the ecology of all living species, including their physiological potential for survival in other habitats, the ecological opportunities they would find in those habitats, the ways in which they can be physically dispersed, and the routes and barriers they would be likely to encounter, and even if we knew in detail the present geography of the earth, we would still be unable fully to explain all the distributions of plants and animals that we now find on the earth. The reason is simple: There is a historical element that must be considered. The earth itself and the organisms on it are constantly changing, and present distributions are in very large part the result of past conditions—conditions that were often very different from those now prevailing. For example, a knowledge of present conditions alone would be insufficient to explain why certain animals occur in South America, Africa, and southern Asia but nowhere else. Only if knowledge of present conditions is combined with evidence from the fossil record and with geological evidence of the past shapes, connections, and climates of the earth's land masses and oceans can we hope to gain insight into the present geography of life.

With these ideas in mind, let us briefly consider some of the major regional patterns of distribution, as these have been described and classified by biologists over the past century (Fig. 18.29).

The Island Continents. The biota (flora and fauna) of the *Australian region* (Australia, New Zealand, and adjacent islands) is by

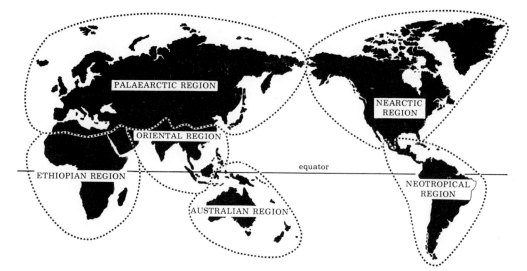

Fig. 18.29. Biogeographic regions of the world.

all odds the most unusual found on any of the earth's major land masses. Large numbers of species common in Australia occur nowhere else in the world. Conversely, many species widespread in the rest of the world are absent from Australia. This biological evidence, together with convincing geological evidence, indicates that Australia has not been connected to the Eurasian land mass for a very long time, if ever. The ancestors of most, if not all, organisms now living in the Australian region must have crossed a water barrier to get there. It is important to realize, however, that that water barrier was dotted by islands (the East Indies, presently the nation of Indonesia) and that organisms could have spread from one island to the next over a period of millions of years; it is not necessary to assume that a great expanse of ocean was crossed at any one time. Furthermore, most of the western islands of the East Indies were probably interconnected as an extension of the Asian land mass several times in the past; hence the distance from Asia to Australia has not always been as great as it is today.

Perhaps the best-known aspect of Australia's curious biota is its mammalian fauna, which is

completely unlike that of any other continent. Other than wild dogs (dingoes) and pigs, both of which were probably brought to the region by prehistoric man, the only placental mammals (those in which the entire embryonic development takes place in the mother's uterus) present in the Australian region before European explorers landed there were a number of species of rodents belonging to a single family and a variety of bats. Bats can, of course, fly across water barriers and would be expected to reach most oceanic islands. The rodents of Australia are apparently relatively recent arrivals, having come from Asia by island-hopping through the East Indies. Most of the ecological niches that on other continents would be filled by placental mammals are in Australia filled by marsupials (mammals whose young develop only a short while in the uterus, are then born, move to a pouch on the mother's abdomen, attach to a nipple, and there complete their embryonic development). Apparently the marsupials reached Australia very early and, encountering no competition from placental mammals, underwent extensive evolutionary radiation. Since they were filling niches similar to those filled in the rest of the world by placentals and were thus subject to similar selection pressures, they evolved striking convergent similarities to the placentals. Certain of the marsupials are very much like placental shrews, others are like placental jumping mice, weasels, wolverines, wolves, anteaters, moles, rats, flying squirrels, groundhogs, bears, etc. The uninitiated visitor to an Australian zoo finds it hard to believe when first looking at an assemblage of these animals that he is not seeing close relatives of the mammals familiar to him from other parts of the world. Not all marsupials look like their ecologically equivalent placentals, however. The kangaroos are markedly different, though some of them play an ecological role very similar to that of horses and other large placental grazers. The Australian marsupials are a fascinating biological development, but most of them are probably doomed to extinction, at least in the wild. The changes brought by civilization have not been favorable for many of them. And most seem unable to compete successfully with the placental mammals that man is introducing.

The South American continent, known to biologists as the *Neotropical region* (meaning "new tropics"), has had a history similar to that of Australia. It too has been an island continent unconnected to the other major land masses of the world through much of its history. And it too had an early mammalian fauna that included a great variety of marsupials, as the fossil record shows. But it also had a variety of placentals that probably reached it during a short period of connection to North America via a Central American land bridge during the early part of the Age of Mammals (about 60 million years ago). After this land bridge disappeared, both the marsupials and the placentals evolved in isolation many characteristics convergent to those evolved by other placentals on the main World Continent. There were times during this period of isolation lasting some 60 million years when the water barrier between South America and what is now northern Central America was not so wide. A few additional placental mammals chanced to get across into South America at such times; among these were the ancestors of the modern New World monkeys and a number of rodents. Finally, not so very long ago (a few million years), connection to North America was reestablished and many additional immigrants arrived in South America. Some species also moved in the opposite direction, from South America to North America; the opossum, the porcupine, and the armadillo are examples. Central America has never been more than a narrow bridge, however, and its climate and rugged terrain have not been hospitable to many northern species. Hence many groups of organisms have never been able to move between the North American and South American continents. The Central American land bridge has never been a corridor for general dispersal; it has been at best a selective or filter route, along which some species but not others could pass. In short, South America, like Australia, has been an island continent through much of its history, but its nearness to North America (Mexico) and its occasional direct connections to North America via the Central American land bridge have given it a more diverse biota with more similarities to that of the World Continent.

The World Continent. Europe, Asia, Africa, and North America have formed a relatively continuous land mass, the so-called World Continent, throughout most of geological time. Consequently their biotas are more alike in many aspects than they are like those of the two island continents. Nevertheless, biologists customarily divide the World Continent into four biogeographical regions: the *Nearctic* ("new northern"), which is North America; the *Palaearctic* ("old northern"), which is Europe and northern Asia; the *Oriental,* which is southern Asia; and the *Ethiopian,* which is Africa south of the Sahara.

The geological feature that looks like the

most obvious barrier between the Palaearctic and Ethiopian regions is the Mediterranian Sea, but this is not really the important barrier. Many species can move between Europe and North Africa by circling around the eastern end of the Mediterranean. The real barrier to species dispersal is the Sahara Desert. Africa north of the Sahara is part of the Palaearctic region.

The Oriental region—tropical Asia—is separated from Palaearctic northern Asia in most places by east–west mountain ranges, of which the Himalayas between India and China are part. It is interesting to note that these east–west mountains constitute important breaks between climatic regions, and that they therefore act as both topographic and climatic barriers between cold-adapted and warm-adapted species. By contrast, north–south mountains such as those in North America tend to facilitate mixing of cold-adapted and warm-adapted species.

That the Palaearctic, Oriental, and Ethiopian regions constitute an essentially continuous land mass is obvious, but you may wonder why the Nearctic is considered part of the same land mass. The answer is that North America and Asia have been connected by a Siberian land bridge through much of their geological history. Part of this bridge, between what are now Alaska and Siberia, is beneath water at the present time. Because the climate of Alaska and Siberia is so severe, you might not expect many organisms to use a bridge in that region. But again present conditions are misleading. The climate of that area has not always been so severe. Fossils of many temperate and even subtropical species of plants and animals are abundant in Alaska. Indeed all the evidence indicates that on many occasions during the past 60 million years or so there has been much

movement between Asia and North America via the Siberian land bridge. In fact, the Nearctic and Palaearctic regions are biologically so similar that many biologists regard them as a single region, which they call the Holarctic.

Once we understand the history of the major land masses and the two principal land bridges (Central American and Siberian), and once we understand that climates have not always been as they are now, we can make more sense of present distribution patterns. The common distribution referred to earlier, where a species occurs disjunctly in South America, Africa, and southern Asia, can be understood if we assume that this species was formerly more widespread, having moved between the New World and the Old World via the Siberian land bridge and between North and South America via Central America, and that it then became extinct in the north, either because of climatic changes or because of intense competition. The fossil record shows that this pattern of dispersal between southern regions via the north has occurred again and again. For example, members of the camel family occur today in South America (llamas, alpacas, vicuñas, etc.), northern Africa, and central Asia, but fossils indicate that the family originated in North America, spread to South America via Central America and to the Old World via Siberia, and later became extinct in North America—hence the disjunct distribution we see today. Many biologists now think that most southern disjunct distributions can be explained in this way, and that the older ideas of direct land bridges between southern continents during the Age of Mammals are not only ruled out by the geological evidence but by the biological evidence as well. Direct connections between the southern continents may have existed during earlier geological eras, however.

REFERENCES

ALLEE, W. C., 1951. *The Social Life of Animals.* Norton, New York.

——, A. E. EMERSON, O. PARK, T. PARK, and K. P. SCHMIDT, 1949. *Principles of Animal Ecology.* Saunders, Philadelphia.

ANDREWARTHA, H. G., and L. C. BIRCH, 1954. *The Distribution and Abundance of Animals.* University of Chicago Press, Chicago.

CAIN, S. A., 1944. *Foundations of Plant Geography.* Harper, New York.

CHRISTIAN, J. J., and D. D. DAVIS, 1964. "Endocrines, Behavior, and Population," *Science,* vol. 146, pp. 1550–1560.

COWLES, H. C., 1899. "The Ecological Relations of the Vegetation on the Sand Dunes of Lake Michigan," *Botanical Gazette,* vol. 27, pp. 95–117, 167–202, 281–308, 361–391.

DARLINGTON, P. J., 1957. *Zoogeography.* Wiley, New York.

ELTON, C. S., 1958. *The Ecology of Invasions by Animals and Plants.* Methuen, London.

HAZEN, W. E., ed., 1964. *Readings in Population and Community Ecology.* Saunders, Philadelphia. (A collection of 25 important articles by prominent ecologists.)

HESSE, R., W. C. ALLEE, and K. P. SCHMIDT, 1951. *Ecological Animal Geography.* Wiley, New York.

KENDEIGH, S. C., 1961. *Animal Ecology.* Prentice-Hall, Englewood Cliffs, N.J.

LACK, D., 1954. *The Natural Regulation of Animal Numbers.* Oxford University Press, New York.

MCINTOSH, R. P., 1958. "Plant Communities," *Science,* vol. 128, pp. 115–120.

NICHOLSON, A. J., 1957. "The Self-Adjustment of Populations to Change," *Cold Spring Harbor Symposium on Quantitative Biology,* vol. 22, pp. 153–172.

OOSTING, H. J., 1956. *The Study of Plant Communities,* 2nd ed. Freeman, San Francisco.

POLUNIN, N., 1960. *Introduction to Plant Geography.* McGraw-Hill, New York.

ROGERS, W. P., 1962. *The Nature of Parasitism.* Academic Press, New York.

SLOBODKIN, L. B., 1961. *Growth and Regulation of Animal Populations.* Holt, Rinehart & Winston, New York.

VIRTANEN, A. I., and J. K. MIETTINEN, 1963. "Biological Nitrogen Fixation," in vol. 3, pp. 539–668, of *Plant Physiology,* ed by F. C. Steward. Academic Press, New York.

WHITTAKER, R. H., 1953. "A Consideration of Climax Theory: The Climax as a Population and Pattern," *Ecological Monographs,* vol. 23, pp. 41–78.

SUGGESTED READING

ANDREWARTHA, H. G., 1961. *Introduction to the Study of Animal Populations.* University of Chicago Press, Chicago. (Paperback edition, Phoenix, Chicago, 1961.)

BATES, M., 1960. *The Forest and the Sea.* Random House, New York.

BILLINGS, W. D., 1964. *Plants and the Ecosystem.* Wadsworth, Belmont, Calif.

CARSON, R., 1952. *The Sea Around Us.* Oxford University Press, New York.

——, 1955. *The Edge of the Sea.* Houghton Mifflin, Boston. (Paperback edition, Signet, New York, 1959.)

COLE, L. C., 1958. "The Ecosphere," *Scientific American,* April. (Offprint 144.)

COOPER, C. F., 1961. "The Ecology of Fire," *Scientific American,* April.

DEEVEY, E. S., 1958. "Bogs," *Scientific American,* October. (Offprint 840.)

FARBER, P., 1963. *Face of North America: The Natural History of a Continent.* Harper, New York.

HAIRSTON, N. G., F. E. SMITH, and L. B. SLOBODKIN, 1960. "Community Structure, Population Control, and Competition," *American Naturalist,* vol. 94, pp. 421–425. (This excellent paper is included in the readings edited by Hazen, listed under REFERENCES above, and also in the readings edited by Kormondy, listed below.)

KORMONDY, E. J., ed., 1965. *Readings in Ecology.* Prentice-Hall, Englewood, Cliffs, N.J. (A collection of passages from 60 important papers.)

LEOPOLD, A. S., 1961. *The Desert.* Time Inc., New York.

ODUM, E. P., 1959. *Fundamentals of Ecology,* 2nd ed. Saunders, Philadelphia.

———, 1963. *Ecology.* Holt, Rinehart & Winston, New York.

OPIK, E. J., 1958. "Climate and the Changing Sun," *Scientific American,* June. (Offprint 835.)

PLASS, G. N., 1959. "Carbon Dioxide and Climate," *Scientific American,* July. (Offprint 823.)

WECKER, S. C., 1964. "Habitat Selection," *Scientific American,* October. (Offprint 195.)

WENT, F. W., 1949. "The Plants of Krakatoa," *Scientific American,* September.

———, 1955. "The Ecology of Desert Plants," *Scientific American,* April. (Offprint 114.)

WOODWELL, G. M., 1963. "The Ecological Effects of Radiation," *Scientific American,* June. (Offprint 159.)

WYNNE-EDWARDS, V. C., 1964. "Population Control in Animals," *Scientific American,* August. (Offprint 192.)

PART V

THE ORIGIN AND DIVERSITY OF LIFE

CHAPTER

19

THE ORIGIN OF
LIFE

WE DISCUSSED THE PRINCIPLE OF BIOGEN-
esis—that life arises from life—in Chapter 3. And we briefly examined Pasteur's classic
experiment in support of this principle. Pasteur's work effectively put to rest, as far as most
biologists were concerned, the long-held idea
of spontaneous generation. No longer did men
of science seriously entertain the notion that the
maggots in decaying meat arise *de novo* from
the meat, or that earthworms arise from the
soil during heavy rains, or that mice arise from
sweaty shirts placed in a dark corner and
sprinkled with wheat, as Jean-Baptiste van
Helmont had suggested, or even that microorganisms appear spontaneously in spoiling
broth. It may seem strange, then, that in the
mid-twentieth century spontaneous generation
should be a topic of major interest in biology.
But there is a big difference between the
modern ideas of spontaneous generation and
those of Pasteur's day. The modern theorists
do not suggest that life can arise spontaneously
under the conditions that now exist on the
earth; indeed, most of them are convinced
that this cannot happen. What they do suggest

is that life could and did arise spontaneously from nonliving matter under the conditions prevailing on the early earth, and that it is from such beginnings that all present earthly life has descended.

It is one of the purposes of this chapter to outline for you a theory of the origin of life that is now widely held by scientists. The basis for this theory was first enunciated clearly and forcefully by the Russian biochemist A. I. Oparin in 1936.[1] You should be aware, however, that although the broad outlines of the theory have wide support many of the details are disputed. And you should realize that we have no direct evidence concerning the origin of life. We cannot be sure how life did arise; we can only gather indirect evidence to show how it could have arisen and how it probably arose.

Formation of the Earth and Its Atmosphere. We are not certain how the solar system formed. We have only hypotheses. But as astronomers probe ever deeper into the secrets of the universe, the evidence upon which these hypotheses are based becomes more and more convincing. The hypothesis most widely held today is that the sun and its planets formed from a cloud of cosmic dust and gas. Most of this material began to condense rapidly into a more compact mass. The condensation produced enormous heat and pressure, which initiated thermonuclear reactions and converted the main condensed mass into the sun. Within the remainder of the dust and gas cloud, which now formed a disc held in the gravitational field of the newborn sun, lesser centers of condensation began to form. These became the planets, of which the earth is one.

As the earth condensed, a stratification of its

---

[1] Oparin had published a brief explanation of his theory earlier (1924), but this book was never translated from the Russian. His ideas had no major impact on scientific thought until *The Origin of Life on Earth* appeared in 1936 (first English edition, 1938).

components took place, the heavier materials, such as iron and nickel, sinking into the core and the lighter substances becoming more concentrated nearer the surface. Among these lighter materials must have been hydrogen, nitrogen, oxygen, and carbon, all of which were to play crucial roles in the later origin of life.

We must know something about the probable composition of the earth's primordial atmosphere if we are to understand the conditions under which life arose. The present atmosphere contains approximately 78 percent molecular nitrogen (N_2), 21 percent molecular oxygen (O_2), and one percent carbon dioxide (CO_2), plus traces of rarer gases such as helium and neon. But available evidence indicates that the primordial atmosphere was quite different. It was not an oxidizing atmosphere, as the present one is, but a reducing one; i.e. it contained much more hydrogen (H_2). Consequently there was little free nitrogen or oxygen and little CO_2. Instead, the nitrogen, oxygen, and carbon were combined with hydrogen. Thus the nitrogen in the atmosphere was probably in the form of ammonia (NH_3), the oxygen in the form of water vapor (H_2O), and the carbon primarily in the form of methane (CH_4). Note that methane is a simple hydrocarbon—an organic compound. Thus the atmosphere of the early earth contained large quantities of an organic compound long before there were any organisms. This sort of atmosphere (containing large percentages of methane, ammonia, and hydrogen) is still found on Jupiter and Saturn.

Initially, most of the earth's water was probably present as vapor in the atmosphere, forming dense clouds many miles thick. Whenever any of this vapor condensed and fell to the surface as rain, the moderately high temperatures of the earth's crust promptly caused the water to evaporate. But eventually the crust cooled sufficiently for liquid water to remain on it. Torrential rains fell, the low places on the crust slowly filled with water, and the first oceans were formed. As rivers rushed down the slopes, they dissolved away and carried with them salts and minerals of various sorts, which slowly accumulated in the seas. Some methane and ammonia (as ammonium ions, NH_4^+) from the atmosphere also dissolved in the waters of the newly formed oceans.

Formation of Complex Organic Molecules. If the early earth had a reducing atmosphere, as Oparin suggested and as many astronomers and chemists have agreed, and the primitive warm seas contained a mixture of salts, ammonium, and methane, how were the more complex organic molecules formed? Methane may be organic, but it is far from being a sufficient base on which to build living things. A mixture of ammonia, methane, water, and hydrogen is thermodynamically stable. There is no tendency for these materials to react with each other to form other compounds. Yet for life to have arisen it would seem at the very least that the critical building-block materials, particularly amino acids and the purine and pyrimidine bases, would have been necessary. How might these compounds have been formed on the abiotic primitive earth?

If more complex organic compounds were produced by reactions in the stable mixture of ammonia, methane, water, and hydrogen, clearly some external source of energy must have been acting on the mixture. One possible source might have been solar radiation, including visible light, ultraviolet light, X rays, etc. Of these different types of solar radiation, ultraviolet light would probably have been the most important. A second important possibility is energy from electrical discharges, such as lightning. A third is heat. There are other possible sources of energy, such as cosmic rays, radioactive disintegration of elements in the earth's interior, and volcanic explosions, but it seems unlikely that these played any appreciable role in organic synthesis. The question thus becomes: Can it be demonstrated that ultraviolet radiation or electrical discharges or heat or a combination of these can cause reactions that produce complex organic compounds from a mixture of ammonia, methane, water, and hydrogen? An answer to this question was provided in 1953 by Stanley L. Miller, who was then a graduate student working under Harold C. Urey at the University of Chicago.

Miller set up an airtight apparatus in which the four gases could be circulated past electrical discharges from tungsten electrodes. He kept the gases circulating continuously in this way for one week, and then analyzed the liquid in the apparatus. He found that an amazing number and variety of organic compounds had been synthesized. Among these were some of the most important amino acids and also such substances as urea, hydrogen cyanide, acetic acid, and lactic acid. Lest it be objected that microorganisms had contaminated his gas mixture and synthesized the compounds, Miller in another experiment circulated the gases in the same way but without any electrical discharges; no significant yield of complex organic compounds resulted. In still another experiment, he prepared the apparatus with the gas mixture inside and then sterilized it at 130°C for 18 hours before starting the sparking. The yields of complex compounds were the same as in his first experiments; a great variety of organic compounds was formed. Clearly, the synthesis was not brought about by microorganisms but was abiotic—a synthesis in the absence of any living organisms, a synthesis under conditions presumably similar to those on the primordial earth. This experiment by Miller, which gave the first conclusive evidence that some of the steps hypothesized by Oparin could really occur, marked a turning point in the scientific approach to the problem of how life began.

In the years since 1953, many investigators have synthesized a great variety of organic compounds (including purines, pyrimidines, and simple sugars) from reducing mixtures of gases in which the only initial carbon source was methane. Thus Miller's results have been confirmed and extended. Still other investigators have used different mixtures of gases or other energy sources (such as ultraviolet light or heat) or both and have also obtained significant yields. This means that abiotic synthesis of organic compounds can occur under so many different conditions that even if the conditions on the primitive earth were only roughly similar to the ones postulated, organic compounds would almost certainly have appeared and become dissolved in the waters of the seas. In other words, synthesis of complex organic compounds on the early earth was not only possible but highly probable.

But, it may be argued, even if organic compounds were synthesized abiotically on the primordial earth, they would surely have been destroyed too fast to have accumulated in sufficient quantities to have formed the basis for later origin of living things. After all, most of these organic compounds are known to be highly perishable. But why are they perishable? There are two main reasons. First, they tend to react slowly with molecular oxygen and become oxidized. And second, they are broken down by organisms of decay, primarily microorganisms. But the prebiotic atmosphere contained virtually no free oxygen, and there were no organisms of any kind. Therefore neither oxidation nor decay would have destroyed the organic molecules, and they could have accumulated in the seas over the course of hundreds of millions of years. No such accumulation would be possible today.

Let us suppose, then, that a variety of hydrocarbons, fatty acids, amino acids, purine and pyrimidine bases, simple sugars, and other relatively small organic compounds slowly accumulated in the ancient seas. This is still not a sufficient basis for the origin of life. Macromolecules are needed, particularly polypeptides and nucleic acids. How might these polymers have formed from the building-block substances present in the "hot soup" of the ancient oceans? This question is not easy to answer, and several hypotheses are currently supported by different investigators. Some think that the concentration of organic material in the seas was high enough for chance bondings between simpler molecules to give rise, over a period of hundreds of millions of years, to considerable quantities of macromolecules. They point out that even though each such polymerization reaction is rather unlikely in the absence of protein enzymes, nevertheless on the time scale here involved enough rare and unlikely events may occur collectively to produce a major change. As George Wald of Harvard University has said, "Given so much time, the 'impossible' becomes possible, the possible probable, and the probable virtually certain."

However, other investigators have been unwilling to agree that organic material in the early oceans was sufficiently abundant for chance polymerizations to produce enough macromolecules to form a basis for life, even granting the immense spans of time involved. They have suggested that the organic building-block compounds may have become more concentrated along the shores of the oceans, particularly in shallow lagoons and ponds. Small amounts of the dilute solution might occasionally have been caught in puddles on the beaches of such lagoons and ponds, and the heat of the sun might have evaporated much of the water and provided energy for polymerization reactions. The resulting polymers might then have been washed back into the pond. A process such as this could slowly have built up a supply of macromolecules in the pond. Sidney W. Fox of Florida State University has shown that if a nearly dry mixture of amino acids is heated, polypeptide molecules are indeed synthesized (particularly if phosphates are present); this hypothesis therefore seems a reasonable one. Alternatively, the energy for polymerization reactions in the puddles might have come from ultraviolet radiation rather than heat.

Formation of Molecular Aggregates and Primitive Cells. We have now reached a point in our model for the origin of life where the "hot soup" of the ancient seas, or at least the "soup" in some estuaries and lagoons, contains a mixture of salts and organic molecules, including polymers such as polypeptides and perhaps nucleic acids. We must next ask how the orderliness that characterizes living things could emerge from this mixture. Oparin pointed out that colloidal protein molecules tend to clump together and form more complex units called *coacervate* droplets. Each such droplet is a cluster of colloidal molecules surrounded by a shell of water in which the individual water molecules are rigidly oriented relative to the colloidal particles. There is thus a definite demarcation or interface between the coacervate droplet and the liquid in which it floats. In a sense, the shell of oriented water molecules forms a membrane around the droplet. Now, coacervate droplets have a marked tendency to adsorb and incorporate various substances from the surrounding solution; sometimes this tendency, which is a selective one, is so pronounced that the droplets may almost completely remove some materials from the medium. In this way, the droplets may grow at the expense of the surrounding liquid. And coacervate droplets have a strong tendency toward formation of definite internal structure; i.e. the molecules within the droplet tend to become arranged in an orderly manner instead of being randomly scattered. As more and more different materials are incorporated into the droplet, a membrane consisting of surface-active substances may form just inside the shell of oriented water molecules, the permeability of the boundary of the droplet thus becoming even more selective than before. Thus, although coacervate droplets are not alive in the usual

sense of the word, they do exhibit many properties ordinarily associated with living organisms. In fact, they look so much like organisms when viewed under a light microscope or even in an electron micrograph that experienced biologists have on occasion mistaken them for bacteria and attempted to assign them to species!

Since a complex coacervate droplet is both structurally organized and sharply separated from the external medium, it follows that the chemical reactions that take place within the droplet depend not only on the conditions of the medium but also on the physico-chemical organization of the droplet itself. Because various substances may be more concentrated in the droplet, the probability of their entering chemical reactions is increased; and because of the organization within the droplet, each reaction that takes place will influence other reactions in ways that are most unlikely when the substances are free in the external medium. Furthermore, catalytic activity of both inorganic substances such as metallic compounds and organic ones such as proteins is enhanced by the regular spatial arrangement of molecules within the droplet. In short, the special conditions within the droplet will exert selective and regulative influence over the chemical reactions taking place within the droplet.

Doubtless vast numbers of different coacervate systems arose in the seas of the early earth. Most were probably too unstable to last long. But a few may have contained particularly favorable combinations of materials, especially complexes with catalytic activity, and may thus have developed unusually harmonious interactions between the reactions occurring within them. They might thus have survived longer and undergone relatively coordinated growth. As such droplets increased in size, they would have been more susceptible to physical fragmentation, which would have produced new smaller droplets with composition and properties essentially similar to those of the original droplet. These, in turn, would have grown and fragmented again. Thus a primitive type of reproduction might have arisen.

According to some workers, the reproduction of the bulk of the droplets was probably not initially under the control of nucleic acids, even though these compounds could have been synthesized under abiotic conditions and may well have been incorporated into some of the droplets. The nucleic acids would, of course, have been able to reproduce themselves exactly if a sufficient pool of nucleotides was present and if there were appropriate catalysts (even weak ones).

The coacervate lineages that survived longest were doubtless those that were most stable, i.e. that had the most harmoniously balanced structural and functional systems. Clearly, if the new droplets formed at each division could have acquired more exact replicates of the favorable features of the parent droplet, their chances of survival would have been greater than without a genetic control system. In other words, chances of survival would have been increased if the sequence of nucleotides in nucleic acids could have come to code not only for more nucleic acid but also for other components of the droplets, particularly proteins. Just how this correlation between nucleotide sequences in nucleic acids and amino acid sequences in proteins would have arisen is not yet clear, but the presumption is that it slowly came into being and thus made possible much more accurate duplication during the reproductive process, and also more precise control over the chemical reactions taking place within the droplets. In effect, a small percentage of coacervate droplets with particularly favorable characteristics slowly developed into the first primitive cells. Notice that there was almost certainly no abrupt transition from "nonliving" coacervate droplets to "living" cells. The attributes that we normally associate with life were acquired gradually. At this stage, the boundary between living and nonliving is an arbitrary one.

Not all biologists accept the sequence outlined above. Some think it more likely that the first cells arose through the self-replication of molecules such as nucleic acids, which would then slowly have accumulated a shell of other substances (a primitive cytoplasm) around themselves. In other words, instead of postulating that droplets capable of reproduction arose first and then slowly developed a genetic control system, they suggest that the control system arose first and that cytoplasm and a membrane then developed around it. According to this hypothesis, the first cells arose from something very like modern viruses, which are simply free nucleic acids with a thin shell of protein around them. It has been argued against this view that all modern viruses are obligatorily parasitic—that they can reproduce only inside living cells—and that consequently they could not have existed before there were any cells. According to this view, viruses are of much more recent origin. But it has been pointed out that, although today the raw materials necessary for virus reproduction can be found only inside living cells (which is why viruses are obligate parasites), these substances would have been available in the "hot soup" hypothesized for the prebiological earth, and that viruses or something like them could, therefore, have been free-living as long as the "hot soup" existed.

Which, if either, of the two alternative models for the origin of the first cells outlined here approximates the facts can perhaps never be settled with finality. But further attempts to duplicate in the laboratory the developmental sequences these models suggest may cast more light on this intriguing subject in the near future.

Evolution of More Complex Biochemical Pathways by Primitive Organisms. According to the view now most widely accepted, the earliest organisms were heterotrophs. They used as nutrients the carbohydrates, amino acids, and other organic compounds free in the environment in which they lived. In other words, they depended upon previous abiotic synthesis of organic compounds. But as the organisms became more abundant and more efficient at removing nutrients from the medium, they must have begun to deplete the supply of nutrients. The rate of formation of organic matter from ammonia, methane, water, and hydrogen was probably never very high, and it took many millions of years for a moderate supply of nutrients to accumulate. Now that supply was being used up at an ever increasing rate, and as the drain on available resources became more and more severe, there must have been increasing competition between the organisms. Forms inefficient at obtaining nutrients doubtless perished; those that were more efficient survived in greater frequency. Natural selection would have favored any new mutation that enhanced the ability of its possessor to obtain or process food.

At first, the primitive organisms probably carried out relatively few complex biochemical transformations. They could obtain most of the materials they needed ready-made. But it would have been these very materials—materials that could be utilized directly with little alteration—that would have dwindled most rapidly. Hence there would have been strong selection for any organisms that could utilize alternative nutrients. Suppose, for example, that compound A, which was necessary for the life of cells, was initially available in the medium but that its supply was being rapidly exhausted. If some cells possessed a mutant gene that coded for an enzyme, a, that catalyzed synthesis of A from another compound, B, available in greater supply in the medium, then those cells would have had an adaptive advantage over cells that lacked the mutant gene. They could survive even when A was no longer available in the medium by carrying out the reaction

$$B \xrightarrow{\;\;a\;\;} A$$

But then there would have been increasing demand for free B, and the rate of its utilization would soon have exceeded the rate of its abiotic synthesis. Thus the supply of B would have dwindled, and there would have been strong selection for any cells possessing a second mutant gene that coded for an enzyme, b, catalyzing synthesis of B from C. These cells would not have been dependent on a free supply of either A or B because they could make both A and B for themselves as long as they could obtain sufficient C:

$$C \xrightarrow{\;\;b\;\;} B \xrightarrow{\;\;a\;\;} A$$

This process of evolution of synthetic ability might have continued until eventually most cells made all the A they required by carrying out a long chain of chemical reactions:

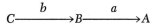

$$G \xrightarrow{\;f\;} F \xrightarrow{\;e\;} E \xrightarrow{\;d\;} D \xrightarrow{\;c\;} C \xrightarrow{\;b\;} B \xrightarrow{\;a\;} A$$

In this way, the primitive cells would slowly have evolved more elaborate biochemical capabilities.

It seems most unlikely that much synthetic ability could have arisen unless the cells possessed some mechanism for handling chemical energy. The fact that all living things, from bacteria to man, utilize ATP as their principal energy currency might be taken as evidence that use of ATP was an early evolutionary development. But what is the evidence that ATP was available to early organisms? The two organic precursors of ATP are adenine, a nitrogenous base, and ribose, a five-carbon sugar. Both of these compounds also occur in nucleic acids, and experiments have demonstrated that both can be synthesized abiotically under presumed prebiological conditions. It seems reasonable to suppose, therefore, that ATP could have been used in coupling exergonic and endergonic reactions as soon as the primitive cells could perform the reactions.

Evolution of Autotrophy. Even though the primitive heterotrophs probably evolved more and more elaborate biochemical pathways that enabled them to utilize a greater variety of the organic compounds free in their environment, and even though some of them probably evolved other methods of feeding, such as saprophytism, parasitism, and predation, nevertheless life would eventually have ceased if all nutrition had remained heterotrophic. Not only must nutrients have been used up much faster than they were being synthesized, but also the organisms themselves must have been altering the environment in ways that decreased the rate of abiotic synthesis of organic compounds. For example, their respiration, which would have been fermentative in the absence of molecular oxygen, would have released carbon dioxide into the atmosphere. Abiotic synthesis of complex organic compounds from CO_2 is much less likely than from methane. And, furthermore, CO_2 in the atmosphere tends to screen out high-energy solar radiation such as ultraviolet light, thus partly blocking one of the major sources of energy for abiotic synthesis.

That life did not become extinct as the supply of free organic compounds dwindled is attributable to the evolution of photosynthetic pathways by some of the primitive organisms. The first such pathway may well have been that of cyclic photophosphorylation, in which light of visible wavelengths is used as an energy source in synthesis of ATP by cells. Later, the much more complex pathways of noncyclic photophosphorylation, in which energy from sunlight is used in synthesis of carbohydrate from carbon dioxide and water (or some other hydrogen source) would have arisen. From this time onward, the continuation of life on earth depended upon the activity of the photosynthetic autotrophs.

The evolution of photosynthesis probably administered the *coup de grâce* to significant abiotic synthesis of complex organic compounds. An important by-product of plant photosynthesis is molecular oxygen. The oxygen released by photosynthesis must have helped convert the atmosphere from a reducing one to an oxidizing one, particularly since much of the hydrogen present initially must by this time have escaped from the planet into space. Once the layer of ozone (O_3) now present high in the atmosphere had been formed by some of the oxygen, this layer effectively screened out most of the ultraviolet radiation from the sun and allowed very little high-energy radiation to reach the earth's surface. In other words, living organisms, once they arose, changed their environment in a way that destroyed the conditions that had made possible the origin of life.

Once molecular oxygen became a major component of the atmosphere, both heterotrophic and autotrophic organisms evolved the biochemical pathways of aerobic respiration, by which far more energy can be extracted from nutrient molecules than by fermentation alone.

The Possibility of Life on Other Planets. If life could arise spontaneously from nonliving matter on the primordial earth, might it also have arisen elsewhere in the universe? This is a question that intrigues modern biologists and astronomers. So far, no one knows the answer. Life may be unique to the planet Earth. But few scientists working in this branch of biology think so; most are convinced that life has probably arisen many times in many places. They point out that there is no reason to think any unduplicable event was necessary to the origin of life on earth, that, on the contrary, all the events now hypothesized and all the known characteristics of life seem to fall well within the general laws of the universe, i.e. that they are natural phenomena susceptible of duplication. Given the immense size of the universe, they argue, it would actually be unreasonable to think that life is restricted to one small planet in one minor solar system.

One interesting series of calculations on the probability of life elsewhere in the universe has been made by Harlow Shapley of Harvard

University. Shapley says that at least 10^{20} stars are visible to us with present-day telescopes (to say nothing about the vast numbers beyond the reach of our telescopes).[2] Many of these stars probably lack planets, but Shapley thinks it reasonable to assume that at least one star in every thousand has a planetary system, which gives a total of 10^{17} stars with planets. Now, if it is assumed that life wherever it occurs is at least roughly similar to earthly life in its basic chemistry, then it must be concluded that only planets with moderate temperatures could support life. The planetary systems of many stars may not include such a planet. Shapley suggests that a very conservative estimate would be that at least one in a thousand of the stars with planets has an appropriate planet; this gives a total of 10^{14} stars with at least one planet of the right temperature. Now, not only must a planet have moderate temperatures if it is to support life, but it must also be within a certain size range to hold a suitable atmosphere. If one out of every thousand of the planets of the right temperature is also of the right size, this gives a total

of 10^{11}. But even if a planet has an appropriate temperature and atmosphere, life still might not have arisen, for any number of reasons. Again Shapley uses an estimate of one in a thousand, which gives 10^8 (one hundred million) planets on which life may well have arisen. Many biologists feel that Shapley's estimate of one hundred million is too conservative, that the figure should be considerably higher, perhaps 10^{14} or more.

If one admits the possibility that life has arisen on a hundred million or more other planets, the question immediately arises whether civilizations as advanced as, or more advanced than, our own might have developed elsewhere. Here there is little on which to base an estimate. Any estimate is only one person's guess. Nevertheless, many scientists believe that there are numerous civilizations in the universe more advanced than our own. Shapley's estimate is that there are at least 100,000 such civilizations. So confident are some scientists that these other civilizations exist that they propose building huge radio receivers for listening for signals from outer space. They think it possible that some day earthly man may be able to communicate with intelligent organisms living on planets in other parts of the universe.

[2] Very large numbers are customarily written as powers of 10. Thus 10^{20} is equivalent to one followed by 20 zeros. Similarly, 10^8 would be one followed by 8 zeros.

REFERENCES

ALFVÉN, H., 1954. *The Origin of the Planetary System.* Oxford University Press, New York.

Fox, S. W., ed., 1965. *The Origins of Prebiological Systems and of Their Molecular Matrices.* Academic Press, New York. (This book contains the proceedings of a conference on problems of the origin of life held in Florida in October, 1963. Included are 24 papers by leading authorities in the field and transcripts of the discussions that followed the presentation of each paper.)

HOYLE, F., 1960. *The Nature of the Universe.* Harper, New York.

MILLER, S. L., 1953. "Production of Amino Acids under Possible Primitive Earth Conditions," *Science,* vol. 117, pp. 528–529.

OPARIN, A. I., ed., 1959. *Proceedings of the First International Symposium on the Origin of Life on the Earth* (International Union of Biochemistry, Symposium Series, vol. 1). Pergamon, Oxford. (A collection of papers by authorities in the field.)

———, 1962. *Life: Its Nature, Origin and Development.* Academic Press, New York.

———, 1964. *The Chemical Origin of Life.* Charles C Thomas, Springfield, Ill.

RUTTEN, M. G., 1962. *The Geological Aspects of the Origin of Life on Earth.* Elsevier, Amsterdam, New York.

UREY, H. C., 1952. *The Planets.* Yale University Press, New Haven, Conn.

SUGGESTED READING

EHRENSVARD, G., 1962. *Life: Origin and Development.* University of Chicago Press, Chicago.

KEOSIAN, J., 1964. *The Origin of Life.* Reinhold, New York.

MILLER, S. L., 1962. "The Origin of Life," in *This Is Life,* ed. by W. H. Johnson and W. C. Steere. Holt, Rinehart & Winston, New York.

OPARIN, A. I., 1938. *The Origin of Life on Earth.* Macmillan, New York. (Also available in paperback under the title *The Origin of Life,* Dover, New York, 1953.)

SHAPLEY, H., 1958. *Of Men and Stars. Beacon,* Boston.

———, 1963. *The View from a Distant Star.* Basic Books, New York.

WALD, G., 1954. "The Origin of Life," *Scientific American,* August. (Offprint 47.)

CHAPTER 20

VIRUSES AND MONERA

L IFE PROBABLY AROSE ON THE EARTH BE-
tween two and three billion years ago.
Evolutionary change has been going on ever
since, bringing with it the increasing organismic
complexity manifest in many lineages and an
increasing diversity expressed in the enormous
variety of organisms now inhabiting this planet.
Biologists would like to unravel the evolutionary relationships among the major groups
formed by this multiplicity of organisms, but
that has proved a difficult task.

THE KINGDOMS OF LIFE

The Pre-Cambrian Fossil Record. The fossil
record is one of our best sources of evidence
concerning the evolutionary history of life on
earth. But unfortunately there are very few
fossils from the first 1½–2½ billion years of
life. The oldest geologic period from which
fossils are fairly abundant is the *Cambrian,*
which began about 600 million years ago (see
Table 21.2, p. 824). Many of the Cambrian
fossils are of relatively complex organisms;
how complex is suggested by the fact that most

of the animal phyla extant today were already represented in the Cambrian. There are a few Pre-Cambrian fossils, but these are mostly of bacteria, simple algae, and a few invertebrates whose relationships are poorly understood.

It is not clear why there are so few Pre-Cambrian fossils. Among the many alternative explanations that have been suggested, one is that most Pre-Cambrian organisms were soft-bodied and hence did not readily form fossils; it is the hard parts of plants and animals that are most often fossilized, because these are the most likely to resist decay and become buried. This explanation is doubtless partly correct, but it alone is not sufficient. It seems most unlikely that the many hard-bodied animals present at the start of the Cambrian period arose suddenly at that time; they almost certainly descended from Pre-Cambrian ancestors that gradually developed shells or exoskeletons or other hard parts. And indeed a few recently discovered beds of Pre-Cambrian fossils, notably in Australia, have confirmed the existence of hard-bodied invertebrate animals before the Cambrian. It is possible, however, that the ranges of these organisms were restricted to areas with rather special environmental conditions that made fossilization unlikely. Furthermore, we must remember that fossils may be destroyed by normal geological processes; the longer the time, the greater the destruction. It is reasonable to suppose, therefore, that a high percentage of any fossils formed as long ago as the Pre-Cambrian would have been destroyed long before there were men to study them. Whatever the explanation for the paucity of Pre-Cambrian fossils, the fact remains that we have very little evidence concerning a most fascinating evolutionary development—the early radiation of life and the origin of the major phyla.

The Difficulty of Kingdom Classification. Because the fossil record is nearly blank for the long span of time when the basic pattern of organismic diversity was coming into being, our ideas about the evolutionary relationships between the major phyla and divisions of organisms are rather vague. We have hardly any notion how bacteria are related to other living things. We have little evidence concerning the relationships between the major groups of algae. We don't know whether fungi evolved from photosynthetic green algae, or directly from heterotrophic organisms such as bacteria, or from some other stock. We are uncertain about the relationships of many Protozoa to multicellular plants or to multicellular animals.

Despite their lack of knowledge concerning the relationships between major groups of organisms, men have traditionally attempted to assign all living things to one or another of a few large categories called **kingdoms.** One of the oldest and most widely used such classifications recognizes only two kingdoms—one for plants and the other for animals. This dichotomy works well as long as the organisms to be classified are the generally familiar ones. Dandelions, grasses, daffodils, roses, and oak trees can easily be recognized as plants; no fancy definitions or elaborate diagnostic keys are necessary. Similarly, cats, horses, chickens, earthworms, and houseflies can easily be recognized as animals. Things become a bit more difficult when the organisms in question are bread mold, sea anemones, or sponges. These don't fit quite so neatly within the common intuitive concept of "plant" and "animal." Nevertheless, bread molds, when their characteristics are carefully examined, seem definitely more "plantlike" than "animal-like," despite their lack of chlorophyll; and biologists can easily convince themselves that sea anemones and sponges are "animals," despite their sedentary way of life.

But what about unicellular organisms? The ones zoologists have traditionally called Protozoa have been particularly troublesome to those who insist on a neat separation between plants and animals. This is true especially of the group of protozoans known as flagellates. These creatures have long flagella that enable them to swim actively in a manner intuitively felt to be "animal-like." Yet some of them possess chlorophyll and carry out photosynthesis, a characteristic ordinarily considered decidedly "plantlike." How can we classify organisms such as these? One possibility would be to rule arbitrarily that all those with chlorophyll are to be considered plants and all lacking chlorophyll are to be considered animals. But this seemingly simple procedure has serious drawbacks. Some green flagellates are clearly very closely related to colorless species; yet our rule would put the green ones in a different kingdom from their colorless close relatives. Furthermore, there are some species of flagellates in which both green and colorless races sometimes occur; our arbitrary rule is unable to deal effectively with such species. Suppose we try a different rule: We decide that, since most Protozoa lack chlorophyll and are rather animal-like, we will consider all of them to be animals, even if they are green. Again there are serious drawbacks. In many cases, unicellular green flagellates are obviously very closely related to species of simple multicellular green algae. Evolutionary patterns within the green algae are best interpreted, in fact, if one includes unicellular green flagellates; transferring them from the algae to the animal kingdom clearly separates closely related organisms and is unacceptable.

No matter what alternative criteria we choose, we shall be unable to make any clean separation of plants and animals that will not cause as many problems as it solves. The reason is obvious. Unicellular organisms (and some multicellular ones) are at an evolutionary level where it is essentially meaningless to talk about "plants" and "animals." The kingdoms are artificial constructions designed by human beings in an effort to cope with the tremendous diversity of the living world. They are not rules of nature; real living things don't come in two convenient categories labeled "plants" and "animals." Once we recognize that kingdoms are only devices that we ourselves have cre-

ated, we can forget about trying to apply the system rigidly at a level where it has little relevance. At the lowest evolutionary levels, about the only distinction between plants and animals that stands up is this: Plants are living things studied by people who say they are studying plants (botanists), and animals are living things studied by people who say they are studying animals (zoologists). Facetious as this distinction sounds, it is basically accurate. Since the unicellular green flagellates are studied by both botanists and zoologists, the first calling them algae and the second calling them Protozoa—without doing violence to any important biological principle—it is practical to classify green flagellates as both plants and animals. They will thus appear in two places in the classification used in this book—in the algal divisions Chlorophyta (green algae), Euglenophyta (euglenoid algae), or Chrysophyta (yellow-green and golden-brown algae) and in the Protozoa.

Like green flagellates, bacteria and blue-green algae are difficult to classify as either plants or animals. These organisms differ in fundamental ways from all other living things. They are procaryotic, whereas all other organisms are eucaryotic. Biologists have usually put these two groups in the plant kingdom, but it is clear that they are not closely related to other plants. Sometimes they have been set apart as a separate kingdom called the *Monera;* we shall follow this practice here.

We have mentioned two possible kingdom classifications—one that recognizes only two kingdoms: *Plantae* (plants) and *Animalia* (animals); and the one used in this book, which recognizes three kingdoms: Monera, Plantae, and Animalia. Other systems recognize a different set of three kingdoms: Protista, Plantae, and Animalia. Still others recognize four kingdoms: Monera, Protista, Plantae, and Animalia. Table 20.1 compares five different kingdom classifications that may be encountered in various textbooks today.

As the table shows, the limits of the kingdom

TABLE 20.1

Various Kingdom Classifications

System 1	System 2	System 3	System 4	System 5
PLANTAE	MONERA	PROTISTA	PROTISTA	MONERA
Bacteria	Bacteria	Bacteria	Bacteria	Bacteria
Blue-green algae	Blue-green algae	Blue-green algae	Blue-green algae	Blue-green algae
Green algae		Protozoa	Protozoa	
Brown algae	PLANTAE	Slime molds	Green algae	PROTISTA
Red algae	Green algae		Brown algae	Protozoa
Slime molds	Brown algae	PLANTAE	Red algae	Green algae
Fungi	Red algae	Green algae	Slime molds	Brown algae
Bryophytes	Slime molds	Brown algae	Fungi	Red algae
Tracheophytes	Fungi	Red algae		Slime molds
	Bryophytes	Fungi	PLANTAE	Fungi
ANIMALIA	Tracheophytes	Bryophytes	Bryophytes	
Protozoa		Tracheophytes	Tracheophytes	PLANTAE
Multicellular	ANIMALIA			Bryophytes
animals	Protozoa	ANIMALIA	ANIMALIA	Tracheophytes
	Multicellular	Multicellular	Multicellular	
	animals	animals	animals	ANIMALIA
				Multicellular
				animals

Protista, which includes both plantlike and animal-like primitive organisms, vary greatly from one classification to another. Thus in some classifications only bacteria, blue-green algae, Protozoa (including the unicellular green flagellates), and slime molds are included, whereas in other classifications all multicellular algae and fungi are included as well. In other words, Protista is sometimes restricted to organisms that are unicellular during much or all of their lives, and sometimes it is expanded to include all plantlike organisms whose bodies show relatively little distinction between tissues. Both usages of Protista have the advantage of clearly separating the plant and animal kingdoms, all the troublesome forms being lumped together under Protista. But the first usage, which restricts Protista to unicellular organisms, separates green flagellates from their close multicellular relatives in the algae, a procedure that the specialists on algae (phycologists) say is not acceptable. And the second usage, which includes all algae and fungi

in the Protista, leaves only bryophytes and vascular plants in the plant kingdom; this classification, accepted by few botanists, combines groups such as the bacteria, the ciliate Protozoa, and the brown algae that are probably not at all closely related, thus making the Protista a phylogenetically meaningless assemblage. In brief, both usages of Protista get around some of the difficulties inherent in the two-kingdom system but create other problems just as troublesome. The admittedly unsatisfactory older and broader usage of the plant and animal kingdoms is retained in this book (except for separation of the Monera), because recognition of the Protista seems only to change the problems without solving them.

VIRUSES

The viruses were not mentioned in the preceding discussion of kingdom classification because they differ in such fundamental ways from cellular organisms that biologists have been hesitant to regard them as living things. Yet they undeniably possess many properties in common with living organisms, and, living or not, their study has come to be a major aspect of modern biology.

The Discovery of Viruses. By the latter part of the nineteenth century, the idea had become firmly established that many diseases are caused by microorganisms. Pioneer bacteriologists such as Louis Pasteur and Robert Koch had isolated the pathogens for a number of diseases that attack man and his domestic animals. But for some diseases biologists, try as they would, could find no causal microorganism. As early as 1796 it had been known that smallpox could be induced in a healthy person by something in the pus from a smallpox victim, and Edward Jenner had demonstrated that a person vaccinated with material from cowpox lesions developed an immunity to smallpox. Yet no bacterial agent could be found.

A crucial experiment was performed in 1892 by a Russian biologist, Dmitri Iwanowsky, who was studying a disease of tobacco plants called tobacco mosaic. The leaves of plants with this disease become mottled and wrinkled. If juice is extracted from an infected plant and rubbed on the leaves of a healthy one, the latter soon develops tobacco mosaic disease. If, however, the juice is heated nearly to boiling before it is rubbed on the healthy leaves, no disease develops. Concluding that the disease must be caused by bacteria in the plant juice, Iwanowsky passed juice from an infected tobacco plant through a very fine porcelain filter in order to remove the bacteria; he then rubbed the filtered juice on the leaves of healthy plants, expecting no disease to develop. But contrary to his expectation, the plants did develop mosaic disease. What could the explanation be? Iwanowsky suggested two possibilities: Either bacteria in the infected plants secrete toxins, and it is these rather than the bacterial cells themselves that are present in infectious juice; or

the bacteria that cause this disease are much smaller than other known bacteria and can pass unharmed through a fine porcelain filter. When it was later demonstrated that the infectious material in filtered juice could reproduce in a new host, Iwanowsky abandoned his first explanation in favor of the second—that some type of extremely small bacterium is the causal agent of the disease. During the next several decades, many other diseases of both plants and animals were found to be caused by infectious agents so small that they could pass through porcelain filters and could not be seen with even the best light microscopes. These microbial agents of disease came to be called filterable viruses, or simply viruses. They were still assumed to be very small bacteria.

There were, however, a few hints that viruses might be something quite different from bacteria. First, all attempts to culture them on media customarily used for bacteria failed. Second, the virus material, unlike bacteria, could be precipitated from an alcoholic suspension without losing its infectious power. But not until 1935 was it conclusively demonstrated that viruses and bacteria are two very different things. In that year, W. M. Stanley of the Rockefeller Institute isolated and crystallized tobacco mosaic virus. If the crystals were injected into tobacco plants, they again became active, multiplied, and caused disease symptoms in the plants. The fact that viruses could be crystallized showed that they were not cells but must be much simpler chemical entities.

As indicated in earlier chapters, we now know that a virus particle consists of a protein shell around a nucleic acid core. The nucleic acid in viruses that attack plants, such as tobacco mosaic virus, is RNA. That in most bacteriophages and viruses that attack animals is DNA, but a few phages and a few animal viruses have RNA. Ordinarily viruses contain neither carbohydrate nor lipid.

Reproduction of Viruses. Because viruses have no metabolic machinery of their own—

they usually lack enzymes and they cannot generate ATP—and because they lack raw materials for synthesis, they cannot reproduce themselves in the sense that living organisms can. It is the host cell, not the virus, that manufactures new virus particles when the old virus provides the instructions. Hence viruses cannot be cultured on artificial media; they require living host cells. Pharmaceutical companies and research laboratories often grow them in fertilized chicken eggs or in cells in tissue cultures.

We have already discussed the reproduction of bacteriophage viruses (see pp. 598–600). You will recall that a free phage particle becomes attached by the tip of its tail to the wall of a bacterial cell. The phage nucleic acid is injected into the host while the protein coat remains outside. Once inside the bacterial cell, the phage DNA provides genetic information for synthesis of new viral DNA and protein and for assembling these into complete new phage particles, which are then released when the cell bursts. We called this series of events the lytic cycle. We also saw that sometimes phage nucleic acid does not immediately take control of the host cell's metabolic machinery and put it to work making new virus particles, but instead becomes attached to the bacterial chromosome and is reproduced with the chromosome for an indefinite number of generations (the lysogenic cycle). Thus a phage virus can exist in three different states: as free infectious particles (sometimes called virions); as vegetative virus, i.e. as viral nucleic acid directing synthesis of new viral components in a host cell; and as provirus, i.e. as viral nucleic acid integrated with the bacterial chromosome and replicated in synchrony with it.

The structure of the free-particle stage of plant and animal viruses is usually simpler than that of bacteriophages. In some cases the particle is rod-shaped, in others "spherical" (actually polyhedral) (Fig. 20.1). The absence of a tail like that of bacteriophage probably

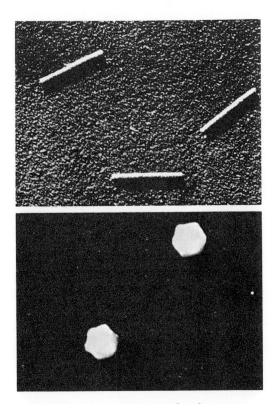

Fig. 20.1. Electron micrographs of two types of viruses. Top: Tobacco mosaic virus, a rod-shaped virus. Bottom: *Tipula* iridescent virus, a polyhedral virus that attacks the larvae of a species of crane fly. [Courtesy Virus Laboratory, University of California, Berkeley.]

means that plant and animal viruses cannot inject their nucleic acid into the host cell; most likely the whole virus particle penetrates into the cell, though the evidence indicates that only the nucleic acid component is necessary for multiplication.

The Origin of Viruses. Viruses are not cells. And viruses do not, in the strict sense, reproduce themselves. Therefore they fail to meet the two essential requisites that, according to the definition in Chapter 3, must be met by living things. Yet they possess other attributes normally associated with life, and many biologists are uneasy about classifying them as non-living and omitting them from the Monera. Some workers have suggested that if we knew more about their origins it would be easier to decide whether viruses should be regarded as a type of organism or as a particularly interesting category of nonliving material object. Of the various hypotheses of viral origin that have been proposed, the three outlined below have received serious consideration.

The first hypothesis suggests that viruses are organisms that have reached the extreme of evolutionary specialization for parasitism. Its proponents point out that loss of structures is commonly seen in internal parasites, and that intracellular parasites might conceivably lose everything but their nucleus. A virus particle resembles a cellular nucleus; hence they conclude that viruses arose from cellular ancestors by a process of gradual loss of all other cellular components. If this hypothesis is correct, then viruses should perhaps be regarded as degenerate cells and classified as living organisms.

The second hypothesis suggests that the ancestors of modern viruses were free-living non-cellular predecessors of cellular organisms. When the organic nutrients of the primordial "hot soup" seas disappeared, their precellular descendants survived by becoming parasites on the cellular organisms that had arisen by that time. According to this view, modern viruses are representatives of an early "nearly living" stage in the origin of life.

The third hypothesis suggests that viruses are neither primitive nor specialized organisms but fragments of genetic material detached from the chromosomes of cellular organisms. They might originally have existed as bare nucleic acid but might later have evolved the capacity of causing their host cells to synthesize a protein shell within which replicates of the nucleic acid could be enclosed. If this hypothesis is correct, some viruses may have arisen as fragments of bacterial chromosomes, others as fragments of RNA from the cells of higher plants, and still others as fragments of the chromosomes of higher animals. The host specificity of viruses might be a reflection of their origin; a given type of virus might be able to parasitize only species fairly closely related to the one from which the virus was originally derived.

Viral Disease. Curiously enough, viral infections seem to be restricted to relatively few groups of organisms. They occur in all major groups of bacteria, but not in Protozoa. They occur in flowering plants (angiosperms), but not in gymnosperms, ferns, mosses, algae, or fungi. They occur in vertebrates and in arthropods but not in most other animals. No explanation for these disparities is known.

Among the many human diseases caused by viruses are chicken pox, mumps, measles, smallpox, yellow fever, rabies, influenza, viral pneumonia, the common cold, poliomyelitis (infantile paralysis), fever blisters, several types of encephalitis, and infectious hepatitis. There is also growing evidence that some, and perhaps all, cancers involve virus pathogens. In some types of cancer, the malignant cells release viral particles during their growth. In other types, no free virus particles are usually associated with the tumors, but there is reason to think that the cells contain proviruses that have modified the cells' metabolic activity and caused them to become malignant. In some cases, cells may contain cancer viruses without actually becoming malignant until induced by an irritant, such as certain carcinogenic chemicals, tobacco smoke, frequent abrasion, or radioactivity.

MONERA

The kingdom Monera includes two divisions: the Schizomycetes (bacteria) and the Cyanophyta (blue-green algae). The cells of both groups are procaryotic; i.e. they lack a nuclear membrane, mitochondria, an endoplasmic reticulum, Golgi apparatus, and lysosomes.

Schizomycetes

The discoverer of bacteria was Antoni van Leeuwenhoek (1632–1723), a Dutchman who was both an extraordinarily skilled maker of microscopes and a careful and inquisitive observer. Though he was a merchant with little formal education, his curiosity about the natural world led him to study an enormous variety of microscopic objects. He made superb observations on the microscopic structure of plant seeds and embryos. He studied many small invertebrate animals. He discovered the existence of spermatozoa. He was the first to see red blood cells, and he was the first actually to observe and describe the capillary circulation that Harvey had hypothesized but not seen. Important as these discoveries were, Leeuwenhoek is best remembered for his discovery of the microbial world; he was the first to describe all the main kinds of unicellular microorganisms—protozoans, algae, yeasts, and bacteria.

Early studies of bacteria were based largely on species belonging to a group now called the eubacteria ("true" bacteria). All of these were rather similar in their basic characteristics. But as the years passed, other groups of organisms with quite different properties also came to be regarded as bacteria. Thus the modern Schizomycetes constitute an assemblage of diverse forms probably not very closely related to one another. The bacteria could easily be divided into three or more groups that would be as distinct from one another as each is from the blue-green algae.

Bacterial Cells. Most bacteria are very tiny, far smaller than the individual cells in the body of a multicellular plant or animal. In fact, some bacteria (e.g. the Rickettsia and the organisms that cause ornithosis and lymphogranuloma) are as small as some of the largest viruses. However, even the smallest bacteria are funda-

mentally different from viruses in that they are cellular. They always contain both RNA and DNA, whereas viruses contain one or the other but never both; they always contain many different proteins with enzymatic functions, whereas viruses carry no enzymatic proteins (except occasionally some concerned with attachment to and penetration into a host cell); they can generate ATP and use it in the synthesis of many other organic compounds, whereas viruses cannot; they provide both the raw material and the metabolic machinery for their own reproduction, whereas viruses do not. No entity truly transitional between viruses and cellular organisms is known to exist.

The cells of most bacteria have one of three fundamental shapes: spherical or ovoid, cylindrical or rod-shaped (Fig. 20.2), or helically coiled (Fig. 20.3). Spherical bacteria are called *cocci* (singular, coccus); rod-shaped ones are called *bacilli;* and helically coiled ones are called *spirilla.*

When cell division takes place, the daughter cells of some species remain attached and form characteristic aggregates. Thus cells of the bacterium that causes pneumonia are frequently found in pairs (diplococci). The cells of some spherical species form long chainlike aggregates (streptococci) (Fig. 20.4), while others form grapelike clusters (staphylococci). Each of the cells in a diplococcal, streptococcal, or staphylococcal aggregate is an independent organism, but there are some bacteria that form either coenocytic[1] or multicellular filaments. A basic difference between a chain of independent cells and a multicellular filament is that adjacent cells of a filament share a common cell wall. Some of the filamentous "bacteria" (e.g. *Beggiatoa*) are in fact probably colorless derivatives of blue-green algae, and some workers place them in the Cyanophyta rather than in the Schizomycetes. Many Actinomycetes, among other filamentous forms, strikingly re-

---

[1] As indicated in earlier chapters, "coenocytic" means having several nuclei in a single cytoplasmic mass or cell.

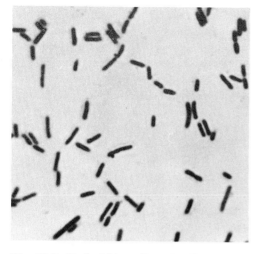

Fig. 20.2. *Escherichia coli,* a bacillus common in the human digestive tract. [Courtesy Carolina Biological Supply Co.]

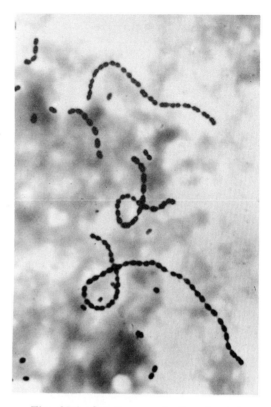

Fig. 20.4. *Streptococcus lactis,* a bacterium common in milk. All streptococci are spherical (coccal) bacteria that are normally grouped in chainlike clusters. [Courtesy General Biological Supply House, Inc., Chicago.]

Fig. 20.3. *Spirillum volutans,* a helically coiled bacterium. The two paramecians (which are Protozoa) are included for size comparison. (See also Fig. 20.6.) [Courtesy General Biological Supply House, Inc., Chicago.]

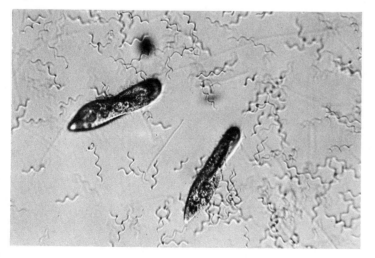

semble molds (which are fungi), but this is probably a case of evolutionary convergence rather than of close relationship, because the cells of Actinomycetes, like those of other bacteria, are procaryotic whereas those of fungi are eucaryotic.

Like the cells of higher plants, most bacterial cells are enclosed in a cell wall, which protects the cell both from physical damage and from osmotic disruption. But the walls of bacteria and blue-green algae differ from those of all higher plants in important aspects of their composition. The walls of eucaryotic cells derive their tensile strength largely from cellulose and related compounds (or from chitin in fungi), those of procaryotic cells from *mucopeptides,* which are compounds composed of amino acids and amino sugars (and their derivatives, particularly muramic acid); neither muramic acid nor amino sugars (sugars with an amino group attached) have been found in the walls of higher plants. This important difference between the chemical composition of procaryotic and eucaryotic cells is the basis for the selective activity of some drugs, such as penicillin. Penicillin inhibits formation of mucopeptides, and hence interferes with bacterial multiplication. It is therefore toxic to growing bacteria but not to resting cells. The drug is nontoxic for higher plants and animals.

Most bacteria are hyperosmotic relative to the fluid medium in which they live; hence they would swell and burst if they did not have well-developed walls. However, many species can be cultured in the laboratory on a medium with an elevated osmotic pressure. Under such conditions, the bacteria can withstand treatment with penicillin; in the presence of the drug, they grow as so-called L-forms, which have very poorly developed walls. Their shape is usually very different from normal, as would be expected. The L-forms are human artifacts, but there are some naturally occurring bacteria that lack rigid walls and can live only in environments where their osmotic relations are such that the absence of a mechanically strong cell

wall is not lethal. These are the pleuropneumonia-like organisms (PPLO), which are probably naturally occurring L-forms, i.e. bacterial cells that have lost the ability to synthesize mucopeptides and have evolved specializations for life in a very restricted habitat. Some of the PPLO cause severe human diseases.

Differences in the relative amounts of certain components in the walls of different types of bacteria make the cells show characteristic reactions to a variety of stains. Since there are few visible morphological characters that can be used in identifying bacteria, diagnostic staining is an important laboratory tool.

Many bacterial cells secrete polysaccharide mucoid materials that accumulate on the outer surface of the cell wall and form a *capsule.* The capsule apparently makes the cell more resistant to the defenses of host organisms; hence encapsulated strains of a given bacterial species are more likely to cause disease than unencapsulated strains.

Some of the eubacteria (mostly rod-shaped ones) can form special resting cells called *endospores,* which enable them to withstand conditions that would quickly kill the normal active cell. Each small endospore develops inside a vegetative cell and contains DNA plus a limited amount of other essential materials from that cell (Fig. 20.5). It is enclosed in an almost indestructible spore coat. Once the endospore has fully developed, the remainder of the vegetative cell in which it formed may disintegrate. Because of their very low water content and refractile coats, spores of many species can survive an hour or more of boiling or an hour in a hot oven. They can be frozen for decades or perhaps for centuries without harm. They can survive long periods of drying. And they can even withstand treatment with strong disinfectant solutions. When conditions again become favorable, the spores may germinate, giving rise to normal vegetative cells that resume growing and dividing. Fortunately, few disease-causing bacteria can form endospores.

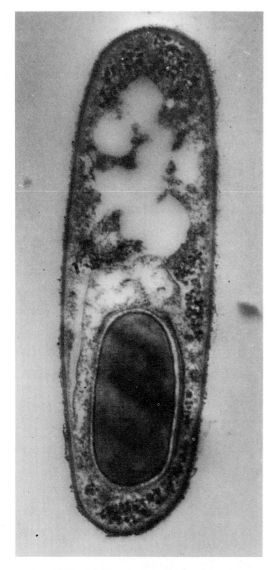

Fig. 20.5. Electron micrograph of a sporulating bacillus. The spore is the dark oval in the lower end of the cell. The developing spore coat is clearly visible. The white areas in the upper end of the cell are not vacuoles but areas filled with fatty material. ×43,000. [Courtesy G. B. Chapman, *J. Bacteriol.*, vol. 71, 1956.]

Many bacteria are motile; i.e. they can move about actively. In some cases, the motion is produced by the beating action of flagella (Fig. 20.6). Bacterial flagella are structurally very

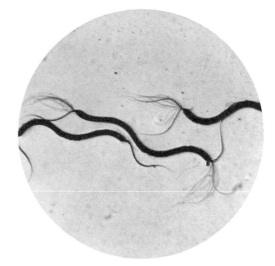

Fig. 20.6. The flagella of *Spirillum volutans*. [Courtesy General Biological Supply House, Inc., Chicago.]

different from the flagella of eucaryotic cells. They are not enclosed within the cytoplasmic membrane, and they do not contain the nine peripheral and two central fibrils found in all flagella of eucaryotic cells. They arise from basal granules, but these granules are much smaller than the basal bodies of eucaryotic cells and are probably not homologous with them. A bacterial flagellum has approximately the same diameter as one of the fibrils from a eucaryotic flagellum. Some bacteria that lack flagella exhibit a peculiar gliding movement that does not involve any visible locomotor organelles; the mechanism of this movement has not yet been discovered.

Bacterial Reproduction. A few bacteria produce special reproductive cells. And a few reproduce by *budding,* a process in which a small protuberance arises on the parent cell and is pinched off as a new cell that is much smaller than the parent. But most bacteria reproduce by *binary fission,* a simple type of cell division in which two equal daughter cells with characteristics essentially like those of the parent cell are produced without mitosis. Near the middle of the cell, the plasma membrane grows inward, cutting the cell in two (Fig. 20.7; see also Fig. 13.3, p. 500). Each cell then lays down its own wall outside its new end membrane. Increased turgor in the growing cells eventually forces them apart.

For many years, bacteria were thought to lack nuclei, and fission was viewed as simply a division of homogeneous cytoplasm. However, newer techniques have revealed the presence of a nuclear area that is not surrounded by a membrane. And analysis has shown that there is DNA in the nuclear area, and that the bacterial genes are arranged in sequence along a single, circular "chromosome" composed only of DNA (see pp. 596–598). Further, it has been established that when a bacterial cell undergoes fission, each daughter cell receives a full set of genes, i.e. a complete chromosome. Therefore nuclear division must have taken place. Why, then, is there no evidence of mitosis? The reason is probably that a bacterium has only one chromosome. The

essential function of the elaborate mitotic apparatus in eucaryotic cells is distributing the multiple chromosomes in such a manner that each daughter cell receives a full set. But when there is only one chromosome, the equipartition can, at least theoretically, be achieved in a far simpler way. We are not yet certain of the details of nuclear division in procaryotic cells, but the evidence indicates that the DNA replicates and that the two chromosomes thus produced move apart into separate nuclear areas long before fission occurs. When the plasma membrane grows inward during fission, it simply partitions the binucleate parent cell into two daughter cells each of which already has its own nuclear area.

Bacteria commonly have an enormous reproductive potential. Many species may divide as often as once every 2 minutes under favorable conditions. If all the descendants of a cell of this type survived and divided every twenty minutes, the single initial cell would have about 500,000 descendants at the end of 6 hours, and by the end of 24 hours the total weight of its descendants would be about 4,000,000 pounds. Although increases of this magnitude do not actually occur, the real increases are frequently huge, which helps explain the rapidity with which food sometimes spoils or a disease develops.

Although the reproductive process itself is asexual, genetic recombination does occur occasionally, at least in some bacteria. As we saw in an earlier chapter, three mechanisms of recombination are known: conjugation, in which part of a chromosome is transferred from a donor cell to a recipient; transformation, in which a living cell picks up fragments of DNA that have been released into the medium from dead cells; and transduction, in which fragments of DNA are carried from one cell to another by viruses. When a normally haploid bacterial cell receives extra DNA by one of these procedures, it becomes partly diploid (usually only partly, because it is very rare for a cell to receive an entire extra chromosome). The di-

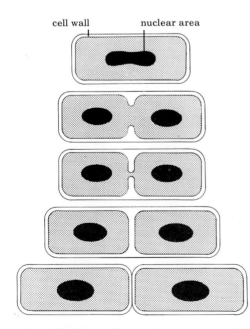

cell wall   nuclear area

Fig. 20.7. Binary fission of a bacterial cell. See text for description.

ploidy is only temporary, however. Haploidy is soon re-established by elimination of all genes that do not become incorporated into the new recombinant chromosome.

Bacterial Nutrition. Most bacteria are heterotrophic, being either saprophytes or parasites. Like animals, the majority of these bacteria are aerobic; i.e. they cannot live without molecular oxygen, which they use in the respiratory breakdown of carbohydrates and other food materials to carbon dioxide and water. Oxygen is lethal to some bacteria, however, which obtain all their energy by fermentation; such bacteria are *obligate anaerobes. Facultative anaerobes,* on the other hand, can live either in the presence or in the absence of molecular oxygen; some of them are simply indifferent to oxygen, obtaining all their energy from fermentation whether oxygen is present or not; others obtain their energy by fermentation when oxygen is not available, but carry out aerobic respiration (via the Krebs cycle) when oxygen is present, and may grow faster under these conditions. Aerobic respiration is, of course, a much more efficient energy-yielding process than fermentation. Certain types of facultative anaerobes do not rely on fermentation when oxygen is absent; they continue to carry out complete respiration by using substitute inorganic substances (such as nitrates, sulfates, or carbonates) as ultimate electron acceptors in place of oxygen.

Besides lactic and alcoholic fermentations, which are the most common fermentative processes in living organisms, there are at least ten other types of fermentations that occur in different groups of bacteria. The products include acetic acid, butylene glycol, butyric acid, and propionic acid. All fermentations are alike, however, in that they are energy-yielding biological oxidation-reduction sequences in which organic molecules serve as the final electron acceptors. ATP is generated in fermentations by phosphorylations on the substrate level.

Bacteria differ considerably in the sorts of molecules they can use as energy sources and in the specific amino acids and vitamins they require. These differences provide valuable diagnostic characters for workers attempting to identify unknown bacteria. Samples of the organisms to be identified are placed on a variety of nutrient media and cultured at standard temperatures. By determining on which of the media the organisms will grow and on which they will not, and, when they grow, by noting what sort (color, texture, etc.) of colony they produce, and by comparing these data with similar data for known species, it is often possible to assign the unknown organisms to the proper group or even to the proper species.

Most bacteria, as we said, are heterotrophs, but some are either chemosynthetic or photosynthetic autotrophs. The chemosynthetic bacteria oxidize inorganic compounds, such as ammonia, nitrite, sulfur, hydrogen gas, or ferrous iron, and trap the released energy. The mechanisms of some of these oxidations were discussed on p. 134. The bacteria that oxidize ammonia or nitrite are the nitrifying bacteria that play such an important role in the nitrogen cycle.

There are two basic types of photosynthetic bacteria, which differ in the type of chlorophyll they possess—the green bacteria and the purple bacteria. Neither group has chlorophyll *a*, which is the chief light-trapping pigment in higher plants. And unlike higher plants, neither group ever uses water as the ultimate electron donor in photosynthesis; hence neither produces molecular oxygen. Depending on the species of bacteria, the electron (and hydrogen) donor is molecular hydrogen, reduced sulfur compounds (such as H_2S), or organic compounds.

The pigments and enzymes of the light-trapping process in photosynthetic bacteria are located in organelles called *chromatophores,* which are composed of vesicles or paired lamellae structurally analogous to the lamellae in eucaryotic chloroplasts. But the chromatophores are not contained within any membrane-bounded structure that could be interpreted as a chloroplast. Therefore the enzymes involved in the "dark" reactions of photosynthesis (i.e. carbon fixation), which are in the stroma portion of plant chloroplasts, are assumed to be in the general cytoplasm of the bacterial cell.

Bacteria as Agents of Disease. Perhaps the bacteria best known to most people are the ones that cause diseases in man, his domesticated animals, or his cultivated plants. Most of the so-called "germs" are either bacteria or viruses (though a few are fungi, protozoans, or parasitic worms). The notion that bacteria can cause disease—often called the Germ Theory of Disease—was first developed by Louis Pasteur in the late nineteenth century. At first there was much opposition to Pasteur's idea, but it soon gained the support of such prominent scientists and physicians of the day as Joseph Lister (1827–1912), Robert Koch (1843–1910), Thomas Burrell (1829–1916), and Ferdinand Cohn (1828–1898). Lister, an English surgeon, was one of the first to realize the implications of Pasteur's discoveries for surgical procedures. He initiated use of antiseptic techniques in the operating room, using carbolic acid solution as a disinfectant. Koch, a German physician, showed that a bacillus was the cause of anthrax in horses, cows, sheep, and human beings, and he later demonstrated that another bacillus caused tuberculosis in man. Burrell, an American botanist at the University of Illinois, showed that a plant disease—fire blight of pears—was caused by bacteria. Cohn, a German botanist who published a classic book on bacteria, is often considered the father of modern bacteriology.

In the course of his investigations of anthrax and tuberculosis, Robert Koch formulated the rules of procedure for proving that a particular microorganism is the cause of a particular disease. A slightly modified version of these rules, traditionally called *Koch's postulates,* is still used today. There are four postulates:

1. It must be shown that the microorganism in question is always present in diseased hosts
2. The microorganism must be isolated from the diseased host and grown in pure culture (i.e. in a culture containing only that one species of microorganism).
3. Microorganisms obtained from the pure culture, when injected into a healthy susceptible host, must produce the disease in that host.
4. Microorganisms must be isolated from the experimentally infected host, grown in pure culture, and compared with the microorganisms in the original culture.

The procedures outlined by Koch have been followed by hundreds of bacteriologists, and bacteria have been shown to cause a long list of human diseases, including bubonic plague, cholera, diphtheria, syphilis, gonorrhea, leprosy, scarlet fever, tetanus, tuberculosis, typhoid fever, whooping cough, bacterial pneumonia, bacterial dysentery, meningitis, strep throat, boils, and abscesses. Equally long lists could be compiled of bacterial diseases of other animals or of bacterial diseases of plants.

Microorganisms cause disease symptoms in a variety of ways. In some cases, their immense numbers simply place such a tremendous material burden on the host's tissues that they interfere with normal function. In other cases, the microorganisms actually destroy cells and tissues. In still other cases, bacteria produce poisons, called *toxins.* These may be exotoxins, which are poisons released from the living bacterial cell into the host's tissues, as in diptheria or tetanus, or they may be endotoxins, which are poisons retained in the cells of the bacteria that produce them and only released into the host when the bacteria die and disintegrate. There are even some cases, as we mentioned in Chapter 16, where the disease symptoms are not caused directly by the microorganisms but result from an excessive immune response to the microorganisms by the host's body.

We discussed in Chapter 16 the ways in which the human body resists attacks by pathogenic microorganisms. The first line of defense, once the pathogens have gotten into the body past the protective epidermal tissues, is phagocytic action by certain kinds of white blood cells; the pathogens are engulfed and destroyed. The second line of defense is production of antibodies that react with the antigens of the pathogens. Production of antibodies the first time a host individual is exposed to a particular antigen is a rather slow process, which may take days or even weeks. However, in most cases the immunity thus built up is relatively long-lasting. For example, a person who has once had whooping cough or chicken pox usually remains immune for life to further infection by the pathogens of those diseases. Immunity to such diseases as influenza and other respiratory infections does not last for life, but may have a duration of several months.

Modern medicine often takes advantage of the body's antigen-antibody reaction to induce prophylactic immunity—immunity that prevents a first case of disease. The patient is inoculated with either a vaccine or an antiserum. A *vaccine* is material containing antigen from the pathogen. Sometimes the antigen consists of dead microorganisms, as in the Salk vaccine for poliomyelitis. Sometimes it consists of attenuated microorganisms, i.e. microorganisms that are alive but have been treated in a manner that weakens them sufficiently to prevent their causing disease; the Sabin oral vaccine for poliomyelitis is an example. Vaccines also sometimes consist either of a small amount of active bacterial toxin (enough to induce formation of antibodies but not enough to produce disease) or of inactivated toxin, called toxoid, as in tetanus toxoid. Vaccines, whatever the kind, induce active immunity in the patient; i.e. they stimulate the patient to produce his own antibodies. They are therefore rather slow-acting, but their effects are long-lasting. By contrast, inoculation with *antiserum* produces almost immediate immunity, but the immunity lasts only a short time, because an antiserum contains presynthesized antibodies instead of antigens, and hence produces passive rather than active immunity. An antiserum is made by injecting antigen into some other animal, usually a horse, waiting until the animal has produced antibodies specific for that antigen, and then removing blood serum containing the antibodies from the animal.

Beneficial Bacteria. Contrary to the popular impression, beneficial bacteria outnumber harmful ones. In an earlier chapter, we mentioned the importance of bacteria as organisms of decay—a process that not only prevents the accumulation of dead bodies and metabolic wastes but also converts materials such as the nitrogen of proteins into a form usable by other living things. We also mentioned the essential role of nitrogen-fixing bacteria. And we discussed the bacteria in the intestine that synthesize vitamins absorbed by the body and that aid in the digestion of certain materials. Anyone who has been given such massive doses of antibiotics as to have his intestinal flora exterminated can testify to the ensuing disturbances in normal intestinal activity.

Bacteria are also of great importance in many industrial processes. Manufacturers often find it easier and cheaper to use cultured microorganisms in certain difficult syntheses than to try to perform the syntheses themselves. Among the many substances manufactured commercially by means of bacteria are acetic acid (vinegar), acetone, butanol, lactic acid, and several vitamins. Bacteria are also used in the retting of flax and hemp, a process that decomposes the pectin material holding the cellulose fibers together; the fibers, once freed, may be used in making linen, other textiles, and rope. Commercial preparation of skins for making leather goods often involves use of bacteria, as does the curing of tobacco.

Many branches of the food industry depend

upon bacteria. You are probably aware of the central role of bacteria in the making of dairy products, such as butter and the various kinds of cheeses; the characteristic flavor of Swiss cheese, for example, is due in large part to propionic acid produced by bacteria. Bacteria are also important in the making of sauerkraut and in the processing of coffee.

Many farmers depend upon bacterial action in the making of silage for use as cattle feed. Also of considerable interest to farmers is the possibility that bacteria pathogenic for destructive insects may eventually be usable in lieu of insecticides.

Particularly interesting is the modern use of bacteria in the production of antibiotics that can help control other bacteria. In fact, most of the antibiotic drugs in use today (but not penicillin) are produced by various species of bacteria of the Actinomycetes group or, if synthesized artificially, were discovered in these organisms. Among these drugs are streptomycin, Aureomycin, Terramycin, and neomycin.

Cyanophyta

The Cyanophyta, or blue-green algae, are procaryotic unicellular or filamentous organisms. The unicellular forms are either rods or spheres, which may occur singly or as colonies embedded in a gelatinous matrix (Fig. 20.8). The filamentous forms are multicellular in the sense that adjacent cells share common end walls. In some species, plasmodesmata penetrate these walls, interconnecting the cytoplasm of the cells. Yet, for the most part, the individual cells remain the important units of function.

The cell walls of blue-green algae differ from those of most bacteria in that they usually contain cellulose, but like those of bacteria they also usually seem to contain some amino sugars and muramic acid. Outside the wall proper, there is often a layer of more or less firm gelatinous material called a sheath, composed of pectic materials. The electron microscope re-

veals numerous fibrils within the sheath; these are oriented nearly parallel to the cell's surface.

The cytoplasm of blue-green algae, which seems to be composed of very dense colloidal material, is unusually viscid. The material is so viscid, in fact, that no Brownian movement can be detected in it, and high-speed centrifugation does not cause rearrangement of its constituents. The large cell vacuole so characteristic of higher-plant cells is absent, as are mitochondria, endoplasmic reticulum, Golgi apparatus, and a nuclear membrane. Many ribosomes are present, however, and there are numerous proteinaceous granules and granules of a stored carbohydrate material called cyanophycean starch, which is very similar (perhaps identical) to the glycogen used as a storage product in animal cells. No blue-green algae ever possess flagella. The peculiar gliding motion exhibited by many species is like that seen in some bacteria, and like it remains unexplained.

All blue-green algae possess photosynthetic pigments located in lamellar structures that appear to be flattened vesicles. These structures are similar to the chromatophores of the photosynthetic bacteria; like the chromatophores, they are not contained within chloroplasts. The chlorophyll of the blue-green algae is chlorophyll *a*, the same pigment as found in higher plants, rather than bacterial chlorophyll. In addition to chlorophyll and various carotenoids (two of which occur only in blue-green algae), these organisms contain **phycocyanin** (blue pigment) or sometimes **phycoerythrin** (red pigment). It is the presence of phycocyanin with the chlorophyll that gives these algae their characteristic blue-green color. However, not all "blue-green" algae are blue-green; black, brown, yellow, red, grass green, and other colors also occur. The periodic redness of the Red Sea is due to a species that contains a particularly large amount of phycoerythrin.

Cell division in blue-green algae is by binary fission, as in bacteria. Reproduction also frequently occurs by fragmentation of filaments. No form of genetic recombination has ever

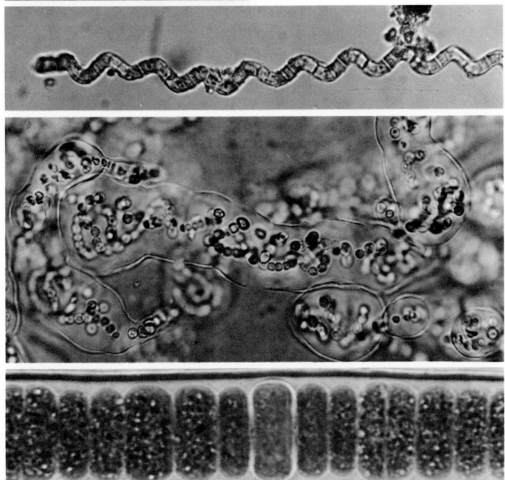

Fig. 20.8. Some representative genera of blue-green algae. (A) *Gloeocapsa*, a genus of unicellular species in which groups of spherical cells are enclosed in layers of gelatinous material (the gelatinous sheaths are faintly visible in this photograph as concentric rings around the cells). The species occur on wet rocks and other damp objects, where they may form large masses of jelly. (B) *Arthrospira*, a genus of coiled filamentous forms without prominent sheaths. They occur on the damp soil of beaches. (C) *Nostoc*, a very common genus in which several beadlike filaments may be grouped in a shared gelatinous matrix. (D) *Scytonema*, a genus of filamentous species with oval, nearly rectangular, cells. The lighter-colored cell in the middle of this section of filament is a heterocyst, a type of cell that often forms in filamentous blue-green algae but whose function is not well understood. [Courtesy J. M. Kingsbury, Cornell University.]

A

B

C

D

been demonstrated in these organisms; they are the only major group in which all reproduction, so far as is known, is totally asexual. It must be admitted, however, that they have not been studied nearly as much as the bacteria, and it seems entirely possible that some form of recombination will eventually be found in them. Almost nothing is known about their genetics.

Blue-green algae occur in numerous and varied habitats. Many live in fresh water, and a few are marine. Some species are very common in or on soil. Others are frequently found growing on the sides of damp rocks and flowerpots and on the bark of trees. They are often particularly abundant on wet cliffs and ledges.

Ponds or lakes containing a rich supply of organic matter, particularly nitrogenous compounds, often develop huge populations ("blooms," as they are called) of blue-green algae, which may make the water so green that objects only a few inches below the surface are entirely invisible. Such blooms may give the water an objectionable odor, clog filters of water supplies, and even be toxic to livestock. A few species live in habitats that are among the most inhospitable known—the hot springs that occur in various parts of the world; these species can grow well at temperatures as high as 85°C (185°F). There are also some species of blue-green algae that live mutualistically with fungi in the compound plants called lichens.

REFERENCES

BROCK, T. D., ed., 1961. *Milestones in Microbiology.* Prentice-Hall, Englewood Cliffs, N.J. (A collection of 55 papers by leading workers.)

BURKHOLDER, P. R., 1934. "Movement in the Cyanophyceae," *Quarterly Review of Biology,* vol. 9, pp. 438–459.

FOGG, G. E., 1956. "The Comparative Physiology and Biochemistry of the Blue-Green Algae," *Bacteriological Reviews,* vol. 20, pp. 148–165.

HAHON, N., ed., 1964. *Selected Papers on Virology.* Prentice-Hall, Englewood Cliffs, N.J. (A collection of 40 papers by leading workers.)

PANKRATZ, H. S., and C. C. BOWEN, 1963. "Cytology of Blue-Green Algae: I. The Cells of

Symploca muscorum," *American Journal of Botany,* vol. 50, pp. 387–399.

PELCZAR, M. J., and R. D. REID, 1965. *Microbiology,* 2nd ed. McGraw-Hill, New York.

RIS, H., and R. N. SINGH, 1961. "Electron Microscope Studies on Blue-Green Algae," *Journal of Biophysical and Biochemical Cytology,* vol. 9, pp. 63–80.

SALTON, M. R. J., 1960. *Microbial Cell Walls.* Wiley, New York.

STANIER, R. Y., M. DOUDOROFF, and E. A. ADELBERG, 1963. *The Microbial World,* 2nd ed. Prentice-Hall, Englewood Cliffs, N.J.

STANLEY, W. M., and E. G. VALENS, 1961. *Viruses and the Nature of Life.* Dutton, New York.

SUGGESTED READING

BRAUDE, A. I., 1964. "Bacterial Endotoxins," *Scientific American,* March. (Offprint 177.)

BURNET, SIR M., 1951. "Viruses," *Scientific American,* May. (Offprint 2.)

DE KRUIF, P., 1926. *Microbe Hunters.* Harcourt, Brace, New York. (Paperback edition, Pocket Books, New York, 1959.)

DUBOS, R., 1960. *Pasteur and Modern Science.* Doubleday, New York.

EDGAR, R. S., and R. H. EPSTEIN, 1965. "The Genetics of a Bacterial Virus," *Scientific American,* February. (Offprint 1004.)

FRAENKEL-CONRAT, H., 1956. "Rebuilding a Virus," *Scientific American,* June. (Offprint 9.)

HORNE, R. W., 1963. "The Structure of Viruses," *Scientific American,* January. (Offprint 147.)

HOTCHKISS, R. D., and E. WEISS, 1956. "Transformed Bacteria," *Scientific American,* November. (Offprint 18.)

ISAACS, A., 1961. "Interferon," *Scientific American,* May. (Offprint 87.)

———, 1963. "Foreign Nucleic Acids," *Scientific American,* October. (Offprint 166.)

JACOB, F., and E. L. WOLLMAN, 1961. "Viruses and Genes," *Scientific American,* June. (Offprint 89.)

LURIA, S. E., 1955. "The T2 Mystery," *Scientific American,* April. (Offprint 24.)

MOROWITZ, H. J., and M. E. TOURTELLOTTE, 1962. "The Smallest Living Cells," *Scientific American,* March. (Offprint 1005.)

RUBIN, H., 1964. "A Defective Cancer Virus," *Scientific American,* June. (Offprint 185.)

SISTROM, W. R., 1962. *Microbial Life.* Holt, Rinehart & Winston, New York.

STANIER, R. Y., and C. B. VAN NIEL, 1962. "The Concept of a Bacterium," *Archiv für Mikrobiologie,* vol. 42, pp. 17–35.

STEWART, S. E., 1960. "The Polyoma Virus," *Scientific American,* November. (Offprint 77.)

WOLLMAN, E. L., and F. JACOB, 1956. "Sexuality in Bacteria," *Scientific American,* July. (Offprint 50.)

ZINDER, N. D., 1958. "Transduction in Bacteria," *Scientific American,* November. (Offprint 106.)

ZINSSER, H., 1935. *Rats, Lice and History.* Little, Brown, Boston.

CHAPTER
21

THE PLANT KINGDOM

THE VARIOUS DIVISIONS[1] OF THE PLANT KING-
dom have traditionally been separated into
two groups: the *Thallophyta* and the *Embryophyta.* Thallophyte plants may be either
unicellular or multicellular. The bodies of multicellular thallophytes usually show very little if
any tissue differentiation. Consequently there is
no anatomical basis for distinguishing roots,
stems, or leaves; the entire plant body is called a
thallus. The reproductive structures of thallophytes are frequently unicellular, and, whether
unicellular or multicellular, they lack a protective wall or jacket of sterile (i.e. nondividing)
cells.[2] The zygotes of thallophyte plants do
not develop into embryos until after they have
been released from the female reproductive organs where they were produced.[3] By contrast,
the multicellular reproductive structures of
embryophyte plants do have a jacket of sterile
cells, and the early stages of embryonic de-

[1] Botanists generally use the term "division" in the
same sense that zoologists use "phylum." The two
terms are thus equivalent.

[2] There are some seeming exceptions, where the
reproductive structures appear superficially to have
jacket cells.

[3] Except in a few rare cases in red algae.

velopment occur while the embryo is still contained within the female reproductive organ.

In older classifications, the Thallophyta and the Embryophyta were recognized as subkingdoms. Now, however, it is generally held that neither the divisions placed together in the Thallophyta, nor the divisions placed together in the Embryophyta, are necessarily closely related; in other words, that the thallophyte-embryophyte dichotomy has little phylogenetic significance. Hence, in modern classifications the names "Thallophyta" and "Embryophyta" are not usually given any formal recognition as taxonomic categories, but are used simply as terms of convenience to designate groups of plants at similar levels of structural complexity. It will be in this sense that we shall use the terms here.

It is also customary to group the thallophyte divisions into two categories on the basis of the presence or absence of chlorophyll. Thus the photosynthetic thallophytes are called *algae*, and the nonphotosynthetic thallophytes are called *fungi*. Neither of these terms is accorded formal taxonomic recognition in most modern classifications, because it is now clear that a close relationship exists neither among the various algal divisions nor among the various fungal divisions. Therefore, like "Thallophyta" and "Embryophyta," the terms "algae" and "fungi" will be used here as terms of convenience without phylogenetic significance.

A formal outline of the classification of the plant kingdom used in this book is given in the Appendix. The following brief outline will provide a basis for the discussion in this chapter:[4]

> "Thallophyta"
> Division Euglenophyta ⎫
> Division Chlorophyta ⎪
> Division Chrysophyta ⎪
> Division Pyrrophyta ⎬ "Algae"
> Division Phaeophyta ⎪
> Division Rhodophyta ⎭
> Division Myxomycophyta ⎫ "Fungi"
> Division Eumycophyta ⎭

> "Embryophyta"
> Division Bryophyta
> Division Tracheophyta

EUGLENOPHYTA (The Euglenoids)

The euglenoids are unicellular organisms that show a combination of plantlike and animal-like characteristics. They are plantlike in that many species have chlorophyll and are photosynthetic; they are animal-like in lacking a cell wall and being highly motile, and the species that lack chlorophyll are heterotrophic, like animals. Zoologists have traditionally regarded the euglenoids as animals and placed them among the flagellated Protozoa. Botanists, on the other hand, have regarded them as plants and placed them among the algae. They seem to have no close relatives among the other algae, however, and for this reason botanical classifications usually put them in a division by themselves. There are about 25 genera of euglenoids, containing approximately 450 species. Most live in fresh water, but a few are found in soil, on damp surfaces, or even in the digestive tracts of certain animals.

A typical cell of *Euglena* is oblong, with an anterior invagination from which a long flagellum emerges (see Fig. 8.7, p. 283).[5] Since the cell lacks a wall, it is fairly flexible, and its shape may change somewhat as it swims about; however, the pellicle by which it is bounded prevents excessive alterations of its shape. The large nucleus contains a prominent nucleolus that is unusual in not disappearing during mitosis. The nuclear membrane too remains intact during mitosis, instead of disappearing as it does in most cells. An orange granule, called the *stigma* (or eyespot), is located near the

---

[4] Since we have put the bacteria and blue-green algae in a separate kingdom, the Monera, they do not appear in this outline. Classifications that recognize only two kingdoms—Plantae and Animalia—place the bacteria among the fungi as the division Schizomycetes (or Schizomycophyta), and the blue-green algae among the algae as the Division Cyanophyta.

[5] Some euglenoids have two, three, or more flagella.

anterior end of the cell and functions as a light detector (there is no stigma in nonphotosynthetic euglenoid species). Most green euglenoids have a special organelle, the **pyrenoid**, that functions in the production of paramylum, a carbohydrate polymer that these organisms use as a storage product instead of starch or glycogen. A large contractile vacuole lies near the anterior end of the cell.

The euglenoid species that lack chlorophyll are obligate heterotrophs. The species that have chlorophyll are facultative heterotrophs and can survive in the dark if they have a source of organic nutrients. It is easy to destroy the chloroplasts of *Euglena* by treatment with streptomycin or heat (or by keeping the cells in the dark for a long time). A colorless strain of *Euglena* can be produced in this way, for chloroplasts are self-perpetuating organelles, which cannot be regained once they are lost. It is thus possible to make a lineage of organisms cross the traditional boundary (presence or absence of chlorophyll) between the plant and animal kingdoms.

Reproduction in euglenoids is by longitudinal mitotic cell division. No sexual reproduction has ever been conclusively demonstrated in them.

CHLOROPHYTA (The Green Algae)

The green algae are of particular interest because they are generally regarded as the group from which the higher plants arose. They are thus probably the only algal division that has not been a phylogenetic dead end. The majority of green algae live in fresh water, but some live in moist places on land, and there are many marine species.

Many divergent evolutionary tendencies, all probably beginning with walled and flagellated unicellular organisms, can be perceived in the Chlorophyta. One tendency has been the evolution of motile colonies. A second has been a change to nonmotile unicells and colonies. A

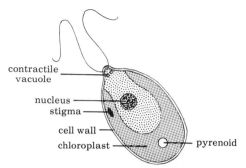

Fig. 21.1. Mature cell of *Chlamydomonas*.

third has been the evolution of extensive tube-like bodies with numerous nuclei but without cellular partitions (coenocytic organisms). Still other tendencies have been the evolution of multicellular filaments and even three-dimensional leaflike thalluses.

***Chlamydomonas* as a Representative Unicellular Green Alga.** *Chlamydomonas* is a genus of modern unicellular green algae that probably resemble the ancestral organisms from which the rest of the plant kingdom arose. Its species are common in ditches, pools, and other bodies of fresh water and in soils. The oval haploid cell has a cellulose wall and two anterior flagella of equal length (Fig. 21.1). It contains a single large cup-shaped chloroplast that fills from one half to two thirds of the basal portion of the cell. Inside the chloroplast are numerous chlorophyll-bearing lamellae, which are often arranged in stacks rather like the grana of higher plants. The chlorophylls are of the same types (chlorophylls *a* and *b*) as are found in vascular plants. The only other pigments are the carotenoids, which are also found in higher plants. (This type of pigmentation is characteristic of all Chlorophyta; unlike many other algae, they have no special accessory pigments or unusual chlorophylls.) A conspicuous pyrenoid in the basal portion of the chloroplast of *Chlamydomonas* functions as the site of starch synthesis. The stigma, or eyespot, is also located inside the large chloroplast. The cell has no large central

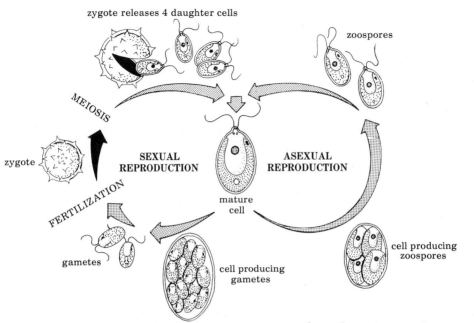

zygote releases 4 daughter cells

zoospores

MEIOSIS

zygote

SEXUAL
REPRODUCTION

ASEXUAL
REPRODUCTION

mature
cell

FERTILIZATION

gametes

cell producing
gametes

cell producing
zoospores

Fig. 21.2. Life history of *Chlamydomonas.* Top: Diagram showing all stages of both the sexual and asexual cycles. Bottom: Schematic diagram of life cycle for comparison with those of other organisms. Note that the zygote is the only diploid stage. This type of life cycle was probably characteristic of the first sexually reproducing unicellular organisms, and it may thus be the type from which all other types arose.

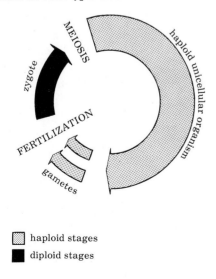

MEIOSIS

zygote

haploid unicellular organism

FERTILIZATION

gametes

⬚ haploid stages
■ diploid stages

vacuole such as is seen in mature cells of higher plants. Two small contractile vacuoles lying near the base of the flagella discharge alternately and rhythmically.[6]

Asexual reproduction is common in *Chlamydomonas* (Fig. 21.2). A vegetative cell resorbs its flagella; then mitotic division of the nucleus and longitudinal cytokinesis take place simultaneously. This process gives rise to two daughter cells, both of which lie within the wall of the original cell. In some species, the two daughter cells are promptly released by breakdown of the wall; in other species, the daughter cells themselves divide while still inside the wall of the parent cell, a total of 4 (as in the figure), 8, 16, or more daughter cells being produced, depending on the species and conditions of growth. The daughter cells develop a wall and flagella just before they are released as free ***zoospores,*** which are motile asexual reproductive cells, i.e. motile reproductive cells not specialized as gametes. In *Chlamydomonas* the zoospores are smaller than

[6] The descriptions of *Chlamydomonas* and other algae given in this chapter are based largely on material in J. M. Kingsbury, *Biology of the Algae,* published privately, Ithaca, N.Y., 1963.

mature vegetative cells but otherwise indistinguishable from them; in many species of algae, however, there are noticeable morphological differences between the zoospores and the mature cells. The free zoospores soon grow to full size, completing the asexual reproductive cycle.

Under certain conditions, *Chlamydomonas* may reproduce sexually. A mature haploid vegetative cell divides mitotically to produce several gamete cells, which develop walls and flagella and are released from the parent cell. The gametes are attracted to each other and form large clumps. Eventually the clumped cells, which have shed their walls, move apart in pairs. The members of a pair lie side by side, and their cytoplasms slowly fuse. Finally, their nuclei unite in the process of fertilization, which produces a single diploid cell, the zygote. The zygote sheds its flagella, sinks to the bottom, and develops a thick protective wall. The zygote can withstand unfavorable environmental conditions, such as the drying up of the pond or the cold of winter. When conditions are again favorable, the zygote germinates, dividing by meiosis to produce four new haploid cells, which are released into the surrounding water. The new cells quickly mature, thus completing the sexual reproductive cycle.

Sexual reproduction in most species of *Chlamydomonas* is at a very simple level, and thus gives us insight into the way sexuality probably arose. There are no separate male and female individuals. Furthermore, the gametes are all alike; they cannot be separated into male gametes (sperms) and female gametes (eggs). Such a condition, where all gametes are alike, is called *isogamy;* it is probably the primitive (ancestral) condition in plants. The isogametes of *Chlamydomonas* are indistinguishable from vegetative cells; they may be viewed simply as small vegetative cells that tend to fuse and act as gametes under certain conditions. This, too, is probably the primitive condition; the specialization of gametes as morphologically distinctive cells—a character-

istic of most higher plants and animals—is surely a later evolutionary development.

Notice that the haploid stages of the life cycle of *Chlamydomonas* are the dominant ones; the only diploid stage is the zygote. Dominance of the haploid stages is characteristic of most very primitive plants, and it seems clear that this was the ancestral condition.

The Volvocine Series. As an example of one of the evolutionary tendencies that can be traced in the Chlorophyta, let us examine the so-called volvocine or motile-colony series. This is a series of genera showing a gradual progression from the unicellular condition of *Chlamydomonas* to an elaborate colonial organization.

Gonium may be taken as an example of the simplest colonial stage. Each colony of *Gonium* is made up of 4, 16, or 32 cells (depending on the species), each of which is morphologically similar to *Chlamydomonas*. The cells are embedded in a mucilaginous matrix and are arranged in a flat or slightly curved plate. In some species, delicate cytoplasmic strands run between the cells; these may provide a route for direct interaction and coordination between the cells of the colony. That some sort of coordination does indeed exist is shown by the organized fashion in which the flagella of all the cells beat together and thus enable the colony to swim as a unit.

When asexual reproduction occurs in *Gonium,* all the cells in a colony divide simultaneously. When each cell of the parent colony has divided enough times to contain within its wall the same number of daughter cells as there are cells in the parent colony, its wall disintegrates and the daughter cells are released. However, the daughter cells from a single parent cell do not swim off independently as separate zoospores as in *Chlamydomonas*. Instead, they remain together in a common matrix and mature into a new *Gonium* colony. Thus each cell of the parent colony gives rise to a complete new colony.

Sexual reproduction in *Gonium* is similar to that in *Chlamydomonas*. Individual cells are released from a colony and function as gametes, fusing in pairs to form zygotes. As in *Chlamydomonas*, the gametes are alike (isogamous). The zygote is the only diploid stage in the life cycle.

Pandorina is a genus of colonial forms slightly more complex than *Gonium*. Each colony is a hollow sphere in which 8, 16, or 32 cells are arranged in a single layer about the periphery, their flagella oriented to the outside of the sphere (Fig. 21.3). Three main advances over *Gonium* are noticeable: (1) The colony shows some regional differentiation; it has definite anterior and posterior halves (detectable both by the orientation of the colony when it is swimming and by the larger size of the stigma in the anterior cells than in the posterior ones). (2) The vegetative cells of the colony are so dependent upon one another that they cannot live apart from the colony, and the colony itself cannot survive if disrupted or broken. (3) Sexual reproduction is **heterogamous** (or anisogamous); i.e. it involves two different kinds of gametes—small male gametes and larger female gametes (but note that in *Pandorina* both types of gametes have flagella and are free-swimming).

Eudorina is a still more advanced genus. The spherical colonies contain 16, 32, or 64 cells. The differences between the anterior and posterior portions of the colony are greater

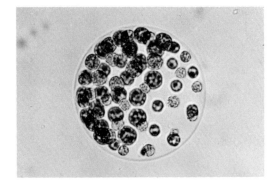

Fig. 21.4. Photograph of *Pleodorina* colony. [Courtesy J. M. Kingsbury, Cornell University.]

than in *Pandorina*, and the heterogamy is more pronounced in that the large female gametes are not released but remain embedded in the matrix of the colony and are fertilized there by the much smaller free-swimming male gametes.

A still more advanced genus is *Pleodorina* (Fig. 21.4), whose spherical colonies are composed of 32 to 128 cells. These large colonies exhibit considerable division of labor. The anterior cells are purely vegetative, never participating in reproduction. The posterior cells, which function in both asexual and sexual reproduction, are much larger. Sexual reproduction is heterogamous; in fact, in some cases the large female gametes lose their flagella and thus become true nonmotile egg cells. This type of advanced heterogamy, where only the male gamete is motile and the female gamete is a nonflagellated nonmotile egg cell, is called **oögamy**.

The culmination of the evolutionary series here being traced is represented by the genus *Volvox* (Fig. 21.5). Its spherical colonies are very large, consisting of about 500–50,000 cells. Most of these cells are exclusively vegetative. A few cells (between 2 and 50) scattered in the posterior half of the colony are much larger than the others and are specialized for reproduction. Each of the female reproductive cells can give rise to an entire new daughter colony. Sexual reproduction is always oögamous.

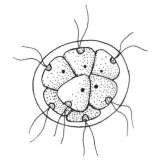

Fig. 21.3. *Pandorina* colony. The cells are embedded in a gelatinous matrix.

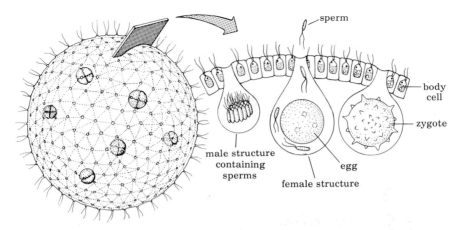

Fig. 21.5. *Volvox*. Left: The colony is very large, containing 500 to 50,000 vegetative cells. Six daughter colonies at various stages of development can be seen still embedded in the matrix of the parent colony. Right: Section through the surface of a colony showing male and female reproductive structures. Sperms released by the male structures enter the female structure and fertilize the egg. After a period of inactivity, the zygote divides meiotically, and the haploid cells thus formed then divide mitotically, producing a new daughter colony, which is eventually released. [Modified from H. J. Fuller and O. Tippo, *College Botany*, Holt, 1949.]

We can summarize the major lines of evolutionary changes manifest in this series as follows: (1) There is a change from unicellular to colonial life, and a tendency for the number of cells in the colonies to increase. (2) There is increasing coordination of activity among the cells. (3) The vegetative cells become so dependent upon one another that they cannot live apart from the colonies, and the colonies cannot survive if disrupted. (4) There is increasing division of labor, particularly between vegetative and reproductive cells. (5) There is a gradual change from isogamy to simple heterogamy to the extreme form of heterogamy called oögamy.

In tracing this *Chlamydomonas–Gonium–Pandorina–Eudorina–Pleodorina–Volvox* series, we do not mean to imply that each genus evolved from the preceding one; the available evidence will not allow us to decide whether it did or not. But it does seem likely that each of these genera evolved from an ancestor that resembled in many important ways the modern genus placed just before it in this series, and therefore that the actual evolutionary progression from some unicellular ancestor to *Volvox* involved a series of stages similar to those represented by the modern genera discussed here. Consequently, study of this series suggests how complex colonial forms may have evolved, and indicates one possible way in which the type of multicellularity characteristic of most animals may have arisen. After all, it is largely an arbitrary decision whether one calls *Volvox* colonial or multicellular. Though multicellular animals certainly did not evolve from *Volvox* or any of the other genera discussed here, a similar evolutionary series, beginning with a nonwalled unicellular organism, might well have been the beginning of multicellularity in the animal kingdom.

Some Multicellular Green Algae. Many green algae have a multicellular stage in their life cycle. In most cases, this stage is a filamentous thallus, which may be either nonbranching or branching, depending upon the species. Let us take *Ulothrix* as a first example.

The species of *Ulothrix* are unbranched filamentous forms, most of which live in fresh

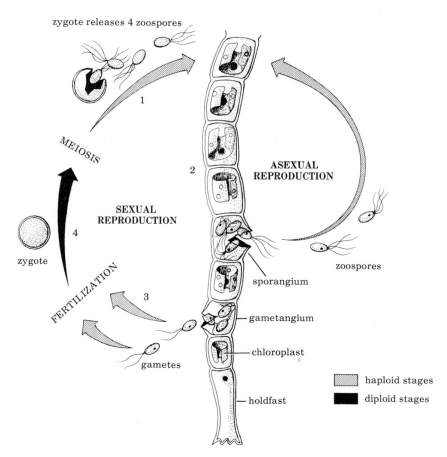

zygote releases 4 zoospores

MEIOSIS

1

2

ASEXUAL
REPRODUCTION

SEXUAL
REPRODUCTION

4

zygote

FERTILIZATION

3

zoospores

sporangium

gametangium

gametes

chloroplast

holdfast

haploid stages

diploid stages

Fig. 21.6. Life history of *Ulothrix*. The haploid plant may reproduce either asexually or sexually (though a single filament would never reproduce both ways at once as shown here). Asexual reproduction is more common; certain cells of the filament develop into sporangia (spore-producing structures) and produce zoospores, which settle down and develop into new filaments. Under certain environmental conditions, the filament may cease reproducing asexually and begin reproducing sexually; a cell becomes specialized as a gametangium (gamete-producing structure) and produces isogametes. Two such gametes may fuse in fertilization, producing a zygote, which divides meiotically and releases zoospores.

water although a few are marine (Fig. 21.6). The filament of each plant is a very small threadlike structure attached to the substratum by a specialized cell called a *holdfast.* Except for the holdfast cell, all the cells of the filament are identical and are arranged end to end in a single series. The filament increases in length as its cells divide horizontally and as the new cells thus added to the chain grow to mature size. Adjacent cells share common end walls— a basic step in the evolution of multicellularity

in algae. Each cell contains a single nucleus and a single large chloroplast.

Ulothrix may reproduce by fragmentation (each fragment growing into a complete plant), by asexually produced zoospores, or by sexual processes. Any cell of the filament except the holdfast may act as a *sporangium* (spore-producing structure), producing zoospores, each of which has four flagella. After they are released, the zoospores swim about for a short while, and then settle down and give rise to a new filament. Sexual reproduction is isogamous. The zygote (stage 4 in Fig. 21.7) formed by the union of two of the biflagellate gametes develops a thick wall and functions as a resting stage capable of withstanding unfavorable environmental conditions. At germination, the zygote divides by meiosis, producing haploid zoospores (stage 1), each of which will grow into a new filament (stage 2). The main difference, then, between this life cycle and that of *Chlamydomonas* is the addition of the haploid multicellular stage (stage 2). As in *Chlamydomonas*, the only diploid stage is the zygote.

Spirogyra (Fig. 21.8) is a rather odd filamentous green alga with a sexual life cycle similar to that of *Ulothrix* except that the gamete cells are not flagellated and are not released from the plant that produces them. Instead, two filaments come to lie side by side; protuberances develop on the sides of the cells where they are in contact; the walls between the protuberances of each pair of cells disintegrate; and then one cell becomes amoeboid, moves through the conjugation tube, and fuses with the other cell, forming a zygote. Relatively few green algae reproduce by this conjugation process.

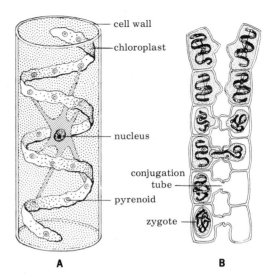

Fig. 21.8. *Spirogyra.* (A) A single vegetative cell removed from the filament. Note the unusual spiral-shaped chloroplast and the numerous pyrenoids. (B) Conjugating filaments. The two filaments lie side by side, and a conjugation tube develops between each pair of cells. One cell acts as the sperm, moving through the tube into the other cell (see third cells from bottom). The zygote thus formed is the only diploid stage in the life cycle. [Modified from H. J. Fuller and O. Tippo, *College Botany,* Holt, 1949.]

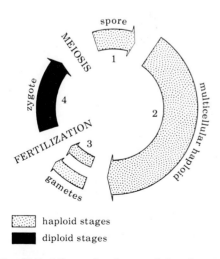

Fig. 21.7. **Life cycle characteristic of most multicellular green algae.** Note that multicellularity is present only in the haploid phase.

Ulva, or sea lettuce, is an example of a green alga with an expanded leaflike thallus two cells thick (Fig. 21.9). Its sexual life cycle is more complex than those of the other green algae discussed here in that it includes both multicellular haploid and multicellular diploid stages (stages 2 and 5 in Fig. 21.10). The entire cycle can be summarized as follows: Haploid zoospores (stage 1) divide mitotically to produce the haploid multicellular thalluses of stage 2. These may reproduce either asexually by means of zoospores or sexually by means of gametes (stage 3). Fusion of pairs of gametes (fertilization) produces diploid zygotes (stage 4). Upon germination, the zygotes divide mitotically (not meiotically as in the green algae previously discussed), producing diploid multicellular thalluses (stage

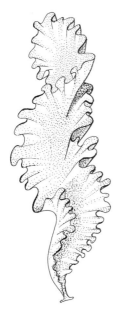

Fig. 21.9. *Ulva*, a marine green alga with a three-dimensional leaflike thallus.

evolution of the sporophyte; there are no green algae in which the sporophyte has become dominant over the gametophyte.

CHRYSOPHYTA (The Yellow-Green and Golden-Brown Algae and the Diatoms)

As the names of the divisions indicate, the earliest classifications of algae were based on color, which in turn depends on the sorts of pigments the cells contain. Fortunately, later study of other important characters, particularly the details of flagellation, the type of reserve materials produced, and the chemistry of the cell wall, showed that algae of like pigmentation usually shared such characters as

5). Eventually certain reproductive cells (sporangia) of these diploid plants divide by meiosis, producing haploid zoospores, which begin a new cycle. A life cycle of this type is said to exhibit *alternation of generations* in that a haploid multicellular plant alternates with a diploid multicellular plant. The haploid multicellular stage is customarily called a *gametophyte* (meaning that it is a plant that can produce gametes), and the diploid multicellular stage is called a *sporophyte* (meaning that it is a plant that can reproduce only by spores).

We have seen that multicellularity in plants arose first in the gametophyte, and that most green algae have no sporophyte stage. *Ulva* shows a more advanced life cycle than most green algae in that both gametophyte and sporophyte stages are present. Furthermore, the two stages are equally prominent in *Ulva*, being nearly equal in duration and almost identical in appearance; in other words, the haploid portion of the life cycle is no longer dominant over the diploid. However, this is as far as any of the Chlorophyta have gone in the

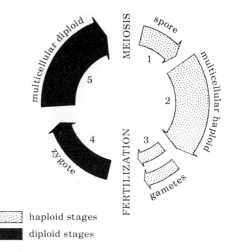

haploid stages

diploid stages

Fig. 21.10. Life cycle of *Ulva* and *Ectocarpus*. The gametophyte (multicellular haploid) and sporophyte (multicellular diploid) stages are equally prominent. *Ulva* and its close relatives are unusual among the green algae in having a life cycle of this sort; most of the Chlorophyta have no alternation of generations, the sporophyte stage being absent. *Ectocarpus*, a brown alga, is also unusual in having a life cycle of this type, but for a different reason: It is one of the few members of the Phaeophyta in which the sporophyte is not more prominent than the gametophyte.

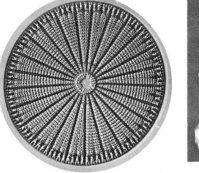
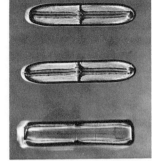

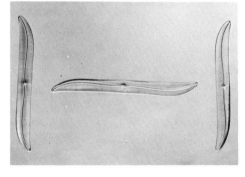

Fig. 21.11. Photographs of representative diatoms. Top (from left to right): *Arachnoidiscus, Pinnularia, Triceratium*. Left: *Pleurosigma*. [Courtesy General Biological Supply House, Inc., Chicago.]

well and that the old color classification was still acceptable. Thus most of the species in the three groups of algae placed together in the division Chrysophyta are some shade of yellow or brown (caused in part by a predominance of carotenoids), and they also resemble each other in not using starch as a reserve material (instead they use oil droplets and a whitish substance of unknown chemical structure called leucosin), in usually having walls of pectic material often impregnated with silica, and in either lacking flagella or having two[7] that are very unequal in length. It must be admitted, however, that despite these similarities the diatoms are quite different in many ways from the yellow-green and the golden-brown algae, and it may eventually be necessary to put them in a separate division of their own.

The majority of the Chrysophyta are unicellular or colonial, although a few have small

[7] A few species have only one flagellum.

simple multicellular bodies. Reproduction is usually asexual, but occasionally sexual. Most of the yellow-green and golden-brown algae live in freshwater, but a few are marine. Diatoms are abundant in both fresh- and salt-water habitats.

The diatoms are of special interest for several reasons. They are unusual in that the vegetative cells are ordinarily diploid—not haploid, as might be expected in such simple and seemingly primitive plants. And their silica-impregnated glasslike walls, which are composed of two pieces that fit together like a box with its lid, often give the cells a jewel-like appearance. The different species exhibit a great variety of shapes and ornamentations (Fig. 21.11). The classification of the diatoms is based almost entirely on the characters of the walls, or shells, as they are commonly called. When the cells die, the shells sink to the bottom, where they may accumulate in large numbers, forming deposits of a material called diatomaceous earth. This material is used as an ingredient in many commercial preparations, including detergents, polishes, paint removers, decolorizing and deodorizing oils, and fertilizers. It is also extensively used as a filtering agent and as a component in insulating and soundproofing products.

The diatoms play an extremely important role in aquatic food webs. They are the most abundant component of marine plankton, for example; it is not unusual for a gallon of sea water to contain as many as one or two million diatoms. *Plankton* consists, by definition, of small organisms floating or drifting near the surface. Planktonic organisms are generally divided into two groups—phytoplankton (plant plankton) and zooplankton (animal plankton). The organisms of the phytoplankton are the principal photosynthetic producers in marine communities.

PYRROPHYTA (The Dinoflagellates)

The dinoflagellates are small, usually unicellular, organisms often regarded as Protozoa by zoologists. A cell wall may or may not be present; if present, it is composed largely of cellulose. Photosynthetic species usually have a yellowish-green to brown color due to an abundance of carotenoids, several of which are unique to these organisms. There are many colorless species that feed on particulate organic matter. The reserve material is either starch or oils. Most species possess two very unequal flagella, which are attached laterally. One of these runs along a groove to the posterior end of the cell and extends behind the cell like a tail; the other lies in a groove that encircles the mid-portion of the cell like a belt. Cell division is unusual in that there is no evidence of a spindle; both the nucleus and the cytoplasm appear to divide by simple constriction.

Dinoflagellates are second only to the diatoms as primary producers of organic matter in the marine environment; they are much less important in fresh water. Some species can produce light and are responsible for much of the luminescence often seen in ocean water at night. A number of species are poisonous; some of these contain red pigments, and when they occur in great abundance they produce the so-called "red tides" that sometimes kill many millions of fish. Red tides are fairly common in the Gulf of Mexico off the coast of Florida.

Fig. 21.12. *Ascophyllum*, a brown alga. This plant covers the rocks exposed at low tide along parts of the northeastern North American coast. [Courtesy J. M. Kingsbury, Cornell University.]

PHAEOPHYTA (The Brown Algae)

The brown algae are almost exclusively marine, the few fresh-water species being quite rare. Many of the plants called seaweeds are members of this division. They are most common along rocky coasts of the cooler parts of the oceans, where they normally grow attached to the bottom in the littoral (intertidal) and upper sublittoral zones. They may be seen in great abundance covering the rocks exposed at low tide along the New England coast (Fig. 21.12). A few species occur in warmer seas, and some of these differ from the majority of brown algae in being able to live and grow when detached from the substratum; e.g. some species of *Sargassum* (Fig. 21.13) form dense floating mats that cover much of the surface of the so-called Sargasso Sea, which occupies some two and a half million square miles of ocean between the West Indies and North Africa.

All brown algae are multicellular, and most are macroscopic, some growing as long as 150 feet or more. The thallus (plant body) may be a filament, or it may be a large and rather complex three-dimensional structure. The latter type of thallus has apparently arisen several times independently; in some species it develops from interwoven and tightly compacted filaments, and in others it results from cell divisions in more than one plane. The individual cells are much like those of higher land plants, having cellulose cell walls with pits through which plasmodesmata pass, large central vacuoles, usually several plastids, and no pyrenoids. However, unlike the cells of most higher land plants, they usually have centrioles.

Like all photosynthetic plants, the Phaeophyta possess chlorophyll *a*. However, they have chlorophyll *c* instead of the chlorophyll *b* found in euglenoids, green algae, and higher land plants. Large amounts of a xanthophyll carotenoid called *fucoxanthin* are also present, and it is this that gives the characteristic brownish color to these algae. A variety of

Fig. 21.13. Photograph of part of a *Sargassum* thallus. Note the characteristic bladders; they are filled with gas and act as floats. [Courtesy J. M. Kingsbury, Cornell University.]

unusual carbohydrates are synthesized and used as structural or storage materials.[8]

Reproduction may be either asexual or sexual, the latter often involving specialized multicellular sex organs. These sex organs are called *antheridia* if they produce male gametes and *archegonia* if they produce female gametes (or gametangia if all the gametes are alike, i.e. if the plant is isogamous). In brown algae, neither the antheridia nor the archegonia are ordinarily enclosed by a protective layer of sterile jacket cells. The life cycle is usually one in which there is an alternation of gametophyte (haploid) and sporophyte (diploid) multicellular generations. In many forms, such as *Ectocarpus*, the gametophyte and sporophyte (stages 2 and 5 in Fig. 21.10) are essentially similar in structure and neither can be said to be dominant. In other forms, such as *Laminaria*, the haploid gametophyte is reduced and the diploid sporophyte is much larger and more

---

[8] Three of the most important polysaccharides synthesized by the Phaeophyta are alginic acid, fucoidin, and laminarin, the principal reserve material.

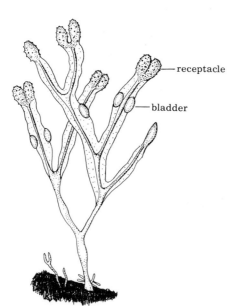

Fig. 21.14. *Fucus,* often called rockweed, a brown alga common along northern coasts. Left: Each thallus is flattened and repeatedly dichotomously branched. Each younger axis consists of a midrib and thin paired wings. In some species (including the one shown here), there are bladders (floats) at intervals along the wings. The tips of fertile thalluses develop swollen reproductive structures called receptacles, whose surface is pocked by numerous tiny openings that lead into cavities (conceptacles) where the sex organs are located. Right: Photograph of *Fucus* growing on a rock. Note the large number of receptacles. [Right: Courtesy J. M. Kingsbury, Cornell University.]

prominent (see Fig. 21.46). In a few, such as *Fucus* (Fig. 21.14), reduction of the haploid stages has progressed so far that there is no longer any multicellular haploid gametophyte and the only haploid cells in the life cycle are the gametes (Fig. 21.15); such a life cycle, which is very rare in plants, is essentially the sort seen in animals.

Let us look more closely at a few representative genera of brown algae. *Ectocarpus* has a branching filamentous thallus (Fig. 21.16). The diploid sporophyte plants (stage 5 in Fig. 21.10) sometimes bear small unicellular sporangia, in which haploid zoospores (stage 1) are produced by meiosis. After swimming about for a while, the zoospores settle down and develop into haploid multicellular gametophyte plants (stage 2). These plants may bear multicellular gametangia, in which morphologically

isogamous gametes (stage 3) are produced. Two gametes (from different plants) may fuse in fertilization to form a zygote (stage 4), which is motile at first but soon settles down and germinates, giving rise to a new diploid multicellular sporophyte plant (stage 5), thus completing the cycle.

Laminaria is an example of the group of brown algae commonly called kelps. The sporophyte thallus is large (6 feet long or more in *Laminaria;* 150 feet long or more in some kelps) and consists of a rootlike **holdfast,** a stemlike **stipe,** and an expanded leaflike **blade** (Fig. 21.17; see also Fig. 6.1, p. 202). Although thallophyte plants normally lack tissue differentiation, the stipe of some kelps has an outer surface tissue (epidermis), a middle tissue (cortex) containing many plastids, and a central core tissue (medulla); it may even have

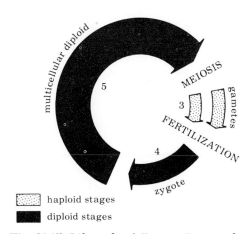

haploid stages

diploid stages

Fig. 21.15. Life cycle of *Fucus*. *Fucus* and its close relatives have a very unusual life cycle. They are the only multicellular plants in which the multicellular haploid stage (the gametophyte) is completely absent. In this respect, their life cycle is like that of animals.

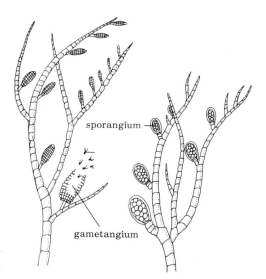

Fig. 21.16. Parts of gametophyte and sporophyte thalli of *Ectocarpus*. Left: The gametophyte (haploid multicellular organism, stage 2 of the life cycle) bears multicellular gametangia, which produce morphologically isogamous gametes. Right: The sporophyte (diploid multicellular organism, stage 5 of the life cycle) bears unicellular sporangia in which zoospores are produced. [Modified from H. J. Fuller and O. Tippo, *College Botany*, Holt, 1949.]

a meristematic layer similar to the cambium of higher vascular plants and, in a few species, a phloemlike conductive tissue in the medulla. In short, these brown algae are complex plants that have convergently evolved many similarities to the vascular plants. However, none of them have a protective layer of sterile jacket cells around their reproductive organs; none develop multicellular embryos while still inside the archegonia; none have a cuticle; and none have xylem.

Fig. 21.17. *Laminaria digitata*. This specimen was detached from the substratum on which it was growing and spread out for photographing. Note the rootlike holdfast, the stemlike stipe, and the leaflike blade. [Courtesy J. M. Kingsbury, Cornell University.]

RHODOPHYTA (The Red Algae)

The red algae are mostly marine seaweeds (Fig. 21.18), but a few live in fresh water or on land. They often occur at greater depths than the brown algae. Most are multicellular and are attached to the substratum, but a few species are unicellular. No red algae attain the very large sizes often seen in brown algae.

The cell walls contain cellulose and also large quantities of mucilaginous material. The reserve product is not starch but a polysaccharide similar to it.[9] Red algae are an important source

[9] This compound is often called floridean starch.

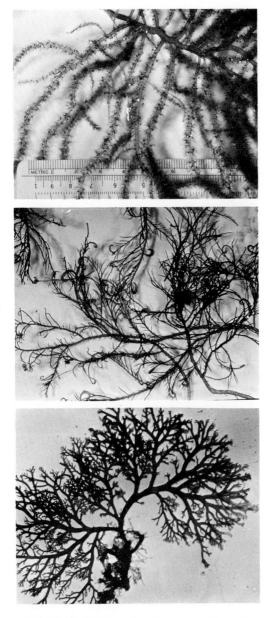

Fig. 21.18. Photographs of representative red algae. From top to bottom: *Dasya pedicellata, Asparagopsis hamifera, Euthora cristata.* [Courtesy J. M. Kingsbury, Cornell University.]

of commercial colloids—among others, agar used in culturing bacteria; suspending agents used in chocolate milk and puddings; stabilizers

used in ice creams, some cheeses, and salad dressings; and moisture retainers used in icings, creams, and marshmallows.

In addition to chlorophyll *a*, which is found in all photosynthetic organisms except the photosynthetic bacteria, the Rhodophyta often possess chlorophyll *d*, which is not found in any other group of plants. They also contain phycocyanins and phycoerythrins.[10] It is the phycoerythrins that give many of these algae their characteristic reddish color. It should be emphasized, however, that "red algae" are not always red; many are black.

The accessory pigments of the Rhodophyta play an important role in absorbing light for photosynthesis. The wavelengths preferentially absorbed by chlorophyll *a* for use in photosynthesis are among those at the ends of the visible spectrum (recall the discussion of the absorption spectrum of chlorophyll in Chapter 4). But those wavelengths do not penetrate to the depths at which the red algae grow, partly because of the imperfect transparency of the water, partly because they are selectively absorbed by pigmented phytoplankton. The wavelengths that do penetrate deep enough are mostly those of the central portion of the spectrum, which are not readily absorbed by chlorophyll *a*. But these wavelengths can be absorbed by the accessory pigments of the Rhodophyta, which then pass the energy to chlorophyll *a*. Thus the accessory pigments make it possible for red algae to live at depths where other algae, lacking these pigments, cannot survive.

The life cycles of red algae are usually very complex, and few of them have been worked out in detail. There is commonly some sort of alternation of generations. Flagellated cells never occur; even the sperm cells lack flagella and must be carried to the egg cells by water currents.

---

[10] The phycocyanins and phycoerythrins of the Rhodophyta are not the same as those found in the Cyanophyta.

MYXOMYCOPHYTA (The Slime Molds)

The slime molds are curious organisms decidedly animal-like at some stages in their life cycle and plantlike at others. Sometimes put among the Protozoa in the animal kingdom, they are more commonly placed among the fungi in the plant kingdom. They are generally found growing on damp soil, rotting logs, leaf mold, or other decaying organic matter in moist woods, where they look like glistening viscous masses of slime; they are sometimes white but are often colored red or yellow.

In many slime molds, the vegetative phase of the life cycle is a large diploid multinucleate (coenocytic) amoeboid mass called a *plasmodium,* which moves about slowly and feeds on particles of organic material by phagocytosis. The behavior of the naked plasmodium is thus animal-like. Under certain conditions, however, the plasmodium becomes stationary and develops fruiting bodies, which may be either simple rounded masses or elaborate stalked organs; at this stage, the appearance and behavior of the organism are plantlike. Meiosis occurs within the sporangia of the fruiting bodies, and the haploid cells thus formed are released as spores; the spores have walls that contain cellulose. When the spores germinate, they produce naked flagellated gametes. These fuse in pairs to form zygotes, which soon lose their flagella and become amoeboid. As this amoeboid form flows along the substratum, engulfing bacteria and other organic particles and digesting them in vacuoles, its diploid nucleus undergoes repeated mitotic divisions without accompanying cytokinesis. In this way, the zygote develops into a multinucleate plasmodium, which may grow to a length of 10 inches (although 2 or 3 inches is a more common size). Some growth may also occur by fusion of the cytoplasms of two or more zygotes or young plasmodia. In summary, then, the life cycle proceeds from diploid amoeboid plasmodium, to stationary spore-

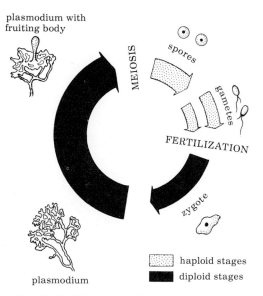

Fig. 21.19. Life cycle of a true slime mold. See text for description.

producing plasmodium, to haploid spores, to flagellated gametes, to zygote, and back to amoeboid plasmodium (Fig. 21.19).

The life cycle described above applies to the so-called true slime molds; the life cycle of the *cellular slime molds* is quite different (Fig. 21.20). The spores do not develop into flagellated gametes, but instead give rise to free-living soil-inhabiting amoeboid cells, each with a single haploid nucleus. The amoebae feed on bacteria and other organic matter. During this feeding stage, the amoebae divide repeatedly (both mitosis and cytokinesis occur), producing independent uninucleate daughter cells. As the local food supply diminishes, the behavior of the amoebae suddenly changes; they cease feeding and begin to stream into central collecting points, where they clump together to form a sluglike pseudoplasmodium. The individual haploid cells retain their separate identities within the slug; they do not fuse. The pseudoplasmodium of the cellular slime molds is thus very different from the diploid multinucleate plasmodium of the true slime molds. The slug may move around as a unit for a

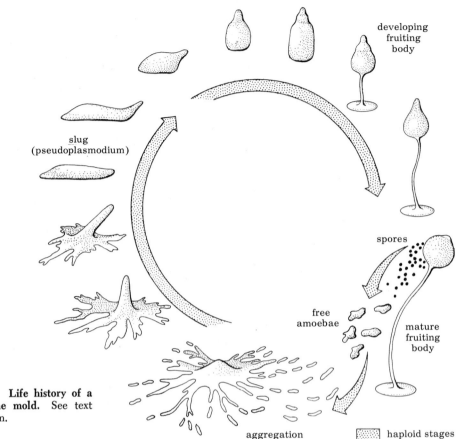

developing
fruiting
body

slug
(pseudoplasmodium)

spores

free
amoebae

mature
fruiting
body

**Fig. 21.20. Life history of a
cellular slime mold.** See text
for discussion.

aggregation   haploid stages

while, but eventually it becomes sedentary and forms a stalked fruiting body in which new spores are produced. Notice that this life cycle does not include any sexual events, and that all stages are apparently haploid.

Cellular slime molds can easily be grown in the laboratory, and they have been used extensively in studies of the factors influencing development. It has been found that the cells release a gas to which other cells respond. During the aggregation period when the slug is being formed, the individual amoebae are guided to the collecting point by a gradient of this gas. The same gas plays a role in controlling the spacing and the orientation of the fruiting bodies.

All the evidence now available indicates that the true slime molds and the cellular slime molds are not closely related and probably should be placed in separate divisions.[11] Their relationships to other organisms are unknown.

EUMYCOPHYTA (The True Fungi)

Fungi are by definition thallophyte plants that lack chlorophyll. Thus the slime molds are fungi, and if bacteria are regarded as plants

[11] The true slime molds constitute the class Myxomycetes, and the cellular slime molds the class Acrasiae. Two other small groups, the Plasmodiophoreae and the Labyrinthuleae, are also usually put in the Myxomycophyta, although they are probably not closely related to either the Myxomycetes or the Acrasiae; their true relationships are unknown.

Authors who wish to emphasize the animal characteristics of the slime molds often use the name "Mycetozoa" instead of "Myxomycophyta."

then they too are fungi. However, the term "fungus" is often used in a more restricted sense to refer only to the members of the Eumycophyta, the so-called true fungi. This is a large group containing thousands of parasitic and saprophytic species, many of economic importance. Some are parasitic on or in animals, including man; many skin diseases, including "ringworm" and athlete's foot, are caused by fungi, and there are several serious fungal diseases of the lungs. Other fungi are parasitic on plants, and some of these may cause loss of millions of dollars when they attack agricultural crops; fungal diseases of plants include stem rust of wheat, white-pine rust, chestnut blight, late blight of potatoes, black spot on roses, mildews of grapes and other plants, apple scab, and corn smut. Still other fungi cause spoilage of bread, fruit, vegetables, and other foodstuffs, and deterioration of leather goods, fabrics, paper, lumber, and other valuable products. However, the numerous pathogenic or destructive fungi should not cause us to forget the many others that are beneficial. Yeasts are used extensively in the manufacture of alcoholic products and to make bread dough "rise." The antibiotic penicillin is obtained from a fungus. Fungi are important in the manufacture of many cheeses, such as Roquefort, Gorgonzola, and Camembert. Certain mushrooms are regularly used as food. And fungi, together with bacteria, decompose vast quantities of dead organic material that would otherwise rapidly accumulate and make the earth uninhabitable.

The body of a fungus is either unicellular or filamentous. The individual filaments are called *hyphae,* and a mass of hyphae is called a *mycelium.* The cell walls sometimes contain cellulose, but more often chitin is their most important component. Most saprophytic fungi secrete digestive enzymes onto their food material and absorb the products of the extracellular digestion (see pp. 174, 176). Parasitic fungi may also carry out extracellular digestion, or they may directly absorb materials produced by the body of their host. Reproduction may be either asexual or sexual, but in both cases the haploid stages are dominant (except in a few exceptional species).

The division Eumycophyta is customarily divided into three classes—Phycomycetes, Ascomycetes, and Basidiomycetes—each of which is given full divisional status in some classifications. Most of the characteristics that distinguish these three groups are related to their sexual reproduction.[12]

Phycomycetes (The Algal Fungi)

The hyphae of the Phycomycetes characteristically lack cross walls although they contain many haploid nuclei (i.e. they are coenocytic). Cross walls appear only during the formation of reproductive structures. Except for their lack of chlorophyll, these fungi resemble the coenocytic green algae, and for this reason they are often called the algal fungi. Some of the aquatic species even produce flagellated zoospores similar to those seen in green algae.

As an example of a member of this class, let us examine the common black bread mold, *Rhizopus.* The hyphae of this mold form a whitish or grayish mycelium on the bread. If the mycelium is examined carefully, it can be seen to include three types of hyphae: hyphae (called stolons) that form a network on the surface of the bread; rootlike hyphae (called rhizoids) that penetrate into the bread and function both in anchoring the plant and in absorbing nutrients; and hyphae (called sporangiophores) that grow upright from the surface and bear globular sporangia on their ends (Fig. 21.21A). Thousands of asexual spores are produced in each sporangium. The spores, which have no flagella, are very tiny and light, and when liberated at maturity (by disintegration of the wall of the sporangium) they may

[12] Other bases of classification are generally unsatisfactory. Hence it is often difficult to classify species for which sexual stages have not been found; such species are customarily assigned to a category called Fungi Imperfecti.

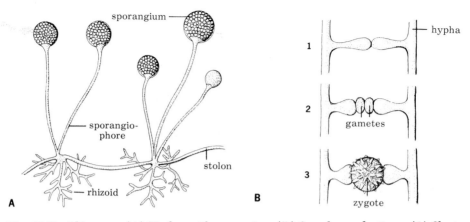

Fig. 21.21. *Rhizopus.* (A) Hyphae with sporangia. (B) Sexual reproduction. (1) Short branches from two different hyphae meet. (2) The tips of the branch hyphae are cut off as gametes. (3) The gametes fuse in fertilization to form a zygote with a thick spiny wall.

be carried long distances by air currents. If a spore lands in a suitable location, where conditions are warm and moist, it germinates and soon gives rise to a new mass of hyphae, thus completing the asexual cycle.

Sexual reproduction in *Rhizopus* resembles that of the green alga *Spirogyra*. Short branches from two different hyphae (which must be of different mating types or sexes) contact each other at their tips (Fig. 21.21B). Cross walls soon form just back of the tip in each hypha,

thus delimiting gamete cells, which then fuse to form a zygote. The zygote develops a thick protective wall and enters a period of dormancy usually lasting from one to three months. At germination, the nucleus of the zygote undergoes meiosis, and a short hypha grows from the zygote. This haploid hypha promptly produces a sporangium, which releases asexual spores that grow into new mycelia. Note that the only diploid stage in the entire sexual cycle is the zygote (Fig. 21.22).

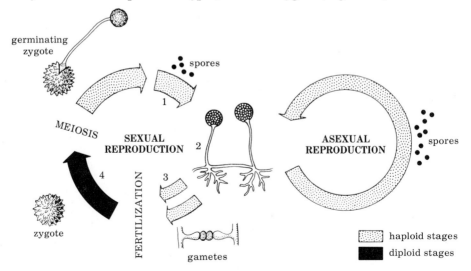

Fig. 21.22. **Life cycle of *Rhizopus.*** See text for description.

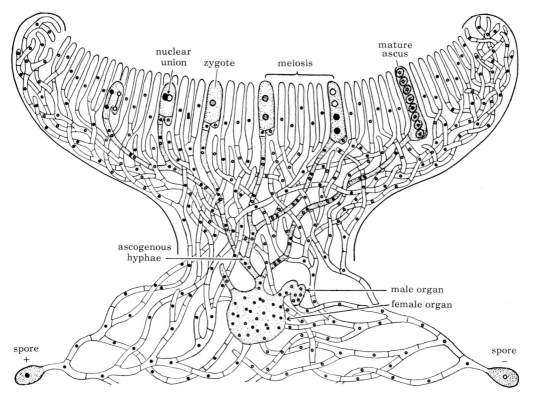

Fig. 21.23. Diagram of a magnified section through a cup fungus. Hyphae of two mycelia, one derived from a plus (female) spore and the other from a minus (male) spore, participate in forming the cup structure and in producing the spores. The plus mycelium bears a female organ, and the minus mycelium bears a male organ. A tube grows from the female organ to the male organ, and then minus nuclei (small circles), acting as male nuclei, move into the female organ and become associated with plus nuclei (black dots). Next, hyphae (gray) grow from the female organ; each cell in these hyphae contains two associated nuclei, one minus and one plus. The terminal cells of these hyphae eventually become elongate, and their nuclei unite, forming a zygote nucleus. The zygote nucleus promptly divides meiotically, and each of the four haploid nuclei thus formed then divides mitotically, producing a total of eight small spore cells, which are still contained within the wall of the old zygote cell, now called an ascus. When the mature ascus ruptures, the spores are released. [From L. W. Sharp, *Fundamentals of Cytology*, McGraw-Hill Book Co., 1943. Used by permission.]

Ascomycetes (The Sac Fungi)

The members of this large class are very diverse, varying all the way from unicellular yeasts through powdery mildews and cottony molds to complex cup fungi. These last form a cup-shaped structure composed of many hyphae tightly packed together (Fig. 21.23). The vegetative hyphae of Ascomycetes, unlike those of Phycomycetes, are septate (i.e. they possess cross walls) and are thus long multi-

cellular filaments rather than coenocytic tubes (though cells with two nuclei each are formed during sexual reproduction).[13]

Despite their differing vegetative structures, all Ascomycetes resemble each other in forming a reproductive structure called an **ascus** during their sexual cycle. An ascus is a sac within

---

[13] Actually the septa (cross walls) are frequently incomplete, having large holes in their centers. The cytoplasm of adjacent cells is thus frequently continuous.

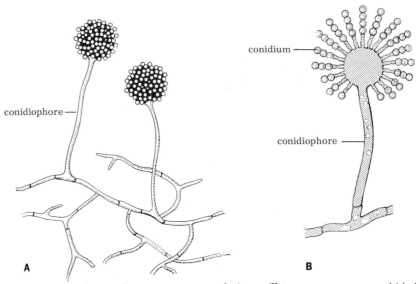

Fig. 21.24. Asexual reproductive structures of *Aspergillus,* an ascomycete. (A) Two conidiophores arise from a mycelium. (B) An enlarged section through a conidiophore shows that the structure bears numerous spores, called conidia, arranged in chains.

which haploid spores (usually eight, but sometimes four) are produced; all the spores in an ascus are derived from a single parent cell (remember discussion of the ascus of *Neurospora;* see p. 572 and Fig. 15.10). The events leading to the formation of a mature ascus are rather complicated (Fig. 21.23). Hyphae from two neighboring haploid mycelia of different mating types develop multinucleate sexual organs. One mycelium (the so-called plus mycelium) bears a large female organ; the other (the minus mycelium) bears a small male organ.[14] A tubular structure grows from the female organ to the male organ, and nuclei from the male pass through this tube into the female organ. But the nuclei do not fuse; hence this process is not true fertilization. A large cell is formed containing many male nuclei and many female nuclei that become associated in pairs. From this strange cell grow numerous hyphae composed of binucleate cells (cells containing one male nucleus and one female nucleus).

Eventually the terminal cell of each of these hyphae becomes converted into a zygote by fusion of its two nuclei. This is the only diploid stage in the life cycle. Within the zygote, the diploid nucleus soon divides by meiosis, producing four haploid nuclei, each of which usually then divides by mitosis. The eight nuclei thus produced, are still inside the wall of the old zygote, which has now become an ascus. Eventually new cell walls develop around each of the eight nuclei and their associated cytoplasm; the resulting eight cells are spores, which are liberated when the wall of the ascus bursts. Each spore, when it germinates, can grow into a new mycelium.

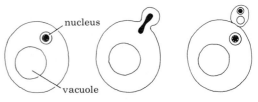

Fig. 21.25. Budding in brewer's yeast. A small new cell is pinched off the larger parent cell.

14 The female organs are called ascogonia and the male organs antheridia.

Fig. 21.26. Photographs of two kinds of lichens. Top: Pixie-cup lichens growing in a clump of moss. Bottom: Common rock lichen growing in grayish scaly patches on a walk. [Courtesy Verne N. Rockcastle, Cornell University.]

Most Ascomycetes also reproduce asexually by means of special spores called *conidia* (Fig. 21.24). Conidia are produced in chains at the end of conidiophore hyphae (but not inside sporangia). Each conidium can grow into a new fungal plant.

It may seem strange that yeasts are considered members of the Ascomycetes. They are unicellular, and their asexual reproduction is by *budding* (Fig. 21.25), not by conidia formation. However, under certain conditions a single yeast cell may function as an ascus, producing four spores. The spores are more resistant to unfavorable environmental conditions than vegetative cells, and they may en-

able yeasts to survive temperature extremes or periods of prolonged drying.

In previous chapters, we mentioned the *lichens,* plants composed of a fungus and an alga growing together in a complex symbiotic relationship (Fig. 21.26). The fungal component of most lichens is an ascomycete, though in a few tropical lichens the fungus is a member of the Basidiomycetes, discussed below. The algal components may be either Cyanophyta or Chlorophyta.

Basidiomycetes (The Club Fungi)

Many of the largest and most conspicuous fungi—puffballs, mushrooms, toadstools, and bracket fungi—are Basidiomycetes (Fig. 21.27). Though the above-ground portion of these plants looks like a solid mass of tissue, and in some is differentiated into a stalk and a prominent cap (Fig. 21.28), it is nevertheless composed of hyphae, as are all fungi (Fig. 21.29). It should be emphasized that the above-ground portion, or fruiting body, of many mushrooms is only a small part of the total plant; there is an extensive mass of hyphae in the soil. The hyphae are septate.

Fig. 21.27. Young shaggy-mane mushrooms *(Coprinus).* This is an edible species. [Courtesy Verne N. Rockcastle, Cornell University.]

Fig. 21.28. Poison *Amanita*. This is one of the most dangerous of mushrooms; to eat it is to risk death. It can be recognized by the cup at the base of the stalk, though this is sometimes buried in fallen leaves or soil and therefore hard to see.

The members of this class are distinguished by their possession of club-shaped reproductive structures called *basidia* (Figs. 21.29, 21.30). The cells of the hyphae that produce basidia are binucleate, containing one haploid male nucleus and one haploid female nucleus (usually designated as minus and plus). Certain terminal cells of these hyphae become zygotes when their two nuclei fuse in fertilization. The zygote then becomes a basidium. Its diploid nucleus divides by meiosis, producing four new haploid nuclei. Four small protuberances develop on the end of the basidium, and the haploid nuclei migrate into these. The tip of each protuberance then becomes walled off as a spore, which falls or is ejected from the basidium. Each spore may give rise to a new mycelium.

THE MOVEMENT ONTO LAND

Let us now turn to the Embryophyta—plants that have evolved numerous adaptations for life on land. We have seen that life probably arose in water, and that many plants, notably the algae, are still largely restricted to the aquatic environment; the few algae that live on land are not truly terrestrial, occurring, as they do, only in very moist places and actually living in a film of moisture. The evolutionary move from an aquatic to a terrestrial existence was not a simple one, for the terrestrial environment is in many ways hostile to life. Among the many problems faced by a land plant are these: (1) obtaining enough water when fluid no longer bathes the entire surface of the plant body; (2) transporting water and dissolved substances from restricted areas of intake to other parts of the plant body, and transporting the products of photosynthesis to those parts of the plant that no longer carry out this process for themselves; (3) preventing excessive loss of water by evaporation; (4) maintaining a sufficiently extensive moist surface for gas exchange when the surrounding medium is air instead of liquid; (5) supporting a large plant body against the pull of gravity when the buoyancy of an aqueous medium is no longer available; (6) carrying out reproduction when there is little water through which flagellated sperms may swim and when the zygote and early embryo are in severe danger of desiccation; (7) withstanding the extreme fluctuations in temperature, humidity, wind, light, and other environmental parameters to which terrestrial organisms are often subjected. Much of the evolution of the embryophyte plants can best be understood in terms of adaptations that help solve these problems.

As we indicated earlier in this chapter, embryophyte plants characteristically possess multicellular sex organs—antheridia and archegonia—which have an outer layer of sterile (i.e. nondividing) jacket cells that help pro-

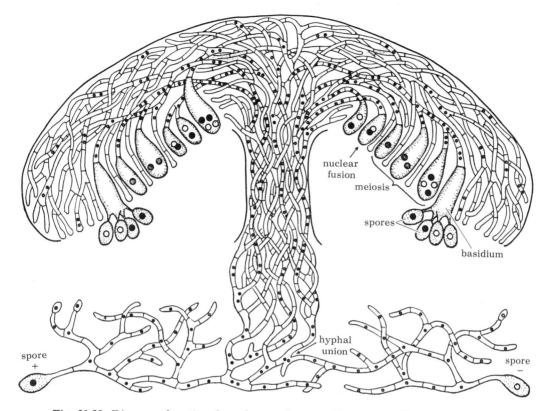

Fig. 21.29. Diagram of section through a mushroom. The entire stalk and cap are composed of hyphae tightly packed together. Spores are produced by basidia on the lower surface of the cap. [From L. W. Sharp, *Fundamentals of Cytology*, McGraw-Hill Book Co., 1943. Used by permission.]

Fig. 21.30. Reproductive structures of Basidiomycetes. The large club-shaped cells at bottom are basidia. A mature basidium bears four round spores at its end. The three shorter basidia in the figure are immature. The one on the far right is an old basidium that has shed its spores.

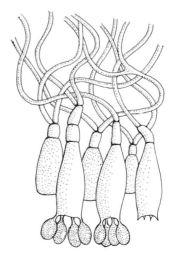

tect the enclosed gametes from desiccation. (The sporangia in embryophytes are also multicellular, and they too have a layer of jacket cells.) All embryophytes are oögamous, and the egg cells are fertilized while they are still contained within the archegonia. Each zygote develops into a multicellular diploid embryo while still inside the archegonium (Table 21.1). The embryo obtains water and nutrients from the parent plant and is thus a parasite on it. This type of embryonic development, which is clearly an adaptation permitting the stages of development that would be most susceptible to desiccation to take place in a favorably moist microenvironment, is strongly reminiscent of the internal gestation of mammals.

The surfaces of the aerial parts of the plant bodies of embryophytes are typically covered by a waxy cuticle, which waterproofs the epidermis and helps prevent excessive water loss.

The principal pigments in embryophytes are chlorophylls *a* and *b*. The reserve material is starch. In other words, these plants are biochemically similar to the Chlorophyta, from which they almost certainly arose.

BRYOPHYTA (The Liverworts, Hornworts, and Mosses)

The bryophytes are relatively small plants that grow in moist places on land—on damp rocks and logs, on the forest floor, in swamps or marshes, or beside streams and pools. Some species can survive periods of drought, but only by becoming dormant and ceasing to grow. In short, the bryophytes live on land, but they have never become fully emancipated from their ancestral aquatic environment, and they have therefore never become a dominant

TABLE 21.1

A Comparison of the Major Plant Divisions

Characteristics	Chloro-phyta	Phaeo-phyta	Rhodo-phyta	Eumyco-phyta	Bryo-phyta	Tracheo-phyta
Usually have flagellated sperms	+	+	−	−	+	+ or −
Possess chlorophyll *a*	+	+	+	−	+	+
Possess chlorophyll *b*	+	−(*c* instead)	−(*d* instead)	−	+	+
Principal reserve material is usually starch	+	−	−	−	+	+
Sporophyte is usually equal or dominant to gametophyte	−	+	+	−	−	+
Usually have multicellular sex organs with jacket cells	−	−	−	−	+	+
Embryo develops within female reproductive organ	−	−	−	−	+	+
Cuticle present	−	−	−	−	+	+
Xylem and phloem present	−	−	−	−	−	+

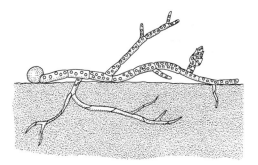

Fig. 21.31. A young moss plant. The spore (round object on surface of soil, at left) gives rise to a filamentous plant (called a protonema) that strikingly resembles a green alga. The protonema develops into the mature moss plant. [Modified from H. J. Fuller and O. Tippo, *College Botany*, Holt, 1949.]

group of plants. Their great dependence upon a moist environment is linked to two characteristics: They retain flagellated sperm cells, which must swim to the egg cells in the archegonia, and they lack vascular tissues, and hence lack efficient long-distance internal transport of fluids.[15] The absence of xylem, which functions as a major supportive tissue in vascular plants, has probably also limited the size they can attain.

The bryophytes are thought to have arisen from filamentous green algae. Indeed, a very young moss plant, called a protonema (Fig. 21.31), often closely resembles a green algal filament. As the plant grows, it forms some branches (rhizoids) that enter the ground and function like roots, anchoring the plant and absorbing water and nutrients. Other branches form upright shoots with stemlike and leaflike parts. Note that we say "like" roots, stems, and leaves: Since bryophytes lack vascular tissue, the anatomical criteria for distinguishing true roots, stems, and leaves cannot be applied to them.

We saw earlier that among the larger and more complex algae, most of which exhibit alternation of generations, there seems to have

been an evolutionary tendency toward reduction of the gametophyte (multicellular haploid) stage and increasing emphasis of the sporophyte (multicellular diploid) stage. Thus in both brown algae and red algae the sporophyte is at least as prominent as the phylogenetically older gametophyte, and it is often much more prominent. As we shall see later, the same evolutionary tendency is found in the vascular plants. But this tendency is not apparent in the bryophytes, where the haploid gametophyte (stage 2 in Fig. 21.32) is clearly the dominant stage in the life cycle. The "leafy" green moss plant or liverwort is the gametophyte. These plants bear antheridia and archegonia in which gametes (stage 3) are produced. The flagellated male gametes (sperms) are released from the antheridia and swim through a film of moisture, such as heavy dew, to archegonia, where they fertilize the egg cells, producing zygotes (stage 4). Each zygote then divides mitotically, producing a diploid sporophyte (stage 5). In a moss, this sporophyte is a relatively simple structure consisting of three parts: a foot embedded in the "leafy"

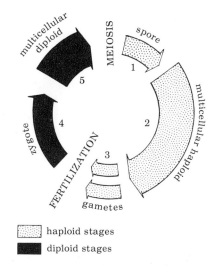

| | haploid stages |
| | diploid stages |

Fig. 21.32. Life cycle of a bryophyte. Both gametophyte (stage 2) and sporophyte (stage 5) are present; the former is dominant.

[15] Some bryophytes possess elongated cells that may function as rudimentary phloemlike vascular elements.

Fig. 21.33. Gametophyte and sporophyte stages of a moss. The lower "leafy" plant is the gametophyte. The sporophyte plant (black stalk and capsule) is attached to the gametophyte.

green gametophyte, a stalk, and a distal capsule, or sporangium (Fig. 21.33). The sporophyte has a few chloroplasts and carries out some photosynthesis, but it also obtains nutrients parasitically from the gametophyte to which it is attached. Meiosis occurs within the mature capsule of the sporophyte, producing haploid spores (stage 1), which are released. These may germinate, developing into protonemata and eventually into mature gametophyte plants (stage 2), thus completing the life cycle.

The gametophyte plants of liverworts often grow as flat green structures lying on the substratum (Fig. 21.34). The antheridia and archegonia are usually borne in discs or capsules located at the tops of stalks that arise from the flat part of the plant body (Fig. 21.35). The life cycle is much like that of mosses except that the sporophyte is more reduced (Fig. 21.36). Asexual reproduction sometimes occurs by production of special cells

called gemmae, usually borne in cuplike structures located on the surface of the flat gametophyte (Fig. 21.34). When detached from the parent plant, the gemmae can grow into new gametophytes.

TRACHEOPHYTA (The Vascular Plants)

We have seen that, though most bryophytes live on land, in a sense they are not fully terrestrial. The tracheophytes, by contrast, have evolved a host of adaptations to the terrestrial environment that have enabled them to invade all but the most inhospitable land habitats. In the process, they have diverged sufficiently from one another for botanists to classify them in five[16] subdivisions as follows:

Division Tracheophyta

Subdivision Psilopsida (psilopsids)
Subdivision Lycopsida (club mosses)
Subdivision Sphenopsida (horsetails)
Subdivision Pteropsida (ferns)
Subdivision Spermopsida (seed plants)

All members of this division (with a few minor exceptions) possess four important characteristics—a protective layer of sterile jacket cells around the reproductive organs, multicellular embryos retained within the archegonia, cuticles on the aerial parts, and xylem— that are lacking in even the most advanced and complex algae (see Table 21.1). All four are obviously fundamental adaptations for a terrestrial existence. Many other such adaptations, absent in the earliest tracheophytes, appear in more advanced members of the division; a history of the evolution of these adaptations is a history of the increasingly extensive exploitation of the terrestrial environment by vascular plants. Let us briefly trace this history of adaptation to the terrestrial environment.

[16] In many classifications, the Pteropsida (ferns) and Spermopsida (seed plants) are combined in a single subdivision usually called Pteropsida.

Fig. 21.34. Liverworts (*Marchantia*). The gametophyte is a flat green organism with a "scaly" appearance. The two cup-shaped structures on the plants in the center of the picture are gemmae cups. [Courtesy Verne N. Rockcastle, Cornell University.]

Fig. 21.35. Reproductive organs of liverworts. Top: The male organs (antheridia) of *Conocephalum* are borne in capsules on the tops of stalks. Bottom: The female organs (archegonia) of *Marchantia* are borne in umbrella-shaped receptacles with fingerlike lobes along their margins. [Courtesy Verne N. Rockcastle, Cornell University.]

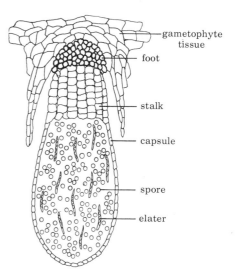

gametophyte tissue

foot

stalk

capsule

spore

elater

Fig. 21.36. Sporophyte of *Marchantia*. The sporophyte of this liverwort is a small structure consisting of a foot, a short stalk, and a capsule. The foot remains embedded in the tissue of the under surface of the umbrella-shaped receptacle of the gametophyte plant (see Fig. 21.35, bottom). The mature capsule contains spores and elaters, which are elongate structures with spirally thickened walls. Eventually the wall of the capsule dries and bursts, releasing the spores. Ejection of the spores is aided by the elaters, which twist and jerk as they dry, thus throwing the spores from the capsule.

TABLE 21.2

The Geologic Time Scale

Era	Period	Epoch	Millions of years (approx.) from start of period to present	Plant life	Animal life
CENOZOIC	Quaternary	Recent	0.01	Increase in number of herbs	Rise of civilizations
		Pleistocene	2		First true men
	Tertiary	Pliocene	12	Dominance of land by angiosperms	Dominance of land by mammals, birds, and insects
		Miocene	25		
		Oligocene	36		
		Eocene	58		
		Paleocene	63		
	—— Building of ancestral Rocky Mountains ——				
MESOZOIC	Cretaceous		135	Angiosperms expand as gymnosperms decline	Last of the dinosaurs; second great radiation of insects
	Jurassic		181	Gymnosperms (esp. cycads and conifers) still dominant; last of the seed ferns; a few angiospermlike plants appear	Dinosaurs abundant; first mammals and birds
	Triassic		230	Dominance of land by gymnosperms; decline of lycopsids and sphenopsids	First dinosaurs
	—— Building of ancestral Appalachian Mountains ——				
PALEOZOIC	Permian		280	Forests of lycopsids, sphenopsids, seed ferns, and conifers	Great expansion of reptiles; decline of amphibians; last of the trilobites
	Carboniferous*		345	Great coal forests, dominated at first by lycopsids and sphenopsids, and later also by ferns and seed ferns; first conifers	Age of Amphibians; first reptiles; first great radiation of insects
	Devonian		405	Expansion of primitive tracheophytes; first liverworts	Age of Fishes; first amphibians and insects
	Silurian		425	Invasion of land by primitive tracheophytes	Invasion of land by a few arthropods
	Ordovician		500	Marine algae abundant	First vertebrates (Agnatha)
	Cambrian		600	Primitive marine algae (esp. Cyanophyta and probably Chlorophyta)	Marine invertebrates abundant (including representatives of most phyla)
	—— Interval of Great Erosion ——				
PRECAMBRIAN				Primitive marine life	

* In North America, the Lower Carboniferous is often called the Mississippian period, and the Upper Carboniferous is called the Pennsylvanian period.

Psilopsida

The oldest undisputed fossil representatives of the vascular plants are from the Silurian period, which means that they lived more than 405 million years ago (Table 21.2). They are classified in the subdivision Psilopsida, most of whose members lived during the Devonian period and then became extinct. There are only two genera of this ancient group still living today (*Psilotum* and *Tmesipteris*).

The Psilopsida are quite simple dichotomously branching plants that lack leaves[17] and have no true roots, although they do have underground stems that bear unicellular rhizoids similar to root hairs (Fig. 21.37A). The aerial stems are green and carry out photosynthesis. There is no cambium and hence no secondary growth. Sporangia develop at the tips of some of the aerial branches, and meiosis occurs within these sporangia, producing haploid spores,

which give rise to subterranean gametophytes (Fig. 21.37B). Each gametophyte (often called a prothallus) bears both archegonia and antheridia and thus produces both eggs and sperms. When the gametes unite in fertilization, they form diploid zygotes that develop into the sporophyte plants described above, thus completing the life cycle. Note that although the diploid sporophyte (stage 5) is more prominent and hence may be said to be dominant, the haploid gametophyte (stage 2) is still relatively large.

Botanists have long noted the resemblance between the Psilopsida and certain branching filamentous green algae, and have assumed that it was from such algae that these primitive vascular plants arose. A difficulty with this theory is that, although the gametophyte is dominant in most green algae, it is the psilopsid sporophyte, not the gametophyte, that most resembles the green algae. If the vascular plants did indeed evolve from green algae, either those algae had a prominent sporophyte stage or the first vascular plants rapidly evolved such a stage.

Lycopsida (The Club Mosses)

The first representatives of the subdivision Lycopsida also appeared in the Silurian period and may be as old as or older than the Psilopsida. During the Devonian and Carboniferous periods, these were among the dominant plants on land. Some of them were very large trees that formed the earth's first forests. Toward the end of the Paleozoic era, however, the group was displaced by more advanced types of vascular plants, and only five genera are alive today. One of these, *Lycopodium* (often called running pine or ground pine), is common in many parts of the United States and is frequently used in Christmas decorations (Fig. 21.38).[18]

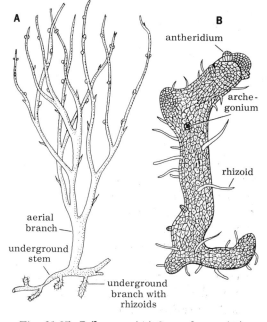

Fig. 21.37. *Psilotum.* (A) Sporophyte. (B) Gametophyte — this stage is entirely subterranean. The two plants are not drawn to the same scale; the sporophyte is actually much larger than the gametophyte. [Modified from H. J. Fuller and O. Tippo, *College Botany*, Holt, 1949.]

[17] Some Psilopsida have small scalelike structures that are sometimes considered to be leaves.

[18] The other living genera of lycopods are *Phylloglossum, Selaginella, Isoetes,* and *Stylites.*

Fig. 21.38. *Lycopodium.* Left: A clump of the plants growing near a fallen log in a pine wood. Right: Plants with reproductive structures (strobili). [Courtesy E. M. Raffensperger, Cornell University.]

Fig. 21.39. Section through strobilus of a fossil lycopsid. [Modified from H. N. Andrews, *Ancient Plants and the World They Lived In,* copyright 1947, Comstock Publishing Co. Used by permission of Cornell University Press.]

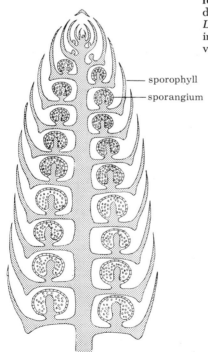

— sporophyll
— sporangium

Unlike the psilopsids, lycopsids have true roots. It is generally supposed that these arose from branches of the ancestral algae that penetrated the soil and branched underground. Lycopsids also have true leaves, which are thought to have arisen as simple scalelike outgrowths (emergences) from the outer tissues of the stem. Certain of the leaves that have become specialized for reproduction bear sporangia on their surfaces. Such reproductive (fertile) leaves are called *sporophylls.* In many lycopsids, the sporophylls are congregated on a short length of stem and form a conelike structure (strobilus) (Fig. 21.39). The cone is rather club-shaped; hence the name "club mosses"

Fig. 21.40. Carboniferous swamp forest. Note the tree sphenopsids with their jointed stems and whorls of leaves. The trunk at right is a lycopsid. [Portion of group in Carnegie Museum, Pittsburgh. Used by permission.]

for the lycopsids (note, however, that lycopsids are not related to the true mosses, which are bryophytes). The spores produced by *Lycopodium* are all alike, and each can give rise to a gametophyte that will bear both archegonia and antheridia. However, some lycopsids (e.g. *Selaginella*) have two types of sporangia, which produce different kinds of spores. One type of sporangium produces very large spores called **megaspores,** which develop into female gametophytes bearing archegonia; the other type produces small spores called **microspores,** which develop into male gametophytes bearing antheridia. Plants that produce only one kind of spore, and hence have only one kind of gametophyte that bears both male and female organs, are said to be **homosporous.** Plants that produce both megaspores (female) and microspores (male) are said to be **heterosporous.**

Sphenopsida (The Horsetails)

The sphenopsids first appear in the fossil record in the Devonian period. They became a major component of the land flora during the late Paleozoic era, and then declined. The species of the one living genus, *Equisetum*, are commonly called horsetails or scouring rushes. Though most of these are small (under 3 feet), some of the ancient sphenopsids were large trees (Fig. 21.40). Much of the coal we use today was formed from the dead bodies of these plants.

Like the lycopsids, sphenopsids possess true roots, stems, and leaves. The stems are hollow and are jointed. Whorls of leaves occur at each joint (Fig. 21.41). Many of the extinct sphenopsids had cambium, and hence secondary growth, but the modern species do not. Spores are borne in terminal cones (Fig. 21.42). In *Equisetum*, all spores are alike (i.e. the plants are homosporous) and give rise to small gametophytes that bear both archegonia and antheridia (i.e. the sexes are not separate).

Pteropsida (The Ferns)

In the opinion of many botanists, the ferns evolved from the Psilopsida. They first appeared in the Devonian period and greatly increased in importance during the Carboniferous. Their decline after the Paleozoic era was much less severe than that of the psilopsids, lycopsids, and sphenopsids, and, as you doubtless know, there are many modern species.

The ferns are fairly advanced plants with a very well developed vascular system and with true roots, stems, and leaves. The leaves are thought to have arisen in a different manner from those of the lycopsids. Instead of being emergences, they are probably flattened and webbed branch stems; i.e. a group of small branches probably became arranged in the

Fig. 21.41. A fossil of a sphenopsid. A whorl of leaves is located at each joint of the stem. [Courtesy Field Museum of Natural History, Chicago.]

same plane (planated), and the interstices filled with tissue.[19] The leaves are sometimes simple, but more often they are compound, being divided into numerous leaflets that may give the plant a lacy appearance.[20] In a few ferns (e.g. the large tree ferns of the tropics), the stem is upright, forming a trunk. But in most modern ferns, especially those of temperate regions, the stems are prostrate on or in the soil, and the large leaves are the only parts normally seen.

The large leafy fern plant is the diploid sporophyte phase. Spores are produced in sporangia located in clusters on the underside of some leaves (sporophylls) (Fig. 21.43). In some species, the sporophylls are relatively

[19] Leaves arising as emergencies are called microphylls. Those arising as planated and webbed branch systems are called megaphylls.

[20] When a fern leaf, or frond, is divided into leaflets, the leaflets are called pinnae. The pinnae may themselves be subdivided into pinnules.

Fig. 21.42. Reproductive stems of Equisetum. Left: Portions of two stems bearing immature terminal cones. The hollow stems can easily be pulled apart at the joints. The leaves, arranged in whorls at the joints, are very small and inconspicuous. Right: Portion of a stem bearing a mature cone. The whorls of leaves along the stem are more evident. [Courtesy Verne N. Rockcastle, Cornell University.]

little modified and look like the nonreproductive leaves. In other species, the sporophylls look quite different from vegetative leaves; sometimes they are so highly modified that they do not look like leaves at all, forming spikelike structures instead (Fig. 21.44).

Most modern ferns are homosporous; i.e. all their spores are alike. After germination, the spores develop into gametophytes that bear both archegonia and antheridia (Fig. 21.45). These gametophytes are tiny (seldom more than one fourth of an inch wide), thin, and often more or less heart-shaped. Although most people are familiar with the sporophytes of ferns, few have ever seen a gametophyte, and even fewer would quess that it had anything to do with a fern. Small and obscure as it is, however, the fern gametophyte is an independent photosynthetic organism. Here, then, is a life cycle in which all five principal stages are present, but in which the multicellular haploid stage has been much reduced and the

Fig. 21.44. Leaves of sensitive fern. The leaf on the left is a mature sporophyll, which bears little resemblance to the sterile leaf on the right. The leaf in the middle is an immature sporophyll. [Courtesy Verne N. Rockcastle, Cornell University.]

Fig. 21.43. Under surface of fertile leaf (sporophyll) of polypody fern. Each of the round dots is a sorus, which is a cluster of many tiny sporangia. [Courtesy Verne N. Rockcastle, Cornell University.]

multicellular diploid stage emphasized (Fig. 21.46).

In some respects, the ferns (and also the three primitive groups of vascular plants discussed above) are no better adapted for life on land than the bryophytes. Their vascularized sporophytes can live in drier places and grow bigger, but for a number of reasons—because their nonvascularized free-living gametophytes can survive only in moist places, because their sperms are flagellated and must have a film of moisture through which to swim to the egg cells in the archegonia, and because the young sporophyte develops directly from the zygote without passing through any protected seedlike stage—these plants are most successful in habitats where there is at least a moderate amount of moisture.

Spermopsida (The Seed Plants)

The seed plants have been by far the most successful in fully exploiting the terrestrial en-

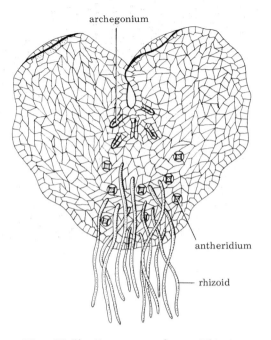

archegonium

antheridium

rhizoid

Fig. 21.45. Fern gametophyte. This is a much-magnified view of the under surface of the tiny heart-shaped organism. [Modified from H. J. Fuller and O. Tippo, *College Botany*, Holt, 1949.]

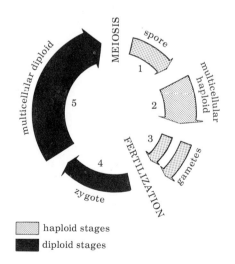

MEIOSIS

spore

multicellular diploid

multicellular haploid

1

2

3

gametes

5

4

FERTILIZATION

zygote

☐ haploid stages

■ diploid stages

Fig. 21.46. Life cycle of ferns and seed plants. Both gametophyte (stage 2) and sporophyte (stage 5) are present; the latter is much the more prominent. Compare this life cycle with that of bryophytes shown in Fig. 21.32.

vironment. They first appeared in the Carboniferous and soon replaced the lycopsids and sphenopsids as the dominant land plants, a position they still hold today. In these plants, the gametophytes are even more reduced than in the ferns—they are not photosynthetic or free-living—and the sperms of most modern species are not independent free-swimming flagellated cells. In addition, the young embryo, together with a supply of nutrients, is enclosed within a desiccation-resistant seed coat and can remain dormant for extended periods if environmental conditions are unfavorable. In short, the aspects of the reproductive process that are most vulnerable in more primitive vascular plants have been eliminated in the seed plants (Table 21.3).

The seed plants have traditionally been divided into two classes, the Gymnospermae and the Angiospermae. In recent years, however, it has become increasingly clear that the relationships between the five groups put together as the gymnosperms are not particularly close and that these groups differ from one another at least as much as they differ from the angiosperms. Consequently many modern classifications recognize each of the gymnospermous groups as a separate class. We have adopted this procedure in the technical classification given in the Appendix and outlined below, but shall discuss the gymnospermous groups together.

Subdivision Spermopsida
 Class Pteridospermae ⎤
 Class Cycadae |
 Class Ginkgoae   ⎬ "Gymnosperms"
 Class Coniferae |
 Class Gneteae   ⎦
 Class Angiospermae

The Gymnosperms. The first gymnosperms appear in the fossil record in the early Carboniferous, but the group probably arose in the Devonian. Many of those first seed plants had bodies that closely resembled the ferns,

TABLE 21.3

A Comparison of the Subdivisions of Tracheophyta

| Characteristic | Psilop-sida | Lycop-sida | Sphenop-sida | Pterop-sida | Spermopsida | |
					Gymno-sperms	Angio-sperms
Have vascular tissue	+	+	+	+	+	+
Have true roots and leaves	−	+	+	+	+	+
Have megaphyllous leaves	−	−	−	+	+	+
Gametophyte not free-living	−	−	−	−	+	+
Sperm cells not flagellated	−	−	−	−	+ (− in primitive groups)	+
Produce seeds	−	−	−	−	+	+
Have flowers and fruit	−	−	−	−	−	+

and indeed for many years their fossils were thought to be fossils of ferns. Slowly, however, evidence accumulated that some of the "ferns" that were such important components of the coal-age forests produced seeds, not spores. Today these fossil plants—usually called the seed ferns—are grouped together as the class Pteridospermae of the subdivision Spermopsida. No members of this class survive today.

Another ancient group, the cycads and their relatives (class Cycadae), may have arisen from the seed ferns. These plants first appeared in the Permian period and became very abundant during the Mesozoic era. They had large palmlike leaves (Fig. 21.47); the palmlike plants so often shown in pictures of the dinosaur age are usually cycads, not true palms. The cycads declined after the rise of the angiosperms in the Cretaceous period, but there are nine genera containing over a hundred species living today. They are generally called sago palms and are fairly common in some tropical regions. One genus (*Zamia*) occurs in Florida.

Fig. 21.47. A living cycad. [Courtesy Field Museum of Natural History, Chicago.]

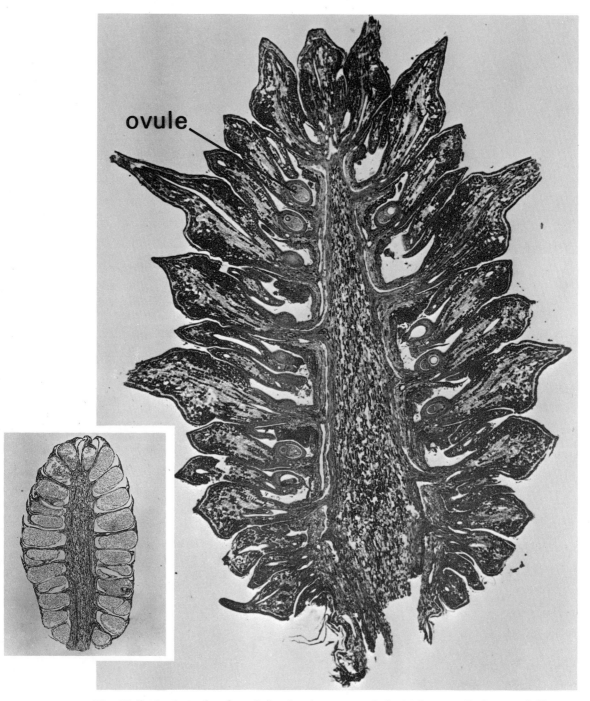

ovule

Fig. 21.48. Sections of male and female pine cones. Left: Male cone. Each sporophyll (cone scale) bears a large sporangium that becomes a pollen sac. Right: Female cone. Ovules can be seen on the surface of the sporophylls, near their base. [Left: Courtesy Thomas Eisner, Cornell University. Right: Courtesy Carolina Biological Supply Co.]

The Ginkgoae are still another group that was once widespread but is now nearly extinct. There is only one living species, the ginkgo or maidenhair tree, which is often planted as a lawn tree but is almost unknown in the wild.

By far the best-known group of gymnosperms is that of the conifers (class Coniferae), which includes such common species as pines, spruces, firs, cedars, hemlocks, yews, and larches. The leaves of most of these are small evergreen needles or scales. This group first arose in the Permian period and was very common during the Mesozoic era. It remains an important part of the earth's flora.

Let us examine in some detail the life cycle of a pine tree as an example of the seed method of reproduction. The large pine tree is the diploid sporophyte stage (stage 5 in Fig. 21.46). This tree produces reproductive structures called **cones.** A cone is a spiral cluster of modified leaves (sporophylls) on a short section of stem.[21] Each sporophyll (often called a cone scale) bears on its surface two sporangia in which haploid spores (stage 1) are produced by meiosis. There are two different kinds of cones: large female cones whose sporangia produce megaspores and small male cones whose sporangia produce microspores (Fig. 21.48). (Production of two kinds of spores—heterospory—is characteristic of all seed plants, both gymnosperms and angiosperms.)

Each scale of a female cone bears two sporangia on its upper (adaxial) surface (Fig. 21.49B). Each sporangium is encased in an integument with a small opening, the **micropyle,** at one end (Fig. 21.49C). Meiosis takes place inside the sporangium, producing four haploid megaspores, three of which soon disintegrate. Next, the single remaining megaspore gives rise, by repeated mitotic divisions, to a multicellular mass, which is the female gameto-

phyte (megagametophyte). When mature, the female gametophyte produces two to five tiny archegonia at its micropylar end. Egg cells develop in the archegonia. Note that the megaspore is never released from the sporangium,

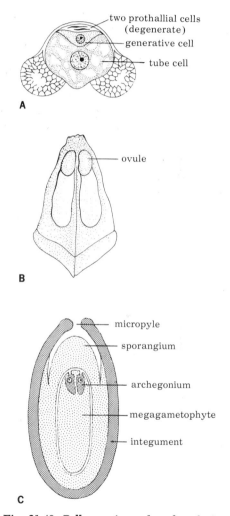

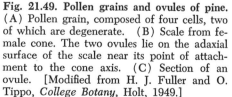

Fig. 21.49. Pollen grains and ovules of pine. (A) Pollen grain, composed of four cells, two of which are degenerate. (B) Scale from female cone. The two ovules lie on the adaxial surface of the scale near its point of attachment to the cone axis. (C) Section of an ovule. [Modified from H. J. Fuller and O. Tippo, *College Botany*, Holt, 1949.]

[21] There is now evidence that the scales of the female cone are not simple sporophylls, but complex structures composed of several fused parts, one of which is the modified leaf.

and that the female gametophyte derived from it remains embedded in the sporangium, which is still attached to the cone scale. The composite structure consisting of integument, sporangium, and female gametophyte is called an *ovule.*

Each microspore produced by the sporangium of a male cone becomes a *pollen grain.* It develops a thick coat, which is highly resistant to loss of water, and winglike structures on each side, which doubtless aid its dispersal by wind. Within the pollen grain, the haploid nucleus divides mitotically several times, and walls develop around each nucleus. In this manner, the pollen grain becomes four-celled (Fig. 12.49A); two of the cells soon degenerate.[22] The mature pollen grain is released from the cone when the sporangium bursts. A single male cone may release millions of tiny pollen grains, which may be carried many miles (sometimes as many as a hundred) by the wind. Note that the pollen grains are multicellular haploid structures (if four cells may be said to be "multi") and that they constitute the male gametophyte (microgametophyte) (stage 2 in Fig. 21.46).

Most of the millions of pollen grains released by a pine tree fail to reach a female cone. But of the few that sift down between the scales of a female cone, some land in a sticky secretion near the open micropylar end of an ovule. As this secretion dries, it is drawn through the micropyle, carrying the pollen grains with it. The arms of the integument around the micropyle then swell and close the opening. When a pollen grain comes in contact with the end of the sporangium just inside the micropyle, it develops a tubular outgrowth, the *pollen tube.* The two functional nuclei of the pollen grain enter the tube, and one of them divides. One of the daughter nuclei thus produced then divides again, pro-

ducing two sperm nuclei.[23] Thus a germinated pollen grain contains four active nuclei plus the two nuclei of the degenerate cells; this six-nucleate condition is as far as the male gametophyte of pine ever develops.

The pollen tube grows down through the tissue of the sporangium and penetrates into one of the archegonia of the female gametophyte. There it discharges its sperm nuclei, one of which fertilizes the egg cell. The resulting zygote (stage 4) then divides mitotically to produce a tiny embryo sporophyte consisting of a hypocotyl and an epicotyl.[24] The embryo is still contained in the female gametophyte, which is itself contained in the sporangium. Finally, the entire ovule is shed from the cone as a *seed,* which consists of three main components: a seed coat derived from the old integument, stored food material (endosperm) derived from the tissue of the female gametophyte, and an embryo.[25]

The main advances of the pine life cycle over the fern life cycle can be summarized as follows: (1) There are two types of sporangia, which produce two types of spores—microspores (male) and megaspores (female). (2) Two different kinds of gametophytes are derived from the two types of spores (i.e. the sexes are separate in the gametophyte stage). (3) The gametophytes are much further reduced than those of ferns; they do not possess chlorophyll and are not free-living. A male gametophyte consists only of the six-nucleate pollen grain and tube. A female gametophyte is only a mass of haploid tissue that remains in the sporangium and is parasitic on it.

---

[22] The two cells that degenerate are called prothallial cells. The other two are the generative cell and the tube cell.

[23] The two nuclei that enter the tube are the generative and tube nuclei. The generative cell divides, producing a stalk cell and a body cell, and the body cell then divides to form two sperms.

[24] As soon as an embryo begins developing in one archegonium, the other archegonia deteriorate; thus only one embryo is formed in each ovule.

[25] As a rule, the sporangium (or nucellus, as botanists generally call the sporangium in the ovule) eventually disintegrates and is not present in the seed, but in a few species it may be preserved, usually as the inner layer of the seed coat.

(4) There are no flagellated sperm cells.[26] (5) The young embryo is contained within a seed.

The Angiosperms. There are a few angiospermlike fossils from the Triassic and Jurassic periods, but the first undisputed representatives of this group are from the Cretaceous. Great expansion of the angiosperms occurred in the Cretaceous, and these plants became the dominant land flora of the Cenozoic era, as they are today.

We have seen that the reproductive structures of gymnosperms are cones (or structures derived from cones) and that the ovules, which later become the seeds, are borne naked on the surface of the sporophylls. In the angiosperms, by contrast, the reproductive structures are flowers, and the ovules are enclosed within modified leaves called carpels.

A flower, like a cone, is a short length of stem with modified leaves attached to it. The modified leaves of a typical flower (Fig. 21.50) occur in four sets attached to the enlarged end (receptacle) of the flower stalk: (1) The *sepals* enclose and protect all the other floral parts during the bud stage. They are usually small, green, and leaflike, but in some species they are large and brightly colored. All the sepals together form the *calyx.* (2) Internal to the sepals are the *petals,* which together form the *corolla.*[27] In flowers pollinated by insects, birds, or other animals, the petals are usually quite showy, but in flowers pollinated by wind they are often reduced or even absent. (3) Just inside the circle of the corolla are the *stamens,* which are the male reproductive organs; i.e. they are the sporophylls that produce the microspores. Each stamen consists of a stalk, called a *filament,* and a terminal ovoid pollen-producing structure called an

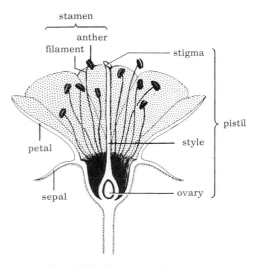

Fig. 21.50. **The parts of a flower.**

anther. (4) In the center of the flower is the female reproductive organ, the *pistil* (some species have more than one pistil per flower). Each pistil consists of an *ovary* at its base, a slender stalk (more than one in some species) called a *style,* which rises from the ovary, and an enlarged apex called a *stigma.* The pistil is derived from one or more sporophylls, which in flowers are called *carpels.*[28] The four kinds of floral organs—sepals, petals, stamens, and pistils—are all present in complete flowers, but some flowers, which are said to be incomplete, lack one or more of them.[29]

Within the ovary are one or more (at least one for each carpel) sporangia, called ovules, which are attached by short stalks to the wall of the ovary. Meiosis occurs once in each ovule, producing four haploid megaspores, three of which usually soon disintegrate. The remaining

[26] The pollen tubes of primitive gymnosperms, such as ginkgoes and cycads, produce flagellated sperm cells, but these have only a very short distance to swim to reach the egg cells, the pollen grains having already been carried to the ovules by the wind.

[27] The calyx and corolla together constitute the perianth.

[28] A simple pistil is composed of only one sporophyll, or carpel. A compound pistil is composed of several fused carpels.

[29] In some species, such as corn, willow, oak, and walnut, the stamens and pistils are in separate flowers. Incomplete flowers of this type, in which only one of the two kinds of reproductive structures is present, are called imperfect flowers. Flowers with both stamens and pistils (whether complete or incomplete) are called perfect flowers.

megaspore then divides mitotically several times, producing, in most species, a structure composed of seven cells, one of which is much larger than the others and contains two nuclei, called polar nuclei (Fig. 21.51A). This haploid seven-celled eight-nucleate structure is the much-reduced female gametophyte (often called an embryo sac).[30] One of the cells located near the micropylar end will act as the egg cell.

Each anther has four sporangia in which meiosis occurs repeatedly, producing numerous haploid microspores. The wall of each microspore thickens, and the nucleus divides mitotically, producing a generative nucleus and a tube nucleus. The resulting thick-walled two-nucleate structure is a pollen grain—a male gametophyte—which is released from the anther when the mature sporangium (Fig. 21.52) splits open.

A pollen grain germinates when it falls (or is deposited) on the stigma of a pistil, which is usually rough and sticky. A pollen tube be-

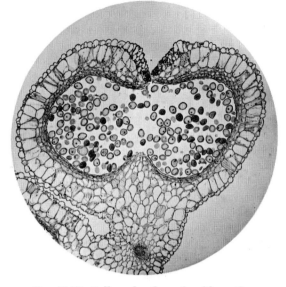

Fig. 21.52. Pollen chamber of a lily anther. When the pollen chamber (derived from the sporangium) opens, the numerous pollen grains within it will be released. [Courtesy General Biological Supply House, Inc., Chicago.]

gins to grow, and the two nuclei of the pollen grain move into it. The generative nucleus then divides, giving rise to two sperm nuclei (Fig. 21.51B).[31] The pollen tube grows down through the tissues of the stigma and style and enters the ovary (Fig. 21.53). When the tip of the pollen tube reaches an ovule, it enters the micropyle and then discharges the two sperm nuclei into the female gametophyte (embryo sac). One of the sperm nuclei fertilizes the egg cell, and the zygote thus formed develops into an embryo sporophyte. By the time fertilization occurs, the two polar nuclei of the female gametophyte have combined to form a diploid *fusion nucleus,* with which the second sperm nucleus unites to form a triploid nucleus. This nucleus undergoes a series of divisions, and a triploid tissue, called *endosperm,* is formed.

---

[30] The embryo sac of some species has more than eight nuclei, and that of a limited number of other species has fewer than eight. Furthermore, in some species no cytokinesis occurs, and all the nuclei lie in the same mass of cytoplasm. However, the most common sort of embryo sac is the seven-celled eight-nucleate type described in the text.

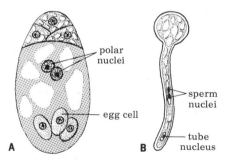

Fig. 21.51. Gametophytes of an angiosperm. (A) Female gametophyte (embryo sac), which is composed of seven cells. One cell is much larger than the others and contains the two polar nuclei. (B) Male gametophyte (pollen grain and tube). [Modified from H. J. Fuller and O. Tippo, *College Botany,* Holt, 1949.]

---

[31] Although the pollen grains of most species are released in the two-nucleate condition and the division of the generative nucleus does not take place until germination, this division occurs earlier in a few species and the pollen grains are released from the anthers in the three-nucleate condition.

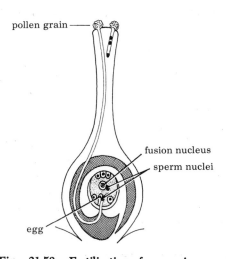

pollen grain

fusion nucleus

sperm nuclei

egg

Fig. 21.53. Fertilization of an angiosperm. Pollen grains land on the stigma and give rise to pollen tubes that grow downward through the style. One of the pollen tubes shown here has reached the ovule in the ovary and discharged its sperm nuclei into it. One sperm nucleus will fertilize the egg cell, and the other will unite with the diploid fusion nucleus (derived from the two polar nuclei) to form a triploid nucleus, which will give rise to endosperm.

The endosperm functions in the seed as a source of stored food for the embryo.

After fertilization, the ovule matures into a seed, which, as in pine, consists of seed coat, endosperm, and embryo. However, the angiosperm seed differs from that of pine in being enveloped by the ovary. It is the ovary that develops into the *fruit,* usually enlarging greatly in the process. Sometimes other structures associated with the ovary, such as the receptacle, are also incorporated into the fruit. The ripe fruit may burst, expelling the seeds, as in peas (where the pod is the fruit). Or the ripe fruit with the seeds still inside may fall from the plant, as in tomatoes, squash, cucumbers, apples, peaches, and acorns. The fruit not only helps protect the seeds from desiccation during their early development, before they have fully ripened, but often also helps disperse them— as when the agent of dispersal is the wind (Fig. 21.54), or when an animal, attracted by the fruit, carries it to other locations or eats both

fruit and seeds and later releases the unharmed seeds in its feces.

The main ways in which the angiosperm life cycle differs from that of gymnosperms can be summarized as follows: (1) The reproductive structures are flowers instead of cones. The sporophylls (stamens and pistils) of flowers are more extensively modified and less leaflike than the sporophylls (scales) of cones. (2) The ovules are embedded in the tissues of the female sporophylls instead of lying bare on their surface. (3) The gametophytes are even more reduced than those of gymnosperms. The male gametophyte (pollen grain and tube) has only three nuclei. The female gametophyte usually has only eight nuclei. (4) In pollination, the pollen grains are not deposited close to the opening of the ovule, as in gymnosperms, but are deposited on the stigma instead. The pollen tube thus has much farther to grow in angiosperms. (5) Angiosperms have "double fertilization," one sperm fertilizing the egg cell and the other uniting with the fusion nucleus to give rise to triploid endosperm. Gymnosperms,

Fig. 21.54. Fruit of the dandelion. Each dandelion "seed" is actually a seed enclosed in a small dry fruit. On one end of the fruit is a parachute, which aids in dispersal by the wind. About three fourths of the seeds with their parachutes have already been blown from the dandelion shown here. [Courtesy Verne N. Rockcastle, Cornell University.]

by contrast, have single fertilization; one sperm fertilizes the egg, and the other soon deteriorates. The so-called endosperm of the gymnosperms is the haploid tissue of the female gametophyte and is thus developmentally quite different from the triploid endosperm of the angiosperms. (6) The seeds of angiosperms are enclosed in fruits that develop from the ovaries and associated structures; gymnosperms have no fruit.

Angiosperms differ from gymnosperms in a variety of characteristics besides reproductive ones—for instance, in the structure of the xylem, which in angiosperms frequently contains vessels, but seldom does in gymnosperms.

The class Angiospermae is customarily divided into two subclasses, the Dicotyledoneae and the Monocotyledoneae. As the names imply, the embryos of dicots (e.g. bean) have two cotyledons, whereas those of monocots (e.g. corn) have only one. There are other basic differences: (1) Dicots often have cambium and secondary growth; monocots usually do not. (2) The vascular bundles in the stems of young dicots are arranged in a circle or fused to form a tubular vascular cylinder; monocots have more scattered vascular bundles. (3) The leaves of dicots usually have net venation; those of monocots usually have parallel venation. (4) The flower parts of dicots occur in fours or fives or multiples of these (e.g. four sepals, four petals, four stamens); those of monocots occur in threes or multiples of three (Fig. 21.55). Most monocots can be recognized by the way the leaf base (which seldom has a petiole) clasps the stem (as in corn). Examples of dicots are oaks, maples, elms, willows, roses, beans, clovers, tomatoes, asters, and dandelions. Examples of monocots are grasses, corn, wheat, rye, daffodils, irises, lilies, and palms.

Fig. 21.55. Easter lily flower. This is a monocot, and all the flower parts are in threes or multiples of three. There are three sepals (the outer three white structures, which resemble petals), three petals, six stamens (one is nearly hidden behind the pistil), and a three-lobed stigma (which shows that the single pistil is compound, formed by fusion of three primordial pistils). [Courtesy Verne N. Rockcastle, Cornell University.]

REFERENCES

ALEXOPOULOS, C. J., 1962. *Introductory Mycology.* Wiley, New York.

ANDREWS, H. N., 1961. *Studies in Paleobotany.* Wiley, New York.

BENSON, L., 1957. *Plant Classification.* Heath, Boston.

BOLD, H. C., 1957. *Morphology of Plants.* Harper, New York.

CHAPMAN, V. J., 1962. *The Algae.* St. Martin's Press, New York.

DELEVORYAS, T., 1962. *Morphology and Evolution of Fossil Plants.* Holt, Rinehart & Winston, New York.

EAMES, A. J., 1961. *Morphology of the Angiosperms.* McGraw-Hill, New York.

ESAU, K., 1960. *Anatomy of Seed Plants.* Wiley, New York.

FOSTER, A. F., and E. M. GIFFORD, 1959. *Comparative Morphology of Vascular Plants.* Freeman, San Francisco.

FRITSCH, F. E., 1945. *The Structure and Reproduction of the Algae,* 2 vols. Cambridge University Press, New York.

GOOD, R., 1956. *Features of Evolution in the Flowering Plants.* Longmans, Green, London.

KINGSBURY, J. M., 1963. *Biology of the Algae.* Published privately, Ithaca, N.Y.

LAWRENCE, G. H. M., 1951. *Taxonomy of Vascular Plants.* Macmillan, New York.

SCAGEL, R. F., *et al.,* 1965. *An Evolutionary Survey of the Plant Kingdom.* Wadsworth, Belmont, Calif.

SMITH, G. M., 1950. *The Fresh-Water Algae of the United States,* 2nd ed. McGraw-Hill, New York.

———, ed., 1951. *Manual of Phycology.* Chronica Botanica, Waltham, Mass.

———, 1955. *Cryptogamic Botany,* 2nd ed. Vol. 1: *Algae and Fungi;* vol. 2: *Bryophytes and Pteridophytes.* McGraw-Hill, New York.

SUGGESTED READING

AHMADJIAN, V., 1963. "The Fungi of Lichens," *Scientific American,* February.

ANDREWS, H. N., 1947. *Ancient Plants and the World They Lived In.* Comstock, Ithaca, N.Y.

———, 1963. "Early Seed Plants," *Science,* vol. 142, pp. 925–937.

BIALE, J. B., 1954. "The Ripening of Fruit," *Scientific American,* May. (Offprint 118.)

BOLD, H. C., 1964. *The Plant Kingdom,* 2nd ed. Prentice-Hall, Englewood Cliffs, N.J.

BONNER, J. T., 1949. "The Social Amoebae," *Scientific American,* June.

———, 1956. "The Growth of Mushrooms," *Scientific American,* May.

———, 1959. "Differentiation in Social Amoebae," *Scientific American,* December.

———, 1959. *The Cellular Slime Molds.* Princeton University Press, Princeton, N.J.

———, 1963. "How Slime Molds Communicate," *Scientific American,* August. (Offprint 164.)

CHRISTENSEN, C. M., 1965. *The Molds and Man,* 3rd ed. University of Minnesota Press, Minneapolis. (Paperback edition, McGraw-Hill, New York, 1965.)

DELEVORYAS, T., 1966. *Plant Diversification.* Holt, Rinehart & Winston, New York.

DOYLE, W. T., 1964. *Nonvascular Plants: Form and Function.* Wadsworth, Belmont, Calif.

EMERSON, R., 1952. "Molds and Men," *Scientific American,* January. (Offprint 115.)

FULLER, H. J., and O. TIPPO, 1954. *College Botany,* rev. ed. Holt, New York. (See esp. Part III.)

GRANT, V., 1951. "The Fertilization of Flowers," *Scientific American,* June. (Offprint 12.)

LAMB, I. M., 1959. "Lichens," *Scientific American,* October. (Offprint 111.)

SINNOTT, E. W., and K. S. WILSON, 1963. *Botany: Principles and Problems,* 6th ed. McGraw-Hill, New York. (See esp. Chapters 16–26.)

WILSON, C. L., and W. E. LOOMIS, 1962. *Botany,* 3rd ed. Holt, Rinehart & Winston, New York. (See esp. Chapters 20–30.)

GUIDES TO IDENTIFICATION

ABRAMS, L., 1940–1960. *Illustrated Flora of the Pacific States*, 4 vols. (vol. 4 with R. S. Ferris). Stanford University Press, Stanford, Calif.

ARMSTRONG, M., 1915. *Field Book of Western Wild Flowers.* Putnam, New York.

BAERG, H. J., 1955. *How to Know the Western Trees.* Wm. C. Brown, Dubuque, Iowa.

BAILEY, L. H., 1949. *Manual of Cultivated Plants,* rev. ed. Macmillan, New York.

CHRISTENSEN, C. M., 1959. *Common Edible Mushrooms.* C. T. Branford Co., Newton Centre, Mass.

COBB, B., 1956. *A Field Guide to the Ferns and Their Related Families.* Houghton Mifflin, Boston.

CONARD, H. S., 1956. *How to Know the Mosses and Liverworts,* rev. ed. Wm. C. Brown, Dubuque, Iowa.

CRAIGHEAD, J. J., F. C. CRAIGHEAD, and R. J. DAVIS, 1963. *A Field Guide to Rocky Mountain Wildflowers.* Houghton Mifflin, Boston.

CUTHBERT, M., 1948. *How to Know the Fall Flowers.* Wm. C. Brown, Dubuque, Iowa.

———, 1949. *How to Know the Spring Flowers,* rev. ed. Wm. C. Brown, Dubuque, Iowa.

DAWSON, E. Y., 1956. *How to Know the Seaweeds.* Wm. C. Brown, Dubuque, Iowa.

DUNHAM, E. M., 1951. *How to Know the Mosses.* Mosher Press, Boston.

DURAND, H., 1949. *Field Book of Common Ferns,* rev. ed. Putnam, New York.

FERNALD, M. L., 1950. *Gray's Manual of Botany,* 8th ed. American Book Co., New York. (Technical and difficult, but the authoritative reference for identification of vascular plants of northeastern U.S.)

GILKEY, H. M., 1951. *Handbook of Northwest Flowering Plants,* 2nd ed. Binfords & Mort, Portland, Ore.

GROUT, A. J., 1947. *Mosses with a Hand-Lens.* Chicago Natural History Museum, Chicago.

HALE, M. E., 1961. *Lichen Handbook.* Smithsonian Institution, Washington.

JAQUES, H. E., 1946. *How to Know the Trees.* Wm. C. Brown, Dubuque, Iowa.

———, 1948. *Plant Families—How to Know Them,* 2nd ed. Wm. C. Brown, Dubuque, Iowa.

———, 1958. *How to Know the Economic Plants.* Wm. C. Brown, Dubuque, Iowa.

JEPSON, W. L., 1951. *A Manual of the Flowering Plants of California.* University of California Press, Berkeley, Calif.

JEWELL, A. L., 1955. *The Observer's Book of Mosses and Liverworts.* Frederick Warne & Co., London.

MATHEWS, F. S., 1915. *Field Book of American Trees and Shrubs.* Putnam, New York.

———, 1955. *Field Book of American Wild Flowers* (revised and enlarged by N. Taylor). Putnam, New York.

MUENSCHER, W. C., 1950. *Keys to Woody Plants,* 6th ed. Comstock, Ithaca, N.Y.

MUNZ, P. A., and D. D. KECK, 1959. *A California Flora.* University of California Press, Berkeley, Calif.

PARSONS, F. T., 1961. *How to Know the Ferns.* Dover, New York.

PETRIDES, G. A., 1958. *A Field Guide to Trees and Shrubs.* Houghton Mifflin, Boston.

POHL, R. W., 1953. *How to Know the Grasses.* Wm. C. Brown, Dubuque, Iowa.

PRESCOTT, G. W., 1964. *How to Know the Fresh-Water Algae,* rev. ed. Wm. C. Brown, Dubuque, Iowa.

PRESTON, R. J., 1961. *North American Trees,* rev. ed. Iowa State University Press, Ames. (Paperback edition, M.I.T. Press, Cambridge, Mass., 1966.)

SMALL, J. K., 1933. *Manual of Southeastern Flora.* Published privately, New York.

SMITH, A. H., 1963. *The Mushroom Hunter's Field Guide,* rev. ed. University of Michigan Press, Ann Arbor.

SMITH, G. M., 1944. *Marine Algae of the Monterey Peninsula.* Stanford University Press, Stanford, Calif.

TAYLOR, W. R., 1957. *Marine Algae of the Northeastern Coast of North America,* 2nd ed. University of Michigan Press, Ann Arbor.

———, 1960. *Marine Algae of the Eastern Tropical and Subtropical Coasts of the Americas.* University of Michigan Press, Ann Arbor.

THOMAS, W. S., 1948. *Field Book of Common Mushrooms,* 3rd ed. Putnam, New York.

WHERRY, E. T., 1948. *Wild Flower Guide: Northeastern and Midland United States.* Doubleday, Garden City, N.Y.

———, 1961. *The Fern Guide: Northeastern and Midland United States and Adjacent Canada.* Doubleday, Garden City, N.Y.

CHAPTER

22

THE ANIMAL KINGDOM

WE NOW TURN TO THE PHYLA OF THE animal kingdom, with many of which you already have some familiarity from our previous discussion of such of their vital processes as nutrient procurement, gas exchange, internal transport, excretion, coordination, and development. In our earlier discussions, we paid particular attention to representatives of the Protozoa, Coelenterata, Platyhelminthes (flatworms), Mollusca, Annelida (segmented worms), Arthropoda, Echinodermata, and Chordata (especially vertebrates). We shall again concentrate on these large and important groups, but we shall also briefly mention many smaller phyla we previously ignored. The aim here is to bring together the various phases of animal life discussed in other chapters and to give some idea both of the immense diversity within the kingdom and of possible evolutionary patterns.

A formal outline of the classification of the animal kingdom used in this book is given in the Appendix. We must stress that this classification, though it is a widely used one, is not accepted by all biologists. Much is uncertain regarding the evolution of animal groups, and different biologists interpret the available data in different ways.

PROTOZOA

Although some biologists, as we indicated earlier, put the Protozoa in the kingdom Protista, we shall follow the tradition that places them in the Animalia. True, Protozoa have little in common with multicellular animals, but then neither do they have much in common with the other organisms usually classified as Protista; hence nothing is gained by moving them from the one category to the other.

Protozoans are usually said to be unicellular. However, as the great student of invertebrate animals Libbie Henrietta Hyman of the American Museum of Natural History has pointed out, "Each protozoan is to be regarded not as equivalent to a cell of a more complex animal but as a complete organism with the same properties and characteristics as cellular animals." Although they "necessarily lack tissues and organs, since these are defined as aggregations of differentiated cells," many do exhibit "a remarkable degree of functional differentiation." Instead of organs, they have functionally equivalent subcellular structures called *organelles.* In recognition of the complexity of Protozoa, which often far exceeds that of other individual cells, Hyman and many other biologists prefer to call them *acellular* organisms, i.e. organisms whose bodies do not exhibit the usual construction of cells.

Protozoans occur in a great variety of habitats, including the sea, fresh water, soil, and the bodies of other organisms—in fact, wherever there is moisture. Most are solitary, but some are colonial. Many are free-living, but others are commensalistic, mutualistic, or parasitic. The great majority are heterotrophic, but some of the flagellates possess chlorophyll and are photosynthetic autotrophs; these plantlike forms, which include *Euglena, Chlamydomonas, Gonium, Pandorina, Volvox,* and the green dinoflagellates, are classified as algae by botanists (see pp. 796–810). The heterotrophic forms usually digest food particles in food vacuoles (see p. 178 and Figs. 5.15 and 5.16). There are no special organelles for gas exchange, the general cell membrane serving as the exchange surface. Many species, particularly those living in hypoosmotic media such as fresh water, possess contractile vacuoles, which function primarily in osmoregulation (see p. 282 and Fig. 8.7). Small amounts of nitrogenous waste may also be expelled by the contractile vacuoles, but most of it is released as ammonia by diffusion across the general cell surface. Locomotion is by formation of pseudopodia or by means of beating cilia or flagella (see p. 431). Where a single individual has many cilia, their action is coordinated by a system of fibrils connecting their basal bodies; these fibrils seem to have conductile properties rather like those of nerves in multicellular animals (see Fig. 10.1, p. 359). Reproduction is sometimes asexual (usually by binary fission, but in some cases by multiple fission or by budding) and sometimes sexual. Most freshwater and parasitic protozoans can encyst when conditions are unfavorable; they secrete a thick resistant case around themselves and become dormant.

The Protozoa have traditionally been divided into four classes: Flagellata, Sarcodina, Sporozoa, and Ciliata. Each of these is a heterogeneous assemblage of structurally similar organisms that are probably not closely related. Furthermore, the relationships of the classes to one another are unclear; this is particularly true of the Ciliata. For these reasons, some biologists choose to divide the Protozoa into two or more separate phyla. Although a more conservative system is used here, the two subphyla treated below (Plasmodroma and Ciliophora) might well be raised to the rank of full phyla.

Subphylum Plasmodroma

Class Flagellata. As their name implies, the Flagellata (also called Mastigophora) are protozoans that possess flagella as the principal locomotor organelles. They appear to be the most primitive of all the Protozoa, and it seems likely that some (and possibly all) of the other protozoan groups arose from them. As indicated in Chapter 21, it also seems likely that the various groups of algae (and through them the higher plants) evolved from flagellates; indeed, many of the modern algae (including all Euglenophyta and Pyrrophyta and many members of the Chlorophyta and Chrysophyta) are classified as flagellate Protozoa by zoologists. Most zoologists (though not all) believe that the flagellates were also the ancestors of the multicellular animals. There is good reason to think, then, that this group of organisms played a key role in the evolution of life on earth, probably giving rise to other Protozoa, to most (and perhaps all) of the plant kingdom, and to the animal kingdom. In saying this, we are not suggesting that any flagellate species still living today was the ancestor of these other organisms, but simply that the ancestral flagellates from which modern flagellates are descended probably also gave rise to other Protozoa and to multicellular plants and animals. We might diagram this relationship as follows:

as symbionts in the bodies of higher plants or animals. Several species, for instance, are found in the gut of termites, where they participate in the digestion of the cellulose consumed by the termite (Fig. 22.1); we mentioned this as an example of mutualism in Chapter 18.

Trypanosoma (Fig. 22.2) is a genus of parasitic zooflagellates that cause several severe diseases in man and his domestic animals. *Trypanosoma gambiense*, for example, is the causative agent in African sleeping sickness.[1] The trypanosomes live in the blood of their host, where they multiply and release the poisonous by-products of their metabolism. In man or domestic animals (but not in the native wild mammals of Africa), they eventually invade the nervous system, causing lethargy and finally death. The trypanosomes are spread from host to host by blood-sucking tsetse flies (genus *Glossina*). When a tsetse fly sucks blood from an infected animal, some of the trypanosomes are sucked into its intestine, where they multiply and undergo several developmental changes. They then migrate to the fly's salivary glands, where they undergo additional developmental changes and continue to multiply. If the fly now bites an uninfected vertebrate, some of the trypanosomes are injected from the salivary glands into the vertebrate host. This disease, which makes large parts of Africa nearly uninhabitable for man, is difficult to control because the many wild animals serve as a con-

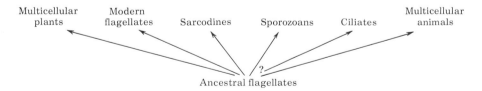

We discussed representatives of the plant-like photosynthetic flagellates (phytoflagellates) in Chapter 21; we have as yet said nothing about the animal-like heterotrophic flagellates (zooflagellates). A few of these are free-living in salt or fresh water, but most live

stant reservoir of trypanosomes. It may eventually be eradicated by extermination of the tsetse flies—admittedly a huge undertaking.

[1] African sleeping sickness should not be confused with ordinary sleeping sickness, or encephalitis, which is caused by a virus.

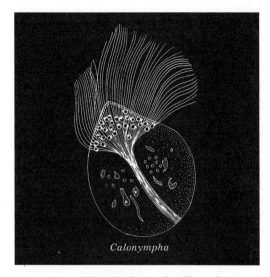

Fig. 22.1. *Calonympha,* a flagellate that inhabits the gut of termites. [Redrawn from C. Janicki, Z. *Wiss. Zool.,* vol. 112, 1915.]

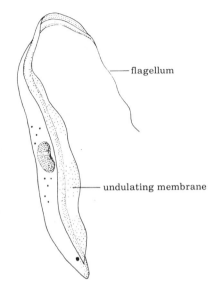

Fig. 22.2. *Trypanosoma,* the cause of African sleeping sickness.

Class Sarcodina. The Sarcodina (also called Rhizopoda) are the amoeboid Protozoa. They are thought to be more closely related to the flagellates than to the other protozoan classes, because some flagellates undergo amoeboid phases, and, conversely, some Sarcodina have flagellated stages. The most familiar sarcodines are the naked fresh-water species of the genera *Amoeba* (Fig. 22.3) and *Pelomyxa,* which have asymmetrical bodies that constantly change shape as new pseudopods are formed and old ones retracted. These pseudopods, which are large and have rounded or blunt ends, function both in locomotion (see p. 430 and Fig. 11.1) and in feeding by phagocytosis (see p. 67 and Fig. 3.14; also p. 178). The food consists of small algae, other protozoans, and even some small multicellular animals such as rotifers and nematode worms.

Also included in the Sarcodina are several groups of protozoans that secrete hard calcareous or siliceous shells around themselves. These shells, often quite elaborate and complex, can be used in species identification. The pseudopods of the shelled Sarcodina are usu-

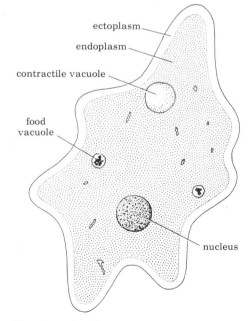

Fig. 22.3. *Amoeba,* a common representative of the Sarcodina.

ally thin and pointed (Fig. 22.4); in some forms, they have no locomotory function, being exclusively feeding devices. This type of pseudopod does not flow around and engulf the prey, but instead functions as a trap. When prey organisms touch it, they become stuck in a mucoid adhesive secretion that coats the pseudopod surface. The secretion apparently contains proteolytic enzymes that initiate digestion of the prey, which is eventually enclosed in a food vacuole and drawn toward the interior of the body of the cell.

Two groups of shelled sarcodines, the Foraminifera and the Radiolaria, have played major roles in the geologic history of the earth. Both groups are extremely abundant in the oceans, and when they die their shells become important components of the bottom mud. The shells of foraminiferans (Fig. 22.5), which are calcareous, are especially prevalent in the mud at

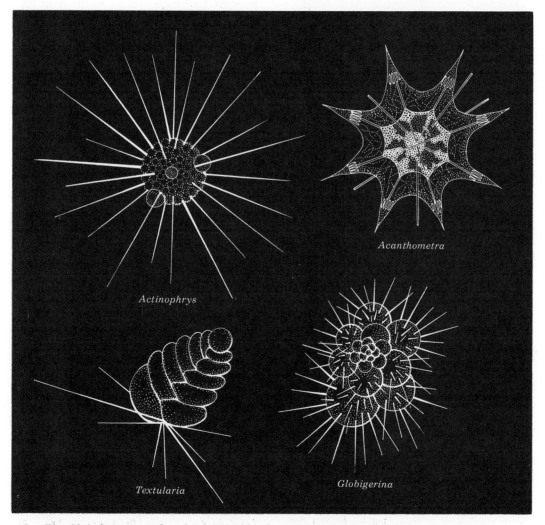

Fig. 22.4. Some examples of Sarcodina that have thin pointed pseudopods. *Acanthometra* is a radiolarian. *Textularia* and *Globigerina* are foraminiferans. [Modified from L. H. Hyman, *The Invertebrates*, McGraw-Hill Book Co., 1940. Used by permission.]

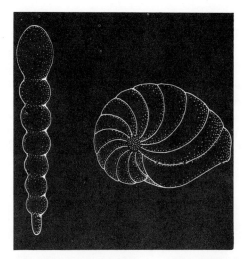

Fig. 22.5. Shells of two foraminiferans. Left: *Rheophax nodulosa*. Right: *Nonion incisum*. [Modified from R. D. Barnes, *Invertebrate Zoology*, Saunders, 1963.]

depths of 8,000 to 15,000 feet; at greater depths, they tend to dissolve, because of the increased carbon dioxide content of the water. The bottom ooze in deeper parts of the ocean is composed chiefly of the siliceous shells of radiolarians. Both these groups have been abundant for a very long time; fossils of foraminiferans go back to the Cambrian period, and fossils of radiolarians occur in Pre-Cambrian rocks. Much of the limestone and chalk now present on the earth was formed from deposits of foraminiferal shells, and radiolarian shells have contributed to the formation of siliceous rocks such as chert.

Class Sporozoa. The Sporozoa lack special locomotor organelles (except in the male gametes). They are parasites of vertebrates and most invertebrates, and usually exhibit complex life cycles. Among human diseases caused by sporozoans are coccidiosis and malaria.

As you probably know, malaria, which is caused by species of the genus *Plasmodium*, is transmitted from host to host by female *Anopheles* mosquitoes. When an anopheline mosquito bites a man and starts to suck blood, it releases saliva containing a chemical that prevents coagulation of the blood and, frequently, also *Plasmodium* cells of a stage called sporozoites. The sporozoites enter the bloodstream of the man and penetrate into red blood cells, where they reproduce asexually. The new cells thus produced are called merozoites. At regular intervals (48 hours in some types of malaria; in one type, 72 hours), all infected red cells burst, releasing numerous merozoites, which enter new blood cells and repeat the asexual reproductive process. Thus, in the most common form of malaria, hordes of merozoites are released into the bloodstream from ruptured red cells every 48 hours. The host experiences attacks of chills and fever each time such a release of merozoites occurs; these symptoms apparently result from toxins discharged into the blood by the rupturing red cells.

Eventually some of the merozoites develop into special sexual cells capable of becoming either male or female gametes; they will not mature as gametes, however, as long as they remain in the blood of the human host. But if an anopheline mosquito sucks blood containing these cells, they complete their development in the stomach of the mosquito. The male gametes then fertilize the female gametes, and the zygote thus produced, which is amoeboid, works its way into the wall of the gut and encysts. Within the cyst, a series of divisions ultimately produce new sporozoites, which are released when the cyst ruptures. These sporozoites migrate to the salivary glands of the mosquito, whence they are discharged into a new vertebrate host when the mosquito feeds. Efforts at malarial control have largely been attempts to eradicate *Anopheles* mosquitoes, either directly by use of insecticides or indirectly by destroying their breeding places.

Subphylum Ciliophora

Class Ciliata. The class Ciliata is the largest of the four protozoan classes and also the most homogeneous. It differs so markedly from the other classes and its relationship to them is so unclear that it is put in a subphylum of its own.

As their name implies, ciliates possess numerous cilia as locomotory organelles. In most species, the cilia are present throughout life, but in a few (Suctoria) they are absent in the adult stages. The ciliates exhibit the greatest elaboration of subcellular organelles of any Protozoa, and it is to them that the term "acellular" applies best. As we saw in our discussion of *Paramecium* (p. 178, Fig. 5.15), they may have a special oral groove and cytopharynx into which food particles are drawn in currents produced by beating cilia, and they often have an anal "pore" through which indigestible wastes are expelled from food vacuoles. Con-

ductile fibrils connect the bases of the cilia, and there may be a system of contractile fibers (sometimes striated) analogous to the muscular system of multicellular animals. Stiffened plates occasionally found in the pellicle of the cell together constitute a "skeleton." In some species, there is a long stalk by which the individual may attach itself to the substratum (Fig. 22.6). A few species have tentacles for capture of prey. Some can discharge toxic threadlike darts called trichocysts that resemble the nematocysts of coelenterates; these may function in defense against predators, in capturing prey, or in anchoring the organism to the substratum during feeding.

Ciliates differ from all other members of the animal kingdom in having two quite different types of nuclei: a large **macronucleus** and one

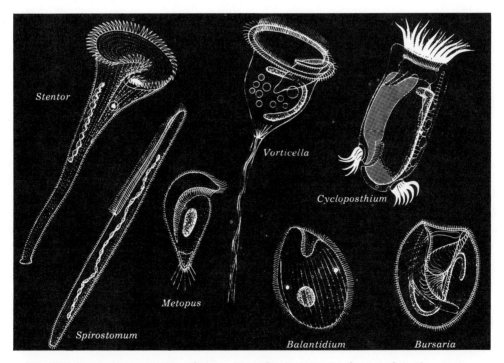

Fig. 22.6. Some representative ciliates. Note the variation in shape and in the arrangement of organelles. *Vorticella* has a long stalk by which it attaches to the substratum. [Modified from L. H. Hyman, *The Invertebrates,* McGraw-Hill Book Co., 1940. Used by permission.]

or more small *micronuclei.* The macronucleus often has a complex shape; it may be like a long string of beads or like a twisted rod, although in some genera, e.g. *Paramecium* (see Fig. 5.15A, p. 178), it may be a simpler bean-shaped structure. The macronucleus controls the normal metabolism of the cell. The micronuclei are concerned only with reproduction and with giving rise to the macronucleus. During asexual reproduction, which is usually by transverse binary fission, the micronuclei divide mitotically,[2] but the macronucleus divides amitotically; i.e. it forms no spindle and appears to divide by simple constriction.

Many ciliates reproduce occasionally by a sexual process called *conjugation.* Two individuals of appropriate mating types come together and adhere in the oral region; there is some fusion in the area of contact. Next, the micronuclei divide by meiosis. Then all but two of the resulting haploid micronuclei in each cell disintegrate; the macronucleus also usually disintegrates. One of the two nuclei in each cell remains stationary and functions as the female nucleus. The other moves into the conjugant cell and fuses with that cell's female nucleus in the process of fertilization. Thus each cell acts as both male and female, donating a nucleus and receiving one in return, and when the two cells part each has a new recombinant diploid nucleus. This nucleus then undergoes one or more divisions, and some of the new nuclei thus produced develop into macronuclei. Following a variable number of cytoplasmic cleavages, the normal number of micro- and macronuclei per cell is restored.

PORIFERA AND MESOZOA

There are two phyla of multicellular animals that differ so greatly from the others that they are often regarded as subkingdoms. These are the Porifera and the Mesozoa.

Porifera (The Sponges)

The sponges are aquatic, mostly marine animals. Although the larvae are ciliated and free-swimming, the adults are always sessile and are usually attached to rocks or shells or other submerged objects. They are multicellular, but show few of the features ordinarily associated with multicellular animals. For example, they have no digestive system, no nervous system,[3] and no circulatory system. In fact, they have no organs of any kind, and even their tissues are not well defined. They thus represent a very low grade of organization.

The body of a sponge is rather like a perforated sac. Its wall is composed of three layers: an outer layer of flattened epidermal cells, a gelatinous middle layer with wandering amoeboid cells, and an inner layer of flagellated cells (Fig. 22.7). The flagellated cells are unusual in that the base of the flagellum is encircled by a delicate collar; such cells are called *collar cells* (or choanocytes).

The wall of a sponge is perforated by numerous pores, each surrounded by a single pore cell. The beating of the flagella of the collar cells produces water currents that flow through the pores (called siphons) into the central cavity (spongocoel) and out through a larger opening at the end of the body. Microscopic food particles brought in by these currents adhere to the collar cells and are engulfed; the food may be digested in food vacuoles of the collar cells themselves or passed to the amoeboid cells for digestion. The water currents also bring oxygen to the cells and carry away carbon dioxide and nitrogenous wastes (largely ammonia).

Sponges characteristically possess an internal

---

[2] Mitosis in the micronuclei of ciliates is unusual in that the nuclear membrane does not disappear and the spindle forms inside the membrane-bounded nucleus.

[3] In some sponges, a few cells of the body wall possess elongate processes that may have special conductile properties.

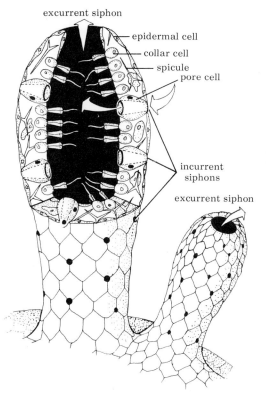

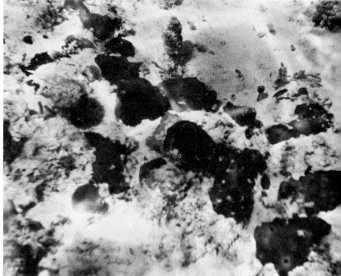

Fig. 22.7. Sponge. Left: Diagram of the parts of a sponge. Right: Photograph of living sponges on the ocean bottom. The siphons are clearly visible. [Right: Courtesy N. F. Snyder, Cornell University.]

skeleton secreted by the amoeboid cells. This skeleton is composed of crystalline *spicules* or of proteinaceous fibers or of both. The spicules are made of calcium carbonate or siliceous material (chiefly silicic acid); their chemical composition and their shape are the basis for sponge classification. The fibrous skeletons of the bath sponges (*Spongia*) are cleaned and sold for many uses. A living bath sponge, which looks rather like a piece of raw liver, bears little resemblance to the familiar object sold as a sponge.

Among the free-living flagellated Protozoa are some collared organisms that closely resemble the collar cells of sponges (Fig. 22.8). Such cells are found in no other organisms. For this reason, many biologists think that the Porifera evolved from collared flagellates. Other biologists disagree, pointing out that larval sponges have no collar cells, and suggest that sponges arose instead from a hollow free-swim-

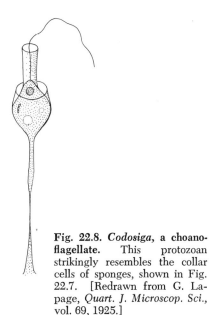

Fig. 22.8. *Codosiga*, a choano-flagellate. This protozoan strikingly resembles the collar cells of sponges, shown in Fig. 22.7. [Redrawn from G. Lapage, *Quart. J. Microscop. Sci.*, vol. 69, 1925.]

ming colonial flagellate. In either case, it seems very likely that sponges arose from the Protozoa independently of the other multicellular animals. If this is so, then the phylum Porifera stands alone as an evolutionary development entirely separate from the rest of the animal kingdom, and it must be concluded that multicellular animals evolved at least twice from the flagellates.

Mesozoa

The phylum Mesozoa contains about 50 species of tiny wormlike animals that live as parasites in the bodies of certain invertebrates, particularly octopuses and squids. They are the simplest of all known multicellular animals, having a solid body composed of about 25 ciliated somatic cells surrounding one or more elongate reproductive cells (Fig. 22.9). They have no distinct tissues or organs. Many biologists consider them to be degenerate flatworms, but there is no good evidence to support this hypothesis, and it seems more reasonable to put them in a phylum of their own. They may indeed have arisen directly from a colonial protozoan ancestor.

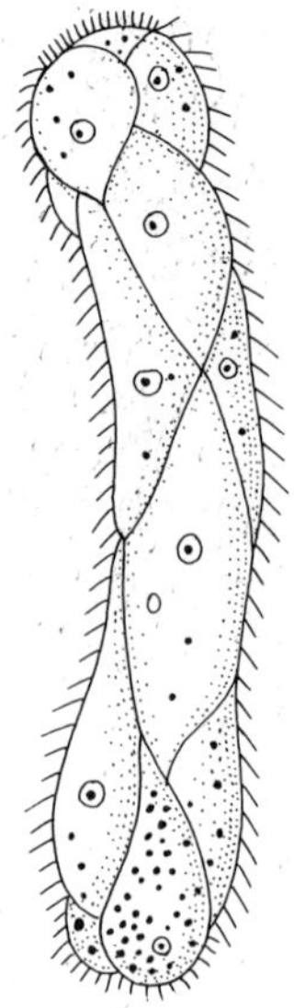

THE RADIATE PHYLA

The two radiate phyla—Coelenterata and Ctenophora—comprise radially symmetrical animals whose bodies are at a relatively simple grade of construction. There are definite tissue layers, but no distinct internal organs. There is no head and no central nervous system, but there is a nerve net (see Fig. 10.3, p. 361). There is a digestive cavity, but it has only one opening, which must serve as both mouth and anus; i.e. it is a gastrovascular cavity. Tentacles are usually present. There is no coelom or other internal space between the wall of the digestive cavity and the outer body wall.

It was once thought that the bodies of these animals consist of only two layers of cells—an

Fig. 22.9. *Pseudicyema*, a mesozoan that lives in the nephridia of squids. [Modified from L. H. Hyman, *The Invertebrates*, McGraw-Hill Book Co., 1940. Used by permission.]

outer epidermis (ectoderm) and an inner gastrodermis (endoderm) (see Fig. 5.17, p. 181) —but it is now known that a third layer called mesoglea (mesoderm) usually occurs between these two, just as it does in higher multicellular animals. However, this mesodermal layer is not as well developed in the radiate phyla as in higher phyla. It is usually gelatinous with a few scattered cells, which may be amoeboid or fibrous.

Coelenterata

The phylum Coelenterata (also called Cnidaria) contains a variety of aquatic organisms, among which are the hydras mentioned so frequently in earlier chapters, jellyfishes, sea anemones, and corals. The hydras live in fresh water, but most other coelenterates are marine.

The coelenterate body shows some cell specialization and division of labor. Thus the outer epidermis contains sensory–nerve cells, gland cells, special cells that produce nematocysts, small interstitial cells, and epithelio-muscle cells. These last are the main structural elements of the epidermis and consist of a columnar cell body with several contractile basal extensions. In other words, the contractile elements of coelenterates are parts of cells that also have other important functions; there are no cells specialized exclusively for contraction—no separate muscle cells. Note also that these contractile elements are ectodermal, not mesodermal as in most higher animals. The gastrodermis also contains contractile elements; these are basal extensions of cells whose cell bodies constitute the bulk of the lining of the gastrovascular cavity and function in digestion. Here again a single cell performs two functions that in higher animals are performed by separate elements. In short, there is some division of labor among cells in coelenterates, but it is never as complete as in most bilateral multicellular animals; and most functions performed by tissues derived from mesoderm in other animals are performed by ectodermal or endodermal cells in coelenterates.

The phylum Coelenterata is divided into three classes: Hydrozoa, Scyphozoa, and Anthozoa.

Class Hydrozoa. The best-known members of this class are the fresh-water hydras. We have discussed their feeding (p. 179), their gas exchange (p. 210), their nervous control (p. 361), and their locomotion (p. 432). Little more need be said about them here. In many ways, in fact, hydras are not typical members of their class. Many hydrozoans are colonial and have a complex life cycle, in which a sedentary hydralike *polyp* stage alternates with, a free-swimming jellyfishlike *medusa* stage (Fig. 22.10). By contrast, hydras are solitary and have only a polyp stage (which is not completely sedentary).

Let us look at *Obelia* as an example of a colonial hydrozoan (Fig. 22.11). Much of the life of *Obelia* is passed as a sedentary branching colony of polyps. The colony arises from an individual hydralike polyp by asexual budding; the buds fail to separate, and the new polyps

remain attached by hollow stemlike connections. The gastrovascular cavities of all the polyps are interconnected via the cavity in the stems. The cells lining the stem cavity have long flagella that circulate the fluid in the cavity. Partly digested food can be passed from one polyp to another in this moving fluid. Both the stems and the polyps (except their mouth and tentacles) are enclosed in a hard chitinous case secreted by the ectoderm. Rings or joints in the case occurring at intervals along the stems permit some flexibility for the colony.

A mature *Obelia* colony consists of two kinds of polyps: feeding polyps with tentacles and nematocysts, and reproductive polyps without

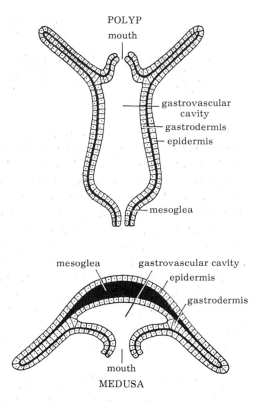

Fig. 22.10. Diagram contrasting polyp and medusa. The basic structure of these two forms is the same. A medusa is like a flattened polyp turned upside down.

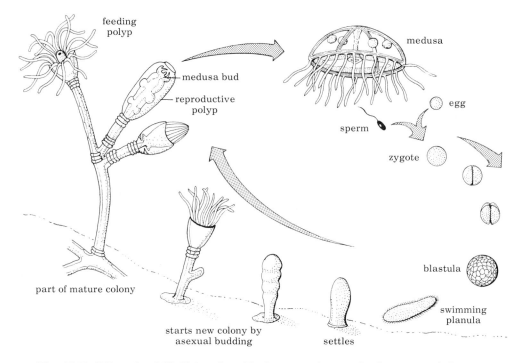

feeding
polyp

medusa bud

reproductive
polyp

medusa

egg

sperm

zygote

part of mature colony

blastula

swimming
planula

starts new colony by
asexual budding

settles

Fig. 22.11. Life cycle of *Obelia*, a colonial hydrozoan. See text for description. (The eggs
and sperms are produced by different individuals, since the medusas are of separate sexes.)
[Modified from T. I. Storer and R. L. Usinger, *General Zoology*, McGraw-Hill Book Co.,
1957. Used by permission.]

tentacles.[4] The reproductive polyps regularly
bud off tiny transparent free-swimming medusas. Each medusa is umbrella-shaped or bell-
shaped, with numerous tentacles hanging from
the margin of the bell. A tube with a mouth at
its end hangs from the middle of the under
surface of the bell (where the clapper of a real
bell would be). The medusas are the dispersal
and sexual stage in the life cycle. They swim
feebly by alternately contracting and relaxing
the contractile cells in the bell, but much of
their movement results from drifting with the
water currents.

Certain cells in mature medusas undergo

meiosis and develop into either sperm cells or
eggs, which are released into the surrounding
water. Fertilization takes place, and the resulting zygote develops into a hollow blastula.
Gastrulation does not take place by the invagination process described in Chapter 16. Instead, endodermal cells proliferated by the
wall (ectoderm) of the blastula wander into
the blastocoel until they completely fill it. This
solid gastrula then develops into an elongate
ciliated larva called a *planula.* The planula
eventually settles to the bottom, attaches by
one end to some object, and develops a mouth
and tentacles at the other end, becoming a
polyp that gives rise to a new colony. The life
cycle is thus completed. Note that the alternation of polyp and medusa stages in a coelenterate like *Obelia* differs from the alternation of
generations in plants in that both polyp and
medusa are diploid; as in all multicellular ani-

[4] In view of this division of labor—the reproductive
polyps are nourished with food captured by the feeding polyps and passed to them through the common
gastrovascular cavity in the connecting stems—and in
view of the structural continuity between the polyps,
it might be argued that the so-called *Obelia* colony
is not really a colony, but a complex individual.

mals, the only haploid stage in the life cycle is the gametes.

Class Scyphozoa. The scyphozoans are the true jellyfishes. In these animals, the medusa is the dominant and conspicuous stage in the life cycle, and the polyp stage is restricted to a small larva. This larva, which develops from the planula, promptly produces medusas by budding (Fig. 22.12). Scyphozoan medusas resemble the hydrozoan medusas already described except that they are usually much larger and have long oral arms (endodermal tentacles) arising from the margin of the mouth; the marginal tentacles may be much reduced as in *Aurelia* (shown in Fig. 22.12), or they may be quite long (Fig. 22.13).

Class Anthozoa. The class Anthozoa includes sedentary polypoid forms such as sea anemones (Fig. 22.14), sea fans, and corals.

All are marine. There is no trace of a medusa stage in their life cycle. They are the most advanced members of the Coelenterata, and their body structure is much more complex than that of simple polyps like the hydras. They possess a tubular pharynx leading into the gastrovascular cavity; their gastrovascular cavity is divided into numerous radiating compartments by longitudinal septa; their mesoderm (mesoglea) is much thicker than that of other coelenterates and is often elaborated into a fibrous connective tissue; and their muscles are much better developed.

The corals, anthozoans that secrete a hard limy skeleton, have played a very important role in the geologic history of the earth, particularly in tropical oceans. As their skeletons have accumulated over the ages, they have formed many reefs, atolls, and islands, especially in the South Pacific. The Great Barrier Reef, a coral ridge many miles wide that ex-

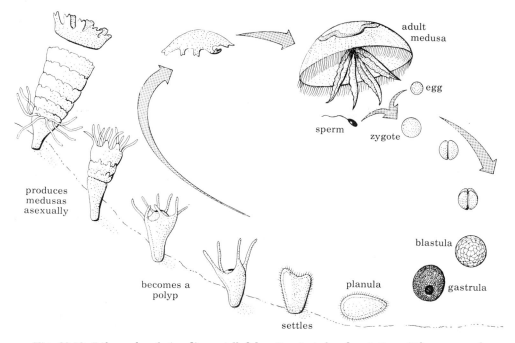

Fig. 22.12. Life cycle of *Aurelia*, a jellyfish. See text for description. (The eggs and sperms are produced by different individuals, since the medusas are of separate sexes.) [Modified from T. I. Storer and R. L. Usinger, *General Zoology*, McGraw-Hill Book Co., 1957. Used by permission.]

Fig. 22.13. *Pelagia*, a jellyfish with oral arms and long marginal tentacles. [Modified from L. H. Hyman, *The Invertebrates*, McGraw-Hill Book Co., 1940. Used by permission.]

tends more than a thousand miles along the eastern coast of Australia, is a particularly impressive example of the way these lowly animals can change the face of the earth.

Ctenophora (The Comb Jellies or Sea Walnuts)

Members of the phylum Ctenophora resemble the coelenterates in being radial animals with a saclike body composed of epidermis, mesoglea, and gastrodermis, in having a digestive cavity of the gastrovascular type, in lacking a coelom, and in lacking definitive organ systems. However, they differ from coelenterates in having independent mesodermal muscles, in lacking nematocysts (the tentacles, when present, may have adhesive cells instead), in lack-

ing the polymorphic life cycle so common in coelenterates, and in characteristically having eight rows of ciliary plates (combs) that run across the surface of the transparent body from the upper pole to the lower pole like the lines of longitude on a globe (Fig. 22.15). The cilia in the eight rows beat in unison and enable the animal to swim feebly. Most ctenophores float near the surface of the sea, chiefly near shore. They are carried about by currents and tides, and large numbers of them may be blown into bays during storms or swept ashore by high waves.

Origin of the Metazoa

Speculation concerning the origin of the Metazoa (all multicellular animals except sponges and mesozoans) has long centered on the radiate phyla just discussed—not only because the radiates, particularly the hydrozoan coelenterates, seems to be among the simplest metazoans, but also because their saclike, essentially two-layered bodies strikingly resemble embryonic gastrulas. Now, a spherical colonial flagellate like *Volvox* certainly resembles an embryonic blastula. As long ago as 1874 Ernst

Fig. 22.14. *Metridium*, a common sea anemone. [Courtesy Carolina Biological Supply Co.]

Haeckel suggested that the ancestor of the multicellular animals was a hollow-sphere colonial flagellate,[5] and that the coelenterates arose from this hypothetical ancestor, called a *blastaea*, by a process of invaginating gastrulation. The higher animals would then have arisen from the early two layered (diploblastic) *gastraea* ancestor of the modern coelenterates by assuming a creeping mode of life and slowly becoming bilateral. According to this hypothesis, the blastula and gastrula stages in the embryonic development of higher animals are recapitulations of early steps in the evolutionary origin of these animals from the Protozoa.

It was soon pointed out that gastrulation in coelenterates does not take place by invagination. Instead, as we have already seen, the endoderm arises by inwandering of cells produced at the inner surface of the ectoderm, and a solid gastrula that develops into a planula larva is formed. Both the hollowing out of the interior to form the gastrovascular cavity and the breaking through of a mouth occur later, when the larva develops into a polyp. Thus it seems likely that the invagination type of gastrulation was a later evolutionary development and not the original method of formation of endoderm. Consequently, although the idea of a hollow blastaea ancestor as the starting point was retained in later versions of Haeckel's theory, the idea of a gastraea stage was abandoned and a *planuloid* stage hypothesized instead.

The hypothesis of metazoan origin from flagellates via blastaea and planuloid steps is widely held by biologists today, but other hypotheses have been proposed, of which the most prominent is that multicellular animals arose from multinucleate ciliates, not from flagellates. According to this hypothesis, the earliest metazoans had syncytial (coenocytic) bodies; i.e. they contained many nuclei each of which controlled the cytoplasm around it,

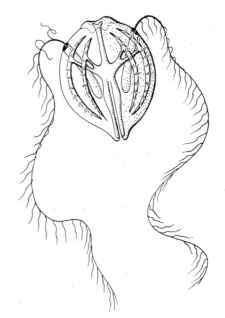

Fig. 22.15. *Pleurobrachia*, **a common ctenophore.** Note the rows of ciliary plates, also the very long antennae, which emerge from sheaths that extend deep into the body.

but there were no cellular partitions. Acquisition of cellular membranes around each nucleus and its associated cytoplasm would have produced a typical multicellular animal, probably resembling some of the simplest flatworms. Note that this hypothesis begins with a bilaterally symmetrical ciliate and hence assumes that the first metazoans were bilateral; it considers the radial symmetry of the Coelenterata and Ctenophora a secondary characteristic.

THE ACOELOMATE BILATERIA

There are two phyla—Platyhelminthes and Nemertina—that contain what most biologists regard as the most primitive bilaterally symmetrical animals.[6] In both phyla, the body is composed of three well-developed tissue layers

---

[5] The colonial flagellate ancestral to multicellular animals would probably have differed from *Volvox* in having cells without walls and without chlorophyll.

[6] Bilateral symmetry is the property of having two similar sides. A bilaterally symmetrical animal has definite dorsal (upper) and ventral (lower) surfaces and definite anterior (head) and posterior (tail) ends.

—ectoderm, mesoderm, and endoderm—and the mesoderm is a solid mass that fills what once was the embryonic blastocoel. In other words, there is no coelom—no cavity between the digestive tract and the body wall (see Fig. 22.24A). For this reason, these two phyla are known as the acoelomate bilateria.

Platyhelminthes (The Flatworms)

The flatworms, as their name implies, are dorsoventrally flattened elongate animals.[7] Their digestive cavity (not always present) resembles that of coelenterates; i.e. it is a gastrovascular cavity—a cavity with a single opening that must serve as both mouth and anus. However, there is a muscular pharynx leading into the cavity, and the cavity itself is often profusely branched, especially in the free-living species (see p. 181 and Fig. 5.18). As in coelenterates, the amount of extracellular digestion is limited, most of the food particles being phagocytized and digested intracellularly by the cells of the wall of the gastrovascular cavity. Respiratory and circulatory systems are absent.[8] However, there is a flame-cell excretory system (see p. 283 and Fig. 8.8), and there are well-developed reproductive organs (usually both male and female in each individual). That both the excretory system, with its flame bulbs and tubules, and the reproductive organs should be present signifies that the flatworms have advanced beyond the tissue-level of construction seen in the radiate phyla to an organ-level of construction. The more extensive development of mesoderm, leading to greater division of labor, was probably a major factor in making this advance possible. Mesodermal muscles are well developed. Several longitudinal nerve cords running the length of the body and a

tiny "brain" ganglion located in the head constitute a central nervous system (see p. 362 and Fig. 10.4).

The phylum is divided into three classes: Turbellaria, Trematoda, and Cestoda. The last two are entirely parasitic.

Class Turbellaria. The members of this class, of which the fresh-water planarians discussed at some length in earlier chapters are examples, are free-living flatworms ranging from microscopic size to a length of several inches. The body is clothed by an epidermal layer, which is usually ciliated (at least in part). Although a few turbellarians live on land, most are aquatic (the majority marine).

Turbellarians usually have a gastrovascular cavity, but most members of one small order, the Acoela, do not (Fig. 22.16). For a variety of reasons (not just the absence of a digestive cavity), many biologists consider the Acoela the most primitive bilateral animals, and suggest that a primitive *acoeloid* organism might well have arisen from a planuloid ancestor. According to these biologists, both the more complex flatworms and the other metazoan phyla probably evolved from such an acoeloid organism. This theory of the early evolution of the Metazoa can be diagramed as follows:

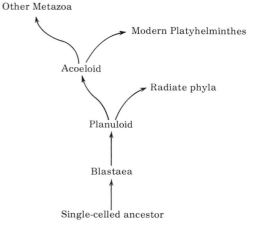

Proponents of the ciliate theory of metazoan origin also assume an acoeloid stage to be at

---

[7] The term "worm" is applied to a great variety of unrelated animals. It is a descriptive, not a taxonomic, term that denotes possession of a slender elongate body, usually without legs or with very short ones.

[8] A so-called "lymphatic system," present in some flukes, may represent a primitive circulatory system.

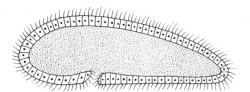

Fig. 22.16. An acoel flatworm. There is a ventral mouth but no digestive cavity; the entire interior of the animal is filled with an almost solid mass of tissue (stippled area) in which cellular boundaries are often poorly defined (i.e. the internal material is often a syncytium).

the root of the Metazoa, but they derive the acoeloid directly from a multinucleate ciliate, not from a planuloid, and they think this acoeloid organism was the ancestor of the radiate phyla as well as of the bilateral phyla. Their ideas can be diagramed as follows:

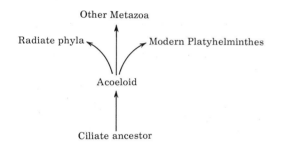

Class Trematoda (The Flukes). The flukes are parasitic flatworms. They lack cilia, and in place of the cellular epidermis of their turbellarian ancestors they have a thick cuticle secreted by the cells below. This cuticle is highly resistant to enzyme action and is thus an important adaptation to a parasitic way of life. Flukes characteristically possess suckers, usually two or more, by which they attach themselves to their host (Fig. 22.17). They have a two-branched gastrovascular cavity, which does not ramify throughout the body like that of turbellarians. Much of their volume is occupied by reproductive organs, including two or more large testes, an ovary, a long much-coiled uterus in which eggs are stored prior to laying, and yolk glands.

The members of one order of flukes are ectoparasites (external parasites) on the gills or skin of fresh-water and marine fishes. A few of these flukes sometimes wander into the body openings of their hosts, and it is probably from such a beginning that the endoparasitism (internal parasitism) typical of the members of the other two orders arose.

The endoparasitic flukes frequently have very complicated life cycles involving two to four different hosts. The blood fluke, *Schistosoma japonicum,* common in China, Japan, Formosa, and the Philippines, is an example of a species with two hosts. The adult worm inhabits blood vessels near the intestine of a human being. When ready to lay its eggs, it pushes its way into one of the very small blood vessels in the wall of the intestine. There it deposits so many eggs that the vessel ruptures,

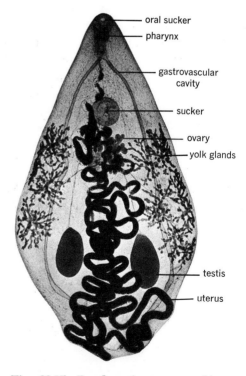

Fig. 22.17. *Prosthogonimus macrorchis,* **a fluke that parasitizes the oviducts of the domestic hen.** [Courtesy General Biological Supply House, Inc., Chicago.]

discharging the eggs into the intestinal cavity, whence they are carried to the exterior in the feces. If there is a modern sewage system, that is the end of the story. But in many Asiatic countries, human feces are regularly used as fertilizer. Thus the eggs get into water in rice fields, irrigation canals, or rivers, where they hatch into tiny ciliated larvae. A larva swims about until it finds a snail of a certain species; it dies if it cannot soon find the correct species. When it finds such a snail, it bores into the body of the snail and feeds on its tissues. It then reproduces asexually, and the new individuals thus produced leave the snail and swim about until they come in contact with the skin of a human being, such as a farmer wading in a rice paddy or a boy swimming in a pond. They attach themselves to the skin and digest their way through it and into a blood vessel. Carried by the blood to the heart and lungs, they eventually reach the vessels of the intestine, where they settle down, mature, and lay eggs, thus initiating a new cycle. Schistosomas in the body of a man cause a serious disease called schistosomiasis, which is characterized initially by a cough, rash, and body pains, followed by severe dysentery and anemia. The disease so saps the strength of its victims that they become weak and emaciated and often die of other diseases to which their weakened condition makes them susceptible.

An example of a fluke with three hosts is the Chinese liver fluke, *Clonorchis sinensis*. The adult lives in the liver of a man, where it lays its eggs. The eggs pass into the intestine with the bile and are carried to the exterior in the feces. If they get into water and are eaten by a certain species of snail, they hatch, and the larvae bore into the lymph spaces of the snail, where they reproduce asexually. The new individuals thus produced live their entire lives in the snail, but they too reproduce asexually, and their progeny leave the snail, burrow through the skin of a fish, and encyst in the fish's muscles. If a man eats the raw or insufficiently cooked fish, his digestive enzymes weaken the walls of the cysts, and the flukes emerge in his intestine, migrate up the bile duct to the liver, and settle down to start a new cycle. All three hosts—snail, fish, and man— are necessary for completion of the reproductive cycle of this fluke.

Class Cestoda (The Tapeworms). Adult tapeworms (Fig. 22.18) live as internal parasites of vertebrates, almost always in the intestine. However, the life cycle usually involves one or two intermediate hosts, which may be invertebrate or vertebrate, depending on the species. The life cycle of the beef tapeworm, in which the intermediate host is a cow and the final host is a man, was outlined on p. 725.

Tapeworms exhibit many special adaptations for their parasitic way of life. Like the flukes, they have a resistant cuticle instead of the epidermis of their free-living ancestors. And they

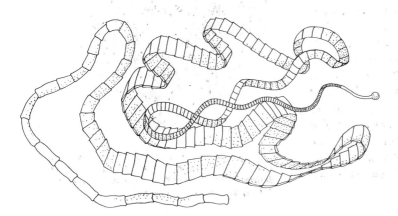

Fig. 22.18. A tapeworm. The body is composed of a small head and neck, followed by a large number of segments called proglottids. As the proglottids ripen, they break off and pass with the host's feces to the outside. New proglottids are produced just back of the neck.

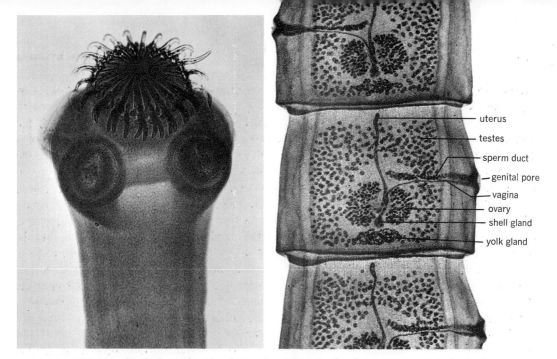

Fig. 22.19. Scolex and proglottids of *Taenia pisiformis,* the dog tapeworm. Left: Scolex. Note the hooks and the suckers. Right: Mature proglottids. [Courtesy General Biological Supply House, Inc., Chicago.]

have neither mouth nor digestive tract. Bathed by the food in their host's intestine, they absorb predigested nutrients across their general body surface. Diffusion, probably augmented by active transport, suffices to provision all the cells, because none are far from the surface.

The head of a tapeworm is a small knoblike structure called a *scolex,* which usually bears suckers, and often also hooks, by which the worm attaches itself to the wall of the host's intestine (Fig. 22.19, left). Immediately behind the scolex is a neck region, which is followed by a very long ribbonlike body (beef tapeworms occasionally grow to 75 feet, fish tapeworms to 60 feet, and pork tapeworms to 25 feet). This long body is usually divided by transverse constrictions into a series of segments called *proglottids* (Fig. 22.19, right).

Each proglottid is essentially a reproductive sac, containing both male and female organs. Sperm cells, usually from a more anterior proglottid of the same animal, enter the genital pore and fertilize the egg cells, which are then combined with yolk from a yolk gland and enclosed in a shell. The fertilized eggs, already

undergoing development, are stored in a uterus, which may become so engorged with eggs that it occupies most of the volume of a mature proglottid. Eventually all the sexual organs except the uterus degenerate, and the proglottid, which is now "ripe," detaches from the worm and passes out of the host's body with the feces. As ripe proglottids are released from the end of the worm, new ones are produced just back of the neck. A single ripe proglottid may contain more than 100,000 eggs, and the annual output of one worm may be more than 600 million.

If an appropriate intermediate host eats food contaminated with feces containing tapeworm eggs, its enzymes digest the shells of the eggs. The embryos thus released bore through the wall of the host's intestine, enter a blood vessel, and are carried by the blood to the muscles, where they encyst. If a man eats the raw or "rare" meat of this intermediate host (e.g. beef, pork, or fish), the walls of the cysts are digested away; the young tapeworms attach themselves to the intestinal wall and, nourished by an abundant supply of food, begin to grow and produce eggs, thus starting a new cycle.

Nemertina (The Nemertine or Proboscis Worms)

The members of the phylum Nemertina (also called Rhynchocoela) are long slender worms characterized by a very long eversible muscular proboscis enclosed in a tubular cavity at the anterior end of the body. This proboscis, which is used in capturing prey and also in defense, is often two or more times the length of the worm's body and is somewhat coiled when enclosed in its sheath. The worms are common along both the Atlantic and Pacific shores of the United States. They are usually found sheltered under stones, shells, or seaweeds, or burrowed in the sand or mud in shallow water.

Although nemertines resemble turbellarian flatworms (their probable ancestors) in their nervous system and in many other ways, e.g. in having a ciliated epidermis, a solid mesoderm, and a flame-cell excretory system, they differ from them in two important characteristics not encountered in the animals considered thus far. First, they have a **complete digestive system**—one that has two openings, a mouth and an anus. Such a system makes possible specialization of sequentially arranged chambers for different functions and thus permits an "assembly-line" processing of food, as we saw in Chapter 5. Second, they have a simple blood circulatory system, which presumably facilitates transport of materials from one part of the body to another.

DIVERGENCE OF THE PROTOSTOMIA AND DEUTEROSTOMIA

We saw in Chapter 16 that the embryonic cavity called the archenteron, formed during gastrulation, becomes the digestive tract of an adult animal. But the archenteron has only one opening to the outside, the blastopore. In animals like coelenterates and flatworms, where the digestive tract is a gastrovascular cavity, the blastopore becomes the combined mouth and anus. But in nemertine worms and the other higher animals that have complete digestive systems, does the blastopore become the mouth, or does it become the anus? Embryologists have shown that in nemertines the site of the embryonic blastopore becomes the mouth and that the anus is an entirely new opening. This is also the case in many other animals, including nematode worms, molluscs, and annelids. But in a few phyla, among them two large and important ones—the Echinodermata and the Chordata—the situation is reversed: The embryonic blastopore becomes the anus, and the mouth is the new opening.

This fundamental difference in embryonic development suggests that a major split occurred in the animal kingdom soon after the origin of a bilateral ancestor. One evolutionary line led to all the phyla in which the blastopore becomes the mouth; these phyla are often collectively called the **Protostomia** (from the Greek *protos*, first, and *stoma*, mouth). The other evolutionary line led to the phyla in which the blastopore becomes the anus and a new mouth is formed; these phyla are collectively called the **Deuterostomia** (from the Greek *deuteros*, second, later, and *stoma*).[9]

As might be expected if the Protostomia and Deuterostomia diverged at a very early stage of their evolution, they differ in a number of other fundamental characters besides the mode of formation of mouth and anus. A further essential difference between them is that the early cleavage stages are determinate in protostomes and indeterminate in deuterostomes; i.e. the developmental fates of the first few cells of a protostome embryo are already at least partly determined, and if these cells are separated no one of them can form a complete individual, but no such determination occurs in the first few cells of a deuterostome embryo

[9] The Protostomia are sometimes called the annelid superphylum, and the Deuterostomia the echinoderm superphylum.

and each cell, if separated, can develop into a normal individual (there can be identical twinning). Furthermore, the two groups exhibit strikingly different patterns of cleavage; the early cleavages are usually oblique to the polar axis[10] of the embryo in protostomes and thus give rise to a spiral arrangement of cells, whereas the early cleavages in deuterostomes are either parallel or at right angles to the polar axis and thus give rise to a so-called radial arrangement of cells (Fig. 22.20). The basic larval types are also quite different in the two groups, as we shall see later in this chapter.

Another fundamental difference between the protostome and deuterostome phyla is seen in the method of origin of the mesoderm in the embryo. The mesoderm of the radiate phyla arises from inwandering cells derived from the ectoderm. A small amount of mesoderm forms this way in the protostomes also, though not in the deuterostomes. Most of the mesoderm in protostomes and all of it in deuterostomes is derived from endoderm instead of ectoderm. However, in protostomes this mesoderm arises as a solid ingrowth of cells from a single initial cell located near the blastopore (Fig. 22.21), whereas in deuterostomes (except vertebrates) it arises by a saclike outfolding of the gut wall, as we saw in Chapter 16.[11]

Still another difference, correlated with the preceding one, has to do with the method of formation of the coelom, if one is present. You will recall from Chapter 16 that a true coelom

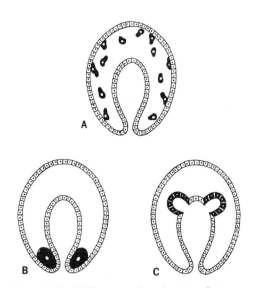

Fig. 22.21. Different modes of origin of mesoderm. (A) In the radiate phyla, mesoderm (black cells) arises from inwandering cells derived from the ectoderm. A small amount of the mesoderm of the protostome phyla arises in this way also. (B) In most protostome phyla, the bulk of the mesoderm arises from initial cells located near the blastopore, at the junction between the ectoderm and the endoderm. (C) In the deuterostome phyla, the mesoderm arises as pouches from the endodermal wall of the archenteron.

is a cavity enclosed entirely by mesoderm and located between the digestive tract and the body wall. In the coelomate protostomes, this cavity usually arises as a split in the initially solid mass of mesoderm. In the deuterostomes, by contrast, the coelom arises as the cavity in the mesodermal sacs as they evaginate from the wall of the archenteron.[12]

To summarize, some of the principal differ-

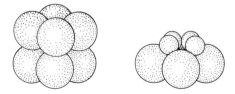

Fig. 22.20. Radial and spiral cleavage patterns. Left: Radial cleavage. The cells of the two layers are arranged directly above each other. Right: Spiral cleavage. The cells in the upper layer are located in the angles between the cells of the lower layer.

[10] The polar axis runs between the animal and vegetal poles.

[11] There are actually a variety of other ways in which mesoderm may arise from endoderm, but embryologists usually interpret them as variants of one or the other of the two processes described here.

[12] A coelom that arises as a split in an initially solid mass of mesoderm is called a schizocoelom. One that forms as the cavity in a pouch of mesoderm is called an enterocoelom. The coelomate protostomes are sometimes called the schizocoelous phyla, and the deuterostomes the enterocoelous phyla.

ences between the Protostomia and the Deuterostomia are differences in the fate of the embryonic blastopore, in the determinateness and pattern of the initial cleavages, in larval type, and in the mode of origin of the meso-

derm and of the coelom (if one is present).

One possible way of diagraming the relationships among the animal phyla, taking into consideration the split between the protostomes and deuterostomes, is shown in Fig. 22.22. This

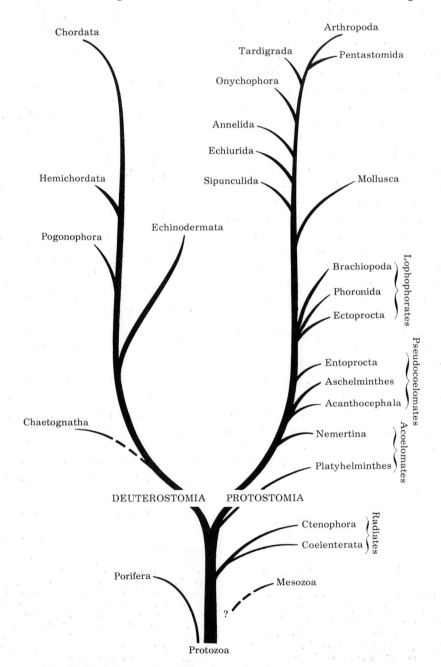

Fig. 22.22. Diagram of possible relationships between the animal phyla.

figure, set up in the traditional fashion of a phylogenetic tree, does not necessarily indicate true relationships; it is only one of many possible schematic representations. Figure 22.23 shows an alternative arrangement.

THE PSEUDOCOELOMATE PROTOSTOMIA

Several protostome phyla have a body cavity functionally analogous to a coelom but differing from a true coelom, which is entirely enclosed by mesoderm, in being partly bounded by ectoderm and endoderm. Such a cavity is called a *pseudocoelom* (Fig. 22.24). It is actually only the remnant of the embryonic blastocoel.

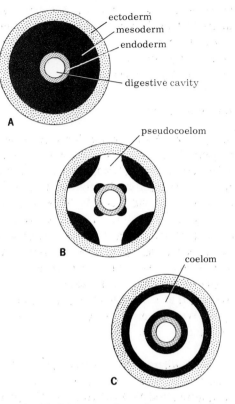

Fig. 22.24. Diagrams of acoelomate, pseudocoelomate, and coelomate body types. (A) Acoelomate body. There is no body cavity, the entire space between the ectoderm and endoderm being filled by a solid mass of mesoderm. (B) Pseudocoelomate body. There is a functional body cavity, but it is not entirely bounded by mesoderm. (C) Coelomate body. The body cavity is completely bounded by mesoderm.

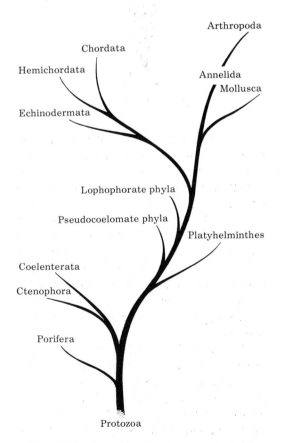

Fig. 22.23. An alternative arrangement of the animal phyla. [After R. D. Barnes.]

Many biologists recognize three phyla of pseudocoelomate protostomes: Acanthocephala, Aschelminthes, and Entoprocta.

Adult Acanthocephala are endoparasites in the digestive tracts of vertebrates; the larvae live in invertebrates. These animals are often called spiny-headed worms because they have a proboscis armed with rows of recurved hooks. They have no digestive tract.

The Entoprocta are tiny sessile, mostly marine, animals that live attached by a stalk to rocks, shells, pilings, or other animals such as crabs or sponges. Most are colonial. Their digestive tract is U-shaped, and both mouth and anus open inside a circle of ciliated tentacles. They feed on small plankton such as diatoms and protozoans.

Aschelminthes

The phylum Aschelminthes includes an array of generally small, wormlike animals, without a definitely delimited head, that have a pseudocoelom, a straight or slightly curved complete digestive tract, and a cuticle. There is no respiratory or circulatory system. A flame-cell excretory system occurs in most classes but not in nematodes, which have a special type of excretory system unique with them.

The phylum is divided into six classes, each recognized as a separate phylum by some biologists. We shall discuss only two: Rotifera and Nematoda.

Class Rotifera. The rotifers—or wheel animalcules, as they are commonly called—are microscopic, usually free-living aquatic animals with a crown of cilia at the anterior end (Fig. 22.25). The cilia are generally arranged in a circle, and when beating they often give the appearance of a rotating wheel; hence the name of the class. When feeding, rotifers attach themselves by a tapering posterior "foot," and the beating cilia draw a current of water into the mouth. In this manner, very small protozoans and algae are swept into a complicated muscular pharynx, where they are ground up by seven hard jawlike structures.[13]

The fresh-water rotifers are extremely abundant. Anyone examining a drop of water for Protozoa under a microscope is likely to see one or more of these interesting animals. In fact, most of them are no larger than protozoans, and it is often difficult, when encountering them for the first time, to realize that they are multicellular.

[13] This complex pharynx is a distinctive feature of the Rotifera. It is called a mastax.

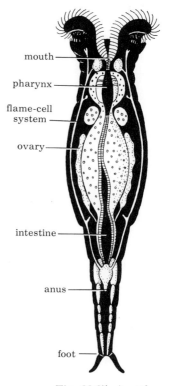

Fig. 22.25. A rotifer.

Class Nematoda (The Nematodes or Roundworms). Nematode worms have round elongate bodies that usually taper nearly to a point at both ends. Unlike flatworms, they have no cilia. The body is enclosed in a tough cuticle (Fig. 22.26). Just under the epidermal layer of the body wall are bundles of longitudinal muscles; there are no circular muscles. The lack of circular muscles and the stiff cuticle severely limit the types of movements possible for the worms, and they usually thrash about in what appears to be a random and inefficient manner.

The wall of the digestive tract consists of a single layer of endodermal cells; there is usually no muscle layer around the intestine, except sometimes at its posterior end. Between the intestine and the body wall is a fluid-filled cavity. As you can see from Fig. 22.26, this cavity is bounded internally by the endodermal wall of the intestine, and it is bounded externally in part by the bands of mesodermal muscle and in part (between the muscle bands) by the ectodermal layer of the body wall. Since the cavity is not entirely enclosed by mesoderm, it is not a coelom, but a pseudocoelom.

Nematodes are extremely abundant, and occur in almost every type of habitat. Of the many free-living in soil or water, most are very tiny, often microscopic. A single spadeful of garden soil may contain a million or more, and a bucket of water from a pond usually contains comparable numbers. Many other nematodes are internal parasites of both plants and animals; these also are often small, but some may attain a length of 3 feet or more. So numerous and widespread are nematodes that one authority has written:

If all the matter in the universe except the nematodes were swept away, our world would still be dimly recognizable, and if, as disembodied spirits, we could then investigate it, we should find its mountains, hills, vales, rivers, lakes, and oceans represented by a film of nematodes. The location of towns would be decipherable, since for every massing of human beings there would be a corresponding massing of certain nematodes. Trees would still stand in ghostly rows representing our streets and highways. The location of the various plants and animals would still be decipherable, and, had we sufficient knowledge, in many cases even their species could be determined by an examination of their erstwhile nematode parasites.[14]

Nematodes parasitic on cultivated plants cause an annual loss of millions of dollars. Others parasitic on human beings cause some serious diseases. *Trichinella spiralis,* for example, causes the disease called trichinosis, often gotten by eating insufficiently cooked pork. Adult *Trichinella* worms inhabit the small intestine of numerous species of mammals, among them hogs. Impregnated females bore through the wall of the intestine and deposit young larvae (which hatched from the eggs while still inside the uterus of the female) in the lymphatic vessels of their host. The larvae are carried by the lymph and blood to all parts of the body. They then bore out of the vessels, eventually entering every organ and tissue. However, only those that bore into skeletal muscles (especially the muscles of the diaphragm, ribs, tongue, and eyes) survive. In the muscles, they grow in size (to about one millimeter) and then curl up and encyst (Fig. 22.27); the thick wall of the cyst is formed by the host's tissues. If insufficiently cooked pork containing such cysts is eaten by a man, the walls of the cysts are digested away and the worms complete their development in the man's intestine. The adult worms then deposit larvae in the lymph vessels in the wall of the intestine, and the larvae move through the body of the man as they do in hogs, eventually encysting in muscles.

Most of the damage of trichinosis occurs

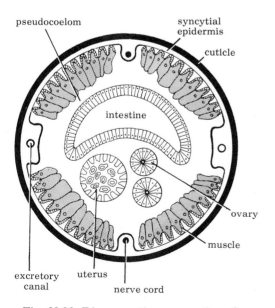

pseudocoelom · syncytial epidermis · cuticle · intestine · ovary · muscle · excretory canal · uterus · nerve cord

Fig. 22.26. Diagrammatic cross section of a nematode worm.

[14] N. A. Cobb, cited in R. Buchsbaum, *Animals Without Backbones,* 2nd ed., University of Chicago Press, 1948, pp. 156–157.

during the migration of the larvae, when half a billion or more may simultaneously bore through the body after one infection. Symptoms include excruciating muscular pains, fever, anemia, weakness, and sometimes localized swellings. Some victims die, and those that do not may sustain permanent muscular damage. Prevention of the disease is simple; pork must be thoroughly cooked to kill the encysted larvae. It is well to remember that one ounce of infected pork in the center of a large chunk of meat where heat does not reach it easily may contain as many as 100,000 encysted worms, each of which, when mature, may produce 1,500 young larvae in the body of a new host.

Among other nematodes that parasitize man are *Ascaris*, a large worm (up to a foot long) that lives in the digestive tract, lays eggs that pass to the outside with the host's feces, and infects new hosts when vegetables grown in soil contaminated with feces are eaten without adequate washing; hookworms, tiny worms common in warm climates, which cause a severely debilitating disease usually gotten by going barefoot on soil contaminated with feces containing eggs; pinworms, tiny worms common in schoolchildren, who usually get infected by putting unclean fingers with eggs on them in their mouths; and filaria worms (spread by the bite of certain mosquitoes in tropical and subtropical areas), which live in the lymphatic system, where they may accumulate in such numbers that they block the flow of lymph, causing accumulation of fluid and often enormous swelling (elephantiasis) of the infected part of the body.

THE COELOMATE PROTOSTOMIA

All the protostome phyla except the ones discussed above possess true coeloms that in most groups arise as a split in an initially solid mass of mesoderm. All have a complete digestive

Fig. 22.27. Photograph of *Trichinella spiralis* encysted in muscle. [Courtesy Bausch and Lomb, *Focus*.]

tract, and most have well-developed circulatory, excretory, and nervous systems.

The Lophophorate Phyla

There are three small phyla—Phoronida, Ectoprocta, and Brachyopoda—that resemble one another in having a *lophophore*—a fold, usually horseshoe-shaped, that encircles the mouth and bears numerous ciliated tentacles. The lophophore is a feeding device; its tentacular cilia create water currents that sweep plankton and tiny particles of detritus into a groove leading to the mouth.

All members of the lophophorate phyla are aquatic, and most are marine. Adults are usually sessile and secrete a protective case, tube, or shell around themselves, but the larvae are ciliated and free-swimming. The digestive tract is U-shaped in Phoronida and Ectoprocta and in some Brachiopoda; the anus lies outside the crown of tentacles.

The phylum Phoronida contains only about 15 species of wormlike animals that inhabit a tube of their own secretion (Fig. 22.28). They are found either buried in the sand or attached to rocks, shells, or other objects in shallow seas.

The Ectoprocta (or Bryozoa) are often called moss animals. They are very tiny (usually less than half a millimeter long), colonial, sessile animals enclosed in a case open only at the lophophore end (Fig. 22.29). Unlike most other coelomate protostomes, they lack both excretory and circulatory systems. They superficially resemble entoprocts, which were formerly included in the same phylum with them, but entoprocts have a pseudocoelom instead of a coelom and their anus is inside the ring of tentacles,[15] which is not a true lophophore.

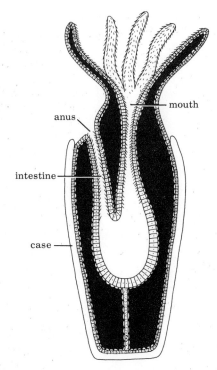

Fig. 22.29. Section through the body of an ectoproct, showing the U-shaped digestive tract. The anus is located outside the ring of tentacles.

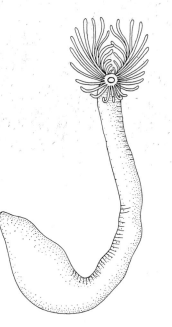

Fig. 22.28. *Phoronis architecta*, a phoronid worm. [Modified from L. H. Hyman, *The Invertebrates,* McGraw-Hill Book Co., 1959. Used by permission.]

The Brachiopoda, shelled animals that superficially resemble molluscs, are often called lamp shells because they are shaped rather like an old Roman oil lamp (Fig. 22.30). They are usually permanently attached to the ocean bottom by a fleshy stalk. There are only about 260

living species of brachiopods, but more than 30,000 fossil species are known; they were among the most common animals in the Paleozoic seas.

The relationships of the lophophorate phyla to the other phyla are very poorly understood.

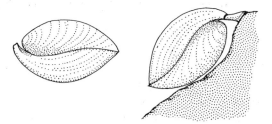

Fig. 22.30. Brachiopods. Left: The shells are shaped rather like an old Roman lamp. Right: The animals usually attach themselves to the substratum by means of a stalk.

---

[15] The name "Entoprocta" means internal anus (i.e. an anus inside the crown of tentacles) and the name "Ectoprocta" means external anus (i.e. outside the crown of tentacles).

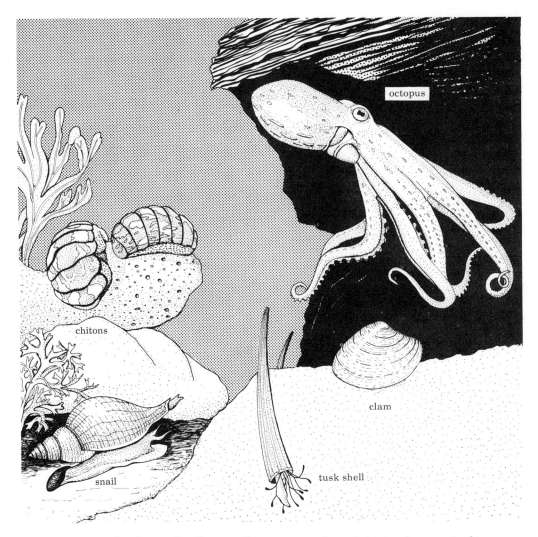

Fig. 22.31. The classes of Mollusca. Chitons are members of the Amphineura. Snails are in the class Gastropoda. Clams are members of the Pelecypoda. Tusk shells belong to the Scaphopoda. The octopus is a representative of the Cephalopoda. (Cutaway at lower right shows clam and tusk shell partly buried in a ridge of sand.)

Mollusca

The phylum Mollusca is the second-largest in the animal kingdom; it contains more than 80,000 living species and 35,000 fossil species. Among the best-known molluscs are snails and slugs, clams and oysters, squids and octopuses.

The various groups of molluscs may differ considerably in outward appearance (Fig. 22.31), but they all have fundamentally similar body plans. The soft body consists of three principal parts: (1) a large ventral muscular *foot,* which can be extruded from the shell (if one is present) and functions in locomotion; (2) a *visceral mass* above the foot, which contains the digestive system, the "kidneys" (actually specialized nephridia), the heart, and

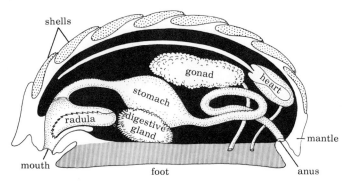

Fig. 22.32. Lateral view of a section of a chiton.

other internal organs; and (3) a heavy fold of tissue called the **mantle,** which covers the visceral mass and which in most species contains glands that secrete a shell. The mantle often overhangs the sides of the visceral mass, thus enclosing a **mantle cavity,** in which gills frequently lie (see Fig. 22.35).

Molluscs have an open circulatory system; i.e. during part of each circuit the blood is in large open sinuses where it bathes the tissues directly. Blood drains from the sinuses into vessels that run out into the gills, where the blood is oxygenated. From the gills, the blood goes to the heart, which pumps it into vessels that lead it back to the sinuses; a typical circuit, then, is heart–sinuses–gills–heart.

Most marine molluscs pass through one or more ciliated free-swimming larval stages, but fresh-water and land snails complete the corresponding developmental stages while still in the egg and hatch as miniature editions of the adult.

The mollusca are customarily divided into six classes: Amphineura, Monoplacophora, Gastropoda, Scaphopoda, Pelecypoda, and Cephalopoda.

Class Amphineura (The Chitons). The chitons are marine molluscs that some zoologists consider very primitive. It is undeniable that they are structurally simpler than most other molluscs, but there is considerable reason for thinking that their simplicity is secondary,

not primitive, and that they therefore probably differ in important ways from the original molluscan ancestors. Nevertheless, because of their simplicity, they are good animals to examine first when one is attempting to understand the basic molluscan body plan.

Figure 22.32 shows a lateral view of a dissection of a chiton. As you can see, the animal has an ovoid bilaterally symmetrical body with an anterior mouth and a posterior anus. Its lack of a distinct head is probably one of the differences between it and the ancestral molluscan. The shell consists of eight serially arranged dorsal plates.

The absence of a distinct head in chitons is probably correlated with their very sluggish, nearly sessile, way of life. They creep about on the surface of rocks in shallow water, rasping off fragments of algae with a horny toothed organ called a **radula.** Their broad flat foot can develop tremendous suction, and when disturbed they clamp down so tenaciously to the rock that they can hardly be pried loose.

Class Monoplacophora. Members of this class have long been known as fossils, but until 1952 it was thought that all had been extinct for hundreds of millions of years. In 1952, however, ten living specimens (genus *Neopilina*) were dredged from a deep trench in the Pacific Ocean off the coast of Costa Rica.

These specimens sparked a lively debate on the ancestry of the Mollusca, because they

Fig. 22.33. Some representative gastropods. (A) Boat shell (*Crepidula*), dorsal and ventral views. (B) Salt-marsh snail (*Melampus*). (C) Moon shell (*Polinices*). (D) Periwinkle (*Littorina*). (E) Channeled conch (*Busycon*). (F) Oyster drill (*Urosalpinx*). (G) Californian keyhole limpet (*Diodora*), lateral and dorsal views. (H) Abalone (*Haliotis*), dorsal and ventral views. [Drawings by Louise G. Kingsbury.]

show some internal segmentation, a characteristic seen in no other members of the phylum. Since it was already known that the early cleavage pattern and larval type of molluscs show striking similarities to the corresponding developmental stages in the segmented worms (Annelida), the segmentation of *Neopilina* led many biologists to conclude that the ancestral molluscs were segmented animals, perhaps primitive annelids. Many other biologists, however, are convinced that the segmentation of *Neopilina* is secondary, not primitive, and that the original molluscan body was unsegmented. Whichever view is correct, it seems clear that the Mollusca and Annelida are fairly closely related.

Class Gastropoda (The Snails and Their Relatives). Most gastropods have a coiled shell.[16] The early larva is bilateral, but, as it develops, the digestive tract bends downward and forward until the anus comes to lie close to the mouth. Then the entire visceral mass is rotated through an angle of 180 degrees, so that it comes to lie dorsal to the head in the anterior part of the body. Most of the visceral organs on one side (usually the left) atrophy, and growth proceeds asymmetrically, producing the characteristic spiral.

Except for the peculiar twisting and coiling of their body, gastropods are thought to be rather like the ancestral molluscs. They have a distinct head with well-developed sense organs, as the ancestral molluscs probably did. Most have a well-developed radula and feed on bits of plant or animal tissue that they grate, rasp, or brush loose with this organ.

Gastropods occur in a great variety of habitats. The majority are marine, and their often large and decorative shells are among the most prized finds on a beach (Fig. 22.33), but there are also many fresh-water species and some that live on land. The land snails are one of the few groups of fully terrestrial invertebrates. In most of them, the gills have disappeared, but the mantle cavity has become very highly vas-

cularized and functions as a lung. Such snails are said to be pulmonate. Some pulmonate snails have secondarily returned to the water and must periodically come to the surface to obtain air.

Class Scaphopoda (The Tusk Shells). Scaphopods have a long tubular shell, open at both ends (Fig. 22.31). One end is usually smaller than the other, and the shell thus has a tusk-like or toothlike appearance. All scaphopods are marine, living buried in mud or sand. The living animals are seldom seen, but the shells of dead ones can sometimes be found washed up on a beach.

Class Pelecypoda (The Bivalve Molluscs). As the term "bivalve" indicates, these animals have a two-part shell. The two parts, or valves, are usually similar in shape and size and are hinged on one side (Fig. 22.34). The animals open and shut them by means of large muscles. Among the most common bivalves are clams, oysters, scallops, cockles, and mussels. Most lead rather sedentary lives as adults, though scallops sometimes swim about by rapidly opening and shutting the valves of their shell.

Pelecypods are filter feeders, straining tiny food particles from the water flowing across their gills. The process is described on p. 183.

Class Cephalopoda (Squids, Octopuses, and Their Relatives). Many of the cephalopods bear little outward resemblance to other molluscs. Unlike their sedentary relatives, they are often specialized for rapid locomotion and a predatory way of life—for killing and eating large prey, such as fishes or crabs. Though fossil cephalopods often had large shells, these are much reduced or absent in most modern forms.[17] The body is elongate, with a large and

---

[16] In some cases, the coiling is minimal. Some species—the slugs—have lost the shell.

[17] *Nautilus* is an exception—a modern form with a well-developed shell.

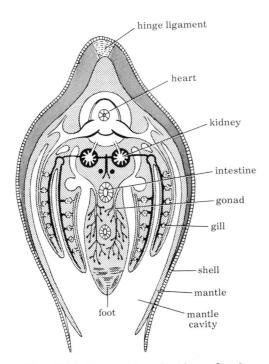

Fig. 22.34. **Cross section of a clam.** [Modified from W. Stempell, *Zoologie im Grundriss*, Borntraeger, 1926.]

well-developed head encircled by long tentacles.

Some species attain a large size, often being several feet long. The giant squids (*Architeuthis*) of the North Atlantic are the largest living invertebrates; the biggest recorded individual was 55 feet long (including the tentacles) and weighed approximately 2 tons. Octopuses never grow anywhere near this size (except in Hollywood).

Cephalopods, particularly squids (see Fig. 6.9B, p. 211), have convergently evolved many similarities to vertebrates. For example, squids have internal cartilaginous supports analogous to the vertebrate skeleton, and they even have a cartilaginous braincase rather like a skull. Furthermore, they have an exceedingly well-developed nervous system with a large and complex brain (see Fig. 10.16, p. 379). Perhaps the most striking of all the squids' simi-

larities to vertebrates are their large camera-type image-forming eyes, which work exactly the way ours do.

Annelida

The Annelida, or segmented worms, have been discussed extensively in other parts of this book. We have examined their digestive system (p. 183), their gas exchange (p. 210), their closed circulatory system (p. 244), their nephridia (p. 284), their nervous system (pp. 363 and 414), and their hydrostatic skeleton, muscle arrangement, and methods of locomotion (p. 433). The discussion here will therefore be brief.

The phylum is usually divided into three classes: Polychaeta, Oligochaeta, and Hirudinea.

Class Polychaeta. Polychaetes are marine annelids with a well-defined head bearing eyes and antennae (Fig. 22.35). Each of the numerous serially arranged body segments usually bears a pair of lateral appendages called *parapodia* that function in both locomotion and

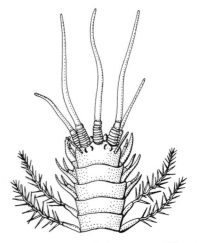

Fig. 22.35. **Head and first two gill-bearing segments of *Diopatra*, a polychaete worm.** [Modified from R. D. Barnes, *Invertebrate Zoology*, Saunders, 1963.]

gas exchange (see Fig. 6.9A, p. 211). There are numerous stiff setae (bristles) on the parapodia (the name "Polychaeta" means many chaetae, i.e. setae).

Some polychaetes swim or crawl about actively; others are more sedentary, usually living in tubes they construct in the mud or sand of the ocean bottom. These tubes may be simple mucus-lined burrows, membranous structures, or elaborately constructed dwellings composed of sand grains cemented together. The tubes of some species are straight, while those of others are U-shaped and have two openings (Fig. 22.36). The beating parapodia keep water currents flowing through the tubes; these currents bring oxygen, and in some cases food particles, to the worm. Many of the tube dwellers are beautiful animals, often colored bright red, pink, or green; some are iridescent. Among the most beautiful are the fanworms, which have a crown of colorful, much-branched fanlike or featherlike processes that they wave in the water at the entrance to their tube (Fig. 22.37).

All the segments of the body are usually much alike. The coelom of each is partly separated from the coeloms of adjacent segments by membranous intersegmental partitions; the partitions of many polychaetes are not complete, however, and in some species they have been entirely lost. Each segment generally has its own ventral ganglion and its own pair of nephridia.[18]

The sexes are separate in the majority of species. In primitive polychaetes most segments produce gametes, but in more advanced species gamete production is restricted to a few specialized segments. The gametes are usually shed into the coelom and leave the body through the nephridia. Fertilization is external. In many species, development includes a ciliated free-swimming larval stage called a *trochophore* (see Fig. 22.57).

[18] In a few species of polychaetes, there is only one pair of nephridia for the whole animal.

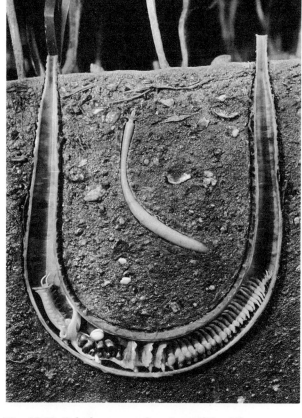

Fig. 22.36. Polychaete and sipunculid. The parchment worm (*Chaetopterus pergamentacus*) is a polychaete that lives in a U-shaped tube. The smaller worm located between the arms of the U tube is a sipunculid (*Phascolosoma gouldii*). [Courtesy American Museum of Natural History.]

Class Oligochaeta. The class Oligochaeta contains the earthworms and many fresh-water species. They differ from polychaetes in lacking a well-developed head, in lacking parapodia, in having fewer setae (the name "Oligochaeta" means few setae), in usually having both male and female organs in each individual, and in usually having more complete intersegmental partitions. We have described most of the important characteristics of earthworms in earlier chapters (see Fig. 5.19, p. 182; Fig. 5.23, p. 186; Fig. 7.20, p. 244; Fig. 8.9, p. 284; and Fig. 10.5, p. 364).

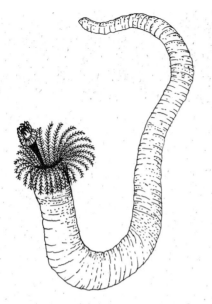

Fig. 22.37. *Hydroides*, a fanworm. The colorful fan of finely branched processes protrudes from the open end of the calcareous tube in which the animal lives.

Class Hirudinea (The Leeches). The leeches, which probably evolved from oligochaetes, are the most specialized annelids. Their body is dorsoventrally flattened and often tapered at both ends. The first and last segments are modified to form suckers, the posterior one being much the larger. We have already described the way these suckers are used in locomotion (see Fig. 11.4, p. 433). Leeches show almost no evidence of internal segmentation; the intersegmental partitions have been completely lost except in a few very primitive species.

Some leeches are predacious, capturing invertebrate prey such as worms, snails, and insect larvae and swallowing them whole. More familiar than this type are the bloodsuckers, which attack a variety of vertebrate and invertebrate hosts. When such a leech attacks a host, it selects a thin area of the host's integument, attaches itself by its posterior sucker, applies the anterior sucker very tightly to the skin, and either painlessly slits the skin with

small bladelike jaws or dissolves an opening by means of enzymes. It then secretes into the wound a substance (hirudin) that prevents coagulation of the blood, and begins to suck the blood, usually consuming an enormous quantity at one feeding and then not feeding again for a fairly long time (some have been known to go unfed for more than a year without apparent harm).

Small Phyla Related to Annelida. Two small phyla of wormlike animals clearly related to the Annelida may be mentioned in passing. One—the Sipunculida—contains about 250 species of unsegmented marine worms that live in the sand or mud of the ocean bottom (Fig. 22.36). The other—Echiurida—are sausage-shaped animals with an anterior proboscis; they show evidence of segmentation during embryonic development but not in the adult.

Onychophora

There are only about 65 living species of this small phylum, all restricted to tropical regions or to the temperate parts of the Southern Hemisphere (Australia, New Zealand, South Africa, and the Andes). They are mostly confined to very moist habitats on land, living beneath leaves, logs, or stones in forests, and are active at night.

Onychophorans look rather like caterpillars, having a wormlike body with from 14 to 43 pairs of short unjointed legs (Fig. 22.38). These animals are of special interest because they have a combination of annelid and arthropod characters and are regarded as an early evolutionary offshoot from the line leading to the arthropods from an ancient annelidlike ancestor (see Fig. 22.42). They have a thin flexible permeable cuticle more like the cuticle of annelids than the exoskeleton of arthropods. Like the annelids, they have a pair of nephridia in each segment. And their movement is more like that of an earthworm than that of an arthropod, though the body is held off the ground

Fig. 22.38. An onychophoran. [Courtesy Ward's Natural Science Establishment, Inc., Rochester, N.Y.]

by the stumpy legs. However, they resemble arthropods in having claws and in having an open circulatory system. The tracheal respiratory system of modern onychophorans probably evolved independently of the tracheae of terrestrial arthropods.

Another small phylum—the Tardigrada—may be related to the Onychophora. It, too, shows a combination of annelid and arthropod characters, with emphasis on the latter. The tardigrades (sometimes called water bears) are very tiny (less than a millimeter long). Some live among the sand grains in shallow water along the coast, others live in fresh water, and still others live in the film of moisture on the surfaces of mosses and lichens.

Arthropoda

The phylum Arthropoda is by far the largest of the phyla. More than 800,000 species have been described, and there are doubtless hundreds of thousands (perhaps millions) more yet to be discovered. Probably more than 80 percent of all the animal species on the earth belong to this phylum.

Arthropods are characterized by their jointed chitinous exoskeleton and jointed legs. The exoskeleton, which is secreted by the epidermis, functions both as a point of attachment for muscles and as a protective armor, but it imposes limitations on growth and must be periodically molted if the animal is to undergo much increase in size (Fig. 22.39; see also Fig. 16.17, p. 619). The arthropod cuticle is not restricted to the exterior surface of the body; long rod-shaped processes that often project from the surface deep into the interior of the animal function as bases for muscle attachment, and both the anterior and the posterior portions of the digestive tract (and the tracheae of land arthropods) are lined with cuticle. These internal extensions of the exoskeleton are also shed at each molt.

Together with their elaborate exoskeleton, arthropods have evolved a complex musculature quite unlike that of most other invertebrates. It comprises not only longitudinal and circular bands, as in so many invertebrates, but also separate muscles that, running in myriad directions, make possible an extensive repertoire of movements. Most of the muscles are striated.

The nervous system is very well developed. Of a similar organization as the annelid nervous

Fig. 22.39. A molting milliped. [Courtesy N. F. Snyder, Cornell University.]

system, it consists of a dorsal brain and a ventral double nerve cord. Primitively there were ganglia in each segment, but in many groups the ganglia have tended to move forward and fuse into larger ganglionic masses. Sensory organs are many and varied. The arthropod nervous system was discussed more extensively in Chapter 10 (p. 363). Hormonal control, too, is well developed (see p. 320).

As we have seen (p. 244, Fig. 7.21), arthropods have an open circulatory system. There is usually an elongate dorsal vessel called the heart, which pumps the blood forward into arteries (the extent of these arteries varies greatly among the various groups of arthropods). From the arteries, the blood goes into open sinuses, where it bathes the tissues directly. Eventually the blood returns to the posterior portion of the heart.

The body spaces through which the blood moves constitute the *hemocoel*—not a true coelom but a cavity derived from the embryonic blastocoel. Although arthropods almost certainly descended from an annelidlike ancestor with well-developed coelomic cavities, and although such cavities develop in arthropod embryos, they are not retained as the functional body cavity of the adults.[19]

In most aquatic arthropods (excluding secondarily aquatic ones, among them some insects), excretion of nitrogenous wastes (primarily ammonia) is principally by way of the gills. Aquatic species usually also have special saclike glands, located near or in the head, that play a minor role in excretion; these glands (usually called coxal glands or green glands) have their own ducts leading to the outside. The excretory organs in most groups of terrestrial arthropods are Malpighian tubules (see Fig. 8.14, p. 291).

The sexes are usually separate. Fertilization is internal in all terrestrial and in most aquatic forms.

---

[19] The cavity of the gonads (and that of the excretory ducts in some arthropods) may be a remnant of the true coelom.

It is generally held that arthropods evolved either from a polychaete annelid or from the ancestor of the polychaetes. The arthropod body plan may be viewed as an elaboration and specialization of the segmented body of that annelid ancestor. The evidence indicates that the first arthropods had long wormlike bodies composed of many nearly identical segments, each bearing a pair of legs. All the legs were alike. Among the host of different modifications of this ancestral body plan that have arisen in the various groups of arthropods during the millions of years of their evolution, four tendencies stand out particularly: (1) a tendency toward reduction of the total number of segments; (2) a tendency toward grouping the segments into distinct body regions, such as a head and trunk, or a head, thorax, and abdomen; (3) a tendency toward increasing cephalization, i.e. toward incorporation of more segments into the head and toward concentration of nervous control and sensory perception in or just behind the head; (4) a tendency toward specialization of the legs of some segments for a variety of functions other than locomotion, and toward complete loss of legs from many other segments.

Subphylum Trilobita. Arthropods were very abundant in the Paleozoic seas, and fossils from that era are plentiful. Particularly common in rocks of the first half of the Paleozoic are the fossils of an extinct group—the Trilobita. The body of these animals was usually oval and flattened (Fig. 22.40). The segments were grouped into three body regions: a head, apparently composed of four fused segments and bearing a pair of slender antennae and often compound eyes; a thorax consisting of a variable number of separate segments; and an abdomen (pygidium), composed of several fused segments. It is not to this tripartite division, however, that the name "Trilobita" refers, but to a division of the body into a median lobe and two lateral lobes by two prominent longitudinal furrows running along the dorsum.

Fig. 22.40. A fossil of a trilobite. [Courtesy N. F. Snyder, Cornell University.]

Trilobites, though certainly different from the first arthropods, and exhibiting specializations of their own (e.g. the longitudinal furrows and the fusion of the abdominal segments), nevertheless approach the hypothetical arthropod ancestor more closely than any other known group. One primitive character stands out particularly—the lack of specialization and structural differentiation of the appendages. Every segment bore a pair of legs, and all these legs, including those of the four head segments, were nearly identical. There were thus no appendages specialized as mouthparts.

Trilobites are so markedly different from all other arthropods that they are often regarded as a separate subphylum. Two other subphyla —Chelicerata and Mandibulata—are usually recognized. In both these groups, the tendency toward specialization of some appendages and loss of others is quite evident; thus in both groups, the appendages of the most anterior segments have been modified as mouthparts and no longer function in locomotion.

Figure 22.41 shows one possible way of representing the hypothetical relationships of the arthropod subphyla and classes.

Subphylum Chelicerata. The chelicerate body is usually divided into two regions: a cephalothorax (prosoma) and an abdomen. There are no antennae. The appendages corresponding to the first pair of postoral legs in ancestral arthropods and trilobites are modified as mouthparts called *chelicerae*, which may be either pincerlike or fanglike. The cephalothorax usually bears five other pairs of appendages besides the chelicerae; in some groups these are all walking legs, while in others only the last four pairs are legs, the first pair being modified as feeding devices called *pedipalps*, which are often much longer than the chelicerae (see Fig. 17.8, p. 669). The legs of the abdominal segments have been either lost or modified into respiratory or sexual structures.

The subphylum Chelicerata includes four classes. One (Eurypterida) consists entirely of animals extinct since the Paleozoic era, and the members of another (Pycnogonida, the sea spiders) are very rare marine animals.

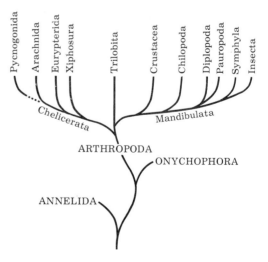

Fig. 22.41. Diagram of possible relationships between the Annelida, the Onychophora, and the subphyla and classes of the Arthropoda.

Members of a third class (Xiphosura) are familiar to anyone who has spent some time on the Atlantic beaches of North America (or the coast of Asia from Japan and Korea to Malaysia and Indonesia). These are the horseshoe crabs, also called king crabs[20] (Fig. 22.42), which are not really crabs at all but living relicts of an ancient chelicerate class most members of which have been extinct for millions of years.

Members of the fourth class of chelicerates —Arachnida—are familiar to everyone. These are the spiders, ticks, mites, daddy longlegs, scorpions, whipscorpions, and their relatives. Though the various groups of arachnids differ structurally in many ways, most have two body regions, a cephalothorax and an abdomen (these are not distinguishable in ticks, mites, or daddy longlegs). There are often simple eyes on the cephalothorax, but never any compound eyes or antennae. The cephalothorax bears six pairs of appendages: a pair of chelicerae, a pair of pedipalps, and four pairs of walking legs. In most groups, prey is seized and

[20] The commercial "king crab" (genus *Paralithodes*) of the north Pacific is a different animal. It is a true crab—a member of the class Crustacea.

torn apart by the pedipalps. The chelicerae may also function in manipulating prey, or they may be modified as poison fangs, as in spiders. The abdomen of arachnids may be long, as in scorpions, or short, as in spiders. In some (including spiders), the bases of one or two pairs of abdominal appendages are retained as much-modified book lungs; in others, no trace of abdominal appendages remains. In addition to the book lungs, many arachnids have tracheae, and some respire by means of tracheae only. Several arachnid groups possess glands that secrete silk.

Subphylum Mandibulata. The members of this subphylum differ from chelicerates in having antennae and in having *mandibles* instead of chelicerae as their first pair of mouthparts. Mandibles are modified from the basal segment (coxa) of the ancestral legs and function in biting and chewing (though in some species they are secondarily modified for piercing and sucking). They are never clawlike or pincer-like, as chelicerae frequently are. In most mandibulates, there are two additional pairs of mouthparts called *maxillae.*

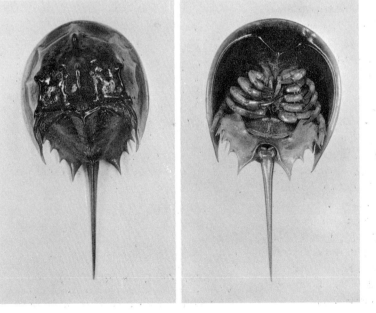

Fig. 22.42. *Limulus poly-phemus,* the horseshoe crab. Left: Dorsal view. Right: Ventral view. [Courtesy American Museum of Natural History.]

The subphylum comprises six classes. We shall mention four of them here: Crustacea, Chilopoda, Diplopoda, and Insecta.

Class Crustacea. Some representatives of this class, such as crayfish, lobsters, shrimps, and crabs (Fig. 22.43), are well known to most people. But there are many other species of Crustacea, which bear little superficial resemblance to these familiar animals; among them are fairy shrimps (e.g. *Branchinecta*), water fleas (e.g. *Daphnia*), brine shrimps (*Artemia*), sand hoppers (*Gammarus*), barnacles (e.g. *Balanus, Mitella*), and sow bugs (e.g. *Porcellio*); many of these are very small odd-looking creatures (Fig. 22.44).

Crustacea characteristically have two pairs of antennae, a pair of mandibles, and two pairs of maxillae. But the rest of the appendages vary greatly from group to group, and whatever could be said about those of one group, such as crayfish and lobsters, would have little relevance to those of other groups. In fact, the Crustacea are an enormously diverse assemblage of animals that can hardly be characterized in any simple way. Some have a cephalothorax and an abdomen; others have a head and a trunk, or a head, thorax, and abdomen, or even a unified body. Most are free-living, but some are parasitic. Most are active swimmers, but some, like barnacles, secrete a shell and are sessile. The majority are marine, but there are many fresh-water species, and a few, such as sow bugs, are terrestrial and have a simple tracheal system. We could go on listing character after character, but the point of the amazing diversity of this group has been made. This is a class in which the basic arrangement of a segmented body with numerous jointed appendages has been modified and exploited in countless ways as the members of the class have diverged into different habitats and adopted different modes of life.

Class Chilopoda. Members of this class are called centipeds (or hundred-legged worms). Their body is divided into two regions, a head

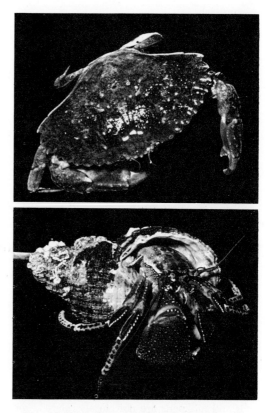

Fig. 22.43. A *Cancer* crab and a hermit crab. This species of *Cancer* (top), which occurs on the west coast of the United States, is used as food. The hermit crabs (bottom) have soft naked abdomens, which they protect by backing into abandoned gastropod shells. They carry the shell around with them and when disturbed may retreat entirely into it. [Courtesy Lynwood S. Smith, University of Washington.]

and a trunk (Fig. 22.45). The trunk is elongate and often somewhat flattened. The head bears a single pair of antennae and three pairs of mouthparts (mandibles and two pairs of maxillae). The animals are carnivorous, and the legs of the first trunk segment are modified as large poison claws. Each of the other trunk segments bears a single pair of walking legs. All centipeds are terrestrial and respire by means of tracheae. Excretion is by Malpighian tubules. The genital ducts open at the rear of the body.

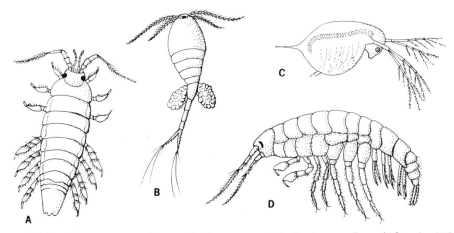

Fig. 22.44. Some representative small Crustacea. (A) Marine sow bug (*Idotea*). (B) Fresh-water copepod (*Cyclops*). (C) Water flea (*Daphnia*). (D) Sand hopper (*Gammarus*). [Based on drawings by Louise G. Kingsbury.]

Class Diplopoda. These animals are called millipeds (or thousand-legged worms). They superficially resemble centipeds and in fact were once placed with them (and with two other smaller groups) in a class called Myriapoda. However, it is now known that centipeds and millipeds are not closely related, and each is placed in a separate class.

The milliped body is divided into a head and a trunk (Fig. 22.46). The head bears a pair of antennae but only two pairs of mouthparts (mandibles, and a pair of maxillae fused to form a platelike underlip). The animals have no poison claws, and are not carnivorous, feeding largely on decaying organic matter of various types. Each of the first four or five trunk segments (depending on the species) bears a single pair of legs, but each of the other segments bears two pairs of legs (and also two pairs of spiracles); it is clear that each of the double-legged segments is formed by the fusion of two segments. Respiration is by tracheae, and excretion is by Malpighian tubules. The genital ducts open anteriorly, on the second segment. In most milliped orders, the legs

(one or both pairs) of the seventh segment in the males are highly modified and function as organs for inserting sperms into the female reproductive tract (see Fig. 17.21, p. 688).

Class Insecta. This is an enormous group of diverse animals that occupy almost every conceivable habitat on land and in fresh water. If numbers are the criterion by which to judge biological success, then the insects are the most successful group of animals that has ever lived;

Fig. 22.45. A centiped. [Courtesy Thomas Eisner, Cornell University.]

Fig. 22.46. Two millipeds. The specimen at the top has a cylindrical body and legs so short that they cannot be seen from above. The bottom specimen has a flattened body and longer legs; note that there are two pairs of legs on each trunk segment.

there are more species of insects than of all other animal groups combined. But there is one qualification to their dominant role—they do not occur in the sea (although a few species walk on the ocean surface); the role played by insects on land is played in the sea by Crustacea.

There are a few insect fossils from the Devonian, but it was in the Carboniferous and Permian periods that insects took their place as one of the dominant groups of animals (see Table 21.2, p. 824). By the end of the Paleozoic era, many of the modern orders had appeared, and the number of species was enormous. A second great period of evolutionary radiation began in the Cretaceous and continues to the present time; this second radiation is correlated with the rise of flowering plants.

The insect body is divided into three regions: a head, a thorax, and an abdomen (Fig. 22.47). The head segments are completely fused, and in adults their boundaries cannot be distinguished. The head bears numerous sensory receptors, usually including compound eyes; one pair of antennae; and three pairs of mouthparts derived from ancestral legs. The mouthparts include a pair of mandibles, a pair of maxillae, and a lower lip, called a *labium,* formed by fusion of the two second maxillae; some biologists think that the upper lip, or *labrum,* is also derived from ancestral legs (Fig. 22.48).

The thorax is composed of three segments—prothorax, mesothorax, and metathorax—each of which bears a pair of walking legs. In many insects (but not all), the second and third thoracic segments each bear a pair of wings.

The abdomen is composed of a variable number of segments (12 or fewer). Abdominal segments are devoid of legs, but highly modified remnants of the ancestral appendages may

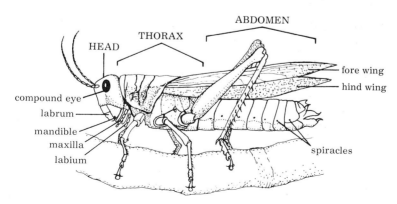

Fig. 22.47. A grasshopper.

be present at the posterior end, where they function in mating and egg laying.[21]

We have already discussed the insects at considerable length in other chapters and need

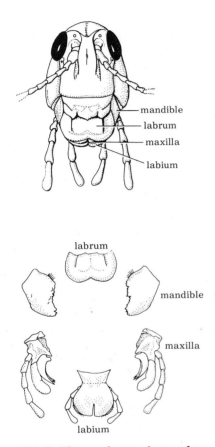

Fig. 22.48. The mouthparts of a grasshopper. Top: Front view of head, with mouthparts *in situ*. Bottom: The mouthparts removed from the head but kept in their proper relative positions. The mandibles and probably the labrum (upper lip) are derived from the basal segments of ancestral legs; all the other segments of those legs have been lost. The maxillae and labium (lower lip) retain more of the segments of the legs from which they are derived; the basal segments are enlarged and the distal segments form slender leglike structures called palps, which bear many sensory receptors. [Modified from T. I. Storer and R. L. Usinger, *General Zoology*, McGraw-Hill Book Co., 1957. Used by permission.]

not repeat ourselves here. See the discussion of the insect tracheal system (p. 218, Figs. 6.17, 6.18), the circulatory system (p. 244, Fig. 7.21), the Malpighian excretory organs (p. 290, Fig. 8.14), hormonal control (p. 322, Fig. 9.18), nervous control and sensory perception (p. 401, Figs. 10.31, 10.32), the exoskeleton and muscles (p. 434, Figs. 11.5A-B, 11.14), behavior (Chapter 12), and development (p. 620, Figs. 16.17, 16.21, 16.22).

The insects are classified in approximately 25 orders (the exact number depends upon the authority cited). The following are among the more familiar.

THYSANURA: bristletails and silverfish. Small, primitive, wingless; chewing mouthparts; long tail-like appendages on rear of abdomen. Incomplete metamorphosis. Common in houses, particularly in kitchens and bathrooms; sometimes damage books in libraries.

ODONATA: dragonflies and damselflies (Fig. 22.49D). Medium to large, rapid-flying, predaceous on other insects; two pairs of long membranous wings; chewing mouthparts; very large compound eyes. Immature stages (nymphs) in fresh water; incomplete metamorphosis.

ORTHOPTERA: grasshoppers, crickets, walking sticks, mantids, cockroaches (Fig. 22.49A), termites, (termites are often put in a separate order called Isoptera). Usually two pairs of wings—the fore wings narrower than the hind wings, coarse-textured, not used in flight, functioning (when animal is at rest) as covers for the folded fanlike hind wings;[22] chewing mouthparts. Gradual metamorphosis.

HEMIPTERA: true bugs (Fig. 22.49I). Usually two pairs of wings—basal half of fore wings thick and leathery, distal half membranous, hind wings membranous; piercing-sucking mouthparts. Gradual metamorphosis.

21 A few primitive insects retain vestiges of appendages on many abdominal segments. These may have a sensory function.

22 The description of the wings of Orthoptera given here does not apply to termites.

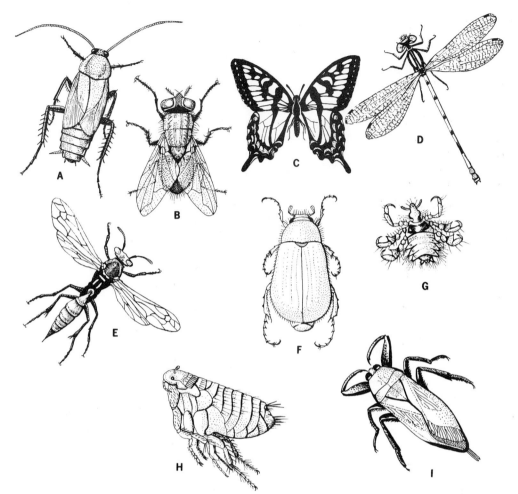

Fig. 22.49. Some representatives of the major insect orders. (A) Cockroach (order Orthoptera). (B) Fly (Diptera). (C) Butterfly (Lepidoptera). (D) Damselfly (Odonata). (E) Wasp (Hymenoptera). (F) Beetle (Coleoptera). (G) Louse (Anoplura). (H) Flea (Siphonaptera). (I) Bug (Hemiptera). The insects are not drawn to the same scale.

ANOPLURA: sucking lice (Fig. 22.49G). External parasites. Wingless; piercing-sucking mouthparts; legs and claws adapted for clinging to host. Gradual metamorphosis.

COLEOPTERA: beetles (Fig. 22.49F). Two pairs of wings—fore wings hard, meeting along middorsal line, forming a protective case for the folded membranous hind wings when at rest; chewing mouthparts. Complete metamorphosis.

LEPIDOPTERA: moths and butterflies (Fig. 22.49C). Two pairs of large scale-covered wings; chewing mouthparts in larvae, sucking (but not piercing) mouthparts in adults. Complete metamorphosis.

DIPTERA: true flies (mosquitoes, gnats, midges, houseflies, horseflies, etc.) (Fig. 22.49B). One pair of membranous wings (the hind wings present as tiny balancing organs); piercing-sucking or sponging mouthparts. Complete metamorphosis.

SIPHONAPTERA: fleas (Fig. 22.49H). Intermittent ectoparasites. Small, body laterally compressed; no wings; piercing-sucking mouthparts; long legs, adapted for jumping. Complete metamorphosis.

HYMENOPTERA: sawflies, ants, bees, wasps (Fig. 22.49E). Usually two pairs of membranous wings, interlocked in flight; chewing or chewing-lapping mouthparts; thorax and abdomen connected by a very narrow waist. Complete metamorphosis.

A more complete listing of the insect orders is given in the Appendix.

THE DEUTEROSTOMIA

There are only five phyla in the Deuterostomia, and only two of these—Echinodermata and Chordata—are major groups. We shall discuss these and a small phylum—Hemichordata—that is important from an evolutionary standpoint. The other two phyla—Chaetognatha (arrow worms) and Pogonophora (beard worms)—contain only a few, exclusively marine species and are not important for our purposes here.

Echinodermata

The echinoderms are exclusively marine, mostly bottom-dwelling animals. They are common in all seas and at all depths from the intertidal zone to the ocean deeps. Included in this distinctive phylum are the starfishes, brittle stars, sea urchins, sand dollars, sea cucumbers, and sea lilies.

The adults are radially symmetrical, but the larvae are bilateral, and it is generally held that echinoderms evolved from bilateral ancestors. The radial symmetry probably arose as an adaptation to a sessile way of life. Most of the modern echinoderms (with the exception of sea lilies) move about slowly and are thus not sessile, but apparently the ancient echinoderms were.

Almost all members of this phylum possess an internal skeleton composed of numerous calcareous plates embedded in the body wall. These plates may be separate, or they may be fused to form a rigid boxlike structure. The skeleton frequently bears many bumps or spines that project from the surface of the animal (these are particularly noticeable in sea urchins; see Fig. 22.53). It is this characteristic that gives the animals the name "Echinodermata" (from the Greek echino-, spiny, and derma, skin).

Echinoderms have a well-developed coelom in which the various internal organs are suspended. The complete digestive system is the most prominent of the organ systems. There is no special excretory system, and the blood circulatory system, though present, is poorly developed. The nervous system is radially organized, consisting of nerve networks that connect to ringlike ganglionated nerve cords running around the body of the animal (there are often three of these cords); there is no brain.

A characteristic unique in echinoderms is their *water-vascular system.* This is a system of tubes (usually called canals) filled with watery fluid. Water can enter the system through a sievelike plate, often called a madreporite, on the surface of the animal. A tube from this plate leads to a ring canal that encircles the esophagus (Fig. 22.50). Five radial canals branch off the ring canal and run along symmetrically spaced grooves or bands on the surface of the animal. Many short side branches from the radial canals lead to hollow *tube feet* that project to the exterior. Each tube foot is a thin-walled hollow cylinder, with a sucker on its end. At the base of each tube foot is a muscular ampulla. When the ampulla contracts, the fluid in it is prevented by a valve from flowing into the radial canal; consequently it is forced into the tube foot, which is thereby extended. The foot attaches to the substratum by its sucker, and then longitudinal muscles in its wall contract, shortening it and pulling the animal forward (while forcing the water back

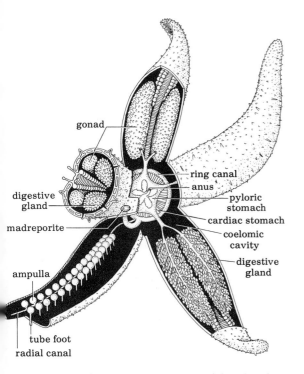

gonad

digestive gland

madreporite

ampulla

tube foot

radial canal

ring canal

anus

pyloric stomach

cardiac stomach

coelomic cavity

digestive gland

Fig. 22.50. Dissection of a starfish (dorsal view).

into the ampulla). This cycle of events, repeated rapidly by the many tube feet of an animal like a starfish, enables it to move slowly. The tube feet may also enable it to hold tightly to a rock or other object by applying suction, or they may be used to pull open the valves of the shell of a clam or oyster, on which the starfish will feed.

The sexes are usually separate. Eggs and sperms are shed into the surrounding water, where fertilization occurs. Cleavage is radial and indeterminate. The larva is ciliated and free-swimming (see Fig. 16.20, p. 620). It has a complete digestive tract; the anus is derived from the embryonic blastopore, the mouth being a new opening.

Class Asteroidea (The Starfishes). Let us examine a starfish (*Asterias*) more closely. The starfish body consists of a central *disc* and five *arms,* each with a groove bearing rows of tube

feet running along the middle of its lower surface. The outer surface of the animal is studded with many short spines and numerous tiny skin gills, which are thin fingerlike evaginations of the body wall that protrude to the outside between the plates of the endoskeleton (see Fig. 6.8, p. 210). The cavity of each skin gill is continuous with the general coelom. Scattered between the spines and skin gills are often numerous small jawlike structures called pedicellariae, which are used for protection and for capturing very small animals. The madreporite is on the upper surface (but not in the center; in this respect, the radial symmetry of the animal is not perfect).

The mouth is located in the center of the lower surface of the disc and the anus in the center of the upper surface (thus the lower surface is the morphological anterior end of the animal, and the upper surface is the morphological posterior end). The digestive tract of a starfish is straight and very short, consisting of a short esophagus, a broad stomach that fills most of the interior of the disc, and a very short intestine. The stomach is divided by a constriction into two parts: a large eversible part (cardiac stomach) at the esophageal (lower) end and a smaller noneversible part (pyloric stomach) at the intestinal (upper) end. Attached to the noneversible part are five pairs of large digestive glands; each pair of glands lies in the coelomic cavity of one of the arms (Fig. 22.50).

When the starfish feeds, it pushes the lower part of the stomach out through the mouth, turning it inside out and placing it over food material such as the soft body of a clam or oyster. The stomach secretes digestive enzymes onto the food, and digestion begins. The partly digested food is then taken into the upper part of the stomach and into the digestive glands, where digestion is completed and the products are absorbed.

Starfishes have amazing regenerative abilities. Even a single detached arm can regenerate an entire new animal (Fig. 22.51).

Other Echinoderm Classes. Although members of the four other echinoderm classes often show little superficial resemblance to starfishes, their structure is fundamentally similar. For example, sea urchins and sea cucumbers lack the five arms of a starfish, but they do have five bands of tube feet and thus show the same basic pentaradiate symmetry.

Class Ophiuroidea. These are the brittle stars, serpent stars, and basket stars (Fig. 22.52). They superficially resemble true starfishes (Asteroidea) in having five arms, but the arms are longer, much slenderer, more flexible, often branched, and grooveless. The body disc is relatively small. The tube feet have no ampullae and are not used in locomotion, which is by rapid lashing of the arms. There is a large stomach but no intestine and no anus. Gas exchange is by invaginated pouches in the periphery of the disc.

Class Echinoidea. These are the sea urchins, sand dollars, and heart urchins. They have no arms, but do have five bands of tube feet. The body is spherical or flattened and oval, and is covered with long spines (Fig. 22.53). The plates of the endoskeleton are fused to form a rigid box or case. There is a complex chewing apparatus just inside the mouth, and the intestine is long and coiled. Gas exchange is by small but highly branched gills or by modified tube feet.

Class Holothuroidea. The sea cucumbers (Fig. 22.54) differ from the other echinoderms in having a much reduced endoskeleton and a leathery body. Also unlike the classes discussed above, they lie on their side rather than on the oral surface. The mouth is surrounded by tentacles attached to the water-vascular system. There is a very long coiled intestine (see Fig. 6.11, p. 213). Gas exchange is usually by complexly branched respiratory trees attached to the cloaca (see p. 211).

Class Crinoidea. This is the oldest and most primitive of the living classes of echinoderms.

Fig. 22.51. A detached arm of a starfish regenerating a new body. [Modified from L. H. Hyman, *The Invertebrates*, McGraw-Hill Book Co., 1955. Used by permission.]

The sea lilies, as most Crinoidea are commonly called, are attached to the substratum by a long stalk and are thus sessile (Fig. 22.55). They have long feathery arms (often branched) around the mouth, which is on the upper side; the sea lilies thus differ from the Asteroidea, Ophiuroidea, and Echinoidea in that their morphological anterior end is directed upward and their morphological posterior end downward. Some modern crinoids—the feather stars —lack a stalk and are not sessile.

Hemichordata

The hemichordates, many of which are called acorn worms (or tongue worms), are marine animals often found living in U-shaped burrows in sand or mud along the coast.[23] They are fairly large worms, ranging from 3½ to 17 inches in length. Their body consists of an anterior conical proboscis (thought by some to resemble an acorn—hence their name), a collar, and a long trunk (Fig. 22.56). The mouth is situated ventrally, at the junction between the proboscis and the collar. A particularly important feature is a series of *gill slits* in the wall of the pharynx. Water drawn into the mouth is forced back into the pharynx and out through these slits. Oxygen is removed from the indrawn water and carbon dioxide released into it by blood in beds of capillaries in the septa between the slits. Another important charac-

[23] Some acorn worms live under rocks or shells instead of burrowing; and not all of the burrowers make a U-shaped tube. There is one class of hemichordates that are not acorn worms.

Fig. 22.52. Brittle stars. The body disc is small, and the arms are long and slender. (A sea urchin is attached to the rock under one arm of the brittle star.) [New York Zoological Society photo.]

Fig. 22.53. A sea urchin. [Courtesy N. F. Snyder, Cornell University.]

Fig. 22.55. A fossil sea lily. [Courtesy American Museum of Natural History.]

Fig. 22.54. A sea cucumber. Notice the rows of tube feet; there are five of these rows, which correspond to the five arms of a starfish. [Courtesy Carolina Biological Supply Co.]

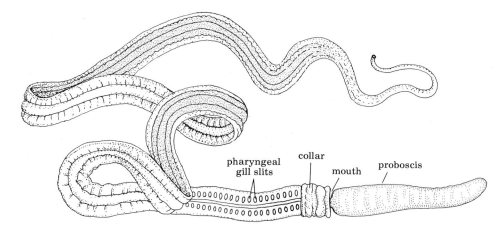

Fig. 22.56. An adult acorn worm.

teristic of hemichordates is the occurrence during development of a ciliated larval stage that strikingly resembles the larvae of some echinoderms.

The Relationships Between Echinoderms, Hemichordates, and Chordates

It may seem strange that Echinodermata is the major phylum generally considered most closely related to our own phylum, the Chordata. After all, starfishes, sea urchins, and sea cucumbers don't look like animals with which one would expect to claim kinship. But as we saw earlier when we discussed the differences between the Protostomia and Deuterostomia, certain characteristics seem to link echinoderms, hemichordates, and chordates and set them apart from all the protostome phyla—among them, formation of the anus from the embryonic blastopore, radial and indeterminate cleavage, origin of the mesoderm as pouches, and formation of the coelom as the cavities in the mesodermal pouches.

The Hemichordata have long held special interest for zoologists because their apparent affinities to both the Echinodermata and the Chordata seem to provide additional evidence of a relationship between those two large and important phyla. The ciliated larvae of hemichordates are so much like those of some echinoderms that they were mistaken for echinoderms when first discovered. This larval type, sometimes called a *dipleurula,* is found only in the echinoderms and hemichordates.[24] It has a band of cilia that forms a ring encircling the mouth (see Fig. 16.20, p. 620). It thus differs from the trochophore larva found in many protostomes (including some turbellarian Platyhelminthes, the lophophorate phyla, Mollusca, and Annelida), which has a band of cilia encircling the body anterior to the mouth (Fig. 22.57). The similar larvae of hemichordates and echinoderms, as well as the similarities in early embryology mentioned above, indicate that these two groups must stem from a common ancestor. In view of the complicated metamorphosis that in echinoderms produces a radial adult from a bilateral larva, it seems likely that echinoderms have deviated greatly from the ancestral type and that hemichordates are probably nearer that ancestral type.

The most obvious resemblance of hemichordates to chordates is their possession of pharyngeal gill slits, which are found in all chordates but nowhere else in the animal kingdom.

[24] The larva of a hemichordate is called a tornaria, and the echinoderm larva it resembles is called a bipinnaria. Both are of the dipleurula type.

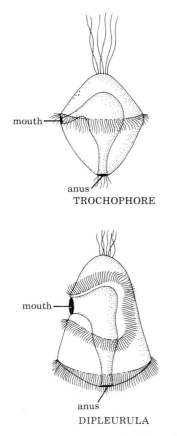

mouth

anus

TROCHOPHORE

mouth

anus

DIPLEURULA

Fig. 22.57. Trochophore and dipleurula larval types. The band of cilia of the trochophore is located anterior to the mouth, whereas that of the dipleurula encircles the mouth.

The hemichordates also have a dorsal nerve cord that is sometimes hollow and resembles the dorsal hollow nerve cord characteristic of chordates. Because of these resemblances, zoologists for many years regarded the hemichordates as primitive members of the phylum Chordata. Though it is now generally agreed that they should be recognized as a separate phylum and that they may actually be closer to the echinoderms than to the chordates, their ties with both Chordata and Echinodermata help clarify the phylogenetic relationship between these two major groups. Note that there is no suggestion here that chordates evolved

from echinoderms, but simply that the two groups diverged from a common ancestor at some remote time.

Some of the important characteristics of the major animal phyla are compared in Table 22.1.

Invertebrate Chordata

Throughout this book, we have used the terms "vertebrate" and "invertebrate," and have assigned all the animals discussed to one or the other of the categories they designate. But this is in many respects an odd way to divide the animal kingdom, because neither category coincides with any phylum or group of phyla. Indeed, the term "vertebrate" designates only a part of one phylum; the rest of that phylum and all the other phyla then fall under the heading "invertebrate." The phylum that contains both invertebrate and vertebrate members is Chordata.

The phylum Chordata is customarily divided into three subphyla: Urochordata, Cephalochordata, and Vertebrata. These share three important characteristics: (1) All have, at least during embryonic development, a structure called a *notochord* (whence the name "Chordata"). This is a flexible supportive rod running longitudinally through the dorsum of the animal just ventral to the nerve cord. (2) All have pharyngeal gill slits (or pouches) at some stage in their development. (3) All have a dorsal hollow nerve cord.

The Urochordata and the Cephalochordata are both invertebrate; i.e. they have no backbone.

Subphylum Urochordata (The Tunicates). In the best-known class of tunicates (sometimes called sea squirts), the adults are sessile marine animals that little resemble other chordates except in having pharyngeal gill slits (Fig. 22.58).[25] These structures function in

[25] Members of two smaller classes of tunicates are free-swimming planktonic organisms.

both gas exchange and feeding, acting as a strainer for removing small food particles from the water flowing through them. According to one hypothesis, the pharyngeal gill slits, which are so distinctive a trait of chordates, first evolved as an adaptation for this sort of filter feeding and only later came to function in gas exchange also.

Larval tunicates, which are motile, show much more resemblance to the other chordates. With their elongate bilaterally symmetrical bodies and long tails, they look rather like tadpoles. They possess a well-developed dorsal hollow nerve cord and a notochord beneath it in the tail region (Fig. 22.59). When the larvae settle down and undergo metamorphosis to the adult form, the notochord and most of the nerve cord are lost.

Some biologists hold that the tunicates and vertebrates descended from a common ancestor that was free-swimming and resembled a mod-

ern tunicate larva. If this is so, then the sessile structure of modern adult tunicates is a later specialization. An alternative hypothesis is that the common ancestor was sessile, more like adult tunicates, and that vertebrates evolved from its motile larva. In other words, in the line leading to the vertebrates, the larval stage increased in importance and duration, until finally it could reproduce without undergoing metamorphosis, and the ancestral sessile stage dropped out of the life cycle entirely.

Subphylum Cephalochordata (The Lancelets). There are about 30 species of these small marine animals. Though capable of swimming, they spend most of their time buried tail-down in sand in shallow water, with only their anterior end exposed. They are filter feeders, taking in water through the mouth and straining it through the pharyngeal gill slits.

The body of a typical lancelet (usually called amphioxus, although the correct name of the genus most commonly studied is *Branchiostoma*) is about 2 inches long, translucent, and shaped rather like a fish (Fig. 22.60). Both the dorsal hollow nerve cord and the notochord are well developed and are retained throughout life. A feature not seen in tunicates but characteristic of both cephalochordates and vertebrates is segmentation. In lancelets, this segmentation is most noticeable in the muscles, which are in V-shaped, segmentally arranged bundles.

Vertebrate Chordata

As the name "Vertebrata" implies, the animals in this group are characterized by an endoskeleton that includes a backbone composed of a series of vertebrae. The vertebrae develop around the notochord, which in most vertebrates is present in the embryo only. The serial

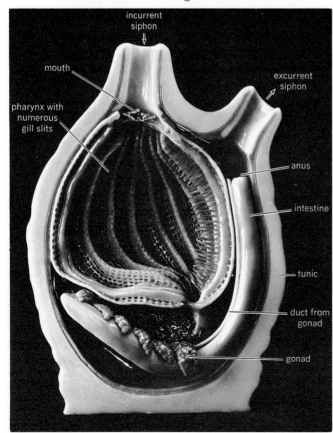

incurrent siphon

mouth

excurrent siphon

pharynx with numerous gill slits

anus

intestine

tunic

duct from gonad

gonad

Fig. 22.58. Cutaway model of an adult tunicate. [Courtesy American Museum of Natural History.]

TABLE 22.1

A Comparison of Some of the Major Animal Phyla

Phylum	Symmetry	Cleavage	Body cavity	Digestive tract	Circulatory system	Ciliated larva	Segmentation
Coelenterata	Radial	Determinate	None	Gastrovascular cavity	Absent	Planula	Absent
Platyhelminthes	Bilateral	Determinate	None	Gastrovascular cavity	Absent	Trochophorelike in some	Absent or correlated with reproduction
Aschelminthes	Bilateral	Determinate	Pseudocoelom	Complete with mouth from blastopore	Absent	None or a unique type	Absent
Mollusca	Bilateral	Determinate	Coelom	Complete with mouth from blastopore	Open	Trochophore	Absent (except in *Neopilina*)
Annelida	Bilateral	Determinate	Coelom	Complete with mouth from blastopore	Closed	Trochophore	Present
Arthropoda	Bilateral	Determinate	Hemocoel (coelom, degenerate)	Complete with mouth from blastopore	Open	None	Present
Echinodermata	Secondarily radial	Indeterminate	Coelom	Complete, with anus from blastopore	A special type; often poorly developed	Diplleurula	Absent
Hemichordata	Bilateral	Indeterminate	Coelom	Complete, with anus from blastopore	Open	Diplleurula	Absent
Chordata	Bilateral	Indeterminate	Coelom	Complete, with anus from blastopore	Closed (except in tunicates)	None	Present

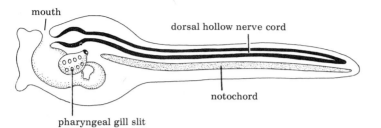

mouth

dorsal hollow nerve cord

notochord

pharyngeal gill slit

Fig.. 22.59. A larval tunicate.

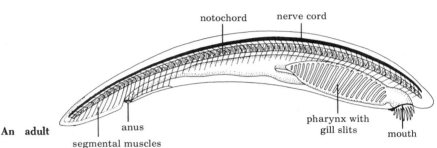

notochord   nerve cord

pharynx with gill slits

mouth

Fig. 22.60. An adult lancelet.

anus

segmental muscles

Fig. 22.61. Reconstruction of an extinct agnath (ostracoderm). Notice that what at first glance appears to be a mouth is just an area of small hard plates. This ancient fish had a mouth (not visible here) but no jaws. [Courtesy Field Museum of Natural History, Chicago.]

arrangement of the vertebrae and the organization of the muscles are the principal tokens of segmentation.

We discussed the anatomy, physiology, behavior, and development of vertebrates at length in other parts of this book. Here we shall be primarily concerned with the evolutionary history of the group.

Class Agnatha. The vertebrates are one of the few major animal groups not represented among the Cambrian fossils. The oldest vertebrate fossils are from the Ordovician period, which began some 500 million years ago (see Table 21.2, p. 824). Those first vertebrate fos-

sils are of bizarre fishlike animals covered by thick plates of bony material (Fig. 22.61). Though they had a skeleton, they lacked an important character found in all later vertebrates—jaws. Furthermore, most of them had no paired fins. These ancient fishes constitute the class Agnatha (which means without jaws). Most were probably filter feeders, straining food material from mud and water flowing through their gill system.

The Agnatha continued as an important group through the Silurian period, sharing the seas with the already abundant sponges, coelenterates, brachiopods (which were far more numerous then than now), molluscs (particu-

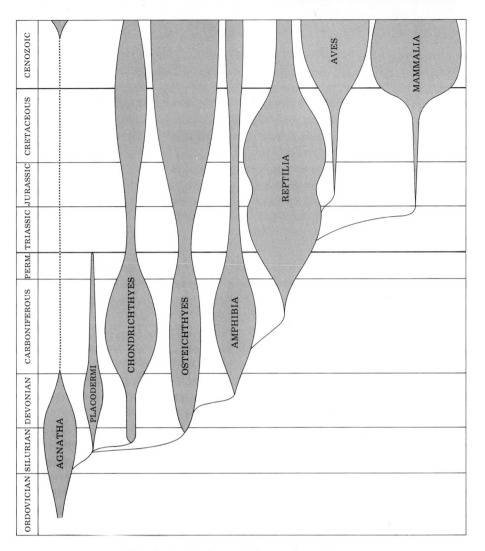

Fig. 22.62. Evolution of the vertebrate classes.

larly gastropods and cephalopods), trilobites and eurypterids, and echinoderms. But by the end of the Silurian the Agnatha had begun to decline, and they disappear from the fossil record by the end of the Devonian (Fig. 22.62).

A few peculiar species living today, the lampreys (Fig. 22.63) and the hagfishes, are generally classified as Agnatha, although they are quite unlike the Paleozoic armored species.[26] They have a soft body without either armor or

scales; they have a cartilaginous skeleton, having lost all trace of bone; and their jawless mouth is modified as a round sucker lined with many horny teeth and accommodating a rasping tongue. They feed by attaching themselves by their sucker to other fishes, rasping a hole in the skin of the prey, and sucking blood and other body fluids. The lampreys have a larval filter-feeding stage that strikingly resembles amphioxus.

Class Placodermi. The decline of the ancient Agnatha coincided with the rise of a second class of armored fishes—the Placodermi—

---

[26] Lampreys and hagfishes are so different from the Paleozoic Agnatha, called ostracoderms, that some biologists erect a separate class for them.

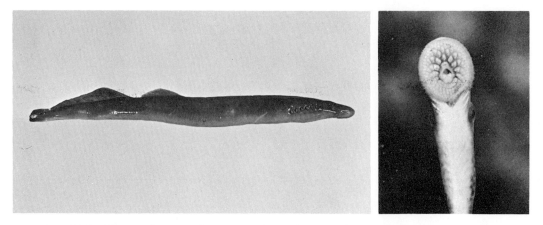

Fig. 22.63. The sea lamprey (*Petromyzon*). Left: Lateral view. Note the pharyngeal gill slits. Right: Ventral view, showing mouth sucker. [Left: Courtesy Carolina Biological Supply Co. Right: New York Zoological Society photo.]

which first appeared in the Silurian, having probably arisen from primitive agnaths. The Placodermi were an important group during the Devonian, but most became extinct by the end of that period; a few survived until the Permian, when they too disappeared.

The Placodermi mark a notable advance in vertebrate evolution in their possession of hinged jaws (Fig. 22.64). The acquisition of hinged jaws was one of the most important events in the history of vertebrates, because it made possible a revolution in the method of feeding and hence in the entire mode of life of early fishes. They became more active and wide-ranging animals, usually with paired fins. Many became ferocious predators. Even those

that remained mud feeders were evidently adaptively superior to the ecologically similar agnaths, which they gradually replaced.

Anatomical and embryological studies have convinced biologists that the hinged jaws of the placoderms were derived from a set of gill-support bars (Fig. 22.65). Notice that hinged jaws arose independently in two important animal groups, the arthropods and the vertebrates, but that, although they are functionally analogous structures, they arose in entirely different ways, in the one case from ancestral legs and in the other from skeletal elements in the wall of the pharyngeal region.

Though the Placodermi themselves have been extinct at least 230 million years, two

Fig. 22.64. Reconstruction of an extinct placoderm. Notice the hinged jaws. [Courtesy Field Museum of Natural History, Chicago.]

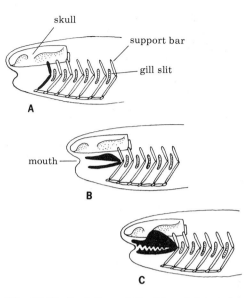

skull

support bar

gill slit

A

mouth

B

C

Fig. 22.65. Evolution of the hinged jaws of vertebrates. (A) The earliest vertebrates had no jaws. The structures (black) that in their descendants would become jaws were gill-support bars. (B) A pair of gill-support bars has been modified into weak jaws. (C) The jaws have become larger and stronger. [Modified from A. S. Romer, *The Vertebrate Body*, Saunders, 1949.]

other classes that arose from them in the Devonian[27] are still important elements of our fauna. These are the Chondrichthyes (sharks, skates, rays, and their relatives) and the Osteichthyes (bony fishes).

Class Chondrichthyes. The modern Chondrichthyes (Fig. 22.66) are distinguished by their cartilaginous skeletons; bone is unknown in the group. Though a cartilaginous skeleton might at first be taken as a primitive trait, it is not thought to be one in Chondrichthyes. Their ancestors among the Placodermi probably had bony skeletons, and loss of the bone must be regarded as an evolutionary specialization. Chondrichthyes have neither swim bladders

[27] Fossils of Chondrichthyes and Osteichthyes first appear in the Devonian, but the lines leading to them may actually have diverged from the Placodermi in the Silurian.

nor lungs. Their osmoregulation is unusual, involving retention of high concentrations of urea in the body fluids (see p. 281). Fertilization is internal, and the eggs have tough leathery shells. Most species are predaceous, but a few are plankton feeders.

Class Osteichthyes. The other class that arose from the Placodermi—the Osteichthyes—includes most of the fishes familiar to you. This is a large class, whose members are the dominant vertebrates in both fresh water and the oceans, as they have been since the Devonian. More than 17,000 species are known, and many remain to be discovered, particularly in the oceans. According to some biologists, the total number of living species may be as high as 40,000. A tremendously varied lot, they range from organisms less than half an inch long when mature to giants more than 20 feet long. They assume a host of different shapes, many of them bizarre and grotesque to our eyes. Some are sluggish and sedentary, while others can swim at speeds as great as 60 miles an hour. Almost every type of food is utilized by some species of fish.

The earliest members of this class probably lived in fresh water. In addition to gills, they had lungs, which they probably used as supplementary gas-exchange devices when the water was stagnant and deficient in oxygen. As we saw in Chapter 6, the ventral lungs have been modified into a dorsal swim bladder in most modern bony fishes (see Fig. 6.16, p. 218), which rely for gas exchange almost exclusively on their gills (see Fig. 6.10, p. 212). But there are still a few living relict species with lungs.

Soon after the Osteichthyes arose from the Placodermi, the class split into two divergent groups. One underwent great evolutionary radiation, giving rise to nearly all the bony fishes alive today. The other radiated considerably in the late Paleozoic, but today is represented by only six relict species—five species of lungfishes (one in Australia, three in Africa, and one in South America) and one species of

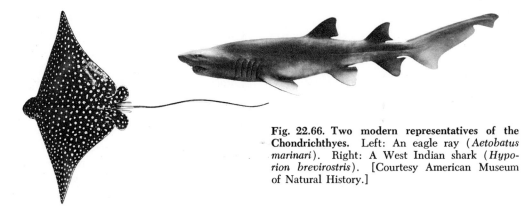

Fig. 22.66. Two modern representatives of the Chondrichthyes. Left: An eagle ray (*Aetobatus marinari*). Right: A West Indian shark (*Hyporion brevirostris*). [Courtesy American Museum of Natural History.]

"lobe-fin" known only from deep waters off the southeast coast of Africa. Despite its rarity in the present fauna, this second group of Osteichthyes is of special evolutionary interest, because it is thought to have been ancestral to the land vertebrates.

Let us look more closely at the ancient lobe-fin fishes.[28] This group has long been known from fossils, but until 1939 it was thought to have been entirely extinct for some 75 million years. In that year, a specimen was caught off the east coast of South Africa; since then, additional specimens of this living fossil, called coelacanths (*Latimeria*), have been caught and studied (Fig. 22.67). The coelacanths are not the particular lobe-fins thought to be the ancestors of land vertebrates, but they resemble those ancestral forms in many ways.

In addition to having lungs, an important preadaptation for life on land, the lobe-fins were characterized by the large fleshy bases of their paired pectoral and pelvic fins. At times, especially during droughts, lobe-fins living in fresh water probably used these leglike fins to pull themselves onto sandbars and mud flats (Fig. 22.68). They may even have managed, albeit with great difficulty, to crawl to a new pond or stream when the one they were in dried up.

Now, by the Devonian period, the land had

already been colonized by plants (see Table 21.2, p. 824), but was still nearly devoid of animal life (there is a fossil of what may have been a land scorpion from the Silurian, and the first insects and millipeds appeared in the Devonian, but they did not become common until the Carboniferous). Hence any animal that could survive on land would have had a whole new range of habitats open to it without competition. Any lobe-fin fishes that had appendages slightly better suited for land locomotion than those of their fellows would have been able to exploit these habitats more fully; through selection pressure exerted over millions of years, the fins of these first vertebrates to walk (or, rather, crawl) on land would slowly have evolved into legs. Thus, by the end of the Devonian, with a host of other adaptations for life on land evolving at the same time, one group of ancient lobe-fin fishes must have given rise to the first amphibians.

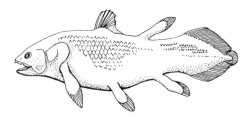

Fig. 22.67. *Latimeria*, a modern lobe-finned fish.

---

[28] Known technically as Crossopterygii.

Fig. 22.68. The movement of vertebrates onto land. Left: A Devonian lobe-finned fish (*Eusthenoperon*), which probably pulled itself out of the water onto mud flats and sandbars. Right: An early amphibian (*Diplovertebron*). Its legs were better suited for locomotion on land than the lobe fins of *Eusthenoperon*, but it too probably spent most of its time in the water. [Courtesy American Museum of Natural History.]

Class Amphibia. Numerous fossils indicate that, as would be expected, the first amphibians were still quite fishlike (Fig. 22.68). In fact, they probably spent most of their time in the water. But as they progressively exploited the ecological opportunities open to them on land, they slowly became a large and diverse group. So numerous were they during the Carboniferous that that period is often called the Age of Amphibians, just as the period before it, the Devonian, is called the Age of Fishes. The amphibians were still abundant in the Permian, but during that period they slowly declined as the members of a new class, the Reptilia, replaced them.

The end of the Permian, which also marked the end of the Paleozoic era, was a time of great change, both geological and biological. The ancestral Appalachian Mountains were built up; the last trilobites and the last placoderms disappeared; the once common brachiopods declined; and older types of corals, molluscs, echinoderms, crustaceans, and fishes were replaced by more modern representatives of those groups. This so-called Permo-Triassic crisis also witnessed the extinction of most groups of amphibians. By the end of the Triassic, the only members of this class that survived were the immediate ancestors of the few small groups of modern Amphibia—the salamanders (order Urodela), the apodes (order Apoda), and the frogs and toads (order Anura) (Fig. 22.69).

Class Reptilia. The first reptiles had evolved from primitive amphibians by the late Carboniferous. The class expanded during the Permian, replacing its amphibian predecessors, and became a huge and dominant group during the Mesozoic era, which is often called the Age of Reptiles.

One might well wonder why the reptiles

Fig. 22.69. Some modern Amphibia. Left top: Spotted salamander (*Ambystoma maculatum*). Left bottom: Bullfrog (*Rana catesbeiana*). Note the very large tympanic membrane (ear) on the side of the head. Right top: American toad (*Bufo americanus*) calling. Note the huge expanded vocal sac. Right bottom: American toads mating. The male clasps the female and releases sperms as she releases eggs. [Left bottom: Courtesy Carolina Biological Supply Co. All others: Courtesy Verne N. Rockcastle, Cornell University.]

were able so effectively to displace the once dominant amphibians. There were doubtless many reasons. But surely one of the most important was that the reptiles were terrestrial in the fullest sense of the word while the amphibians were not. Amphibians continued to use external fertilization and to lay fishlike eggs —eggs that had no amnion or shell and hence had to be deposited either in water or in very moist places on land lest they dry up (Fig. 22.70). Larval development remained aquatic.

Amphibians were thus bound to the ancestral fresh-water environment by the necessities of their mode of reproduction. Furthermore, even adult amphibians probably had thin moist skin and were in danger of desiccation if conditions became very dry.[29] But in both these respects, reptiles had completed the transition to land

[29] All modern amphibians have thin moist skin that functions as a respiratory organ (in addition to the gills and/or lungs), but this may not have been true of all ancient amphibians.

Fig. 22.70. Eggs of a spotted salamander attached in a cluster to a submerged twig. [Courtesy Verne N. Rockcastle, Cornell University.]

life; they used internal fertilization, laid amniotic shelled eggs (Fig. 22.71), had no larval stage, and had dry, scaly, relatively impermeable skin. Evolution of the amniotic egg—often called the "land egg"—which provides a fluid-filled chamber in which the embryo may develop even when the egg itself is in a dry place, was an advance as important in the conquest of land as the evolution of legs by the Amphibia.

The Reptilia had many other characteristics that made them better suited for terrestrial life than the Amphibia. The legs of the ancient amphibians were small, weak, attached far up on the sides of the body, and oriented laterally; hence they were unable to support much weight, and the belly of the animal often dragged on the ground; walking was doubtless slow and labored, as it is in salamanders today. The legs of reptiles were usually larger and

stronger and could thus support more weight and effect more rapid locomotion; in many (though not all) species, they were also attached lower on the sides and oriented more vertically, so that the animal's body was lifted clear of the ground. Whereas the lungs of amphibians were poorly developed and inefficiently ventilated, those of reptiles were fairly well developed, and greater rib musculature made their ventilation more efficient. Whereas the amphibian heart was three-chambered (two atria and one ventricle), that of reptiles was four-chambered (though the partition between the ventricles was seldom complete); hence there was little mixing of oxygenated and deoxygenated blood (see Fig. 7.25, p. 248).

The class Reptilia is represented in our modern fauna by members of four groups: turtles (order Chelonia), crocodiles and alligators (order Crocodylia), lizards and snakes (order Squamata), and the tuatara (order Rhynchocephalia) (Fig. 22.72). The last, the tuatara (*Sphenodon punctatum*), is the sole surviving member of its ancient order; it is found only on a few islands off the coast of New Zealand.

Fig. 22.71. Young pine snake hatching from egg. The egg has a tough shell and was laid on land. [Courtesy R. B. Fischer, Cornell University.]

Fig. 22.72. Some modern Reptilia. Left top: Tuatara (*Sphenodon punctatum*). Left middle: Saltmarsh crocodile (*Crocodylus palustris*). Left bottom: Snapping turtle (*Chelydra serpentina*). Right top: Black racer (*Coluber constrictor*), a common snake in the eastern United States. Right bottom: Fence lizard (*Sceloporus undulatus*). [Left top and middle: Courtesy American Museum of Natural History. Left bottom and right top: New York Zoological Society photos. Right bottom: Courtesy Verne N. Rockcastle, Cornell University.]

Members of the other three orders are fairly abundant, totaling about 6,000 living species.

All the living reptiles except the crocodilians are directly descended from an important Permian group called the stem reptiles or root reptiles (cotylosaurs) (Fig. 22.73). This group also gave rise to several other lineages, including two (ichthyosaurs and plesiosaurs) that returned to the aquatic environment (Fig. 22.74), one (therapsids) (Fig. 22.75) that ultimately led to the mammals, and one (the-

codonts) that in its turn gave rise to crocodilians, to birds, to the flying reptiles called pterosaurs, and to the great assemblage of reptiles called dinosaurs. The dinosaurs were extremely abundant and varied during the Jurassic and Cretaceous periods (Figs. 22.76, 22.77, 22.78).

By the end of the Cretaceous (which also was the end of the Mesozoic era), all the ichthyosaurs, plesiosaurs, and dinosaurs had disappeared from the earth. Only members of the four groups of modern reptiles remained. It is true that the decline of the dinosaurs was not as sudden as is often supposed; it took place over a span of tens of millions of years. But it was a dramatic event in the history of life on earth nonetheless. Why there should have been such widespread extinction of previously successful animals has never been satisfactorily explained. The extinction was not limited to reptiles; many invertebrates, such as a widespread and abundant group of shelled cephalopods (ammonites), also disappeared. Yet many other groups living in the same sorts of habitats

not only did not become extinct but did not even undergo significant change.

Class Aves. By the late Triassic or early Jurassic, two different lineages of reptiles, descended from the thecodonts, had developed the power of flight. One of these lineages (pterosaurs) included animals with wings consisting of a large membrane of skin stretched between the body and the enormously elongated arm and fourth finger. Some of these had wingspreads as great as 26 feet. They were common for a time, but eventually be-

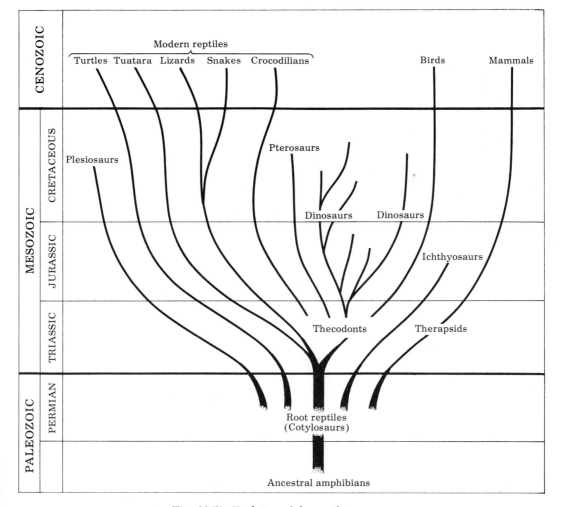

Fig. 22.73. Evolution of the reptilian groups.

Fig. 22.74. Plesiosaurs and ichthyosaurs. [From a mural by Charles R. Knight. Courtesy Field Museum of Natural History, Chicago.]

Fig. 22.75. Restoration of a therapsid reptile. Fossil evidence indicates that the mammals evolved from the therapsids. [Courtesy American Museum of Natural History.]

Fig. 22.76. *Triceratops* and *Tyrannosaurus,* two ancient dinosaurs. *Triceratops* (left) was a herbivore. *Tyrannosaurus* was a giant carnivore, about 47 feet long and 19 feet high. [From a mural by Charles R. Knight. Courtesy Field Museum of Natural History, Chicago.]

Fig. 22.77. *Brontosaurus*, a giant amphibious dinosaur. Adults probably weighed as much as 25–35 tons. [From a mural by Charles R. Knight. Courtesy Field Museum of Natural History, Chicago.]

Fig. 22.78. *Stegosaurus*, an armored herbivorous dinosaur. [From a mural by Charles R. Knight. Courtesy Field Museum of Natural History, Chicago.]

came extinct. The other lineage developed wings of an entirely different sort, in which many long feathers, derived from scales, were attached to the modified forelimbs. This line eventually became so different from the other reptiles that we designate it as a separate class —Aves—the birds.

The oldest known fossil bird (*Archaeopteryx*), from the middle Jurassic, still had many reptilian characters; e.g. it still had teeth and a long jointed tail. Neither of these traits is present in modern birds, which have a beak instead of teeth and only a tiny remnant of the ancestral tail bones (the tail of a modern bird consists only of feathers).

Along with wings, birds evolved a host of other adaptations for their very active way of life. One of the most important was warm-bloodedness (homeothermy)—the ability to maintain a high and constant metabolic rate, and hence great activity, despite fluctuations in environmental temperature. An anatomical feature that helped make possible the metabolic efficiency necessary for homeothermy was the complete separation of the two ventricles of the heart; birds have completely four-chambered hearts. The insulation against heat loss provided by the body feathers plays an important role in temperature regulation; in modern birds, all the scales except those of the feet are modified as feathers. Among other adaptations for flight are light hollow bones and an extensive system of air sacs attached to the lungs (see Fig. 6.15, p. 217). Birds also have very keen senses of vision, hearing, and equilibrium.

The newly hatched young of birds are usually not yet capable of complete temperature regulation, and they cannot fly. In many species, in fact, they are featherless, blind, and almost entirely helpless. Accordingly, most birds exhibit elaborate nest-building and parental-care behavior (Fig. 22.79).

Class Mammalia. Both birds and mammals evolved from reptiles, and both became hemeothermic and highly successful organisms, but

Fig. 22.79. Song Sparrow feeding its young. [Courtesy N. F. Snyder, Cornell University.]

the two groups did not arise from the same ancestral reptilian stock. The line leading to the mammals split off from the stem reptiles early in the Permian (Fig. 22.73), while that leading to the birds diverged from the thecodonts in the Triassic.

The mammals themselves, it should be clearly understood, did not appear in the Permian. But in that period a lineage began that slowly evolved mammal-like characteristics. Precisely at what point along this lineage therapsid reptiles (Fig. 22.75) ceased and mammals began, it is impossible to say: There was no sudden transformation of reptile into mammal, no dramatic event to mark the appearance of the first member of our class. Accordingly, no attempt is made in our review below of some of the characters that distinguish modern mammals from stem reptiles to specify when each of these characters appeared.

Mammals have a four-chambered heart and are homeothermic. They have a diaphragm, which increases breathing efficiency. There is increased separation (by the palate) of the respiratory and alimentary passages. The body is covered with an insulating layer of hair. The limbs are oriented ventrally and lift the body high off the ground. The lower jaw is composed of only one bone (compared with six or more in most reptiles), and the teeth are complexly differentiated for a variety of functions. There are three bones in the middle ear (compared with one in reptiles and birds). The brain, particularly the neocortex, is much larger than in reptiles, and behavior is more easily modifiable by experience. No eggs are laid (except in monotremes); embryonic development occurs in the uterus of the mother, and the young are born alive. After birth, the young are nourished on milk secreted by the mammary glands of the mother.

As indicated above, there is one small group of mammals—the monotremes—that are fundamentally different from all other members of the class. They lay eggs; yet they secrete milk. In many other ways, they are a curious blend of reptilian traits, mammalian traits, and traits peculiar to themselves. It seems clear that they were a very early offshoot of the mammalian lineage and were not ancestral to the other mammals. Some biologists think they should be considered mammal-like reptiles instead of reptile-like mammals. The only living monotremes are the spiny anteater and the duck-billed platypus, both found in Australia and New Zealand (Fig. 22.80).

The main stem of mammalian evolution split into two parts very early, one leading to the marsupials and the other to the placentals. As we have seen in other chapters, marsupial embryos remain in the uterus for a relatively short time and then complete their development

Fig. 22.81. Euro kangaroo with young in pouch. [New York Zoological Society photo.]

while attached to a nipple in an abdominal pouch of the mother (Fig. 22.81). Embryos of placental mammals complete their development in the uterus.

The living placental mammals are classified in approximately 16 orders, several of which contain species familiar to almost everyone. A few of the most important orders are listed below:

INSECTIVORA:　moles and shrews

CHIROPTERA:　bats

PRIMATES:　lemurs, monkeys, apes, men

EDENTATA:　sloths, anteaters, armadillos

LAGOMORPHA:　rabbits, hares, pikas

RODENTIA:　rats, mice, squirrels, gophers, beavers, porcupines

CETACEA:　whales, dolphins, porpoises

CARNIVORA:　cats, dogs, bears, raccoons, weasels, skunks, minks, badgers, otters, hyenas, seals, walruses

PROBOSCIDEA:　elephants

PERISSODACTYLA: odd-toed ungulates (hoofed animals)—horses, zebras, tapirs, rhinoceroses

ARTIODACTYLA:　even-toed ungulates—pigs, hippopotamuses, camels, deer, giraffes, antelopes, cattle, sheep, goats, bison

Fig. 22.80. Duck-billed platypus, an egg-laying mammal. [New York Zoological Society photo.]

The oldest fossils identified as placental mammalian ones are from the Jurassic. They are of small, probably secretive creatures that are thought to have fed primarily on insects. They remained a relatively unimportant part of the fauna until the end of the Mesozoic. Of the modern orders, Insectivora is closest to this ancient group. The great radiation from the insectivore ancestors dates from the beginning of the Cenozoic era, as the mammals rapidly filled the many niches left open by the demise of the dinosaurs. The Cenozoic, which includes the present, is aptly termed the Age of Mammals.

Evolution of the Primates

As members of the mammalian order Primates, we naturally have a special interest in its evolutionary history, and, in particular, in that part of its history that concerns the origin of man.

Fossil evidence indicates that the primates arose from an arboreal stock of small shrewlike insectivores very early in the Cenozoic. The groups soon split into several evolutionary lines that have had independent histories ever since. Though the modern representatives of these evolutionary lines are a rather heterogeneous lot, most of them share the following characteristics: (1) retention of the clavicle (collarbone), which is greatly reduced or lost in many other mammals; (2) development of a shoulder joint permitting relatively free movements in all directions, and an elbow joint permitting some rotational movement; (3) retention of five functional digits on each foot; (4) enhanced individual mobility of the digits, especially the first digits (thumb and big toe), which are usually apposable; (5) modification of the claws into flattened nails; (6) development of sensitive tactile pads on the digits; (7) abbreviation of the snout or muzzle; (8) elaboration of the visual apparatus and development of binocular vision; (9) expansion of the brain, particularly the cerebral cortex;

(10) usually only two mammae; (11) usually only one young per pregnancy. Most of these traits are correlated with an arboreal way of life.

In quadrupedal terrestrial mammals, the limbs function as props and as instruments of propulsion for running and galloping; they have tended to evolve toward greater stability at the expense of freedom of movement. Think of the forelimbs of a dog or a horse: The clavicle is greatly reduced or lost; the two limbs are positioned close together under the animal, and their movement is largely restricted to one plane (i.e. they can move easily back and forth but cannot be spread far to the side like human arms). By contrast, in an animal leaping about in the branches of a tree, there is an obvious advantage in having limbs more suited for grasping, clasping, and swinging; free mobility at the shoulder, elbow, and digit joints facilitates such activities, as does attachment of the limbs (braced by the clavicle) far apart at the sides of the body instead of underneath.

The eyes of many quadrupedal terrestrial mammals (e.g. horses, cows, dogs) are located on the sides of the head. As a result, they can survey a very wide total visual field, but the fields of the two eyes overlap only slightly; i.e. the animals do not have binocular stereoscopic vision. But stereoscopic vision aids in localizing near objects, and an animal jumping from limb to limb must obviously be able to detect very accurately the position of the next limb. Hence the arboreal way of life of the early primates doubtless led to selection for stereoscopic vision and, consequently, for eyes directed forward rather than laterally. This change, in turn, would have led to the distinctive flattened forward-directed face of most higher primates.

Now, hands capable of grasping the next limb and keen eyes with broadly overlapping fields of vision would not by themselves have met the requirements of an arboreal way of life. It would have been essential, in addition, to have neural and muscular mechanisms capable of very precise eye-hand coordination.

This need was doubtless one of the factors that led to the early expansion of the primate brain.

We could continue in this manner, relating other characteristics of primates to the demands of arboreal life, but the point has been made: Many of the traits most important to us as human beings probably would not have evolved if our distant ancestors had not lived in trees.

The Prosimians. The living primates are usually classified in two suborders: Prosimii and Anthropoidea. The first, the prosimians ("pre-monkeys"), are a miscellaneous group of more or less primitive primates, including the lemurs, aye-ayes, lorises, pottos, galagos, and tarsiers.

The living lemurs and aye-ayes are found only on the island of Madagascar off the east coast of Africa. Their relatives, the lorises, pottos, and galagos, inhabit southern Asia and

Fig. 22.83. Tarsier. [New York Zoological Society photo.]

tropical Africa. Most lemurs are fairly small arboreal animals with a bushier coat than is usual among higher primates. They have fairly long foxlike snouts and bushy tails, and hardly resemble the higher primates (Fig. 22.82). But they have apposable first digits, and in all except the aye-aye the digits are provided with flattened nails.

The tarsier, which is a small crepuscular animal found in the Philippines and the East Indies, is a more advanced and specialized prosimian than the lemurs (Fig. 22.83). In some respects, it shows more superficial resemblance to monkeys, though it differs in many ways from all other primates. It has a much shorter muzzle than lemurs, and thus has a more distinct face. The eyes are enormous and are directed more completely forward than in lemurs. The hind limbs are long and specialized for leaping. The long tail is naked except at the end.

The Monkeys. The first members of the suborder Anthropoidea had diverged from a prosimian stock by the Oligocene epoch. Actu-

Fig. 22.82. Ring-tailed lemur. The animal has a long snout and a bushy tail, but its feet have apposable first digits, as can be seen by the way the animal grasps the branch. [New York Zoological Society photo.]

ally, two lines of anthropoids probably arose at about the same time from closely related prosimians. One of these led to the New World monkeys (including the marmosets), and the other led to the Old World monkeys and the apes. The Old World line itself probably soon split into separate monkey and ape lineages. We may diagram these hypothetical relationships as follows:

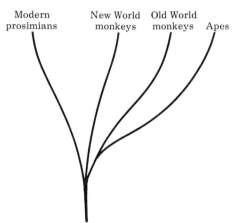

Modern prosimians   New World monkeys   Old World monkeys   Apes

Early prosimians

The following is the formal classification within the anthropoid suborder:

Suborder Anthropoidea
  Superfamily Ceboidea
    Family Cebidae, New World monkeys
    Family Callithricidae, marmosets
  Superfamily Cercopithecoidea
    Family Cercopithecidae, Old World monkeys and baboons
  Superfamily Hominoidea
    Family Pongidae, apes
    Family Hominidae, men

The New World and Old World monkeys differ in far more ways than we can mention here. Three differences, however, are easily seen even on a casual visit to a zoo: (1) Most New World monkeys have a prehensile tail that they use almost like another hand for grasping branches; the tail of Old World monkeys is not prehensile. (2) The nostrils of New World monkeys are separated by a wide par-

tition and are thus oriented in a lateral direction; the nostrils of Old World monkeys are not widely separated and are directed forward and down. (3) New World monkeys lack the naked brightly colored areas on the buttocks (ischial callosites) so common in Old World monkeys. Among the best-known New World monkeys are capuchins (the traditional organ-grinders' monkeys, Fig. 22.84), howlers, spider monkeys, and squirrel monkeys. Examples of Old World monkeys are macaques, mandrills, baboons, proboscis monkeys, mona monkeys, and the sacred hanuman monkeys of India. One of the macaques, commonly called the rhesus monkey, has been used extensively in physiological and psychological research; when physiologists or psychologists refer to "the monkey," this is usually the species they mean.

The Apes. The living great apes (Pongidae) fall into four groups: gibbons, orang-

Fig. 22.84. An organ-grinders' monkey. This is one of the New World monkeys, with a prehensile tail. [New York Zoological Society photo.]

Fig. 22.85. White-handed gibbon with young clinging to her. [New York Zoological Society photo.]

utans, gorillas, and chimpanzees. All are fairly large animals that have no tail, a relatively large skull and brain, and very long arms. All have a tendency, when on the ground, to walk semi-erect.

The gibbons, of which several species are found in southeast Asia, represent a lineage that probably split from the others soon after the pongid line itself arose. They are the smallest of the apes (about 3 feet tall when standing) (Fig. 22.85). Their arms are exceedingly long, reaching the ground even when the animal is standing erect. The gibbons are amazing arboreal acrobats and spend almost all their time in trees.

The one living species of orangutan is native to Sumatra and Borneo. Though the orangs are fairly large (males average about 165 pounds), and their movements slow and deliberate, they nevertheless spend most of their time in trees and only rarely descend to the ground.

Gorillas, of which there are two forms in Africa, are the largest of the apes; wild adult males may weigh as much as 450 pounds (up to 600 pounds in zoos) and stand 6 feet tall. Their arms, while proportionately much longer than those of man, are not as long as those of gibbons and orangs. Unlike gibbons and orangs, gorillas spend most of their time on the ground. Despite their fierce appearance, they are not usually aggressive.

Chimpanzees, which are native to tropical Africa, have been used extensively in psychological experiments. In general appearance, they are the most manlike of the living apes (Fig. 22.86). They are about the same size

Fig. 22.86. Chimpanzee. [New York Zoological Society photo.]

as orangs, but their arms are shorter. Although they spend most of their time in trees, they descend to the ground more frequently than orangs, and sometimes even adopt a bipedal position (their usual locomotion, however, is quadrupedal, with the knuckles of the hand used for support). They are quite intelligent and can learn to perform a variety of tasks, such as opening doors and manipulating household gadgets. However, attempts to teach them to speak have failed.

The Evolution of Man. The earliest members of the family Hominidae (men) probably arose from the same pongid stock that produced the gorillas and chimpanzees. Both paleontological evidence and recent biochemical and serological data indicate that gorilla, chimpanzee, and man are more closely related, in terms of recency of common ancestry, than any one of them is to orangutans or gibbons. We can diagram this relationship as follows:

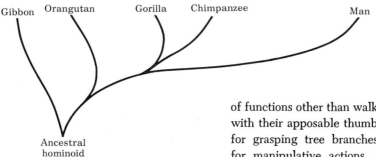

In the course of evolution from ape ancestor to modern man, many anatomical changes occurred; we can mention only a few here. (1) The jaw became shorter (making the muzzle shorter), and the teeth became smaller. (2) The point of attachment of the skull to the vertebral column shifted from the rear of the braincase to a position under the braincase, so that the skull was balanced more on top of the vertebral column. (3) The braincase became much larger, and, as it did, a prominent vertical forehead developed. (4) The eyebrow

ridges and other keels on the skull were reduced as the muscles that once attached to them became smaller. (5) The nose became more prominent, with a distinct bridge and tip. (6) The arms (though probably never as long as in the modern apes) became shorter. (7) The feet became flattened, and then an arch developed. (8) The big toe moved back into line with the other toes and ceased being apposable. The various fossil men are intermediate in these characteristics.

Several traits that man inherited from his ape ancestors were important in leading to the development of one of his most important abilities—the making and using of tools. The long widely spaced arms of apes, with their special shoulder and elbow joints, may have been excellent for moving about in trees, but they were not well suited for terrestrial locomotion. Hence, when on the ground, the animals tended to adopt an upright or semi-upright posture, the forelimbs being thus left free for the performance of functions other than walking. And the hands, with their apposable thumbs originally evolved for grasping tree branches, were preadapted for manipulative actions. Again we see that our "human" traits owe much to our ape ancestors' arboreal existence.

The first fossil human bones were found in 1856 in Germany by Johann Karl Fuhlrott. They excited lively debate, with Fuhlrott and his supporters maintaining that they were remnants of an ancient man quite different from modern man, and his opponents objecting that they were simply the remains of a modern-type man who had suffered several deformities. It was many years before enough similar fossils were found to establish the validity of Fuhlrott's claim conclusively.

In the years since 1856, bones of many ancient men have been discovered. Until very recently, the tendency of anthropologists was to erect both a new genus and a new species for each new find, without regard to biological criteria for erecting such categories. The result was a very long list of names that gave no indication of the probable relationships of the organisms they designated. During the last few years, however, the modern biological ideas concerning speciation and intraspecific variation have been increasingly applied to the study of fossil man, and this, together with the discovery of many new fossils, particularly in Africa, has begun to improve our understanding of human evolution and to bring some order out of what was becoming a chaotic jumble of information. Much is still unknown, however, and there is still considerable controversy over how the data should be interpreted; you should therefore take the brief sketch given here as only one of a number of possible interpretations.

The oldest fossils now assigned to the family Hominidae are of *Ramapithecus punjabicus* from the late Miocene. This was an apelike creature, but it exhibited early stages of some of the changes mentioned above. Of special interest is the reduction of the size of the incisors and canines, a change that may have been correlated with increased use of the hands rather than the teeth in obtaining food.

The oldest known truly manlike hominids lived near the beginning of the Pleistocene epoch nearly two million years ago. They are usually assigned to the genus *Australopithecus* (from *australis,* southern, and *pithecus,* ape— "southern," because the first specimens were found in South Africa), but some recent authors have placed them in *Homo,* the genus to which modern man belongs. These ancient creatures, often called South African ape men, were apparently fully bipedal, and they probably used simple bone tools. They had large jaws but almost no forehead or chin, and their cranial capacity was only about 450–700 cubic

centimeters (compared with 350–450 for normal chimpanzees and 1,200–1,600 for normal modern men). Most of the fossils of these early men are from eastern and southern Africa, but specimens have also been found in North Africa and Java. There were probably at least two species, one of which had considerably larger teeth than the other.[30]

A later stage in human evolution is represented by fossils that may be classified as *Homo erectus*[31] (originally described as *Pithecanthropus erectus,* often called Java man) (Fig. 22.87). Specimens have been found in Asia and Africa, and perhaps Europe. This species first appeared about 600,000 years ago. The cranial capacity was considerably larger than that of *Australopithecus,* normally ranging from 775 to 1,100 cubic centimeters. However, the facial features remained primitive, with a projecting massive jaw, large teeth, almost no chin, a receding forehead, heavy bony eyebrow ridges, and a broad low-bridged nose. Not only did *H. erectus* make and use tools, but he also used fire. Casts of the interior of the skulls indicate the presence of the speech areas of the brain; of course we have no way of knowing whether or how language was used.

Modern man is given the Latin name *Homo sapiens* (wise man). Early representatives of this species, which probably first appeared about 50,000 years ago (the date is disputed), are often called Cro-Magnon man (Fig. 22.87). Unfortunately, we are uncertain where the early evolutionary stages of *Homo sapiens* occurred. The species appeared rather suddenly in Europe, probably having migrated from Africa or southern Asia.

[30] The smaller-toothed species may be called *Australopithecus africanus* (or *Homo africanus*); it includes specimens from Olduvai Bed I (in Tanzania) called *Homo habilis* by Leakey. The larger-toothed species is *Australopithecus paleojavanicus;* it includes the specimens denominated *Paranthropus robustus* and the forms originally described in *Meganthropus* and *Zinjanthropus.*
[31] *Homo erectus* includes the specimens from Olduvai Bed II called *Homo habilis* by Leakey, and also the forms originally described in *Pithecanthropus, Sinanthropus, Telanthropus,* and *Atlanthropus.*

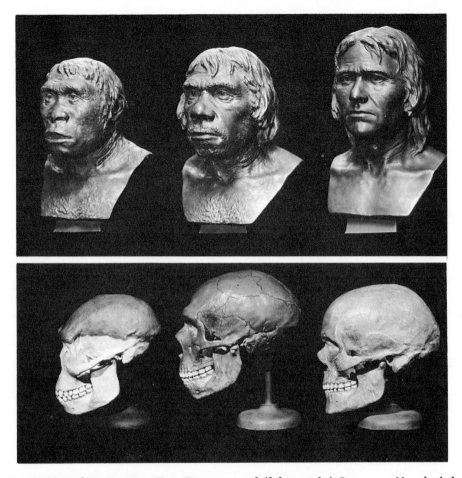

Fig. 22.87. Prehistoric men. Top: Restorations of (left to right) Java man, Neanderthal man, and Cro-Magnon man. Bottom: Lateral view of restored skulls of the same three men. Note differences in size of braincase, height of forehead, size of eyebrow ridge, length of jaw, size of teeth, etc. [Courtesy American Museum of Natural History.]

When *Homo sapiens* first settled in Europe, he coexisted for a time with a related form already established there. This form, called Neanderthal man (*Homo neanderthalensis*),[32] is the one to which the bones discovered by Fuhlrott belonged (Fig. 22.87). Neanderthal

man was about 5–5½ feet tall, and had a receding forehead, prominent eyebrow ridges, and a receding chin, but his brain was as big as that of modern man (perhaps a little bigger). He made many kinds of tools and even buried his dead, which has been interpreted as an indication that he was capable of abstract and religious thought. Neanderthal man disappeared soon after *Homo sapiens* arrived in his range, presumably eliminated either by combat or by competition.

As we saw in an earlier chapter, widespread

[32] Neanderthal man is here regarded as a separate species. Some workers, who consider this form a subspecies of *Homo sapiens* and designate it *Homo sapiens neanderthalensis,* have suggested that Neanderthal man's disappearance may not have been so much an elimination as an absorption into *Homo sapiens sapiens* as a result of interbreeding.

species often tend to become subdivided into geographic races. Man is no exception. *Homo sapiens* is an extremely variable species, and regional populations are often recognizably different (or were before the great mobility of the last few centuries began). Thus Scandinavians tend to have blue eyes and a fair complexion, while south Europeans tend to have brown eyes and a darker complexion. Eskimos look different from Mohawk Indians, and they in turn look different from Apaches. Pygmies of the Congo are obviously different from their taller neighbors. Many of the differences probably reflect adaptations to different environmental conditions. Thus, for example, the prevalence of darker skin in tropical and subtropical regions may be an adaptation giving protection against damaging ultraviolet solar radiation.

Now, races, by definition, are regional populations that differ genetically but have no effective intrinsic isolating mechanisms. There are seldom sharp boundaries between them, and they intergrade over wide areas. Designation of races in most species is thus an arbitrary matter, and there is no such thing as a "pure" race. An almost unlimited number of different races of the snake *Coluber constrictor* could be erected, depending on which of the characters whose distributions are illustrated in Fig. 17.16 (p. 682) are chosen for emphasis. The same considerations apply to man. Some authorities have chosen to recognize as many as 30 different races, while others recognize only three: the traditional Caucasoid, Mongoloid, and Negroid. Another widely used system recognizes five: the traditional three, plus American Indians and Australian aborigines.

No one of these systems has any more biological validity than the others, since races, as categories, are human inventions. What is biologically real is the geographic variation within the species *Homo sapiens,* a variation that will increasingly break down as men move about more and more. The main barriers to interbreeding in many parts of the world are now cultural or social rather than geographic, and it seems very unlikely that such barriers will even approach the effectiveness of the original geographic barriers. Hence whatever races are recognized now, it seems probable that they will become less and less distinct as time goes on. This, too, is a phenomenon that has occurred countless times in other species.

The Interaction of Cultural and Biological Evolution. One of the most interesting discoveries of recent years is that early hominids used tools long before their brains were much larger than those of apes. Thus the old idea that a large brain and high intelligence were necessary prerequisites for the use of tools has been discredited. Early man's use of tools may, in fact, have been an important factor in leading to evolution of higher intelligence. Once tool use and tool making began, individuals that excelled in these endeavors would surely have had an advantage over their less talented fellows. There would thus have been strong selection for neural mechanisms making possible improved tool making and use. Thus perhaps, instead of considering culture the crown of man's fully evolved intelligence, we should regard early cultural development and increasing intelligence as two faces of the same coin; in a sense, the highly developed brain of modern man may be as much a consequence as a cause of culture.

Cultural evolution can proceed at a far more rapid pace than biological evolution. Words as units of inheritance are much more effective than genes in spreading new developments and in giving dominance to new approaches originating with a few talented individuals. But the two types of evolution continue to be interwoven just as they were in tool use; they may well be even more so in the future.

Man now has the ability to alter deliberately some aspects of the future evolution of his species (and of other species). Modern medicine, by saving people with gross genetic defects that would once have been fatal, permits perpetuation of genes that natural selection would formerly have eliminated. Man could, if he chose, practice eugenics—deliberately restrict the perpetuation of some genetic traits and encourage the perpetuation of others. And the day will surely come when the DNA of genes can deliberately be altered in order to design, at least in part, new human beings. When that day comes, how do we decide what to design? And who decides? And who controls the one who decides? And in the meantime, how do we handle the problem of controlling the size of human populations, a problem becoming increasingly serious as a result of our interference with the action of many of the former regulating factors? These are important questions that are at once biological, economic, political, and moral. They must be faced soon. We have already gone too far toward modifying biological evolution to pull back. Like it or not, the next few generations of human beings must answer these and many similar questions. The answers they choose to give may well have as profound an influence on the future of life as anything that has happened since the first cells appeared in the primordial seas.

REFERENCES

BARNES, R. D., 1963. *Invertebrate Zoology.* Saunders, Philadelphia.

BROWN, F. A., 1950. *Selected Invertebrate Types.* Wiley, New York.

CLARK, W. E. LE GROS, 1959. *The Antecedents of Man.* Edinburgh University Press, Edinburgh. (Paperback edition, Harper Torchbooks, New York, 1963.)

COMSTOCK, J. H., 1940. *An Introduction to Entomology,* 9th ed. Comstock, Ithaca, N.Y.

CORLISS, J. O., 1961. *The Ciliated Protozoa.* Pergamon, Oxford.

EASTON, W. H., 1960. *Invertebrate Paleontology.* Harper & Row, New York.

GREGORY, W. K., 1951. *Evolution Emerging* (2 vols.). Macmillan, New York.

HALL, R. P., 1953. *Protozoology.* Prentice-Hall, Englewood Cliffs, N.J.

HYMAN, L. H., 1940–1955. *The Invertebrates* (5 vols.). Vol. 1: *Protozoa through Ctenophora,* 1940; vol. 2: *Platyhelminthes and Rhynchocoela,* 1951; vol. 3: *Acanthocephala, Aschelminthes, and Entoprocta,* 1951; vol. 4: *Echinodermata,* 1955; vol. 5: *Smaller Coelomate Groups,* 1959. McGraw-Hill, New York.

IMMS, A. D., 1957. *A General Textbook of Entomology,* 9th ed. Methuen, London.

KUDO, R. R., 1966. *Protozoology,* 5th ed. Charles C Thomas, Springfield, Ill.

LAGLER, K. F., J. E. BARDACH, and R. R. MILLER, 1962. *Ichthyology.* Wiley, New York.

NOBLE, G. K., 1931. *The Biology of Amphibia.* McGraw-Hill, New York. (Paperback edition, (Dover, New York, 1954.)

PARKER, T. J., and W. A. HASWELL, 1940. *A Text-Book of Zoology* (2 vols.). Macmillan, New York.

ROMER, A. S., 1962. *The Vertebrate Body,* 3rd ed. Saunders, Philadelphia.

———, 1966. *Vertebrate Paleontology,* 3rd ed. University of Chicago Press, Chicago.

SNODGRASS, R. E., 1935. *Principles of Insect Morphology.* McGraw-Hill, New York.

STORER, T. I., and R. L. USINGER, 1965. *General Zoology,* 4th ed. McGraw-Hill, New York.

VAN TYNE, J., and A. J. BERGER, 1959. *Fundamentals of Ornithology.* Wiley, New York.

VILLEE, C. A., W. F. WALKER, and F. E. SMITH, 1963. *General Zoology,* 2nd ed. Saunders, Philadelphia.

WEISZ, P. B., 1966. *The Science of Zoology.* McGraw-Hill, New York.

WELTY, J. C., 1962. *The Life of Birds.* Saunders, Philadelphia.

YOUNG, J. Z., 1957. *The Life of Mammals.* Oxford University Press, New York.

———, 1962. *The Life of Vertebrates,* 2nd ed. Oxford University Press, New York.

SUGGESTED READING

AUSTIN, O. L., 1961. *Birds of the World*. Golden Press, New York.

BRUES, C. T., 1951. "Insects in Amber," *Scientific American*, November. (Offprint 838.)

BUCHSBAUM, R., 1948. *Animals Without Backbones*, 2nd ed. University of Chicago Press, Chicago.

———, and L. J. MILNE, 1960. *The Lower Animals: Living Invertebrates of the World*. Doubleday, Garden City, N.Y.

CLARK, J. D., 1958. "Early Man in Africa," *Scientific American*, July. (Offprint 820.)

COCHRAN, D. M., 1961. *Living Amphibians of the World*. Doubleday, Garden City, N.Y.

COLBERT, E. H., 1949. "The Ancestors of Mammals," *Scientific American*, March. (Offprint 806.)

GILLIARD, E. T., 1958. *Living Birds of the World*. Doubleday, Garden City, N.Y.

GLAESSNER, M. F., 1961. "Pre-Cambrian Animals," *Scientific American*, March. (Offprint 837.)

HANSON, E. D., 1964. *Animal Diversity*, 2nd ed. Prentice-Hall, Englewood Cliffs, N.J.

HERALD, E. S., 1961. *Living Fishes of the World*. Doubleday, Garden City, N.Y.

KLOTS, A. B., and E. B. KLOTS, 1959. *Living Insects of the World*. Doubleday, Garden City, N.Y.

MILLOT, J., 1955. "The Coelacanth," *Scientific American*, December. (Offprint 831.)

NEWELL, N. D., 1963. "Crises in the History of Life," *Scientific American*, February. (Offprint 867.)

PILBEAM, D. R., and E. L. SIMONS, 1965. "Some Problems of Hominid Classification," *American Scientist*, vol. 53, pp. 237–259.

ROMER, A. S., 1959. *The Vertebrate Story*, 4th ed. (titled *Man and the Vertebrates* in older editions). University of Chicago Press, Chicago.

SAHLINS, M. D., 1960. "The Origin of Society," *Scientific American*, September. (Offprint 602.)

SANDERSON, I. T., 1955. *Living Mammals of the World*. Doubleday, Garden City, N.Y.

SCHMIDT, K. P., and R. F. INGER, 1957. *Living Reptiles of the World*. Doubleday, Garden City, N.Y.

SIMONS, E. L., 1964. "The Early Relatives of Man," *Scientific American*, July. (Offprint 622.)

WASHBURN, S. L., 1960. "Tools and Human Evolution," *Scientific American*, September. (Offprint 601.)

———, and I. DeVORE, 1961. "The Social Life of Baboons," *Scientific American*, June. (Offprint 614.)

WECKLER, J. E., 1957. "Neanderthal Man," *Scientific American*, December. (Offprint 844.)

GUIDES TO IDENTIFICATION

ANTHONY, H. E., 1928. *Field Book of North American Mammals*. Putnam, New York.

BISHOP, S. C., 1947. *Handbook of Salamanders*. Comstock, Ithaca, N.Y.

BLAIR, W. F., *et al.*, 1957. *Vertebrates of the United States*. McGraw-Hill, New York.

BREDER, C. M., 1948. *Field Book of Marine Fishes of the Atlantic Coast from Labrador to Texas*. Putnam, New York.

BRUES, C. T., A. L. MELANDER, and F. M. CARPENTER, 1954. *Classification of Insects*, rev. ed. Museum of Comparative Zoology, Cambridge, Mass.

BURCH, J. B., 1962. *How to Know the Eastern Land Snails*. Wm. C. Brown, Dubuque, Iowa.

BURT, W. H., and R. P. GROSSENHEIDER, 1964. *A Field Guide to the Mammals*, 2nd ed. Houghton Mifflin, Boston.

CARR, A., 1952. *Handbook of Turtles*. Comstock, Ithaca, N.Y.

CHU, H. F., 1949. *How to Know the Immature Insects*. Wm. C. Brown, Dubuque, Iowa.

CONANT, R., 1958. *A Field Guide to Reptiles and Amphibians of Eastern North America*. Houghton Mifflin, Boston.

EDDY, S., 1957. *How to Know the Freshwater Fishes*. Wm. C. Brown, Dubuque, Iowa.

EHRLICH, P. R., 1961. *How to Know the Butterflies*. Wm. C. Brown, Dubuque, Iowa.

GLASS, B. P., 1951. *A Key to the Skulls of North American Mammals*. Burgess, Minneapolis.

HAMILTON, W. J., 1943. *The Mammals of Eastern United States*. Comstock, Ithaca, N.Y.

HEADSTROM, R., 1949. *Birds' Nests: A Field Guide*. Ives Washburn, New York.

HELFER, J. R., 1963. *How to Know the Grasshoppers.* Wm. C. Brown, Dubuque, Iowa.

HUBBS, C. L., and K. F. LAGLER, 1964. *Fishes of the Great Lakes Region,* rev. ed. University of Michigan Press, Ann Arbor.

JAHN, T. L., 1949. *How to Know the Protozoa.* Wm. C. Brown, Dubuque, Iowa.

JAQUES, H. E., 1947. *How to Know the Insects,* 2nd ed. Wm. C. Brown, Dubuque, Iowa.

———, 1951. *How to Know the Beetles.* Wm. C. Brown, Dubuque, Iowa.

KASTON, B. J., 1953. *How to Know the Spiders.* Wm. C. Brown, Dubuque, Iowa.

KLOTS, A. B., 1951. *A Field Guide to the Butterflies of North America, East of the Great Plains.* Houghton Mifflin, Boston.

LUTZ, F. E., 1948. *Field Book of Insects,* 3rd ed. Putnam, New York.

MINER, R. W., 1950. *Field Book of Seashore Life.* Putnam, New York.

MORGAN, A. H., 1930. *Field Book of Ponds and Streams.* Putnam, New York.

MORRIS, P. A., 1951. *A Field Guide to the Shells of Our Atlantic and Gulf Coasts,* rev. ed. Houghton Mifflin, Boston.

———, 1952. *A Field Guide to the Shells of the Pacific Coast and Hawaii.* Houghton Mifflin, Boston.

MURIE, O. J., 1954. *A Field Guide to Animal Tracks.* Houghton Mifflin, Boston.

PENNAK, R. W., 1953. *Freshwater Invertebrates of the United States.* Ronald, New York.

PETERSON, R. T., 1947. *A Field Guide to the Birds,* 2nd ed. Houghton Mifflin, Boston.

———, 1961. *A Field Guide to Western Birds,* 2nd ed. Houghton Mifflin, Boston.

———, 1963. *A Field Guide to the Birds of Texas and Adjacent States.* Houghton Mifflin, Boston.

———, F. G. MOUNTFORT, and P. A. D. HOLLOM, 1966. *A Field Guide to the Birds of Britain and Europe,* 2nd ed. Houghton Mifflin, Boston.

SAUNDERS, A. A., 1951. *A Guide to Bird Songs.* Doubleday, Garden City, N.Y.

SCHMIDT, K. P., and D. D. DAVIS, 1941. *Field Book of Snakes of the United States and Canada.* Putnam, New York.

SCHRENKEISEN, R., *Field Book of Freshwater Fishes of North America North of Mexico.* Putnam, New York.

SMITH, H. M., 1946. *Handbook of Lizards.* Comstock, Ithaca, N.Y.

STEBBINS, R. C., 1954. *Amphibians and Reptiles of Western North America.* McGraw-Hill, New York.

WRIGHT, A. H., and A. A. WRIGHT, 1949. *Handbook of Frogs and Toads of the United States and Canada,* 3rd ed. Comstock, Ithaca, N.Y.

———, 1957. *Handbook of Snakes of the United States and Canada* (2 vols.). Comstock, Ithaca, N.Y.

A CLASSIFICATION OF LIVING THINGS

THE CLASSIFICATION GIVEN HERE IS ONE OF many in current use. Some other systems recognize more or fewer divisions and phyla, and combine or divide classes in a variety of other ways. Chapters 20–22 discuss certain of the points at issue between advocates of different systems. Compared with the large areas of agreement, however, the differences between the various classifications are minor.

Most classes are listed here, and for some classes (e.g. Insecta and Mammalia) orders are also given. Except for a few extinct groups of particular evolutionary importance (e.g. Placodermi), only groups with living representatives are included. A few of the better-known genera are mentioned as examples in each of the taxons.

KINGDOM MONERA

DIVISION SCHIZOMYCETES. Bacteria

CLASS MYXOBACTERIA. *Myxococcus, Chondromyces, Cytophaga, Sporocytophaga*

CLASS SPIROCHETES. *Leptospira, Cristispira, Spirocheta, Treponema*

CLASS EUBACTERIA. *Staphylococcus, Escherichia, Salmonella, Pasteurella, Streptococcus, Bacillus, Spirillum, Caryophanon, Actinomyces*

CLASS RICKETTSIAE. *Rickettsia, Coxiella*

DIVISION CYANOPHYTA. Blue-green algae. *Gloeocapsa, Microcystis, Oscillatoria, Nostoc, Scytonema*

KINGDOM PLANTAE

DIVISION EUGLENOPHYTA. Euglenoids. *Euglena, Eutreptia, Phacus, Colacium*

DIVISION CHLOROPHYTA. Green algae

CLASS CHLOROPHYCEAE. True green algae. *Chlamydomonas, Volvox, Ulothrix, Spirogyra, Oedogonium, Ulva*

CLASS CHAROPHYCEAE. Stoneworts. *Chara, Nitella, Tolypella*

DIVISION CHRYSOPHYTA

CLASS XANTHOPHYCEAE. Yellow-green algae. *Botrydiopsis, Halosphaera, Tribonema, Botrydium*

CLASS CHRYSOPHYCEAE. Golden-brown algae. *Chrysamoeba, Chromulina, Synura, Mallomonas*

CLASS BACILLARIOPHYCEAE. Diatoms. *Pinnularia, Arachnoidiscus, Triceratium, Pleurosigma*

DIVISION PYRROPHYTA. Dinoflagellates. *Gonyaulax, Gymnodinium, Ceratium, Gloeodinium*

DIVISION PHAEOPHYTA. Brown algae. *Sargassum, Ectocarpus, Fucus, Laminaria*

DIVISION RHODOPHYTA. Red algae. *Nemalion, Polysiphonia, Dasya, Chondrus, Batrachospermum*

DIVISION MYXOMYCOPHYTA. Slime molds

CLASS MYXOMYCETES. True slime molds. *Physarum, Hemitrichia, Stemonitis*

CLASS ACRASIAE. Cellular slime molds. *Dictyostelium*

CLASS PLASMODIOPHOREAE. *Plasmodiophora*

CLASS LABYRINTHULEAE. *Labyrinthula*

DIVISION EUMYCOPHYTA. True fungi

CLASS PHYCOMYCETES. Algal fungi. *Rhizopus, Saprolegnia, Phytophthora, Albugo*

CLASS ASCOMYCETES. Sac fungi. *Neurospora, Aspergillus, Penicillium, Saccharomyces, Morchella, Ceratostomella*

CLASS BASIDIOMYCETES. Club fungi. *Ustilago, Puccinia, Coprinus, Lycoperdon, Psalliota, Amanita*

DIVISION BRYOPHYTA

CLASS HEPATICAE. Liverworts. *Marchantia, Conocephalum, Riccia, Porella*

CLASS ANTHOCEROTAE. Hornworts. *Anthoceros*

CLASS MUSCI. Mosses. *Polytrichum, Sphagnum, Mnium*

DIVISION TRACHEOPHYTA. Vascular plants

Subdivision Psilopsida. *Psilotum, Tmesipteris*

Subdivision Lycopsida. Club mosses. *Lycopodium, Phylloglossum, Selaginella, Isoetes, Stylites*

Subdivision Sphenopsida. Horsetails. *Equisetum*

Subdivision Pteropsida. Ferns. *Polypodium, Osmunda, Dryopteris, Botrychium, Pteridium*

Subdivision Spermopsida. Seed plants

CLASS PTERIDOSPERMAE. Seed ferns. No living representatives

CLASS CYCADAE. Cycads. *Zamia*

CLASS GINKGOAE. *Ginkgo*

CLASS CONIFERAE. Conifers. *Pinus, Tsuga, Taxus, Sequoia*

CLASS GNETEAE. *Gnetum, Ephedra, Welwitschia*

CLASS ANGIOSPERMAE. *Flowering plants*

SUBCLASS DICOTYLEDONEAE. Dicots. *Magnolia, Quercus, Acer, Pisum, Taraxacum, Rosa, Chrysanthemum, Aster, Primula, Ligustrum, Ranunculus*

SUBCLASS MONOCOTYLEDONEAE. Monocots. *Lilium, Tulipa, Poa, Elymus, Triticum, Zea, Ophrys, Yucca, Sabal*

KINGDOM ANIMALIA

SUBKINGDOM PROTOZOA

PHYLUM PROTOZOA. Acellular animals

Subphylum Plasmodroma

CLASS FLAGELLATA (or Mastigophora). Flagellates. *Trypanosoma, Calonympha, Chilomonas* (also *Euglena, Chlamydomonas,* and other green flagellates included in Plantae as well)

CLASS SARCODINA (or Rhizopoda). Protozoans with pseudopods. *Amoeba, Globigerina, Textularia, Acanthometra*

CLASS SPOROZOA. *Plasmodium, Monocystis*

Subphylum Ciliophora

CLASS CILIATA. Ciliates. *Paramecium, Opalina, Stentor, Vorticella, Spirostomum*

SUBKINGDOM PARAZOA

PHYLUM PORIFERA. Sponges

CLASS CALCAREA. Calcareous (chalky) sponges. *Scypha, Leucosolenia, Sycon, Grantia*

CLASS HEXACTINELLIDA. Glass sponges. *Euplectella, Hyalonema, Monoraphis*

CLASS DESMOSPONGIAE. *Spongilla, Euspongia, Axinella*

SUBKINGDOM MESOZOA

PHYLUM MESOZOA. *Dicyema, Pseudicyema, Rhopalura*

SUBKINGDOM METAZOA

SECTION RADIATA

PHYLUM COELENTERATA (or Cnidaria)

CLASS HYDROZOA. Hydrozoans. *Hydra, Obelia, Gonionemus, Physalia*

CLASS SCYPHOZOA. Jellyfishes. *Aurelia, Pelagia, Cyanea*

CLASS ANTHOZOA. Sea anemones and corals. *Metridium, Pennatula, Gorgonia, Astrangia*

PHYLUM CTENOPHORA. Comb jellies

CLASS TENTACULATA. *Pleurobrachia, Mnemiopsis, Cestum, Velamen*

CLASS NUDA. *Beroe*

SECTION PROTOSTOMIA

PHYLUM PLATYHELMINTHES. Flatworms

CLASS TURBELLARIA. Free-living flatworms. *Planaria, Dugesia, Leptoplana*

CLASS TREMATODA. Flukes. *Fasciola, Schistosomum, Prosthogonimus*

CLASS CESTODA. Tapeworms. *Taenia, Dipylidium, Mesocestoides*

PHYLUM NEMERTINA (or Rhynchocoela). Proboscis worms. *Cerebratulus, Lineus, Malacobdella*

PHYLUM ACANTHOCEPHALA. Spiny-headed worms. *Echinorhynchus, Gigantorhynchus*

PHYLUM ASCHELMINTHES

CLASS ROTIFERA. Rotifers. *Asplanchna, Hydatina, Rotaria*

CLASS GASTROTRICHA. *Chaetonotus, Macrodasys*

CLASS KINORHYNCHA (or Echinodera). *Echinoderes, Semnoderes*

CLASS PRIAPULIDA. *Priapulus, Halicryptus*

CLASS NEMATODA. Round worms. *Ascaris, Trichinella, Necator, Enterobius, Ancylostoma, Heterodera*

CLASS NEMATOMORPHA. Horsehair worms. *Gordius, Paragordius, Nectonema*

PHYLUM ENTOPROCTA. *Urnatella, Loxosoma, Pedicellina*

PHYLUM ECTOPROCTA (or Bryozoa). Bryozoans, moss animals

CLASS GYMNOLAEMATA. *Paludicella, Bugula*

CLASS PHYLACTOLAEMATA. *Plumatella, Pectinatella*

PHYLUM PHORONIDA. *Phoronis, Phoronopsis*

PHYLUM BRACHIOPODA. Lamp shells

CLASS INARTICULATA. *Lingula, Glottidia, Discina*

CLASS ARTICULATA. *Magellania, Neothyris, Terebratula*

PHYLUM MOLLUSCA. Molluscs

CLASS AMPHINEURA. Chitons. *Chaetopleura, Ischnochiton, Lepidochiton, Amicula*

CLASS MONOPLACOPHORA. *Neopilina*

CLASS GASTROPODA. Snails and their allies (univalve molluscs). *Helix, Busycon, Crepidula, Haliotis, Littorina, Doris, Limax*

CLASS SCAPHOPODA. Tusk shells. *Dentalium, Cadulus*

CLASS PELECYPODA. Bivalve molluscs. *Mytilus, Ostrea, Pecten, Mercenaria, Teredo, Tagelus, Unio, Anodonta*

CLASS CEPHALOPODA. Squids, octopuses, etc. *Loligo, Octopus, Nautilus*

PHYLUM SIPUNCULIDA. *Sipunculus, Phascolosoma, Dendrostomum*

PHYLUM ECHIURIDA. *Echiurus, Urechis, Thalassema*

PHYLUM ANNELIDA. Segmented worms

CLASS POLYCHAETA (including Archiannelida). Sandworms, tubeworms, etc. *Nereis, Chaetopterus, Aphrodite, Diopatra, Arenicola, Hydroides, Sabella*

CLASS OLIGOCHAETA. Earthworms and many fresh-water annelids. *Tubifex, Enchytraeus, Lumbricus, Dendrobaena*

CLASS HIRUDINEA. Leeches. *Trachelobdella, Hirudo, Macrobdella, Haemadipsa*

PHYLUM ONYCHOPHORA. *Peripatus, Peripatopsis*

PHYLUM TARDIGRADA. Water bears. *Echiniscus, Macrobiotus*

PHYLUM PENTASTOMIDA. *Cephalobaena, Linguatula*

PHYLUM ARTHROPODA

Subphylum Trilobita. No living representatives

Subphylum Chelicerata

CLASS EURYPTERIDA. No living representatives

CLASS XIPHOSURA. King crabs. *Limulus*

CLASS ARACHNIDA. Spiders, ticks, mites, scorpions, whipscorpions, daddy longlegs, etc. *Archaearanea, Latrodectus, Argiope, Centruroides, Chelifer, Mastigoproctus, Phalangium, Ixodes*

CLASS PYCNOGONIDA. Sea spiders. *Nymphon, Ascorhynchus*

Subphylum Mandibulata

CLASS CRUSTACEA. *Homarus, Cancer, Daphnia, Artemia, Cyclops, Balanus, Porcellio*

CLASS CHILOPODA. Centipeds. *Scolopendra, Lithobius, Scutigera*

CLASS DIPLOPODA. Millipeds. *Narceus, Apheloria, Polydesmus, Julus, Glomeris*

CLASS PAUROPODA. *Pauropus*

CLASS SYMPHYLA. *Scutigerella*

CLASS INSECTA. Insects

ORDER COLLEMBOLA. Springtails. *Isotoma, Achorutes, Neosminthurus, Sminthurus*

ORDER PROTURA. *Acerentulus, Eosentomon*

ORDER DIPLURA. *Campodea, Japyx*

ORDER THYSANURA. Bristletails, silverfish, firebrats. *Machilis, Lepisma, Thermobia*

ORDER EPHEMERIDA. Mayflies. *Hexagenia, Callibaetis, Ephemerella*

ORDER ODONATA. Dragonflies, damselflies. *Archilestes, Lestes, Aeshna, Gomphus*

ORDER ORTHOPTERA (including Isoptera). Grasshoppers, crickets, walking sticks, mantids, cockroaches, termites, etc. *Schistocerca, Romalea, Nemobius, Megaphasma, Mantis, Blatta, Periplaneta, Reticulitermes*

ORDER DERMAPTERA. Earwigs. *Labia, Forficula, Prolabia*

ORDER EMBIARIA (or Embiidina or Embioptera). *Oligotoma, Anisembia, Gynembia*

ORDER PLECOPTERA. Stoneflies. *Isoperla, Taeniopteryx, Capnia, Perla*

ORDER ZORAPTERA. *Zorotypus*

ORDER CORRODENTIA. Book lice. *Ectopsocus, Liposcelis, Trogium*

ORDER MALLOPHAGA. Chewing lice. *Cuclotogaster, Menacanthus, Menopon, Trichodectes*

ORDER ANOPLURA. Sucking lice. *Pediculus, Phthirius, Haematopinus*

ORDER THYSANOPTERA. Thrips. *Heliothrips, Frankliniella, Hercothrips*

ORDER HEMIPTERA (including Homoptera). Bugs, cicadas, aphids, leafhoppers, etc. *Belostoma, Lygaeus, Notonecta, Cimex, Lygus, Oncopeltus, Magicicada, Circulifer, Psylla, Aphis*

ORDER NEUROPTERA. Dobsonflies, alderflies, lacewings, mantispids, snakeflies, etc. *Corydalus, Hemerobius, Chrysopa, Mantispa, Agulla*

ORDER COLEOPTERA. Beetles, weevils. *Copris, Phyllophaga, Harpalus, Scolytus, Melanotus, Cicindela, Dermestes, Photinus, Coccinella, Tenebrio, Anthonomus, Conotrachelus*

ORDER HYMENOPTERA. Wasps, bees, ants, sawflies. *Cimbex, Vespa, Glypta, Scolia, Bembix, Formica, Bombus, Apis*

ORDER MECOPTERA. Scorpionflies. *Panorpa, Boreus, Bittacus*

ORDER SIPHONAPTERA. Fleas. *Pulex, Nosopsyllus, Xenopsylla, Ctenocephalides*

ORDER DIPTERA. True flies, mosquitoes. *Aedes, Asilus, Sarcophaga, Anthomyia, Musca, Chironomus, Tabanus, Tipula, Drosophila*

ORDER TRICHOPTERA. Caddisflies. *Limnephilus, Rhyacophila, Hydropsyche*

ORDER LEPIDOPTERA. Moths, butterflies. *Tinea, Pyrausta, Malacosoma, Sphinx, Samia, Bombyx, Heliothis, Papilio, Lycaena*

SECTION DEUTEROSTOMIA

PHYLUM CHAETOGNATHA. Arrow worms. *Sagitta, Spadella*

PHYLUM ECHINODERMATA

CLASS CRINOIDEA. Crinoids, sea lilies. *Antedon, Ptilocrinus, Comactinia*

CLASS ASTEROIDEA. Starfishes. *Asterias, Ctenodiscus, Luidia, Oreaster*

CLASS OPHIUROIDEA. Brittle stars, serpent stars, basket stars, etc. *Asteronyx, Amphioplus, Ophiothrix, Ophioderma, Ophiura*

CLASS ECHINOIDEA. Sea urchins, sand dollars, heart urchins. *Cidaris, Arbacia, Strongylocentrotus, Echinanthus, Echinarachnius, Moira*

CLASS HOLOTHUROIDEA. Sea cucumbers. *Cucumaria, Thyone, Caudina, Synapta*

PHYLUM POGONOPHORA. Beard worms. *Siboglinum, Lamellisabella, Oligobrachia, Polybrachia*

PHYLUM HEMICHORDATA

CLASS ENTEROPNEUSTA. Acorn worms. *Saccoglossus, Balanoglossus, Glossobalanus*

CLASS PTEROBRANCHIA. *Rhabdopleura, Cephalodiscus*

PHYLUM CHORDATA. Chordates

Subphylum Urochordata (or Tunicata). Tunicates

CLASS ASCIDIACEA. Ascidians or sea squirts. *Ciona, Clavelina, Molgula, Perophora*

CLASS THALIACEA. *Pyrosoma, Salpa, Doliolum*

CLASS LARVACEA. *Appendicularia, Oikopleura, Fritillaria*

Subphylum Cephalochordata. Lancelets, amphioxus. *Branchiostoma, Asymmetron*

Subphylum Vertebrata. Vertebrates

CLASS AGNATHA. Jawless fishes. *Cephalaspis,* *Pteraspis,* *Petromyzon, Entosphenus, Myxine, Eptatretus*

CLASS PLACODERMI. No living representatives

CLASS CHONDRICHTHYES. Cartilaginous fishes. *Squalus, Hyporion, Raja, Chimaera*

CLASS OSTEICHTHYES. Bony fishes

SUBCLASS SARCOPTERYGII

ORDER CROSSOPTERYGII (or Coelacanthiformes). Lobe-fins. *Latimeria*

ORDER DIPNOI (or Dipteriformes). Lungfishes. *Neoceratodus, Protopterus, Lepidosiren*

SUBCLASS BRACHIOPTERYGII. Bichirs. *Polypterus*

SUBCLASS ACTINOPTERYGII. Higher bony fishes. *Amia, Cyprinus, Gadus, Perca, Salmo*

CLASS AMPHIBIA

ORDER ANURA. Frogs and toads. *Rana, Hyla, Bufo*

ORDER URODELA. Salamanders. *Necturus, Triturus, Plethodon, Ambystoma*

ORDER APODA. *Ichthyophis, Typhlonectes*

CLASS REPTILIA

ORDER CHELONIA. Turtles. *Chelydra, Kinosternon, Clemmys, Terrapene*

ORDER RHYNCHOCEPHALIA. Tuatara. *Sphenodon*

ORDER CROCODYLIA. Crocodiles and alligators. *Crocodylus, Alligator*

ORDER SQUAMATA. Snakes and lizards. *Iguana, Anolis, Sceloporus, Phrynosoma, Natrix, Elaphe, Coluber, Thamnophis, Crotalus*

CLASS AVES. Birds. *Anas, Larus, Columba, Gallus, Turdus, Dendroica, Sturnus, Passer, Melospiza*

* Extinct.

CLASS MAMMALIA. Mammals

SUBCLASS PROTOTHERIA

ORDER MONOTREMATA. Egg-laying mammals. *Ornithorhynchus, Tachyglossus*

SUBCLASS THERIA. Marsupial and placental mammals

ORDER MARSUPIALIA. Marsupials. *Didelphis, Sarcophilus, Notoryctes, Macropus*

ORDER INSECTIVORA. Insectivores (moles, shrews, etc.). *Scalopus, Sorex, Erinaceus*

ORDER DERMOPTERA. Flying lemurs. *Galeopithecus*

ORDER CHIROPTERA. Bats. *Myotis, Eptesicus, Desmodus*

ORDER PRIMATES. Lemurs, monkeys, apes, man. *Lemur, Tarsius, Cebus, Macacus, Cynocephalus, Pongo, Pan, Homo*

ORDER EDENTATA. Sloths, anteaters, armadillos. *Bradypus, Myrmecophagus, Dasypus*

ORDER PHOLIDOTA. Pangolin. *Manis*

ORDER LAGOMORPHA. Rabbits, hares, pikas. *Ochotona, Lepus, Sylvilagus, Oryctolagus*

ORDER RODENTIA. Rodents. *Sciurus, Marmota, Dipodomys, Microtus, Peromyscus, Rattus, Mus, Erethizon, Castor*

ORDER CETACEA. Whales, dolphins, porpoises. *Delphinus, Phocaena, Monodon, Balaena*

ORDER CARNIVORA. Carnivores. *Canis, Procyon, Ursus, Mustela, Mephitis, Felis, Hyaena, Eumetopias*

ORDER TUBULIDENTATA. Aardvark. *Orycteropus*

ORDER PROBOSCIDEA. Elephants. *Elephas, Loxodonta*

ORDER HYRACOIDEA. Coneys. *Procavia*

ORDER SIRENIA. Manatees. *Trichechus, Halicore*

ORDER PERISSODACTYLA. Odd-toed ungulates. *Equus, Tapirella, Tapirus, Rhinoceros*

ORDER ARTIODACTYLA. Even-toed ungulates. *Pecari, Sus, Hippopotamus, Camelus, Cervus, Odocoileus, Giraffa, Bison, Ovis, Bos*

INDEX

Illustrations are identified by **boldface** page numbers; explanations of basic terms by *italic* page numbers. Organisms are indexed both under their scientific names and under their common names (e.g. Mammalia, mammal) according to usage in text, with cross references between entries only where they are alphabetically separated.